Automotive Technology

Volume 1

Automotive Technology Volume 1

ISBN 978-94-93249-62-2

1st edition

© 2021 Electude Beheer B.V.

All rights reserved. No part of this book may be reproduced or transmitted in any form or by any means, electronic or mechanical, including scanning, photocopying, recording or by any information storage and retrieval system, without written permission from the publisher.

Graphical illustrations, animations and photographs are owned by Electude Beheer BV or used under license.

This book is not intended to replace instructional or service information designed to diagnose, repair or maintain any specific motor vehicle or its components, nor use of any related product sold by any manufacturer or retailer, such as tools, shop equipment or other devices or substances as typically used when working on an automobile. Publisher does not warrant or guarantee any product or service procedure described herein. The reader willingly assumes all risks in connection with undertaking any activity or procedure as described in this book. The reader is expressly warned to learn and adopt safety precautions that might be required to safely undertake the activities described herein and to avoid all potential hazards. The publisher shall not be liable for any damages resulting, in whole or in part, resulting from the reader's use of or reliance upon this material.

United States Office:	Netherlands Office:
Electude USA, LLC	Electude International BV
303 Wyman Street, Suite 300	Collseweg 30, 5674 TR
Waltham, MA 02451-1208	Nuenen, Netherlands

Printed in the United States of America

To learn more or request a free trial of Electude online products, contact our team at sales@electude.com or request a trial at www.electude.com/free-trial

ELECTUDE

W=LCOME

To the Student,

My name is Koen Berends and I am co-founder and Chief Development Officer of Electude. Our goal at Electude has always been to give you the best online courses in order to make learning about automotive interesting, challenging and the right start to your career as a technician. Using interactive animations and simulations on every screen, we help you understand even complex topics as clearly and simply as possible. Your success is our success!

Until now, Electude has only created online learning. We thought automotive books were outdated and usually had way too much content in them. But many teachers and students still like printed books in addition to great online experiences, so we decided to add printed books to what we offer. I asked my team to think about how to make a book that matches the online learning found in Electude. I also said these books should be "just the facts" -- no "extra" reading and details, just the words, pictures and exercises that match what you will be tested on and truly need to know. I am confident this book, used with our online learning, will give you a complete solution and a great learning experience!

Wishing you success in your learning and your career!

Koen Berends

To the Instructor,

This book is part of the Electude Classroom series and represents our approach to supporting instructors with instructional tools. Classroom combines Electude's digital learning materials with, for the first time, companion books. With this we will deliver a complete solution to support every aspect of the learning path - from classroom to shop, covering every required ASE task.

To ensure every ASE task is covered, we developed digital labs fully correlated to ASE. We developed "How-to" modules to bring those procedures to life with step-by-step photos in the book and video online. This way learning objectives align to theory modules, then how-to modules and matching lab tasks.

The Companion Guide is one part of a solution that includes our online courses, lab activities, quizzes, tests and analytics. In addition, with Classroom you may select from a collection of partner products with solutions for vehicle-specific service information, safety, training aids and soft skills. Learn about our partner products at https://www.electude.com/partnerproducts
Whether your class is held in a classroom, online, or blended format we are confident Electude will keep your students focused and engaged in learning automotive technology!!

CONTENTS
ELECTRICAL SYSTEMS

1. INTRODUCTION TO ELECTRICAL FUNDAMENTALS   1
    Electrical Fundamentals   1
    DC and AC Voltage   6
    Ohm's Law   9
    Calculations Using Ohm's Law   12
    Watt's Law   14

2. ELECTRICAL MEASURING EQUIPMENT   21
    Voltmeter   21
    Ohmmeter   23
    Ammeter   24
    Current Clamp   26

3. SERIES AND PARALLEL CIRCUITS   33
    Series Circuits   33
    Parallel Circuits   36
    Series-Parallel Circuits   39

4. BASIC ELECTRICAL COMPONENTS   43
    Resistor   43
    Potentiometer   50
    Relay   53
    How To: Test the Relay   56
    Diode   60

5. ELECTRIC MOTOR   65
    Electromagnetism   65
    Electric Motor   69
    Electric Motor: Permanent Magnet Motor   73

6. SCHEMATICS   79
Electrical Symbols   79
Electrical Diagrams   83
Symbols and Identification Codes   87
Manufacturer's Diagrams   90

7. CIRCUIT PROTECTION   99
Fuse   99
Overloading   103
Short Circuit   105
How To: Find a Short Circuit   107

8. BASIC ELECTRICAL DIAGNOSIS   113
Ground-Switched and Positive-Switched   113
Voltage Drop   115
Fault Finding   119

9. WIRING AND WIRE REPAIR   123
Determining the Cross-Sectional Area of a Conductor   123
How To: Repair Wiring and Replacing a Relay Contact   125
How To: Repair Wiring With Soldered Connections   128

10. BATTERIES   133
Lead-Acid Battery: Introduction USA   133
Battery: Electrical Capacity   135
Battery: Cranking and Charging Amps   137
Battery: Electrolyte   138
Lead-Acid Battery: Basic Principles   140
Lead-Acid Battery: Designs   145
Lead-Acid Battery: Measuring   148
Hydrometer   151
Battery: Charging   154
How To: Clean the battery terminals and maintain the battery   159
How To: Jump start a car   163

11. STARTING SYSTEM — 167

- Starter Motor: Introduction — 167
- Lorentz Force — 170
- Electrical Properties of a Starter Motor — 174
- Starter Motor Properties — 180
- Starter Motor: Components — 182
- Starter Motor: Shift Lever and Overrunning Clutch — 187
- Starter Motor: Solenoid — 190
- How To: Check the Starter Motor — 195

12. CHARGING SYSTEM — 201

- Kirchhoff's First Law — 201
- Alternator: Introduction — 204
- Charging System: Introduction — 206
- Induction — 209
- Alternator: Rotor — 211
- Alternator: Stator — 215
- Alternator — 217
- Alternator Power — 221
- Determining the Required Alternator Power — 224
- Three-Phase Voltage Star Connection — 226
- Alternator: Voltage Regulation — 230
- Charging System: Diagnosis — 234
- How To: Test the Alternator — 239
- Serpentine Belt — 243

13. ENERGY MANAGEMENT — 249

- Battery Management — 249
- Energy Management — 252
- Energy Management Diagnosis — 259

14. LIGHTING SYSTEMS — 267

Lighting Diagrams	267
Reading Lighting Wiring Diagrams	273
Reflector Operation	277
Headlights	280
How To: Adjust the Headlights	283
Low and High Beam	286
Low and High Beam with LED Technology	288
How To: Replace an HID Bulb	291
Headlight Cleaning Systems	294
Tail Lights	296
Turn Signals	298
Cornering Lights	302
Trailer Lights	305
Light Inspection	312
How To: Diagnose the dipped headlights relay	314

CONTENTS
GASOLINE ENGINE
CONSTRUCTION AND OPERATION

1. COMBUSTION ENGINE FUNDAMENTALS — 332
- Engine Mechanical Components — 332
- Piston Engines — 325
- Engine Block Types — 327
- 4-Stroke Piston Engine — 329
- 2-Stroke Piston Engine — 331
- Otto Engine — 333
- Diesel Engine — 336
- Power Diagram — 340

2. ENGINE MAIN PARTS — 345
- Engine Block — 345
- Cylinder — 349
- Cylinder Head — 351

3. PISTON AND CONNECTING ROD — 357
- Pistons — 357
- Measuring Piston Wear — 365
- Measuring Piston Pin Wear and Clearance — 366
- Determining Piston Clearance — 368
- Piston Ring Gap and Piston Ring Clearance — 370
- Connecting Rod — 372
- Measuring Connecting Rod Bearing Clearance — 375
- Polishing the Connecting Rod — 381
- Piston Bore Offset — 382

4. CRANKSHAFT 385

Crankshaft	385
Measuring Radial Main Bearing Wear	390
Measuring Axial Crankshaft Wear	395
Crankshaft Runout Inspection	397
Line Boring	399
Crankshaft Damage and Causes	400
Flywheel	402

5. VALVES AND CAMSHAFT 407

Valves	407
Camshaft	412
Valve Operation	415
Timing System	419
Valve Timing	422
Valve Overlap	425
Camshaft Adjustment	426
Measuring Cam Lobe Wear	431
Camshaft Runout Inspection	433
Camshaft Radial and Axial Bearing Clearance	434
Replacing a Valve Seal	438
Checking Valve Length, Valve Head Thickness and Valve Head Diameter	439
Checking the Wear and Clearance of Valve Guides and Valve Stems	440
How To: Checking valve clearances	442
Visual Inspection of Valve Seat and Valve	447
How To: Replace Valve Cover Gasket	449

6. ENGINE MECHANICAL PRINCIPLES 457

Stroke Volume	457
Compression Ratio	460
Engine Performance Graph	463
Internal Combustion Engine Efficiency	466

7. LOAD ON ENGINE COMPONENTS — 471
Load on Engine Components — 471
Irregular Loading — 476
Load and Driving Behavior — 479

8. ENGINE VIBRATIONS — 483
Engine Vibrations — 483
Balancing Reciprocating Masses — 485
Balancing Rotating Masses — 492
Balancing Ignition Forces — 496
Harmonic Vibration Dampener — 498

9. MEASURING ENGINE CONDITION — 503
Measuring Compression — 503
How To: Cylinder Compression Test Otto Engine — 508
How To: Relative Cylinder Compression Test — 510
Measure Cylinder Leakage — 512
Power Balance Test — 516
Measuring Cylinder Wear — 517
Boring and Honing the Cylinder — 520

10. LUBRICATION SYSTEM: FUNDAMENTALS — 523
Lubrication — 523
Lubrication Types — 526
Lubricating Oil: Properties — 528
Lubricating Oil: Types — 533
Engine Oil Classifications and Ratings — 536

11. LUBRICATION SYSTEM: COMPONENTS — 545

Lubrication System	545
Dry Sump Lubrication System	548
Oil Pump	551
Lubrication System: Pressure Relief Valve	560
Oil Filter	562
Oil Cooler	569
Oil Pressure Sensor	572
Lubrication System: Oil Seals	575
Crankcase Ventilation	580

12. LUBRICATION SYSTEM: MAINTENANCE — 585

Contamination of the Lubrication System	585
Changing Oil	588
Checking Oil Level	594
Oil Level Sensor	596
Oil Quality Sensor	598

13. LUBRICATION SYSTEM: DIAGNOSTICS — 601

Oil Loss	601
Oil Pressure	608
Oil Temperature	609

14. COOLING SYSTEM: FUNDAMENTALS — 613

Heat Balance	613
Sankey Diagram: Power Loss	615
Cooling Systems	616
Electronic Controls of Modern Cooling Systems	618

15. COOLING SYSTEM: COMPONENTS — 621

Engine Coolant	621
Mechanical Water Pump	624
Electric Water Pump	626
Thermostat	627
Electric Thermostat	633
How To: Replacing the Thermostat	635
Radiator	640
Expansion Tank	642
Pressure Cap	644
Heater Core	647
Engine Coolant Hoses	650
Thermostatically Controlled Fan	651

16. COOLING SYSTEM: MAINTENANCE — 657

Cooling System Monitoring: Instrumentation	657
Antifreeze Gauge	661
Replacing Engine Coolant	663

17. COOLING SYSTEM: DIAGNOSTICS — 671

Cooling System Pressure Tester	671
Combustion Leak Detector	675

18. INTAKE SYSTEM — 679

Intake System Introduction	679
Air Filters	684
How To: Use a Smoke Machine	687

19. EXHAUST SYSTEM — 691

Exhaust System Introduction	691
Exhaust Pipes	695
Mufflers	699
How To: Exhaust Gas Back-Pressure Test	701

CONTENTS
AIR CONDITIONING AND ELECTRICAL ACCESSORIES

1. INTRODUCTION TO AIR CONDITIONING SYSTEMS — 709
- Air Conditioning Principles — 709
- Types of Heat — 711
- Refrigerant: Properties — 713
- Refrigerant Cycle — 719

2. CLIMATE CONTROL — 723
- Climate Control: Operation — 723
- Heater — 726
- Interior Fragrance Devices — 729

3. MECHANICAL HVAC COMPONENTS — 733
- Compressor with a fixed displacement — 733
- Variable Displacement Compressor — 736
- Air Conditioning Compressor Drive — 739
- Air Conditioning System Components — 741
- Air Conditioning Systems with Fixed Orifice Tube — 747
- Climate Control: Pipes, Hoses, and Couplings — 750

4. ELECTRICAL HVAC COMPONENTS — 757
- Air Conditioning Electrical Components — 757
- Compressor Controls — 760
- Radiator Cooling Fan Control — 762
- Evaporator Temperature — 765
- The Heater Assembly — 771
- HVAC System Sensors — 779

5. HVAC SERVICE AND MAINTENANCE — 791

Refrigerant Recovery and Recharging	791
Sniffer Leak Detection	798
Nitrogen Leak Detection	801
UV Leak Detection	803
Diagnosing a Malfunctioning Air Conditioner	805
Air Conditioning Lubrication Oil Types	811
How To: Detect a Leak in the Air Conditioning System	814
How To: Measure the Air Conditioning Temperature	817

6. SAFETY SYSTEMS — 821

Introduction to Safety Systems	821
SRS: Airbags	823
Acceleration Sensor	827
SRS: Gas Generator	830
SRS: Working on Airbags	831
Seat Belt	833

7. ELECTRICAL ACCESSORIES — 837

Central Locking System	837
Electric Windows	839
Mirrors	843
Mirror Operation	847
Seat Control	849
Seat Heating and Ventilation	851

CONTENTS
ADVANCED AUTOMOTIVE ELECTRONICS

1. ADVANCED ELECTRICAL AND ELECTRONIC COMPONENTS — 859

- NTC Thermistor — 859
- PTC Thermistor — 861
- Light Dependent Resistor — 863
- Magnetic Dependent Resistor — 864
- Positive Temperature Coefficient (PTC) Heater — 865
- LED — 867
- Zener Diode — 869
- Transistor — 870
- Capacitor — 873
- Coil — 878

2. OSCILLOSCOPE — 883

- Oscilloscope: Introduction — 883
- Oscilloscope: Guided Tour — 887
- Oscilloscope: Step-by-Step Plan — 890
- Oscilloscope: Using Two Channels — 894

3. SENSORS, SIGNALS AND ACTUATORS — 897

- Introduction to Sensors — 897
- Signals — 901
- Amplitude Modulation — 907
- Frequency Modulation — 908
- Pulse Width Modulation — 910
- Principle Operation of Actuators — 912
- Switching Actuators On and Off — 917

4. IN-VEHICLE NETWORK COMMUNICATION — 925

CAN Bus: Introduction	925
CAN Bus: Network Topology	930
CAN Bus: Transmission Lines	932
CAN Bus: Electrical Operation	934
CAN Bus: Network Protocol Introduction	938
CAN Bus: Network Protocol	940
CAN Bus: Network Arbitration	945
CAN Bus: Error Detection and Rectification	946
CAN Bus: Diagnosis	950
CAN Bus and Flexray	954
LIN bus	959

5. INTRODUCTION TO HYBRID/EV SAFETY — 963

Working with Voltage	963
Introduction to hybrid and electric powertrains	967
Electric Drive - Recognition	969
Working On Hybrid Vehicles	971
HV Safety Switch	973
How To: De-Energize a Hybrid Car's HV Circuit	977
How To: Turn on a Hybrid Car's HV Circuit	979
Towing a Hybrid Vehicle	981

ELECTUDE

ELECTUDE

Electrical Systems

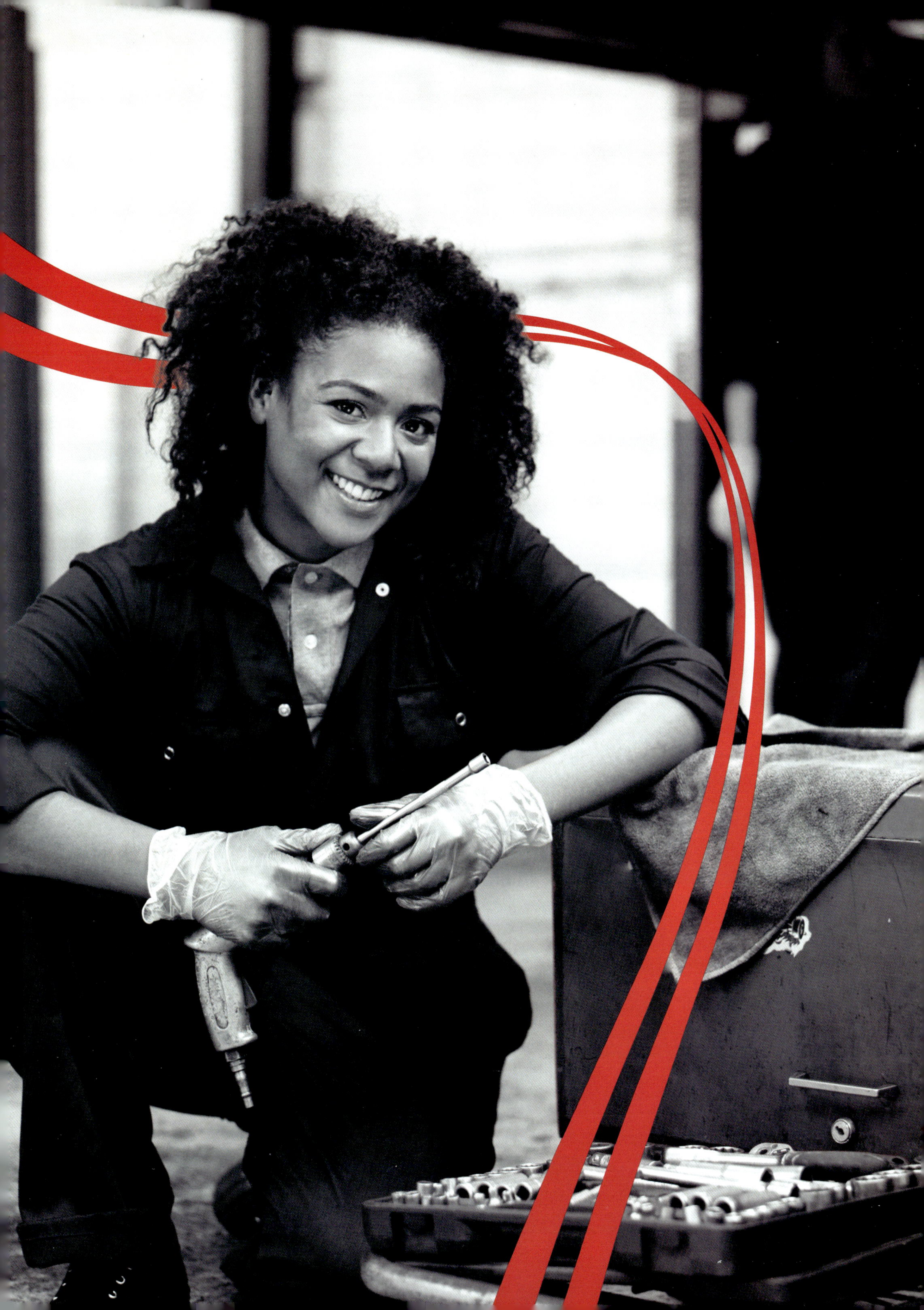

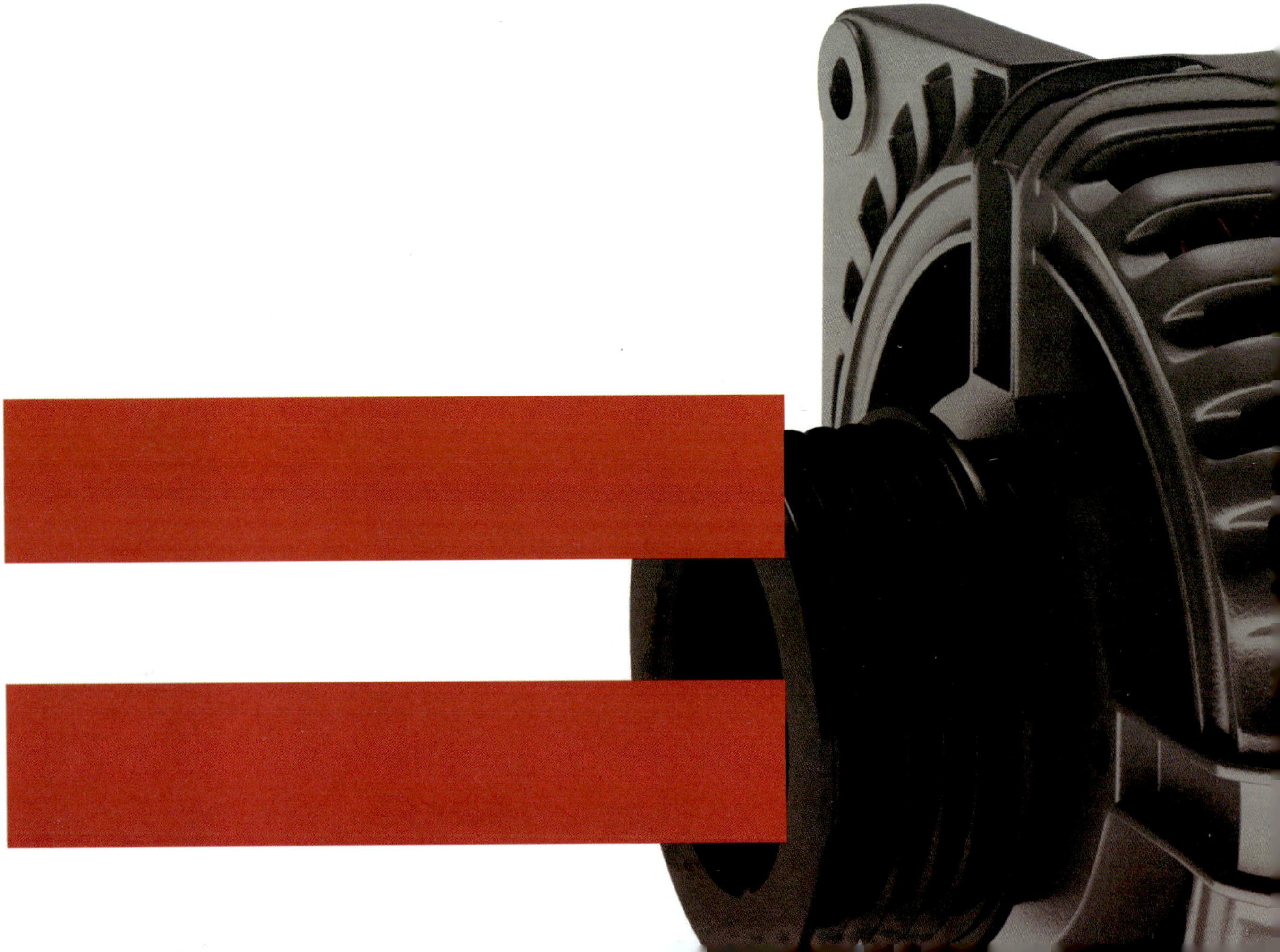

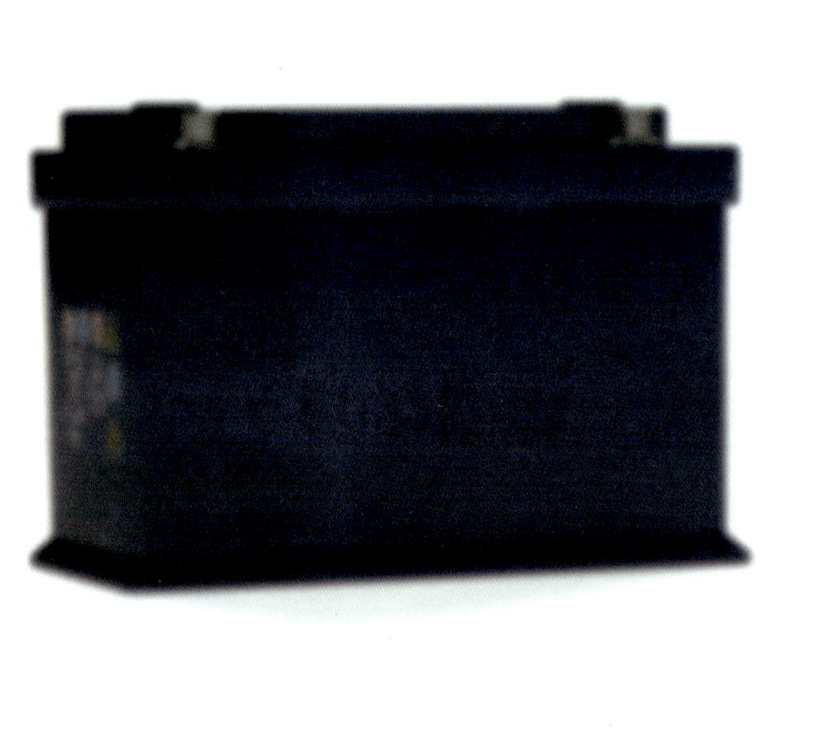

1. Introduction to Electrical Fundamentals

ELECTRICAL FUNDAMENTALS

1. Atom

To understand how electricity works, you first need to understand how materials are constructed.

All matter consists of molecules. These molecules are built from atoms. An atom has a nucleus built of neutrons (•) which have no charge and positively charged protons (+).

Negatively charged electrons (-) orbit around the nucleus. If there are as many protons in a nucleus as there are electrons orbiting around it, then the material is said to be neutral or balanced. This is because the positive and negative particles cancel each other out.

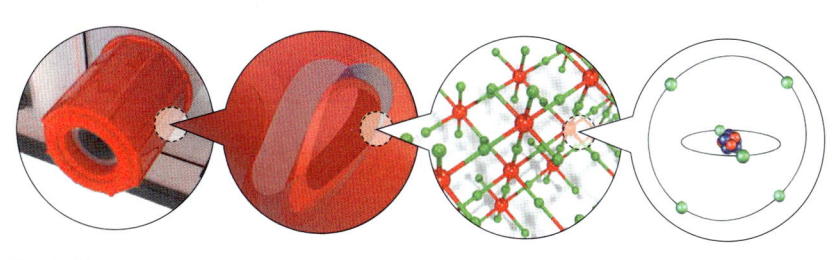

Fig. 1 If you magnify a material you will see a molecule and an atom.

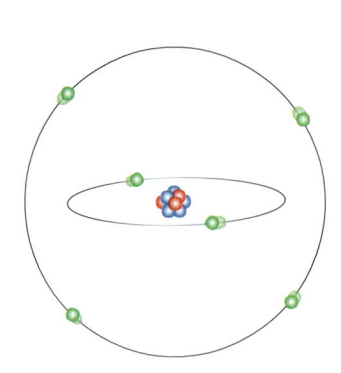

Fig. 2 Structure of an atom

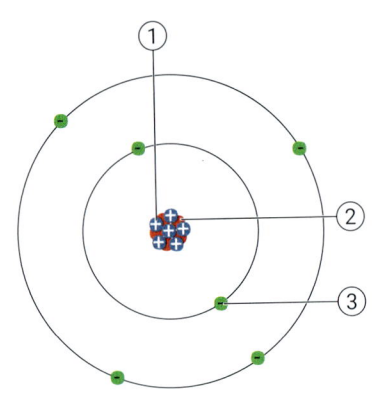

Fig. 3 Neutral charged atom:
1. Proton. 2. Neutron. 3. Electron.

2. Electrical Charge

In their normal state, atoms are neutral or balanced, which means they have the same number of protons and electrons.

In addition to neutral atoms, both positively and negatively charged atoms can exist.
— A positive atom has more protons than electrons.
— A negative has more electrons than protons.

A positively charged atom is called a positive ion. A negatively charged atom is called a negative ion.

An ion is made only by adding or pulling away electrons.

Electrical charge is indicated with the letter Q. The unit for measuring the quantity of electrical charge is the Coulomb (C). One Coulomb is equal to 6.214×10^{18} electrons (or) 1 C = 1 Amp per-second.

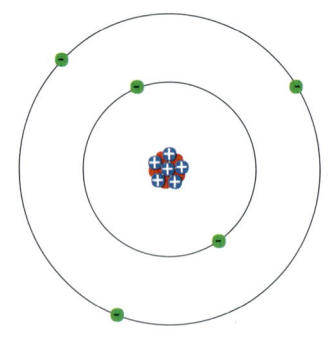

Fig. 4 A positively charged atom with 5 electrons and 6 protons

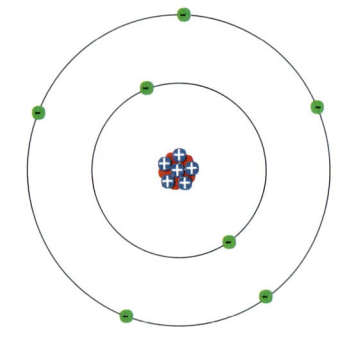

Fig. 5 A negatively charged atom with 7 electrons and 6 protons

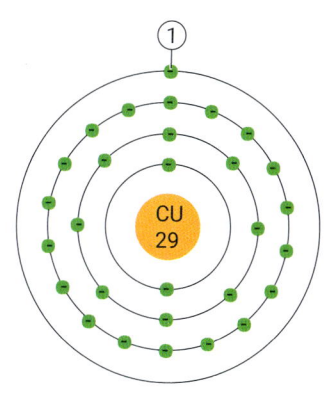

Fig. 6 A copper atom (Cu) has a free electron (1)

3. Free Electron

Here you see a schematic representation of a copper atom. A copper atom consists of 29 protons and 29 electrons.

This atom is built of four shells (rings). The further the electrons are apart from the nucleus, the less force of attraction the electrons have to the nucleus.

The electrons in the outer shell are called valence electrons, and the outer shell is often called the 'valance shell.' These electrons can easily break away from the parent atom. Therefore, they're called free electrons.
- An electric conductor can easily dispose of free electrons. Copper, aluminum, and gold are examples of good conductors.
- An electric insulator has five or more electrons in the outer orbit and rarely disposes of them. This is because it's difficult to move electrons that have a strong magnetic pull toward the protons in the nucleus out of orbit. Glass, PVC, air, and ceramic are examples of good insulators.

4. Electron Current

When positive and negative charged poles are connected via a conductor, an electron current will begin to flow.

Electrons move from the negative pole to the positive pole; the electron current flows from negative (-) to positive (+).
- The drift velocity of electrons, the speed at which they flow from one atom to another, is very slow (millimeters per hour).
- The propagation velocity of electrons, however, is very fast, equal to the speed of light (186,000 miles a second or 300,000 km/s).

You can compare the propagation velocity with a garden hose filled with small balls. If a ball enters from one end, a ball leaves from the other end. But the balls themselves are moving very slowly (drift velocity).

Propagation velocity, also known as velocity factor (VF), refers to the change of the electrical voltage in a wire relative to the speed of light.

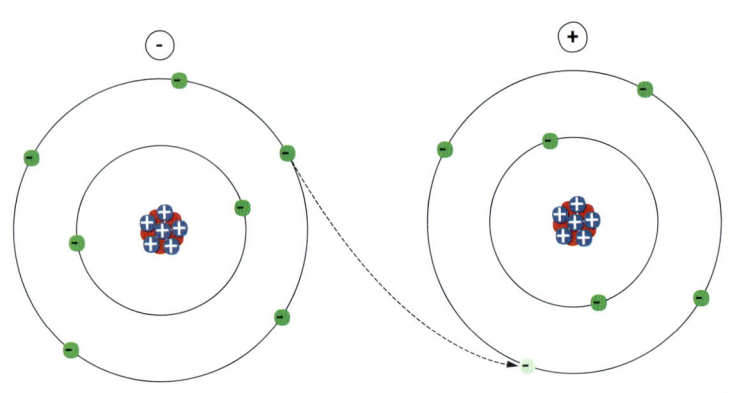

Fig. 7 An electron moves from a negatively (-) charged atom to a positively (+) charged atom

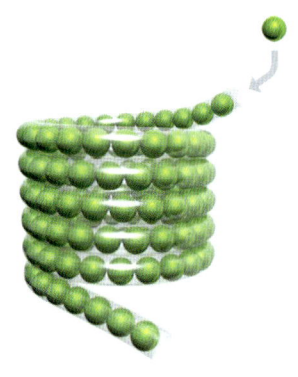

Fig. 8 The propagation velocity and drift velocity

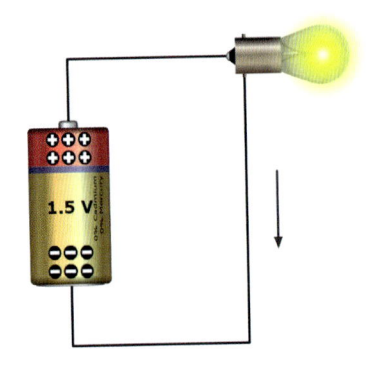

Fig. 9 The electric current flows from + to -.

5. Electric Current

Although modern science has determined electric current flows from negative to positive, early science instead believed that electric current flowed from positive (+) to negative (-). This early current flow theory is known as **conventional theory**.

Conventional theory remains relevant today because we use it to describe the direction of current flow in automotive circuits. This is because modern automobiles utilize a negative ground. When a negative ground is used, the positive side becomes the "hot" side of the circuit, requiring that it be insulated from the common ground (negative). Therefore, it makes more sense to use conventional theory to describe the flow of current in an automotive circuit, even though the electrons are moving from negative to positive.

The term "hole theory" is sometimes used to support conventional theory. Hole theory suggests that as an electron is drawn forward (toward the positive), a "hole" or space opens up behind it for another electron to occupy. In other words, as the electrons move in one direction (from negative to positive), the "holes" move in the opposite direction (from positive to negative).

Current is indicated with the letter (I) which stands for intensity. The unit of measurement for current is ampere (A).

Fig. 10 Measuring the electrical voltage

6. Voltage

Electromotive force or *potential difference* is the force by which electrons exercise power on each other, which causes them to move.

The difference in electrical charge between two points determines the electromotive force. Potential difference exists even when there's no load applied and no current flowing.

The letter (E) stands for electromotive force. It refers to the force or electrical pressure that causes electrons to move.

Electromotive force (potential difference) is measured in voltage. A single unit of voltage is referred to as a volt (V). Most European service manuals use the letter (U) to indicate voltage, while service manuals in North America use the letter (V) for voltage.

DC AND AC VOLTAGE

1. Voltage Sources

There are two different voltage sources: a direct current (DC) voltage source, and an alternating current (AC) voltage source.

EXAMPLE A bicycle generator and a wall socket in the home each supply AC voltage.

An alternating current is one in which the positive and negative poles are constantly switching many times per second, so the current flows first in one direction and then the other. This is a result of the design and operation of the generator.

Fig. 11 AC and DC sources

The abbreviations (AC) and (DC) represent the different types of voltages.
— DC stands for Direct Current.
— AC stands for Alternating Current

2. DC Voltage

With a DC voltage, the positive pole and negative pole remain unchanged and current flows in one direction only. Square-wave and triangular-wave voltages that do not cross the zero line are examples of direct voltage. The magnitude of the voltage may change, but current always flows in the same direction.

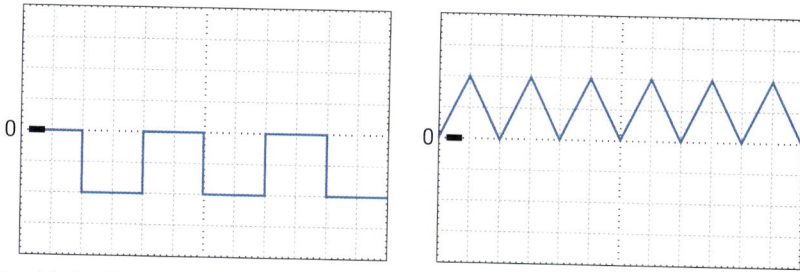

Fig. 12 Oscilloscope traces show that Direct Current voltage never crosses the zero line.

It's also possible to have a positive and negative DC voltage. Current can flow in either direction, but the direction remains constant when the circuit is turned on.

Examples of a DC voltage source are a car battery, a battery, and a solar cell.

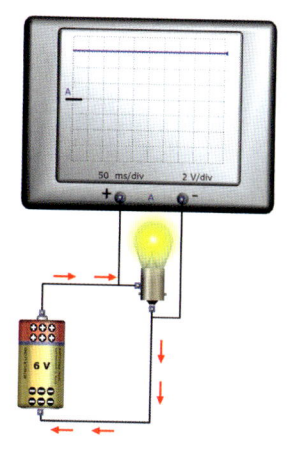

Fig. 13 A positive DC voltage

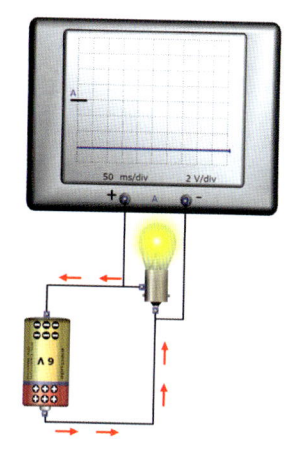

Fig. 14 A negative DC voltage

3. AC Voltage

An AC voltage can be generated by moving a magnet up and down in a coil of wire. A bicycle dynamo works according to this principle. The only difference is that the magnet turns and does not move back and forth.

When the magnet turns in the coil of wire, the coil generates a sine wave voltage. When the magnet has rotated once, the voltage has been positive once and negative once. This is one cycle.

The amount of voltage generated depends on:

— the rotation speed of the magnet
— the strength of the magnet

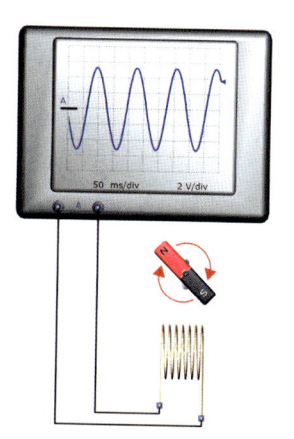

Fig. 15 Generating an AC voltage with a coil and a magnet

— number of turns in the coil
— the distance between the coil and the magnet

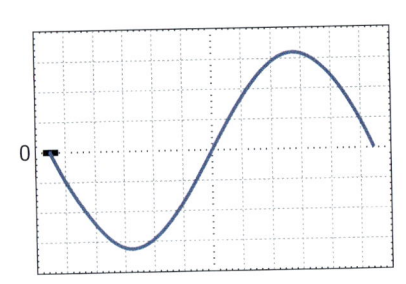

Fig. 16 One complete AC cycle

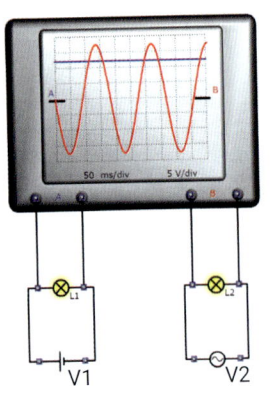

Fig. 17 Two voltages with the same effective value

4. Effective Voltage

The effective value of an AC voltage is the electrical energy that has the same effect as a DC voltage of the same value.

A lab scope will display the peak values of the AC voltage sine wave, but a multimeter measures the effective value of that same AC voltage.

The effective value of an AC voltage is 70.7% of the peak value. The effective value is calculated by multiplying the peak value by 0.707. This is also called the Root Mean Square or RMS voltage of a sinusoidal waveform.

OHM'S LAW

1. Voltage, Current and Resistance

A battery has a positive (+) and a negative (-) terminal. The chemical reaction within a battery causes a measurable difference in electrical force (pressure) between the two terminals.

If a conductor is connected between the two terminals, a circuit is created and electron current will flow for as long as there remains a measurable difference in force between the two terminals.

Normal circuit resistance limits how much current passes through the circuit per second.

The unit of electrical force is: Voltage (volts).
The symbol for voltage is: V, although in some formulas you might also see the symbols U or E (electromotive force) used interchangeably.

The unit of current is: Ampere (Amp).
The symbol for current is: I (intensity).

The unit of resistance is: Ohm (Ω).
The symbol for resistance is: R

2. Ohm's Law

Ohm's law is a mathematical equation that defines the relationship between voltage, current, and resistance.

The voltage and current are directly proportional to each other. This means that if you make the voltage twice as large, the current also becomes twice as large.

Ohm's law states:
- $V = I \times R$
  voltage = current x resistance

From here it follows that:

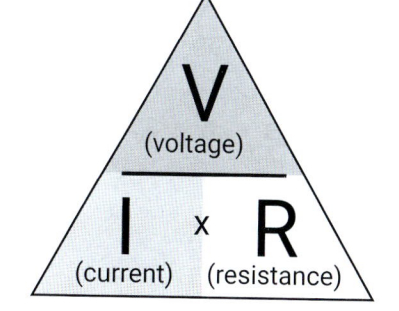

Fig. 18 Ohm's law in a triangle

- $I = V / R$
  current = voltage/ resistance
- $R = V / I$
  resistance = voltage/ current

You can place Ohm's law in a triangle so that you can easily find the right formula. You do this by putting your finger on the unit you want to calculate. If you want to calculate the current you put your finger on the I (current). You then see that you have to divide the V (voltage) by the R (resistance).

3. Calculations

With Ohm's law you can calculate comparisons with one unknown.

Calculation example 1:
Calculate the voltage of the battery.

Given:
I = 2 A
R = 6 Ω

Solution:
V = I x R
V = 2 A x 6 Ω
V = 12 V

Fig. 19 Calculation example 1

Calculation example 2:
Calculate the current through the lamp.

Given:
V = 4 V
R = 2 Ω

Solution:
I = V / R
I = 4 V / 2 Ω
I = 2 A

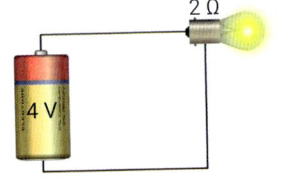

Fig. 20 Calculation example 2

Calculation example 3:
Calculate the resistance of the lamp.

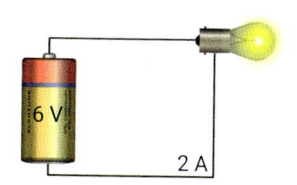

Fig. 21 Calculation example 3

Given:
V = 6 V
I = 2 A

Solution:
R = V / I
R = 6 V / 2 A
R = 3 Ω

4. Potential Difference

A battery or electrical storage device has a surplus of electrons at one terminal and a shortage of electrons at the other. When a battery is discharged, the difference in electrons between the two terminals is cancelled out, thus lowering the available voltage.

You can discharge a battery by connecting a lamp or other electrical load across the terminals.
Since a lamp only allows a limited number of electrons to pass through it acts as a resistor, which impedes current flow. This resistance causes friction, which heats the filament. The filament then becomes white hot, emitting light.

When the lamp is lit, the battery discharges. When the battery is completely discharged, the battery voltage is 0 V.

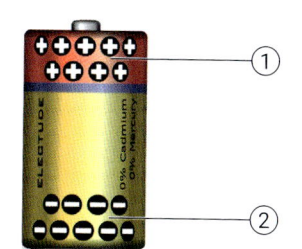

Fig. 22 Battery terminals: 1. Positive terminal (electron shortage); 2. Negative terminal (electron surplus).

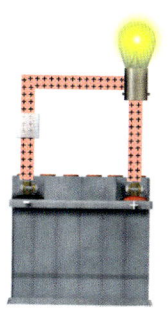

Fig. 23 Large lamp, low resistance, large current

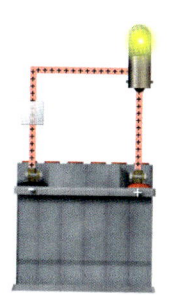

Fig. 24 Small lamp, high resistance, small current

CALCULATIONS USING OHM'S LAW

With Ohm's law you can calculate the voltage, current, or resistance of a circuit or component. When you know two of the units, you can determine the other.

V = I x R

Use the knowledge from the Ohm's law chapter to answer the question.

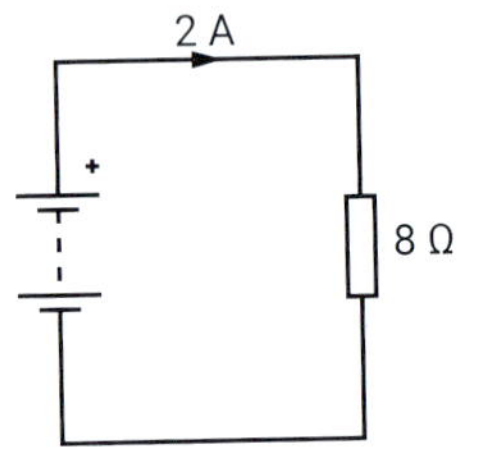

Fig. 25 Calculation example 1

Calculation example 1:
Calculate the supply voltage.
Given:
I = 2 A
R = 8 Ω

Solution:
V = I x R
V = 2 A x 8 Ω
V = 16 V

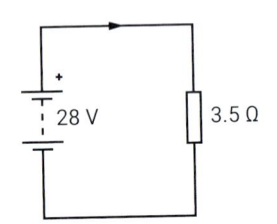

Fig. 26 Calculation example 2

Calculation example 2:
Calculate the current through the resistor.
Given:
V = 28 V
R = 3.5 Ω

Solution:
I = V / R
I = 28 V / 3.5 Ω
I = 8 A

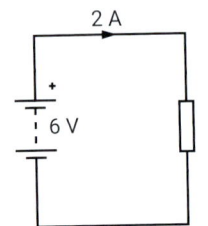

Fig. 27 Calculation example 3

Calculation example 3:
Calculate the resistance.
Given:
V = 6 V
I = 2 A

Solution:
R = V / I
R = 6 V / 2 A
R = 3 Ω

1. Units

Some values are so small or so large that several numbers are shown before or after the decimal point. It is better to write these values as milli (m), kilo (k), or Mega (M).

The difference between 1 mV and 1 V, for instance, is a factor of 1000. In other words: 1000 mV is equal to 1 V and 1 kV is equal to 1000 V.

You could compare this to millimeters and meters. 1000 mm is equal to 1 m, and 1000 m is equal to 1 km.

Fig. 28 1 m is equal to 1000 mm.

Calculation example 4:
Calculate the supply voltage.

Given:
I = 200 mA
R = 160 kΩ

Solution:
V = I x R
V = 0.2 A x 160,000 Ω
V = 32,000 V = 32 kV

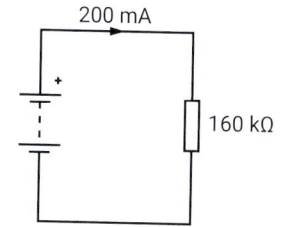

Fig. 29 Calculation example 4

Calculation example 5:
Calculate the resistance.

Given:
V = 500 mV
I = 25 mA

Solution:
R = V / I
R = 500 mV / 25 mA
R = 20 Ω

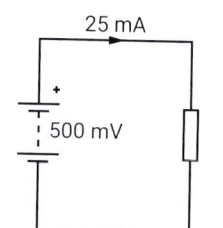

Fig. 30 Calculation example 5

WATT'S LAW

1. Power

The total power consumed by a lamp is converted into heat and light.

Heat is generated by the friction of the electron current moving through the filament. Light is generated because the filament in the lamp gets hot and begins to glow.

Power is the work done per unit of time and is dependent on the electromotive force (voltage) and the current (amperage).

When the voltage and/or current through the lamp increases, the amount of power consumed also increases; this in turn causes the lamp to give off more heat and light.

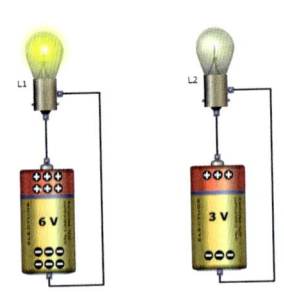

Fig. 31 A higher voltage on the same lamp provides more power.

Fig. 32 A lamp with a high resistance ensures a low current and therefore a low power.

Fig. 33 A lamp with a low resistance ensures a large current and therefore a high power.

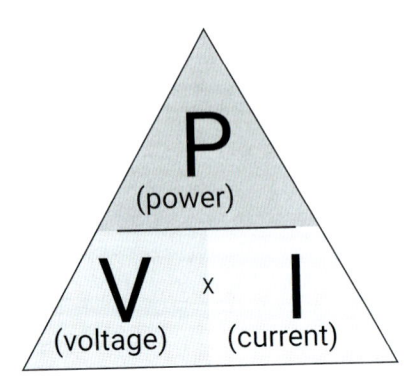

Fig. 34 The relationship between P, V, and I

2. Power Consumed

The amount of power consumed cannot be measured with a multimeter.
Power consumption can be calculated using the formula:

P = V x I

power (P) = voltage (V) x amperage (I)

Placing the formula in a triangle makes it easy to use.

For instance, if you want to calculate the voltage, keep V covered. The formula for calculating V will appear in the triangle.

The unit of power is: Watt
The abbreviation for power is: W
The symbol for power is: P

The unit of voltage is: Volt
The abbreviation of voltage is: V
The symbol for voltage is: V

The unit of current is: Ampere
The abbreviation of current is: A
The symbol for current is: I

3. Calculating the Power

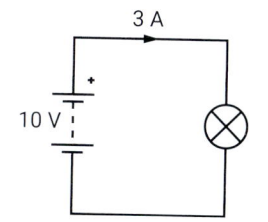

Fig. 35 The power is: P = V x I = 10 x 3 = 30 W

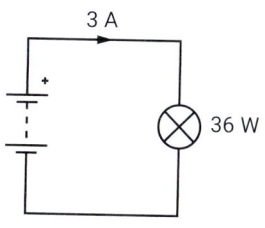

Fig. 36 The voltage is: V = P / I = 36 / 3 = 12 V

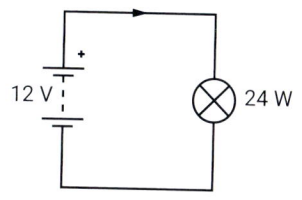

Fig. 37 The current is: I = P / V = 24 / 12 = 2 A

Using Watt's law allows you to calculate the power, voltage, and current.

Unknown current flow or voltage figures can often be calculated using Ohm's Law.

Calculation example 1:
Calculate the power of the circuit with the following data:
V = 12 V
R = 6 Ω

First calculate the current using Ohm's law.
I = V / R
I = 12 V / 6 Ω
I = 2 A

Now you can calculate the power.

P = V x I

P = 12 V x 2 A

P = 24 W

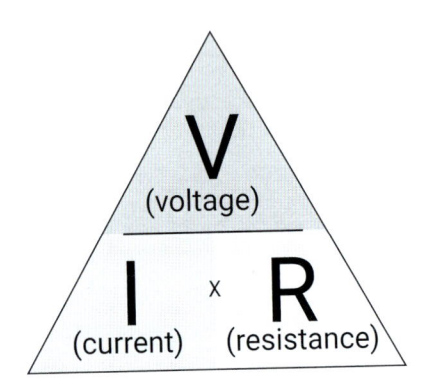

Fig. 38 Ohm's law

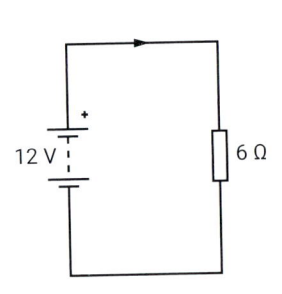

Fig. 39 Calculation example 1: the current is not yet known.

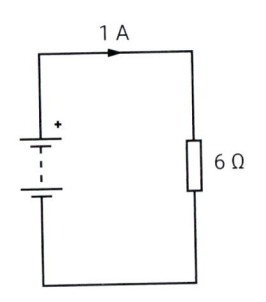

Fig. 40 Calculation example 2: the voltage is not yet known.

Calculation example 2:

Calculate the power of the circuit with the following data:

I = 1 A

R = 6 Ω

First calculate the voltage using Ohm's law.

V = I x R

V = 1 A x 6 Ω

V = 6 V

Now you can calculate the power.

P = V x I

P = 6 V x 1 A

P = 6 W

4. Watt's Law in Practice

Watt's law can sometimes be useful in practice. The following are two situations concerning the power of the glow plug system. In the first situation you will calculate the power of the complete system. In the second situation there is a resistance in the ground circuit.

$1/Rv_{glow} = 1 / R1 + 1 / R2 + 1 / R3 + 1 / R4$

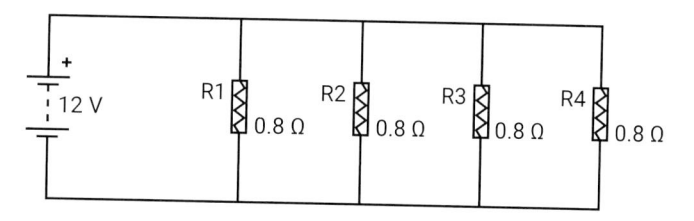

Fig. 41 Calculation example 3: normal situation

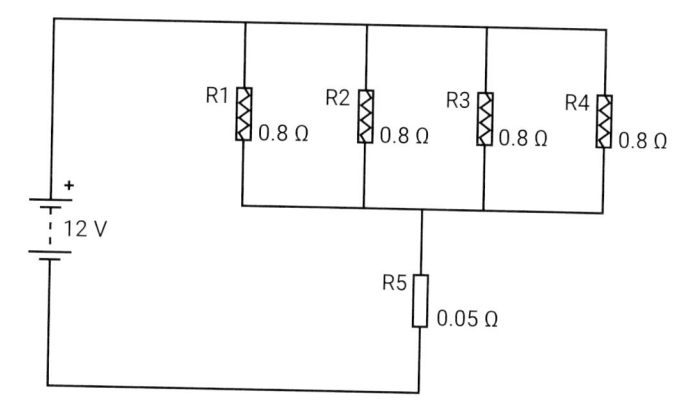

Fig. 42 Calculation example 4: with resistance in the ground circuit

Calculation example 3:

Calculate the power in a properly functioning circuit.

Step 1. Calculate the current through resistor R1:
$V = I_{R1} \times R1$
$I_{R1} = V / R1$
$I_{R1} = 12\,V / 0.8\,\Omega$
$I_{R1} = 15\,A$

Step 2. Calculate the total current:
$I_t = I_{R1} + I_{R2} + I_{R3} + I_{R4}$
$I_t = 15\,A + 15\,A + 15\,A + 15\,A = 60\,A$

Step 3. Calculate the power:
$P = V \times I$
$P = 12\,V \times 60\,A = 720\,W$

Calculation example 4:

Due to a resistance in the ground connection, the consumed power of the glow plug filament changes.

Step 1. Calculate the total resistance of all glow plug filaments.
$1/Rv_{glow} = 1/R1 + 1/R2 + 1/R3 + 1/R4$
$1/Rv_{glow} = 1/0.8\,\Omega + 1/0.8\,\Omega + 1/0.8\,\Omega + 1/0.8\,\Omega$

$1/Rv_{glow} = 1.25 + 1.25 + 1.25 + 1.25$
$1/Rv_{glow} = 5$
$Rv_{glow} = 1/5$
$Rv_{glow} = 0.2\ \Omega$

Step 2. Calculate the total resistance of the circuit:
$R_{to} = Rv_{glow} + R5$
$R_{to} = 0.2\ \Omega + 0.05\ \Omega$
$R_{to} = 0.25\ \Omega$

Step 3. Calculate the current through the circuit:
$V = I_{to} \times R_{to}$
$I_{to} = V / R_{to}$
$I_{to} = 12\ V / 0.25\ \Omega$
$I_{to} = 48\ A$

Step 4. Calculate the voltage drop across the glow plug filament:
$V_{R1} = I_{to} \times R1$
$V_{R1} = 48\ A \times 0.2\ \Omega$
$V_{R1} = 9.6\ V$

Step 5. Calculate the power through all glow plug filaments:
$P_{glow} = V_{R1} \times I_{to}$
$P_{glow} = 9.6\ V \times 48\ A$
$P_{glow} = 460.8\ W$

Due to the resistance in the ground circuit, the power of the glow plugs drops from 720 W to 460.8 W. This "small" resistance can have major consequences for the correct functioning of the glow plug system.

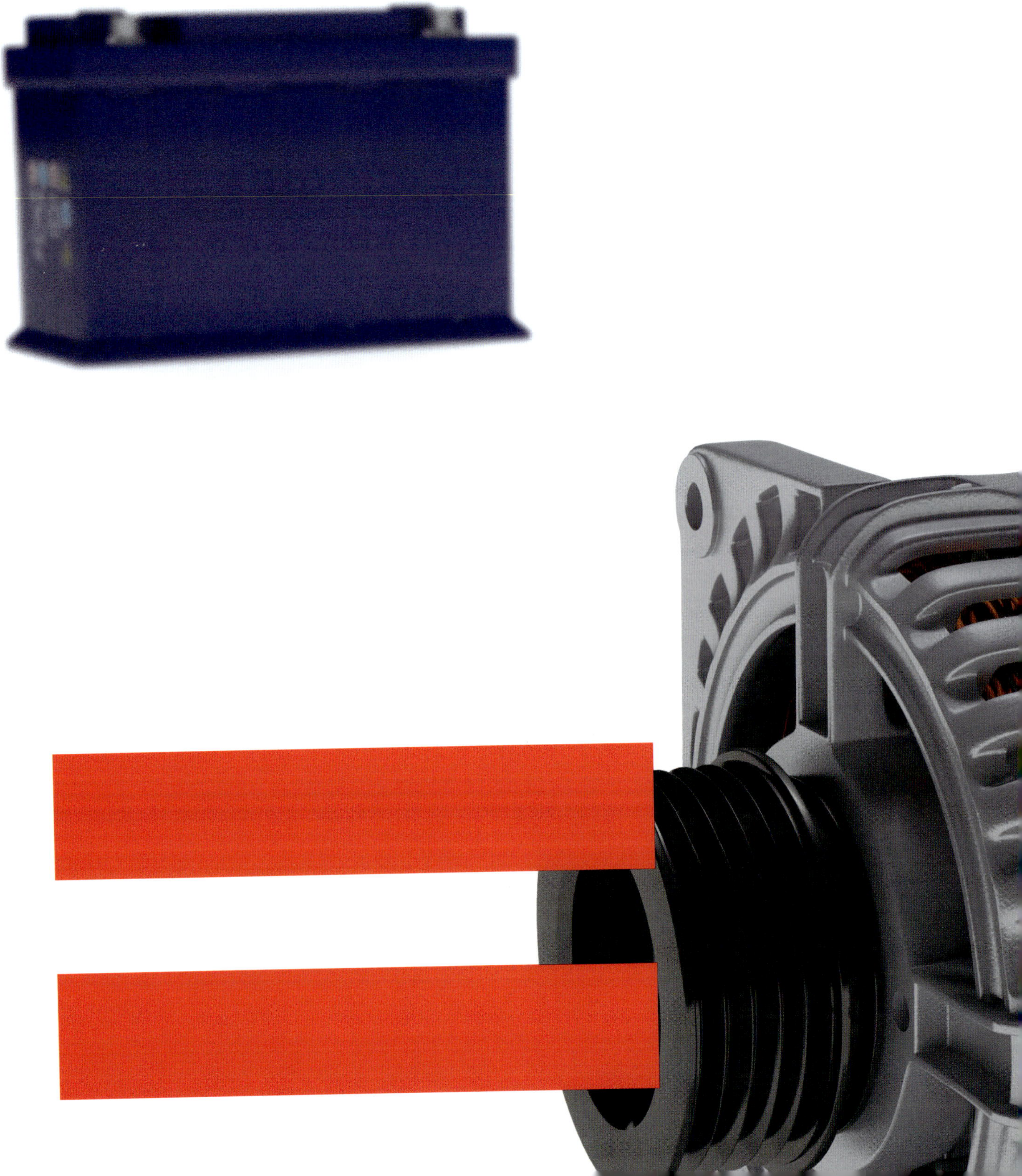

2. Electrical Measuring Equipment

VOLTMETER

1. Multimeter

The multimeter is an instrument used for measuring electrical components and circuits.

The most common units we measure with a multimeter are:

— direct and alternating current voltages, in volts (V)
— direct and alternating currents, in amperes (A)
— resistance, in ohms (Ω)

Fig. 43 The multimeter is set to be able to measure the battery voltage.

2. Measuring Voltage with a Voltmeter

A voltmeter measures the difference in voltage (potential difference) by connecting the meter in parallel between two measuring points.

If you want to measure the voltage difference across lamp R1, you connect the measuring probes to connection points 12 and 19. This makes a parallel connection to the circuit.

If you want to measure the voltage at connection point 12, you connect the red probe to connection point 12 and the black probe to

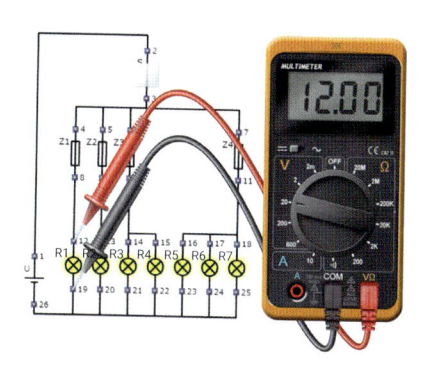

Fig. 44 Measuring the voltage difference across R1

the negative terminal of the battery (point 26).

You can use the measuring probes to measure the voltage-drop across any component in the circuit.

You cannot make a short circuit with a voltmeter, because it has very high internal resistance. Therefore, the current flowing through a voltmeter is extremely low.

3. Setting a Voltmeter

Before you can effectively use a multimeter it must be setup correctly for the type of measurement you need to take.

For measuring the battery voltage, for example, you set the following:

1. Place the test probes (1) in the correct connections; black (negative) in the "COM" connection, red (positive) in the "V Ω" connection.
2. Set the selector button AC voltage/DC voltage (2) to DC voltage.
3. Turn the rotary switch (3) to the correct measuring range. The expected voltage is around 12 volts, so you would set the switch to 20 V. If you have no idea how high the voltage will be, set the switch to the highest range and view the measured value. If the measured voltage falls within a different range, choose the correct range for an accurate measurement.

Fig. 45 Multimeter set to measure voltage. 1 test probes 2. selector button AC/DC voltage 3 rotary switch measuring range

OHMMETER

An ohmmeter allows you to measure the electrical resistance of a circuit or component.

To obtain the correct readings, you must set the multimeter to the correct settings for the circuit or component you are attempting to measure.

Fig. 46 Measuring with an Ohmmeter

1. Measuring with an Ohmmeter

You must disconnect the circuit or component from battery power before taking a resistance measurement.

This is because an ohmmeter uses its own source of voltage for taking resistance measurements.

Fig. 47 Measure resistance of a component

Fig. 48 Measuring the resistance of the ground connection

2. Accuracy

If you need to make a very precise resistance measurement, you must take into account that most ohmmeters measure to an accuracy of 0.1 Ω.

For example, the meter may indicate a value of between 0.9 Ω and 1.1 Ω, but the actual resistance of the component is 1.0 Ω.

AMMETER

With an ammeter you can measure the current in a circuit.

An ammeter is always connected in series with the load; meaning you must create an open in the circuit and place the measuring probes between the two points. This allows the meter to complete the circuit.

Using the multimeter shown, you can measure a maximum current of 10 A without overloading the internal meter fuse.

Fig. 49 Multimeter set as an ammeter

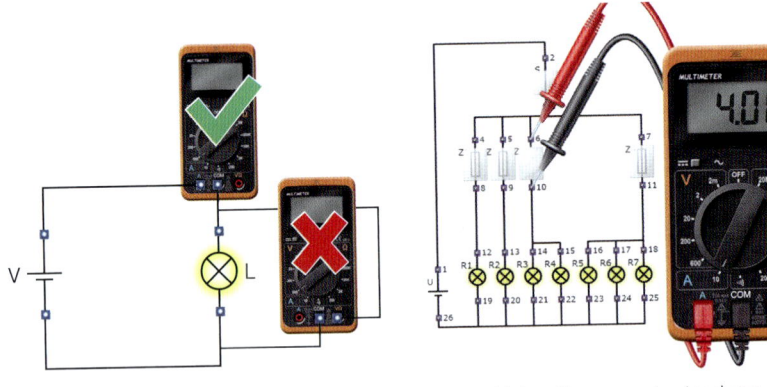

Fig. 50 You always connect an ammeter in series.

Fig. 51 Using the ammeter in place of a fuse

1. Measuring with an Ammeter

You can measure current in a circuit by replacing the circuit fuse with the meter. The current that normally flows through the fuse will now go through the ammeter. The resistance of the ammeter is very low. As a result, the measurement has no influence on the circuit.

PLEASE NOTE With an ammeter you can create a short circuit, because an ammeter has a very low resistance.

2. Setting an Ammeter

You need to set the multimeter correctly before you attempt to take any measurements.

To measure the current intensity in a circuit, set the multimeter as follows:

1. Place the test probes in the correct connections: black (negative) in the "COM" connection, red (positive) in the "A" connection.
2. Set the AC/DC voltage selector to DC voltage.
3. Turn the rotary switch to the correct measuring range. With the multimeter in this example, there is only one position to measure current intensity. It says "10," which means that a maximum of 10 amps can be measured with this meter.

Determine in advance what current you can expect to see in the circuit. If the expected current is less than 10 A, you can connect the multimeter and take your measurement. If the expected current is more than 10 A, you will have to find another way to measure the current or use a different ammeter. If you allow too much current to pass through the multimeter, the fast-blow fuse in the meter will burn out.

CURRENT CLAMP

Fig. 52 A current clamp connected to a voltmeter

1. Introduction

With a current clamp, you can measure a current through a wire without disturbing the circuit.
Since the current does not physically pass through the current clamp as it would an ammeter, current clamps are capable of measuring much larger currents compared to an ammeter; modern low-amps-type current clamps can also measure down to milli-amperes.

The current clamp sends its reading by releasing a voltage signal that correlates to the strength of the electrical current passing through the clamp. You must therefore connect the current clamp to a voltmeter before taking any measurements.

When connecting the current clamp you need to setup the multimeter correctly. The multimeter must be in the mV position. The outputs of the current clamp are connected to the inputs of the voltmeter.

Before taking any measurements, you must zero the current clamp with it being removed from any source of electric current. This calibrates the current clamp. The voltmeter should read 0mV when the clamp is connected to a de-energized circuit.

2. Magnetic Field

The current clamp measures the magnetic field that is generated around a conductor when current flows through it. If the current flow goes up, the magnetic field will increase proportionately.

The magnetic field causes the sensor in the current clamp to generate a voltage signal.
An output voltage of 1 mV, for example, is equal to 1 A being measured through the wire.

When connecting the current clamp, you must keep in mind the direction of the current flow.

If the current through the cable comes in on the positive (+) side of the current clamp, then you get a positive voltage reading. If the current comes in on the negative (-) side, then you get a negative voltage reading.

Fig. 53 Pay attention to the direction of current flow in the circuit when connecting the current clamp: Shown is the positive-biased orientation of the clamp.

Fig. 54 Pay attention to the direction of current flow in the circuit when connecting the current clamp: Shown is the negative-biased orientation of the clamp.

3. Measurement

Before you start taking measurements you must first set the appropriate current-measuring range of the current clamp. You have to choose between 1 mV/1A (600A) or 10mV/1A (100A), depending on the amount of the current that you expect to measure.

At position 1mV/1A, 1mV corresponds to 1A.
At position 10mV/1A, 10mV corresponds to 1A.

The current clamp must then be correctly connected to the multimeter, and the multimeter must be placed in the correct voltage-measuring range (mV scale).

Finally, the zero point of the current clamp must be set. There should be no current flowing when this is done!

To measure the current through a component, the current clamp must be placed around the wire of that component.

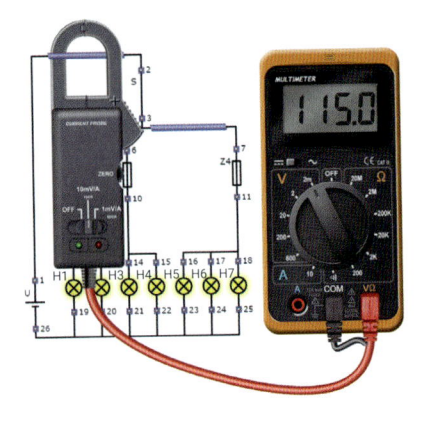

Fig. 55 Place the current clamp around the wire of the circuit that you want to measure.

Fig. 56 Measuring the Total Current Flow

Position the current clamp (10 mV/A) around the cable that leads directly from the battery to determine the total current intensity. The value read is 115 mV. This means that the measured value is 115/10 = 11.5 A.

The values for both wires are added together when measuring current through two wires at the same time. This means that if 10 A is measured through each wire, a total value of 20 A is measured.

When the current directions differ from each other, the magnetic fields will (partially) cancel each other out. If the current intensity in the upper circuit is 7 A and the current intensity in the lower circuit is 5 A, then 2 A will be measured.

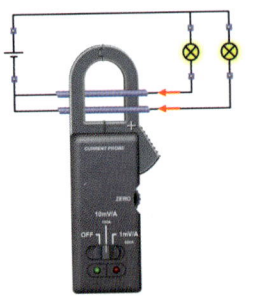

Fig. 57 Current values are added up.

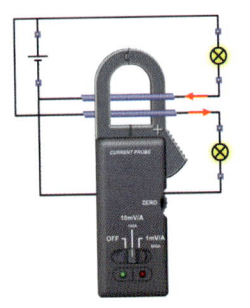

Fig. 58 Current values (partially) cancel each other out.

4. Voltage Drop Across Fuses

The current flowing through a circuit can be determined using a voltmeter without interrupting the circuit.
Ohm's law states that measuring the current drop across resistance allows you to determine if, and how much, current is flowing through the resistance.
This method is used to detect a minor current drain in the vehicle.

It can take up to half an hour to switch off all the systems in a modern car. A waiting period needs to be observed following the removal and/or replacement of fuses or plugs, or opening and/or closing the door.
This obviously hinders the detection of current drain.
The use of a current clamp is not practical in this situation as the wires are part of the wiring harness.

Every fuse has resistance, even if only a minimal amount. A voltage drop will be visible if current is flowing across the fuse.
Measuring the voltage drop across the fuses will allow you to determine whether or not current is flowing through the circuit.

The voltage drop measured is extremely small. That is why the multimeter is set to the mV scale.
The resistance of the fuse depends on the type and rating of the fuse. Depending on the type of fuse and the voltage drop measured, the corresponding current can be found in a table.

Fig. 59 A voltage drop is measured across the fuse, and this means the current is flowing.

Standard fuse.	5 A	10 A	15 A	20 A	25 A	30 A	Mains fuse.	40 A	60 A
	mA	mA	mA	mA	mA	mA		mA	mA
0.5 mV	28	65	104	148	198	254		132	294
1 mV	56	130	208	296	397	508		263	588
1.5 mV	84	195	313	444	595	761		395	882
2 mV	112	260	417	592	794	1015		526	1176
2.5 mV	140	325	521	740	992	1269		658	1471
3 mV	168	390	625	888	1190	1523		789	1765
3.5 mV	196	455	729	1036	1389	1777		921	2059
4 mV	224	519	833	1183	1587	2030		1035	2553
4.5 mV	252	584	938	1331	1786	2284		1184	2647
5 mV	280	649	1042	1479	1984	2538		1316	2941
5.5 mV	308	714	1146	1627	2183	2792			

Fig. 60 Lookup table for determining the current.

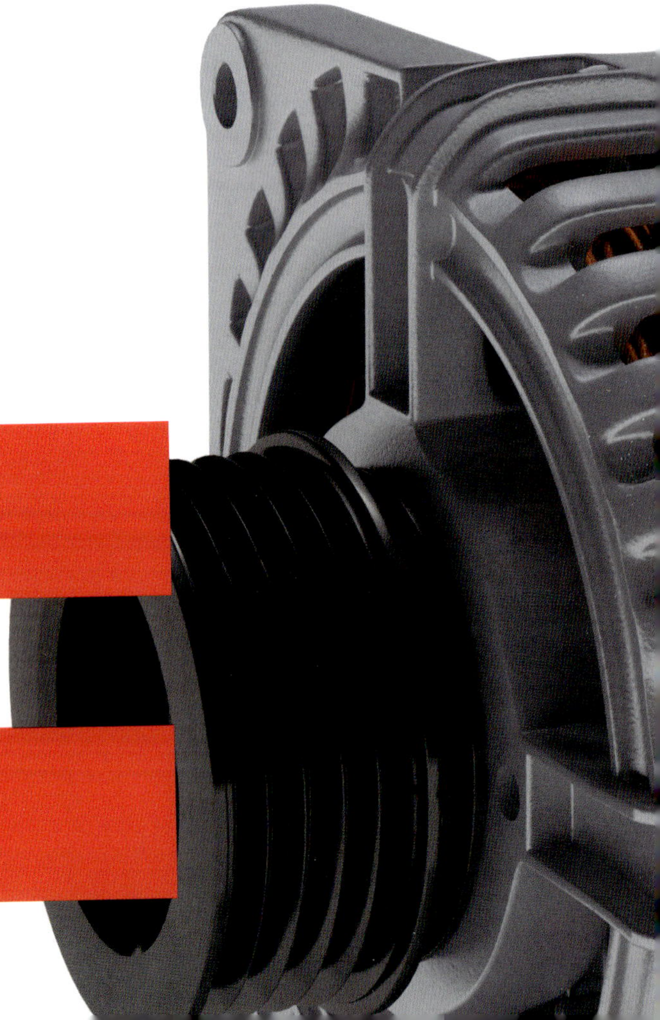

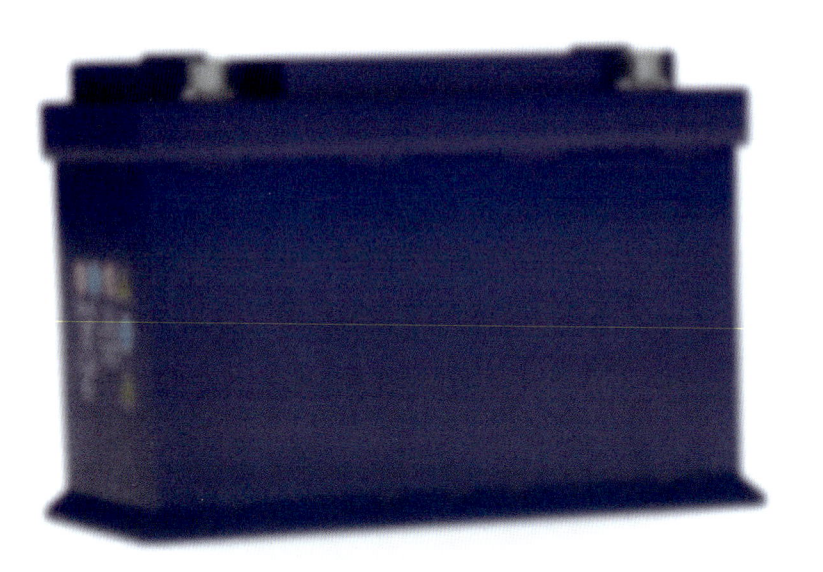

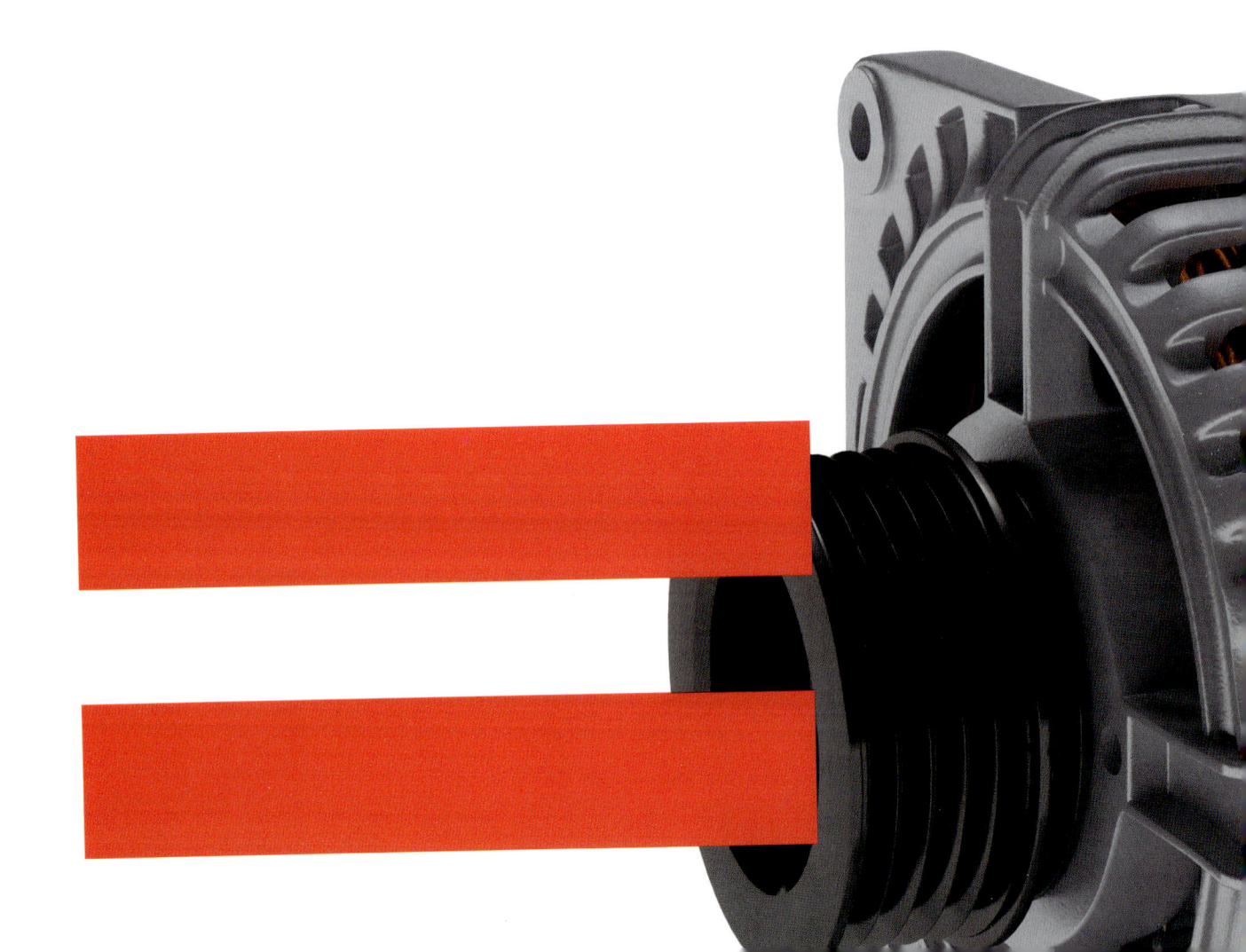

3. Series and Parallel Circuits

SERIES CIRCUITS

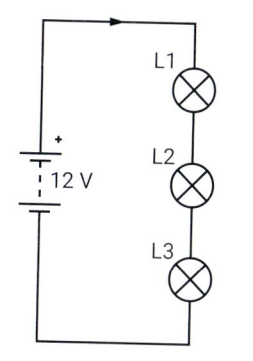

Fig. 61 Three lamps connected in series

1. Introduction

In series circuits, the components are connected in a loop, or series.

The current flow is the same at every point in the circuit; two different current loads cannot flow through one wire.
In a series circuit, the available voltage is divided amoungst the resistors or loads which are in series, so measured voltage can be different in different parts of the circuit.

One disadvantage of a series circuit is that no current will flow and none of the components will function if there is an open anywhere in the circuit.

Examples of series circuits are:
— A switch for operating a lamp is in series.
— Strings of Christmas lights are all in series.
— Several cells in vehicle batteries are connected in series so their voltages are all added together.

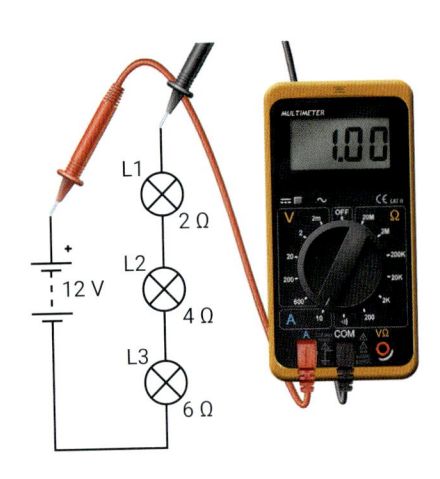

Fig. 62 The current flow in a series circuit is the same at all points in the circuit.

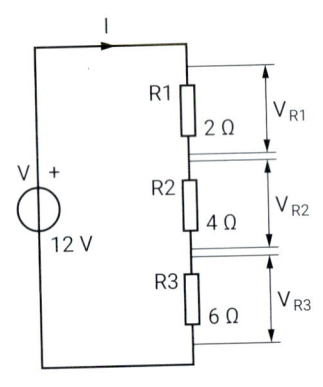

Fig. 63 Calculation example 1

2. Characteristics

The characteristics of a series circuit are:

— The current through a series circuit is the same at any given point in the circuit.
— If you add up the individual voltage drops in a series circuit, the result will be the total applied voltage.
— If you add up the resistance values, the result will be the total resistance.

Ohm's law (V = I x R) can be used to calculate the voltage, current and resistance in a series circuit.

Using the diagram, you will test each characteristic of the series circuit.

Calculation example 1:

First you calculate the total resistance. You do this by adding up all the resistances in the circuit.

R_{tot} = R1 + R2 + R3
R_{to} = 2 Ω + 4 Ω + 6 Ω
R_{to} = 12 Ω

The total resistance of this series circuit is 12 Ω.

Because the current through all of the resistors is the same and you know the supply voltage, you can calculate the total current for the circuit:

I = V / R
I = 12 V / 12 Ω
I = 1 A

A current of 1 ampere is flowing through the circuit.

You can also calculate the individual voltage drops across each resistor. The sum of all of these voltage drops should equal source voltage.

V_{R1} = I x R
V_{R1} = 1 A x 2 Ω
V_{R1} = 2 V

V_{R2} = I x R
V_{R2} = 1 A x 4 Ω
V_{R2} = 4 V

V_{R3} = I x R
V_{R3} = 1 A x 6 Ω
V_{R3} = 6 V

This proves that adding all of the voltage drops together equals the source voltage:
V = V_{R1} + V_{R2} + V_{R3}
V = 2 V + 4 V + 6 V
V = 12 V

PARALLEL CIRCUITS

1. Introduction

In parallel circuits, the loads are connected separately. The advantages of parallel circuits are:

— All loads operate at the same voltage, equal to source voltage.
— The loads can be controlled to operate at the same time or separately.

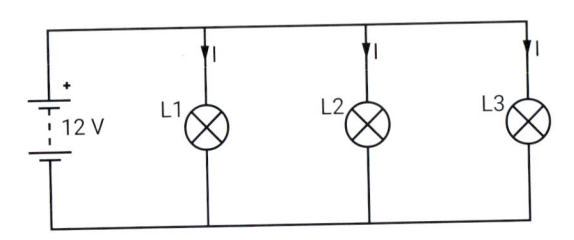

Fig. 64 Three lamps connected in parallel

Examples of parallel circuits include:
— The lamps in a tail lamp circuit
— The windshield wiper motor speed control circuit.

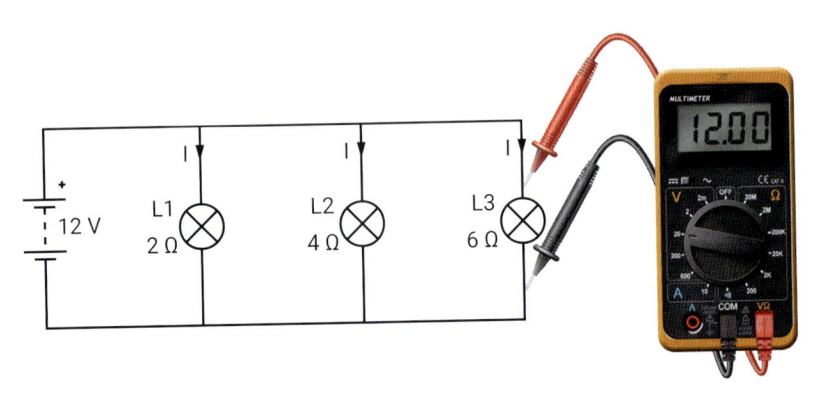

Fig. 65 The voltage across each lamp is the same.

2. Characteristics

The characteristics of a parallel circuit are as follows:
— The voltages across the components connected in parallel are equal to source voltage
— Current can be different in different branches of the circuit. To find the total current in the circuit, add up the current values of each of the parallel branches

— To calculate the equivalent (total) circuit resistance, divide the total voltage by the total current.

With Ohm's law (V = I x R) you can calculate the voltage, current, and resistance in a circuit. With the help of the diagram, you will determine whether the characteristics for a parallel circuit are correct.

Calculation example 1:

Because every lamp is directly connected to the power supply, the applied voltage on each lamp will be equal to source voltage.

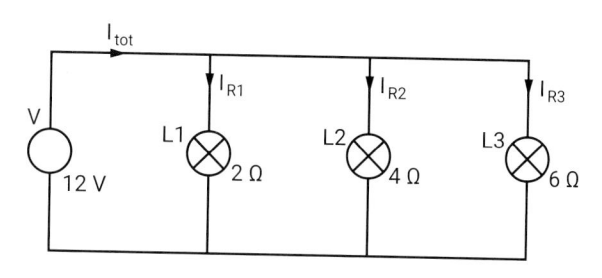

Fig. 66 Calculation example 1

To calculate the total circuit current you must first know the current flow for each branch of the circuit, which is calculated using Ohm's law.

I_{R1} = V / R
I_{R1} = 12 V / 2 Ω
I_{R1} = 6 A

I_{R2} = V / R
I_{R2} = 12 V / 4 Ω
I_{R2} = 3 A

I_{R2} = V / R
I_{R2} = 12 V / 6 Ω
I_{R2} = 2 A

Now that you have calculated the current flow for each branch, the total circuit current can be calculated by adding these values together.

$I_{to} = I_{R1} + I_{R2} + I_{R3}$
$I_{to} = 6\ A + 3\ A + 2\ A$
$I_{to} = 11\ A$

To calculate the equivalent (total) circuit resistance, divide the total current by the source voltage.

$R_v = V / I_{to}$
$R_v = 12\ V / 11\ A$
$R_v = 1.09\ Ω$

NOTE With a parallel circuit, the total resistance of the circuit is always smaller than the smallest branch resistance.

SERIES-PARALLEL CIRCUITS

1. Calculating series parallel circuits

To arrive at a good outcome, it's important to make a plan in advance.

Sometimes you cannot solve a circuit in one attempt; It's necessary to tackle the solution step-by-step.

Use Ohm's law:
$$V = I \times R$$

And the formulas for calculating the total resistance:
Series circuits:
$$R_V = R_1 + R_2 + R_3 \text{ etc.}$$
Parallel circuits:
$$1/R_V = 1/R_1 + 1/R_2 + 1/R_3 \text{ etc.}$$

Calculation example 1:
Calculate the current through the resistors R2 and R3.

Given:
V = 11 V
R1 = 7 Ω
R2 = 5 Ω
R3 = 5 Ω

Solution:
First calculate the total resistance of R2 and R3.
R_{2-3} = R2 + R3
R_{2-3} = 5 Ω + 5 Ω
R_{2-3} = 10 Ω

Now calculate the current with Ohm's law.
I_{R2-3} = V / R
I_{R2-3} = 11 V / 10 Ω
I_{R2-3} = 1.1 A

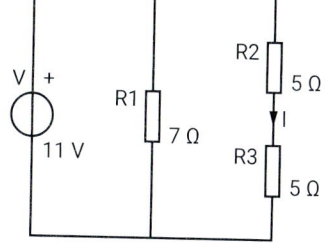

Fig. 67 Calculation example 1

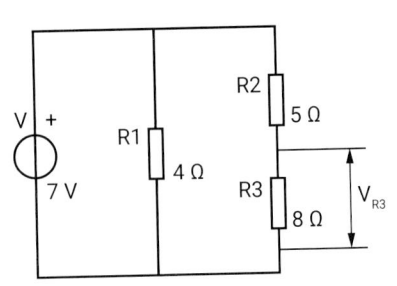

Fig. 68 Calculation example 2

Calculation example 2:

Calculate the voltage across the resistor R3.

Given:

V = 7 V

R1 = 4 Ω

R2 = 5 Ω

R3 = 8 Ω

Solution:

First calculate the total resistance of R2 and R3.

R_{2-3} = R2 + R3

R_{2-3} = 5 Ω + 8 Ω

R_{2-3} = 13 Ω

Now calculate the current with Ohm's law.

I_{R2-3} = V / R

I_{R2-3} = 7 V / 13 Ω

I_{R2-3} = 0.54 A

Now you can calculate the voltage across resistor R3 with Ohm's law.

V_{R3} = I_{R2-3} x R3

V_{R3} = 0.54 A x 8 Ω

V_{R3} = 4.32 V

Calculation example 3:

Calculate the voltage across resistor R3.

Given:

V = 14 V

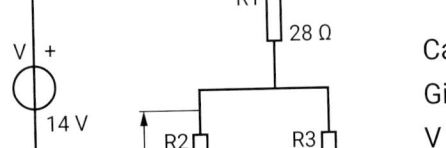

R1 = 28 Ω

R2 = 9 Ω

R3 = 12 Ω

Fig. 69 Calculation example 3

Solution:

First calculate the total resistance of R2 and R3.

$1/R_{2-3}$ = 1/R2 = 1/9 + 1/12

$1/R_{2-3}$ = 0.11 + 0.08

$1/R_{2-3}$ = 0.19

R_{2-3} = 1 / 0.19

R_{2-3} = 5.26 Ω

Calculate the total resistance.
$R_V = R1 + R_{2-3}$
$R_V = 28 \, \Omega + 5.26 \, \Omega$
$R_V = 33.26 \, \Omega$

Calculate the total current through the circuit.
$I = V / R_V$
$I = 14 / 33.26 \, \Omega$
$I = 0.42 \, A$

Now you can calculate the voltage across R2 with Ohm's law.
$V_{R2} = I \times R_{2-3}$
$V_{R2} = 0.42 \, A \times 5.26 \, \Omega$
$V_{R2} = 2.21 \, V$

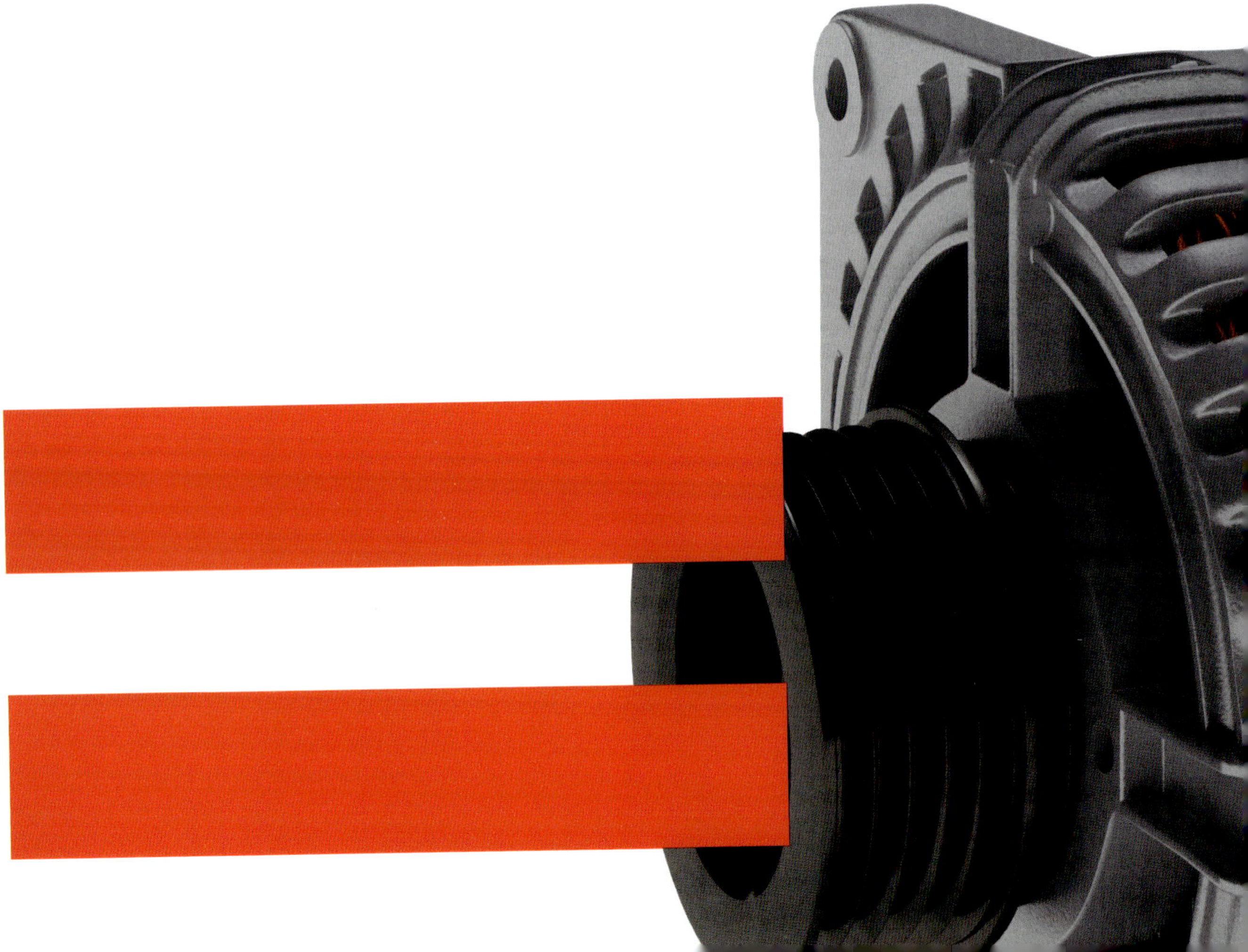

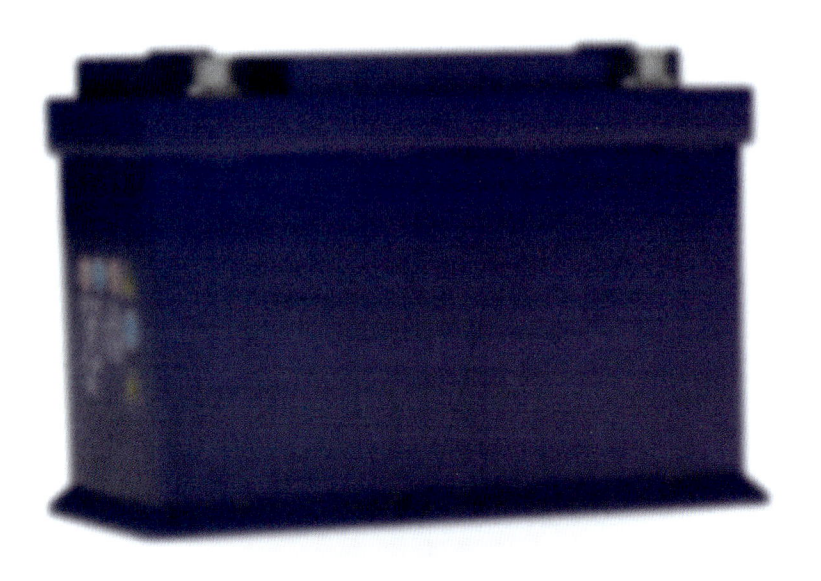

4. Basic Electrical Components

RESISTOR

1. Introduction

Electronics are unthinkable without resistors. Every circuit board contains resistors.

A resistor limits the electric current through a circuit. They also convert electric energy to heat.

The symbol (R) indicates resistance. The unit of resistance is ohm (Ω), from the Greek letter Omega.

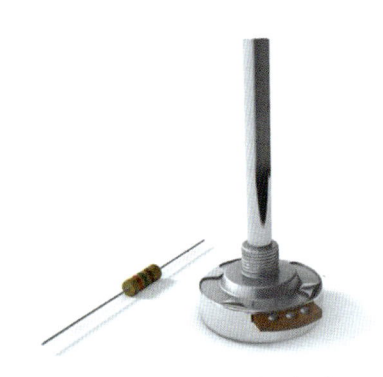

Fig. 70 A resistor with a fixed value and a variable value.

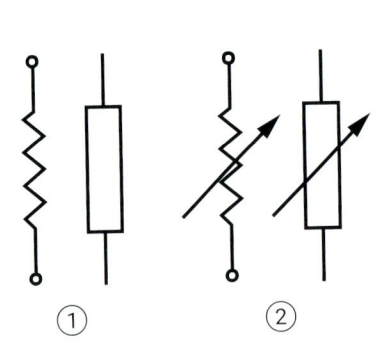

Fig. 71 The symbol of a fixed resistor (1) and variable resistor (2).

Fig. 72 Carrying out a resistance measurement

Resistors may have a fixed value or a variable value.
— Resistors with a fixed value can be recognized by the colored bands around the component.
— Resistors with a variable value can usually be set with a rotary switch.

You can perform a resistance measurement with a multimeter.

It's important to ensure the correct settings before you start measuring.

2. Operation

A conductor with a larger diameter or cross-section has more free electrons. Electric current can move much easier through larger conductors.
— The resistance increases, when the area (A) is smaller (inversely proportional).
— The resistance increases, when the length (l) increases (directly proportional).

When the cross-sectional area is doubled, the resistance is halved. When the length is doubled, the resistance is doubled.

Current flows more easily through some materials than through others. This is indicated by *specific resistance* (ρ).

The *specific resistance* of silver is the smallest. Copper and aluminium are also good conductors.

Specific resistance:

— Silver = 0.0160×10^{-6} Ωm

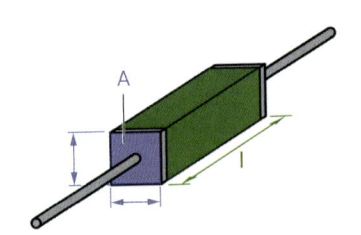

Fig. 73 Determining the cross-sectional area and the length of a resistor

- Copper = 0.0175 x 10⁻⁶ Ωm
- Aluminium = 0.028 x 10⁻⁶ Ωm

3. Types

Carbon and Metal Film Resistors
- A layer of vaporized carbon or metal is deposited onto a ceramic tube. Afterwards, a precision helix groove is cut into the deposited carbon or metal to ensure the correct resistance value.
- Because the deposited layer is very thin, the power rating (watts) of the resistor is small.

Wire Wound Resistors
- A resistor wire is wound around a ceramic tube.
- Because thick resistor wire is used, it can be used in higher power circuits.

SMD Resistors
- Soldered wires are replaced by solder pads.
- These resistors are soldered on the surface of a printed circuit board.
- Advantages are low production costs, smaller, lighter, and better properties.

Variable Resistors
- The resistance can easily be changed.
- There are linear and logarithmic variable resistors.

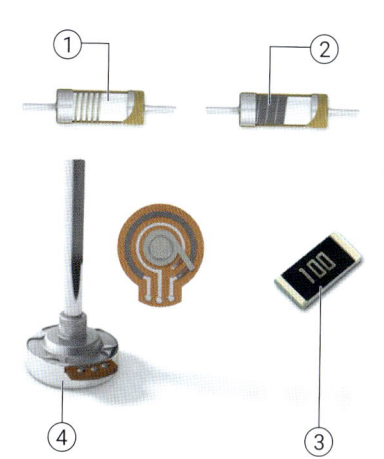

Fig. 74 1. Carbon and metal film resistor. 2. Wire wound resistor. 3. SMD resistor. 4. Variable resistors.

4. Characteristics

Maximum voltage:
When a resistor is used above the maximum voltage, a breakdown occurs that can influence the resistor's value.

Maximum power:
When the power of a resistor is exceeded, the temperature of the resistor will become too high. The resistor value can change.

Powers:
- Carbon resistors: 0.25–1 Watt.
- Wire wound resistors: 3–20 Watt.

Tolerance:

The actual resistance value is never exactly what's marked on the resistor housing. This deviation in percentage is due to precision tolerances in the production process. Environmental temperature also has an influence on the actual resistance value.

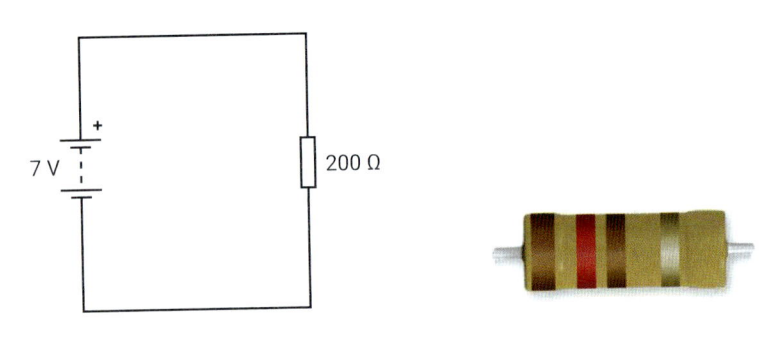

Fig. 75 Calculating the power through a resistor

Fig. 76 Resistance of 120 Ω with a tolerance of 5%

Calculating the power of a resistor:

You have a carbon film resistor rated at 0.25 W connected to a voltage source of 7 V. The resistance value of the resistor is 200 Ω. What is the power flowing through this resistor?

I = V / R
I = 7 V / 200 Ω
I = 0.035 A = 35 mA

P = V x I
P = 7 V x 0.035 A
P = 0.245 W

The power rating of this resistor is barely adequate. If the voltage increases, then the current flowing through the resistor will also increase and the resistor will overheat and break down.

Calculate the tolerance:

A resistance value of 120 Ω with a tolerance of 5 % means the actual resistance can be a maximum of 126 Ω and a minimum of 114 Ω.

5. Color Code

The numeral value of the resistor and tolerance are represented through a color code. There are different colored bands around a resistor.

It is important to start reading from the correct end.
- The first band is nearest to one end.
- The last rings can be silver or gold.
- The first band can be wider.

On resistors with four bands:

- Band 1 and 2 = numeral value.
- Band 3 = multiplication factor.
- Band 4 = tolerance.

Resistors are not made in all values. They are made in sets of standard values for each tolerance rating. The most common set is the E12 series, which includes 12 different resistor values with a +/- 10% tolerance rating

10, 12, 15, 18, 22, 27, 33, 39, 47, 56, 68, 82

These values can be multiplied or divided with 10 to get more values.

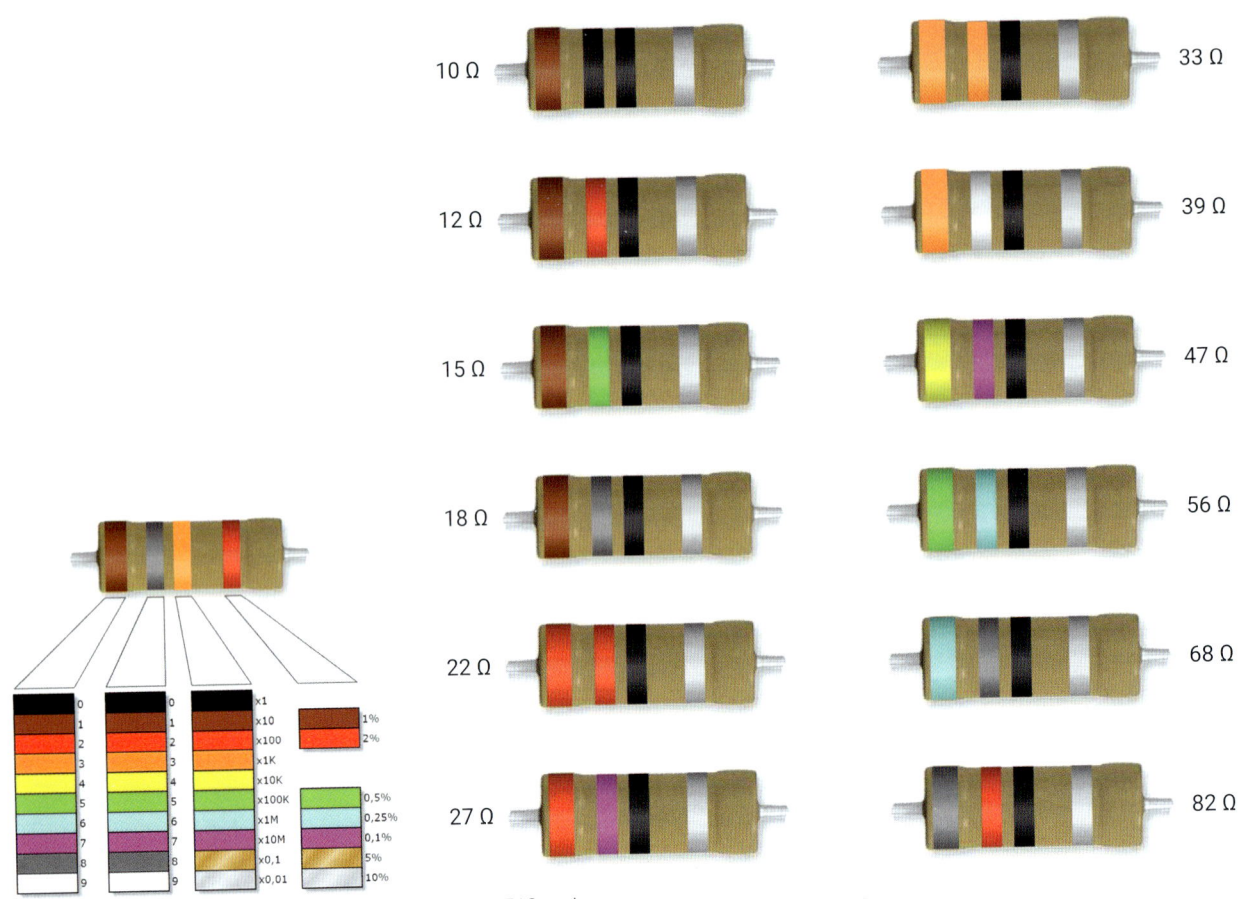

Fig. 77 Color coding of resistor (18 kΩ 2%)

Fig. 78 E12 series

You can also find the resistor of 10 Ω in the E12 series as 1 Ω, 100 Ω, 1 kΩ, and so on.

There are other systems used to indicate the size of a resistor, for example:
— A resistor of 560 Ω can be noted as 560R.
— A resistor of 5600 Ω can be noted as 5k6.

6. Application

Here you see a printed circuit board of an amplifier.

Different components are used for the correct operation of this amplifier.

You can recognize the components on a circuit board using their symbols.

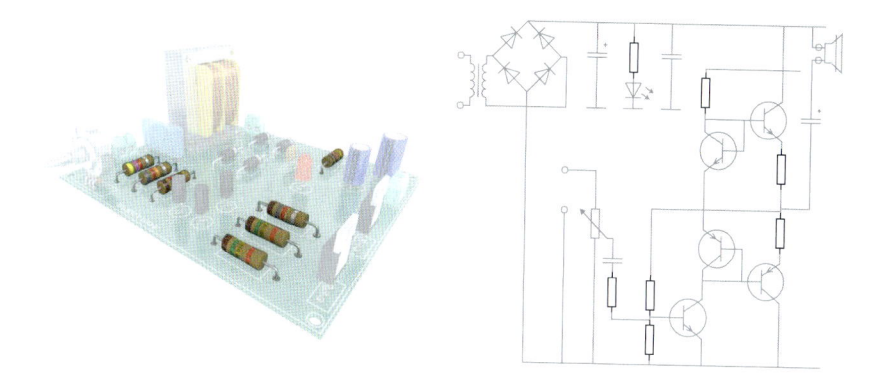

Fig. 79 Printed circuit board with resistors

Fig. 80 Electrical diagram with resistors

Resistors are essential here.

All resistors have a fixed value, except the variable resistor on the input.

POTENTIOMETER

1. Determining Position

A potentiometer behaves like a variable resistor.

The resistance can be adjusted with the help of a knob that fits over the shaft. When the knob is turned, this creates a variable voltage.

The symbol of the potentiometer is a resistor with an arrow through it. The arrow is the third connection and indicates the variable resistance.

Potentiometers have many applications in modern electronics. In automotive applications you can find them in the throttle position sensor and the accelerator pedal position sensor.

Fig. 81 Potentiometer

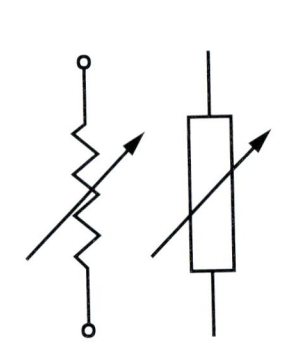

Fig. 82 2 Symbols of a potentiometer.

Fig. 83 A potentiometer is used to determine the position of the throttle valve and the accelerator pedal.

2. Components

A potentiometer contains the following parts:
— electrical connections
— adjustment axis
— track without variable resistance
— carbon track for the variable resistance
— wiper (sliding contact)
— wiper carrier (arm)
— housing

4. BASIC ELECTRICAL COMPONENTS

A potentiometer has two circular tracks. The outer track is made of carbon so that it has a resistance. The inner track is made of a highly conductive material.

Because the wiper connects both tracks with each other, a resistance is created between the connections of the outer carbon track and the connection of the middle conductive track.

By turning the knob and attached wiper, it is possible to set the resistance value.

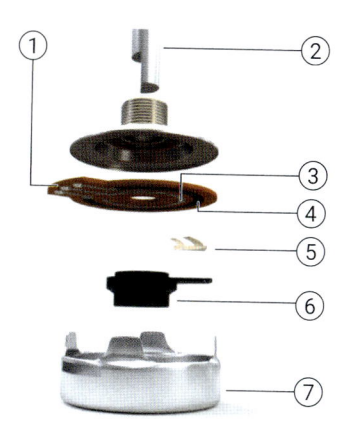

Fig. 84 Parts of a potentiometer: 1. connections 2. adjustment axis 3. track without variable resistor 4. carbon track for the variable resistor 5. stylus 6. stylus carrier 7. housing

3. Potentiometer Resistance

Some potentiometers have a linear resistance change. This means that the resistance increases in a straight line, in relation to the rotation of the stylus.

In logarithmic potentiometers, the resistance value increases with a logarithmic function. When you plot this line on the same graph, you will see a curved line.

The potentiometer shown here has a rotational angle of 270°.

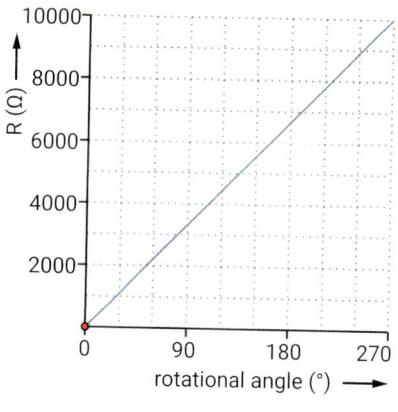

Fig. 85 Resistance value of a linear potentiometer

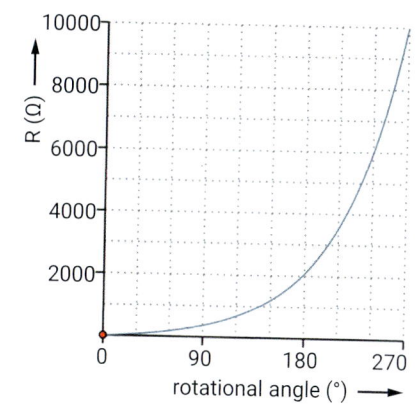

Fig. 86 Resistance value of a logarithmic potentiometer

4. Application

Here you see a printed circuit board of an amplifier.

Different components are used for the correct operation of this amplifier.

You can recognize the components on a circuit board using their symbols.

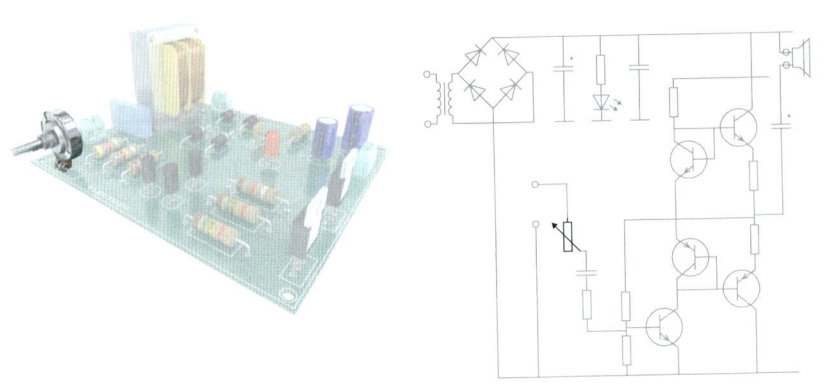

Fig. 87 Printed circuit board with variable resistor

Fig. 88 Electrical diagram with variable resistor

In the diagram you can recognize the variable resistor by the arrow in the resistor.

The variable resistor is used here to adjust the volume of the amplifier.

RELAY

A relay consists of a coil with a soft iron core. When a current flows through the coil, a magnetic field is generated. This current is called the control current.

The magnetic field exerts a force on the lever. A switch is attached to the lever. The force of the magnetic field moves the lever and closes the switch for the main current.

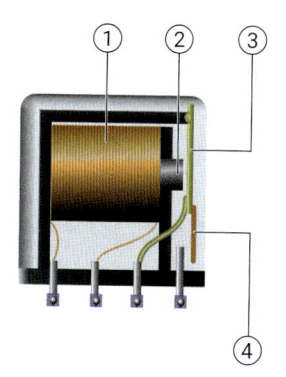

Fig. 89 De-energized relay: 1. coil 2. soft iron core 3. switch lever 4. switch contact

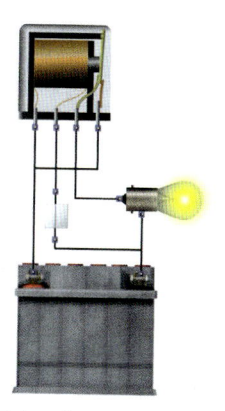

Fig. 90 Relay circuit with energized relay

1. Operation

The purpose of a relay is to switch a large main current, using a small control current.

A small switch can handle the control current without burning out. The relay contacts switch the current to the load and are large enough to handle this.

A standard relay has four electrical terminals.
These are: (1) main current input, (2) main current output, (3) control current input, and (4) control current output.

For example, relays can be used to switch current to the starter solenoid, horn, and headlamps.

54 ELECTRICAL SYSTEMS

Fig. 91 Mini relay

Fig. 92 Micro relay

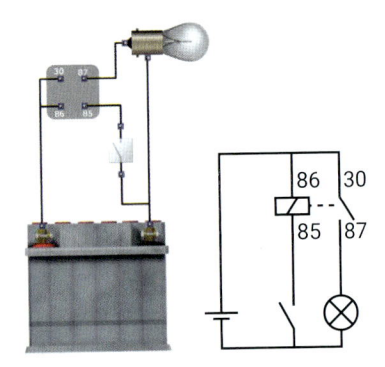

Fig. 93 Relay connected in a circuit

2. Types

Relays are divided into three types:

1. Normally-open (NO) contact relay—this type of relay closes the circuit when energized.

2. Normally-closed (NC) contact relay—this type of relay breaks the circuit when energized.

3. Changeover relay—this type of relay closes one circuit when energized and another when de-energized.

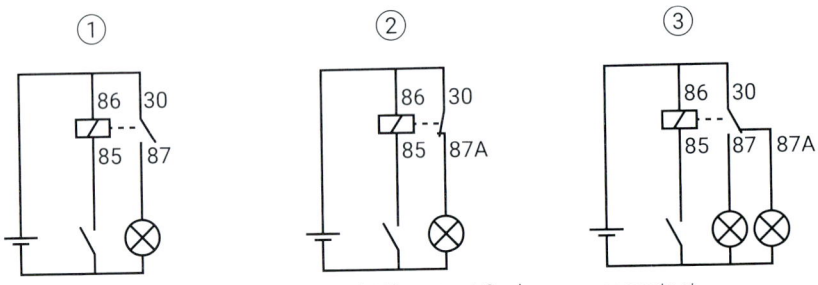

Fig. 94 Relay with: 1. (NO) contact 2. (NC) contact 3. changeover contact

A relay sometimes has a resistor or a diode. The resistor or diode is connected in parallel across the coil and used to dampen the induced voltage spike after the coil circuit is switched off.

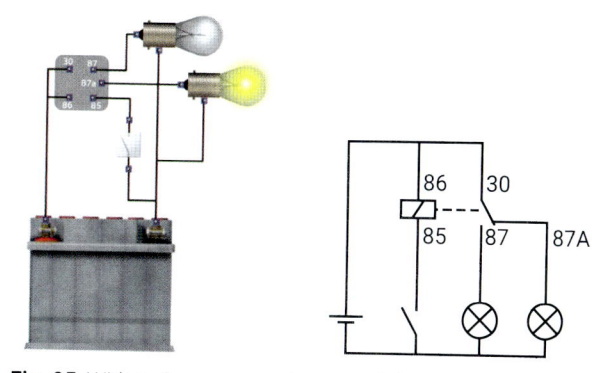

Fig. 95 With a changeover relay, one of the contacts is always connected.

HOW TO: TEST THE RELAY

1. Tools Required

We test the relay by checking the relay coil and the relay switch. We will also look at how the relay functions when it is connected in the car.

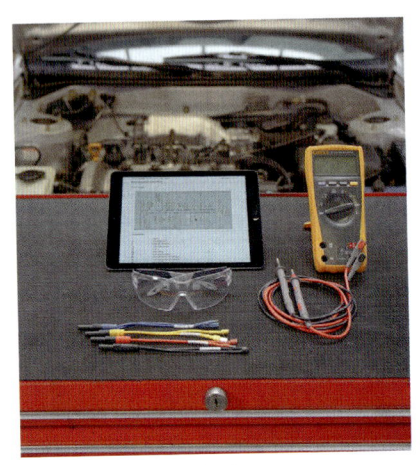

Fig. 96 Tools Required

2. Electrical diagram of the EFI relay

The diagram shows the EFI relay; this is the relay that we are testing.

4. BASIC ELECTRICAL COMPONENTS

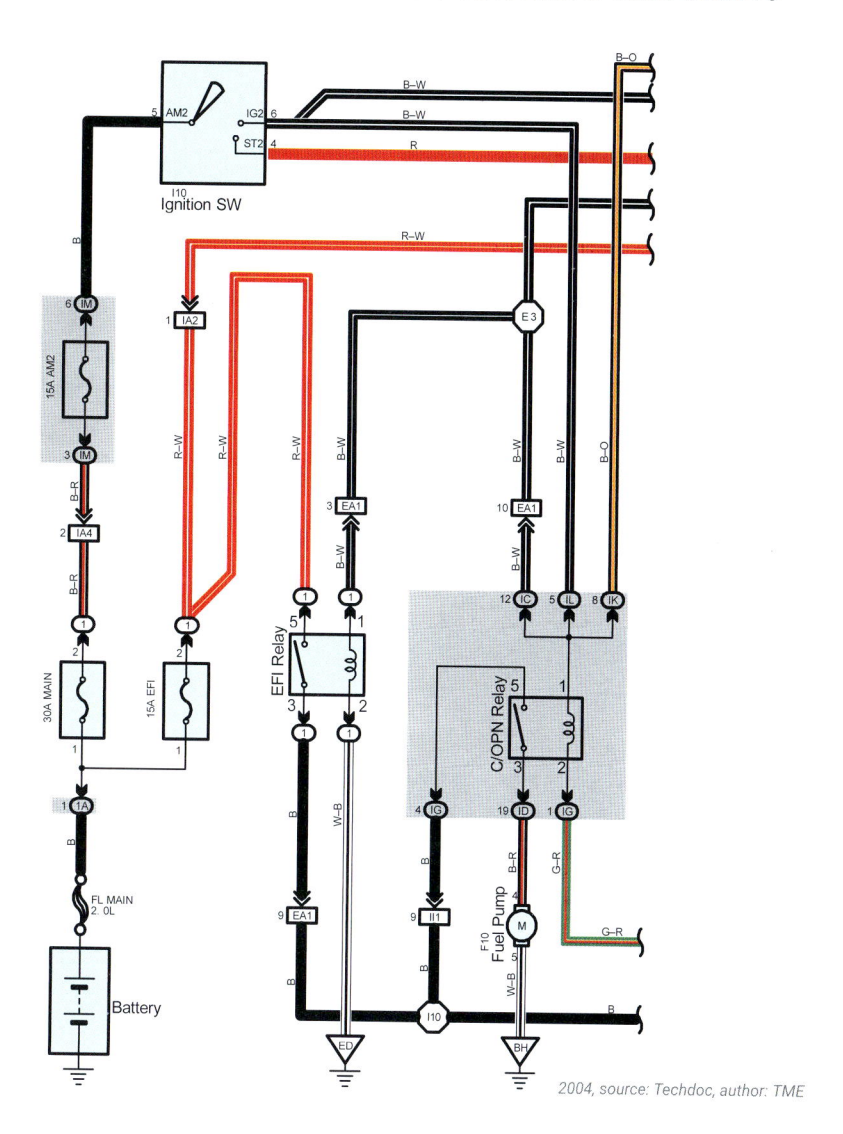

57

3. Test the relay coil and the relay switch.

The resistance of the coil is checked. The switch is also measured without power to see if it is stuck open or closed.

Fig. 97 Remove the relay from the relay box. Measure the resistance of the relay coil, between pins 1 and 2 of the relay. This is 91.6 Ω. You can find out if this is correct in the shop manual.

Fig. 98 Measure the resistance of the switch, between pins 3 and 5 of the relay. This relay is a normally-open (NO) relay, the switch is open without assistance. The resistance should be very high.

4. Test the operation of the relay.

By using Y cables we can connect the relay to its circuit while taking measurements to see if the relay functions properly.

Fig. 99 Connect the relay to the Y cables.

Fig. 100 Connect both multimeters to the Y cables. The left multimeter is connected to the control of the relay coil, pins 1 and 2. The right multimeter is connected to the two switch connections, pins 3 and 5.

Fig. 101 The left multimeter shows 0 V. There is no voltage on the coil. The right multimeter indicates 12.8 V, which is battery voltage. In the diagram, pin 5 is connected to the battery because the switch is open, and there is 0 V on the other side of the switch.

Fig. 102 Switch on the ignition. The coil of the relay is now energized. The voltage difference is then 12.6 V on the left multimeter. The voltage difference across the switch with the switch closed is now 0 V. The relay works properly.

DIODE

1. Introduction

Diodes belong to the category of semiconductors. The current through a diode can only flow in one direction. A diode can operate in either *forward bias* or *reverse bias*.

A diode is indicated with the letter D.

A diode can be compared with a one-way check valve because the current can only go through in one direction.

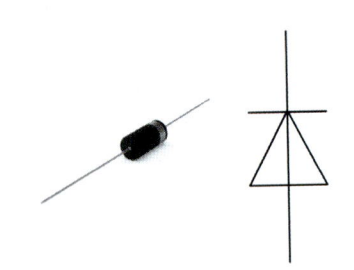

Fig. 106 Diode

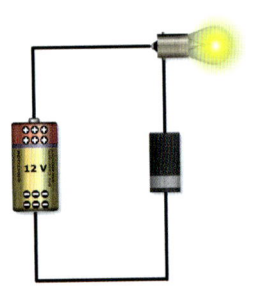

Fig. 107 Diode in forward direction

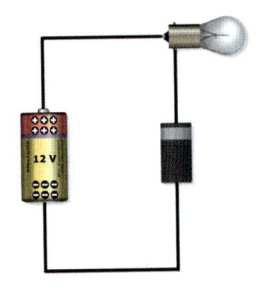

Fig. 108 Diode in reverse direction

Fig. 109 The cathode can be recognized by the colored ring.

2. Construction

A diode has two terminals, the anode and cathode. It's crucial to recognize these two terminals in order to determine forward and reverse bias.

When the current flows from the anode to the cathode, the diode will conduct.

The cathode is often recognized by a colored ring around one end of the casing.

Diodes can be made of different materials. Two of the most common elements used are:
— silicon
— germanium

4. BASIC ELECTRICAL COMPONENTS

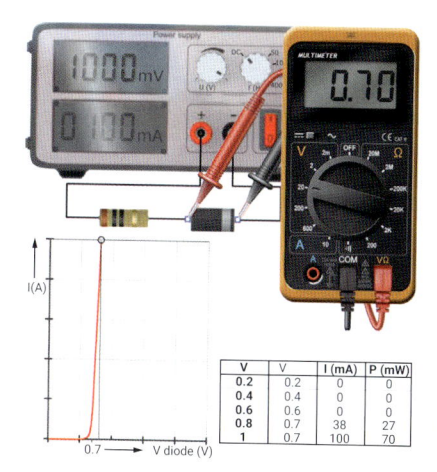

Fig. 110 Example

3. Operation

Each diode has a threshold voltage. When the diode conducts, a voltage drop occurs across the diode. The level of the threshold voltage depends on the material of the diode.
— germanium is 0.3 V
— silicon is 0.7 V

Power dissipation developed in a diode is defined by the multiplication of the threshold voltage x the forward current.

$$P_{diode} = V_{threshold} \times I$$

EXAMPLE

Given:
V_{source} = 0.8 V
$V_{threshold}$ = 0.7 V
I = 40 mA

Requested:
What is the developed power in the diode?

Answer:
P_{diode} = V x I
P_{diode} = 0.7 x 40
P_{diode} = 28 mW

4. Application

Here you see a printed circuit board of an amplifier.

Various electronic components are used for the correct functioning of this amplifier.

Use your acquired knowledge to identify the components on the circuit board.

Fig. 111 Printed circuit board with diodes

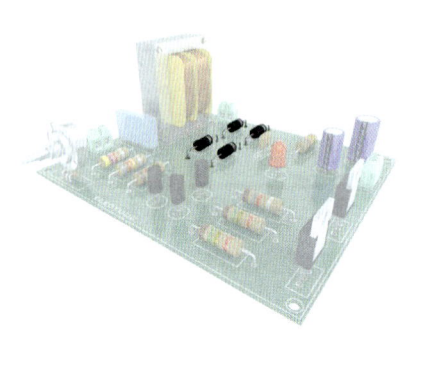

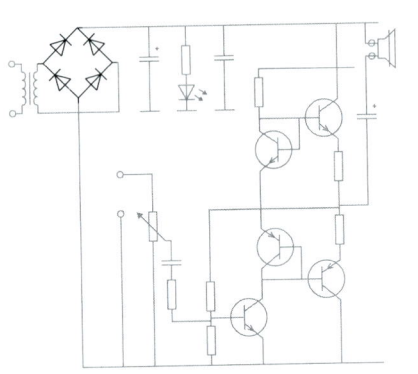

Fig. 112 Electrical diagram with diodes

5. Testing Diodes

A diode can be tested in different ways. Two common ways are:
— By means of a light and power source.
— With the aid of a multimeter.

The use of a lamp is a cheap but reliable solution. The lamp is connected to the battery and the diode. If the diode is in the reverse direction, the lamp should not light up. The lamp should light up in the forward direction. Usually a 12 V/10 W lamp is used for this test.

You can also test a diode with a multimeter. This is possible in two ways:
— resistance measurement
— diode test function

With both methods, the multimeter sends a small current through the diode. In the case of a resistance measurement, a resistance value can be read on the multimeter. If the diode test function is used, the threshold voltage can be read on the display.

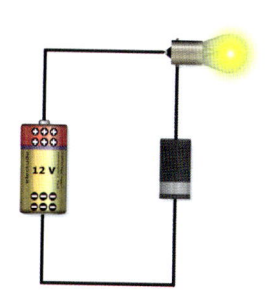

Fig. 113 Testing with a lamp

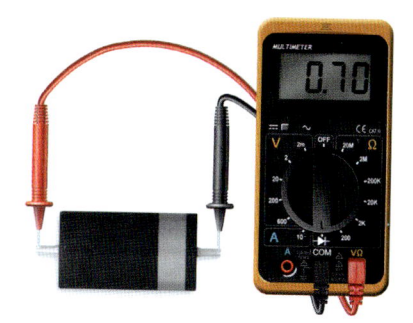

Fig. 114 Testing with a multimeter

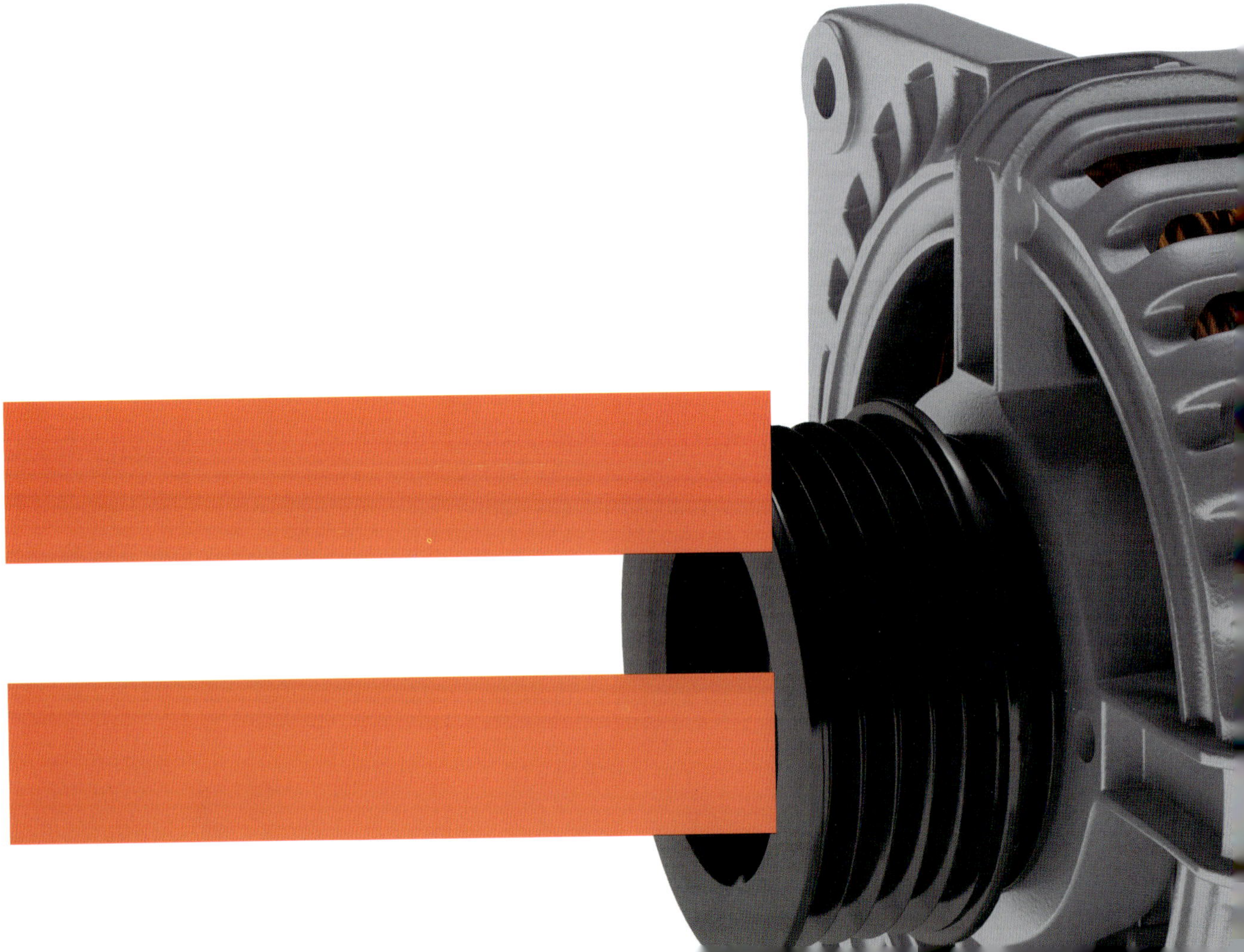

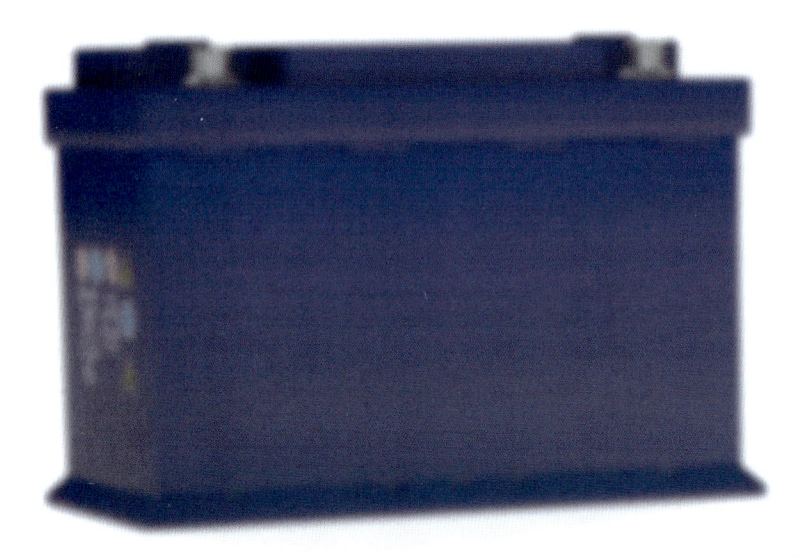

5. Electric Motor

ELECTROMAGNETISM

1. Introduction

There are two types of magnets:
- Permanent magnets; these are always magnetic.
- Electromagnets; these can be switched on and off, therefore it is possible to control the force. These magnets can also be stronger than permanent magnets.

Examples of devices, which use electromagnetism are:

- electric motor
- speaker
- relay

In the case of an iron recycling plant, powerful electromagnets are used to lift iron.

Fig. 115 Electromagnetic components:
1. Electric motor 2. Loudspeaker.
3. Relay.

Fig. 116 An electromagnet is used to move scrap metal.

An electromagnet is made out of a coil of wire and an iron core. The moment a current flows through the coil, the coil becomes magnetic. Magnetism travels more easily through iron than through air. The magnetic field of the coil is strengthened by using an iron core.

2. Magnetic Field Around a Conductor

When current runs through a wire, there will be a magnetic field around the conductor. This magnetic field is used to make an electromagnet.

A magnetic field can be visualized using a schematic showing magnetic field lines. In electromagnets these are also referred to as lines of induction.

To determine the direction of the field lines, the **right-hand rule** is applied.

By taking hold of a wire and positioning your thumb in the direction of the current. The direction that your fingers are pointing, is the same direction of the magnetic field lines.

In the schematic the green **arrow** represents the direction of current.

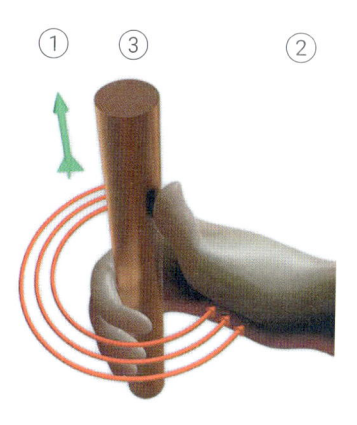

Fig. 117
Right hand rule:
1. Current direction 2. Right hand 3. Conductor.
The direction of the field currents (red) is determined by the current direction.

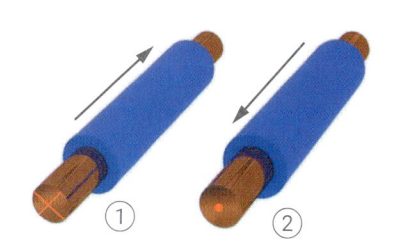

Fig. 118 With a conductor with a cross (1) the current flows away from you. With a conductor with a point (2) the current comes towards you.

3. Magnetic Field Through a Coil

The magnetic field around a single wire is very weak. The coil was developed for electrical devices that require a strong magnetic field to operate. The magnetic field can be increased by having a greater number of winding turns.

The magnetic field at either end of the coil can be compared with the ends of a permanent magnet; because both a north and south pole is created.

The force of an electromagnet is proportional to the number of turns and the electrical current flowing through it.
In other words: *The field strength of a coil with 5 turns and 1 A is just as powerful as a coil with 1 winding and 5 A.*

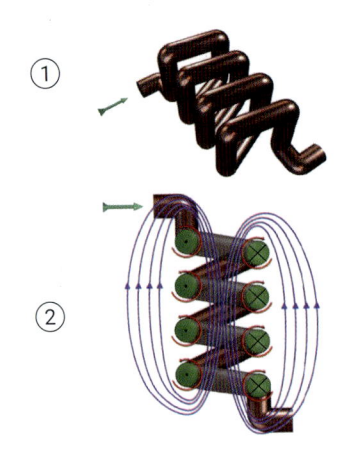

Fig. 119 1. The current through the coil
2. The current direction and magnetic field.

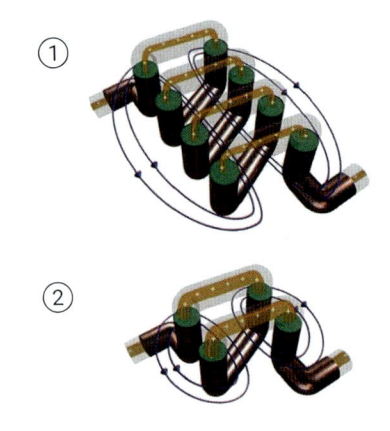

Fig. 120 1. Magnetic field with 2A with 4 windings is as strong as the magnetic field with 4A with 2 windings.

4. Calculations Based on a Coil

Ampere's law describes how an electric current generates a magnetic field.

The following formula applies in respect of the field strength in a coil:

$$H = N * \frac{I}{l_{coil}}$$

- H = field strength in (A/m)
- N = number of windings
- I = current in (A)
- l_{coil} = length of coil in (m)

ELECTRIC MOTOR

1. Introduction

In 1821, Michael Faraday was the first to succeed in developing an electric motor. With an electric motor, *electrical energy* is converted into *mechanical energy*. This conversion takes place through *Lorentz forces*.

An electric motor consists of:
— Stator or permanent magnet: the fixed part of the motor.
— Armature (or rotor): the moving part of the motor.

The commutator or collector ensures that the current flows through the armature in the right direction.

Fig. 121 You stand still and push every passing outer ring.

Fig. 122 The stator or magnet (1) stands still; the armature (2) rotates. 3. Commutator.

You can compare the operation of the electric motor with a children's carousel on a playground. You stand still (stator or magnet) and drive the outer ring by continuously giving a push (Lorentz force) on the carousel (armature) as each outer ring comes along (commutator).
With an electric motor, the stator or permanent magnet creates a magnetic field within the housing of the electric motor. The north and south poles do not change and remain in the same position. The armature is the rotating part of the electric motor. If the electric motor rotates a little further to the left, the commutator must ensure

that the current flows on the other winding. This allows the armature to continue turning.

2. Commutator

A commutator is used to make an electrical connection to the armature. Another word for a commutator is collector.
A commutator can be seen as a rotary switch.
The current flows through the carbon brushes to the copper plates of the commutator. This is in turn connected to the windings in the armature.
The commutator has the following functions:
— Changing the direction of current as a mechanical rectifier.
— Ensuring an electrical connection to the armature.

One disadvantage of the commutator is that voltage loss occurs across the carbon brushes. The carbon brushes also wear out.
An electric motor is equipped with multiple windings to eliminate dead spots. This also makes the torque higher and more even.

Operation:
The "+" carbon brush comes into contact with the commutator, whereby the current flows through the upper part of the winding and through the lower part back to the "-" carbon brush. The current in the upper part must always flow away from the carbon brush to keep the armature rotating. If the armature turns a little further, the "+" carbon brush will come into contact with the next winding. The commutator therefore ensures that the current reverses in the winding. (Just as with a children's carousel, you push the next passing outer ring forward.)

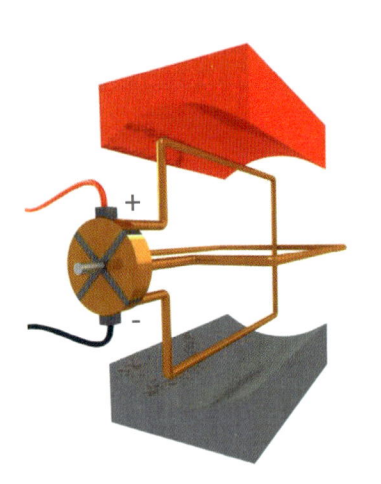

Fig. 123 The top of the armature is connected with "+" and the bottom is always the "-".

3. Electromagnetic Field

There are two different ways to obtain a magnetic field. By means of *permanent magnetism* or *electromagnetism*.

If the field is generated by means of electromagnetism, the permanent magnets are replaced with stator windings (field windings). In this way, the stator windings are responsible for generating electromagnetism.

Fig. 124 Principle of a motor with permanent stator field.

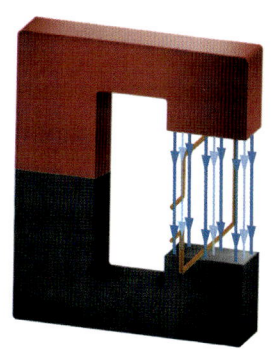

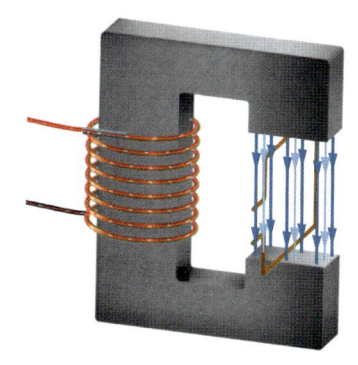

Fig. 125 Principle of a motor with electromagnetic stator field.

If a motor has permanent magnets, you can change the rotational direction of the electric motor by changing the direction of the current through the motor.

If you have a motor with electromagnets, you cannot change the rotational direction of the electric motor. Motors with electromagnets are therefore **never** used for operating windows, sun roofs, seats or adjusting mirrors.

Because motors with electromagnets do not yet have a counter voltage when they start to rotate, a very large current flows through the stator and armature windings. This therefore creates a very strong magnetic field in the stator and the armature. This provides maximum starting torque.

4. Structure of a Motor

There are various types of motors on the market with different properties and constructions. We can look at these motors to identify all the parts:

Permanent magnet motor:
— This motor has a laminated rotor to reduce eddy currents.

Universal motor (electromagnetic motor):
— This motor is equipped with stator segments; permanent magnets are replaced by field windings. Pole shoes are needed to evenly distribute the field magnetism.

Squirrel cage armature motor:
— This motor does not require a commutator. The armature bars are short-circuited at both ends by the end rings; this is called a rotor cage.

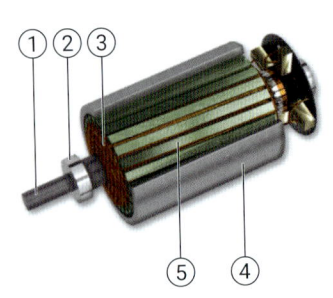

Fig. 126 Permanent magnet motor:
1. Shaft. 2. Bearing. 3. Armature.
4. Permanent magnets.
5. Laminated motor.

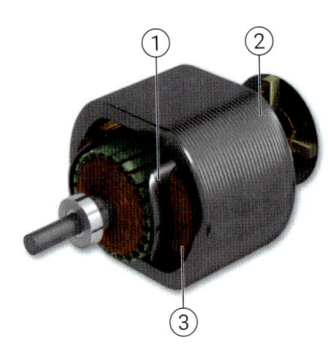

Fig. 127 Universal motor:
1. Pole shoes. 2. Laminated stator.
3. Field windings.

Fig. 128 Squirrel cage armature motor.
The armature consists of conductive bars short-circuited at both ends by end rings.

ELECTRIC MOTOR: PERMANENT MAGNET MOTOR

1. Introduction

A permanent magnet motor (pm motor) uses permanent magnets. This motor is often used in:
- starter motors
- wheelchair motors
- cordless drills

No field windings are used in the construction, therefore permanent magnet motors are typically smaller and more energy efficient.

Permanent magnet motors are not always suitable for large capacities; this is because the strength of permanent magnets is limited. That said, new magnetic materials have been developed which are several times stronger.

Fig. 129 A permanent magnet motor (PM motor).

Fig. 130 Motors with permanent magnets are used in: 1. Wheelchair motors. 2. Cordless drills. 3. Starter motors.

Very powerful permanent magnets can be made using rare materials such as neodymium and samarium. Electric motors equipped with these powerful magnets can deliver high torque with a compact design. The use of these rare materials in the required permanent magnets makes these electric motors more expensive than when standard magnets are used.

2. Motor Construction

Permanent magnet motors have a commutator. The commutator is responsible for an electrical connection with the rotor.

Permanent magnets are used in the stator construction. These are responsible for generating the magnetic field in the stator.

You can see through the illustration, that in the case of a pm motor, current only flows through the rotor (armature).

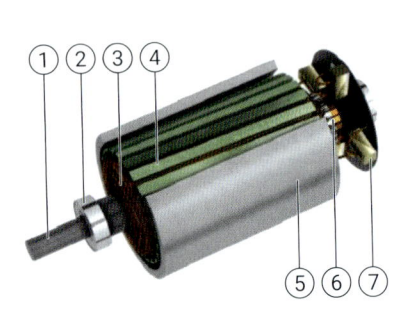

Fig. 131 A permanent magnet motor or PM motor. 1. Shaft. 2. Bearing. 3. Winding. 4. Laminated rotor. 5. Permanent magnets. 6. Commutator. 7. Carbon brush.

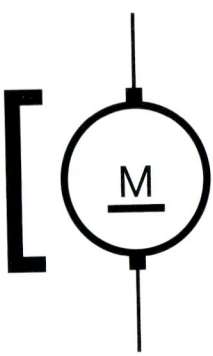

Fig. 132 The electrical symbol for PM motors.

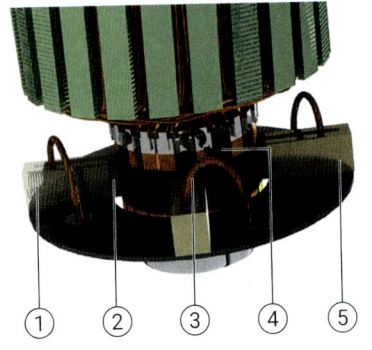

Fig. 133 The commutator with carbon brushes. 1. Carbon brush spring. 2. Carbon brush. 3. Connecting wire. 4. Commutator lamellae. 5. Carbon brush housing.

3. Operation

The most important components of this motor are the field magnets and the rotor winding.

The direction of motor rotation can be changed by reversing the supply voltage.

The current through the rotor winding creates a magnetic field around the winding. Because the magnetic field in the winding acts conversely to the magnetic field in the permanent magnets, the winding is pushed away. We call this force the Lorentz force.

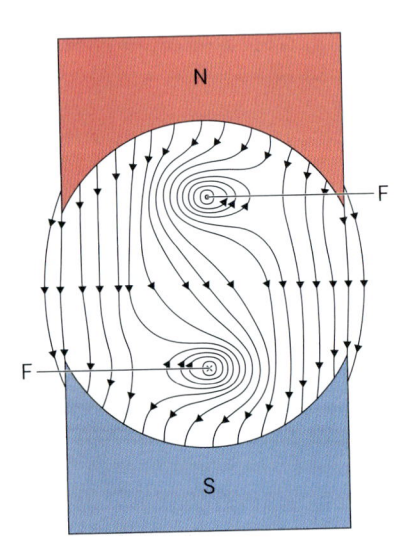

Fig. 134 Magnetic lines of force that push the winding away clockwise. These Lorentz forces provide the torque.

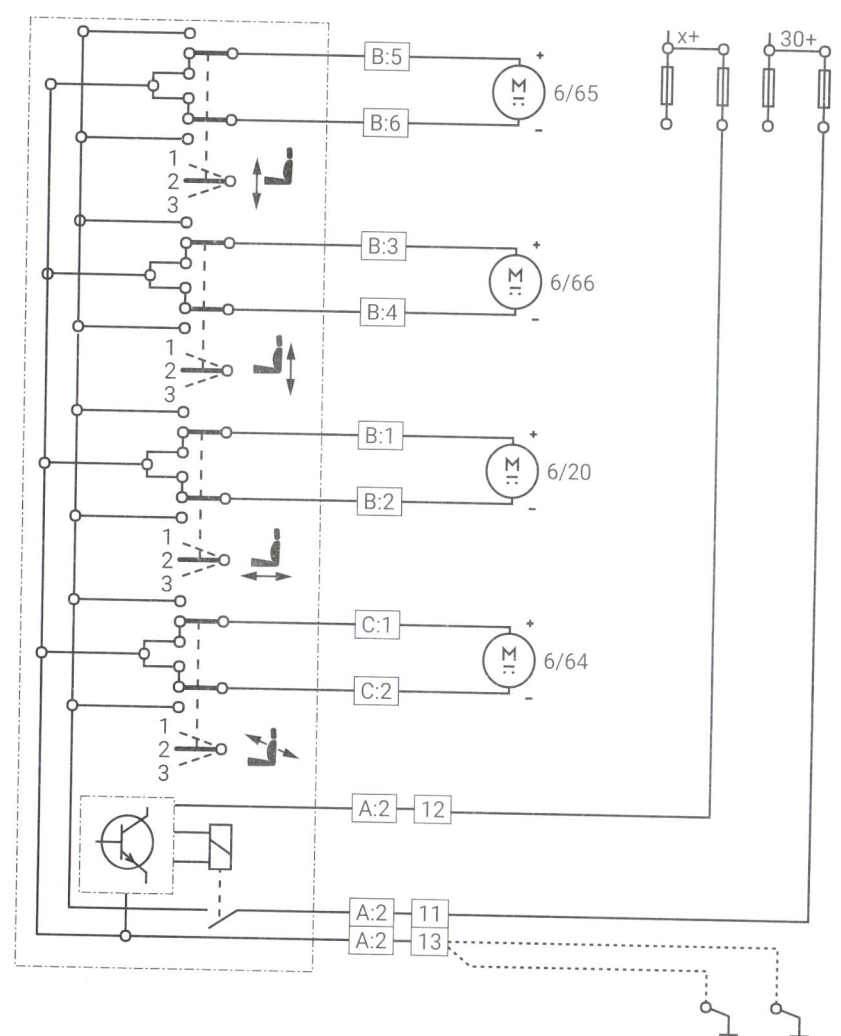

Fig. 135 An electric motor applied to the height adjustment of a seat. The motor's direction of rotation can be changed by reversing the supply voltage and ground.

4. Electrical Characteristics

The rotation of an electric motor generates a voltage. This voltage is called counter electromotive force (CEMF), also known as back electromotive force (back EMF, E_b).

The CEMF increases as the rotational speed increases. No CEMF is generated when the motor is prevented from rotating.

When calculating the current, you need to take into account that CEMF is generated. The formula for this is:

$$V_{terminal} - E_b = I_{rotor} \times R_{rotor}$$

Because an electric motor only has copper as an electrical

conductor, when controlling the motor the resistance will never be higher than a few ohms.

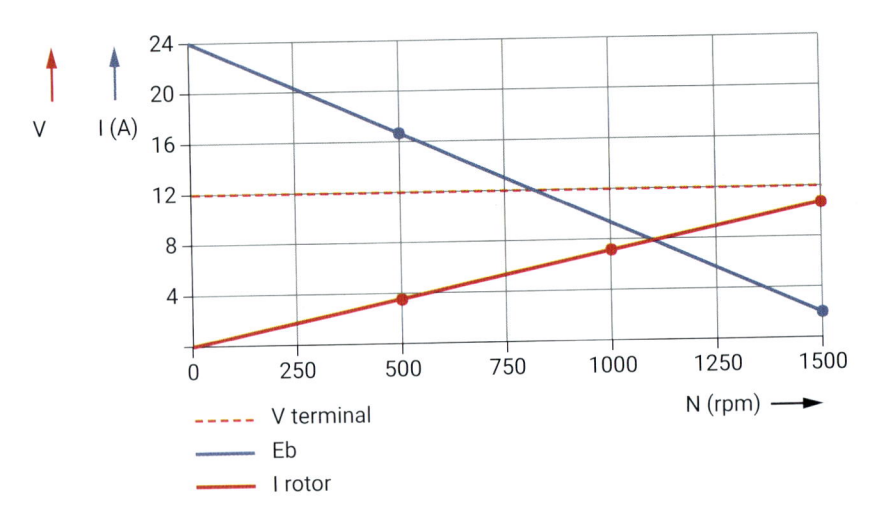

Fig. 136 Counter voltage.

5. Speed Control

The speed of an electric motor can be controlled by increasing or decreasing the voltage. Because vehicle electric systems function with a fixed source voltage, the voltage on the electric motor is reduced by:
— Resistors.
— PWM control.

In a speed control system with resistors, one or more resistors are connected in series with the electric motor. This controls the voltage difference across the motor. The less voltage difference, the lower the speed.

In speed control systems that use a PWM control, the voltage across the motor is adjusted by regulating the average voltage across the motor. At a duty cycle of 50%, there are 12 volts across the motor for half the time. There is no voltage across the motor for the remaining 50% of the time. The average voltage across the motor is then 6 volts. The motor runs at a constant speed by switching the voltage on and off quickly.

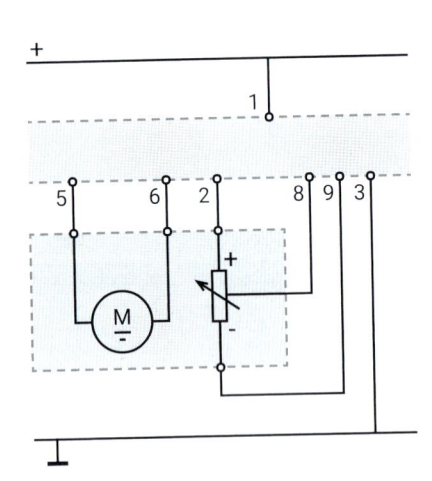

Fig. 137 Diagram of an electric motor with feedback.

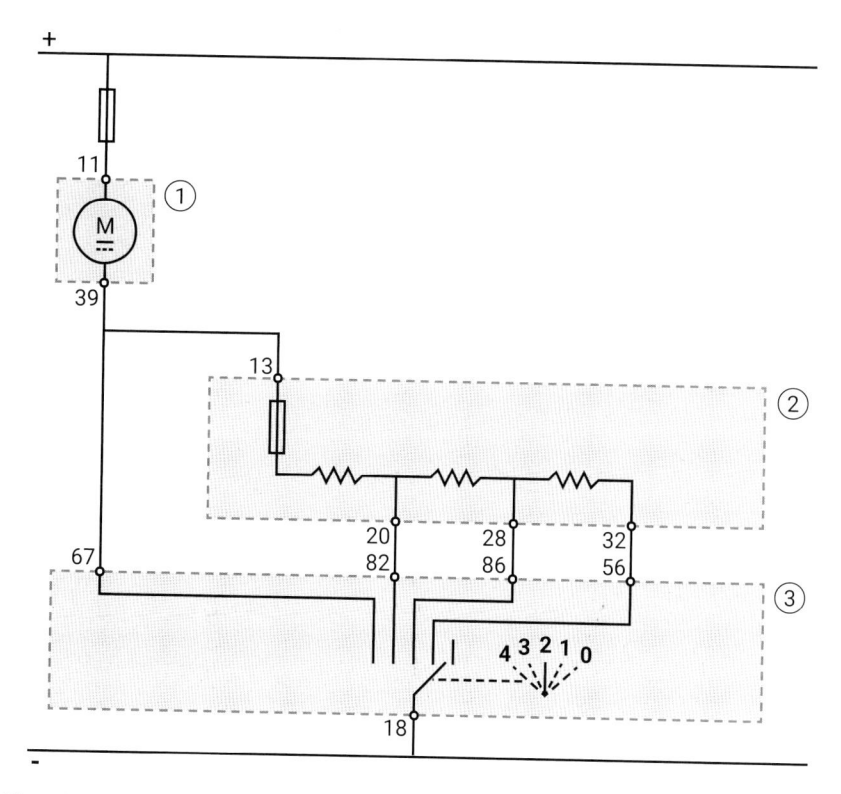

Fig. 138 Electric motor with resistors for different speeds.

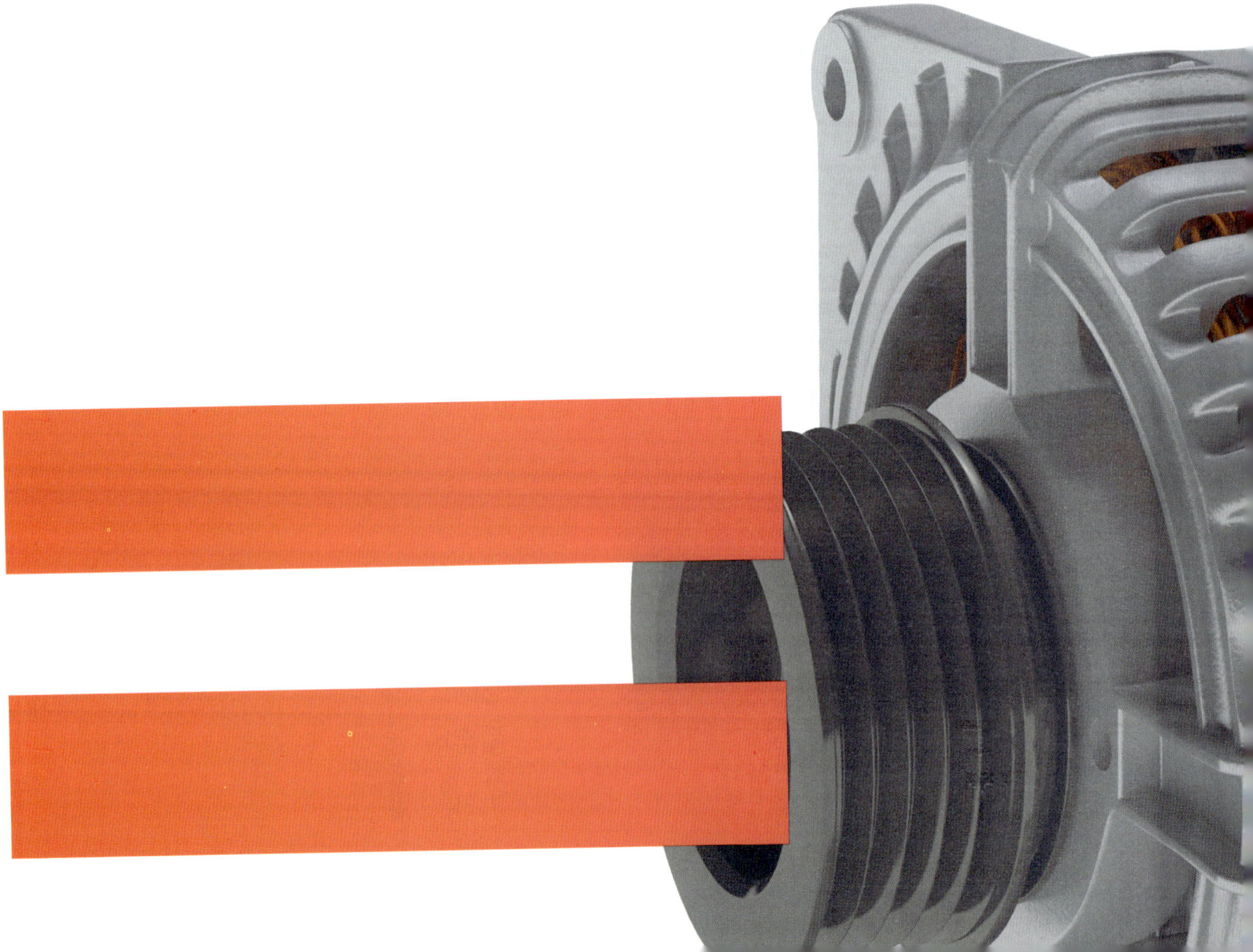

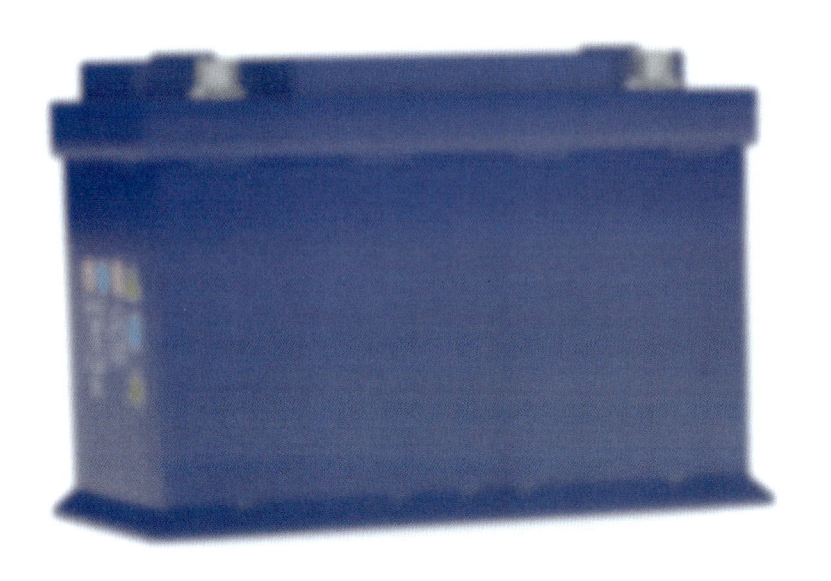

6. Schematics

ELECTRICAL SYMBOLS

Electrical symbols are used to help technicians read and understand wiring diagrams.

Every electrical load can be represented as a symbol.

Most symbols are standardized. Consider, for example, the symbols for a lamp and a resistor. These symbols are specified in accordance with the DIN standard DIN. DIN stands for "Deutsches Institut für Normung" (German Institute for Standardization).

Other symbols, such as those for active sensors, are not standardized. Here the designer chooses their own design.

General symbols

conductor	ground connection	permanent connection	detachable connection	earth connection	plug connection	cell
battery	ideal voltage source	ideal power source	change voltage source	voltmeter	ammeter	

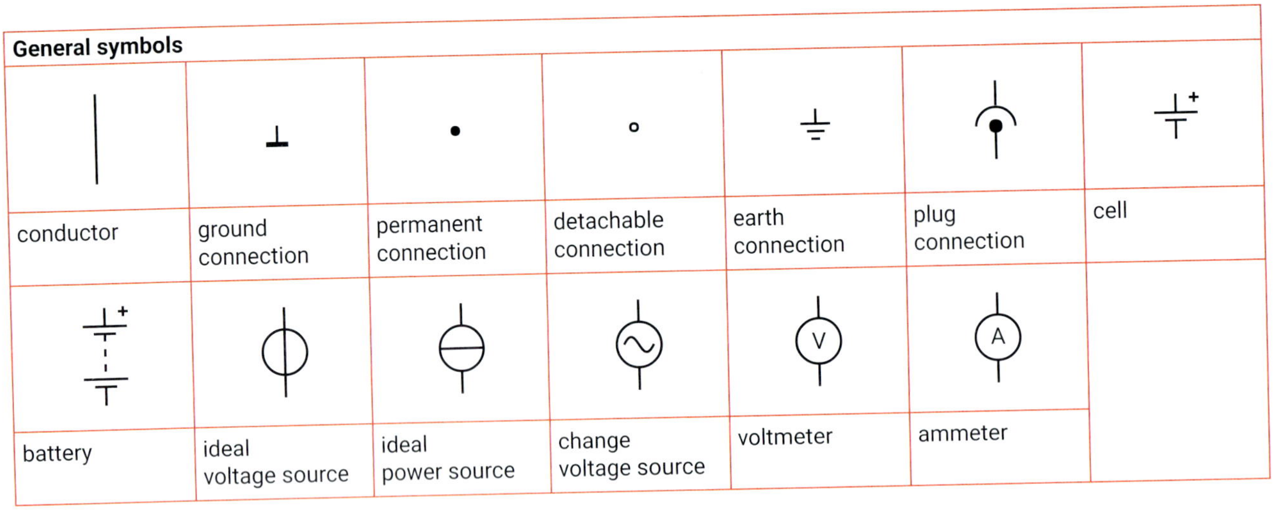

Fig. 139 General symbols

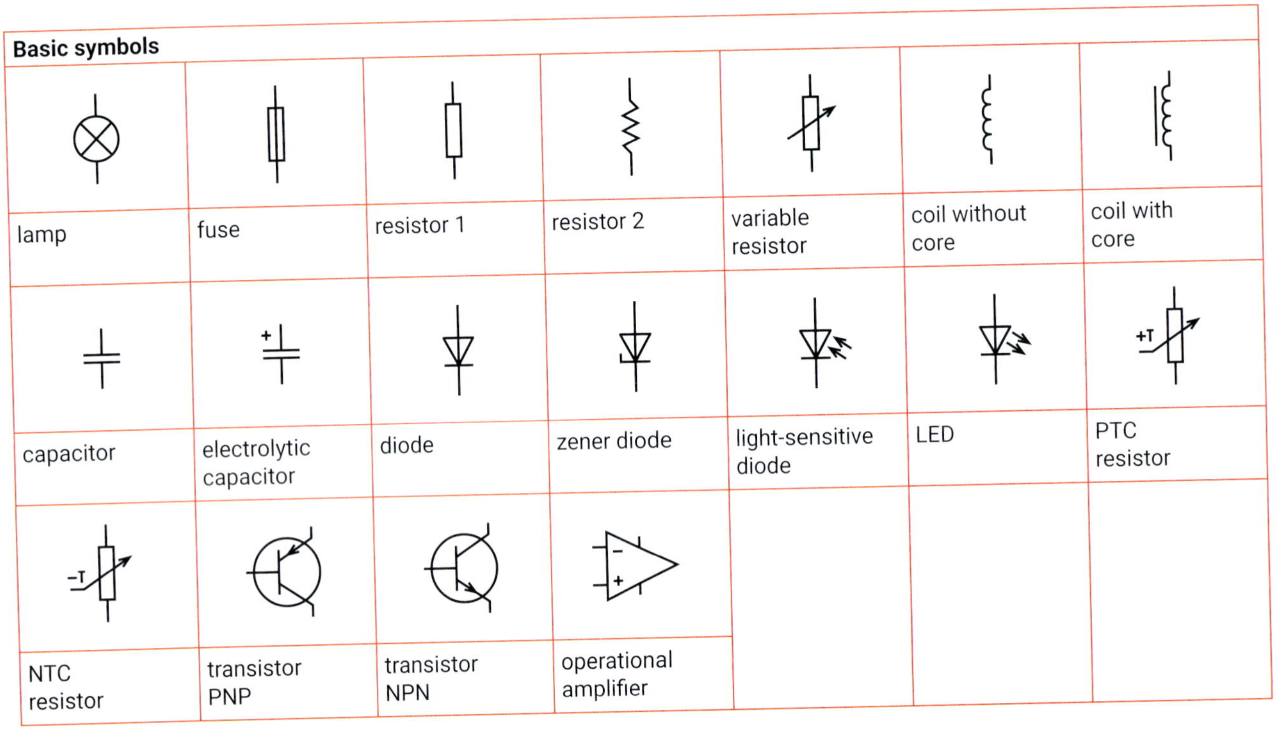

Basic symbols

lamp	fuse	resistor 1	resistor 2	variable resistor	coil without core	coil with core
capacitor	electrolytic capacitor	diode	zener diode	light-sensitive diode	LED	PTC resistor
NTC resistor	transistor PNP	transistor NPN	operational amplifier			

Fig. 140 Basic symbols

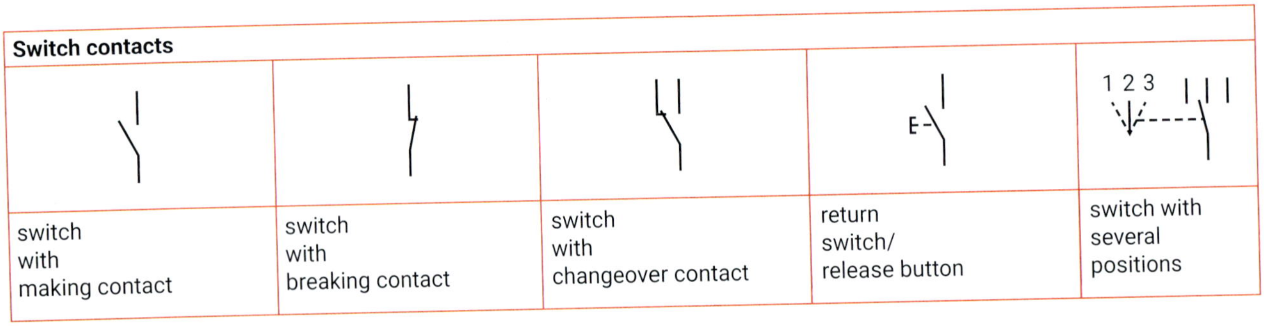

Switch contacts

switch with making contact	switch with breaking contact	switch with changeover contact	return switch/ release button	switch with several positions

Fig. 141 Switch contacts

Relay

relay with making contact	relay with breaking contact	relay with several contacts	relay with changeover contact

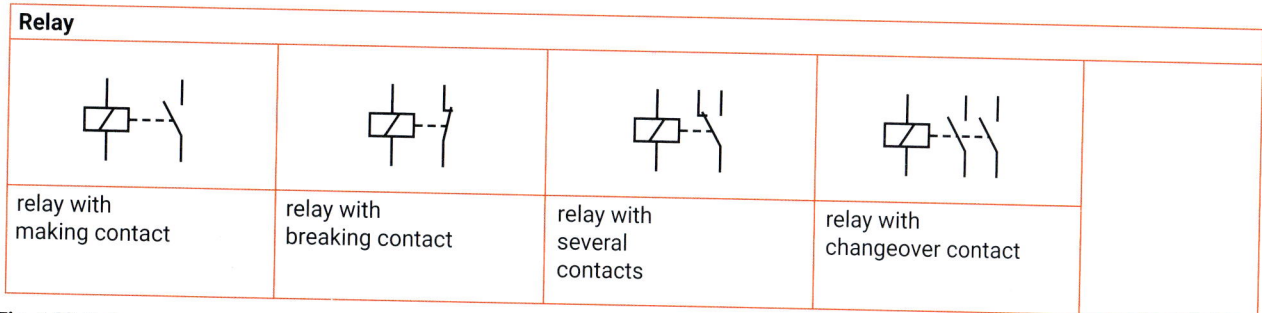

Fig. 142 Relay

Other

transformer	electric motor	three phases electric motor	three phases generator	inverter	heating element	solenoid valve
speaker	frequency regulator	AND port	OR port	NOT port	NAND port	NOR port
XOR port	MOSFET P	MOSFET N	JFET N	JFET P	IGBT-N	IGBT-P

Fig. 143 Other symbols

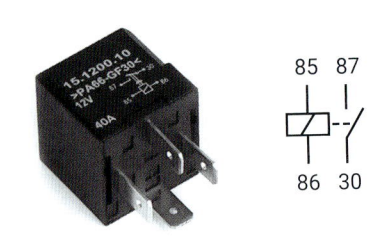

Fig. 144 Standardized terminal numbers on a relay

1. Terminal markings

Most electrical consumers (loads) have a terminal number that allows you to easily identify which connection you are dealing with. The terminal numbers are standardized in the DIN-72552 standard. Below you can see some common terminal numbers:

30 battery positive (B+), direct
15 battery positive from the ignition switch
31 vehicle ground, battery negative
50 starter engine control, direct
56 headlights
56a high beam
56b low beam
58 rear light

A relay also has standardized terminal numbers. You can usually find this on the bottom or on the side.

85 relay coil ground
86 relay coil positive
30 (B+)
87 load (relay on)
87a load (relay off)

ELECTRICAL DIAGRAMS

An electrical diagram provides insight into an electrical circuit.

An electrical diagram uses electrical symbols connected with lines, creating interconnections.

There are small easy diagrams for simple circuits or controls and more complex diagrams for larger circuits and systems. Often these diagrams are divided into sub-diagrams.

Below are some examples that you may encounter in the field.

1. Simple circuit diagram

This diagram has three symbols: a battery (12 V), a switch (S1), and a lamp (L1).

It is clearly visible how the current flows through the circuit. When switch S1 is closed, then the current from the battery can flow back to the battery via the lamp L1.

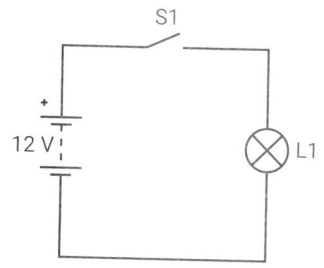

Fig. 145 A simple circuit diagram

2. Cascade Diagram

In a cascade diagram the electrical current runs from top to bottom. A horizontal line is drawn at the top; this is the positive voltage and can be any voltage, however, 12V is commonly used in most automotive electrical diagrams. At the bottom there is a horizontal line representing ground. This can be indicated with a ground symbol or with 0V.

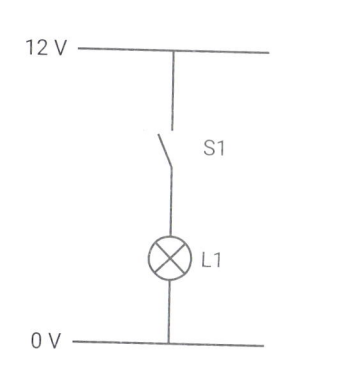

Fig. 146 A simple cascade diagram

Simple cascade diagram:
The simple cascade diagram is the same as the previous diagram. The current in this diagram does not run in a "circle," but from top to bottom. You could say that the positive pole of the battery is set at the top of the diagram, and the negative pole at the bottom. In reality, just like in the previous diagram, these two come together at the battery, and this cascade diagram still represents a complete circuit.

Low and high beam:

The cascade diagram of the headlight low- and high-beam circuits is a bit more complicated.

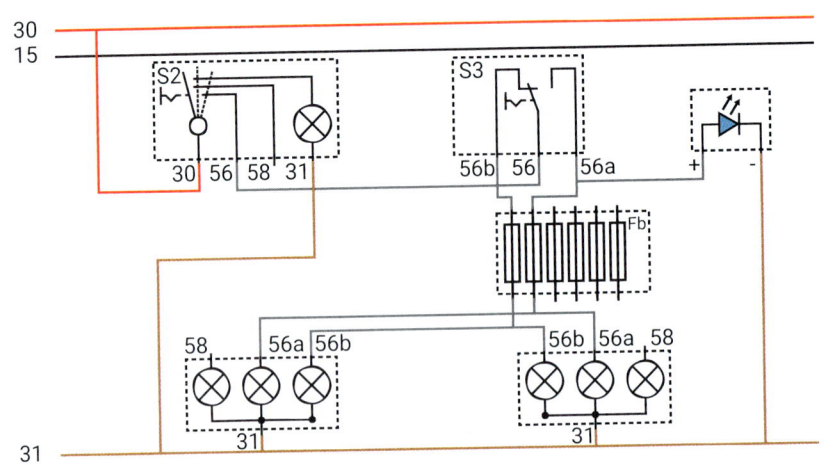

Fig. 147 Cascade diagram of the low- and high-beam headlights.

The supply voltage is not indicated with 12 V in this diagram, but instead the DIN coding is used. Number 30 means that battery voltage is present at all times and number 31 is the ground connection for the circuit.

You can switch on the headlights with the selector switch S2. This switch has three positions; These are off, sidelight, and sidelight with low/high beam. With changeover switch S3 you can switch between low or high beam. Both switch positions have a separate fuse.

3. Automotive Diagrams

Automotive diagrams (network diagrams) do not always describe how a circuit operates. It's often more important to recognize the sensor type and how it is connected to the control unit.

6. SCHEMATICS 85

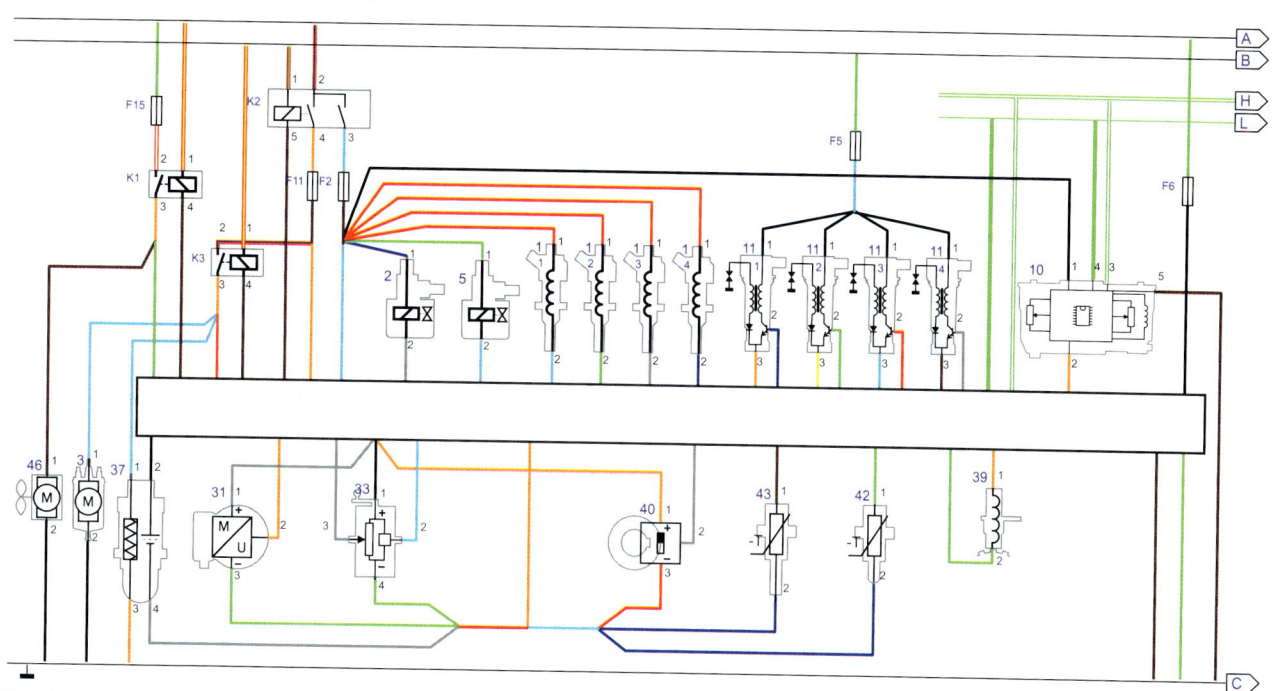

Fig. 148 The diagram of an engine management system

Number 100 in the diagram is the engine control unit; this controls the internal combustion engine. At the top of the control unit you can see all the actuators. For example the injectors (nr. 1), the ignition coils (nr. 11)

For many parts you can see what kind of measuring principle is used. Two temperature sensors are included in this system (Nr. 42 and 43). From this symbol you can deduce that they are NTC sensors, but the temperature/resistance values are not shown.

These types of diagrams give you a practical insight into how control units are connected to each other, which sensors are used, how many connections a sensor has, what wire color is used and how all components are connected.

4. Electrotechnical Diagram

In an electrotechnical diagram symbols are connected with lines. These diagrams explain how circuits work electrically.

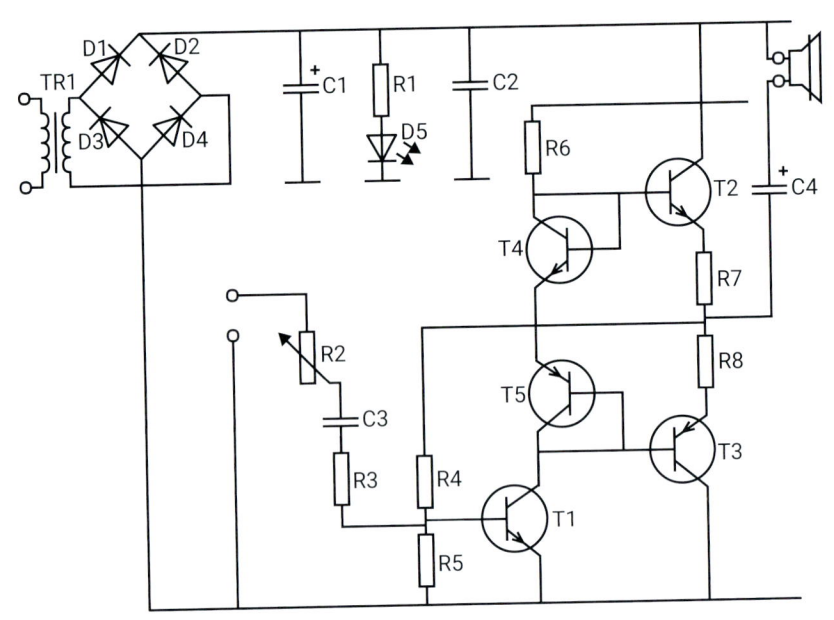

Fig. 149 An electrical diagram of an amplifier

Here you see an example of an amplifier circuit. The transformer TR1 ensures that the supply voltage is transformed down and the new voltage is rectified with four diodes (D1-4). With capacitor C1, the voltage is leveled off so that an even, direct-current voltage remains.

Resistor (R1) and LED (D5) indicate whether the amplifier is switched on. Capacitor (C2) reduces interference.

The two connections at the variable resistor are the ports of the amplifier. The volume of the amplifier can be adjusted with a variable resistor (R2). Capacitor (C3) blocks a DC voltage at the input.

Transistor T1 to T5 provide amplification for the signal.

SYMBOLS AND IDENTIFICATION CODES

1. Introduction

Electric symbols are used in diagrams. They are used to identify a component, wire, connection, or a control unit in a diagram.

2. Ignition Switch

The ignition switch is an important part in motor vehicles. It switches all components that are powered via the ignition switch and provides a start signal to start the vehicle. The ignition switch is also used to switch the vehicle off.

The symbol for an ignition switch has four positions:
- Position 0 = off
- Position 1 = only accessories switched on
- Position 2 = ignition and accessories switched on
- Position 3 = start signal

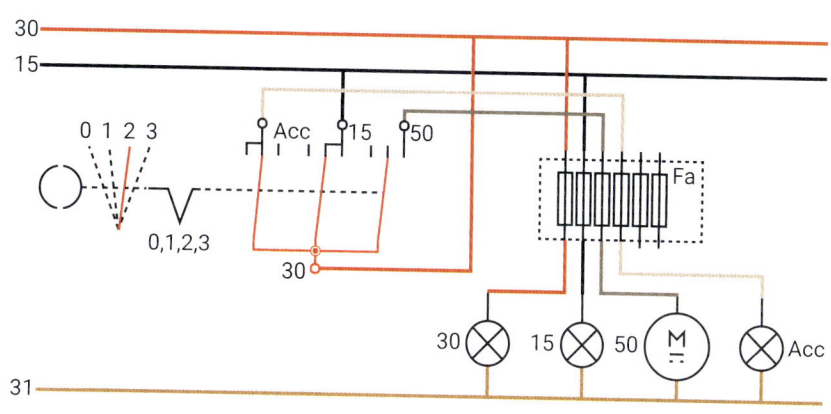

Fig. 150 Electrical Diagram of an Ignition Switch, with the switch in Position 2.

The circle on the left of the symbol shows that we must use a key to operate this switch. The broken line from the key to the electrical contacts represents the mechanical portion of the switch. We see a "V" shape in the broken line pointing to the position the switch will return to after it has been turned to the 'start' position and then released. In this case, that is position 2.

88 ELECTRICAL SYSTEMS

If we turn the ignition switch to position 3 and release it, the ignition switch automatically returns to position 2 to prevent the starter motor from continuing to run.

Constant voltage is present on terminal 30. If we turn the key to position 1, all the contacts will move to the right. Now the Acc connection has a connection to terminal 30, and the accessories (radio, etc.) will be supplied with voltage.

If we turn the key to position 2, the contacts move one position further to the right, and now the connections Acc and 15 (positive via ignition) will be connected to terminal 30.

If we turn the key to position 3, the connection between 30 and Acc will break. Connection 15 remains connected, and connection 50 is connected to terminal 30. At this moment the starter motor will be operated.

The moment we release the key, the switch will return to position 2, and the connections Acc and 15 will be connected to terminal 30 again.

If we return the ignition switch to position 0, the connection 15 will no longer have any voltage, and the vehicle will switch off.

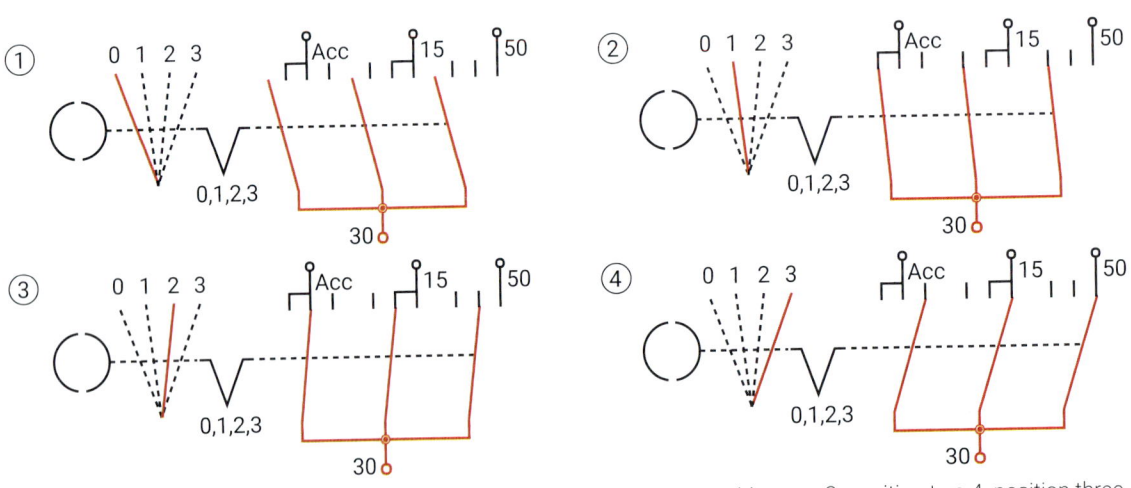

Fig. 151 Ignition switch symbol with different positions: 1. position zero 2. position one 3. position two 4. position three

Fig. 152 Lighting switch

3. Light Switch

Motor vehicles are equipped with different lighting on the front and the rear. To be able to switch these separately, we use a light switch.

The light switch has three positions:
Position 0 = everything switched off
Position 1 = sidelights, rear light, license plate lighting, and instrument lighting switched on
Position 2 = sidelights, rear light, license plate lighting, instrument lighting, and headlights switched on.

There is constant voltage on terminal 30. If we set the switch to position 1 (diagram 2), all internal contacts will move to the left and terminal 30 will be connected to connections 58, 58L, and 58R. Now the sidelights, rear lights, license plate lighting, and instrument lighting are supplied with voltage.

If we set the switch to position 2 (diagram 3), the internal contacts move one position further to the left, and connections 58, 58L, and 58R are still connected to terminal 30. Now connection 56 is also connected to connection 15. As a result, the headlights will only illuminate when the ignition switch is switched on.

If we turn the lighting switch back to position 0 (diagram 1), all connections will be open, and all the lights will go off.

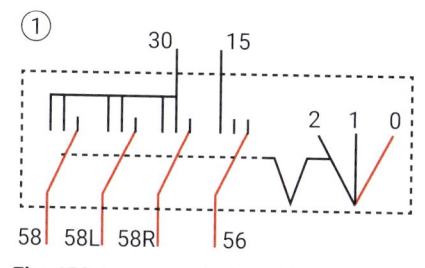

Fig. 153 Ignition switch positions

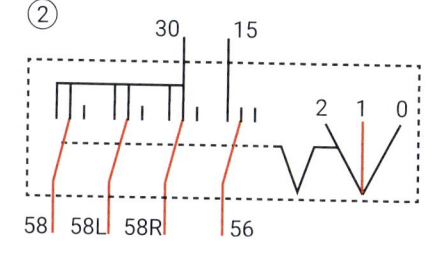

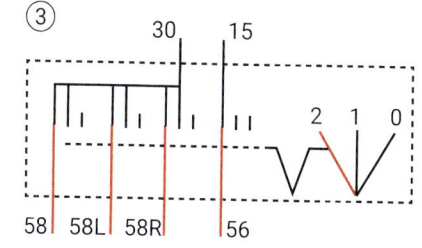

MANUFACTURER'S DIAGRAMS

1. Introduction

Electrical wiring diagrams are of great importance in the search for failures. How the diagram is structured is determined by the manufacturers themselves. They can decide how the components are shown and connected in the diagram. In order to show the difference between the manufacturers, we are going to look at original diagrams from two manufacturers.

2. Toyota Wiring Diagram

In the Toyota headlights diagram we see how Toyota draws its diagrams. Toyota uses its own symbols to display the components. To read these diagrams, start with the component in the diagram and follow the wiring. This way you get to the components that are connected to it or to the fuse that protects this component against excessive current. To make it even easier, images of the color and location of the plugs are shown. With each component the number of the plug is shown, and so is the pin number to which the wire is connected. This way you can take different measurements of the component and its wiring. If you know what to measure and where, you can easily solve a problem in this way.

6. SCHEMATICS

Headlight

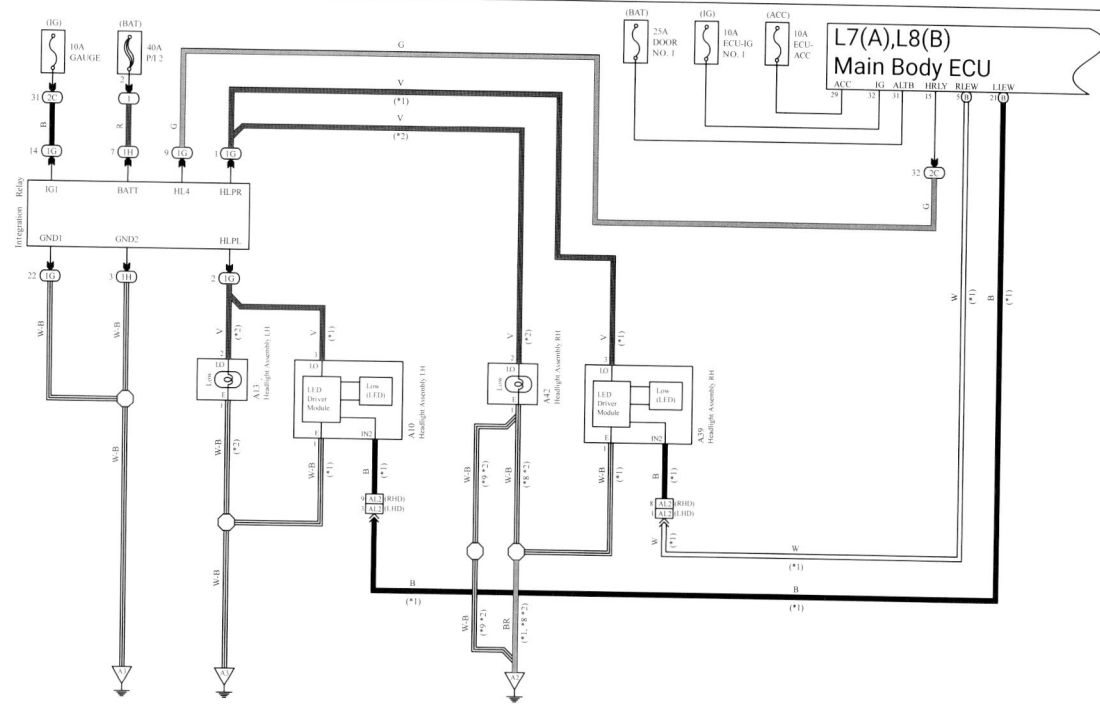

Fig. 155 Headlight diagram from Toyota 1 of 3

Headlight

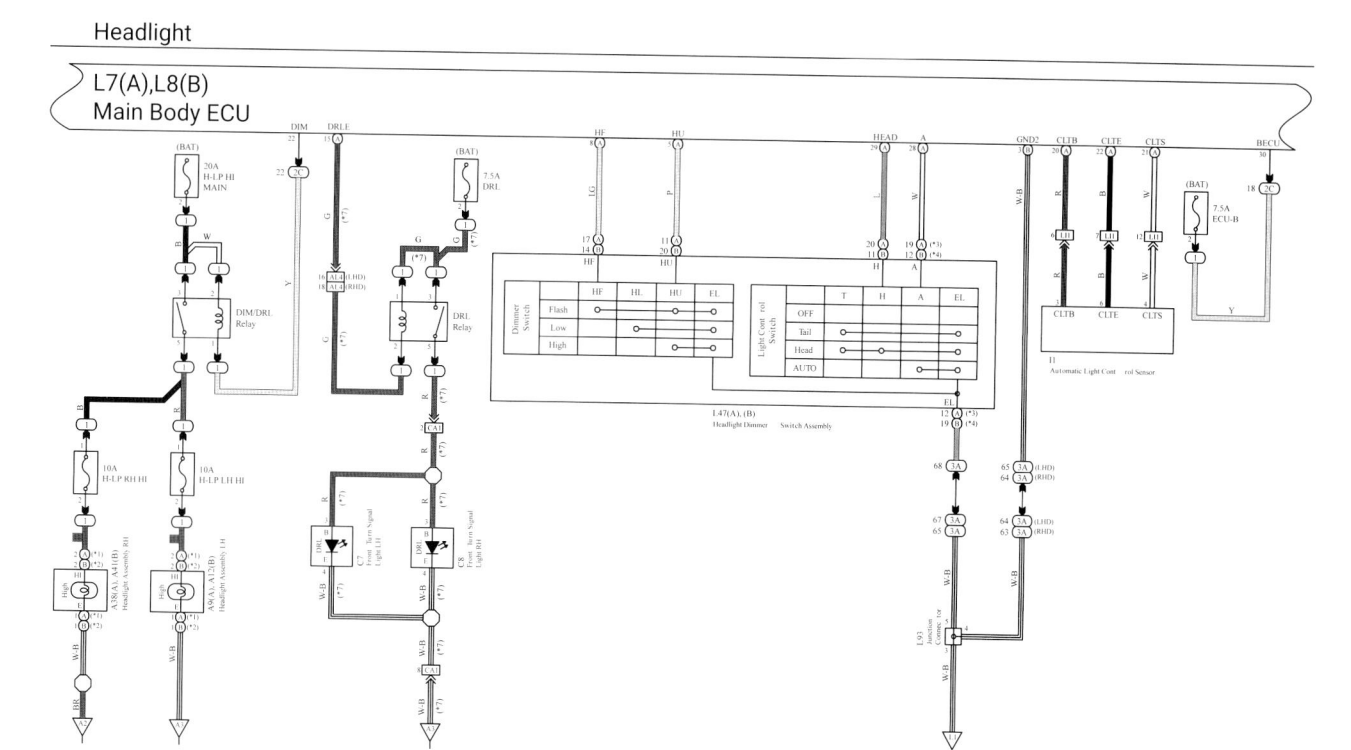

Fig. 156 Headlight diagram from Toyota 2 of 3

Headlight

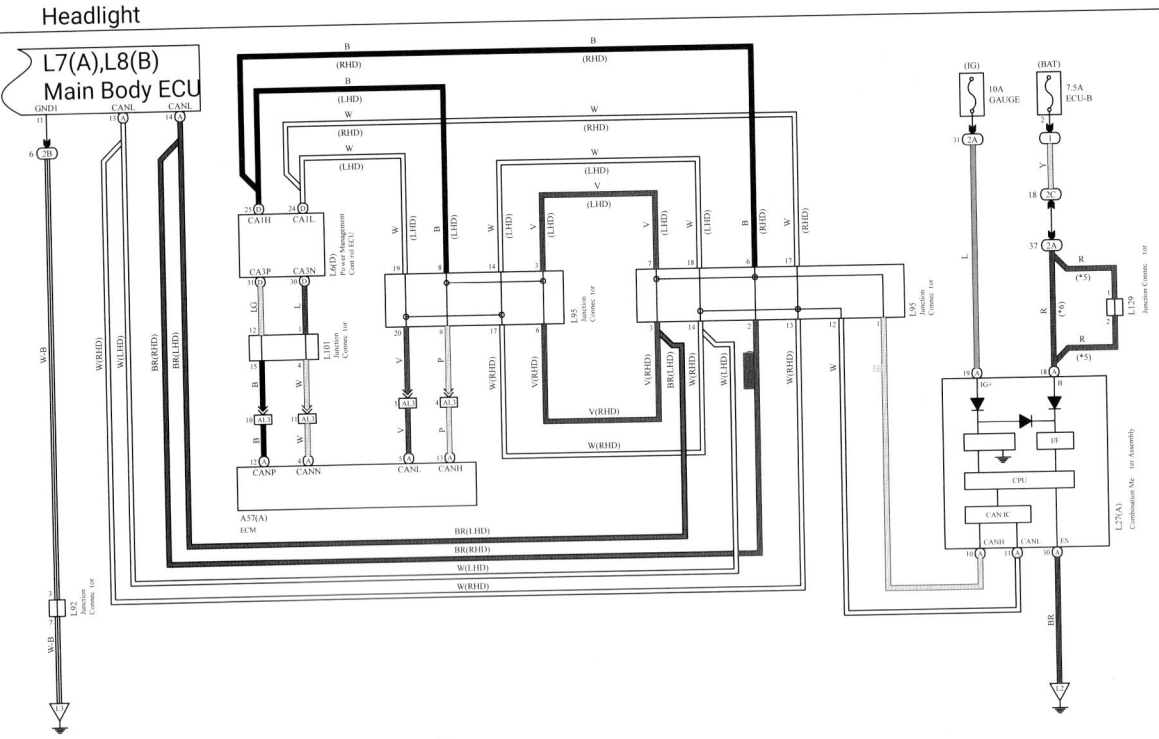

Fig. 157 Headlight diagram from Toyota 3 of 3

Toyota wiring diagram legend:
(*1) LED type
(*2) Except LED type
(*3) Light control switch LH side type
(*4) Light control switch RH side type
(*5) From Dec. 2011 production
(*6) Before Dec. 2011 production
(*7) W/Daytime running light from Dec. 2011 production
(*8) Before Jul. 2012 production
(*9) From Jul. 2012 production.

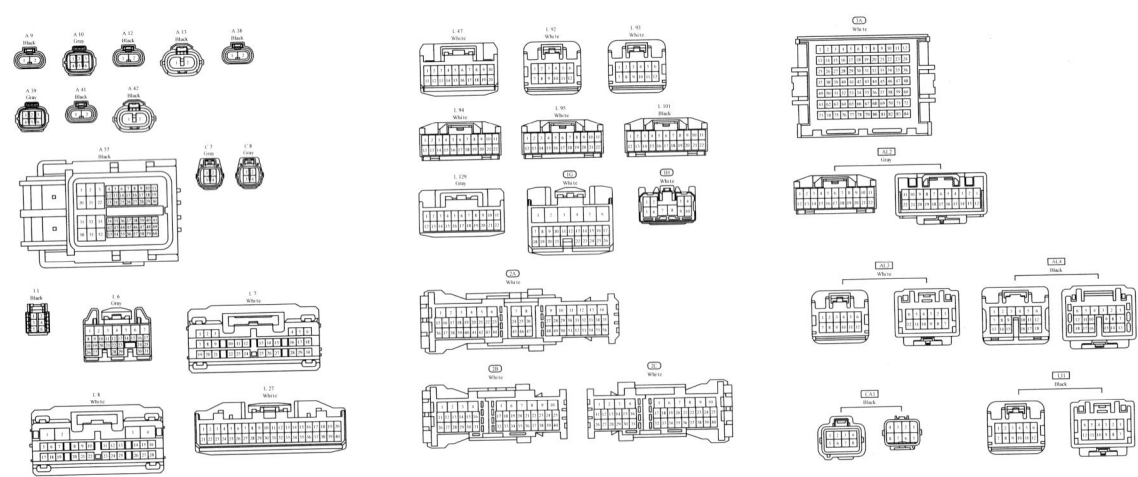

Fig. 158 Connector plugs with wiring diagram number, color and pin numbers

3. Peugeot Wiring Diagram

In the Peugeot wiring diagram we see that each component has its own sequential number. Based on this number, we can find the component in the table with component names. To be able to read this diagram easily, find the component that you need to take measurements from in the table of components. Now find the component in the diagram. Peugeot doesn't use colors in the diagrams but instead uses numbers on the wire. These numbers can also be found on the wire in the car. If you have found the wire with this number in the plug at the component, you can take your measurements and detect a failure.

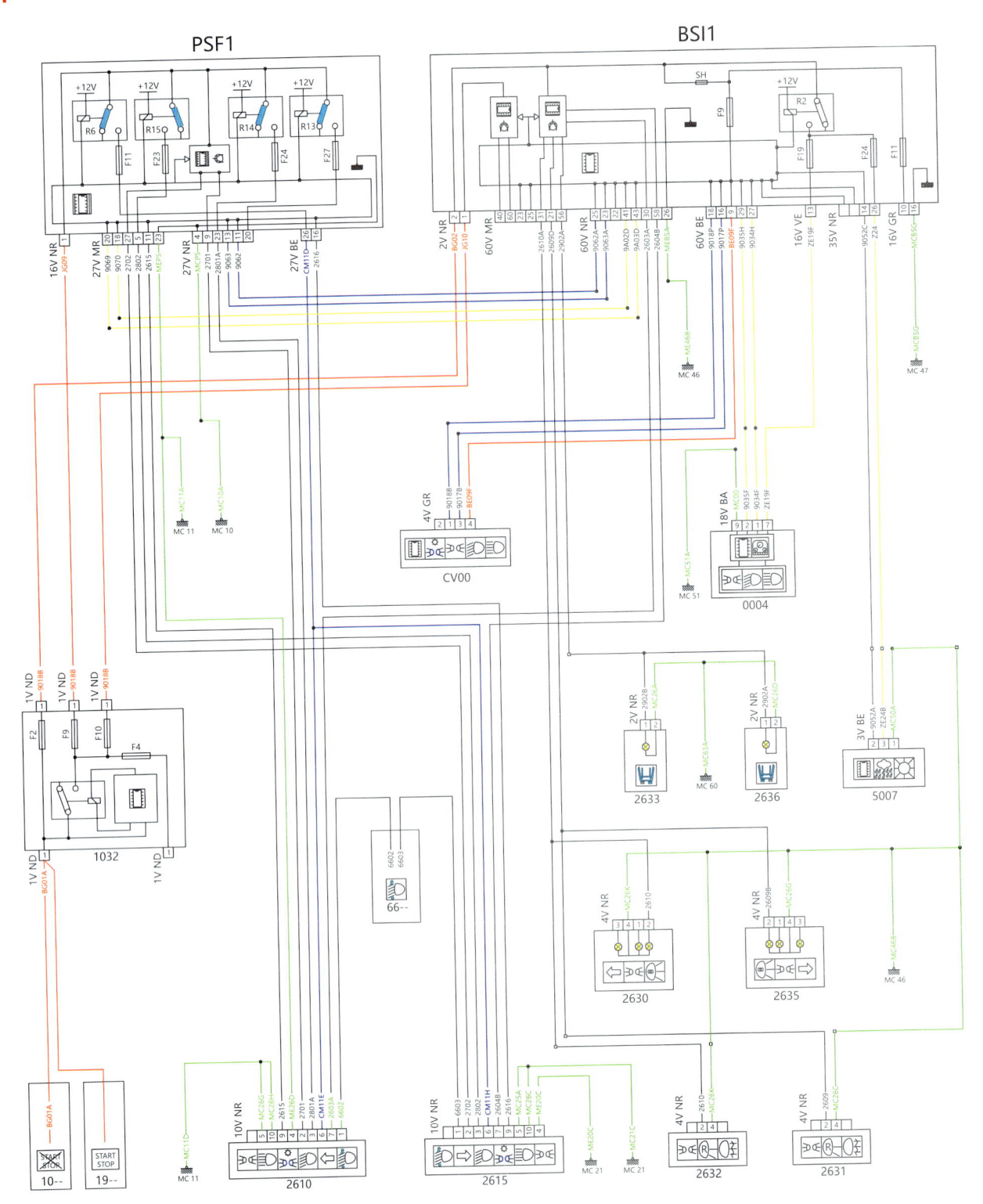

Fig. 159 Peugeot lighting and signaling diagram

6. SCHEMATICS

part code	information
0044	Instrument panel.
1032	unit protection and control electrical power supplies
2610	left headlight
2615	right headlight
2630	left rear light on the body
2631	right rear light on tailgate/trunk lid
2632	left rear light on tailgate/trunk lid
2633	right license plate lighting unit
2635	right rear light on body
2636	left license plate lighting unit
5007	rain/light sensor
6606	electronic unit adaptive headlight adjustment
BB01	12V battery
BSI1	body control module (BCM)
CONN	plugs overview
CV00	steering column switch
E260	wire connection of a signal wire (or with equal voltage 260)
E261	wire connection of a signal wire (or with equal voltage 261)
E290	wire connection of a signal wire (or with equal voltage 290)
E907	wire connection of a signal wire (or with equal voltage 907)
E908	wire connection of a signal wire (or with equal voltage 908)
E912A	wire connection of a signal wire (or with equal voltage 912)
E912B	wire connection of a signal wire (or with equal voltage 912)
E913A	wire connection of a signal wire (or with equal voltage 913)
E913B	wire connection of a signal wire (or with equal voltage 913)
E917A	wire connection of a signal wire (or with equal voltage 917A)
E918A	wire connection of a signal wire (or with equal voltage 918A)
E934A	wire connection of a signal wire (or with equal voltage 934)
E935	wire connection of a signal wire (or with equal voltage 935)
EC11	interconnection of a "+ after contact" protected via fuse number 11
EM10A	ground connection (ground point number 10A)
EM11A	ground connection (ground point number 11A)
EM11D	ground connection (ground point number 11)

ELECTRICAL SYSTEMS

EM21C	ground connection (ground point number 21C)
EM46B	ground connection (ground point number 46B)
EM46D	ground connection (ground point number 46D)
EM46G	ground connection (ground point number EM46G)
EM51A	ground connection (ground point number 51A)
EM63A	ground connection (ground point number 63A)
MC10A	ground point bodywork number 10A
MC11A	ground point bodywork number 11A
MC11B	ground point bodywork number 11B
MC21B	ground point bodywork number 21B
MC21C	ground point bodywork number 21C
MC46B	ground point bodywork number 46
MC46D	ground point bodywork number 46
MC47D	ground point bodywork number 47
MC51A	ground point bodywork number 51
MC60D	ground point bodywork number 60D
PSF1	fuses/relay box engine compartment

Fig. 160 Table with sequence numbers and names of components

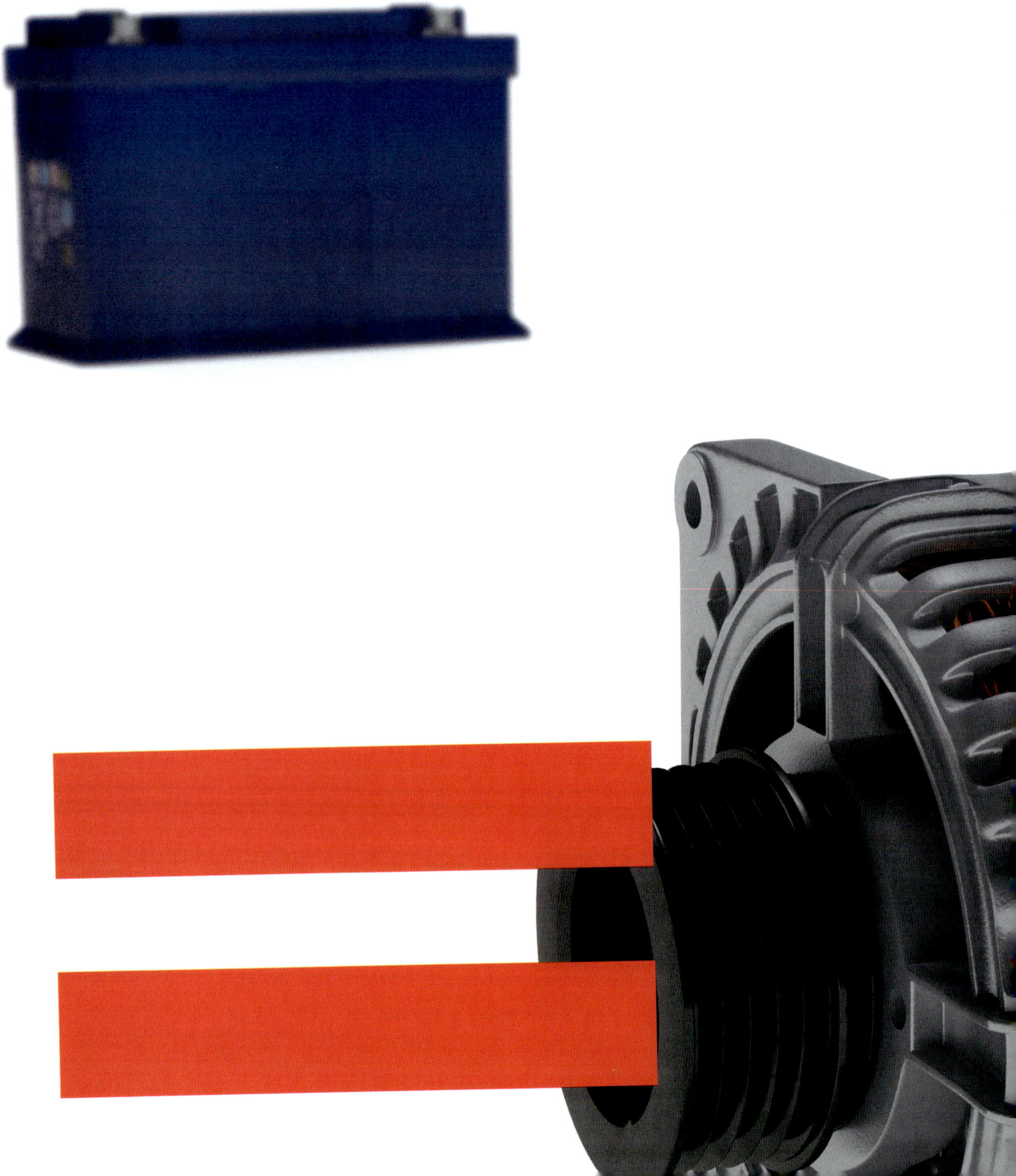

7. Circuit Protection

FUSE

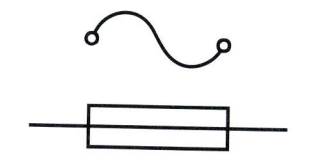

Fig. 161 2 Symbols for a fuse.

A fuse protects an electrical circuit against short circuits and overcurrents. All electrical loads are protected with a fuse. Another word for a a fuse is a safety fuse.

A fuse is always placed as close as possible to the power supply to protect as much of the circuit as possible.

There are many different fuses; examples include:
- maxi blade fuse, mini blade fuse and micro blade fuse
- glass fuse
- torpedo fuse
- main fuse

Main fuses are used for large currents. The starter motor has one fuse; the alternator and other loads also use one or more main fuses. They form a protection for the fuse box if it is further away from the battery.

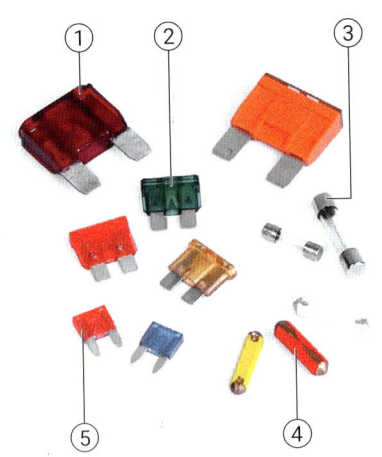

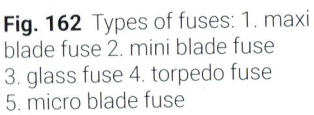

Fig. 162 Types of fuses: 1. maxi blade fuse 2. mini blade fuse 3. glass fuse 4. torpedo fuse 5. micro blade fuse

Fig. 163 Main fuses

1. Fuse Compartment

The fuse compartment can be found in different places.

Some examples are:
— under the hood
— in the dashboard

The relays are also often placed in this compartment.

If additional electrical loads are added to a vehicle, it may be necessary to fit an accessory fuse. You will always find this near the battery.

Fig. 164 Fuse compartment under the hood

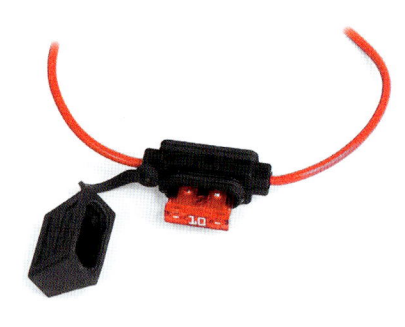

Fig. 165 Accessory fuse

2. Operation

A fuse is the weakest link in an electrical circuit. It protects the wires against overcurrent, which can cause the insulation to melt. Electric loads are also protected. A fuse can prevent damage to the wiring and a possible fire.

If a high current flows through a conductor, it becomes hot. This also happens with a fuse. If an over-current or short circuit occurs, the fuse wire will melt. The circuit is opened when a fuse blows.

If a fuse has blown, it's important to first find the cause before installing a new fuse.

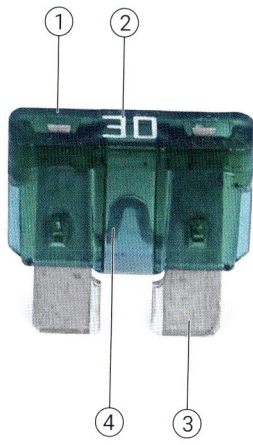

Fig. 166 Parts of a fuse: 1. housing 2. value 3. connection 4. fuse wire

Fig. 167 A blown fuse

3. Color Code

The value of a fuse is not only indicated by a number on the fuse, but also by its color.

Some examples are:
- Light brown 5 A
- Dark brown 7.5 A
- Red 10 A
- Blue 15 A
- Yellow 20 A
- Clear 25 A
- Green 30 A
- Orange 40 A

PLEASE NOTE Never install a fuse with a higher value than specified. This can lead to a lot of damage to the wiring and electrical components.

OVERLOADING

The wiring and fuses in the car are designed to function at a certain maximum current.

Overloading occurs if the current through a circuit exceeds this value. Wiring, connections and loads can then become hot as a result of the (too) high current. This can melt the insulation off of wires and create an electrical short-circuit

1. Fuse Overload

A fuse is overloaded if the current flowing through a circuit exceeds the rating of the fuse. Because of this the fuse will blow.

Every fuse has a fusing characteristic; you can find out how long it takes for the fuse to blow if you overload it.

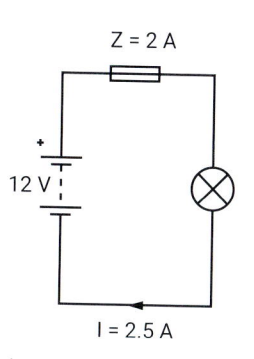

Fig. 168 Fuse overload

In the example you see a fuse that is overloaded by a lamp. If the current through the fuse is not much greater than the value of the fuse, it may take awhile for the fuse to blow.

If the overload increases, the melting time decreases. This makes a fuse the most suitable for short circuit protection.

2. Wire Overload

The insulating properties of the wiring can decrease due to high temperature caused by overloading.

Overloading a wire brings great danger. The insulating properties can reduce or the wire can even melt. This can cause a short circuit and a fire hazard.

Causes of overloading in wiring can be:
— Connecting a load with too small a conductor cross section.
— Using too large a fuse with too high a load.

3. Overloading an Electric Motor

Fuses only protect a motor against short circuits, not against overloading.

The starting current of an electric motor is several times greater than the nominal current. This means that protection against overload with a fuse is not possible.

A fuse never responds immediately to an overload. If a motor has been overloaded, there is a chance of damage. The temperature developed in an electric motor during overloading can cause it to fail.

SHORT CIRCUIT

1. Introduction

If a new connection is made parallel to the electrical circuit, it is called a short circuit. A short circuit is often an unintentional and harmful connection.

2. Cause and Effect

Short circuits can have various causes, such as:
– Incorrect connection.
– Corrosion.
– Damaged insulation due to sharp edges or high temperature.

When the insulator of a conductor becomes compromised, an unintentional connection may occur.

Power-side short circuits:
– Occur when a positive lead of a component is constantly connected to the positive of the battery.
– May cause the component to always be switched on if the short bypasses the circuit control device.
– Loads are therefore unintentionally switched on.

Ground-side short circuits:
– Occurs when a positive lead of a component is constantly connected to the ground of the battery, bypassing the load./li>
– Can create a direct path to ground which will cause the current flow through the conductor or circuit to be very high.
– Increased current flow causes the conductor to become hot and may cause a fire.

Short circuits:
– Occur when two or more conductors or circuits form an electrical connection in an unintended place.
– Will often cause a very large current will flow through the conductor, which will overheat the conductor and may cause a fire.

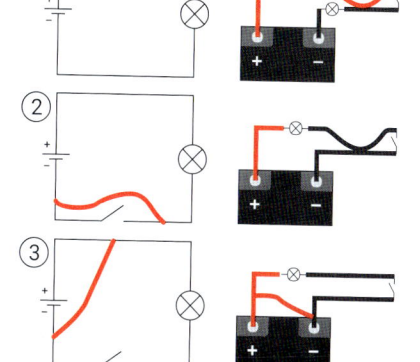

Fig. 169 1. Positive short circuit. 2. Ground short circuit. 3. Short circuit.

- May cause components to operate unintentionally if the short bypasses the circuit control device
- If present, the fuse may burn out in the circuit.

3. Path of Least Resistance

Because electrical current always wants to choose the path of least resistance, a large current will be created in the event of a short circuit. This is because the current depends on the voltage and the resistance:

$$I = \frac{V}{R} \Rightarrow current = \frac{voltage}{resistance}$$

I = current
V = voltage
R = resistance

Because a short circuit is a connection that is parallel to the electrical circuit, the resistance of the entire circuit can decrease. This increases the current in the circuit and often results in heat generation.

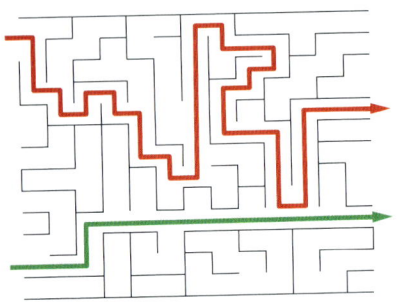

Fig. 170 Current chooses the path of least resistance, just like choosing the easiest route in a maze.

7. CIRCUIT PROTECTION 107

HOW TO: FIND A SHORT CIRCUIT

1. Issue

The customer comes in complaining that the left rear light and the left side light are not working.
The electrical diagram shows that both lights are on the same fuse. Maybe the fuse has blown. If necessary, first check the bulbs and the battery voltage.

Fig. 171 Identify the problem by checking the lights.
The left side light is not working.

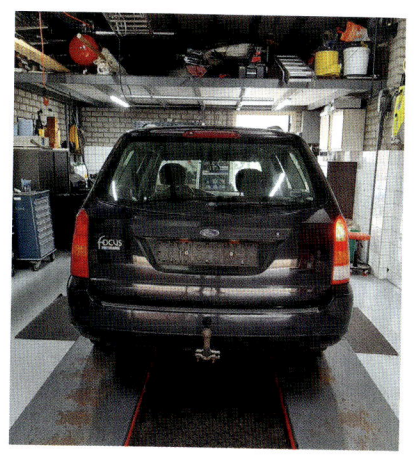

Fig. 172 The left rear light is also not working.

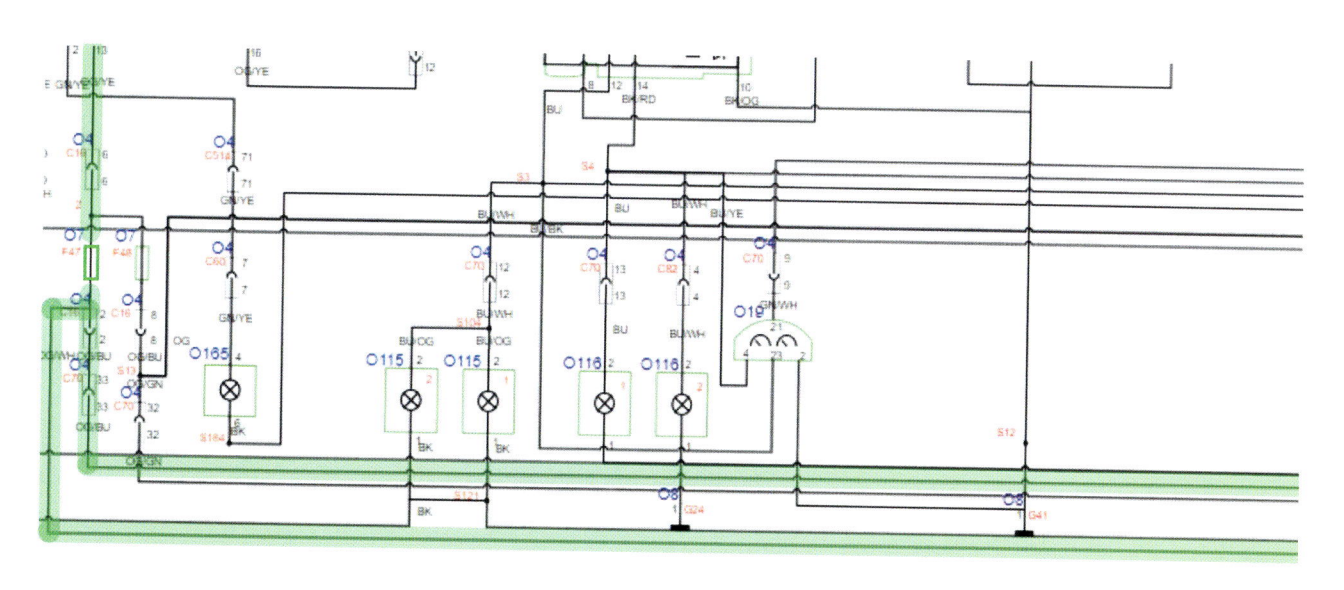

2018, source: WorkshopData, author: HaynesPro

Fig. 173 Diagram part 1.
Check the electrical diagram to see how the bulbs are connected. The fuse, F47, branches into two wires.

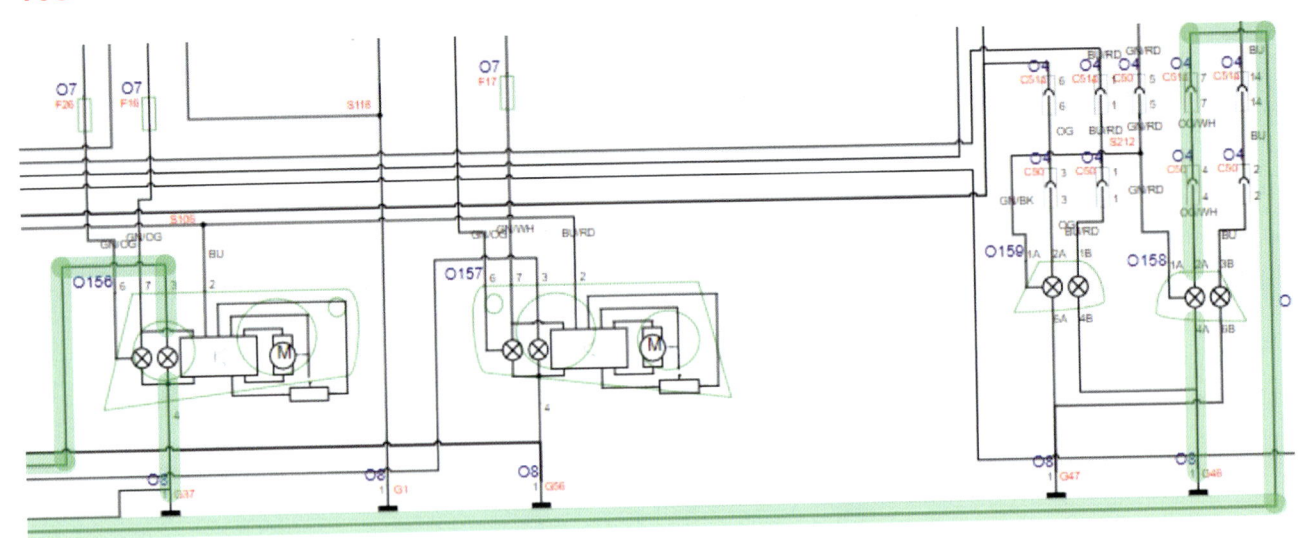

Fig. 174 Diagram part 2.
Note that the wires run to both the side light (O156) and the rear light (O158). This means that both bulbs are on the same fuse in this car.

2. Fuse

You can use a test lamp or consult the documentation of the car in order to find the blown fuse.

First we check the function of the test lamp. The test bulb may be defective.

Fig. 175 You can use a test lamp to find a short circuit.

Fig. 176 Always check the function of the test lamp first. You can do this by connecting the test lamp to the battery for a moment.

3. Short Circuit

Fuses usually do not blow for no reason. The current through the circuit has become too high. This can happen because the circuit has a short circuit. The fuse then blows to prevent greater damage. There are different types of short circuit, but in this case it is probably a short circuit of a positive wire to the ground.

Fig. 177 Open the fuse box to check the fuse for the side light and the rear light.

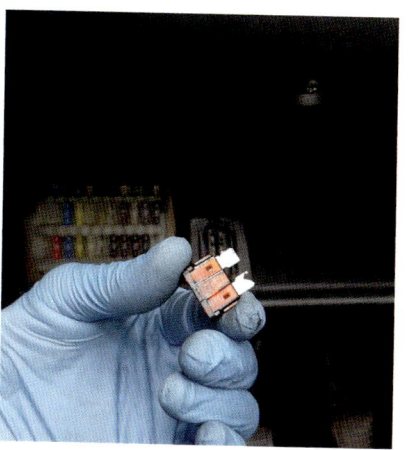

Fig. 178 The fuse for the light has blown. The fuse legs are also damaged. So check the contacts of the fuse as well.

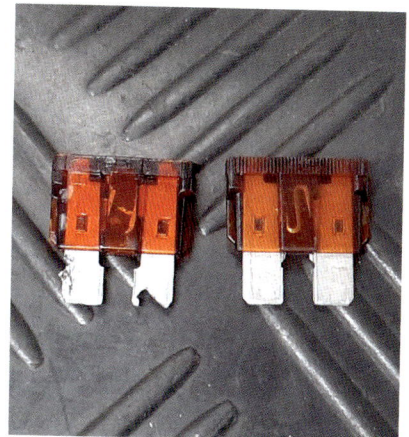

Fig. 179 Here is the difference between a blown fuse (left) and a new fuse (right).

4. Finding a Short Circuit

Detecting a short circuit with the help of a test lamp has a number of advantages:
— The fuse does not always blow again.
— The current through the circuit is limited by the test lamp.
— You can easily see whether current is flowing or not. This makes the search for a short circuit easier.

You can exclude places where the short circuit could be located by disconnecting one of the consumers from the circuit. As long as the test lamp is on, there is a short circuit. Once the test lamp goes off, there is no connection to the ground anymore. This means that the short circuit is in the disconnected part.

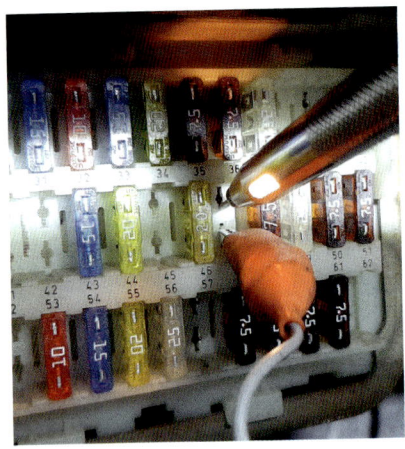

Fig. 180 You can see whether current is flowing by connecting the test lamp over the fuse connections. The bulb lights up if the current is flowing, and the bulb goes out when the short circuit is removed from the circuit.

Fig. 181 Note: the bulbs in the headlight and the rear light make a connection to the ground. This means the test lamp continues to light up as long as both are connected. Disconnect these current consumers to determine whether the short circuit is still present afterward.

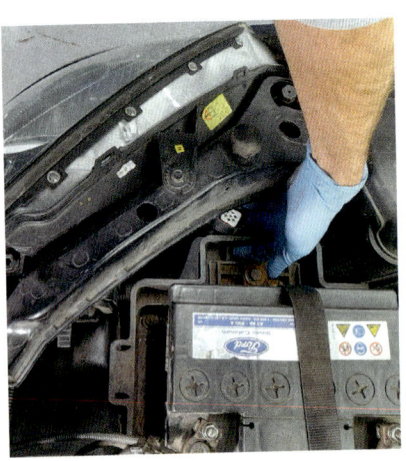

Fig. 182 Undo the headlight plug. The test lamp remains on after disconnection because the rear light is still connected.

Fig. 183 Now disconnect the rear light plug. If the test lamp goes out after this, there is a problem in the rear light.

Fig. 184 The test lamp is still on. Now look for other places that could cause a fault in the electrical circuit.

5. Tow Bar Socket

The socket of the tow bar is often connected to the wiring of the lights. The socket is located on the underside of the car. This makes the component more sensitive to faults, such as a short circuit.

7. CIRCUIT PROTECTION 111

Fig. 185 This car also has a tow bar. A short circuit can be located in the socket.

Fig. 186 Open the socket to check the wiring.

Fig. 187 Remove the outer housing of the socket.

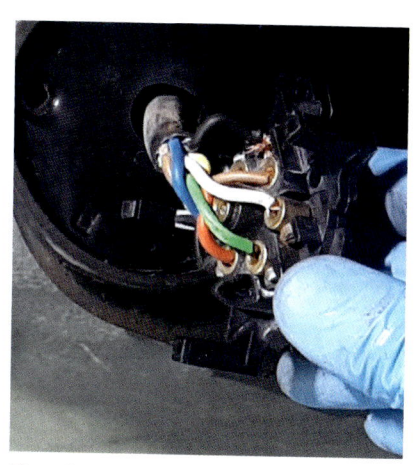

Fig. 188 The black wire is loose and seems to be touching another wire.

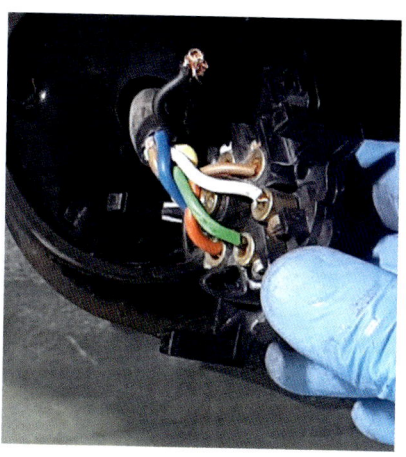

Fig. 189 Take the wire aside and check with test lamp again.

Fig. 190 The test lamp has gone out now. That means this is where the short circuit is.

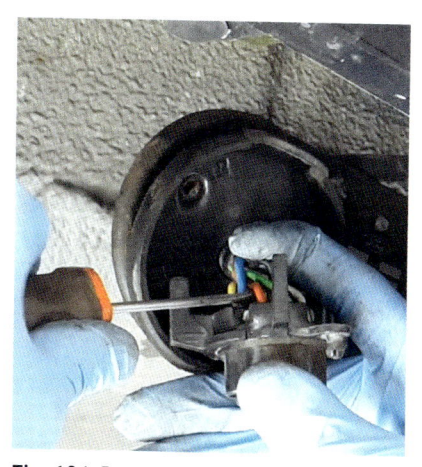

Fig. 191 Reconnect the wire to the correct place in the socket.

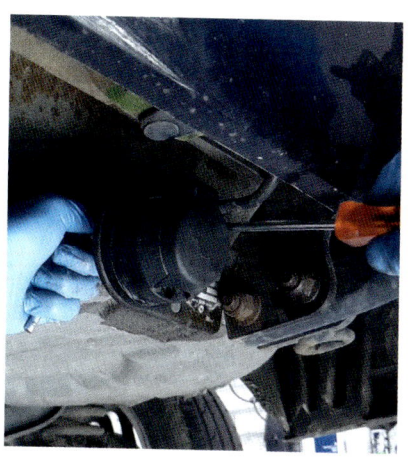

Fig. 192 Mount the socket.

Fig. 193 Insert a new fuse with the correct current rating in the fuse box and check the lights.

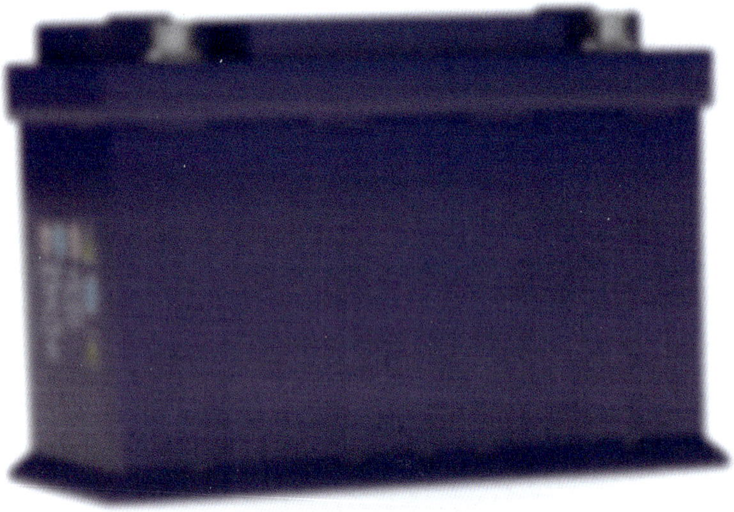

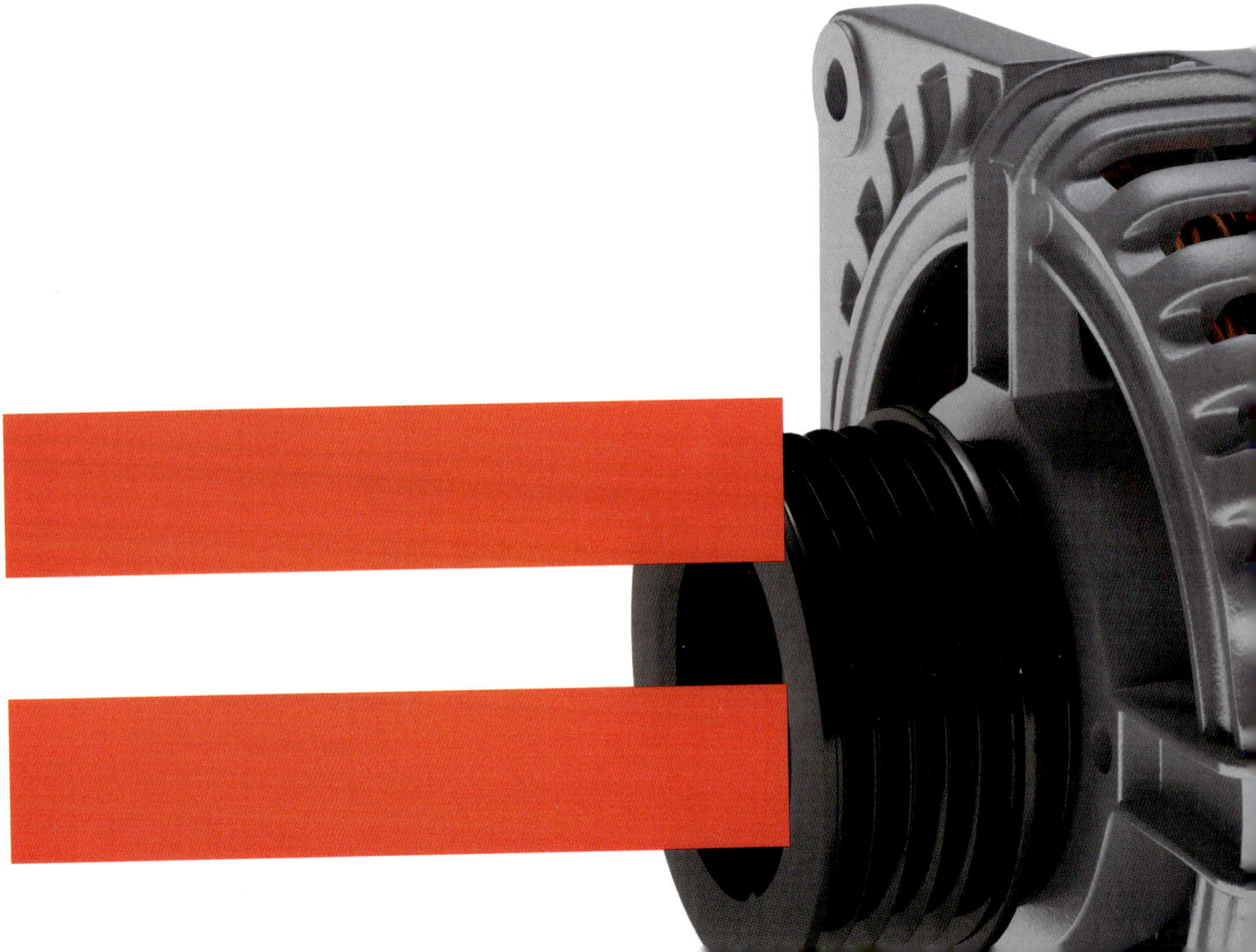

8. Basic Electrical Diagnosis

GROUND-SWITCHED AND POSITIVE-SWITCHED

There are two ways to control a load (consumer):

— ground-switched
— positive-switched

Ground-switched connections are often used in automotive electronics. Many actuators are controlled by switching the ground on and off with the control module.

Ground-switched means that the switch is positioned on the ground side of the load.

Positive-switched means that the switch is positioned on the positive side of the load.

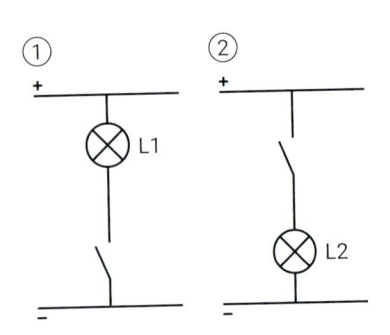

Fig. 195 1. Ground-switched lamp
2. Positive-switched lamp

Fig. 196 With a ground-switched circuit, supply voltage is always present on the positive side of the circuit.

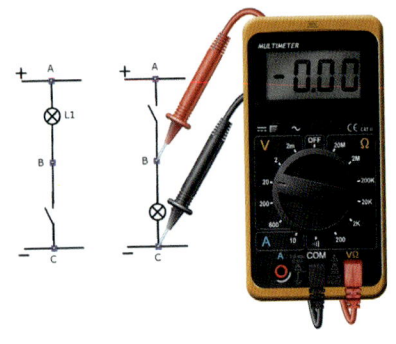

Fig. 197 With a positive-switched circuit, supply voltage is only present on the positive side of the circuit when the switch is closed.

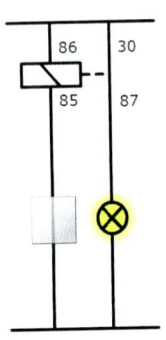

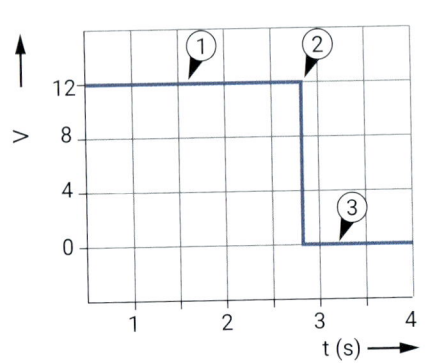

Fig. 198 Voltage measurement across terminals 30 and 87: 1. This is a normally-closed (NC) relay contact; When the relay is not energized, the voltage present at terminal 30 is connected to terminal 87. 2. When the relay is energized, the NC contacts between 30 and 87 open. 3. When these contacts open, there is no voltage across the contacts.

VOLTAGE DROP

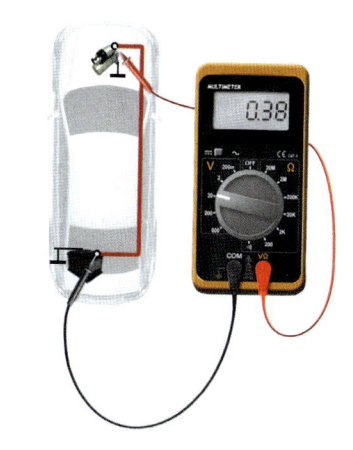

Fig. 199 Measuring voltage drop

Voltage drop is a loss or drop in voltage due to a resistance in an electrical circuit.

If a voltage drop occurs, a voltage division occurs between the load and the resistance. As a result, the load has a lower voltage, and there is a good chance that it will no longer be able to function.

The amount of voltage drop depends on the resistance (R) of the wire and the current (I) through the wire.

If you use Ohm's law, you can use this data to calculate the voltage drop.

V = I x R

Because the resistances are usually very small, you don't measure with an ohmmeter but you switch on the loads and measure the voltage drop with a voltmeter.

Calculation example 1

Suppose you have a wire with a resistance of 0.1 Ω. You switch on the side lights and 2 A flows. The voltage drop across this wire is then:

V = I x R
V = 2 A x 0.1 Ω
V = 0.2 V

This is acceptable for a 12 V installation.

Calculation example 2

But if the high beam is also switched on the same wire, a current of around 10 A flows. Then the voltage drop across this wire is:

V = I x R
V = 10 A x 0.1 Ω
V = 1 V

This is much too high for a 12 V installation, because there are now only 11 V left for the load devices.

1. Causes of Voltage Drop

Voltage drop can occur in the wiring, contacts, and connections. The total voltage drop must not exceed 5% of the supply voltage.

High currents can create a fire hazard due to resistance causing heat build-up in connections, contacts, and switches.

With a 12 V installation, the voltage drop may not exceed 12 V x 5/100 = 0.6 V.

Voltage drop in wiring:
Every electrical conductor or wire has a resistance, so you can say that voltage drop occurs in every wire. It's also possible that a break has occurred internally. This may also increase the resistance of the wire.

Voltage drop in contacts and connections:
Contacts and connections can oxidize. Just as iron starts to rust, other metals can oxidize. Because oxidized metals are poor electrical conductors, a contact resistance is created. Oxidized copper contacts can often be recognized by their green deposits.

Switch contacts can also burn out. When the current through the contact becomes too high, the contact gets hot and resistance through the contact increases, causing even more heat. Eventually the contact burns out. This can be caused by adding too large of a load to the circuit or by high induction voltages generated when the contacts open.

Calculation example 3
In the circuit diagram you see an example where contact resistances can occur. The current through this circuit is 2 A, with a supply voltage of 12.6 V.

If you calculate the voltage drop across all resistors then you know the voltage that is across the lamp.

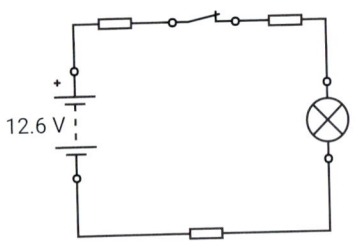

Fig. 200 Voltage drop in a circuit

- Each connection has a resistance of 0.01 Ω. There are six connections in this diagram with a total resistance of 0.06 Ω.
- The switch contact of the switch has a resistance of 0.02 Ω.
- Every wire in this diagram has a resistance of 0.03 Ω. These three wires together have a resistance of 0.09 Ω.

The total contact resistance is:

0.06 Ω + 0.02 Ω + 0.09 Ω = 0.17 Ω

The voltage drop is:

$V = I \times R$
$V = 2 A \times 0.17 Ω$
$V = 0.34 V$

This voltage drop is less than 5% of the supply voltage. This circuit works correctly.

The voltage left over for the lamp is then:

12.6 V - 0.34 V = 12.26 V

2. Fault Finding

You can trace a voltage drop with a voltmeter.

Before you begin to locate the failure, ask yourself a few questions. Which loads aren't functioning properly? Which loads still function correctly?

If you have found out in which partial circuit you have to search, it's important to know whether the load is positive or ground switched.

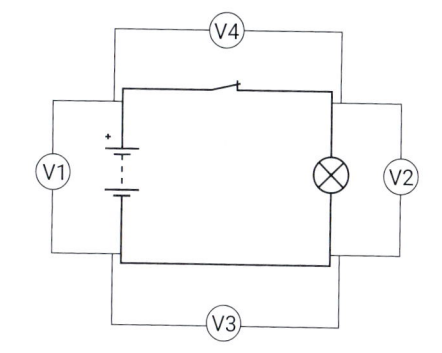

Fig. 201 Check for failures

You can determine where the contact resistance is based on four measurements.

PLEASE NOTE Make sure the switch is closed before you start the measurements. Always measure voltage drop in a loaded circuit (load switched on)

V1: check supply voltage
You measure the voltage across the battery and use this reading to compare the losses.

V2: voltage across the load
You measure the voltage across the load, checking for oxidized contacts and whether the load is still functioning properly.

V3: check ground circuit
You can check the ground circuit by measuring the voltage from the negative pole to the load.

V4: check positive circuit
You can check the positive circuit by measuring the voltage from the positive pole to the load.

These four measurements form the "V4 measurement."

Calculation example 4
As you can see in calculation example 4, measurements V1, V2, and V3 were performed. Because the voltage across the load is much too low, you can conclude that voltage is lost somewhere.

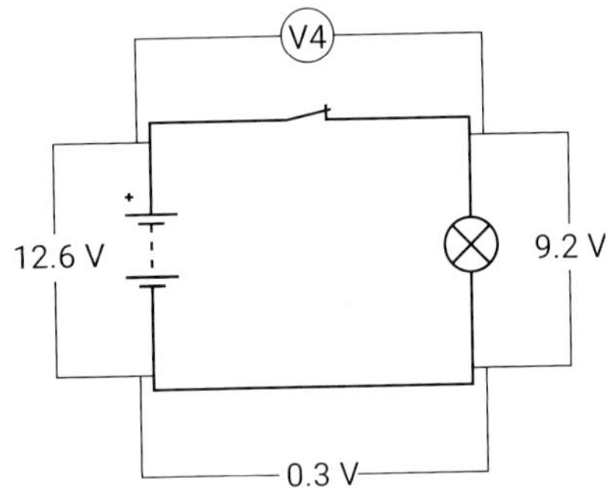

Data:
V1 = 12.6 V
V2 = 9.2 V
V3 = 0.3 V

From this data you can calculate the voltage drop across the positive circuit, V4.

V2 + V3 + V4 = V1
9.2 V + 0.3V + V4 = 12.6 V
V4 = 3.1 V

This means that you will check step-by-step whether the contact resistance is in the wiring of the positive circuit, in the fuse or switch connections or in the switch contact of the switch.

Fig. 202 Calculation Example 4

FAULT FINDING

1. V4 method

The V1-V4 method is often used in fault finding. The term indicates you are measuring voltage across four different parts of one circuit. It is also referred to as 'measuring voltage drop' and is a fast way to accurately locate the faulty component or circuit.

Before you use the V1-V4 method, you must switch on the load.

V1: Measure the terminal voltage.
Measure the voltage across the battery.

V2: Measure the applied voltage.
This is the voltage across the load.

V3: Measure the voltage loss in the ground circuit.
This is the voltage across the wire from the negative side of the load to the negative terminal of the battery. This may be a maximum of 0.5 V.

V4: Measure the voltage loss in the positive side of the circuit.
This is the voltage across the wire from the positive terminal of the battery to the positive side of the load. This may be a maximum of 0.5 V.

Check V1-V4 method
V1 = V2 + V3 + V4
The terminal voltage must be equal to the individual voltage drops.

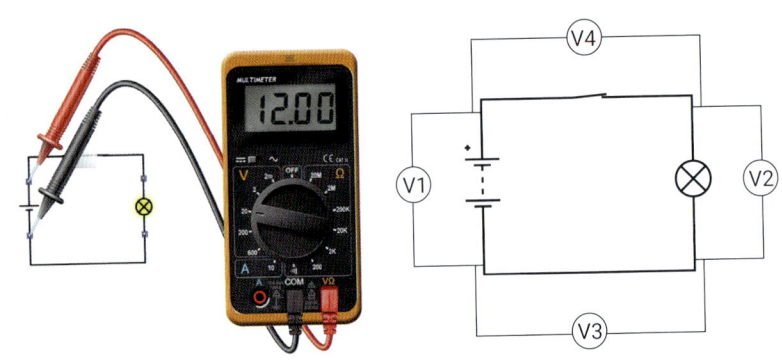

Fig. 203 Measuring the terminal voltage (V1)

Fig. 204 V4 method

2. Voltage Drop

An electrical load is usually connected in series with wires, connectors, fuses, and switches. All these components must have the lowest possible resistance in order to provide the load with sufficient voltage. The maximum voltage loss that may be caused by a contact resistance is 0.5 V.

If these conductors have oxidized connections, contact resistance is formed, and less voltage is provided to the load.

If there is a contact resistance in series with the rear window heating element, the glass will not defrost properly.

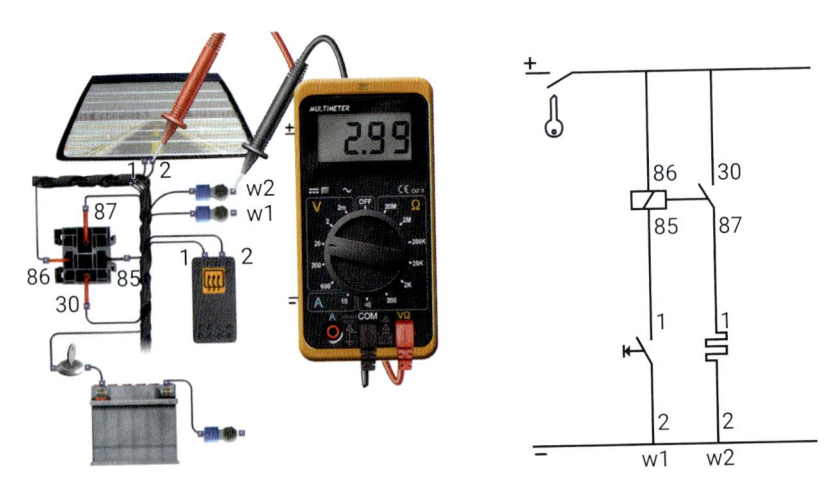

Fig. 205 Measuring the voltage drop

EXAMPLE During the main circuit check you will find a voltage drop of 2.99 V in the ground circuit. The voltage drop across the ground circuit is much too high.

The voltage drop across the ground circuit ensures that there is not a full voltage across the rear window heater. This means that the rear window is not completely free of condensation.

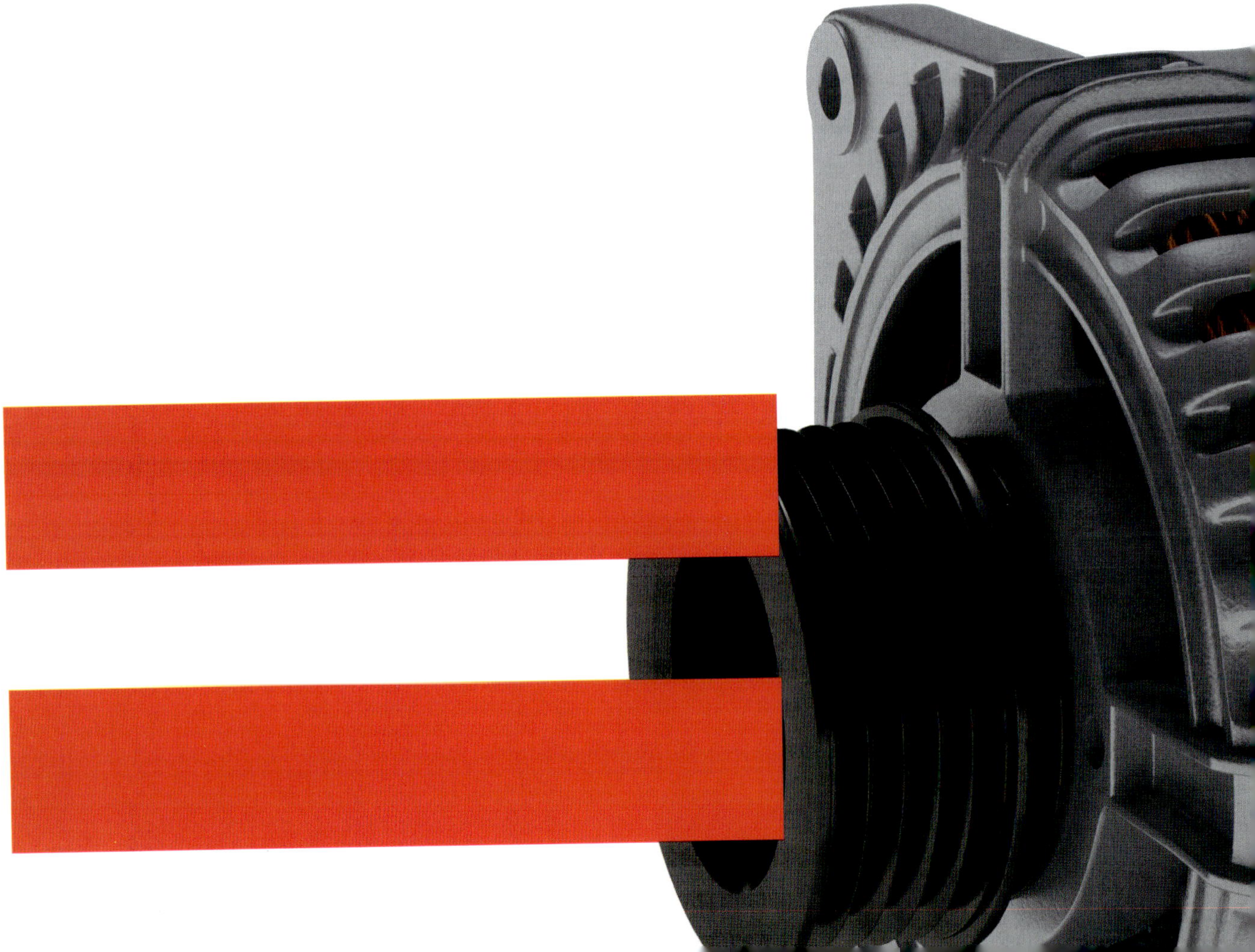

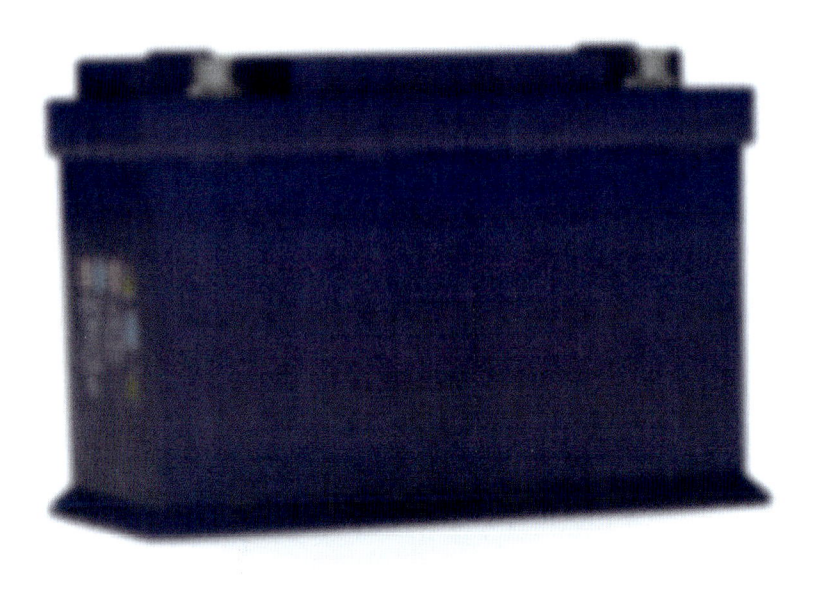

9. Wiring and Wire Repair

DETERMINING THE CROSS-SECTIONAL AREA OF A CONDUCTOR

1. Dilemmas in the workshop

Replacing a cable should be done with care; the cross-sectional area of the cable is very important.

When a current runs through an electric conductor, heat is generated. If the current increases, so will the generated heat.

If you connect a load, you need to choose a cable that can handle the current flow of the circuit. In a 12V installation you can assume:
— 1 mm^2 for turn signals and brake lights
— 1.5 mm^2 for horn and wipers
— 2.5 mm^2 for a starter relay
— 4 mm^2 for a charging circuit
— 6 mm^2 for light switches
— 10 mm^2 for a pre-heating system
— 50 mm^2 for a starter cable

Fig. 206 Different types of cables.

Fig. 207 Cables with different cross-sections.

2. Introduction

The resistivity of a conductor depends on a few factors:
- length
- cross-sectional area
- resistivity

These are the relationships between these three:
- The resistance increases with decreasing cross-sectional area (A) (inversely proportionate).
- The resistance increases with added length (l) (proportional).
- Certain conductors allow current to flow more easily than others; this is known as resistivity (ρ).
    - $\rho_{silver} = 0.0160 \times 10^{-6}\ \Omega m$
    - $\rho_{copper} = 0.0175 \times 10^{-6}\ \Omega m$
    - $\rho_{aluminum} = 0.028 \times 10^{-6}\ \Omega m$

HOW TO: REPAIR WIRING AND REPLACING A RELAY CONTACT

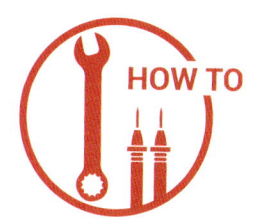

1. Repair of Wiring

Wiring often needs to be repaired in a car. In this case, the wiring is repaired with crimping pliers. A relay contact is also replaced.

2. Repair of the Wiring With Crimping Pliers

Fig. 210 Tools Required

Fig. 211 Remove the insulation from the first wire. Removing about 5 mm from the insulation is sufficient.

Fig. 212 For the cross section of the wire, choose the correct size of crimp connector and place the connector in the crimping pliers in the correct way.

Fig. 213 Turn the stripped ends around. Place the stripped end of the first wire in the crimp connector.

Fig. 214 Squeeze the connector so that the wire is clamped. Remove the connector from the crimping pliers and place the other side of the connector in the crimping pliers.

Fig. 215 Place the stripped end of the second wire in the connector.

The connection is made. Check whether both wires are attached properly in the crimp connector.

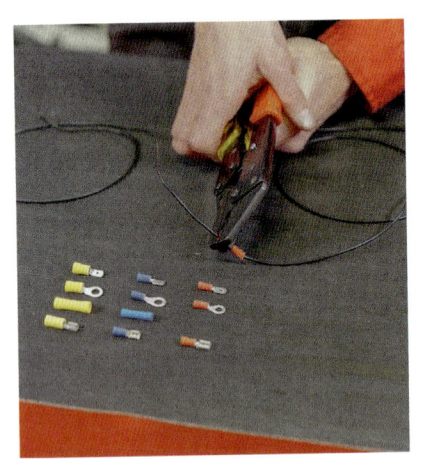

Fig. 216 Squeeze the connector so that the second wire is clamped.

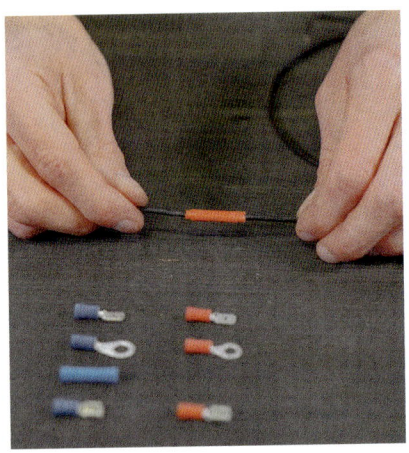

Fig. 217 Remove the connector from the crimping pliers. Check whether both wires are attached properly.

3. Repair of a Plug in a Relay Socket

The plug in the relay socket is broken. The plug no longer makes good contact with the relay pins.

Fig. 218 Remove the plug from the relay socket. Use plug unlocking tools for this.

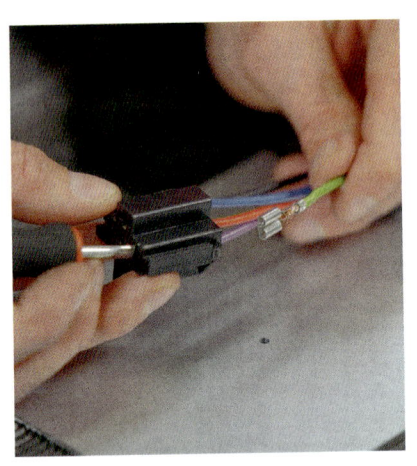

Fig. 219 Plug unlocking tools are available in different sizes. Use the size that is suitable for the size of the plug.

Fig. 220 Cut the defective plug off the wire.

Place a new plug on the wire and mount the plug in the relay socket.

9. WIRING AND WIRE REPAIR

Fig. 221 Remove the insulation from the wire. Removing about 5 mm from the insulation is sufficient.

Fig. 222 Place a new plug in the correct way in the crimping pliers.

Fig. 223 Place the stripped end in the plug.

Fig. 224 Squeeze the connector closed. Take the wire and connector out of the pliers. Check whether the plug is attached properly.

Fig. 225 Look to see wheres the plug lock is located on the plug. Put the plug back in the relay socket in the correct way.

Fig. 226 Check whether the plug is mounted properly.

HOW TO: REPAIR WIRING WITH SOLDERED CONNECTIONS

1. Repair of Wiring With Soldered Connections

If a wire has become damaged or it is cut through, you can solder the parts back together.
CAN bus connections can also be soldered.

2. Repair of a Single Wire

Two ends of a wire are connected here by means of a soldered connection. A soldered connection conducts current well and also results in a proper connection from a mechanical perspective.

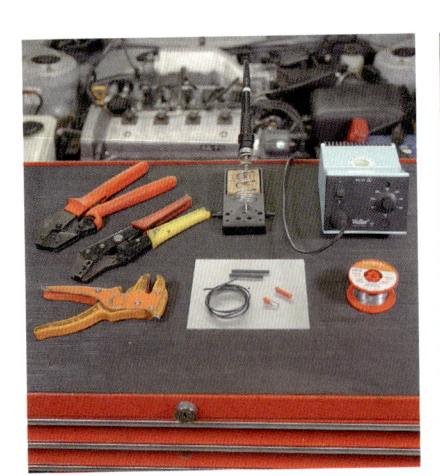

Fig. 228 Tools Required

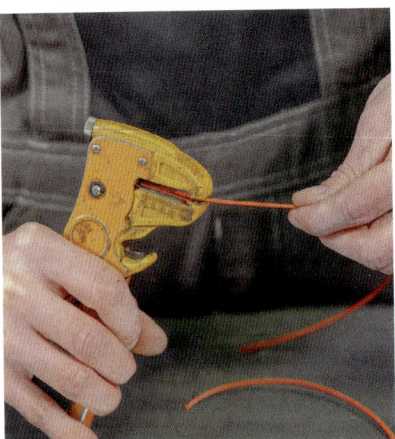

Fig. 229 Remove the insulation (5 - 7 mm) from the first wire with stripping pliers.

Fig. 230 Remove the insulation (5 - 7 mm) of the second wire and twist the loose wires on each end together.

Fig. 231 Put a crimping sleeve of the correct size around one of the ends. Then twist both ends together and place the whole thing on a metal plate.

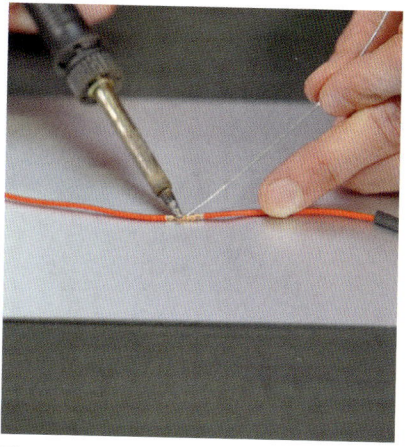

Fig. 232 Take the soldering iron and heat the twisted wire ends. Place the solder near the wire ends and ensure that the solder flows properly across the wire ends.

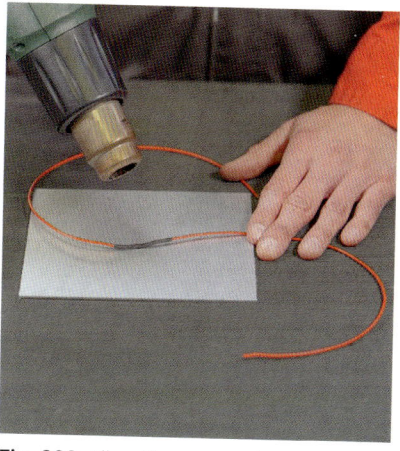

Fig. 233 Allow the connection to cool briefly and slide the crimping sleeve over the soldered wire ends. Take the hot air gun and heat the crimping sleeve all around so that the sleeve shrinks around the joint and contacts well.

3. Repair of a CAN Bus Connection

CAN bus connections consist of two wires. These wires are twisted around each other. It is called a "twisted-pair." This is done to avoid electromagnetic interference.

When repairing a CAN bus connection, special attention must be paid to restoring the "twisted pair." In other words, we have to make sure that the wires are twisted around each other.

Fig. 234 The CAN bus wire is damaged.

Fig. 235 Cut the damaged part out of the wiring. Twist the wiring apart on both sides.

Fig. 236 Remove the insulation (5 - 7 mm) from the four wires. Twist the loose wires together.

Fig. 237 Slide the crimping sleeve over two of the four wire ends.

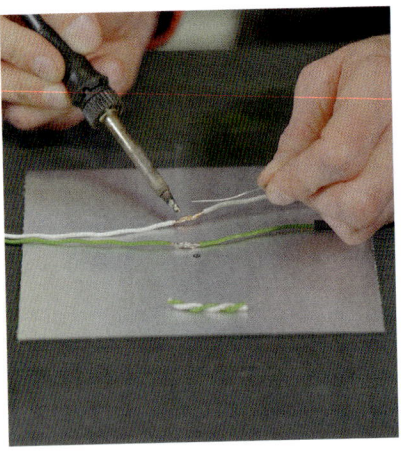

Fig. 238 Twist together the two stripped wire ends that belong together. Heat the wire with the soldering iron and make sure that the whole wire is covered with solder.

Fig. 239 Allow both wires to cool briefly. Then slide both crimping sleeves over the soldered parts. Point the hot air gun at the crimping sleeve and heat the sleeve all the way around.

Fig. 240 Twist the wires so that both wires are twisted around each other again.

Fig. 241 After the repair, test whether the connection is intact again. You can do this by viewing the signals with an oscilloscope.

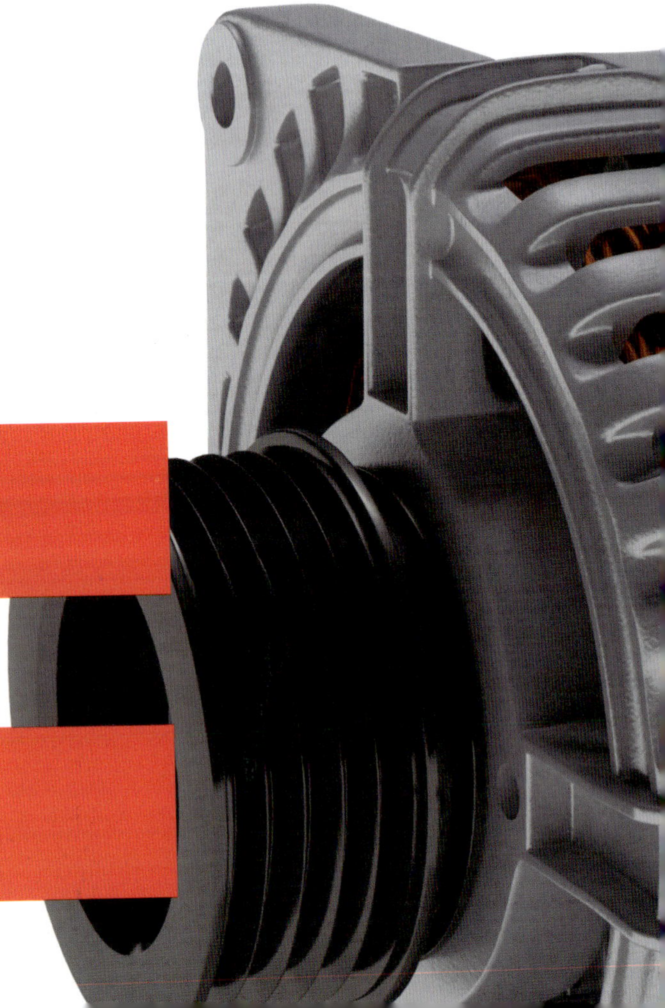

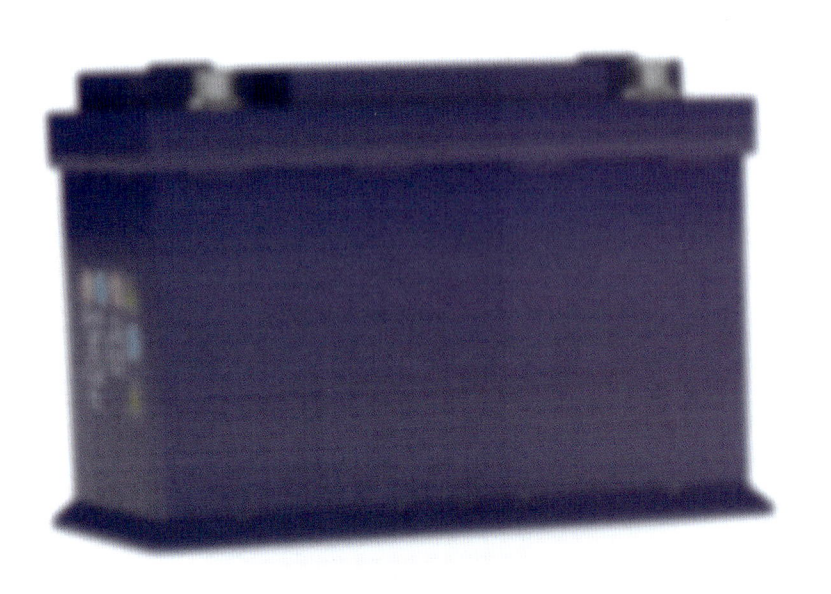

10. Batteries

LEAD-ACID BATTERY: INTRODUCTION USA

1. Introduction

In lead batteries, a chemical reaction takes place on the battery plates, which are submerged in an acid (electrolyte). The plate thickness and the surface area of the plate have a great influence on the capacity and the (cold) starting current of a battery.

Batteries with plates that have a large plate surface can supply a lot of current for a short time, necessary when starting a piston engine, for example.

Batteries with thick plates can supply a constant current over a longer period of time.

To increase the surface of a plate, battery plates are made from a grid with porous lead paste. The cavities in this paste ensure that the surface area is increased. The paste loosens with age. That's why each plate is equipped with a plastic envelope. This ensures that the individual parts of the battery plates cannot touch each other.

2. Battery Symbols

Because batteries contain dangerous acids, there are several symbols on the battery that indicate how to handle the battery safely.

The symbols indicate that:
— You must keep the battery away from children.
— The battery can explode while charging.
— The battery must be kept away from flames.
— Hazardous corrosive acid is present.
— You should always wear safety goggles.
— You should always read the manual first.
— The battery must be disposed of at a special collection point.
— You should never dispose of the battery with regular trash because batteries contain lead.

3. Battery Standards

Important information is listed on every battery, to help you identify the type of battery you're working with. This information must comply with standards established by one of the following world organizations:
— SAE: Society of Automotive Engineers
— DIN: Duitse Industrie Normen [German Industry Standards]
— EN: EN: Europese Norm [European Standard]
— IEC: International Electrotechnical Commission

Each organization performs battery tests differently. Therefore, battery specifications differ according to organization. For this reason, most electronic battery test equipment require that you indicate which battery standard you're dealing with.

BATTERY: ELECTRICAL CAPACITY

1. Capacity

The capacity of a battery is the measure of the amount of electrical energy that a battery can contain. The capacity is given in the unit **Ah (Ampere-hour)**. The capacity (Ah) is the current (A) that a battery can supply during a given time (h).

Capacity (Ah) = current (A) x time (h).

In automotive engineering, the capacity of a battery is almost always determined over a period of 20 hours at a temperature of 81 °F (27 °C).

2. Battery Plates

In lead batteries, a chemical reaction takes place on the battery plates, which are submerged in an acid (electrolyte). The plate thickness and the surface area of the plate have a great influence on the capacity and the (cold) starting current of a battery.

Batteries with plates that have a large plate surface can supply a lot of current for a short time, necessary when starting a piston engine, for example.

Batteries with thick plates can supply a constant current over a longer period of time.

To increase the surface of a plate, battery plates are made from a grid with porous lead paste. The cavities in this paste ensure that the surface area is increased. The paste loosens with age. That's why each plate is equipped with a plastic envelope. This ensures that the individual parts of the battery plates cannot touch each other.

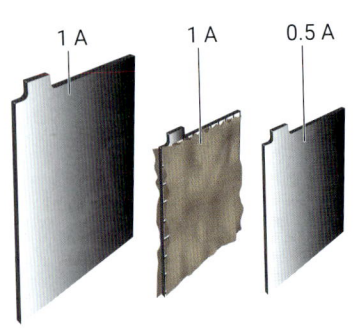

Fig. 243 The larger the surface, the greater the (cold) starting current.

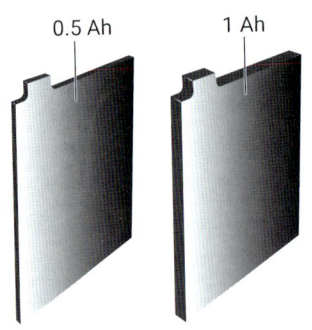

Fig. 244 The thicker the plate, the greater the capacity.

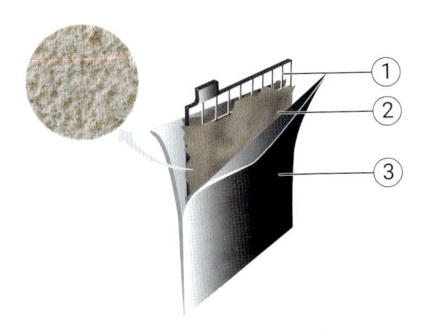

Fig. 245 1. Grid. 2. Porous paste. 3. Envelope/separator.

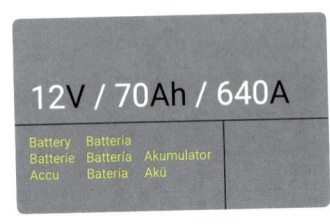

Fig. 246 The label on a battery.

3. Standard

The capacity of vehicle batteries is determined according to a set standard. This standard lays down a number of values:
— Discharge time.
— Temperature.
— Residual voltage.

One of these standards is the German DIN standard. According to the DIN standard, a 70 Ah battery should be tested in the following way:
— 20 hour discharge time.
— At a temperature of 77° F (± 4° F).
— The residual voltage must not fall below 1.75 V per cell.
— The following then applies to the entire battery: 6 x 1.75 = 10.5 V.

The capacity of a battery is not a fixed value. The capacity may increase or decrease depending on various factors.

BATTERY: CRANKING AND CHARGING AMPS

1. Cold Start

A cold start is described as starting a car under very cold conditions. Cold conditions slow the chemical reactions in a battery, which reduces the battery's capacity and source voltage. This makes starting a car in cold weather difficult. In addition to the reduced performance of the battery, cold weather also has adverse consequences for the combustion engine. For example, the oil in the oil sump is thicker, causing the starter motor to experience more resistance during start-up.

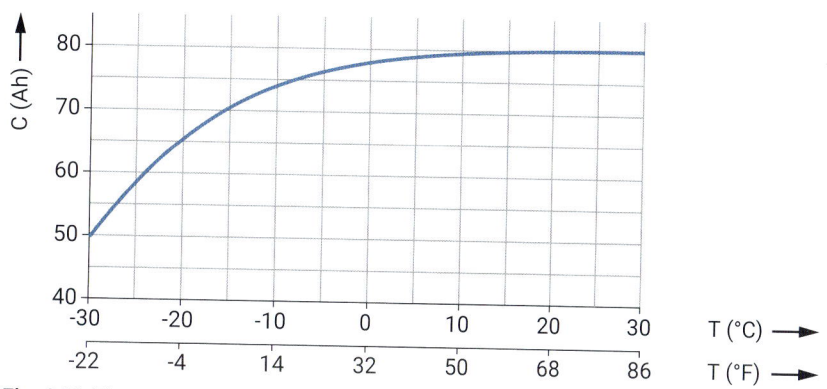

Fig. 248 The capacity in relation to the temperature.

Cold start current:
The cold start current stated on a battery tells us about the speed with which the battery can deliver electrical energy. The cold starting current or CCA (Cold Cranking Amps) is a value determined by the battery manufacturer. This value is tested according to a certain standard. This standard specifies how much residual voltage must be present in the battery after a cold start drawing a given current at a given ambient temperature.

EXAMPLE
— CCA: 280 A at -0.4 °F (-18 °C).
— According to the DIN standard, the residual voltage must be:
  — At least 1.5 V per cell after 30 seconds.
  — At least 1 V per cell after 150 seconds.

BATTERY: ELECTROLYTE

1. Electrolyte Density

The density of the electrolyte tells us about the state of charge of the battery and therefore about the capacity. A battery that is 50% discharged obviously has a lower capacity than a fully charged battery.

Electrolyte density is expressed as specific gravity, which is the density of the electrolyte compared to the density of water. The specific gravity of water is 1.000, and the electrolyte in a typical automotive lead/acid battery should have a specific gravity between 1.200 and 1.280. The electrolyte of a fully charged battery has a specific gravity of 1.265.

The state-of-charge and therefore the battery's capacity decreases 3% with a decrease in specific gravity of only 0.010.

EXAMPLE
— Battery with a capacity of 70 Ah.
— Specific gravity is 1.265.
— Specific gravity decreases by 0.010
— Capacity decrease of 3% (3 x 0.7 = 2.1 Ah)
— Capacity = 70 - 2.1 = 67.9 Ah.

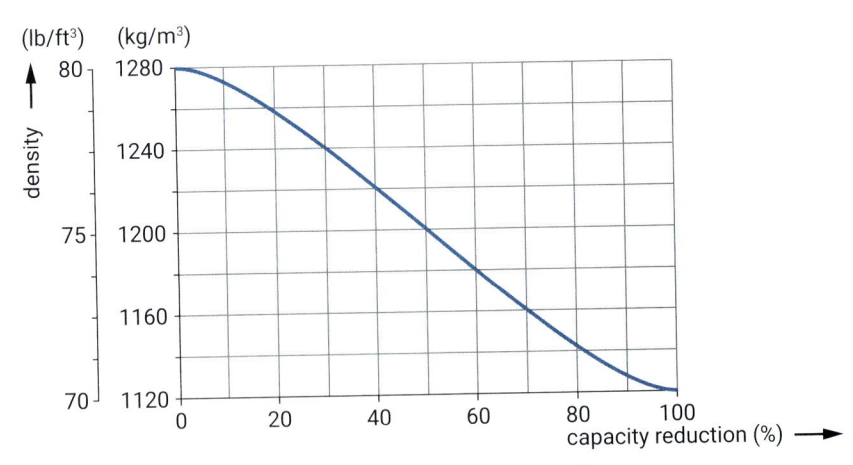

Fig. 250 The density of the electrolyte relative to the capacity.

2. Self-Discharge

Batteries that are not in use can still lose capacity after a certain amount of time. This is called self-discharge. Because small internal circuits are created in the battery, small discharge currents will start running. The cause of this can be:
— Contamination of the electrolyte by components of the plates.
— Electrochemical reactions between the metals that make up the plates.

Self-discharge is accelerated when the battery is stored at a high temperature. The rate of self-discharge doubles with every 18 °F (10 °C) rise in temperature. Batteries must therefore always be stored under a number of conditions:
— The battery must be fully charged.
— The battery must be stored in a cool, dark place.
— The state of charge of the battery must be checked regularly and the battery may need to be recharged.

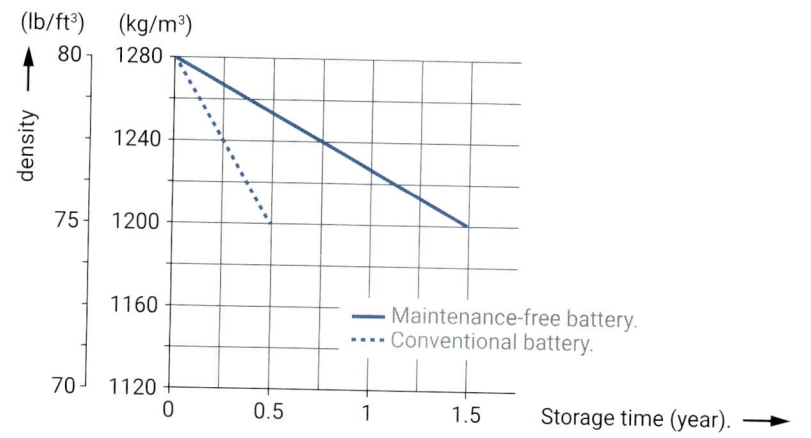

Fig. 251 The specific gravity of the electrolyte also decreases when the battery is not being used.

LEAD-ACID BATTERY: BASIC PRINCIPLES

1. Purpose of the Battery

A vehicle needs electrical energy to make the lamps and control units work. When the engine is running, this energy comes from the alternator, but when the engine is not running or needs to be started, this energy must come from somewhere else.

While it is difficult to store electrical energy for a long time, a battery stores energy in chemical form, which is much easier to store. When the engine is not running, the battery converts chemical energy into electrical energy to run the vehicle. After the engine is running, the alternator recharges the battery, converting electrical energy back to chemical energy, where it is stored for later use.

Fig. 252 When starting, the battery supplies energy to the starter motor.

Fig. 253 When the engine is started, the alternator supplies energy to the battery.

Starting
When starting the vehicle, the battery will convert stored chemical energy into usable electrical energy to power the starter motor and start the internal combustion engine.

Charge
When the internal combustion engine is started, the alternator will ensure that electrical energy is supplied to the battery. The battery converts this electrical energy into chemical energy and stores it for later use.

2. Battery Discharging Principle

There are two lead plates in a container filled with electrolyte.

In the fully **charged** state, there's a **surplus** of negatively charged particles on the **negative plate**. The voltage difference between the two plates is great.

If you connect an electrical accessory (load device) to the plates, the discharging process begins. Electrons move from the negative plate, via the lamp, to the positive plate.

The voltage difference between the two plates is constantly decreasing during the discharging process.

Fig. 254 The battery is fully charged.

Fig. 255 The battery is supplying current and being discharged.

Fig. 256 The battery is completely discharged.

When the number of negatively-charged particles in both plates are equal, there will no longer be a voltage difference between the plates. The battery is completely discharged.

3. Battery Charging Principle

In a **discharged** state, there's a **state of equilibrium** between the negatively-charged particles on the **positive plate** and on the **negative plate**. There's no voltage difference.

The charging process starts by connecting a charger to the plates. Electrons travel from the positive plate through the charger to the negative plate.

The voltage difference between the plates is constantly increasing as charging takes place.

Fig. 257 The battery is completely discharged and connected to the battery charger.

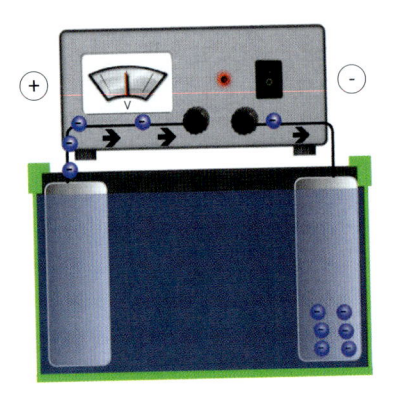

Fig. 258 The battery is being charged.

Fig. 259 The battery is fully charged.

4. Chemical Reaction Through Discharging

The electrolyte consists of sulfuric acid (H_2SO_4) and water (H_2O). In the charged state, the positive plate consists of lead dioxide (PbO_2) and the negative plate consists of lead (Pb).

While discharging takes place, the sulfuric acid reacts with the lead on the negative plate turning into lead sulfate (pBSO$_4$). During this process, negatively-charged electrons are released. Positively-charged hydrogen atoms (H+) are left behind in the electrolyte.

The electrons flow through the lamp to the positive plate. The hydrogen travels through the electrolyte to the positive plate.

On the positive plate, the lead dioxide reacts with the sulfuric acid and the hydrogen turns into lead sulfate. The electrons are absorbed during this process, and water is released.

Because sulfuric acid is turned into water while discharging takes place, the acidity of the electrolyte decreases as the battery discharges.

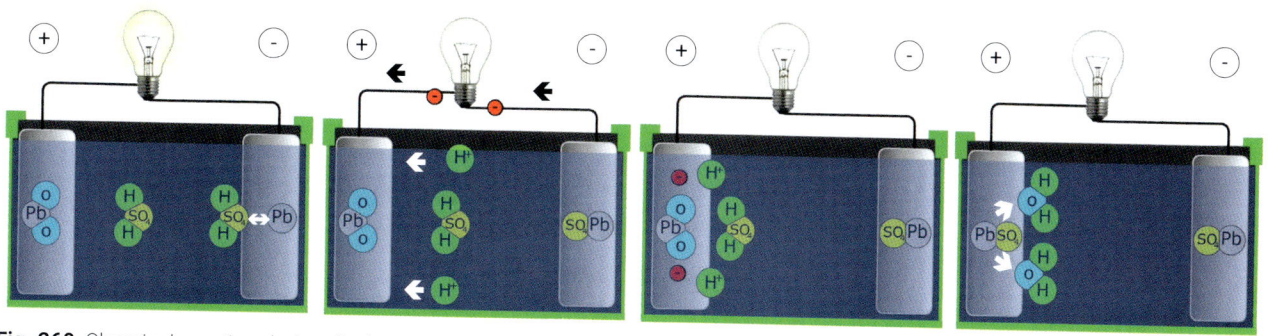

Fig. 260 Chemical reaction during discharge.

5. Chemical Reaction Through Charging

In a discharged state, the positive and negative plates both consist of lead sulfate (pBSO$_4$).

While charging, the water (H$_2$0) reacts with the lead sulfate on the positive plate which converts it into lead dioxide and sulfuric acid. Negatively-charged electrons are released in the process, and positively-charged hydrogen atoms are created (H+).

The electrons flow through the charger to the negative plate. The hydrogen also travels through the electrolyte to the negative plate.

On the negative plate, the hydrogen reacts with the lead sulfate to turn into sulfuric acid (H$_2$SO$_4$) and leaves behind a lead (Pb) negative plate.

Because sulfuric acid is formed while charging is taking place and water disappears, the acidity increases.

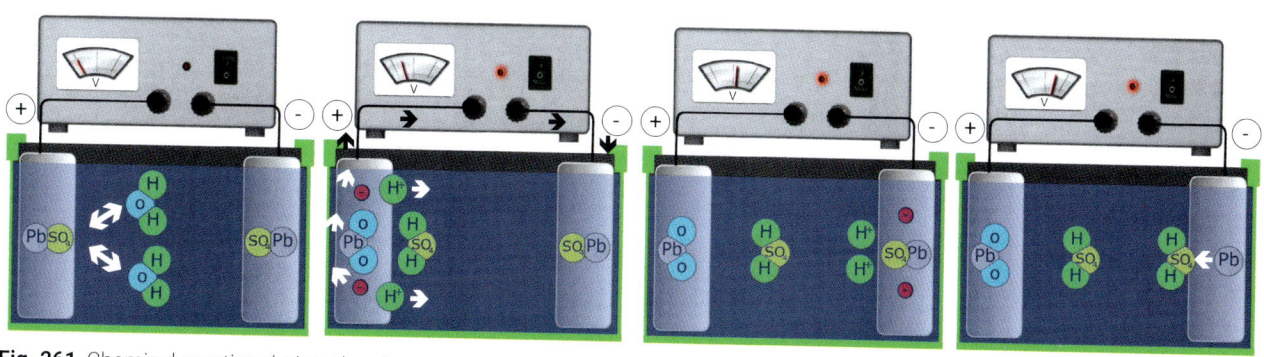

Fig. 261 Chemical reaction during charging

6. Lead-Acid Battery Design

A 12-volt lead-acid battery consists of a battery box with six cells, a positive terminal, and a negative terminal.

Each cell is able to deliver a voltage of 2.1 volts. By connecting the cells in series, using cell connections, the battery delivers a voltage of 12.6 volts.

A cell is made up of:
— positive plates
— negative plates
— separators
  This allows the positive and negative plates to be separated from one another.
— Cell connecting bars
  With one bar, all positive plates are connected to one another, and with another bar all negative plates are connected to one another.

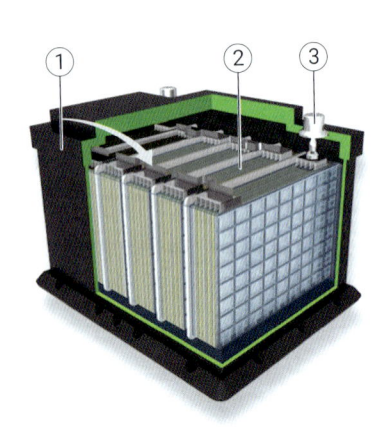

Fig. 262 1. battery box 2. battery cell 3. battery post

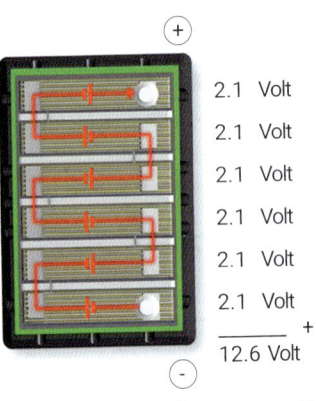

Fig. 263 2.1 volt cells connected in series

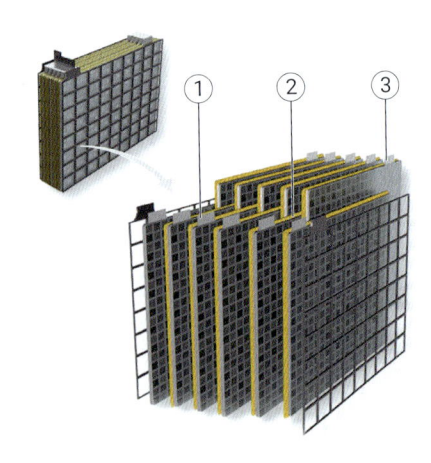

Fig. 264 1. negative plate 2. separator 3. positive plate

LEAD-ACID BATTERY: DESIGNS

1. Lead-Acid Battery Categories

There are different types of lead-acid batteries. These can be divided into two main groups.
— Vented lead-acid batteries:
  These can be topped up with distilled water.
— Sealed lead-acid batteries:
  These cannot be refilled. Many of these batteries can be checked by looking at the test indicator.
    — Green:
      The battery is more than 65% charged and the electrolyte is up to the correct level.
    — Black: The battery is less than 65% charged and the electrolyte is up to the correct level.
    — Clear: The electrolyte level is too low.

Fig. 265 1. Battery case. 2. Filler cap.

Fig. 266 1. Clear. 2. Black. 3. Green.

2. Standard Lead-Acid Battery

In standard lead-acid batteries there is a liquid electrolyte between the plates.

Lead-acid batteries are ideally suited as starter batteries. Starter batteries need to be able to deliver a very high current in a short time. It also needs to be possible to recharge the battery quickly.

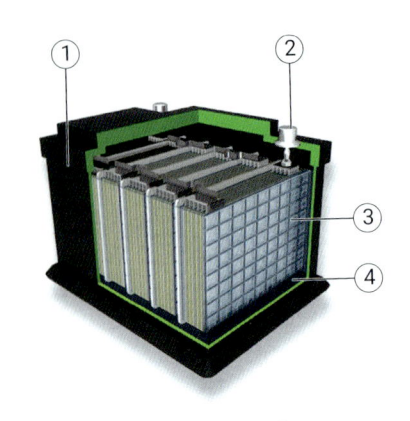

Fig. 267 1. Battery case. 2. Battery terminal. 3. Battery cell. 4. Electrolyte.

In addition to these advantages, the following disadvantages also apply:
— Lead-acid batteries have a relatively low capacity.
— Only a limited proportion of the capacity can be used.

3. EFB battery

An EFB (Enhanced Flooded Battery) is actually an "enhanced lead battery." The electrolyte is in liquid form, just like in a lead battery. Modifications make these batteries suitable for use in vehicles with heavy demands such as start-stop systems.
Poly-fleece fabric is attached to the positive plate of the battery. The electrolyte continues circulating through the battery using an acid circulator in combination with the labyrinth in the lid.

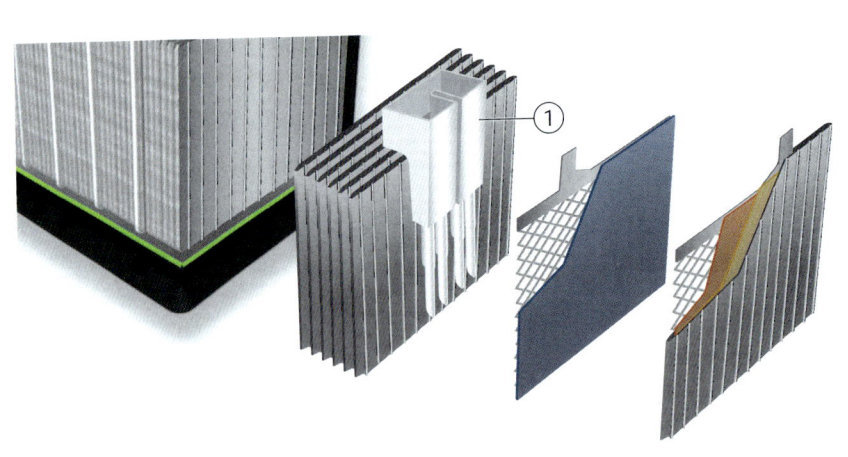

Fig. 268 EFB battery with acid circulator (1).

The construction of EFB batteries provides the following characteristics:
— Longer service life.
— Discharge up to a maximum of 5%.
— Maintenance-free.
— Suitable for vehicles with a start-stop system.
— Positioned between a standard lead-acid battery and an AGM battery.

4. Gel Battery

A thickening agent is added to the liquid electrolyte in gel batteries. This creates an almost solid gel.

Advantages of gel batteries:

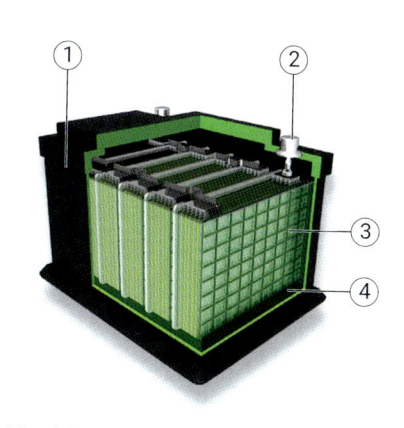

Fig. 269 1. Battery case. 2. Battery terminal. 3. Battery cell. 4. Gel.

— Electrolyte is not able to leak from the battery, even if the battery case breaks.
— Self-discharge is less than in the case of standard lead-acid batteries. (Self-discharging: discharging without drawing any current from the battery.)
— They can be placed anywhere, but must be upright.

Disadvantages of gel batteries:
— Overcharging the battery adversely affects its service life and the battery's capacity.
— The battery must be charged more slowly than standard lead-acid batteries.
— Higher price.

Gel batteries are sealed and can only be checked by taking terminal measurements.

5. AGM battery

AGM (Absorbed Glass Mats) batteries contain fiberglass mats soaked with electrolyte between the plates. AGM batteries do not leak either.

Advantages of AGM batteries in relation to gel batteries:
— While the capacity of a battery is reduced at lower temperatures, AGM batteries are less sensitive to cold.
— Longer service life.
— They can be put anywhere in any position; even upside down.

The disadvantages of gel batteries also apply to AGM batteries.

AGM batteries are also sealed and can only be checked by means of terminal measurements.

No space is required for fluid supply (electrolyte) inside the battery. This means that the cells can be almost as high as the battery case. This allows a small battery to have a greater capacity.

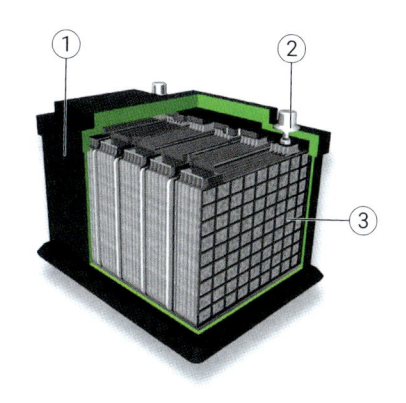

Fig. 270 1. Battery case. 2. Battery terminal. 3. Battery cell with fiberglass mats.

LEAD-ACID BATTERY: MEASURING

1. Series and Parallel Connections

Sometimes batteries are connected in series or in parallel to attain the desired battery capacity or battery voltage.

If the batteries of the same voltage are connected in **series**, their voltages are added together but the capacity of the pair remains the same as the capacity of one battery.

If batteries of the same voltage are connected in **parallel**, their capacities are added together but the voltage remains the same as the voltage of one battery.

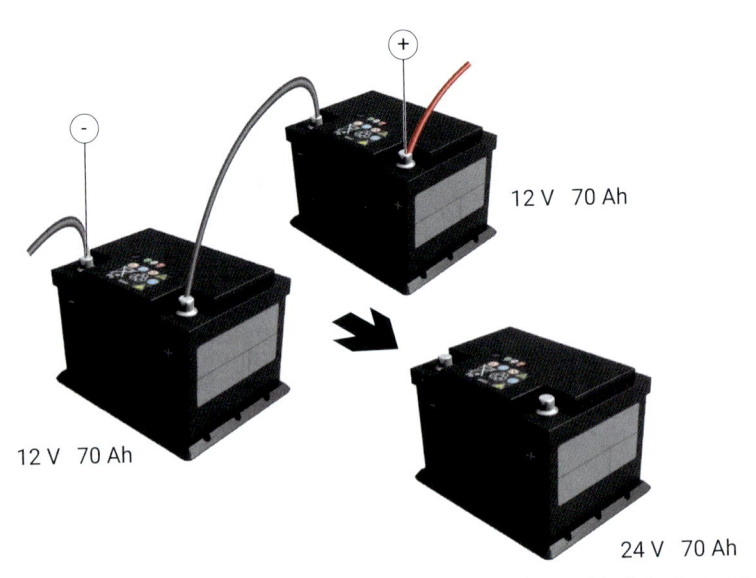

12 V 70 Ah

12 V 70 Ah

24 V 70 Ah

Fig. 271 With two batteries connected in series, the voltage of both batteries is added together.

12V 70Ah

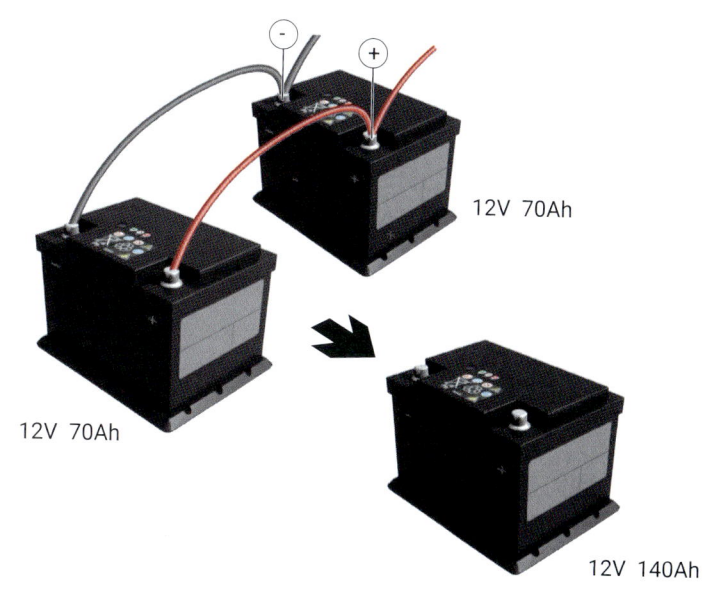

12V 70Ah

12V 140Ah

Fig. 272 With two batteries connected in parallel, the capacity of both batteries is added together.

The capacity of a battery is expressed in Ampere hours (Ah). This is the maximum amount of electrical energy that a battery can deliver.

2. Source Voltage and Terminal Voltage

The **source voltage** of a battery is the voltage difference between the positive and negative terminal of the battery free of load (battery voltage when no current is flowing).

The **terminal voltage** of a battery is the voltage difference between the positive and negative terminal of the battery under load (battery voltage when current is flowing).

Fig. 273 Measuring the open voltage (battery free of load, where current through the meter is ignored

Fig. 274 Measuring the closed circuit voltage (battery under load)

The open circuit voltage of a battery decreases over time because of the internal resistance of the battery, and it decreases faster as the battery ages. The lead plates gradually deteriorate with age, increasing their resistance.

3. Battery Conductance Tester

A battery conductance tester is able to determine the state of the battery by taking measurements. The measurements are taken both free of load and with the battery under load.

The battery tester must be connected to the battery. The tester asks questions that must be answered, including:
— test standard
— type of battery
— battery voltage
— battery capacity
— battery cold cranking amperage (CCA)

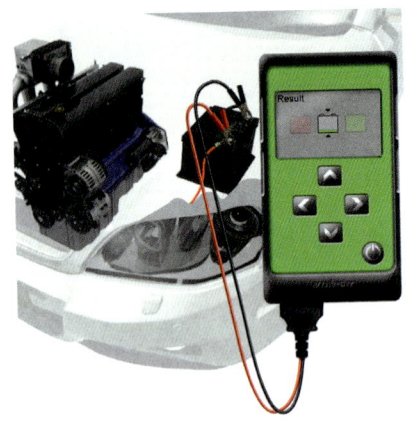

Fig. 275 The conductance tester.

After testing is complete, the tester indicates one of the following states:
— Battery good and charged. (Green: full battery icon)
— Battery good, but must be charged. (Green: empty battery icon)
— Battery not OK and needs to be replaced. (Red battery icon)

This test is called a conductance test. During testing, the internal conductivity of the battery is tested. This is done by charging the battery for a very short amount of time. The measurements then show how much of the active plate surface of the battery is still present and not deteriorated or covered with scale.

PLEASE NOTE This is only possible if the correct battery information is entered.

This method of testing has a number of advantages, such as:
— The battery does not have to be fully charged.
— The battery does not have to be disassembled.
— It is a passive test method, which means no sparking or consequences for sensitive electronics.

This measurement should only be taken on batteries in a state of rest. If the engine has been running, the lights must be switched on for one minute, then switched off for one minute before the measurement can be taken.

HYDROMETER

1. Introduction

A hydrometer is a tool that allows you to accurately measure the state of charge of a battery.

Operation

The state of charge is determined by measuring the specific gravity of the electrolyte. Hydrometers can only be used with vented lead-acid batteries.

Hydrometers consist of a transparent tube, a rubber bellows, a suction tube and a float. The float will continue to float on the electrolyte that is suctioned up when measuring the state of charge. The lower the specific gravity of the electrolyte, the deeper the float will sink.

A scale on the float clearly shows how far the float sinks and that is used to determine the exact specific gravity of the electrolyte.
— A properly charged battery has a specific gravity of 1.28.
— A half-charged battery has a specific gravity of 1.2.
— A discharged battery has a specific gravity of 1.1.

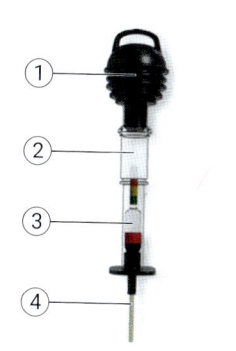

Fig. 278 1. Bellows. 2. Tube. 3. Float. 4. Suction tube.

2. Using a hydrometer

Before getting started with the hydrometer, ensure that you're wearing safety goggles and protective clothing.

Next unscrew all six cell caps. You must place the suction tube of the hydrometer into the electrolyte for the cell you're testing. When you squeeze and release the rubber bulb, electrolyte will be drawn into the tube.

Make sure the float moves freely inside the glass tube. Only then will you be able to determine the battery state-of-charge.

3. Reading the hydrometer

If the float is able to move freely, then you can measure the specific gravity of the liquid. The specific gravity of the liquid is a measure of the state of charge of the battery.

Make sure that you hold the hydrometer vertically and read the number on the float at eye level with the surface of the liquid.

The line under the number indicates the value of the specific gravity.

NOTE If you have measured the state of charge of a cell, always make sure that the liquid is returned back into the cell that you have just measured.

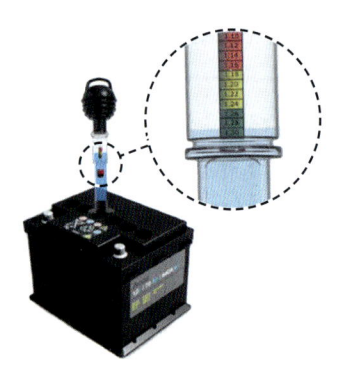

Charging. State. battery	Specific. weight	Idling-voltage
100%	1.28	12.72
80%	1.245	12.51
60%	1.21	12.3
40%	1.16	12.09
20%	1.14	11.88
10%	1.1	11.64

Fig. 279 Reading the hydrometer.

4. Refractometer

There is also a different way to test the specific gravity of the battery acid. The specific gravity of a cell can be determined with one drop of battery acid by means of what is called a refractometer. This is done by measuring the refraction of light by the liquid.

Battery acid is taken from a cell using a pipette. A drop of battery acid is placed under the lid. By looking in the refractometer, the specific gravity of the battery acid can be determined on the basis of a scale.

A refractometer can also be used to test coolant and washer fluid.

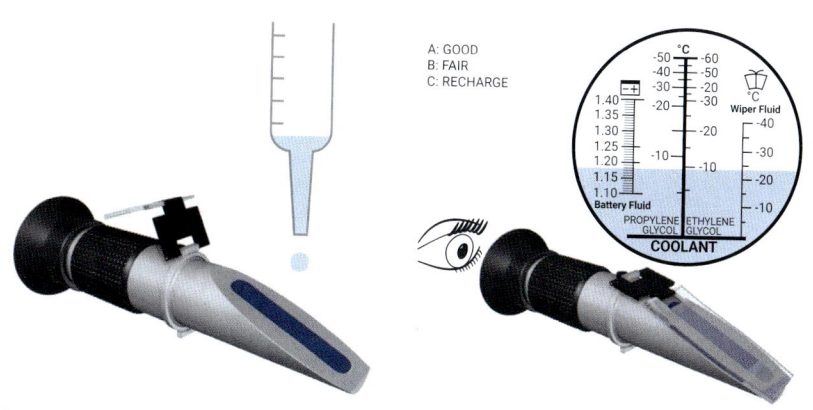

Fig. 280 A drop of battery acid.

Fig. 281 Reading the refractometer.

5. Sulfation

With a sulfated battery, the lead sulfate has resulted in the formation of a coarse crystal structure because of a deep discharge. This greatly reduces the capacity of the battery. In many cases it is not possible to restore the crystal structure. The battery has then become unusable.

Deep discharge, resulting in sulfation, can occur if the battery is not used for a long time and is insufficiently charged.

To prevent sulfation of batteries that are not being used, you must ensure that the specific gravity of the battery acid does not fall below 1.13. Sometimes it is not possible to determine the specific gravity. In such a case, measure the open circuit voltage of the battery. This may not fall below 11.5 V. The battery must be regularly charged.

A (deeply) discharged, sulfated battery has a high internal resistance. Due to the high internal resistance, a lot of heat will be generated in the battery during charging. This results in hazardous explosive gases (oxyhydrogen).
Some battery chargers have a special program for charging (repairing) a sulfated battery.

BATTERY: CHARGING

1. Charging

Starter batteries are normally charged by the vehicle's charging system. However, starting the vehicle discharges the battery considerably. Because of this, it takes a while before the battery is fully charged again.

If the vehicle is only driven for a short time after starting, the battery will not be charged enough. It may then be necessary to charge the battery with a battery charger. Even when a battery is rarely used, such as in cars in a showroom, it is still necessary to charge the battery.

Gas voltage.
When lead-acid batteries are charged with too high a voltage, gases are released. The hydrogen gas and oxygen that is then released together form a very explosive gas (oxyhydrogen). The charging voltage at which these gases arise is called the gas voltage. To prevent the formation of these gases, the charging voltage per cell must not exceed 2.4 V. For the complete battery, the charging voltage may not be greater than: 2.4 x 6 = 14.4 V.

2. Charging Methods

In short, charging is the supply of electrical energy to the battery. This supply can be achieved in various ways. There are different types of charging systems. Different charging methods are sometimes combined in one charger.

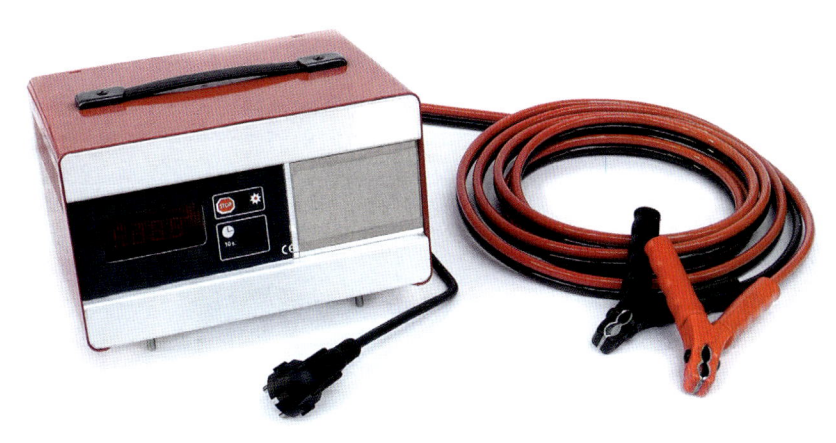

Fig. 282 Conventional Battery Charger

Normal Charge.

Normal charging of a battery is done with a conventional battery charger. This is not much more than a device that converts AC voltage from the socket to a suitable DC voltage. Nowadays, this type of charger is equipped with a safety feature that ensures that the battery cannot be overcharged.

Conventional battery chargers often provide an unstable DC voltage that causes voltage peaks. This can cause damage to sensitive electronics in the vehicle's onboard system.

Trickle charger.

These chargers are not intended to fully charge a battery from a discharged state. Trickle chargers ensure that a battery that is (nearly) full is kept charged up. Because trickle chargers charge the battery when the battery voltage drops below a certain level and stop charging when the battery is full, trickle chargers can remain connected to a battery for a longer period of time. Trickle chargers that operate only as needed are called "maintenance chargers." Trickle chargers are used, among other things, for vintage cars, motorbikes and yachts, because they are often not used for long periods of time (winter months).

Fig. 283 Trickle Charger

3. Automatic Battery Charger

Modern battery chargers are equipped with smart electronics that can monitor the condition of the battery. Charging batteries with an automatic charger often involves several steps. One charger uses all intermediate steps, while another only uses a few steps. There are a number of standard steps that a battery charger can use:

Fig. 284 Automatic Battery Charger

- Desulfation:
  The battery is charged with pulses to remove sulfate deposits.
- Soft start:
  This tests whether the battery can accept the charge. The charger only starts charging when the battery is okay.
- Bulk charging:
  The battery is charged to approximately 80% with maximum current.
- Absorption charging:
  The battery is charged to 100% with constant voltage and decreasing current.
- Analysis:
  A test is done to see whether the battery retains energy. If this not the case, then the battery may need to be replaced.
- Reconditioning:
  This function can be used to recondition a fully discharged battery.
- Float:
  The battery voltage is kept at a maximum level
- Trickle charging:
  When the battery is fully charged, the charger switches to trickle charging or maintenance mode.

Many automatic battery chargers ensure stable voltage without the risk of any voltage peaks. This makes these chargers suitable for the sensitive electronics in the vehicle.

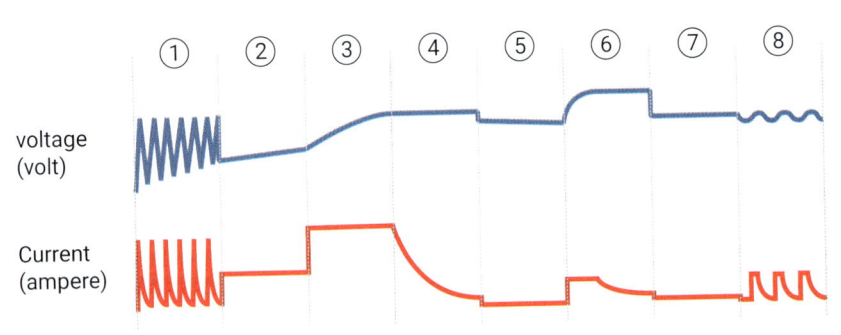

Fig. 285 Voltage and current with: 1. Desulfation. 2. Soft start. 3. Bulk charging. 4. Absorption charging. 5. Analysis. 6. Reconditioning. 7. Float. 8. Trickle charging.

4. Special Conditions

It will occasionally be necessary to replace a battery if it is not used for a long time or if it is discharged only with short trips. There are other conditions where it is necessary to put a battery on a charger.

Diagnosis:
When a vehicle needs to be diagnosed, it's possible the ignition switch and various loads will be switched on for a long time. This will drain the battery. Many modern battery chargers are suitable for recharging the battery during diagnosis without affecting measurements.

In addition, stable voltage is very important when programming a control unit or loading new software. In some cases, a control unit can end up in what is called "safe mode". This happens when the supply voltage falls below a certain value, and will cause the control unit to malfunction.

Fig. 286 A "memory saver".

Replacing the battery:
Cars are equipped with different memories to maintain settings. If the battery is removed, all of the settings in the memory will be deleted. To prevent this, some chargers can power the vehicle while the battery is removed. There are also special devices that can supply the memory via the vehicle's diagnostic connection (OBD) when the battery is being replaced. These devices are called "memory savers".

Jump Starter:
Sometimes the battery has been discharged to such an extent that the engine can no longer be started. Instead of fully charging the battery, a jump starter can be used. This is a device that can deliver a high current in a short amount of time. It is important to protect against incorrect connection of a jump starter.

Starting with another car:
In an emergency, the battery of another car can be used to start a car by connecting the battery poles to jumper cables. There are special transfer points that need to be used. This is not possible with some cars. The manufacturer of the car will indicate whether jump starting is possible in the manual and, if so, how it should be done.

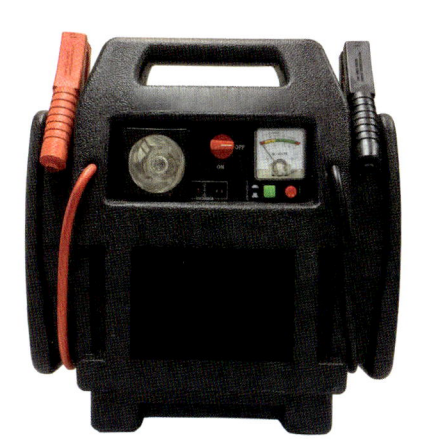

Fig. 287 Jump starter.

Fig. 288 Jump starting with jumper cables.

HOW TO: CLEAN THE BATTERY TERMINALS AND MAINTAIN THE BATTERY

1. Connecting the EOBD memory saver

If the battery is disconnected, the entire car is disconnected from the power supply. This will cause the switch box memories and the security codes of the radio or other equipment to be deleted. This can be prevented by connecting a memory saver to the EOBD plug.

Fig. 289 Tools Required

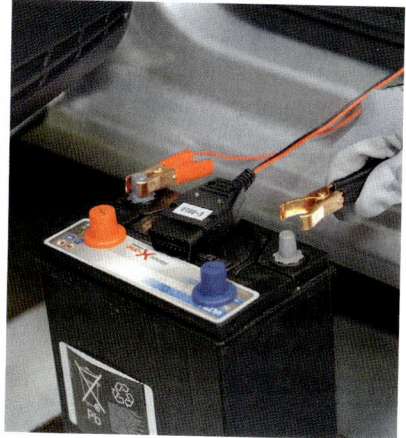

Fig. 290 Use a second battery by connecting the memory saver to it.

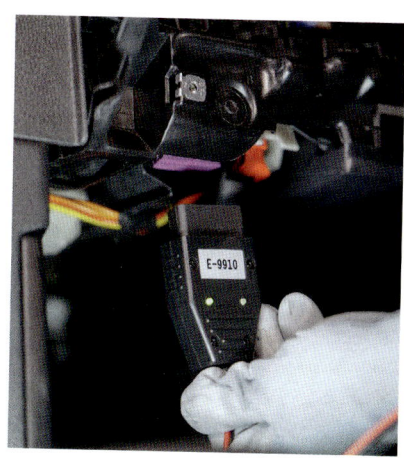

Fig. 291 Next, connect the plug to the EOBD connector. The car's battery can now be safely disconnected.

2. Disconnect the battery and remove it from the car

Disconnect the negative terminal first, then the positive terminal. Loosen the bracket which holds the battery in place.

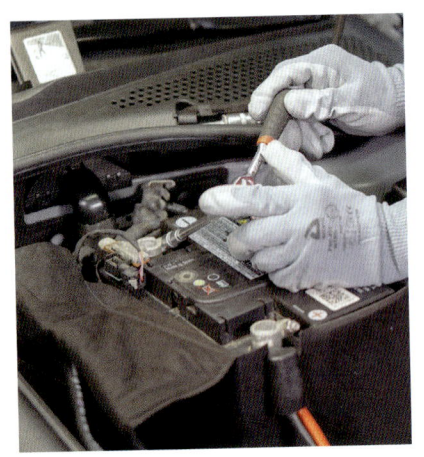

Fig. 292 Set aside the battery's protective housing. Remove the protective cap from the battery's negative terminal.

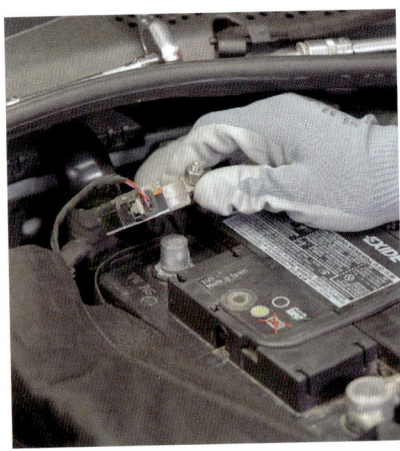

Fig. 293 Disconnect the negative pole connector from the battery. Clean it with battery cleaner. Place it behind the battery, to prevent it from making contact with the battery's negative terminal.

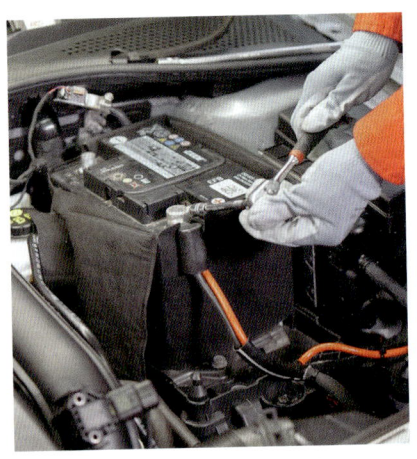

Fig. 294 Disconnect the battery's positive pole connection first. Clean it with battery cleaner. Isolate the positive terminal connection and place it away from the positive terminal.

Fig. 295 Unscrew the bracket that holds the battery in place.

Fig. 296 Remove the bolt and the bracket.

3. Clean the battery terminals, the battery and the battery tray

Remove the battery from the car and remove the protective housing. Clean the battery terminals and the battery tray.

Fig. 297 Clean both battery terminals with battery terminal cleaner. This removes lead oxide from the battery terminals and increases electrical conduction.

Fig. 298 Clean the battery with a slightly damp cloth.

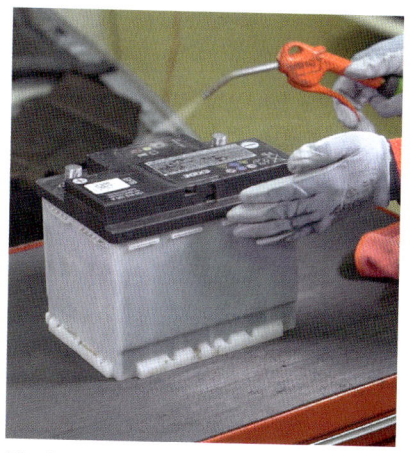

Fig. 299 Use an air gun to blow away any remaining dust or dirt.

Fig. 300 Clean the car's battery tray. You can use a vacuum cleaner for this.

Fig. 301 Place the protective housing around the battery and set the battery back in the battery tray.

Fig. 302 Tighten the bracket to secure the battery in place.

4. Replace the positive and negative terminals and check whether the battery is functioning properly again.

Secure the positive connector on the battery's positive terminal and do the same for the negative connector on the negative terminal.

Fig. 303 First, mount the positive connector on the positive terminal.

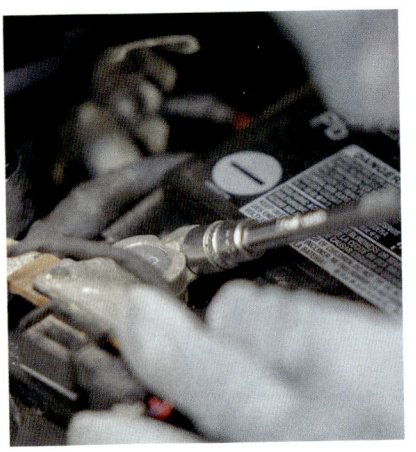

Fig. 304 Next, mount the negative connector on the negative terminal.

Check whether the battery's voltage is correct, also with the engine running.

Fig. 305 Measure the battery voltage with a multimeter. The engine is switched off. The voltage is correct, 12.1 V.

Fig. 306 Now, with the engine running, measure the terminal voltage with the multimeter. The voltage is correct, 14.2 V.

HOW TO: JUMP START A CAR

1. Jump start a car

Dead car batteries are a common occurrence. You can start the car with the help of another car or a battery booster. In this case, we will use the battery from a working car. This is connected via jumper cables to the battery in the affected car.

Position the cars opposite each other so that the jumper cables can reach both batteries.

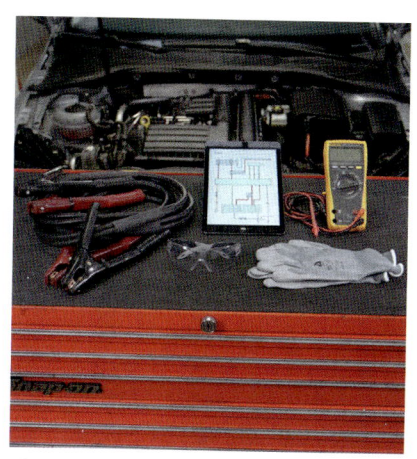

Fig. 308 Tools required. Start the engine in the working car.

Fig. 309 Attach the jumper cable's positive pole (red) to the positive battery terminal of the working car.

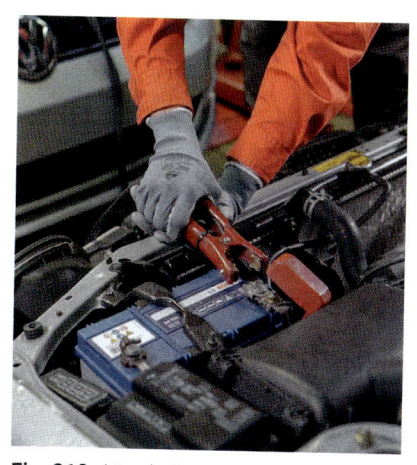

Fig. 310 Attach the jumper cable's other positive pole (red) to the positive battery terminal of the affected car.

164 ELECTRICAL SYSTEMS

Attach the negative clamps to the engine blocks in both cars. You can now start the engine in the affected car.

Fig. 311 Attach the negative clamp (black) to the engine block in the working car.

Fig. 312 Now connect the negative clamp (black) to the engine block in the affected car.

Fig. 313 Start the affected car and leave the engine running so it can charge.

2. Remove the jumper cables and check whether the affected car's alternator is charging properly

Fig. 314 Turn on the lights and electrical devices in both cars to prevent any voltage peaks. Remove the negative clamps from both cars. Remove them from the affected car first.

Fig. 315 Now disconnect the positive clamps, first from the affected car and then the working car.

Fig. 316 Use a multimeter to check the voltage on the battery terminals. The voltage should be 14.6 volts. That is sufficient to charge the battery; it may even be a bit too high.

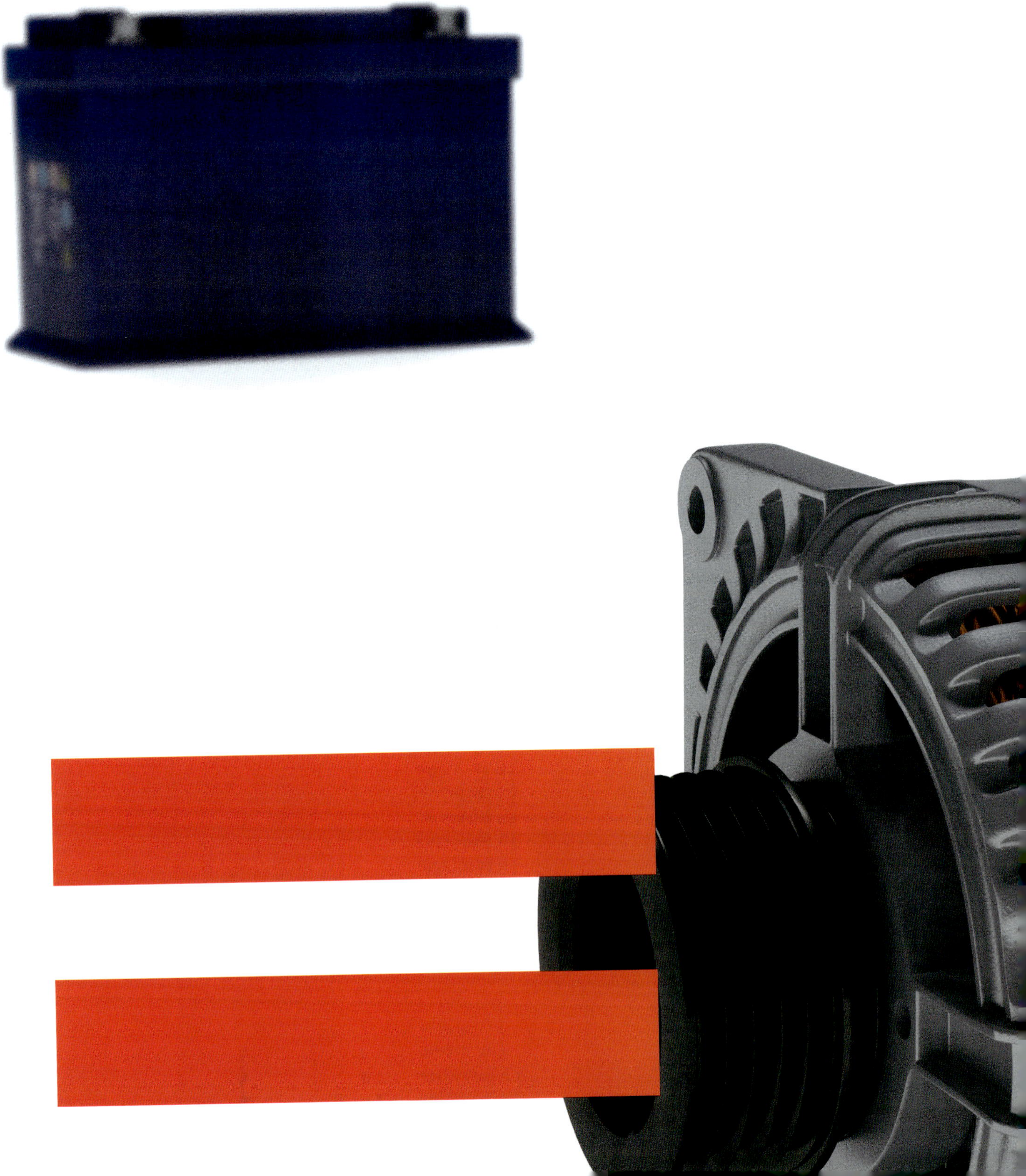

11. Starting System

STARTER MOTOR: INTRODUCTION

1. Introduction

The starting system consists of an energy source (battery), start switch, starter motor, and a flywheel ring gear.

With diesel engines, the starting system is often supplemented with a pre-heating system for a quicker start at colder temperatures.

Today's vehicles are all equipped with a start immobilizer system. This system is mandatory for vehicles in a certain price range or as dictated by some insurance companies.

The start switch can be designed as an actual switch, but the starter can also be operated by giving a "start" command with a start button. The computer then switches the starter motor on and off again when the engine starts running. With today's Start/Stop system, starting is controlled by a control unit.

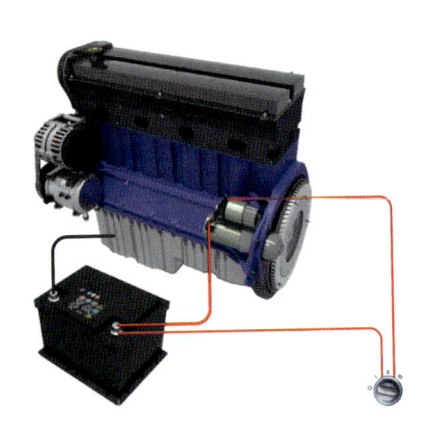

Fig. 318 Complete starter system with start switch

Fig. 319 Start button

2. Introduction

The starter motor is mounted to the engine block.

The role of the starter motor is to initiate the starting sequence by cranking the engine. It engages via a small gear (pinion gear) on the end of the motor that is meshed with the teeth on the internal combustion engine's flywheel.

The basis of the starter is an electric motor. The energy required to run the starter motor is supplied by the battery.

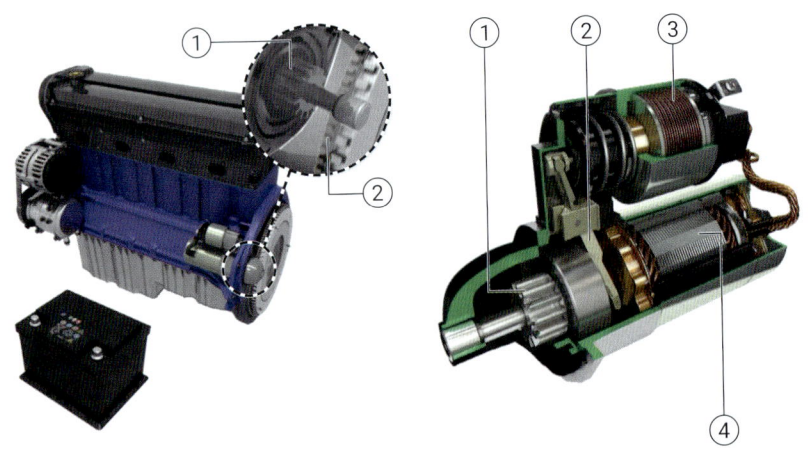

Fig. 320 1. pinion gear 2. flywheel ring gear

Fig. 321 1. pinion gear 2. drive lever 3. solenoid 4. electric motor

The flywheel ring gear is a ring with teeth that is placed around the flywheel of the internal combustion engine.

3. Main Components

The main components and functions of the starter motor are:
- **Starter solenoid**

  When the ignition key is operated, the solenoid switches on the electric motor and simultaneously engages the starter drive mechanism.
- **Starter drive shift lever**

  This shift lever moves the pinion gear over the shaft of the electric motor so that it engages with the flywheel. After the engine starts and you release the ignition key, the pinion is retracted so the engine is prevented from driving the electric motor.
- **Electric motor**

  This drives the flywheel of the internal combustion engine by means of the pinion gear.

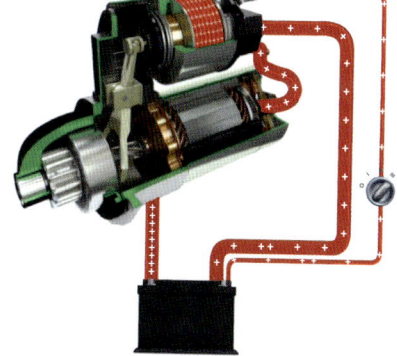

Fig. 322 Pinion gear in rest position

Fig. 323 Pinion gear during starting. When the starter solenoid is operated, the main current starts to flow.

The starter solenoid is energized with a small current. When the starter solenoid closes, a large current (main current) will flow through the electric motor. This then runs through the engine block to ground. The movement of the starter solenoid is also used to operate the drive lever.

LORENTZ FORCE

1. Left Hand Rule

When current flows through a wire, it generates a magnetic field that rotates around the wire. If that wire is in an existing magnetic field, it experiences a force called the Lorentz force.
It is important to know which direction this force is going. For this you use the *left hand rule*:

1. With an extended left hand, palm up, the field lines of the permanent magnetic point down through the palm of your hand.
2. Your fingers point in the direction of the current flow.
3. Your thumb indicates the direction of rotation of the magnetic field surrounding the wire. So if the current through the wire flows away from you, the magnetic field in the wire is turning clockwise.

Magnetic lines of force always radiate from the north to the south pole.
So if the magnet's north pole is on the top and south pole is on the bottom with the conductor in between, the magnetic two fields repel each other on the left side of the conductor. And since the entire magnetic field from the permanent magnet surrounds the wire, the lines of force attract on the right.

11. STARTING SYSTEM 171

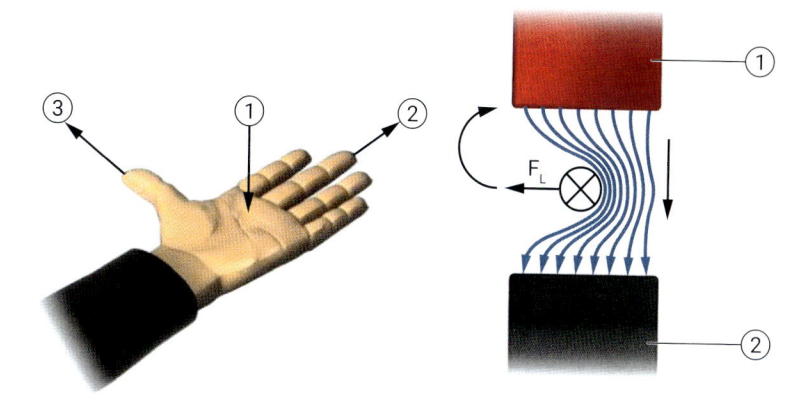

Fig. 324 1. Field lines. 2. Direction of current. 3. Lorentz force.

Fig. 325 1. North pole. 2. South pole. Current passes through the conductor away from you, perpendicular to the field lines; the magnetic field around the conductor, the Lorentz force, rotates clockwise. On the left, the magnetic fields oppose each other; on the right, they combine with each other.

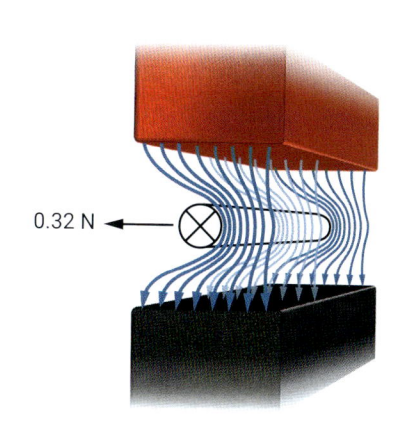

Fig. 326 Example 2

2. Principle

The size of the Lorentz force F_L depends on:
- the strength of the homogeneous magnetic field (B). The unit is Tesla:
- the amount of current through the electrical conductor (I). The unit is Ampere:
- the length of the conductor in the magnetic field (l). The unit is meters.

The formula with which we calculate the Lorentz force is:

$$F_L = B * I * l$$

The definition is as follows:
Lorentz force is the force exerted on a conductor by an electromagnetic field.

Example 1 Given:
$B = 4$ Tesla
$I = 2$ Ampere
$l = 0.8$ inches (2 centimeters)

Objective:
Calculate the Lorentz force F_L in Newtons.

Answer:
$2cm = 0.02m$
$F_L = B * I * l$
$F_L = 4 * 2 * 0.02$
$F_L = 0.16N$

Example 2 Given:
$B = 4$ Tesla
$I = 2$ Ampere
$l = 1.6$ inches (4 centimeters.

Objective:
Calculate the Lorentz force F_L in Newtons.

Answer:
$4cm = 0.04m$

$F_L = B * I * l$
$F_L = 4 * 2 * 0.04$
$F_L = 0.32N$.

3. Application

Electric motors work with Lorentz force. Even alternators and solenoid valves do not work without this force.

We place a conductor in the shape of a loop through the permanent magnetic field. This creates a Lorentz force on both sides of the loop in the opposite direction. These Lorentz forces provide a torque and the conductor will turn.

When the conductor comes into a horizontal position, the Lorentz forces work outwards, there is no torque. The conductor will stop.

Fig. 327 Lorentz forces provide torque.

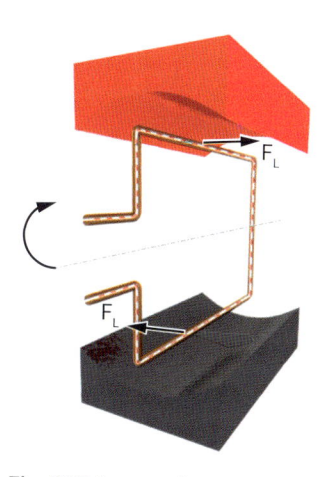

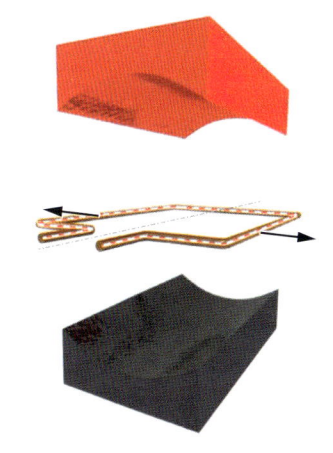

Fig. 328 Lorentz force is present, but there is no torque.

In the image, only one winding (conductor) and one pole pair are visible. If current flows through the vertical winding, it will turn a quarter turn and stop again. The torque that is supplied is greatest when the windings are vertical. As the winding rotates and comes to the horizontal position, the torque will become less and less until the winding comes to a standstill. The torque supplied is then 0 Nm.

ELECTRICAL PROPERTIES OF A STARTER MOTOR

1. Electrical Characteristics

The effect of Lorentz force on a winding creates a force. The Lorentz force wants to push the winding to the left at the top of the winding, while the winding is pushed to the right at the bottom. The winding starts to rotate on its axis due to the resulting torque. The magnitude of the torque depends on the strength of the Lorentz force and the diameter of the winding.

A torque is created by force x radius (perpendicular distance from turning point to the force).
In formula form:

$$T = F * r$$

This is:
$T =$ torque Nm
$F =$ force N
r = radius of the winding m

The F stands for the Lorentz force, and the "r" in the formula stands for the radius of a winding from the electric motor. Because this also applies to the other half of the winding, the formula must be multiplied by 2. So for an electric motor the formula applies:

$$T = F_L * (r * 2)$$

that is:

$$T = F_L * d$$

This is:
$T =$ Torque Nm)
$F_L =$ Lorentz force N
$d =$ diameter armature m

If we made a calculation, we would see that the electric motor has an uneven torque variation. The torque is maximum if the winding is perpendicular to the Lorentz force, but if this is turned 90°, the winding will stand still and no longer provide torque. The torque will decrease with every degree that the winding turns.

To solve this problem, multiple windings are applied, which increases the torque delivered. Every winding in the electric motor delivers a torque. We can therefore multiply the previously discussed formula about the delivered torque of an electric motor by the number of windings. That eventually gives the formula:

$$T = F_L * d * N$$

This is:
$T =$ Torque $Nm)$
$F_L =$ Lorentz force N
$d =$ diameter armature m
$N =$ number of windings

For the Lorentz force it applies:

$$F_L = B * I * l$$

This is:
$B =$ strength of magnetic field in Tesla.
$I =$ current intensity through the conductor in (A), thus determining the magnetic field around the conductor
$l =$ the length of the conductor in meters (m)

EXAMPLE

Given:
B = 4 Tesla
I = 2 Ampere
l = 2 centimeters
Diameter is 4 cm
Number of windings = 20

Requested:
Calculate the torque the electric motor supplies?

Answer:

Length = 2 cm = 0.02 m
Diameter = 4 cm = 0.04 m

First we calculate the Lorentz force:
$F_L = B * I * l$
$F_L = 4 * 2 * 0.02$
$F_L = 0.16 N$

We can then calculate the torque:
$T = F_L * d * N$
$T = 0.16 * 0.04 * 20$
$T = 0.1344 Nm$

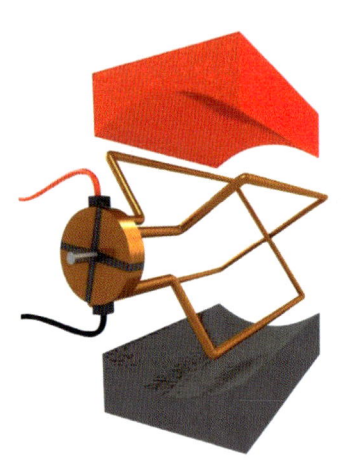

Fig. 329 Multiple windings ensure a more even torque.

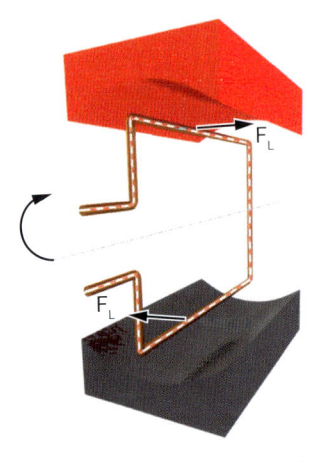

Fig. 330 Lorentz forces provide torque.

2. Counter Voltage in an Electric Motor

Multiple windings are used, making the delivered torque of the electric motor larger and more even. Every winding that is constructed in the electric motor and that is in contact with a carbon brush produces a torque. But not all windings are connected to a carbon brush; this current-free winding rotates through a magnetic field. Such a winding is therefore a conductor that rotates through a magnetic field. A changing magnetic field around a conductor, generates voltage in that conductor. The moment the winding comes into contact with the carbon brush, this voltage counteracts the supplied voltage.

So two conflicting things happen in the electric motor.

1. A torque is generated in the armature of the electric motor by the Lorentz force that arises when a current flows through a

winding.

2. A voltage is generated in the armature of the electric motor with the winding through which no current is flowing. This is referred to as the counter voltage

The counter voltage increases as the speed of the armature in the electric motor increases. When starting the electric motor, the counter voltage is 0 volt, because the speed is 0. But because the speed increases, the counter voltage will also be higher. Because the counter voltage becomes higher, the voltage difference between battery and electric motor will become smaller. As a result, the current strength decreases, and thus also the Lorentz force of the electric motor.

The formula for the counter voltage:

$$E_t = c * \phi * n$$

This is:

E_t = counter voltage
c = motor constant (determined by the construction of the electric motor)
ϕ = magnetic flux
n = speed

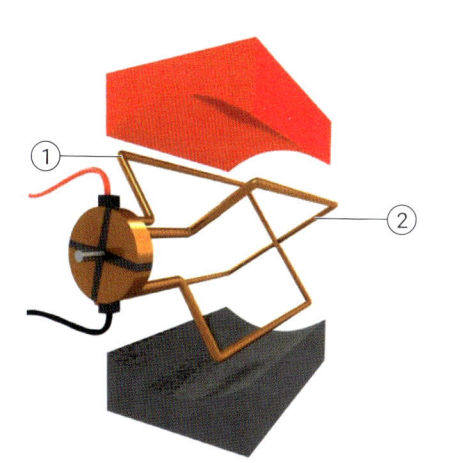

Fig. 331 No current flows through conductor 2, but it does rotate through a magnetic field.

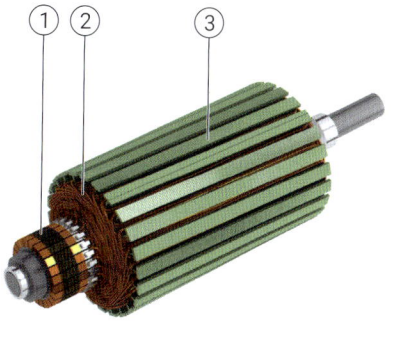

Fig. 332 1. collector 2. windings 3. armature segments

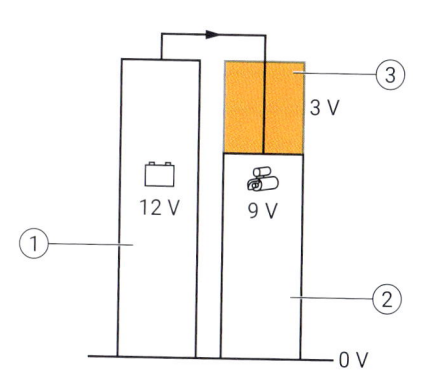

Fig. 333 Counter voltage generated in the armature approaches the battery voltage level 1. battery 2. starter motor counter voltage 3. voltage difference on which the starter motor operates

3. Effect of counter voltage in an electric motor

The moment the starter motor is operated, it will have to set the crankshaft in motion. A large starting torque is required for this.

There is no counter voltage yet as the engine is not running. The voltage difference across the starter motor is 12 volts. The resistance in the starter circuit is 0.02Ω.

The starting current at that moment is:
$$V = \frac{I}{R} \Rightarrow I = \frac{V}{R} \Rightarrow I = \frac{12V}{0.02\Omega} = 600A$$

When the crankshaft is moving, counter voltage is generated in the armature. This counter voltage can rise to 10 volts in the starter motor. The voltage difference across the starter motor is 12 V − 10 V = 2 V. The voltage during starting is then 2 V :

$$V = \frac{I}{R} \Rightarrow I = \frac{V}{R} \Rightarrow I = \frac{2V}{0,02\Omega} = 100A$$

That brings us to the following formula:

$$V_k = U_t + (I_{startercircuit} * R_{startercircuit})$$

V_k = terminal voltage
U_t = counter voltage
$I_{startercircuit}$ starting current
$R_{startercircuit}$ resistance starter circuit

The formula entered at the time of starting to start:

$$V_k = V_t + (I_{startercircuit} * R_{startercircuit})$$
$$12V = 0V + (600A * 0.02\Omega)$$

The formula entered at the time of starting:

$$V_k = U_t + (I_{startercircuit} * R_{startercircuit})$$
$$12V = 10V + (100A * 0.02\Omega)$$

During starting, the crankshaft works against compression and slows down in speed. The starter motor will decrease in speed at that moment. The counter voltage will decrease with the result that the current through the starter motor increases.

Once through the compression, you get the power stroke and the crankshaft accelerates. This also speeds up the speed of the starter motor and generates more counter voltage. The current intensity through the armature motor will decrease again.

During starting, the current through the starter motor and the battery will become larger and smaller due to the generated counter voltage in the armature of the starter motor.
Each battery has an internal resistance. This is very low, but, due to the high current, there is a varying voltage drop in the battery during starting. The terminal voltage across the battery changes during starting and follows the compression/power strokes of the engine. This can be observed by measuring the voltage on the battery with an oscilloscope. Various test equipment is also available that measures the average starting current during starting in order to get an indication of the compression per cylinder.

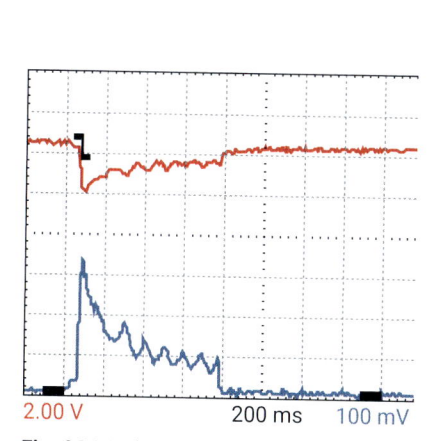

Fig. 334 Voltage measured on the battery and starting current through the starting circuit

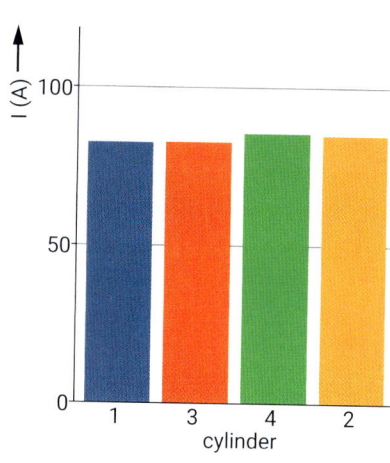

Fig. 335 The starting current with a good motor

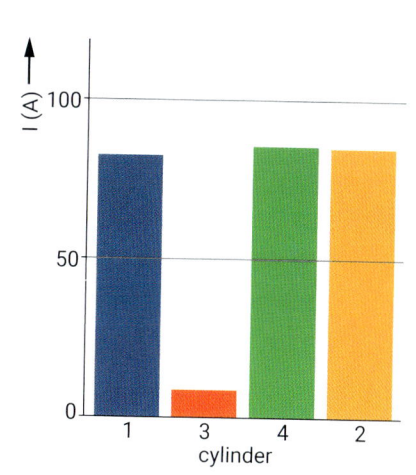

Fig. 336 The starting current with an engine where there is compression loss

STARTER MOTOR PROPERTIES

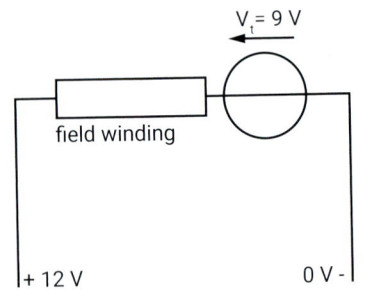

Fig. 337 Field and armature windings are in series, counter voltage influences field strength

1. Electromagnetic Field (Series Motor)

Of all the types of electric motors and starter motors, the permanent magnet motors and the universal motors (with an electromagnetic field) are most frequently used. The earlier starter motors were almost always designed as a motor with an electromagnetic field. The starting torque was very high due to the high current through the field and armature winding.

Today it is possible to make "super magnets." These super magnets are so strong that the starting torque approaches that of the motors with an electromagnetic field.

Motors with an electromagnetic field have the disadvantage that they could "run-on" without load if the ignition key is held in the start position while the combustion engine starts running. Then there is no more power to be supplied, and the speed rises sharply. With increasing speed, the counter voltage will also increase, and the current through the motor will decrease. No power is needed if the combustion engine is already running. This sort of operation will cause the electric motor to run at high speed, and potentially damage the starter. To prevent this, an "armature brake" is sometimes used on these motors. An armature brake can be as simple as a copper bushing on one end of the armature shaft that offers more resistance to rotation than a ball bearing. An additional advantage is that you can make a quick restart if the engine does not start. If a starter motor has ball bearings at both ends of the shaft, the armature shaft will rotate for too long because there is no longer any magnetic field.

2. Permanent Magnetic Field (Similar to Shunt Motor)

A shunt motor is a motor where the field winding and armature winding are in parallel. With an electric motor in operation, a counter voltage is generated in the armature, as a result the current becomes lower and therefore a weaker magnetic field exists at the armature. But the counter voltage does not arise in the field winding. The magnetic fields at the field winding therefore remain equally strong despite the counter voltage. The characteristics of a motor with permanent magnets are similar to those of a shunt motor because the field strength does not change under the influence of the counter voltage.

Motors with permanent magnets are usually smaller and lighter than motors with an electromagnetic field.

Due to the permanent presence of a magnetic field, the armature cannot increase in speed indefinitely. The higher the speed of the armature, the more counter voltage will be generated. Less current will flow through the armature and it will stop increasing speed. The turning of the armature shaft will also be much shorter because it is slowed down by the magnetic field.

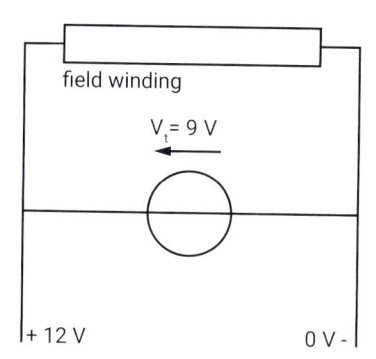

Fig. 338 Shunt motor, field, and armature windings are in parallel, counter voltage has no influence on the field strength.

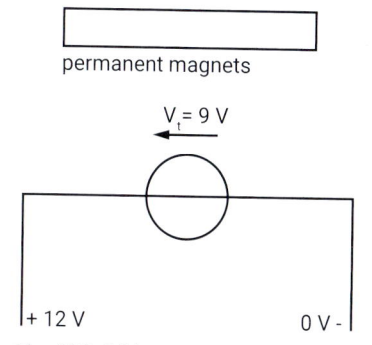

Fig. 339 With permanent magnets, the counter voltage also has no influence on the field strength.

STARTER MOTOR: COMPONENTS

1. Introduction

Starter motors can be categorized as follows.

In terms of energizing:

1. Electromagnetic field.
2. Permanent magnetic field.

In terms of drive:

1. Direct drive.
2. Indirect drive.
3. Planetary drive.

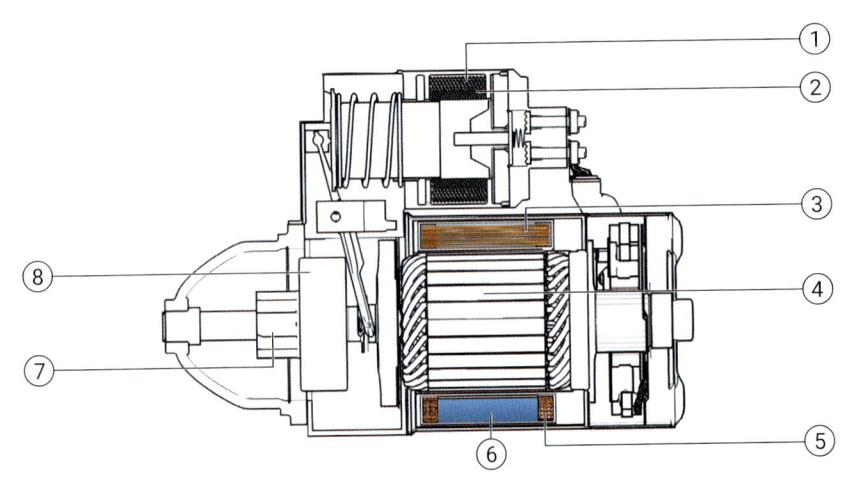

Fig. 340 Starter motor with electromagnets and direct drive: 1. Pull-in coil. 2. Hold-in coil. 3. Field winding. 4. Armature. 5. Field winding. 6. Electromagnet. 7. Pinion gear. 8. Freewheel.

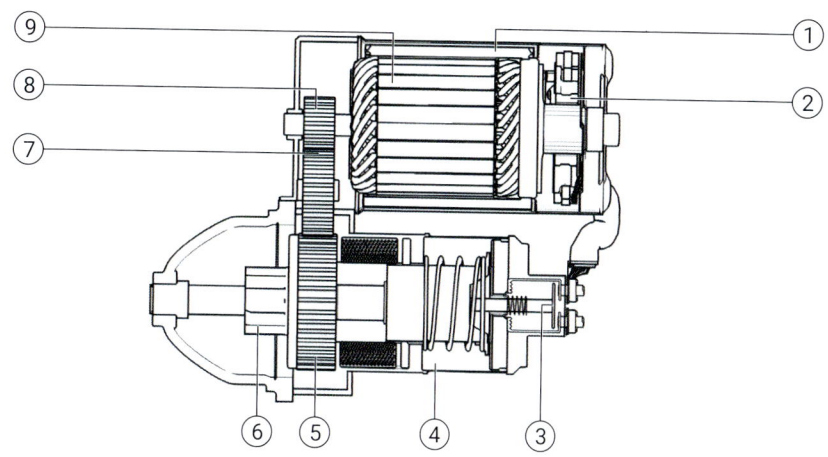

Fig. 341 Starter motor with electromagnets and indirect drive: 1. Field winding/electromagnets. 2. Carbon brush. 3. Contact bridge. 4. Starter solenoid. 5. Gear with freewheel clutch. 6. Pinion gear. 7. Intermediate gear. 8. Armature shaft gear. 9. Armature.

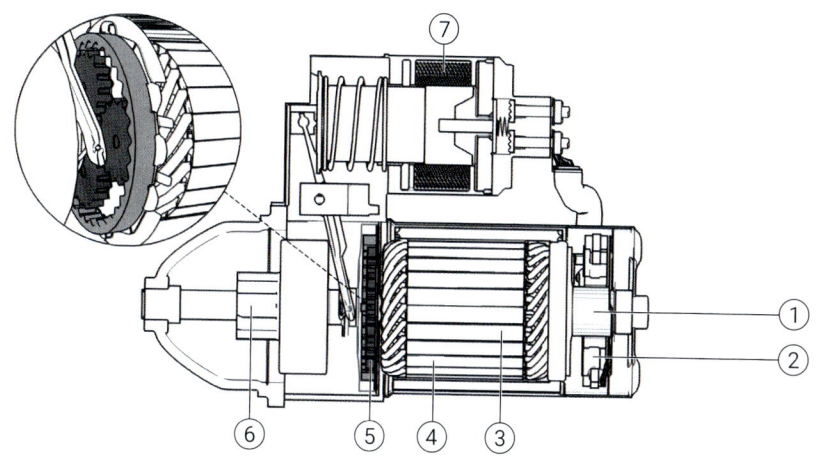

Fig. 342 Starter motor with permanent magnets and planetary drive: 1. Commutator. 2. Brush holder with carbon brushes. 3. Armature. 4. Permanent magnets. 5. Planetary transmission. 6. Pinion gear. 7. Pull-in coil.

2. Starter Motor with Electromagnets and Permanent Magnets

The diagram of a permanent magnet motor shows that current only flows through the armature. The stator is shown as a permanent magnet.
In the diagram of a motor with electromagnets, the current passes through the field winding after the starter solenoid.

Permanent magnets don't use any energy. This increases the efficiency of the motor. A motor with permanent magnets is more compact because permanent magnets take up less space than electromagnets with a pole shoe and field winding.

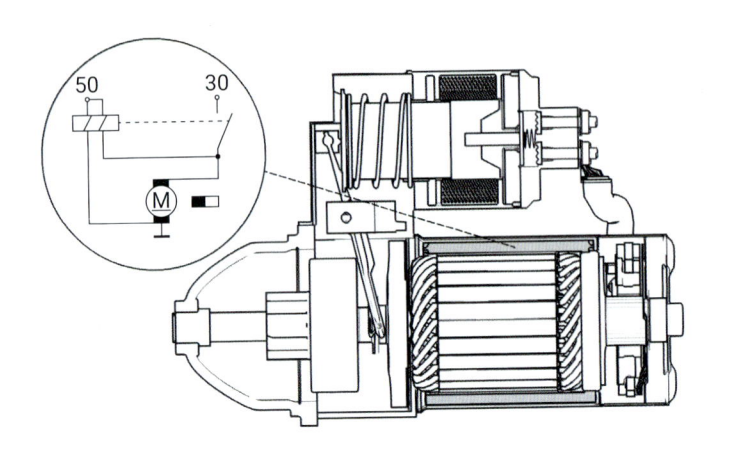

Fig. 343 Starter motor with permanent magnetic field and direct drive.

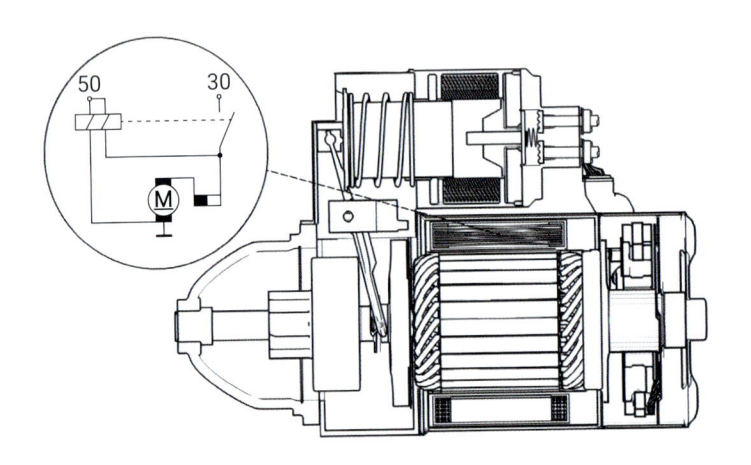

Fig. 344 Starter motor with electromagnetic field and planetary gear system.

3. Difference in the Induced Counter Voltage in Electric Motors

The rotation of an electric motor generates a voltage. This voltage is called counter voltage (E_t).

The counter voltage increases as the speed increases. No counter voltage is generated if the motor is stopped.

When calculating the current you must therefore take into account the generated counter voltage. The formula for this is:

$$E_{counter} = V_{terminal} - (I_{armature} * R_{armature}).$$

Because an electric motor only has copper as an electrical conductor, the resistance ($R_{armature}$) will be very low when checking the motor (<1Ω).

The formula for the counter voltage:

$$E_t = c * \phi * n$$

$E_t =$ counter voltage
$c =$ motor constant (determined by the construction of the electric motor)
$\phi =$ magnetic flux (the higher the field strength, the higher the counter voltage)
$n =$ the speed.

If you look at the value of the formula, there is a difference between the motors with permanent magnets and with electromagnets when comparing the magnetic flux.

If the speed increases, the counter voltage will increase for both motors. This also reduces the current through the electric motor.

Because the magnetic flux in series motors with electromagnets is determined by the current intensity in the field coils (ϕ), the speed (n) can run very high. (For this, take a look again at the formula for the counter voltage: speed can go up, while flux goes down. The counter voltage does not change). For that reason, an armature brake is often used, in the form of bushings instead of ball bearings.

Because the magnetic flux on motors with permanent magnets (ϕ) always remains the same, the speed (n) is limited.

4. Indirect Drive Through an Intermediate Gear

Starter motors also need to become increasingly compact and lighter. One possibility for this is to use an electric motor with a smaller diameter.

The advantage of a smaller diameter is that it is possible to achieve a higher speed. The weight of the armature shaft is much smaller. Partly because of this, the armature shaft will stop much faster after an attempted start so this type of electric motor can be equipped with ball bearings. The disadvantage of this type of electric motors as a starter motor is that less torque is delivered. The torque is increased again by a gear transmission.

With this type of starter motor, the armature is not in line with the pinion shaft. As a result, no lever is needed to direct the pinion gear in the flywheel ring gear.

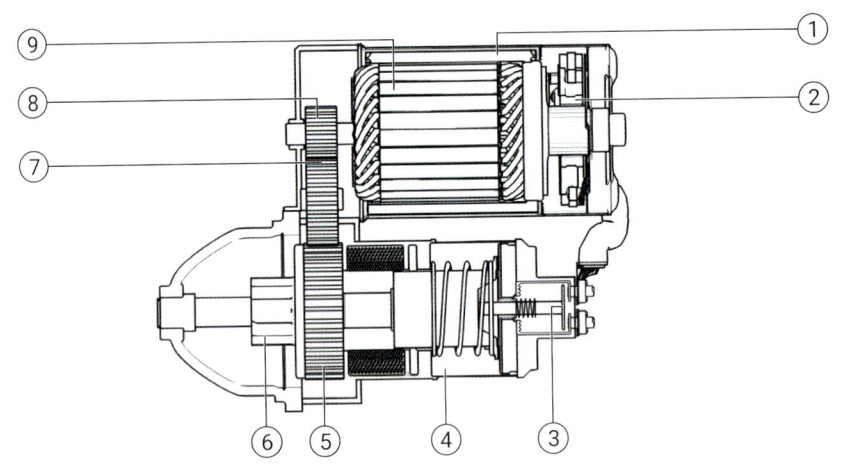

Fig. 345 Starter motor with electromagnets and indirect drive: 1. Field winding/electromagnets. 2. Carbon brush. 3. Contact bridge. 4. Starter solenoid. 5. Gear with freewheel clutch. 6. Pinion gear. 7. Intermediate gear. 8. Armature shaft gear. 9. Armature.

5. Planetary Gear Systems With Starter Motors

Another way in which the starter motor can be made small and lightweight is by using a planetary gear system. With a starter motor, transmission is achieved by fixing the ring gear to the starter motor housing. This causes a delay. Then a lever and gear shift fork are used.

Fig. 346 1. Ring gear. 2. Sun gear on armature shaft. 3. Planet gear. 4. Planetary carrier axle.

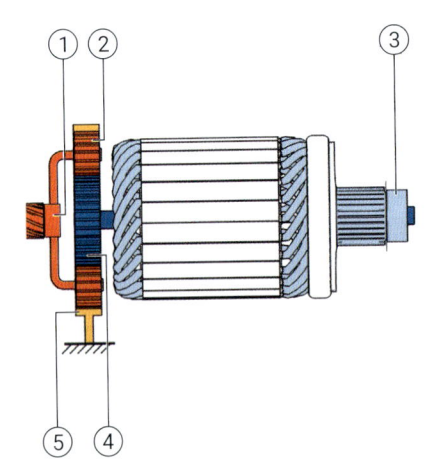

Fig. 347 1. Planetary carrier axle. 2. Planet gear. 3. Armature shaft bearing. 4. Sun gear. 5. Ring gear.

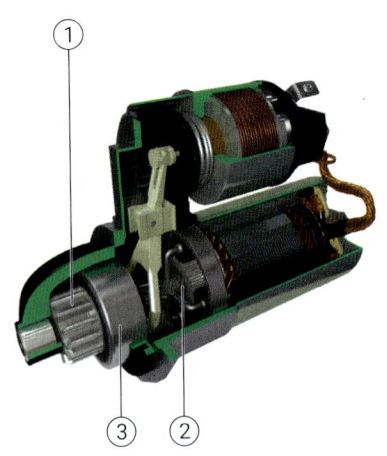

Fig. 348 Parts 1, 2 and 3 form the transmission to the flywheel ring gear.

STARTER MOTOR: SHIFT LEVER AND OVERRUNNING CLUTCH

1. Introduction

The shift lever sometimes called a drive lever, together with the overrunning clutch are two of the main components of the starter motor.

The functions of this mechanism are:
— to engage the starter drive pinion when the starter motor is switched on.
— prevent the internal combustion engine from driving the starter motor after the engine has started.

Note: The overrunning clutch is an integral component of the starter drive mechanism, which also includes the pinion gear.

Fig. 349 1. Overrunning clutch. 2. Lever. 3. Starter solenoid. 4. Screw thread. 5. Fork.

2. Operation

When the ignition key is turned to the start position, the starter solenoid engages the shift lever, which is also attached to the starter drive at the opposite end.

The shift lever pushes the drive pinion into mesh with the flywheel ring gear.

When the ignition key is released, the starter motor turns off. The solenoid spring pushes the solenoid plunger and shift lever back to resting position, pulling the drive pinion out of mesh with the flywheel ring gear.

Spiral grooves cut into the armature shaft cause the pinion to rotate and mesh more easily with the ring gear during engagement and out of mesh during disengagement.

If the fork lever is operated during a start, and one tooth of the pinion comes straight onto the head of the tooth of the flywheel ring gear, the solenoid would not be able to complete its movement

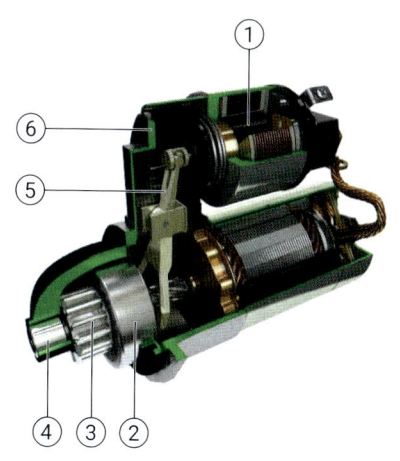

Fig. 350 1. Solenoid core. 2. Overrunning clutch. 3. Starter motor pinion. 4. Bearing ring. 5. Fork lever. 6. Housing.

towards the main contacts. The tracking spring, which is mounted between lever and clutch housing, is compressed at that moment so that the solenoid core can always complete its movement, and the rear contacts always close in the process. As a result, the armature starts to rotate, turning the blocked pinion so it can mesh into the flywheel ring gear.

3. Overrunning Clutch

The overrunning clutch is a one-way clutch that allows the pinion to turn freely in one direction and locks it in the other. It's designed to prevent the engine from driving the starter motor if the pinion remains engaged after the engine has started (for example, if the ignition key is not released right away).

When the starter motor drives the engine, the rollers wedge between the clutch housing and the pinion. Because of this, the starter motor is able to drive the clutch housing and pinion together.

However, if the engine is running and the starter motor is engaged, the engine will begin to drive the pinion faster than the starter motor is turning. The rollers are pushed away against the spring pressure. Small springs force the rollers into an open area to spin freely. This releases the connection between the pinion and the clutch housing, allowing the clutch housing and the rest of the starter motor to spin independently from the engine. This design is often called a sprag clutch.

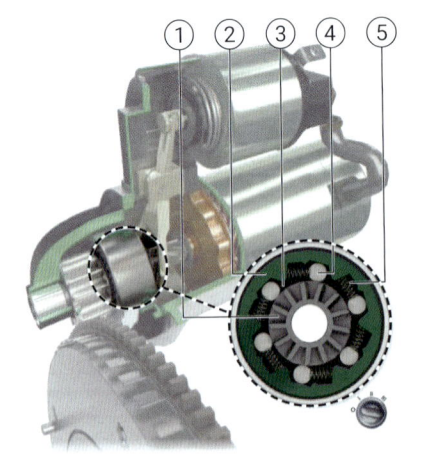

Fig. 351 1. Starter motor pinion. 2. Clutch housing. 3. Roller bed. 4. Roller. 5. Compression spring.

Fig. 352 The overrunning clutch in operation.

4. Gear Ratio

The gear ratio between pinion and flywheel ring gear is very large. Consider what the diameter of the flywheel ring gear is and what the diameter of the pinion is.

The flywheel ring gear is very large but it is driven by a pinion with 10 to 14 teeth. If a driver starts the engine and the overrunnng clutch does not release, the armature shaft would be driven by the engine at a very high speed.

A customer may hear something wrong and decide to drive carefully to the repair shop. During such a drive, an engine speed of 2,000 revolutions per minute is quickly reached. The gear ratio is around 20 to 1. This means that the armature shaft will reach a speed of 20 x 2,000 revolutions per minute = 40,000 RPM.

There is a chance that the windings in the armature shaft will fly apart because of the resulting centrifugal force and short to ground against the starter housing.

STARTER MOTOR: SOLENOID

1. Introduction

The starter solenoid is an important part of the starter motor. The starter solenoid has two functions:
- To actuate the shift lever
- To switch on the main current to armature

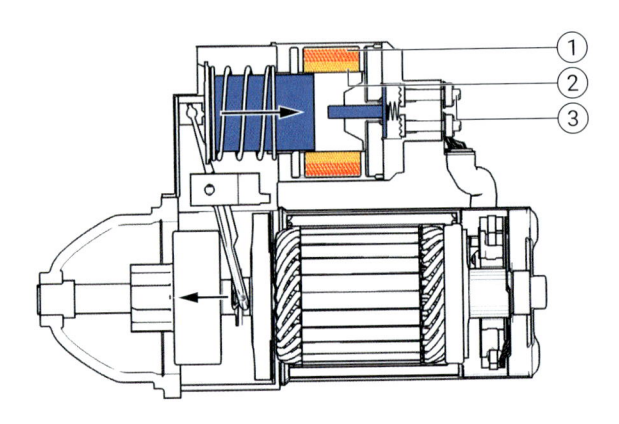

Fig. 353 A solenoid with 2 coils: 1. pull-in coil 2. hold-in coil 3. battery connection

2. Operation

The starter solenoid has two coils: a **strong pull-in coil** and a **lighter hold-in coil**. The operation of the solenoid is achieved by dividing these two coils into three phases of operation.

During the **first phase** a current runs through both coils of the solenoid, creating a magnetic field. The iron core of the starter solenoid is pulled in and operates the shift lever of the starter motor.

During the **second phase** the solenoid switches on the main current to the starter motor. The hold-in coil remains activated in order to keep the core in place, but current is no longer running through the pull-in coil.

During the **third phase** the ignition switch is released and the current is turned off. The spring pushes the iron core back to the starting position.

Because both the movement of the lever and the engagement of the pinion gear must occur in the first phase, the most force is required at this moment. That's why two coils are used at the same time.

Once the pinion gear is engaged with the flywheel ring gear, less force is required to hold the pinion gear in place.

3. Electrical Operation

The starter solenoid consists of two coils and has three connections. The coils are connected in parallel.

During the **first phase** a current runs through the pull-in coil via the armature to ground. The current through the hold-in coil runs via the housing of the starter motor to ground. By switching on the two coils, the solenoid responds more quickly.

During the **second phase** the main contacts are connected, and a large current runs through the armature. To prevent the solenoid from becoming too hot when re-starting for lengthy periods, no more current runs through the pull-in coil.

No current flows during the **third phase**, during which the ignition switch is no longer operated.

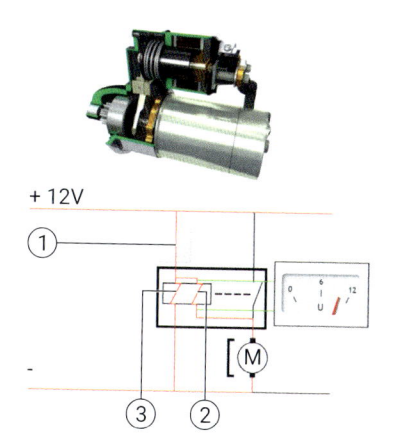

Fig. 354 Current flow in the first phase: 1. ignition switch 2. pull-in coil 3. hold-in coil

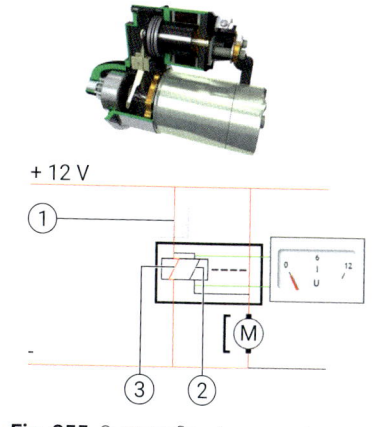

Fig. 355 Current flow in second phase: 1. ignition switch 2. pull-in coil 3. hold-in coil

First phase:
The hold-in coil receives 12 V via the starter switch and is directly grounded via the starter motor housing. The pull-in coil also

receives 12 V from the starter switch, but has its ground through the armature and possibly through field windings from the starter motor.

Second phase:
Now current only flows through the hold-in coil. Closing the solenoid contacts also supplies 12 V on the armature and possibly field windings of the starter motor. The *voltage difference* across the pull-in coil is now 0 V.

4. Testing a Starter Solenoid

A starter solenoid has three electrical parts: the two coils and the main contacts. The main contacts can only be checked with a voltmeter when the solenoid is switched on.

The solenoid coils can be checked by means of a resistance measurement. The measurements that can be performed are:
— open circuit
— short circuit to ground
— coil resistance

The pull-in coil is only energized when the starter motor is switched on, which is for a very brief moment, because once switched on and during starting, only the hold-in coil is energized. Because engagement takes longer than retraction, the hold-in coil becomes warmer.

Because engagement requires more force it must have more current; the diameter of the wiring of the pull-in coil is thicker than that of the hold-in coil.

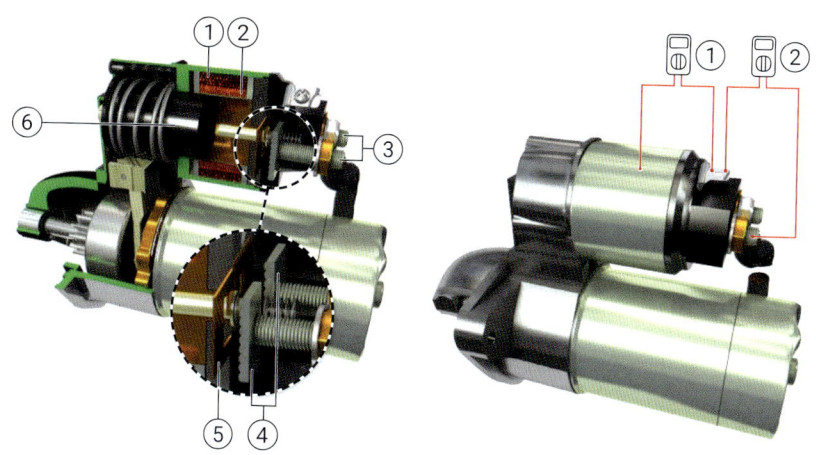

Fig. 356 Cross section of the starter solenoid: 1. pull-in coil 2. hold-in coil 3. main battery contacts 4. contacts 5. contact bridge 6. magnetic core

Fig. 357 Check hold-in coil: 1. short circuit to ground or open circuit 2. coil short circuit Check pull-in coil: 1. open circuit 2. coil short circuit

5. Starter solenoid clicking during starting when the battery voltage is too low

With older types of vehicles where an ignition key (15) and start switch (50) are used, the starter motor will switch on and off when the battery voltage is too low. Not much current is required to engage the starter solenoid. When the starter solenoid is closed, the current flows from the "+" pole directly to the starter motor. Now much more current must be supplied. As a result, the battery voltage drops below 9 V. That's not enough to keep the starter solenoid engaged so it releases again. The main contacts release, and the current to the starter motor is interrupted again.
At this moment there is again enough voltage to engage the starter solenoid.

The newer starting systems check the battery voltage before the starter motor is switched on and actually prevent starter operation if battery voltage is too low. Low voltage during starting can disrupt the communication between the control units, and some control units would stop working and/or loose volatile memory.

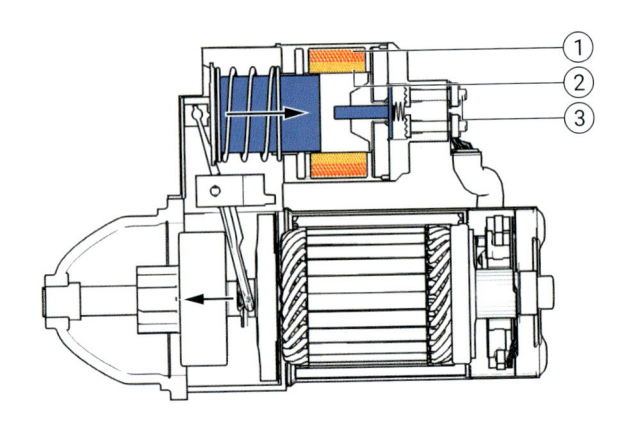

Fig. 358 Starter solenoid opened: 1. pull-in coil 2. hold-in coil 3. battery connection

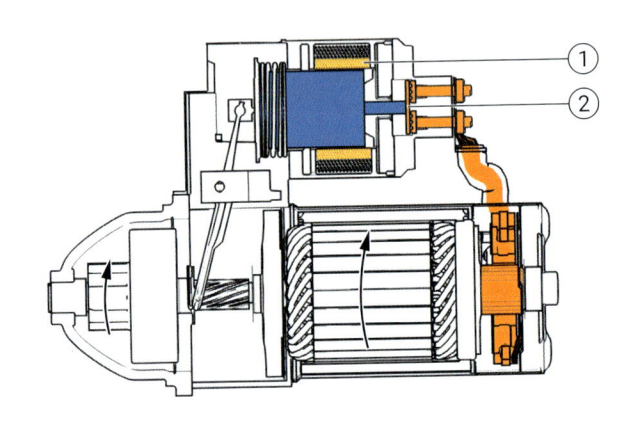

Fig. 359 Starter solenoid closed: 1. hold-in coil 2. contact bridge

Fig. 356 Cross section of the starter solenoid: 1. pull-in coil 2. hold-in coil 3. main battery contacts 4. contacts 5. contact bridge 6. magnetic core

Fig. 357 Check hold-in coil: 1. short circuit to ground or open circuit 2. coil short circuit Check pull-in coil: 1. open circuit 2. coil short circuit

5. Starter solenoid clicking during starting when the battery voltage is too low

With older types of vehicles where an ignition key (15) and start switch (50) are used, the starter motor will switch on and off when the battery voltage is too low. Not much current is required to engage the starter solenoid. When the starter solenoid is closed, the current flows from the "+" pole directly to the starter motor. Now much more current must be supplied. As a result, the battery voltage drops below 9 V. That's not enough to keep the starter solenoid engaged so it releases again. The main contacts release, and the current to the starter motor is interrupted again.
At this moment there is again enough voltage to engage the starter solenoid.

The newer starting systems check the battery voltage before the starter motor is switched on and actually prevent starter operation if battery voltage is too low. Low voltage during starting can disrupt the communication between the control units, and some control units would stop working and/or loose volatile memory.

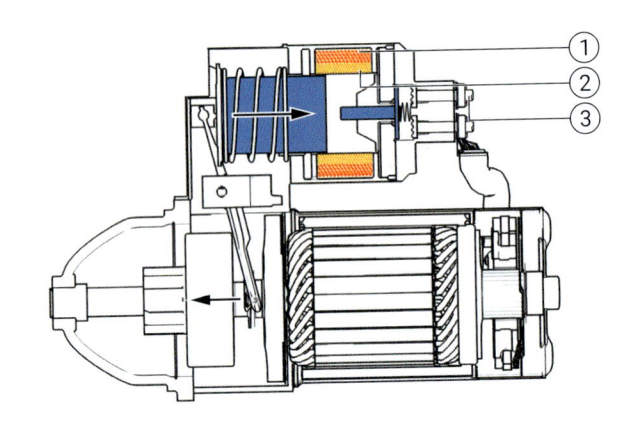

Fig. 358 Starter solenoid opened: 1. pull-in coil 2. hold-in coil 3. battery connection

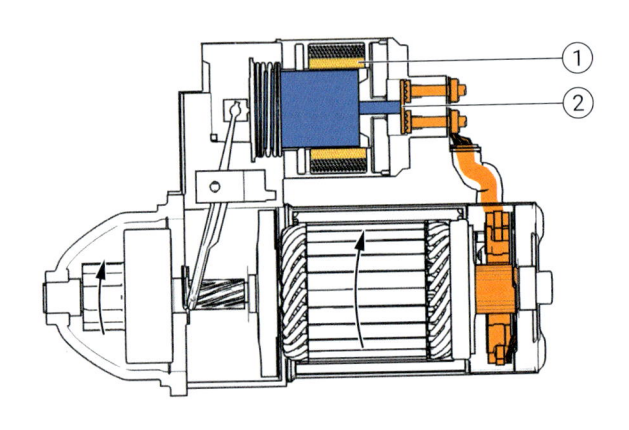

Fig. 359 Starter solenoid closed: 1. hold-in coil 2. contact bridge

HOW TO: CHECK THE STARTER MOTOR

1. Tools Required

During the electrical check of the starter motor, the voltage drop during starting is measured on the starter motor and the starter motor relay. Also the voltage loss across the power supply and ground circuits during starting is checked.
The current through the starter motor can be seen using an amps clamp and an oscilloscope.

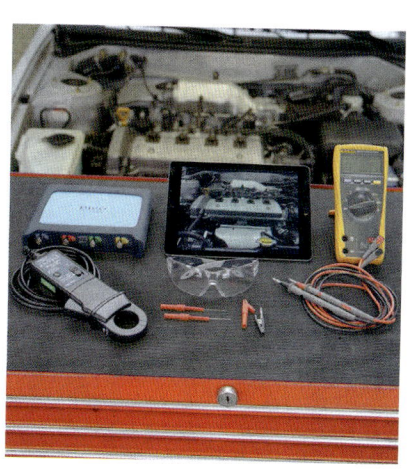

Fig. 360 Tools Required

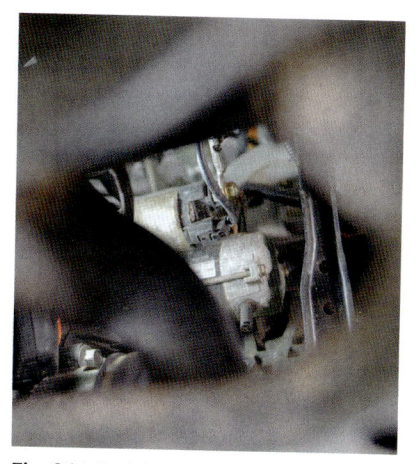

Fig. 361 In this case the starter motor is installed at the rear of the engine, under the intake manifold.

2. The electrical diagram for the starter motor

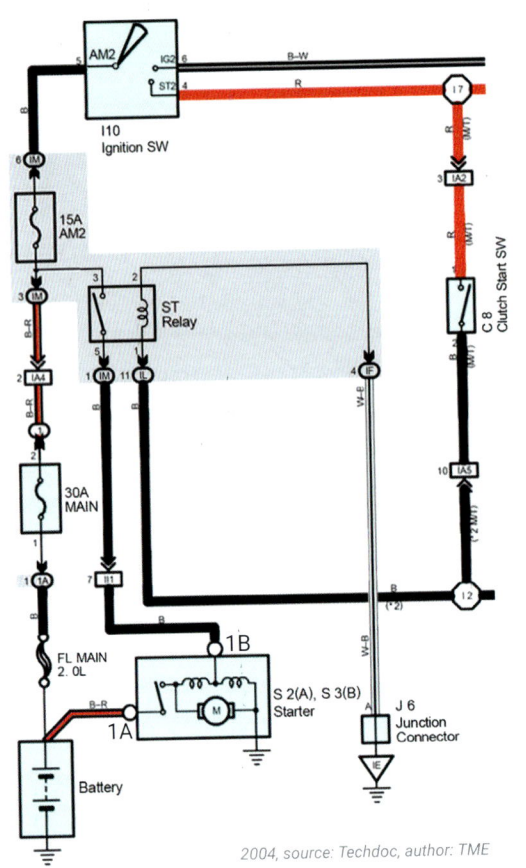

Fig. 362 This is the starter circuit diagram. The ignition switch (I10) powers the starter relay (ST). As soon as the key is turned to start, 12 V will appear on the starter relay. The starter relay then closes and powers the starter motor solenoid (S2A0). The starter motor solenoid closes and the starter motor is powered.

3. Measure the voltage drop during starting

Connect the measuring probes of the multimeters between the power supply of the starter motor solenoid and the starter motor.

Fig. 363 Connect the measuring probe to the power supply of the starter motor solenoid (pin 1B of the starter motor in the diagram). Connect the other measuring probe to the power supply of the starter motor (pin 1A).

Fig. 364 Connect both ground probes of the two multimeters with the negative battery terminal. Remove the fuel pump relay so that the engine doesn't start during cranking.

Fig. 365 The multimeter on the left is connected to the starter motor relay. The multimeter on the right is connected to the starter motor. During starting we read 8.7 V on the left and 8.9 V on the right. Both values are on the low side. It would take further investigation to find out what's wrong here: the battery, wiring, or ground.

4. Check the voltage drop across the positive and the ground sides of the circuit.

By measuring the voltage between the negative battery terminal and the ground connection of the starter motor, and the positive battery terminal and positive connection of the starter motor, you check the voltage drop of both positive and ground circuits when the engine is cranked over.

198 ELECTRICAL SYSTEMS

Fig. 366 Check the ground connection. Connect the ground probe of the multimeter with the negative battery terminal; connect the positive probe with the ground of the engine.

Fig. 367 Crank the engine and read the value on the multimeter. This is the voltage drop at the ground connection that occurs when the engine is starting. Here it is 0.2 V. This value is correct.

Fig. 368 Check the positive connection. Connect the ground probe of the multimeter with the positive battery terminal; connect the positive probe with the positive connection of the starter motor. During cranking the voltage drop is 0.19 V. This is okay.

5. Check the starter current draw with the amp clamp during starting.

Use the amps clamp to measure the current to the starter motor. The voltage is also measured to check that it doesn't get too low.

Fig. 369 Connect the measuring probe of the oscilloscope with the positive battery terminal, and the ground of the oscilloscope with the negative terminal. Connect the amps clamp around the positive cable of the starter motor and the other end to the measuring channel of the oscilloscope.

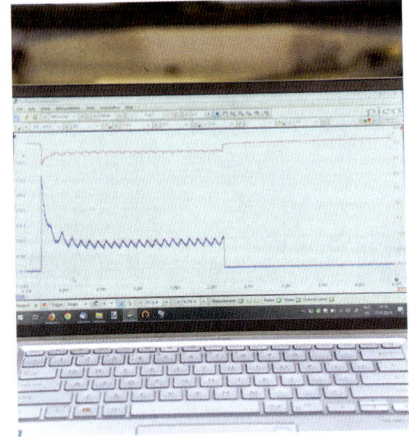

Fig. 370 On the oscilloscope you can read that the maximum current is 420 A (blue). The minimum value of the voltage is 11 V (red). These values must both be checked in the shop manual. Both values are good here.

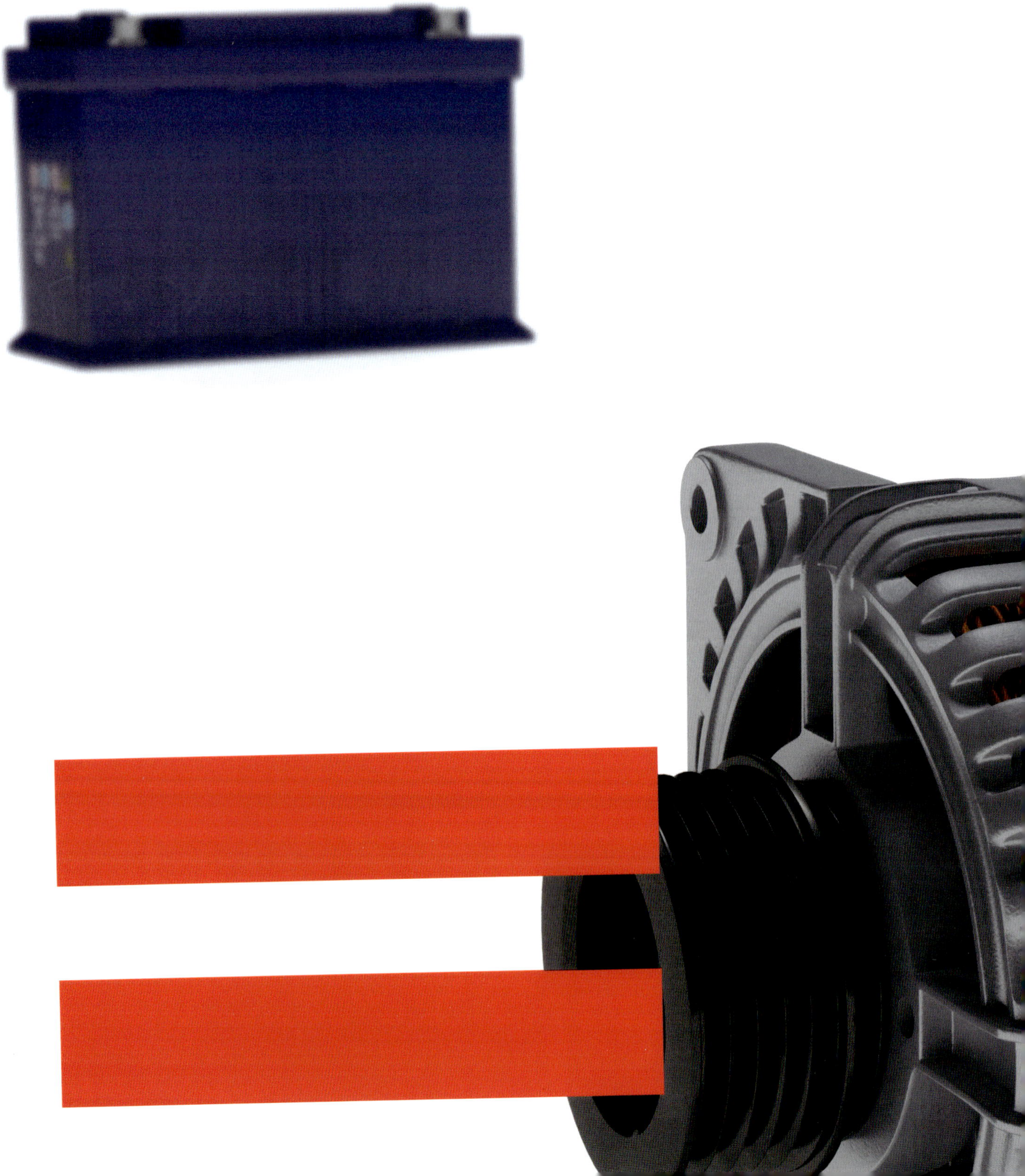

12. Charging System

KIRCHHOFF'S FIRST LAW

Under normal circumstances, the alternator supplies the electrical energy to power all electrical accessories and keep the battery charged whenever the engine is running.

There are times, however, when the alternator is not supplying energy or not enough energy to keep up with electrical demand. During these times, the battery supplies reserve energy and becomes discharged.

A battery is discharged:

— during start-up
— when electrical load exceeds alternator output
— when the engine is not running and electrical accessories are switched on

Using Kirchhoff's first law, you can determine whether the battery is either being charged or discharged.

Kirchhoff's first law states that:

the sum of all currents in a junction equals zero Amperes:

I1 + I2 + I3 + I4 + I5 = 0

In other words: the current flowing toward the junction is positive (alternator output and/or battery output), and the sum of current flowing away from the junction (electrical loads) is negative.

If you add up all the loads, you'll find that it's the same as the energy that's being supplied, either by the alternator, battery, or a combination of the two.

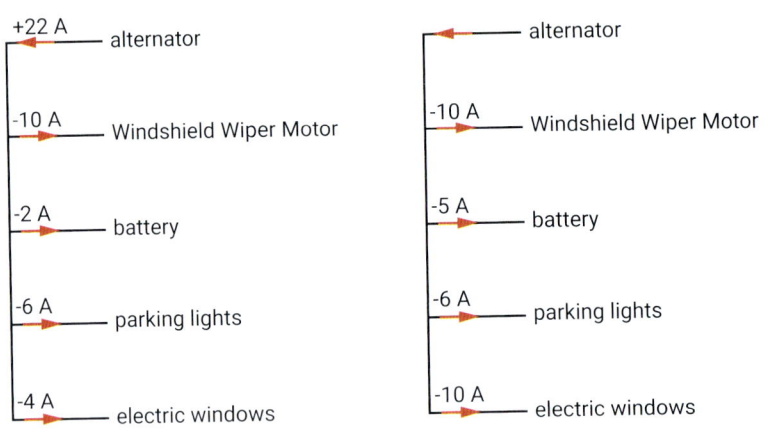

Fig. 373 Example 1: Kirchoff's law

Fig. 374 Example 2: an unknown current

Example 1
If you add all the currents together you will come to zero.

If you add the currents from the example, you will see that this is correct.

The alternator (+22 A), the windshield wiper motor (-10 A), the current charging the battery (-2 A), the sidelights (-6 A), and the electric windows (-4 A) together have a sum of 0.

22 A - 10 A - 2 A - 6 A - 4 A = 0

Example 2
If you have one unknown, you can use this method to calculate this value.

$I_{alternator} - 10\text{ A} - 5\text{ A} - 6\text{ A} - 10\text{ A} = 0$

$I_{alternator} - 31\text{ A} = 0$

$I_{alternator} = 31\text{ A}$

if you bring $I_{alternator}$ to the other side of this sign, you can calculate that the alternator supplies a current of +31 A.

ALTERNATOR: INTRODUCTION

Fig. 375 The alternator is mounted on the engine block.

1. Task and Location

The alternator is located in the engine compartment and is mounted to the engine block.

The alternator converts the kinetic energy of the engine into electrical energy.

The alternator provides all electrical consumers (loads) in the vehicle with current and ensures that the battery is charged, so that there's always an energy reserve.

2. Components

The main components of the alternator are:
- Housing.
  This attaches the alternator to the block. It protects the alternator components.
- Pulley.
  The engine drives the alternator via a pulley.
- Rotor.
  This creates a magnetic field to generate voltage.
- Stator.
  This is comprised of three coils in which alternating current is generated.
- Rectifier.
  This converts alternating current to direct current.
- Voltage regulator.
  This ensures a constant controlled alternator voltage.
- Fan.
  This cools the alternator.

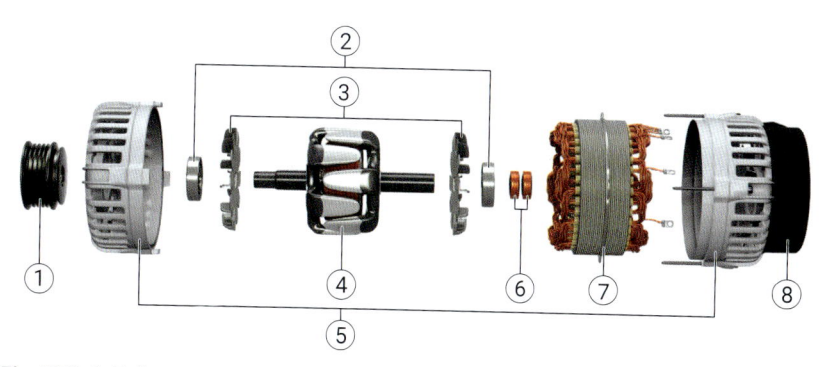

Fig. 376 1. Pulley. 2. Bearings. 3. Fan. 4. Rotor. 5. Housing. 6. Slip rings. 7. Stator. 8. Rectifier and voltage regulator.

The alternator housing is equipped with bearings to make the rotor run smoothly. Slip rings ensure that the current required for generating a magnetic field can be supplied to the rotor.

CHARGING SYSTEM: INTRODUCTION

Fig. 377 1. Alternator. 2. Engine. 3. Battery. 4. Ignition key. 5. Charging current warning light.

1. Tasks and Components

Vehicles have a large number of electrical loads such as the starter motor, lights, rear window heater and navigation system.

The charging system supplies current to all of these loads and charges the battery. The battery has to be fully charged after each trip to be able to start the vehicle again. When the battery is only partly charged, the positive and negative plates start to sulfate.

The charging system consists of:
— Engine.
— Alternator.
— Battery.
— Ignition key.
— Charging current warning light.

2. Operation

The engine drives the alternator so that it can supply electrical energy to the loads (consumers).

The amount of energy that the alternator supplies depends on what is being demanded by the load devices and the battery. The alternator must be capable to supply current to all loads and charge the battery at the same time. The amount of energy required drops significantly when the battery is fully charged and few loads are switched on.

The instrument panel warning light illuminates when there's a problem with the charging system.

Fig. 378 Energy flow from the battery to the starter motor.

Fig. 379 When the engine is stopped, the battery supplies energy to the loads.

Fig. 380 With the engine running, the alternator supplies energy to the loads and charges the battery.

3. ETL model

Every system in which energy is converted can be represented schematically. These schematics make it clearly visible which forms of energy transfer take place. ETL stands for Energy Transfer Load. The following components can be displayed in an ETL model:
— E: Energy source.
— T: Transfer.
— L: Load.
— B: Buffer.

The charging system of a vehicle can also be displayed in an ETL model. The distribution can be as follows:
— E: Alternator.
— O: Onboard network.
— L: Loads.
— B: Battery.

The arrows in the ETL model indicate the energy flows that run to and from the various components.

Energy source.	Transfer.	Load.
alternator	Onboard network.	loads

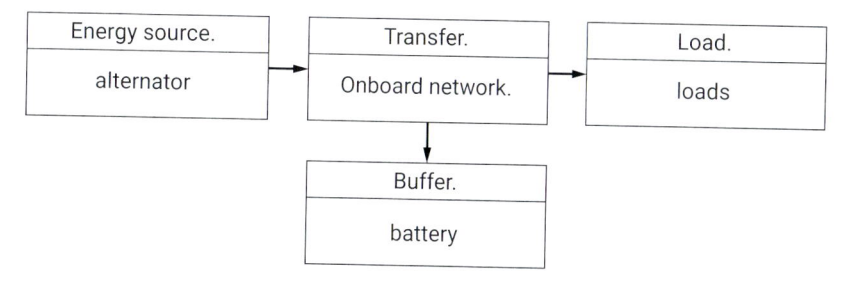

Buffer.
battery

Fig. 381 ETL model with engine running and activated loads.

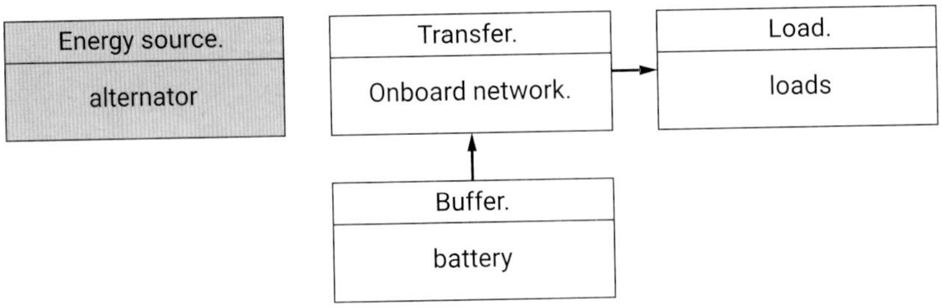

| Energy source. | | Transfer. | | Load. |
| alternator | | Onboard network. | → | loads |

| Buffer. |
| battery |

Fig. 382 ETL model with engine stopped and loads activated.

INDUCTION

1. Induction

The physical principle of induction tells us that when a conductor undergoes a change in its magnetic field, a voltage is generated/induced in the conductor.

The generated voltage depends upon the speed and the direction with which the magnetic field changes.

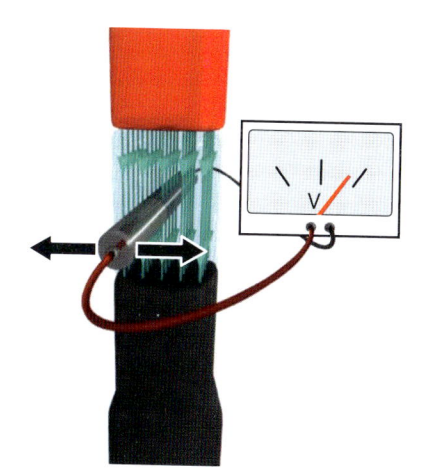

Fig. 383 A voltage is generated when the magnetic field is moved sideways.

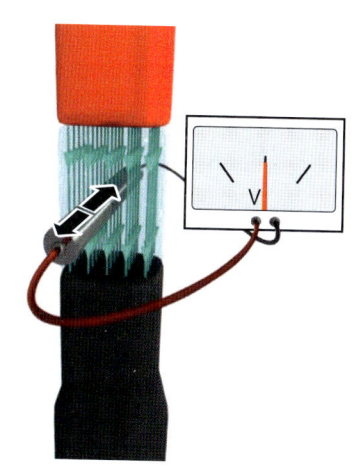

Fig. 384 No voltage is generated when the conductor is moved forward and backward.

Fig. 385 A voltage is generated when the magnetic field is moved sideways.

2. Voltage Generated

The voltage generated by induction depends on the following:
- The speed at which the magnetic field changes
- The direction in which the magnetic field changes
- The strength of the magnetic field
- The number of windings in the coil (conductor)

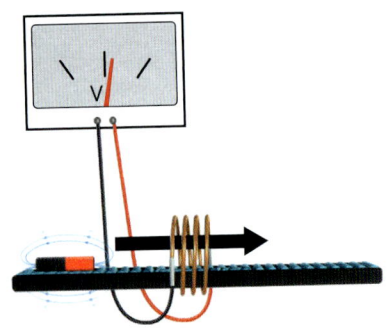

Fig. 386 In this test set-up, a magnet is placed on a motorized conveyor belt. The magnet can move through the coil. The speed of the belt can be regulated. The higher the speed, the higher the generated voltage.

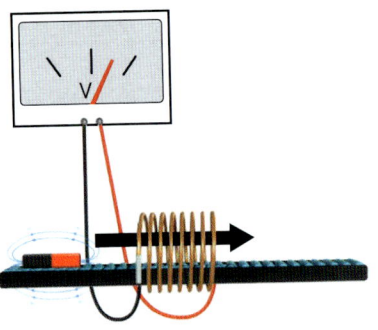

Fig. 387 When the coil has more windings, the generated voltage is greater.

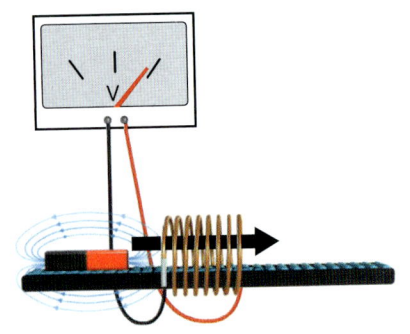

Fig. 388 When the magnetic field is increased, the generated voltage is greater.

3. Rotating Magnet

Note: In practice it may be easier to rotate the magnet.

A sine wave AC voltage is generated in the conductor.

When the change in the magnetic field is the greatest, the voltage generated is at its highest. When the change in the magnetic field is the smallest, the voltage generated is at its lowest.

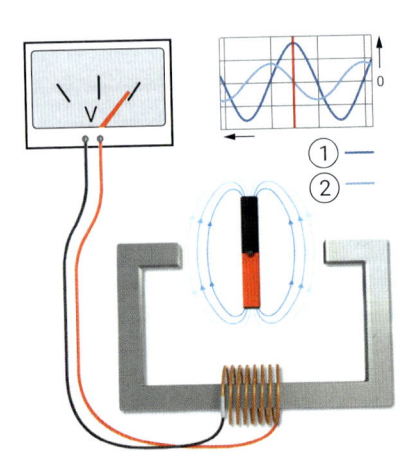

Fig. 389 The voltage (1) is the highest because the change of the magnetic field (2) is the greatest.

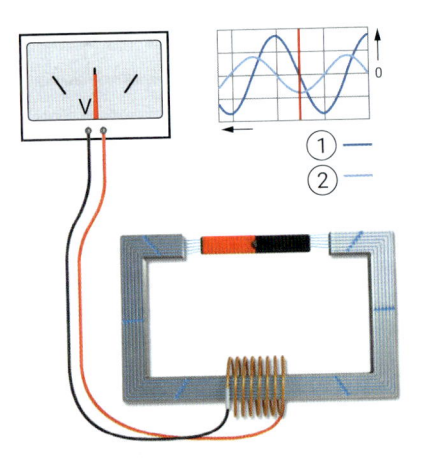

Fig. 390 The voltage (1) is the lowest because the change of the magnetic field (2) is the smallest.

ALTERNATOR: ROTOR

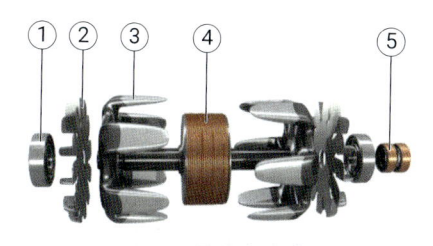

Fig. 391 1. bearing 2. fan 3. claw pole 4. field winding 5. slip rings

1. Construction and Operation

The rotor provides a magnetic field so a voltage can be generated in the stator windings of the alternator.

The rotor consists of:
- **Claw poles**: these are magnetic north and south poles.
- **Core**: this amplifies the magnetic field.
- **Rotor winding**: this generates a magnetic field.
- **Slip rings & brushes**: these handle the supply current to the rotor winding.

The components of the rotor are pressed onto a shaft with bearings on each end so it can rotate. The fan is also attached to the rotor shaft and provides cooling for the alternator.

Fig. 392 The complete rotor

Fig. 393 Each end of the field winding is connected to a slip ring.

2. Operation

The magnetic field in the alternator is created when the rotor is actuated. To do this a field current is passed through the rotor winding. This field current is transferred to the rotor winding via the carbon brushes and the slip rings.

When current flows through the rotor winding, one claw pole changes to north poles, and the other claw pole changes to south poles. Which claw pole is a north pole or south pole depends on the direction of the current through the rotor winding.

Fig. 394 The field winding in the energized state

Fig. 395 The rotor winding and claw poles in the energized state

Fig. 396 The rotor in the alternator

The claw poles that are equipped with six "fingers" ensure that the magnetic force of the rotor is divided into six pole pairs.

3. Rotor Diagnosis

The rotor of an alternator can have various defects, which can cause the alternator to no longer generate voltage. Typical rotor defects are:
- ground short circuit
- coil winding short circuit
- open circuit

Ground short circuit

A measuring probe of the multimeter is held against one of the slip rings. The other measuring probe is held against the metal (for example the shaft or a claw pole) of the rotor. By performing a resistance measurement, it is possible to find out whether there is a connection between the coil and the metal of the rotor.

If the meter indicates a small resistance, there is a short circuit to ground.

Fig. 397 Short circuit to ground

Field Winding Short Circuit

A field winding short circuit occurs when the wires in the coil are connected to each other. A good rotor coil winding has a resistance value specified by the manufacturer. When measuring with a multimeter on both slip rings, the resistance must correspond to the specified value. If the value deviates a lot, the rotor is no longer okay.

Fig. 398 Field winding short circuit

Open Circuit

If the field winding is broken, it is called an open circuit. By performing a resistance measurement with a multimeter on both slip rings, a wire break can be diagnosed. When the multimeter indicates an infinite resistance value, there is an open circuit in the field winding.

Fig. 399 Wire break

ALTERNATOR: STATOR

1. Construction and Operation

The current supplied by an alternator is generated in the stator. The stator of a three-phase alternator consists of one stator core and three stator coils.

The stator core consists of stacked, ring-shaped plates. The plates are separated from each other by insulating material. The stator core amplifies the magnetic field in the alternator and, as a result, increases the voltage generated.

The stator core contains recesses into which the stator coils are inserted. Voltage is generated in the stator coils.

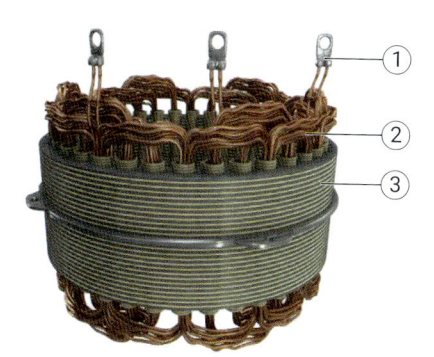

Fig. 400 1. Connection. 2. Stator coils. 3. Stator core.

2. Stator Circuits

There are two ways to connect the three stator coils:
— Delta circuit.
  Can be recognized by three pairs of connection wires.
— Wye (Y) circuit / star circuit.
  Has four connections, three of which are single wire connections and one connection where the three ends of the coils are connected to each other.

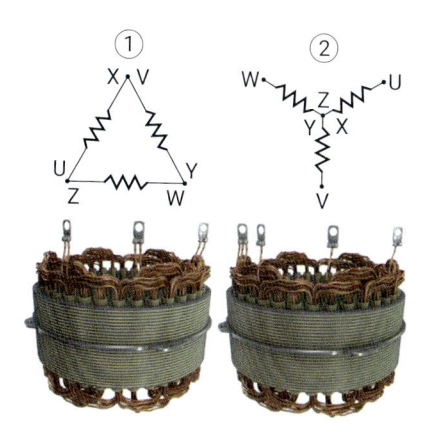

Fig. 401 1. Star circuit. 2. Delta circuit.

Wye circuits are the most common because they can achieve sufficiently high voltage more quickly.

Delta circuits are used if the alternator has to supply a lot of current.

3. Faults

The stator ceases to function correctly if one of the stator coils makes contact with the stator core (short circuit to ground) or if one of the coils is an open circuit (broken wire).

You can check this using a multimeter.
The resistance of the coils must be small (approximately 0.05 Ω).

The resistance between the stator coils and the stator core must be infinite.

Fig. 402 This stator doesn't have a short circuit to ground.

Fig. 403 A small amount of resistance is measured between the coils and the stator core. This indicates a short circuit to ground.

Fig. 404 Coil V has a small amount of resistance. The coil is still good.

Fig. 405 The resistance is infinite. So there is an open circuit in coil V.

If the stator coils short-circuit to each other, this is referred to as a copper short circuit. This cannot be checked with an ohmmeter because the resistance of the coils is already very low. The stator can be checked for a copper short circuit by means of a current measurement while the alternator is operating.

ALTERNATOR

1. Pre-Exciting

An alternator generates a voltage when the rotor is magnetized and spun within the stator windings. The current passing through the rotor of the alternator that produces the magnetic field is generated by the alternator itself. This process is called self-excitation.

To begin the self-excitation process, the rotor first needs to be pre-excited. The pre-excitation circuit runs via the ignition switch and the charging system indicator light on the dashboard. The rotor is excited so that the alternator is able to generate current to excite itself. During pre-excitation, the charging system indicator lamp lights up. The voltage generated by the alternator comes to D+, which causes the charging system indicator lamp to switch off.

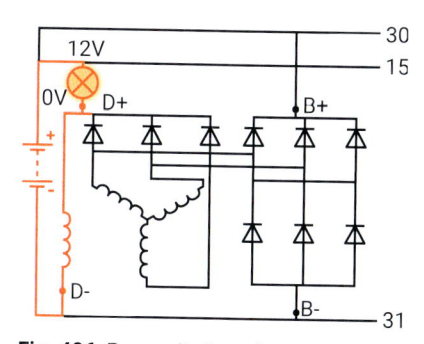

Fig. 406 Pre-excitation of an alternator

Fig. 407 Inside of an alternator

2. Generating Voltage

When the rotor is excited and rotating, a three-phase alternating voltage is generated in the stator coils by means of induction.

Field diodes

Three diodes provide voltage for the rotor (orange). These diodes are called the field diodes. The diodes ensure that the AC voltage of the stator is converted to a DC voltage for the rotor. The rotor uses this DC voltage to create a magnetic field.

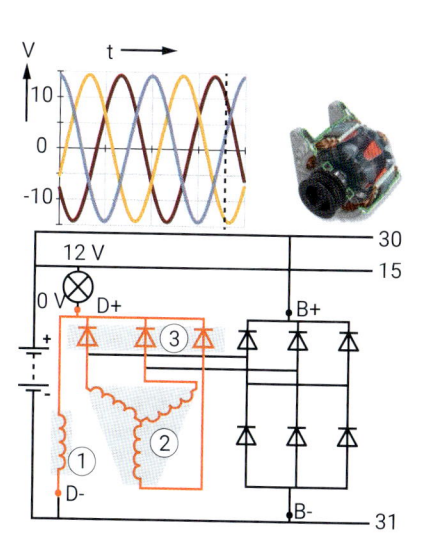

Fig. 408 1. rotor winding 2. stator windings 3. field diodes

3. Voltage Rectifying

The voltage, which is generated in the stator, is converted into a DC voltage using a rectifier circuit (diode bridge).

The generated voltages are sinusoidal, thus creating a ripple voltage after rectification. Many times a sinusoidal wave is referred to as a sine wave.

Fig. 409 The diode bridge on the alternator

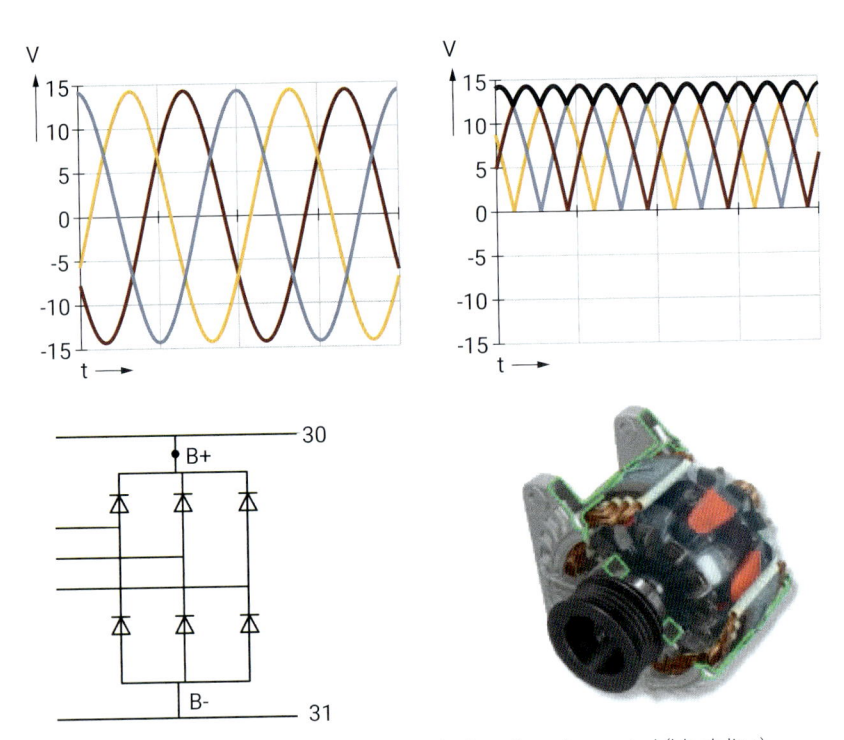

Fig. 410 After rectifying the AC voltage, a ripple voltage is created (black line).

4. Voltage Regulator

The ripple voltage is applied to the voltage regulator. The voltage regulator guarantees a constant output voltage from the alternator.

The output voltage must be high enough to power electrical loads and charge the battery. The voltage should not be too high, otherwise it might cause damage to the load devices and the battery.

Fig. 411 The voltage regulator on the alternator

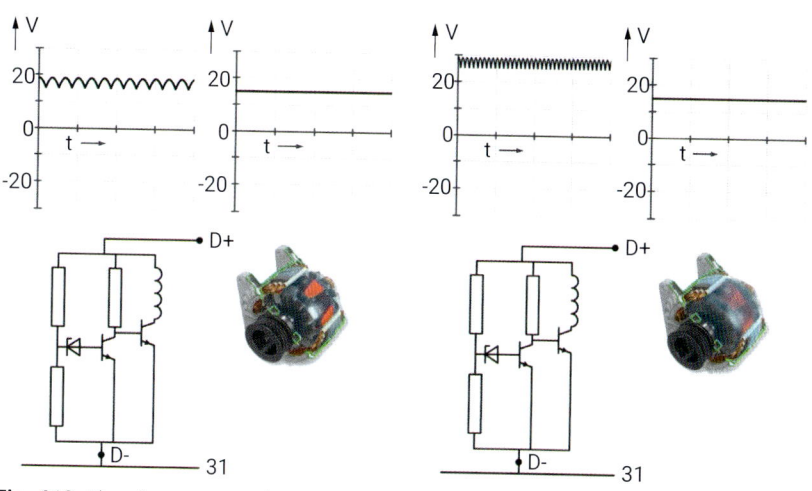

Fig. 412 The alternator at a low speed

Fig. 413 The alternator at a high speed

Intelligent Voltage Regulator

An alternator can use its own voltage regulator and the vehicle's control unit to regulate output voltage. The generated power is communicated to the engine management and/or the battery management unit. This allows the generated voltage to be optimally regulated, increasing the efficiency.
If the vehicle is started with a fairly low battery, these control units will ensure that the alternator speed is high enough to generate sufficient charging current during idle speed.

If the vehicle has a fullly-charged battery, the control units can decide to limit the current generated. As a result, the combustion engine needs to deliver less power, and fuel will be saved.
The alternator can be equipped with a data bus connection with which it can communicate with the onboard network and the engine management system.

5. Wiring Diagram

All the sub-diagrams viewed previously are now shown together, forming the complete wiring diagram for the alternator.

The alternator has three connections:
- B+: battery charging current
- D+: control voltage of the rotor for setting the alternator voltage
- D-: alternator ground

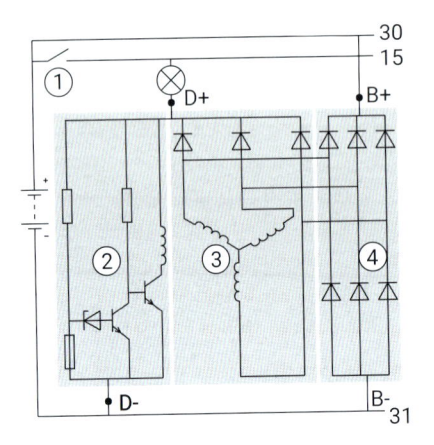

Fig. 414 1. pre-excitation 2. regulate voltage 3. generate voltage 4. rectify

Fig. 415 1. D- ground connection 2. B+ charging current connection 3. D+ rotor control voltage

ALTERNATOR POWER

1. Introduction

An alternator must generate enough power to provide all loads in a vehicle with energy. In addition, the alternator must also charge the onboard network battery so that it retains sufficient capacity.

Vehicles with many or large load devices need an alternator with a larger capacity; those with fewer or small loads need a smaller capacity.

2. Alternator Power

An alternator always charges with a higher voltage than the battery voltage. This is around 14 V. The maximum charging current determines the maximum power (volts x current) of an alternator. The identification plate shows the data of an alternator. For example, an alternator can generate a current of 80 A at the nominal speed (alternator speed: 6000 rpm). Sometimes a second current is mentioned. This indicates the current at an idle speed. The idle speed (alternator speed: 1800 rpm) is 45 A for some types.

With the power law (P = V x I) you can determine the nominal power of this alternator: 14 V x 80 A = 1120 W.

In order to reach the nominal charging current, the alternator must be running at a speed of 6000 rpm. This does not mean that the crankshaft also has to rotate at this speed.
Suppose the pulley of the crankshaft has a diameter of 4.33 inches and the pulley diameter of the alternator is 2.16 inches. You then have a gear ratio of 1:2 between these two pulleys. The crankshaft only needs to rotate 3000 rpm to give the alternator a rotation speed of 6000 rpm.

Fig. 416 Alternator identification plate

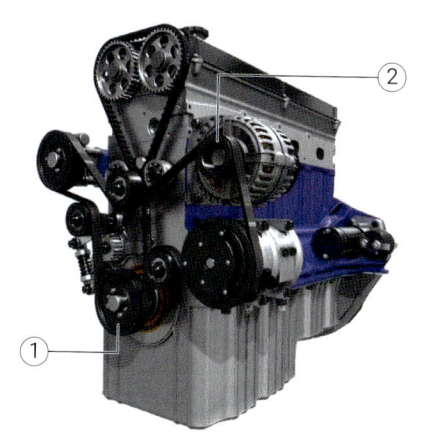

Fig. 417 1. crankshaft pulley
2. alternator pulley

3. Energy Supply

In a "normal" situation, the alternator always generates enough energy to supply the vehicle's electrical loads with energy. The surplus energy is stored in the onboard battery, so that there is sufficient energy in the battery to provide the vehicle with energy to start the engine next time.

Modern alternators have an energy surplus, which means the alternator generates more energy than the loads demand. When the power of the alternator is insufficient three things can happen:

1. The engine management increases the engine speed. This allows the alternator to deliver a greater power (idle speed).
2. The engine management reduces the number of load devices.
3. Energy from the onboard battery is used, and the battery is slowly drained. This situation can only occur briefly.

With the 1st law of Kirchhoff you can determine the power distribution. When the battery is charged, the current towards the battery is positive, and when the battery is discharged, the current towards the battery is negative.

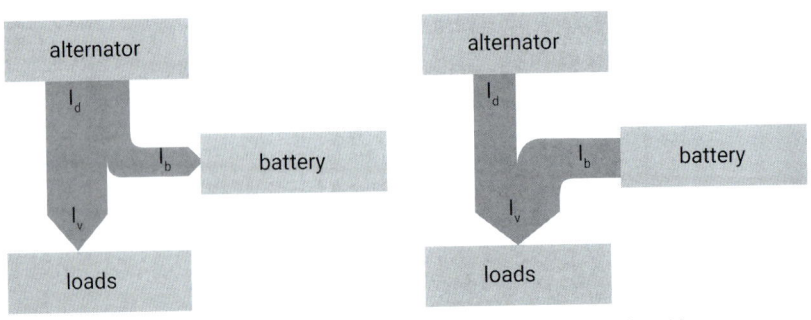

Fig. 418 Energy supply with an energy surplus

Fig. 419 Energy supply with an energy shortage

It is important to match the loads, the battery, and the alternator so that a reliable energy supply takes place.

If additional loads are added to a vehicle, it is important to check whether the power of the alternator is still sufficient.

4. The power of load devices

To be able to determine the total electrical power requirements of a vehicle, a distinction must be made based on the operating time of the loads. There are:
— long-term loads
— short-term loads

Long-term loads can be switched on for long periods; examples are the ignition, the car radio, and all control units.

Short-term loads are only used for shorter periods; examples are the brake lights, the horn and the reversing lights.

continuos load devices	long-term power (W)
control units	200
ignition	20
electric fuel pump	50
low beam	110
rear lights	20
license plate light	10
instrument lighting	10
climate control blower motor	55
car radio	25
total	**500**

short-term loads	long-term power (W)
ABS/ESP/SRS assistance systems	100
oxygen sensors	100
turn signals	40
brake lights	63
high beam	70
interior lighting	5
window wipers	90
horn	30
reverse lights	21
radiator fan	120
starter motor	1200
rear fog lights	35
rear window heater	120
electric windows	150
total	**2145**

Fig. 420 Average power requirement of long-term loads in a vehicle

Fig. 421 Average power requirements of short-term loads in a vehicle.

DETERMINING THE REQUIRED ALTERNATOR POWER

An alternator does not need to supply power to all loads simultaneously. To determine the required power, the short-term loads are multiplied by a switch-on factor. The size of this factor depends on the power used over a longer period.

In the table you can see that, for example, the rear window heating does not have to be included for the full 120 W, but that with a factor of 0.5 it results in a power of 60 W. With the turn signals, even a factor of 0.1 can be used because they consume only a fraction of the total power over a longer period.

	long-term power (W)	factor	consumed power (W)
continuos load devices			
control units	200	1	200
ignition	20	1	20
electric fuel pump	50	1	50
low beam	110	1	110
rear lights	20	1	20
license plate light	10	1	10
instrument lighting	10	1	10
climate control blower motor	55	1	55
car radio	25	1	25
total	**500**		**500**
short-term loads			
ABS/ESP/SRS assistance systems	100	0.5	50
oxygen sensors	100	0.5	50
turn signals	40	0.1	4.1
brake lights	63	0.1	6.3
high beam	70	0.5	35
interior lighting	5	0.1	0.5
window wipers	90	0.5	45
horn	30	0.1	3
reverse lights	21	0.5	10.5
radiator fan	120	0.5	60
starter motor	1200	0	0
rear fog lights	35	0.5	17.5
rear window heater	120	0.5	60
electric windows	150	0.1	15
total	**2145**		**356**

Fig. 422 Total power of long-term and short-term loads in a vehicle

If you have determined both powers you can calculate the total to be sure that the alternator always has sufficient power at idle and nominal speed.

Idle Power

At idle speed you can multiply the long-term loads by a factor of 1.3 to ensure sufficient power.

$P_{idle} = P_{continuous} \times 1.3 = 500\ W \times 1.3 = 650\ W$

With the power law you can calculate the minimum current of the alternator at idle speed:

$I_{idle} = P_{idle} / V = 650\ W / 14\ V = 46.4\ A$

Nominal Power

You calculate the nominal power by adding the powers together:

$P_{nominal} = P_{idle} + P_{short} = 650\ W + 356.9\ W = 1006.9\ W$

With the power law you can calculate what the nominal current of the alternator must be:

$I_{nominal} = P/V = 1006.9\ W / 14\ V = 71.9\ A$

If you compare the calculated data with the alternator identification plate, you can conclude that this alternator has sufficient power to power the vehicle both at idle speed and at nominal speed.

Fig. 423 Alternator identification plate

THREE-PHASE VOLTAGE STAR CONNECTION

1. Generator

Here you see an example of a single-phase generator.

In the coils of the generator an AC voltage is generated by means of induction.

The phase voltage is the generated voltage in a coil, measured with respect to ground.

The induction voltage that is generated is a sinusoidal AC voltage.

The faster the electromagnet turns, the higher the voltage generated.

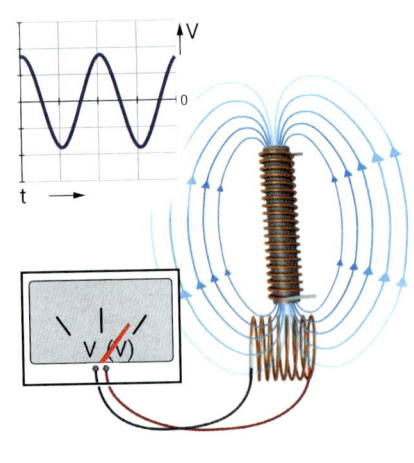

Fig. 424 A single-phase generator.

2. Three-Phase Voltage

Three coils are rotated 120 degrees in relation to one another. As a result, the phase voltages are offset by 1/3 of a period in relation to one another.

The sum of the phase voltages is 0 V at any given time. The ends of the coils are connected to one another and form a *star connection*.

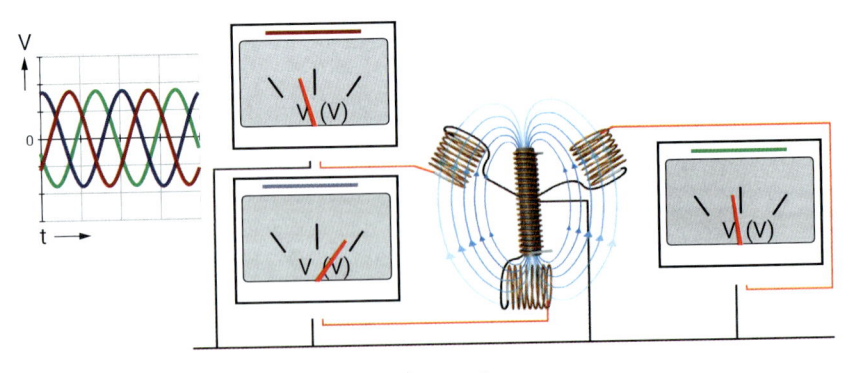

Fig. 425 A three-phase generator in star connection.

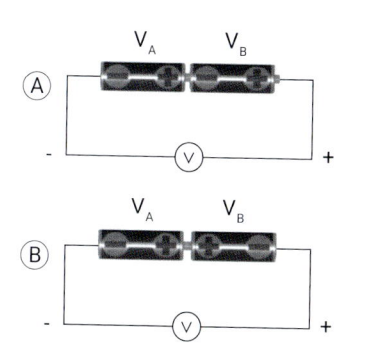

Fig. 426 Voltage measurement with two batteries in series.

3. Line Voltage

The line voltage is the voltage generated by a coil, measured in relation to another coil.

The line voltage can be determined by subtracting the phase voltages from one another.

It becomes clear how this works when you connect two batteries in series.

$V_A = 1.5$ V
$V_B = 1.5$ V.
Situation A: $V_V = V_A + V_B = 1.5$ V $+ 1.5$ V $= 3$ V.
Situation B: $V_V = V_A + V_B = 1.5$ V $+ -1.5$ V $= 0$ V.

In a vehicle alternator, it is not batteries, but coils, that generate a voltage. The calculation of these coils is comparable to the example.

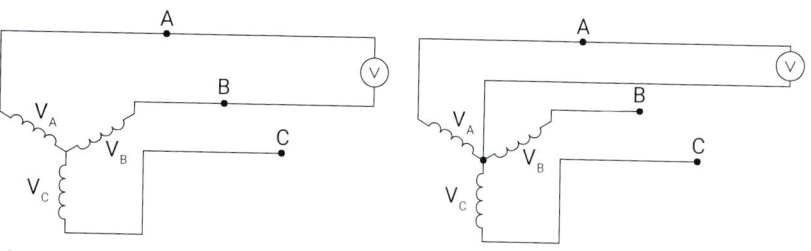

Fig. 427 Measuring the line voltage.

Fig. 428 Measuring the phase voltage.

4. Determining the line voltage

You can also graphically determine how large the line voltage is. This is not done by adding up the voltages as with the batteries, but by subtracting them.

You see the two-phase voltage V_A and V_B. In the diagram you can see how the line voltage (V_{A-B}) is measured. But you can also calculate it yourself.

$V_{A-B} = V_A - V_B.$

With this calculation, you determine the distance between the two-phase voltages V_A (red) and V_B (green). This is the line voltage V_{A-B} (brown).

At **time T1**, the voltage is V_A 7 V and the voltage V_B -7 V.
$V_{A-B} = V_A - V_B$
$V_{A-B} = 7V - -7V$
$V_{A-B} = 7V + 7V$
$V_{A-B} = 14V$.

At **time T2**, the voltage is V_A -4 V and the voltage is V_B -4 V.
$V_{A-B} = V_A - V_B$
$V_{A-B} = -4V - -4V$
$V_{A-B} = -4V + 4V$
$V_{A-B} = 0V$.

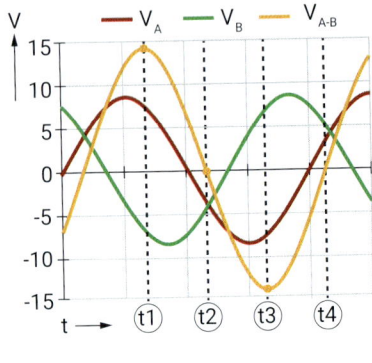

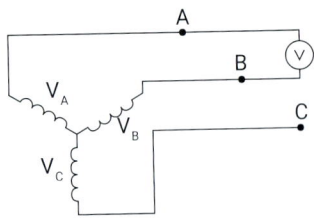

Fig. 429 The phase voltage V_A and V_B and the line voltage V_{A-B}.

At **time T3**, the voltage is V_A -7 V and the voltage V_B 7 V.
$U_{A-B} = V_A - V_B$
$V_{A-B} = -7V - 7V$
$V_{A-B} = -14V$.

At **time T4**, the voltage is V_A 4 V and the voltage V_B 4 V.
$V_{A-B} = V_A - V_B$
$V_{A-B} = 4V - 4V$
$V_{A-B} = 0V$.

5. Terminal Pairs

Instead of a rotating magnet with one pole pair, the rotating magnet has six pole pairs. This magnet is referred to as the rotor.

In one revolution of the rotor, a sinusoidal AC voltage with six periods is generated, rather than one period.

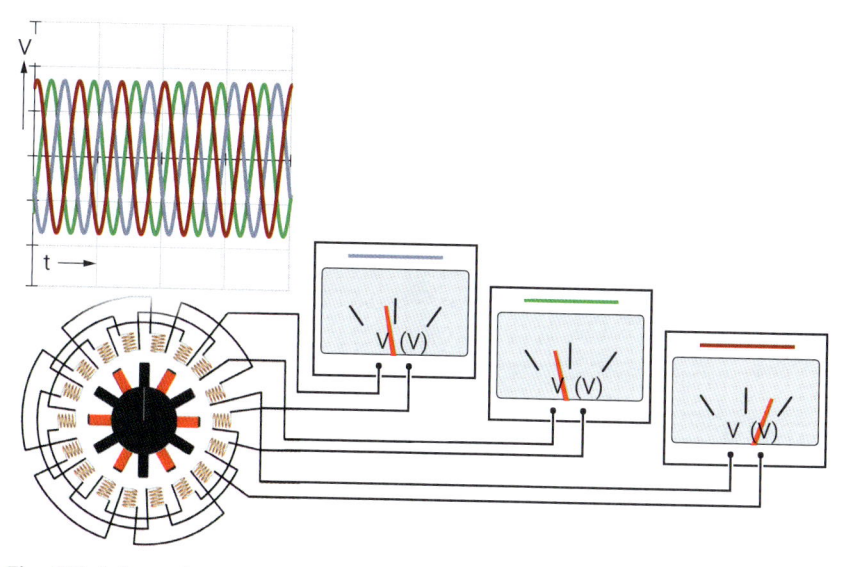

Fig. 430 A three-phase generator with six pole pairs.

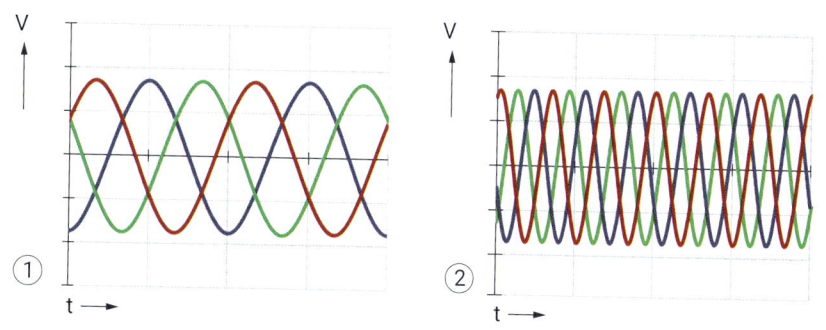

Fig. 431 1. The voltage of two rotations with one pole pair. 2. The voltage of one rotation with six pole pairs.

For one revolution, the following applies: the more pole pairs, the more periods.

ALTERNATOR: VOLTAGE REGULATION

1. Rotational Speed

The magnitude of alternator output voltage depends on many variables, including the rotational speed of the rotor. The speed of the rotor depends on the rotational speed of the engine.

The alternator is designed so that a sufficient voltage (approximately 14.4 volts) can be generated when the engine is idling.

However, as the rotational speed of the engine increases, the voltage generated may become too high. To prevent this from happening, the alternator's voltage regulator limits output voltage by controlling the rotor's magnetic field strength.

On today's vehicles, the voltage regulator may be part of within the alternator or contained within the engine control unit.

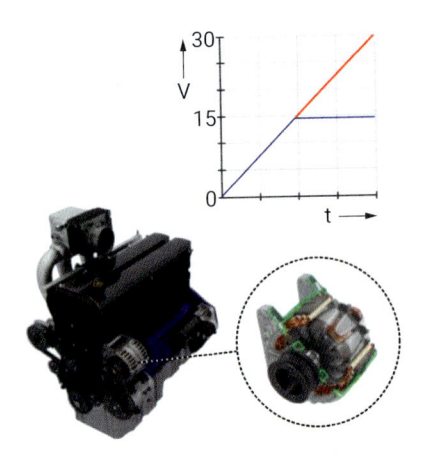

Fig. 432 The blue line indicates the alternator voltage controlled with a voltage regulator. The red line shows the voltage without voltage regulator control.

2. Field Strength

In addition to the rotational speed of the rotor, the alternator output voltage is also influenced by the number of stator windings and the magnetic field strength of the rotor.

The engine determines the rotational speed of the rotor. The number of stator windings is determined by the construction of the alternator. Only the magnetic field strength of the rotor is adjustable.

The magnetic field strength is adjusted by pulsing the rotor's magnetic field on and off. If the output voltage gets too high, the pulse is decreased. If the output voltage is too low, the pulse is increased. Controlling the pulse width controls the magnetic field strength of the rotor.

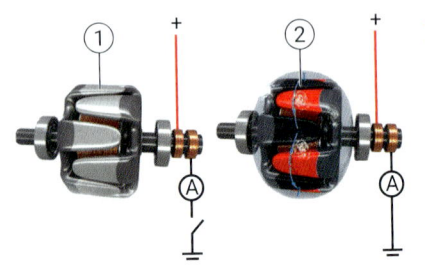

Fig. 433 The rotor in the non-energized state (1) and energized state (2). The ammeter shows where the rotor current can be measured.

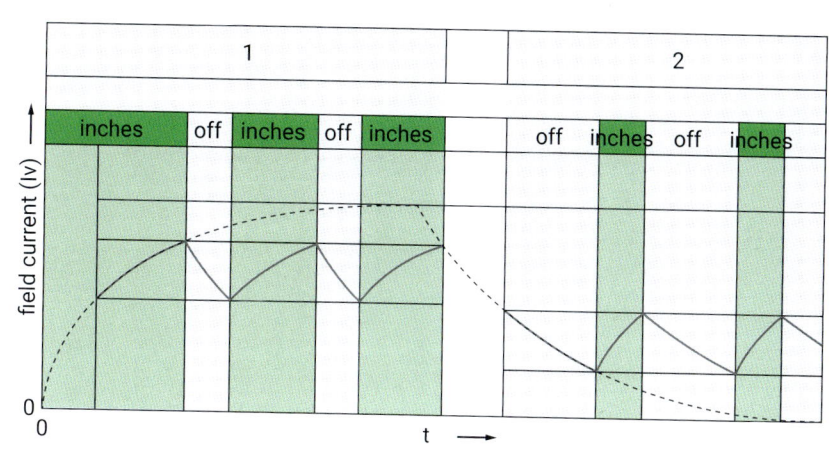

Fig. 434 The rotor current at low speed (1) and high speed (2)

Controlling the voltage in the rotor also controls the current flowing through the rotor (V = I * R). Therefore the average magnetic field strength depends on the current flowing through the rotor.

The rotor current can be displayed in a graph. This shows that an average rotor current is constant. Notice that the current through the rotor is switched on for a shorter period of time at a higher speed than at a lower speed. Switching at a high speed is therefore faster than at a low speed.

3. Voltage Regulation

The voltage regulator is responsible for switching the magnetic field on and off by controlling the current flowing through the rotor windings.

If the **voltage** across **D+** (alternator positive connection) is **lower** than the **reference voltage** (for example, 14.4 V), then a current flows from D+ through the rotor to D- (alternator negative connection). A **voltage** is generated in the alternator. The voltage generated is supplied at connection D+.

If the **voltage** across **D+ becomes higher** than the **reference voltage**, then the Zener diode voltage is reached and the transistor T2 becomes conductive. The threshold voltage of a silicon transistor is 0.7 V.
Transistor T1 no longer conducts and no current flows through the rotor. **No voltage** is generated.

When the voltage falls below the Zener diode voltage, T2 turns off and T1 conducts again, and the cycle repeats itself.

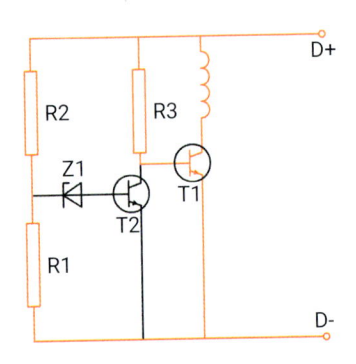

Fig. 435 If T2 is not conducting, the rotor is energized.

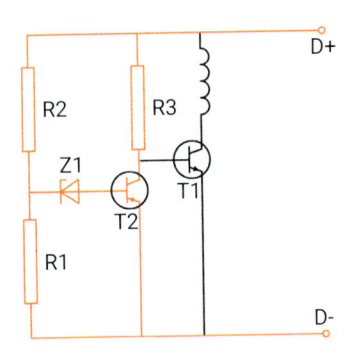

Fig. 436 If the zener diode opens, T2 will start conducting and the rotor will not be energized.

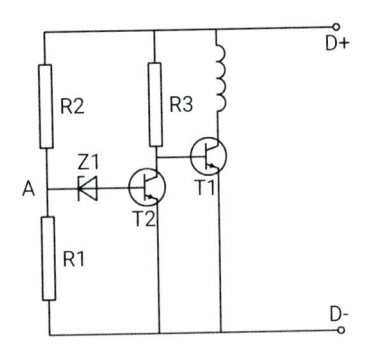

Fig. 437 Calculating the voltage regulator voltage

Calculate the voltage regulator voltage

T2 only starts conducting when the Zener diode threshold voltage is reached. The threshold voltage of a transistor is 0.7 V. To reach this threshold voltage, a voltage from the zener voltage + the threshold voltage must be present at point A.

Example 1

Given:

$R1 = 2000\Omega$

$R2 = 2000\Omega$

$R3 = 2000\Omega$

$V_{D+} = 14.6V$

$V_Z = 6.6V$

Requested:
Is the rotor switched on or off in this situation?

Answer:
Because resistors R1 and R2 have the same value, the voltage is divided. The voltage on point A is therefore: $\frac{14.6V}{2} = 7.3V$.

The voltage required to switch off the rotor is the zener voltage + the threshold voltage: $6.6V + 0.7V = 7.3V$.
So the rotor will be switched off.

Example 2

Given:
$R1 = 46\Omega$

$R2 = 100\Omega$
$R3 = 20\Omega$
$U_{D+} = 14.6V$
$V_Z = 3.9V$

Requested:
Is the rotor switched on or off in this situation?

Answer:
Because not all resistors in this circuit are the same, the current in the circuit first needs to be calculated.

First the equivalent (total) resistance of R1 and R2 is calculated:
$R_v = R1 + R2$
$R_v = 100\Omega + 46\Omega$
$R_v = 146\Omega$

Then the current through the resistors is calculated:
$I_{Rv} = \frac{V}{R_v}$
$I_{Rv} = \frac{14.6V}{146\Omega}$
$I_{Rv} = 0.1A$

The voltage across R1 can now be calculated:
$V_{R1} = I * R1$
$V_{R1} = 0.1A * 46\Omega$
$V_{R1} = 4.6V$

The rotor is switched off when T2 starts to conduct. T2 becomes conductive if the voltage point A is equal to the zener voltage + the threshold voltage of transistor T2.

$3.9V + 0.7V = 4.6V$

The transistor will therefore start conducting, and the rotor will be switched off.

CHARGING SYSTEM: DIAGNOSIS

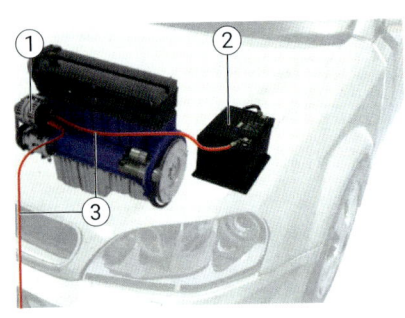

Fig. 438 Parts of the charging system: 1. Alternator. 2. Battery. 3. Wiring.

1. Charging System

When the engine doesn't start or the charging current control indicator remains lit while the engine is running, there may be a problem with the charging system.

In the event of problems with the charging system, the cause of the problem may be in one of the following components:
— Battery.
— Alternator.
— Wiring.

Before you start performing diagnostics on the charging system, you first need to find all of the actions and data in the workshop documentation.

2. Alternator Connections

When performing diagnostics on the charging system, you need to take some measurements on the alternator connections.

The alternator has three connections.
— B+: battery charging current.
— D+: controlled rotor excitation voltage for regulating the alternator output voltage.
— D-: alternator ground.

Fig. 439 1. B+ charging current connection. 2. D- ground connection. 3. D+ rotor control voltage.

3. Charge Current Warning Indicator

Watching how the warning indicator lamp is illuminated during pre-excitation and when the engine is running can assist in carrying out some overall diagnostics. (In the workshop documentation, look at how the charge indicator light displays faults.)

Fig. 440 Checking the charging current indicator lamp.

The following situations can occur:

1. The charge indicator lights up as **normal** during **pre-excitation** (before start-up), and then turns **off** when the engine is

running.
2. The charge indicator lights up as **normal** during **pre-excitation**, but remains **faintly** illuminated when the **engine is running**.
3. The charge indicator lights up **faintly** during **pre-excitation** and then turns **off** when the engine is running.
4. The charge indicator does **not** light up during **pre-excitation** and also **not** while the **engine is running**.

In all cases, a faulty alternator may be the cause. Scenarios 3 or 4 may also occur because of a wiring fault. Furthermore, in scenario 4 the charge indicator light or its wiring may also be faulty.

After this overall diagnosis you can start to detect the cause of the fault by taking some targeted measurements.

4. Charging Current Check

The charging current of the alternator must reach or exceed the minimum specification. You can check this by completing the following actions:

- Look up the alternator's minimum charging current and engine rotational speed. Often this information is on the alternator cover.
- Connect the tester to the battery.
- Start the engine and increase its speed.
- Load the alternator with the tester so the voltage drops to about 13.5 V.
- Using a current clamp, measure the charging current.

If the charging current is not OK and the battery cables and connections are OK, then the alternator needs to be replaced.

Fig. 441 When you have completed the steps you can check the charging current.

Fig. 442 1. Regulated voltage. 2. Current at 1,800 rpm (alternator speed). 3. Current at 6,000 rpm (alternator speed).

5. Voltage Regulator Check

The voltage generated by the alternator must be high enough to recharge the battery, but should not get too high.

You can check voltage regulation by completing the following actions:
— Find the specified voltage output range of the alternator. In this case, the voltage must be between 13.8 and 14.5 V.
— Start the engine.
— Measure the voltage between the B+ connection and the alternator housing at 2,000 engine rpm.

If the regulated voltage is not correct and the battery cables and connections are OK, the alternator needs to be replaced.

Fig. 443 Once you have completed these steps, you can check the regulated alternator voltage.

6. Supply Circuit Check

A voltage drop test of the positive battery cable is required if the charging current or the regulated voltage is not OK.

You can check the supply circuit by carrying out the following actions:
— Start the engine and increase the rotational speed to 2,000 rpm.
— Load the alternator with the tester so that the voltage has dropped to about 13.5 V.
— Connect a voltmeter between the positive battery terminal and the B+ connection on the alternator.

Fig. 444 Once you have completed these steps, you can check the power supply circuit.

— Check whether the voltmeter is showing a voltage lower than 0.3 V.

If the voltage drop is more than 0.3 V, the positive battery cable or connector must be checked.

7. Ground Circuit Check

If the battery ground cable or connector are faulty, not only will you have problems with the charging system, but also with other systems.

You can check the ground circuit by checking the voltage drop of the negative battery cable:
— Start the engine and increase the rotational speed to 2,000 rpm.
— Load the alternator with the tester so that the voltage has dropped to about 13.5 V.
— Connect a voltmeter between the negative battery terminal and the alternator housing.
— The voltmeter should read less than 0.3 V.

If the voltage drop is more than 0.3 V, then the ground cable or connector must be checked.

Fig. 445 Once you have completed these steps, you can check the ground circuit.

8. Battery Check

By calculating the internal resistance of the battery, you can assess the condition of the battery. In the case of this battery, service information states the maximum acceptable internal resistance value should not exceed 2.5 ohms divided by the battery's cold cranking amp rating (CCA). To determine the actual internal resistance of the battery, you should proceed as follows:
1. Make sure the battery is fully charged.
2. Measure the open-circuit battery voltage (unloaded)(V_B).
3. Connect a load to the battery and measure the voltage again (loaded). For a car battery, a high load such as the starter is recommended. (V_K).
4. Calculate the voltage drop across the internal resistance ($V_{ri} = V_B - V_K$).
5. Measure the load current (I).
6. Calculate the internal resistance ($R_i = V_{ri} / I$).

In case of an excessively high, internal resistance, the battery should be replaced.

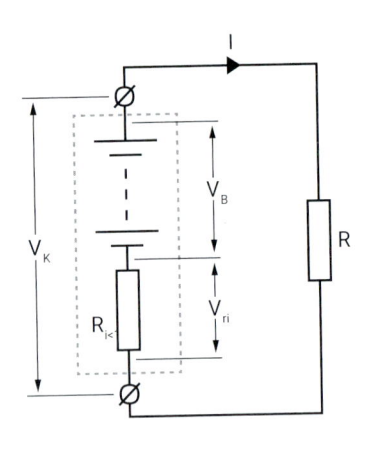

Fig. 446 Simplified electrical diagram of a battery that is loaded by a resistor (R).

Fig. 447 The internal resistance of this battery should not exceed 0.0039 Ω.

EXAMPLE

You have measured the source and terminal voltage of a battery. The terminal voltage (V_K) is 12.6 V and the source voltage (V_B) is 12.48 V. The voltage drop (V_{ri}) across the internal resistance (R_i) in this situation is:

$V_{ri} = V_B - V_K$
$V_{ri} = 12.6\ V - 12.48\ V$
$V_{ri} = 0.12\ V$.

A charging current (I) of 60 A is used during this measurement.

Now that you know the voltage (V_{ri}) across the resistor and the current (I) through the resistor, you can determine the internal resistance:

$R_i = V_{ri} / I$
$R_i = 0.12\ V / 60\ A$
$R_i = 0.002\ Ω = 2\ mΩ$.

The battery shown in the picture has a cold start current of 640 A. This battery may have a maximum resistance of:

$R_i = 2.5$ / cold start current
$R_i = 2.5 / 640\ A$
$R_i = 0.0039\ Ω = 3.9\ mΩ$.

HOW TO: TEST THE ALTERNATOR

1. Tools Required

The electrical test of the alternator tests the voltage and current output of the alternator. We will also check the voltage drop across the positive and ground connections.

Fig. 448 Tools Required

2. The electrical diagram of this vehicle's alternator

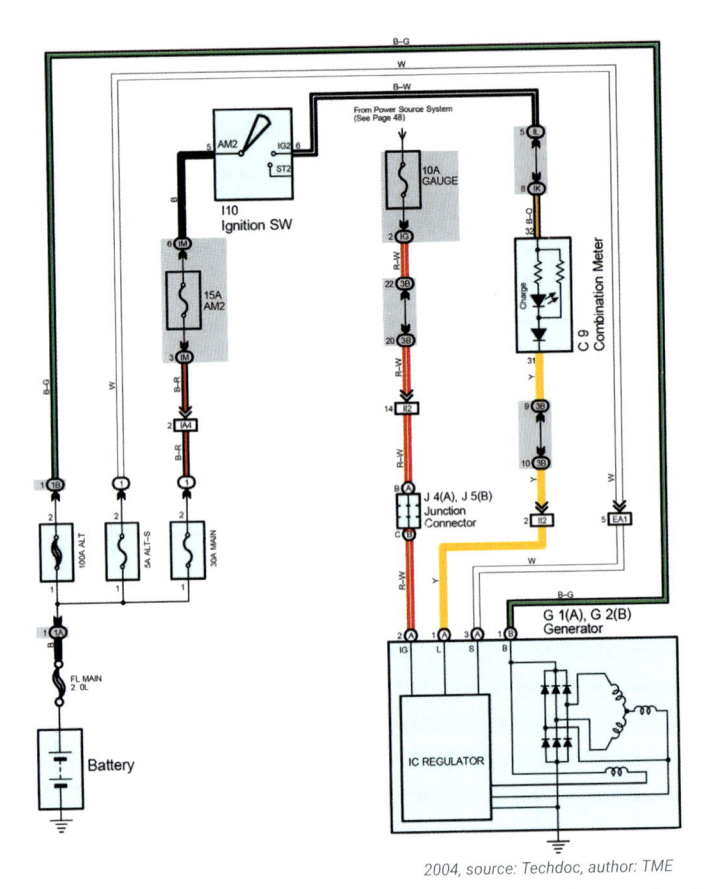

Fig. 449 This is the diagram of the alternator circuit. The alternator has four connections: the connection to the positive battery terminal (B), the power supply to the regulator (IG), the connection to the alternator warning light (L), and the voltage-sensing connection (S). The ground is connected to the alternator housing, which in turn is connected to the engine.

3. Test the voltage generated by the alternator and the current supplied by the alternator.

The voltage generated by the alternator depends on the current supplied. To properly test the alternator, the check must be carried out under load.

Fig. 450 Connect the amp clamp to the positive connection of the alternator and connect it to the left multimeter. Connect the positive of the right multimeter with the positive battery terminal, and the ground of the multimeter with the negative battery terminal.

Fig. 451 Let the engine run at idle speed, between 1500 and 2000 rpm.

Fig. 452 Read the values from the multimeters. The left multimeter displays the value from the amp clamp: 19.5 mV. This corresponds to 19.5 A. The right multimeter shows the voltage of the battery: 14.4 V. Both values are correct.

4. Check the voltage of the battery and the current supply from the alternator under load.

First switch on the rear window heating, then switch on the high beam.

Fig. 453 Turn on the rear window heater and then the high beam to increase the load on the alternator.

Fig. 454 The current goes up considerably, to 29.6 A. The voltage goes down slightly, from 14.4 V to 13.9 V.

Fig. 455 The voltage drop across the positive connection is measured under load. The negative connection of the right multimeter is connected to the positive of the alternator (B). The voltage drop between the positive battery terminal and the positive connection of the alternator is 172 mV.

5. Check the voltage drop across the negative connection of the alternator and the alternator AC ripple.

Fig. 456 The voltage drop across the negative connection is less than 26 mV. This is good for this vehicle. The alternator's voltage is visible on the oscilloscope.

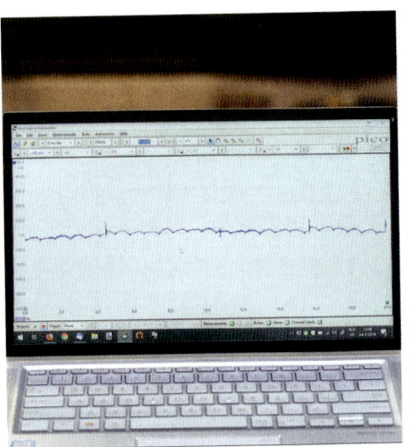

Fig. 457 For this measurement, the oscilloscope is set to AC, making the signal we want to see more visible. The alternator voltage is rectified in the alternator. In the oscilloscope image you can see the remains of a wave pattern. We call this the alternator AC ripple.

SERPENTINE BELT

1. Powertrain

The serpentine belt replaces the old-fashioned V-belt. The serpentine belt drives accessory units, such as the alternator, power steering pump, and air conditioning compressor.

The serpentine belt is a wide, flat belt with lengthwise grooves. Other names for it are micro-V-belt, poly-V-belt, or multi-rib belt.

2. Serpentine Belt

The main advantage of the serpentine belt is that it can drive multiple pulleys. This is because the serpentine belt is flatter and therefore more flexible than a V-belt. The serpentine belt can transfer more force than a V-belt.

The minimum pulley size along which the serpentine belt can run is smaller than that of a V-belt; 50 mm as compared to 80 mm for a V-belt.

The serpentine belt consists of several layers. The ribs are made of neoprene, a synthetic rubber. On top of this is a polyester cord ply that provides the belt's strength. The back of the serpentine belt is made of polyester and cotton. The serpentine belt can resist oil, dirt, and water.

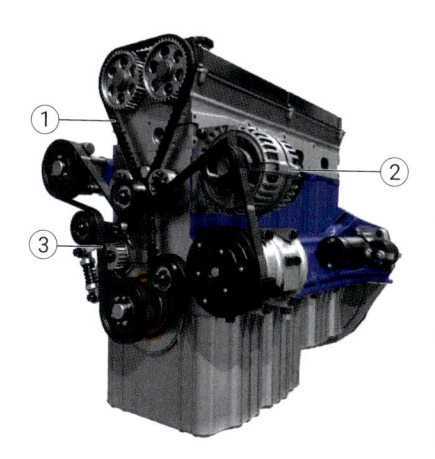

Fig. 459 1. timing belt 2. alternator 3. serpentine belt

Fig. 460 1. V-belt 2. serpentine belt

Fig. 461 The pulley of a V-belt is larger than that of a serpentine belt.

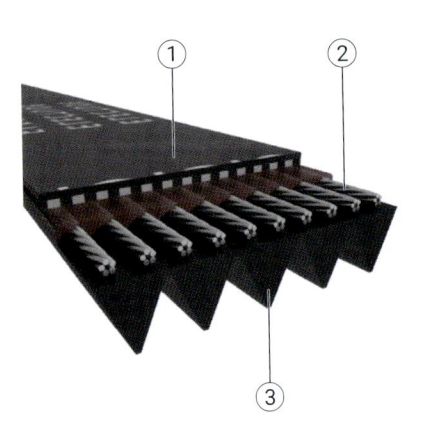

Fig. 462 1. polyester/cotton back 2. polyester cord ply 3. neoprene ribs

3. Wear and Coding

The serpentine belt must be replaced periodically in accordance with the manufacturers service schedule. The belt must be checked during the interim time to determine whether unusual wear or damage has occurred.

Coding is added on the packaging of each serpentine belt. You can extract data from this.
5PK1650 is an example of such coding.
— 5 represents the number of ribs.
— PK represents the profile type; a PK serpentine belt is always used in the automotive sector.
— 1650 represents the circumference of the serpentine belt in millimeters.

Fig. 463 1. circumference in millimeters 2. profile type 3. number of ribs

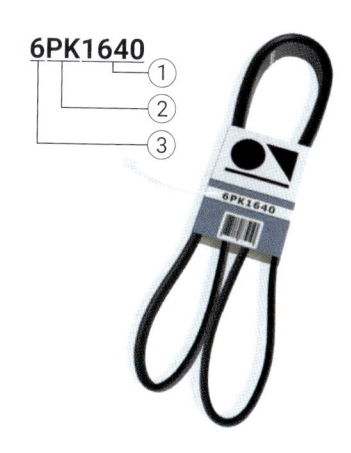

Fig. 464 1. damaged serpentine belt 2. worn out serpentine belt

A serpentine belt can show unusual wear; this can be, for example, a:

— worn out serpentine belt
— damaged serpentine belt

4. Types

Auxiliary units demand a high drive power from the serpentine belt. This is the reason why the belt must be tensioned correctly. The tension of a serpentine belt is 5x higher than that of a timing belt.

There are two different tensioning devices: a system with a manual tensioner and a system with an automatic tensioner. You use a belt tension meter to check the tension of a belt with regard to a manual tensioner.

There is also a system without a tensioner. Here an *elastic* serpentine belt is being used. This serpentine belt must be installed using special tools.

Fig. 465 1. manual tensioner 2. automatic tensioner 3. elastic serpentine belt

5. Pulley Designs

Two common types of alternator pulleys are:
— Solid pulleys.
— Overrunning alternator pulleys (with one-way clutch).

Uneven running of the engine causes vibrations. The serpentine belt transmits these vibrations to the components driven by the serpentine belt, including the alternator.

The rotor in an alternator is continuously accelerated and slowed down by this vibration. This puts a lot of strain on the serpentine belt. The serpentine belt can wear out faster. This means that the chance of premature tearing and breaking is high.

An overrunning alternator pulley with a one-way clutch is used to prevent this accelerated wear. This allows the rotor of the alternator to freely rotate, but not to be braked.

Fig. 466 Alternator with a one-way clutch pulley.

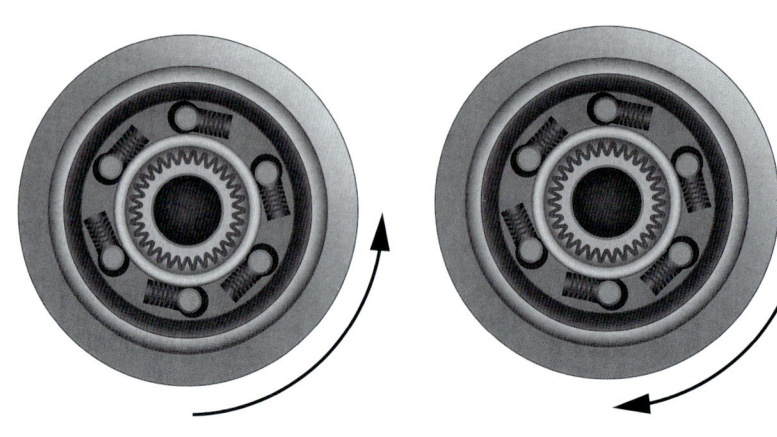

Fig. 467 Balls and springs in the one-way clutch. The direction of the arrow indicates the pull direction.

Fig. 468 The direction of the arrow indicates the free direction.

6. Maintenance and Repair

The auxiliary units can only function properly if the drive is working properly. That is why it is important that the belt tension is correct and that the belt is installed correctly.

The workshop documentation specifies what the correct belt tension and how it should be checked. The belt tension can be checked in different ways:

— **Manually**
   The belt is pressed down by hand and it must not deflect more than the specified distance.
— **Mechanical belt tension meter**
   This belt tension meter uses a spring-loaded gauge. The belt tension can be measured by turning the gauge against the belt.
— **Sonic belt tension meter**
   A sonic belt tension meter measures the vibration of the belt when tapping it.

Serpentine belts cannot be repaired. If they are damaged, they need to be replaced in accordance with the vehicle service information. The workshop manual may also indicate whether pulleys need to be replaced during maintenance. The overrunning alternator pulley is a part that experiences heavy wear and tear.

Fig. 469 Manual belt tension measurement

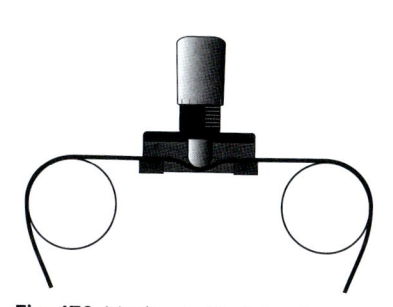

Fig. 470 Mechanical belt tension measurement

Fig. 471 Sonic belt tension measurement

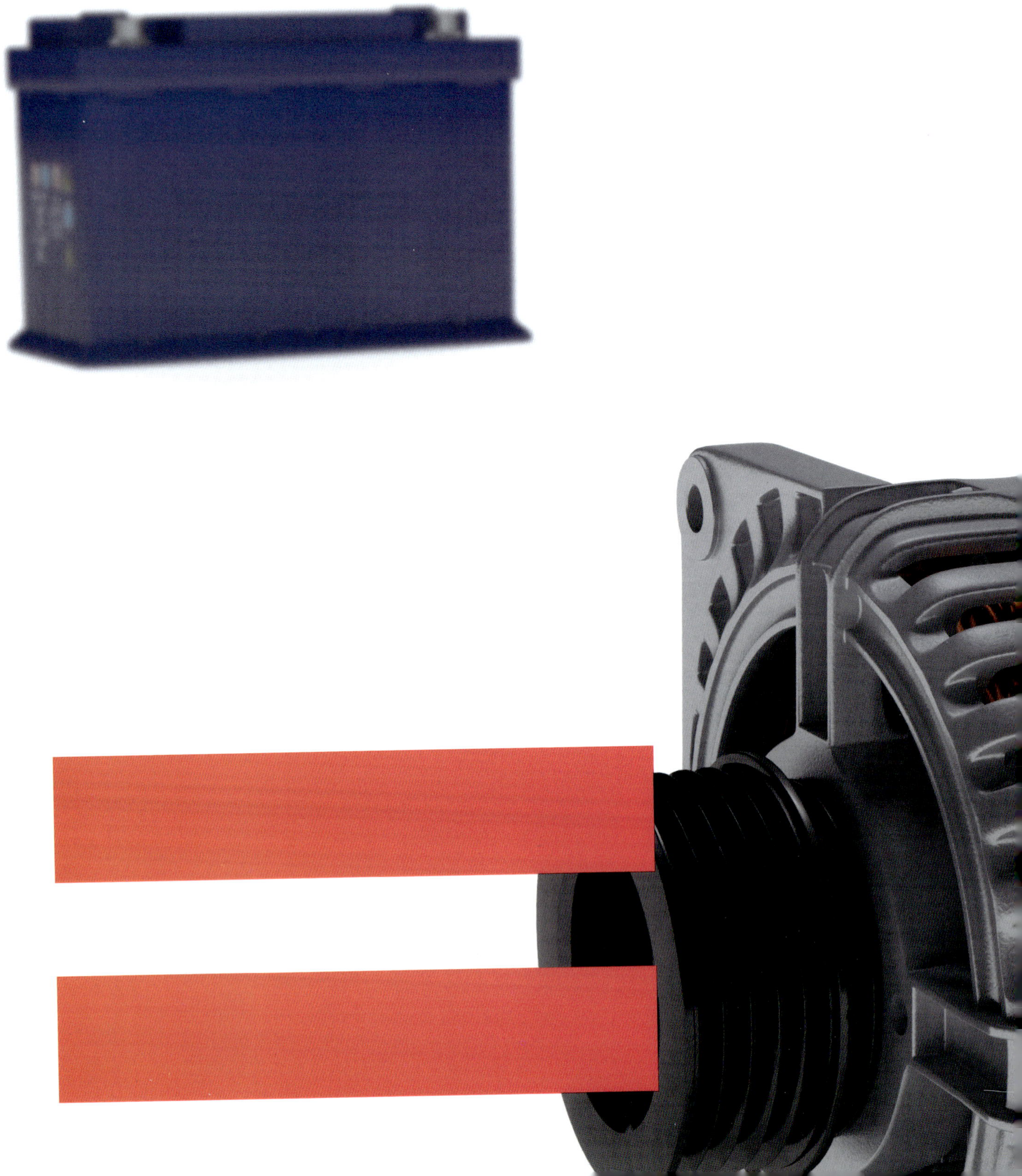

13. Energy Management

BATTERY MANAGEMENT

1. Battery Management System

The battery management system is capable of determining the condition of the battery, controlling the alternator and potentially switching off loads when necessary. The system can thus ensure that there is always enough energy left in the battery to restart the vehicle.

2. Components

The battery management system consists of the following components:
— Battery sensor.
— Battery management control unit.

The battery management control unit is connected to the vehicle's onboard control system. If the battery is not sufficiently charged, the battery management control unit can cause the idle speed of the combustion engine to increase. The system can also switch off loads when necessary.

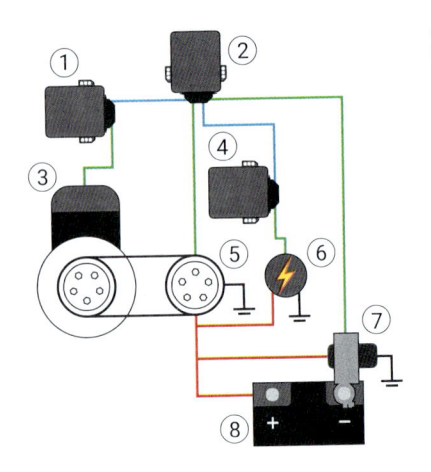

Fig. 472 Battery management system: 1. Engine control unit. 2. Battery management control unit. 3. Internal combustion engine. 4. Onboard control unit. 5. Alternator. 6. Loads. 7. Battery sensor. 8. Battery.

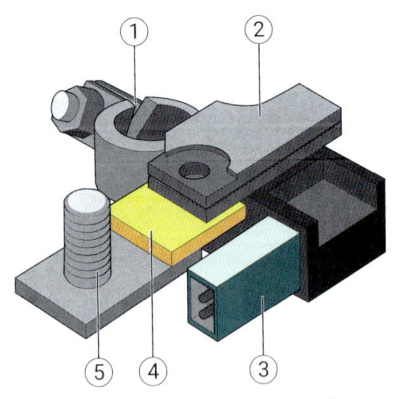

Fig. 473 1. Negative pole terminal. 2. Battery sensor. 3. Connector. 4. Shunt. 5. Vehicle ground connection.

3. Battery Sensor

The battery management system measures and remembers exactly what the state of charge of the battery is. If the battery needs to be charged, it is therefore important that this is done according to factory requirements. This often means that the charger is connected in such a way that the sensor and the battery are located between the charging terminals. This is necessary because the sensor cannot otherwise measure how much energy is entering the battery.

In many vehicles that are equipped with a battery sensor, special charging and connection points can be found so that no mistakes can be made.

4. Charging and Jump Starting

The battery management system measures and remembers exactly what the state of charge of the battery is. If the battery needs to be charged, it is therefore important that this is done according to factory requirements. This often means that the charger is connected in such a way that the sensor and the battery are located between the charging terminals. This is necessary because the sensor cannot otherwise measure how much energy is entering the battery.

In many vehicles that are equipped with a battery sensor, special charging and connection points can be found so that no mistakes can be made.

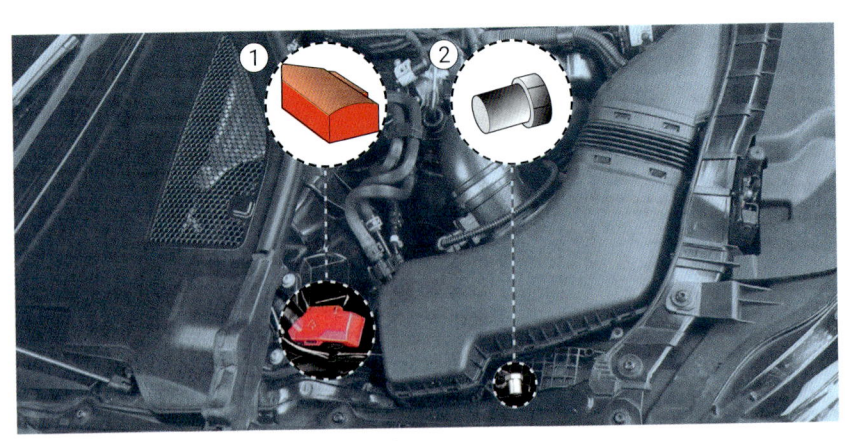

Fig. 474 1. Positive pole. 2. Negative pole.

5. Replacing the Battery

When replacing a battery with a battery sensor, the management system may need to relearn the new battery. This means that the battery management system will know exactly what type of battery is being placed in the system. Relearning the battery can usually be done with the diagnostic scan tool.

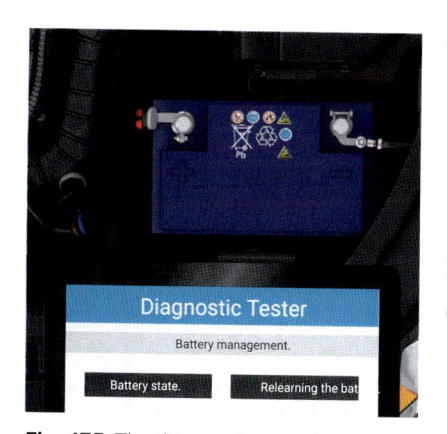

Fig. 475 The diagnostic scan tool can be used to view the condition of the battery and to relearn a new battery.

ENERGY MANAGEMENT

Energy management is used to achieve a reduction in CO_2 emissions. A combination of control strategies is needed to achieve this.

This allows manufacturers, in a smart way, to:
— Use the alternator.
— Recover energy.
— Use the battery dynamically.
— Divide the on-board power supply into sub-circuits.
— Manage network activities.

During normal use, it is important to optimize all these controls to ensure that energy management runs as efficiently as possible. There are several ways to do this:
— Selective shutdown.
— Power mode management.
— Stop-start management.

1. Selective Shutdown

First of all, energy management ensures efficient control of energy. This management system can also intervene in the emergence of critical situations.

The capability of reducing electrical loads can be applied in both situations. This means that various comfort loads can be reduced or switched off. This is often called 'load shedding.'

When a battery's State of Charge goes too low or the intelligent alternator is at its maximum output, load shedding plus an increase in idle speed will increase the charging voltage. Electric heating is one of the loads that demands a relatively large amount of power. A power of up to 1200 Watts is not unusual.

Order.	Function.	control
1	rear window heater	pulsed signal
2	Rear seat heating.	Position 2.
	Rear electric heating.	75%
3	Front seat heating.	Position 2.
	Rear seat heating.	50%
4	Rear electric heating.	50%
5	Front seat heating.	50%
	Rear seat heating.	Position 1.
6	Rear electric heating.	25%
	Heated steering wheel.	50%
7	Rear electric heating.	off
	Mirror heating.	off
	Windshield washer heating.	off
8	Heated steering wheel.	off
9	Front seat heating.	off
	Rear seat heating.	off
10	rear window heater	off
11	Multimedia system.	Max. 30 A.

Fig. 476 Possibilities for reducing energy consumption.

Reducing or switching off electrically heated components is the first step. The measures are taken in the order shown. When the battery's State of Charge returns to normal range and the alternator load has decreased, then it switches over to the "normal" control.

Specifically switching comfort loads off and on saves energy and reduces the load on the intelligent charging system. This also applies to control units, of course. Functions that are not being used while driving can be turned off. This is also referred to as a selective sub-operation. Some examples include trailer lights (if no trailer is coupled) or electric parking heaters (at high outside temperatures).

The energy management control unit determines the partial operation status on the basis of various parameters, such as vehicle status and required functions. Control units that are not needed are notified via the network to enter sleep mode. However, the receiver module in the control unit remains active, as does communication from other control units on the same network. If a "wake up" message is sent over the network for the relevant control unit, the control unit becomes active again.

2. Power Mode Management

The ignition switch of a traditional car has three positions:
— Position 0: Car off.
— Position 1: Accessories on.
— Position 2: Ignition on/engine on.

There are several modes of operation a vehicle can operate in. Typically, the driver chooses which mode the vehicle should be in. If the occupants of the vehicle want to remain in the car to work or to wait for something, then they will need to choose position 0, 1 or 2 on the ignition switch.

In position 0, the car is off and no accessory or comfort functions can be used. In position 1, you can use the radio, for example, but the question is whether there are enough accessory or comfort functions to allow you to stay in the car for a longer period of time. In position 2, all functions work, but there is now a high discharge current and the engine may need to idle for a long time.
The three fixed states do not optimally meet the wishes and needs of the occupants.

Another way to optimize energy management is called power mode management. It is important that the occupants always perceive that vehicle is in the correct mode. Power modes are not manually selected by the driver, but are automatically chosen via the driver-oriented power mode management software.

A vehicle with power mode management can operate in three power modes:
— **Parked:**
  — Functions of the car are switched off.
  — There are no occupants in the car.
  — The car is locked.
  — The car has not been used for some time.
— **Occupied:**
  — Stationary functions are enabled.

- The car is not ready to drive.
- There are occupants in the car.
- **Driving:**
  - All functions in the car work.
  - The car is ready to drive.
  - There are occupants in the car.

The power mode management system switches between the power modes by monitoring the behavior of the driver. Behaviors such as used controls in the vehicle, opening and/or closing doors or the use of multimedia are analyzed and can be used to determine the needed power mode. An example of switching between power modes is shown in the picture.

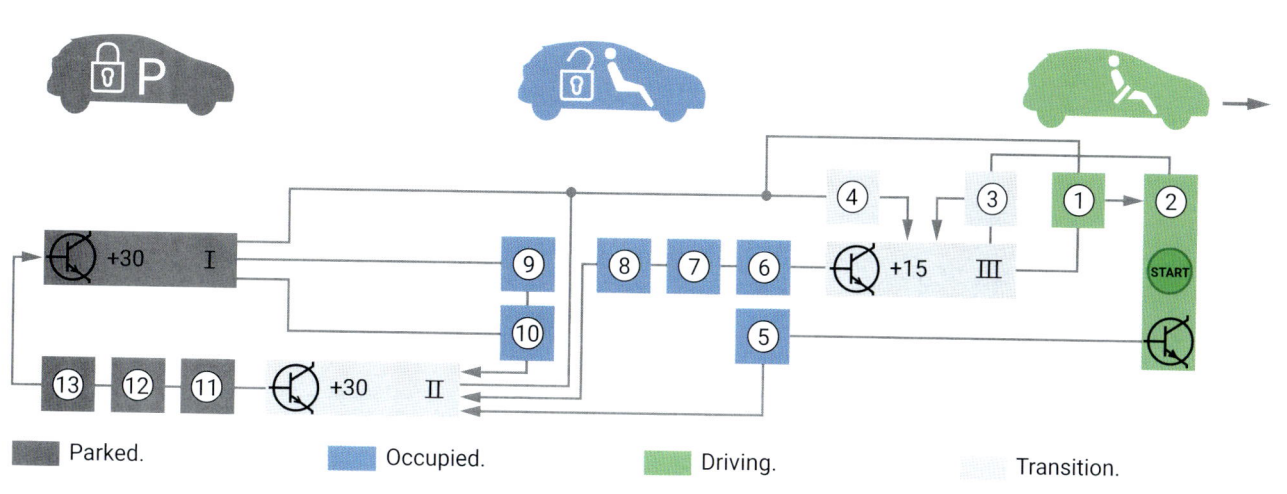

Fig. 477 Power modes:
I. Constant positive parked. All functions disabled.
II. Constant positive basic. Stationary functions work.
III. Positive switched (+15). All functions work (engine stop).

1. **Start-stop button + brake pedal + valid key:**
   The engine is started.
2. **The engine is started:**
   Ready to drive.
3. **Start-stop button + gearbox neutral:**
   The car goes to the transition from driving mode to <> occupied. The engine is off and all functions are working.
4. **Start-stop button + valid key:**
   All functions start working, the car leaves occupied mode and enters the transition from occupied to <> driving.
5. **Start-stop button with engine running:**
   The engine stops. The car goes directly from driving mode to occupied mode.

6 / 7 / 8. Remove driver's seat belt + open driver's door + start/stop button.

Transition from driving mode to <> occupied mode. Occupied mode is activated. Stationary functions are activated.

9. Using the key (open):

Occupied mode is activated from parking mode.

10. Opening the driver's door with keyless entry:

Occupancy mode is activated from Parking mode.

11. Using the key (close):

Parking mode is switched on. Service and comfort functions are switched off.

12. Ten minutes of inactivity:

Parking mode is switched on. Service and comfort functions are switched off.

13. Holding down the off button on the multimedia system:

Parking mode is switched on. Service and comfort functions are switched off.

After the car has been turned off, it automatically goes into occupied mode. When leaving the car, it remains in occupied mode. Parking mode starts when the driver locks the car or after ten minutes of inactivity. The required electrical energy comes from the battery.

Certain settings can often be changed via the vehicle menu. For example, the direct switch from occupied mode to parking mode. This is adjustable in the "doors/ignition key" menu. Activating this option means the car mode switches directly to parking after the driver's door is opened, saving energy.

Doors/Key

- [ ] Relock automatically
- [ ] Lock after pulling away
- [x] **Unlock at end of journey**
- [x] **Switch off after door opening**
- [ ] Flash for lock/unlock

Fig. 478 Doors/ignition key menu.

3. Key-Off Current Drain

The electrical current that is drawn from the battery during the car's "off period" is called key-off current drain. The current draw needs to be low enough to ensure a subsequent engine start. Key-off currents of approximately 10 mA to 25 mA are normal values. When the key-off current exceeds a maximum value of 80 mA, for example, an "increased battery discharge when stationary" error message is registered in the energy management system's fault memory and displayed via the multimedia system. A subsequent engine start can no longer be guaranteed. If the car is equipped with telematics services and the owner has a subscription, then a message is sent from the car to the dealer. The dealer can then contact the car owner to make an appointment. The driver can also contact the dealer directly, based on the message in the multimedia system.

Key-off current is measured directly on the battery by the battery monitor sensor, and the readings are stored in memory. The readings begin a few minutes after the car is completely at rest and lasts until the ignition key is turned on again. The key-off current draw can be measured directly if there is a suspicion of excessive power consumption.

The minimum key-off current drain is not immediately reached after the car is switched off. Power consumption decreases in phases following the consumer shutdown protocol.

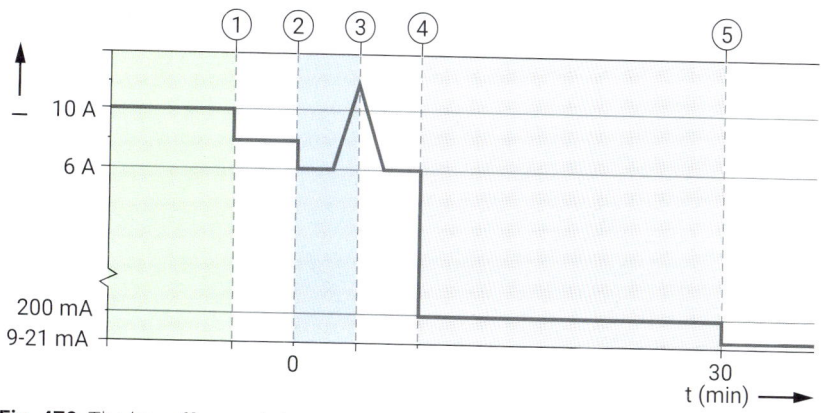

Fig. 479 The key-off current decreases in phases.

1. The start-stop button is operated causing the engine to stop, the car goes to the transition from driving mode to occupied mode.

2. The car enters the occupied mode, in which stationary service and comfort functions work.
3. The car is locked.
4. When you use the key (lock), the car enters parking mode and service and comfort functions are deactivated.
5. Consumer shutdown comes to an end and all consumers are in sleep mode (idle).

ENERGY MANAGEMENT DIAGNOSIS

1. Introduction

Diagnosing a car equipped with an energy management system can be quite a task due to the complexity of the system. It is therefore important to work systematically when dealing with a complaint. Knowledge of the system and the influence on the functioning of (sub)systems and the car as a whole is essential. A car that won't start is a familiar complaint for every workshop. This is annoying for the customer and difficult for the technician in charge of the diagnosis, especially if the usual causes are ruled out or if there is a repeated complaint. Problems related to the energy management system can be a reason for this problem. But how to diagnose this?

PLEASE NOTE The diagnosis options differ depending on the make, type and year of a car. The described diagnostic options are therefore examples.

Fig. 480 Deactivation/activation of the intelligent alternator control.

2. Intelligent Charging System

An energy management system uses an intelligent charging system. How can this be diagnosed?

To test the alternator, the diagnostic tester has the option to switch off the intelligent alternator control. The charging system then works in a conventional way and can be approached in that way.

The output of the alternator voltage and current can then be determined in deactivated mode under varying loads and speeds. These values can be measured with an oscilloscope or diagnostic tester.

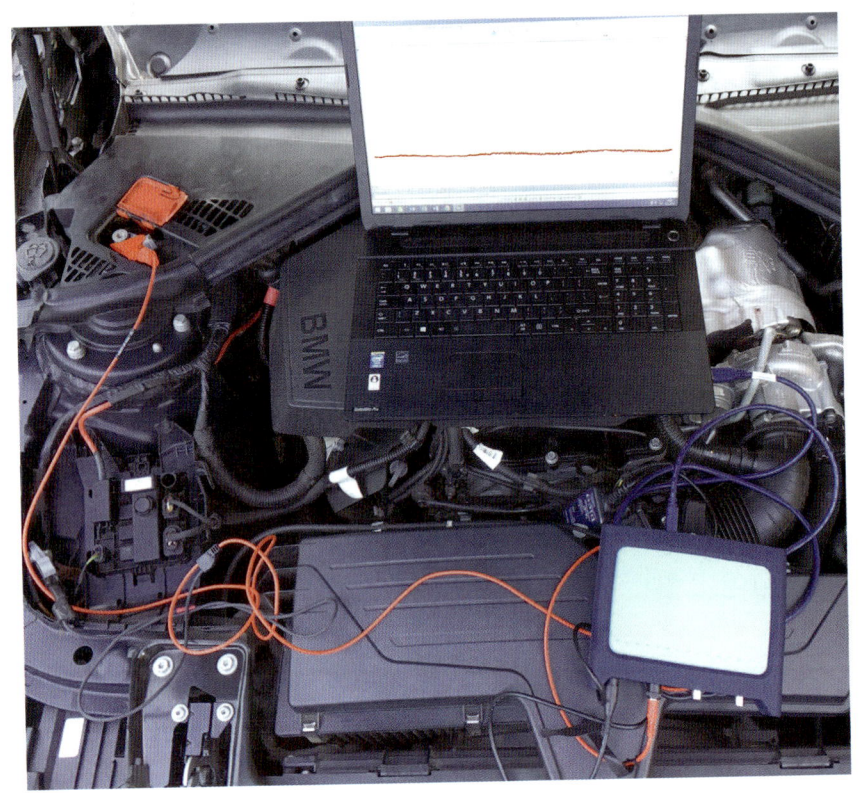

Fig. 481 Alternator control using an oscilloscope.

3. Battery

The battery plays a central role in energy management. The state of the battery has a major influence on the functioning of the energy management system. For example, conflicts arise when:
— A battery charger is used incorrectly.
— An incorrect battery is installed.
— A battery is not registered correctly after replacement.
— A battery becomes defective or very old.

The above points must be taken into account during maintenance checks. If there is a malfunction, it is important to check these points. A diagnostic tester can be used to find information about the specified and registered battery. In this case, the manufacturer specified an AGM battery with a capacity of 105 Ah. This should also be the type that is registered in the system, but in such a situation it is still important to check this data matches up with the actual installed battery. The specified, registered and installed battery should be the same.

In addition to information about the battery type, it is also possible to find out when the battery was last replaced and check the current SOC (State of Charge). The SOC obviously does not say anything

Procedure

Original battery capacity according to the vehicle order: 90 Ah
Original battery type according to the vehicle order: AGM battery

Current registered battery capacity in the engine electronics: 90 Ah
Current registered battery type in the engine electronics: AGM battery

- Last battery change at odometer reading: 0 km
- Current odometer reading: 10272 km

State of charge of the battery is too low.
Recharge battery!

- Current state of battery charge: 37 %
- Current startability limit: 30 %

2019, source: ISTA+, author: BMW

Fig. 482 The specified, registered and installed battery must be the same.

about the SOH (State of Health) of the battery. A battery test is required to determine this. Batteries can be tested in parallel with a correct battery tester, but also serially with a (brand-specific) diagnostic tester. In serial battery tests, batteries are tested by means of charge absorption and discharge.

The battery charge test is carried out by an external battery charger when the engine is stopped. The test has a fixed duration, five minutes for example, in which parameters such as battery voltage, battery current and battery temperature are monitored.

In discharge tests, the reverse happens and the battery is subjected to a discharge current. The battery is loaded when the engine is started, with particular attention paid to the battery's voltage drop.

In addition to an active test, the history of the charge status can also be found. This shows whether the car has had an overly-discharged battery in the last six cycles. This is not the case in this example.

However, a battery can also be overly discharged during operation due to "incorrect" use of the car.
Too many short trips, leaving the ignition on too long and too many locking/unlocking events place a high load on the battery if the charging system doesn't have enough of an opportunity to recharge the battery sufficiently. The car's "use" or deployment is stored in an internal data log. An analysis of the data can be read with a diagnostic tester. Based on this, the technician can form an opinion on the "use" of the car.

The use of the car in this example does not lead to a failure from a deeply discharged battery.
The car has completed 179 trips in the last five weeks with an average distance of 8.38 miles. In addition, the car has not gone longer than 5 days without being driven.
What is remarkable is that this car was used once for a period of 160 minutes while remaining stationary. For example, it may have been a situation where the car wasn't being driven but the doors were open and the radio was in use.

Fig. 483 History of the last six SOC determinations.

Fig. 484 Duration of the "service life" of the car.

4. Key-Off Current Drain

Another reason that a battery can become deeply discharged is too high a key-off current drain. The battery monitor sensor measures the incoming and outgoing electrical current from the battery. This is measured not only during periods when the car is on but also during the key-off periods.

The current draw during key-off must not be too high. These current values are stored in memory and analyzed by the software. The results can be read with a (brand-specific) diagnostic tester. The maximum key-off current draw in this example needs to be below 80 mA. As you can see, all of the "off periods" are fine.

Conclusion: The car does not have too much key-off current drain, which could otherwise lead to a deeply discharged battery.

If serial diagnosis shows too high a key-off current drain, it would be a reason to start further investigation. One way to do this is to log and analyze the electric current in parallel with an oscilloscope.

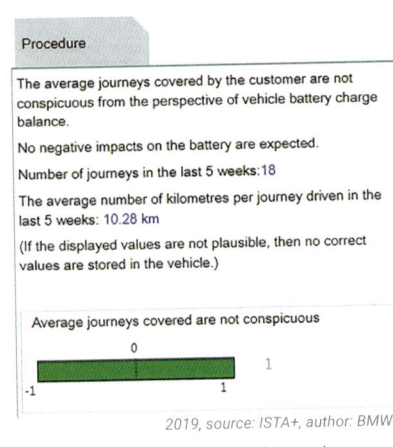

Fig. 485 History of recently made trips.

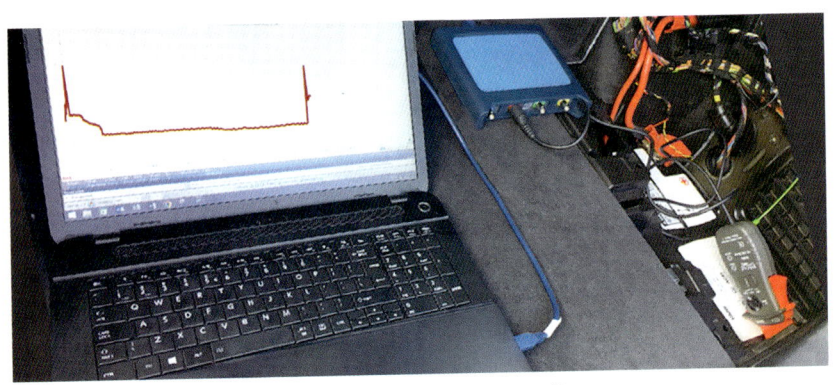

Fig. 486 Parallel key-off drain measurement with the oscilloscope.

5. Stop-Start Management

A failure of the battery also affects the operation of the stop-start management system. The operation of the stop-start management system is based on many parameters, including in particular the operation and behavior of the driver. In the event of complaints from the driver about the stop-start management system's operation, it is important to first get as much information as possible by having a conversation. From there, it can be determined whether the complaints are related to the driver or whether a system diagnosis should be started.

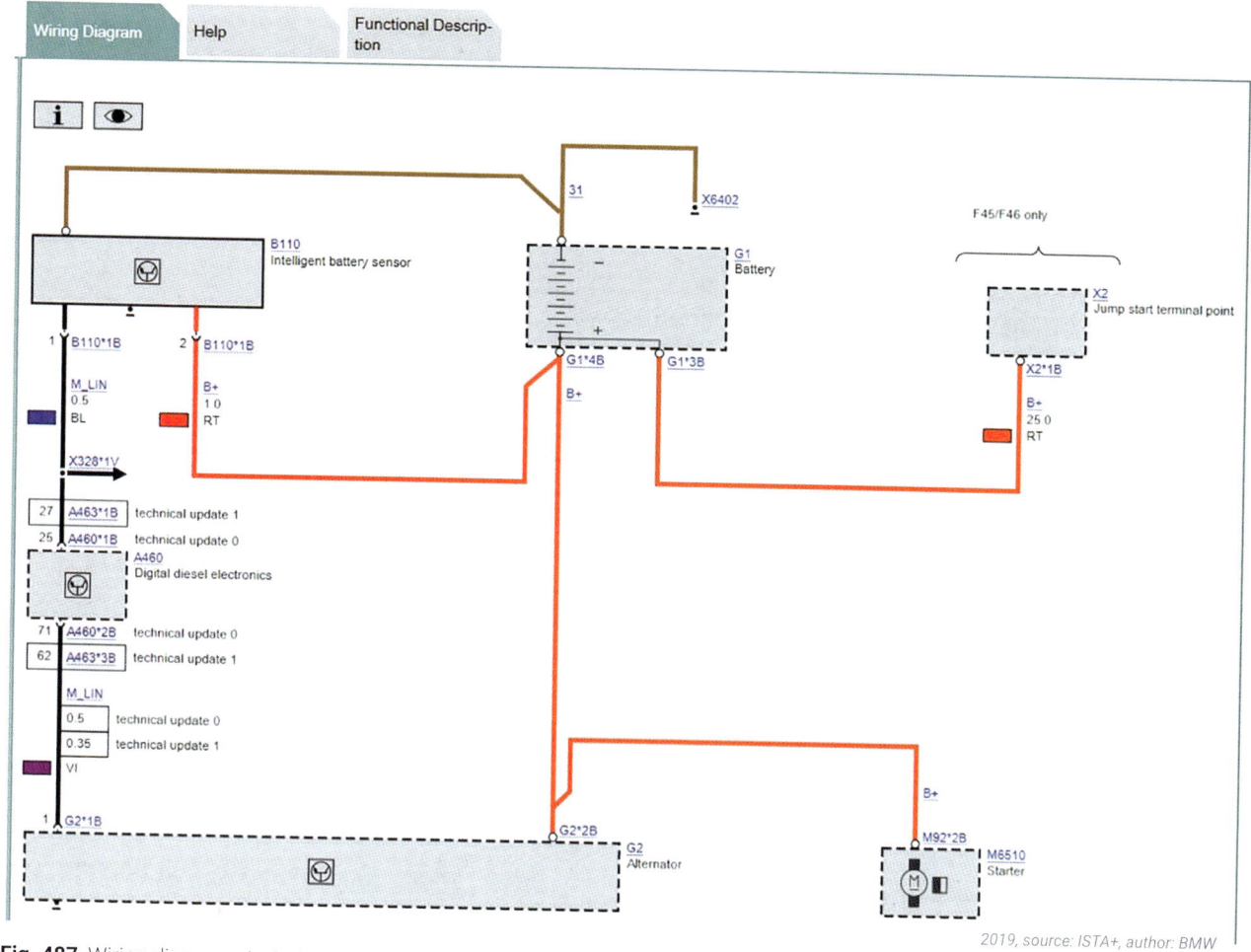

Fig. 487 Wiring diagram start-stop management.

Below are some examples of questions that can be asked to get a better description of the complaint:

Complaint: The engine is expected to stop but the engine continues running.
— Is the seat belt inserted?
— Was the engine at operating temperature?
— Was the car stationary?
— What position was the gear lever in?
— How were the pedals operated?
— Was the car reversed beforehand?
— What condition is the battery in (was the car not driven for a long time, only short trips)?
— Are any additional accessories built in?
— Was the "stop-start" button pressed?
— Was there any visible condensation on the windshield?
— Was the steering wheel moved?
— Was the air conditioning on?

— Was there a traffic jam?
— Is the navigation software up to date?
— Was there a moving vehicle in front?
— What was the outside temperature?

Complaint: The engine starts prematurely during the stop phase.
— Did the car start rolling?
— Was there any condensation on the windshield?
— Was the interior heating recently switched on?
— Was the steering wheel moved at all?
— How long did the stop phase last?
— Was the brake pedal pressed multiple times?
— Did the vehicle in front start driving?
— Were the pedals operated?

If the complaint can be traced back to the customer, advice or a system explanation should be given. However, if the discussion does not point to a solution, a system diagnosis should be started. Checking parameters, switch-off inhibitor and switch-on condition is particularly important. The relevant parameters for checking the stop-start management system can be checked using a (brand-specific) diagnostic tester.

6. Step-by-Step Plan

In the introduction, we took our case as a starting point to dive into the topic of energy management. The knowledge gained and the insight into a number of diagnostic options should now allow you to answer the previously asked questions:
— Is the correct battery installed?
— Is the battery properly registered?
— How is the battery's health?
— What is the car's key-off current drain?
— Do any (sub)networks or control units remain active when not in use?
— Is the charging system working properly?
— Are there any accessories installed?
— Is there a malfunction in the car's sensor system?
— How is the car used?

A practical diagnosis of the energy management system can be made by applying your knowledge and skills in the following step-by-step diagnostic plan:

Step 1 Vehicle Identification:
Determine which car you are dealing with. What trim level does the car have?
Which systems are available?

Step 2 Function Check (Verify the Complaint):
Check whether systems are functioning correctly.
Replicate for yourself what the customer experiences. Technicians use all of their senses, looking critically at the car, listening to impact noises, perhaps a noticeable smell or resonance.

Step 3 Make a Diagnosis Using the Diagnostic Tester:
Check for recorded faults and work your way through a troubleshooting guide. If necessary, parallel measurements are also carried out here with, for example, an oscilloscope or current clamp.

Step 4 Draw a Conclusion:
Diagnose the cause of the complaint.

Step 5 Advise the Customer:
Advise the customer about further work required to diagnose and correct the fault. The advice may be implemented as necessary.

Step 6 Final Inspection:
Check whether the fault has been repaired.

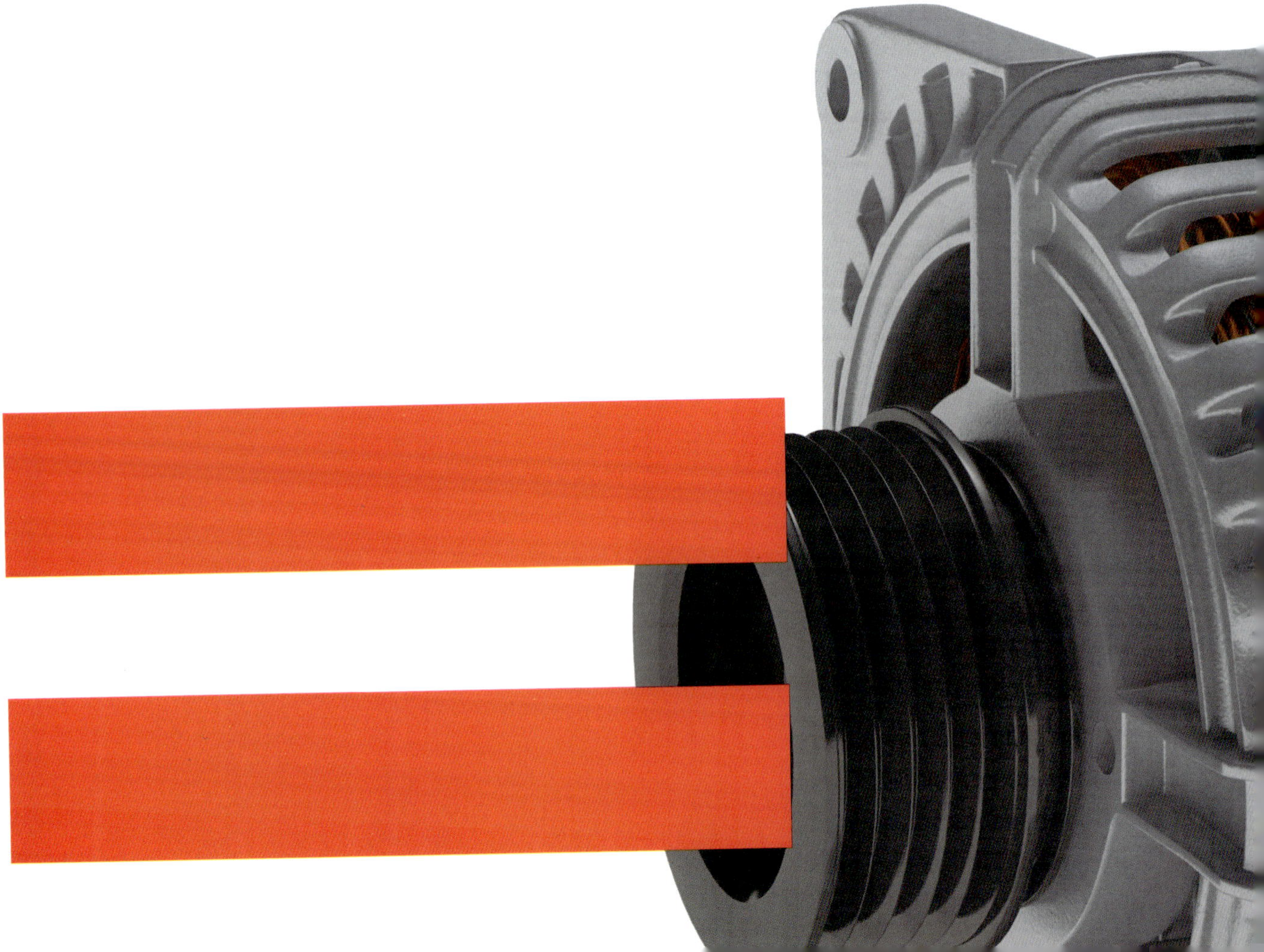

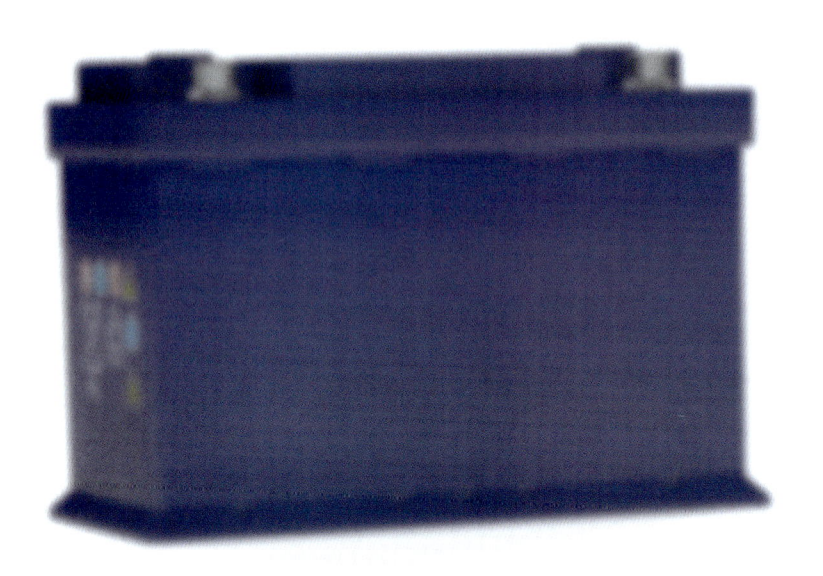

14. Lighting Systems

LIGHTING DIAGRAMS

1. Diagram showing parts as they are located in the car

With lighting wiring diagrams, where parts are shown in their positions in the car, we can roughly see where each component is located.

We can see that the fuse box is to the left of center, the indicator lights are central, and the automatic indicator is to the right of center. These components are probably on the dashboard. Switches S1 and S2 are in front, so they will probably be at the steering wheel.

We can also see that the battery is right at the rear. This will probably be under the back seat.

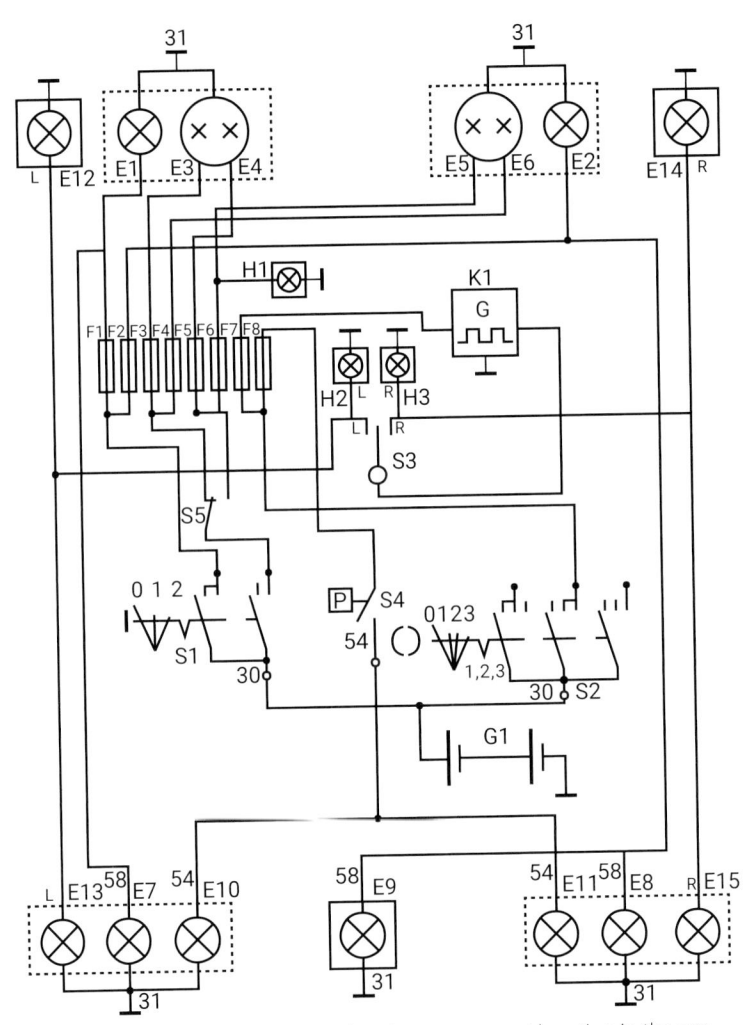

Fig. 488 Lighting wiring diagram also showing component location in the car

E1	Sidelight left	E12	Turn signal left front	F8	Fuse brake lights
E2	Sidelight right	E13	Turn signal left rear	G1	Battery
E3	Low beam left	E14	Turn signal right front	H1	High beam indicator light
E4	High beam left	E15	Turn signal right rear	H2	Left turn signal indicator light
E5	High beam right	F1	Sidelights fuse and left rear light	H3	Right turn signal indicator light
E6	Low beam right	F2	Sidelights fuse, right rear lights and license plate light	K1	Turn signal flasher
E7	Rear light left	F3	Left low beam fuse	S1	Light Switch
E8	Rear light right	F4	Right low beam fuse	S2	Ignition switch
E9	License plate lighting	F5	Left high beam fuse	S3	Indicator switch
E10	Brake light left	F6	Right high beam fuse and indicator light	S4	Brake light switch
E11	Brake light right	F7	Indicator fuse installation	S5	Dimmer switch

Fig. 489 Table of components with their identification code and sequence numbers

2. Diagram According to the Cascade Principle

With a lighting wiring diagram according to the cascade principle, we see that the power supply is shown at the top and the ground is shown at the bottom. In between are all the components and the way in which they are connected.

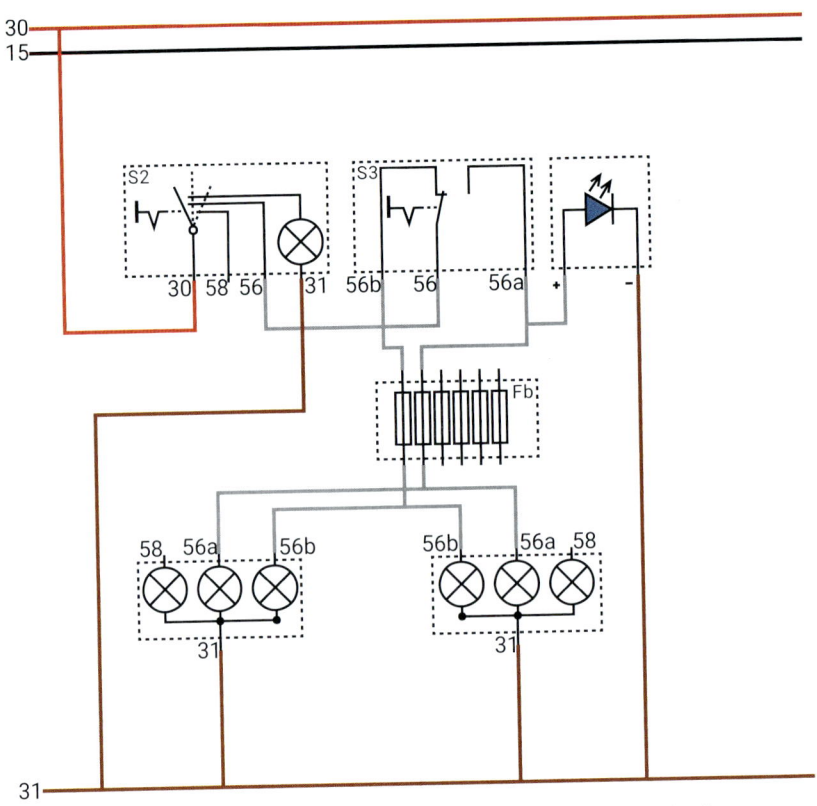

Fig. 490 Power supply is identified circuit number 30 and ground is circuit number 31.

3. Detailed wiring diagram according to cascade principle

Cascade wiring diagrams are widely used in motor vehicle technology. They are easy to read. You look for a certain component and then go from top to bottom to see how this component gets its voltage and where it is connected to ground. Supply voltage is always at the top, and ground is always at the bottom.

For example, we see that component S13 (brake pedal switch) receives its power via fuse F20 and when this switch is turned on, the lamps H3 (brake light left) and H4 (brake light right) illuminate. If this is not the case, we can find out from the diagram where we should measure.

14. LIGHTING SYSTEMS

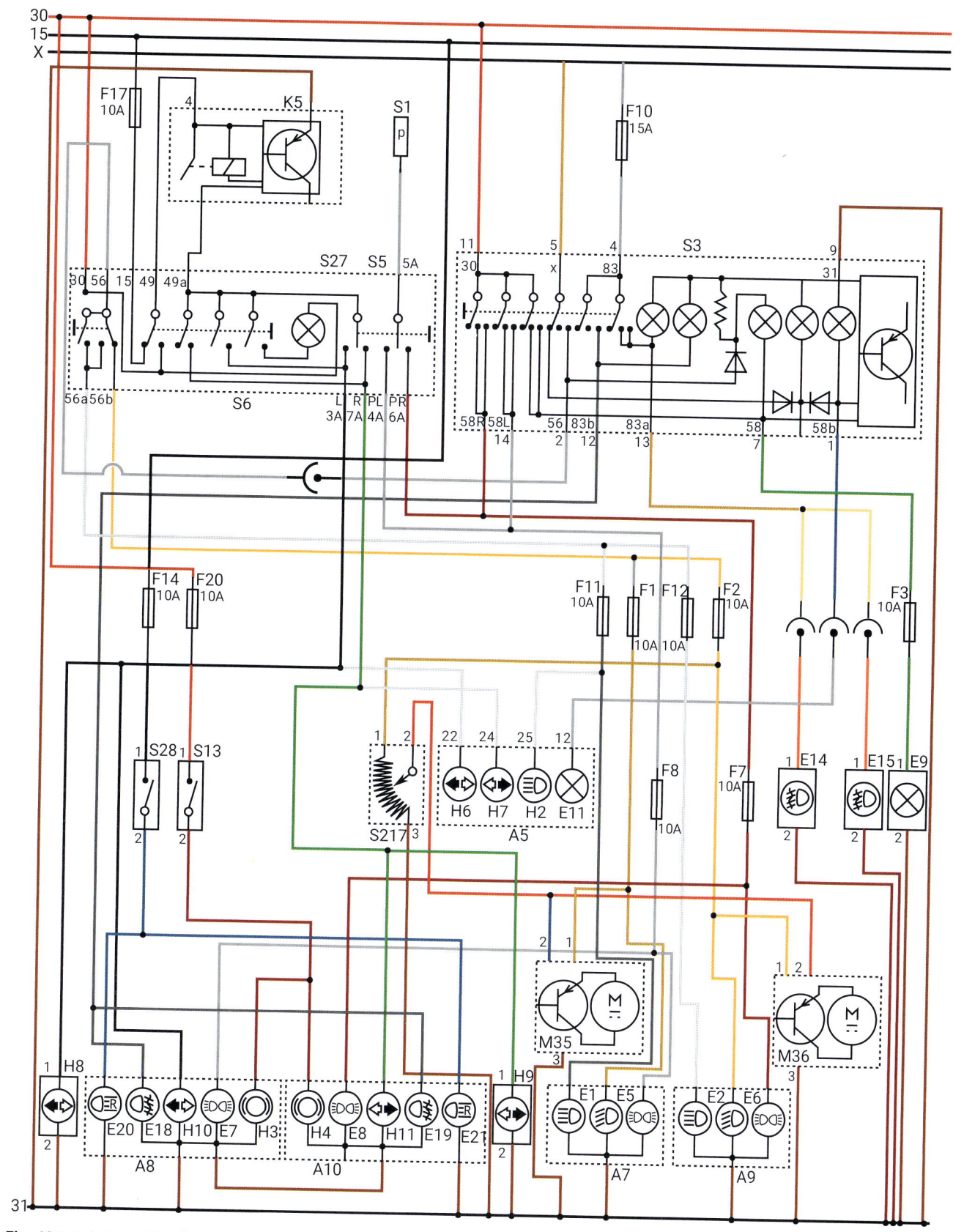

Fig. 491 Lighting wiring diagram according to cascade principle

15	Ignition switch - contact ON	E9	License plate lighting, left or only one	H9	Indicator, front right
30	Battery positive (B+)	E11	Lamp(s) instrument panel	H10	Turn signal left rear
31	Battery negative	E14	Fog light, left	H11	Turn signal, right rear
A5	Instrument panel	E15	Fog light, right	K5	Turn signal relay
A7	Headlight unit, left	E18	Rear fog light, left or only one	M35	Motor headlight adjustment, left or only one
A8	Rear light unit, left	E19	Rear fog light, right	M36	Motor headlight adjustment, right
A9	Headlight unit, right	E20	Reverse light, left or only one	S1	Ignition switch
A10	Rear light, right	E21	Reverse light, right	S217	Headlight adjustment switch
E1	Headlight, left	H2	High beam warning lamp	S3	Headlight switch
E2	Headlight, right	H3	Brake light, left	S5	Parking light switch
E5	Sidelight, left	H4	Brake light, right	S6	Combination switch
E6	Sidelight, right	H6	Turn signal indicator, left or only one	S13	Switch brake pedal position
E7	Rear light, left	H7	Turn signal indicator, right	S27	Switch hazard warning lights
E8	Rear light, right	H8	Turn signal, left front	S28	Reverse gear switch

Fig. 492 Table of components with their identification code and sequence numbers

READING LIGHTING WIRING DIAGRAMS

1. Introduction

To be able to diagnose faults in a vehicle it's important to be able to read wiring diagrams. Every car manufacturer connects components as they think they should be. Reading a wiring diagram shows exactly how the components are connected and how the current flows through them. We also know immediately at which points and where we should measure if we look for a fault.

To better understand electrical diagrams for lighting, we use simplified sub-diagrams below.

2. Sidelights, Rear Lights and License Plate Lighting

The current will run from 30 (constant positive) to the switch S2, connection 30. The moment the switch S2 is set to position 1, all internal contacts will move one position to the right.
The current will flow via connection 58 of S2, via fuse Fb1 to the left sidelights 58 and left rear lights 58L.
The current will also flow via fuse Fb2 to the license plate lighting, right sidelights and right rear lights 58R. The light in switch S2 will also illuminate.
In this diagram the left and the right sides are fused separately. This is to ensure that with a short circuit on one of the lamps the other side continues working.

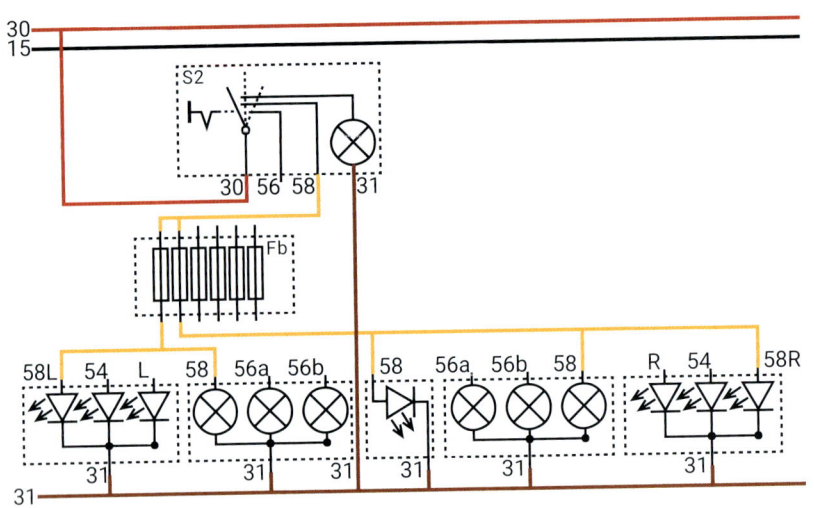

Fig. 493 Wiring diagram for sidelights, rear lights, and license plate lighting

3. Low and High Beam

When the switch S2 is set to position 2 the switch will make internal contact with connection 56. It's now possible to switch on the low beam or high beam via S3.
The sidelights, rear lights, and license plate lighting will still be switched on via connection 58.

If combination switch S3 is switched on, the current will flow via connection 56 to 56b. The current then continues to Fb1 and to the low beam. The low beam will now illuminate.
If the high beam switch of S3 is operated, the current will flow via 56a to Fb2 and to the high beam circuit and both high beams will illuminate. A blue high beam indicator (an LED in this diagram) also lights up on the instrument panel.

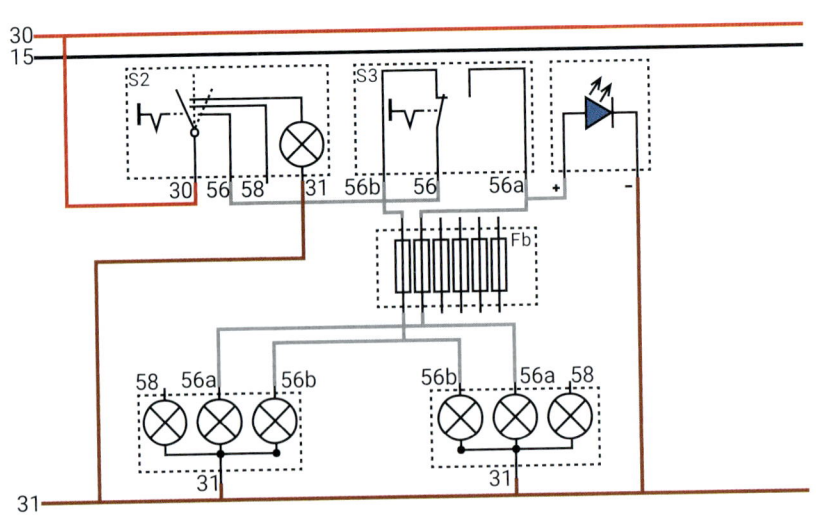

Fig. 494 Wiring diagram for low beam and high beam

4. Brake, Horn and Reverse Lighting

The brake lights work via the constant positive (30). The current will flow from connection 30 via fuse Fb1 to switch S9. The moment the switch is operated, the current will flow through the switch to the brake lights and come on. When the switch is released, the power will be interrupted and the lights (the LEDs in this diagram) will go off.

Horn and Reverse Lighting

The horn is controlled via switch S8. The horn is positive-switched.

The reverse light is controlled via switch S7 and is also positive-switched.

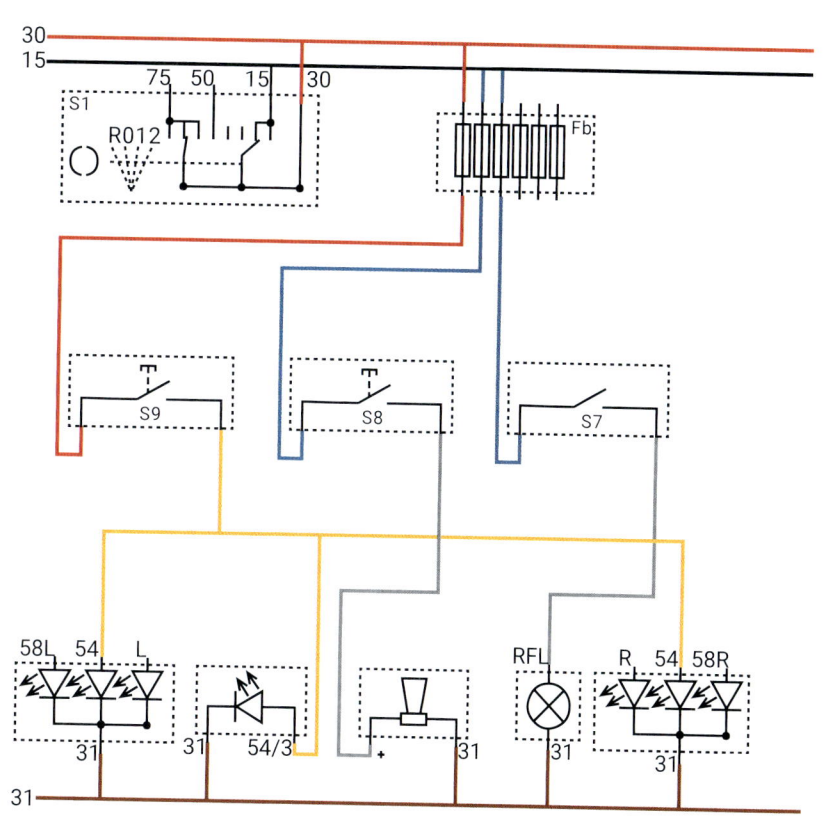

Fig. 495 Wiring diagram for brake, horn and reverse lights

5. Fog Light Front and Rear

The current will run from 30 to switch (S2). After the switch, the circuit continues from connection number 58 to the fog light switch connection number 83.
The front fog lights are switched on in position 1 of switch 6.

The front fog lights (through connection 83a) are controlled via the relay K2 on connection 86.
The front fog lights only illuminate when the vehicle ignition is on. From connection 15 the main current goes to the fuse. The wire goes from the fuse to the relay K2, connection 30. The current then flows from connections 87 to connection 55 of the front fog lights.

When switch S6 is set to position 2, the rear fog light will be switched on. The front fog lights remain switched on.
The current flows via connection 83b and the switch to connection 83b and then via the fuse to the rear fog light (NSL).
The indicator lamp (yellow/orange) in the switch will also illuminate.

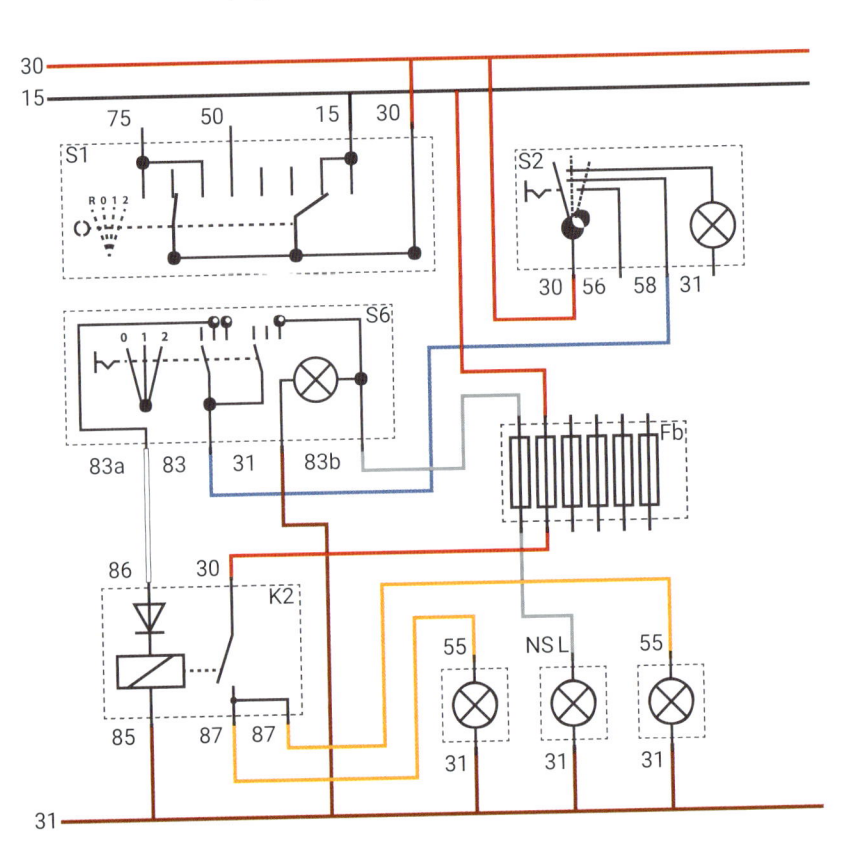

Fig. 496 Wiring diagram for front and rear fog lights

REFLECTOR OPERATION

1. General

In order to get as much light as possible in the best beam pattern from a headlight, the light from the lamp needs to be reflected and focused. To achieve this, there is a reflector behind/around the light source that reflects the light and sends it in the desired direction (forwards). A reflector can be made of metal or plastic with a special reflective coating.

2. Operation

A reflector is really just a mirror with a special shape. When a light beam falls on a mirrored surface at an angle, the light beam will be reflected away at the same angle. The rule is therefore: Angle of incidence = angle of reflection. A light bulb radiates light all around. You need a reflector that is curved around the lamp to bundle all the light from this light bulb and to reflect it forwards.

Conventional reflectors are often parabolic reflectors. A major disadvantage with high and low beams in a single parabolic reflector is that the low beam only uses part of the reflector. The light output is therefore less than with the high beam.

Fig. 497 Reflection of light: 1. Incident light beam. 2. Reflected light beam. 3. Mirror. α. Angle of incidence. ß. Angle of reflection.

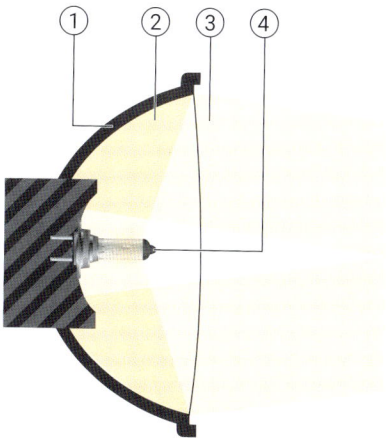

Fig. 498 Reflection of light in a headlight: 1. Reflector. 2. Incident light beam. 3. Reflected light beam. 4. Lamp.

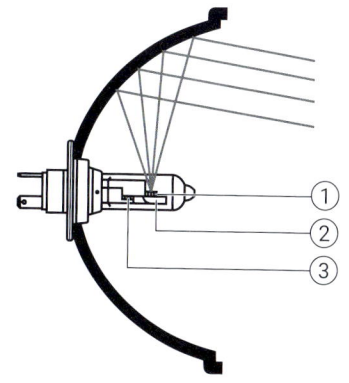

Fig. 499 Low beam with a parabolic reflector: 1. Low beam. 2. Cover plate. 3. High beam.

3. Focal Point

When light falls parallel to a reflector, the reflected light comes together at one point. This point is called the focal point.

If a lamp is placed exactly at the focal point of a reflector, the opposite applies. The light will reflect out of the reflector in parallel.

If multiple reflectors are used, there are multiple focal points.

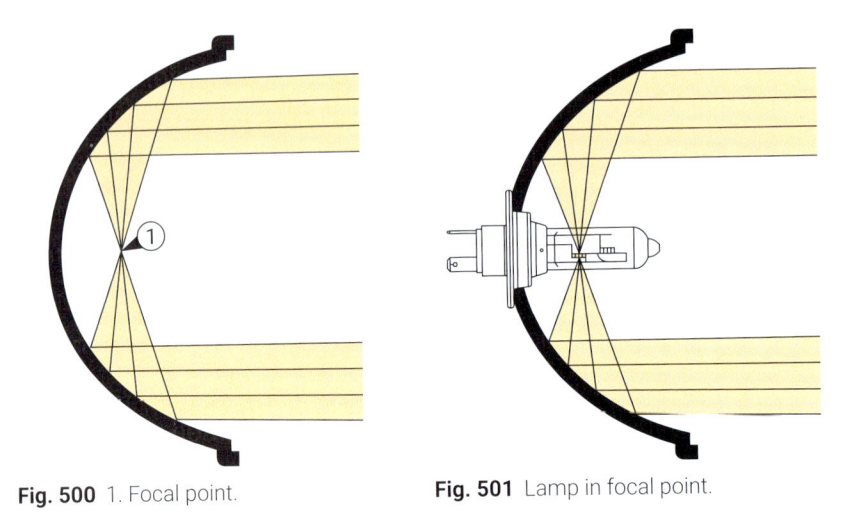

Fig. 500 1. Focal point.

Fig. 501 Lamp in focal point.

4. Different Types of Reflectors

Deviating reflectors have been constructed in order to be able to use as much light as possible without blinding oncoming traffic.

Homofocal reflectors (one focal point): This type of reflector is made up of a basic reflector with sector-shaped auxiliary reflectors. The auxiliary reflectors have a smaller focal length than the basic reflector. The reflectors are constructed in such a way that their focal points converge on one point. This headlight uses a two-filament lamp. The auxiliary reflectors provide better lighting for the sections of road directly in front of and directly next to the car.

Bifocal reflectors (two focal points): Bifocal reflectors consist of two parts. Each reflector part has a different focal point, but the reflector parts are constructed in such a way that the focal points come together on the filament. With low beams, the lower part of the reflector can therefore also be used without blinding the driver of the oncoming vehicle Low and high beams are each housed in a separate headlight unit (four-headlight system). The lamps are usually type H1.

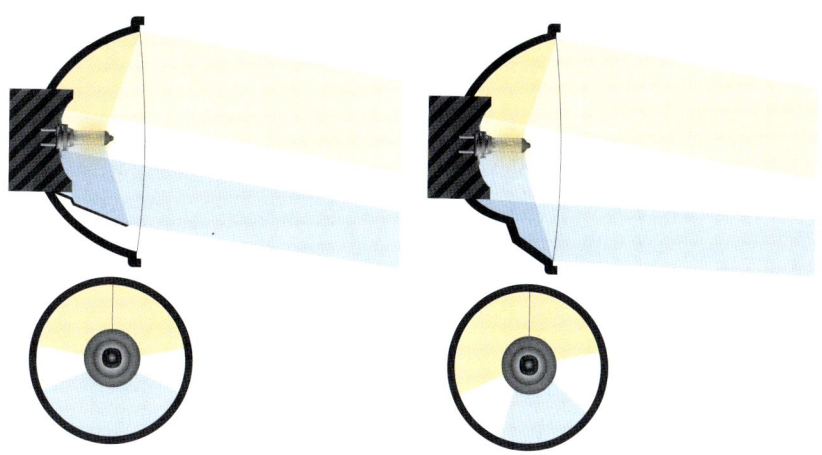

Fig. 502 Low beam with a homofocal reflector.

Fig. 503 Low beam with a bifocal reflector.

HEADLIGHTS

1. Types of Headlights

Headlights can be divided into two main groups:
- Reflector headlights.
- Projector headlights.

Projector headlights are becoming increasingly popular because they have a greater light output.
The light output is on average 8% greater in comparison to that of a reflector headlight. The light/dark separation is also better in comparison to reflector headlights. Projector headlights are also more compact than reflector headlights.

Fig. 504 Different types of headlights: 1. Reflector module. 2. Projector module.

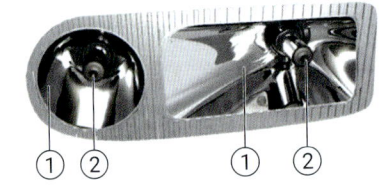

Fig. 505 Reflector headlight: 1. Reflector. 2. Halogen lamp.

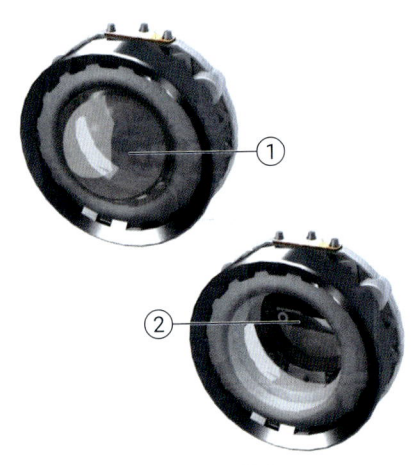

Fig. 506 Projector headlight: 1. Lens. 2. Light beam shielding.

2. Reflector Headlights

Reflector headlights can be divided into two groups:
- Paraboloid (or parabolic) headlights.
- Functional faceted headlights.

The paraboloid headlight is older. It has a reflector and profiled headlight glass for optimal light distribution.

The functional faceted headlight has adjacent reflector areas on the reflector instead of the glass. Virtually the entire reflector surface can be used to reflect light. This type of lamp has clear headlight glass.

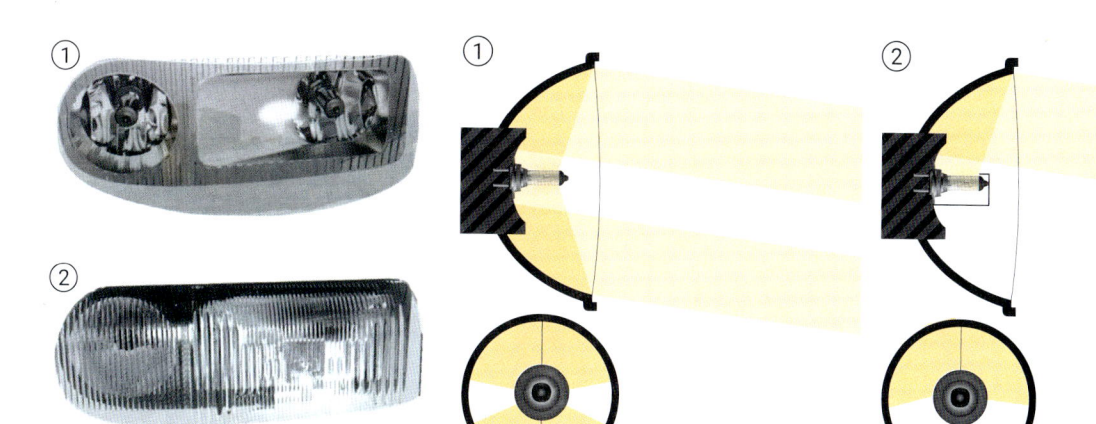

Fig. 507 Reflector headlights:
1. Functional faceted headlight.
2. Paraboloid headlight.

Fig. 508 Reflector headlights, light beam: 1. Functional faceted headlight. 2. Paraboloid headlight

3. Projector Headlights

Projector headlights can be divided into two groups:
— Ellipsoid headlights.
— Superellipsoid headlights.

Superellipsoid headlights are an improved version of the ellipsoid headlight. The difference is hard to discern from the outside but superellipsoid headlights are often used in combination with clear headlight glass.

Both have a reflector, separation from the lower part of the reflector and a lens. Superellipsoid headlights use a larger part of the available reflector surface and, therefore, greater light output.

Fig. 509 Projector headlights:
1. Superellipsoid headlight.
2. Ellipsoid headlight.

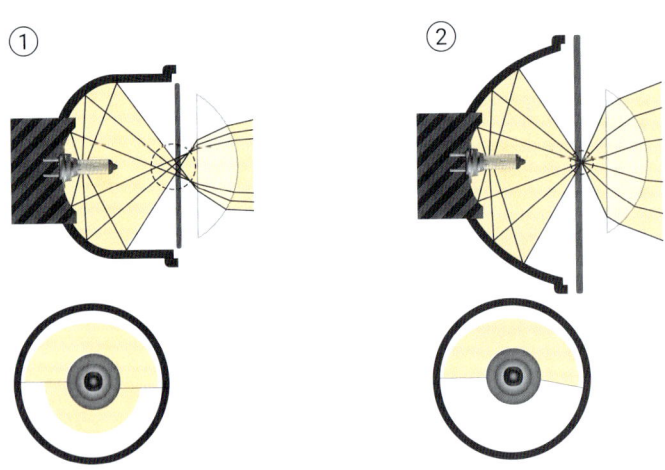

Fig. 510 Projector headlights, light beam: 1. Superellipsoid headlight. 2. Ellipsoid headlight.

HOW TO: ADJUST THE HEADLIGHTS

1. Adjusting the Headlights

The position of the headlights should be checked regularly. The aiming of the headlights can change over time, causing on-coming drivers to be blinded and providing poor visibility for the driver.

Fig. 511 Tools Required

Fig. 512 Place the car on a level surface. If the vehicle is equipped with manual headlight height correction, set the height setting to 0. Switch on the low beam.

Fig. 513 Place the headlight adjustment device in front of the first headlight. Adjust the height so that the headlight is at the same height as the adjustment device.

2. Set the headlight adjustment device properly.

Make sure that the device is parallel to the car and that the mirror is properly adjusted. Check the headlight image.

Fig. 514 Check if the adjustment device is parallel to the car.

Fig. 515 Look at the headlight beam and adjust the angle of the mirror.

Fig. 516 Adjust the mirror to the value indicated on the car.

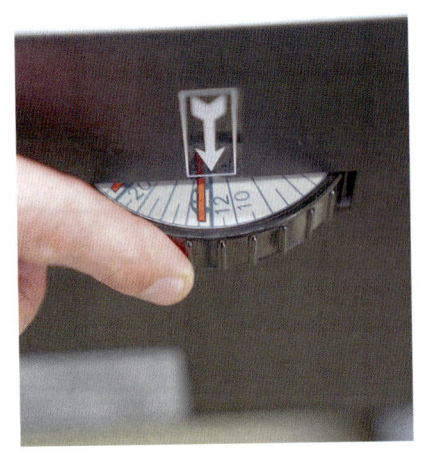

Fig. 517 Set the dial to the specified value.

Fig. 518 Check whether or not the image of the headlight is correct in the adjustment device.

Fig. 519 The image follows the slanting arrow and follows the horizontal line to the left. This is good.

3. Check the Second Headlight

The second headlight is set too high. The headlight is adjusted with a screwdriver.

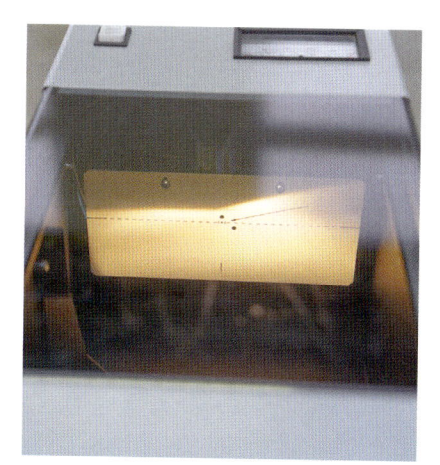

Fig. 520 Check the image of the second headlight. The image is too high, and the headlight must be adjusted.

Fig. 521 Adjust the headlight to the correct height with a screwdriver.

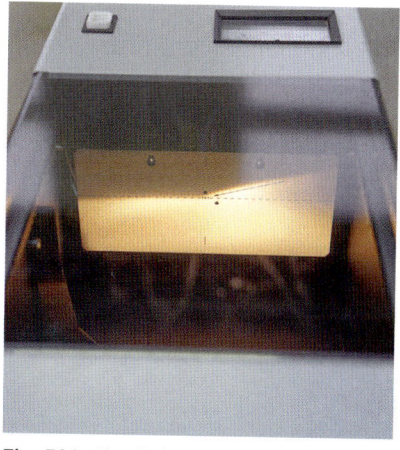

Fig. 522 Check the adjustment device to see if the height is correct.

LOW AND HIGH BEAM

1. Introduction

For a headlight with low and high beam in a reflector, we use a two-filament lamp. In most cases, an H4 halogen lamp is used.
H4 lamps are designed in such a way that the rear filament is used for high beam, and the front filament (filament with a shield underneath) for low beam.

2. Low Beam Headlights

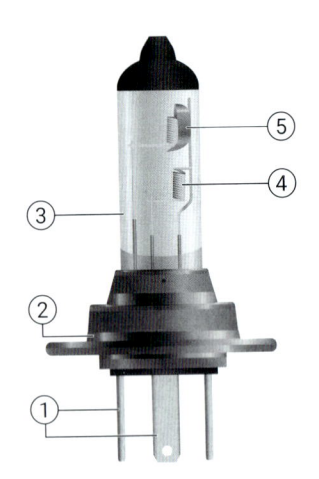

Fig. 524 1. connector 2. lamp base 3. lamp glass 4. high beam 5. low beam filament with filament shield

With an H4 lamp, the filament of the low beam is placed just before the focal point. As a result, the light rays from the lamp pointing upward and downward will be reflected. A filament shield is attached to the bottom of the filament. This ensures that the light rays emitted downward do not reach the reflector, but are reflected to the top of the reflector. This prevents the oncoming traffic from being blinded.
A black coating is applied to the front of the lamp to prevent blinding light to the front.

Asymmetric Low-Beam Headlights

The beam pattern of low-beam headlights runs upwards on one side at an angle of 15°. This will cause the light beams to be higher on the verge side. This creates a kind of verge lighting.

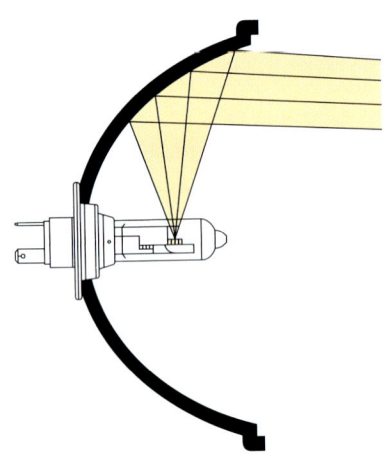

Fig. 525 Light beam from a low beam

In countries where vehicles drive on the right-hand side, the right-hand verge is additionally illuminated by the asymmetrical part of the low-beam headlights.
If the same car is used in a country where vehicles drive on the left side of the road, the headlights will need to be adjusted so they don't blind oncoming traffic.
Depending on the design, this adjustment can be made by:
— Masking off part of the glass on the headlights.
— Using a lever on or in the headlight units.
— Setting the lights via the vehicle's menu.

3. High Beam

The high beam filament is placed behind the focal point of the reflector without a filament shield. The light rays that are emitted against the reflector are thus reflected to the front.

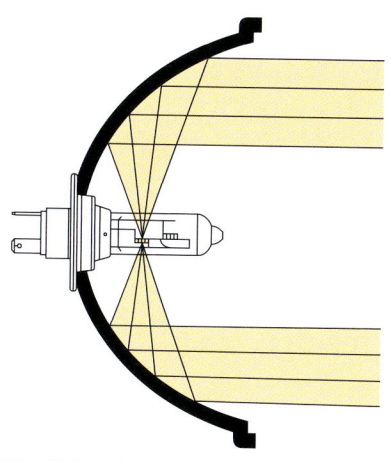

Fig. 526 Light beam from a high beam

LOW AND HIGH BEAM WITH LED TECHNOLOGY

1. Introduction

With the optical LED system the lighting can be adjusted to increase safety.

The LED headlights are divided into five reflectors. Each reflector is made up of several LEDs that are controlled independently.

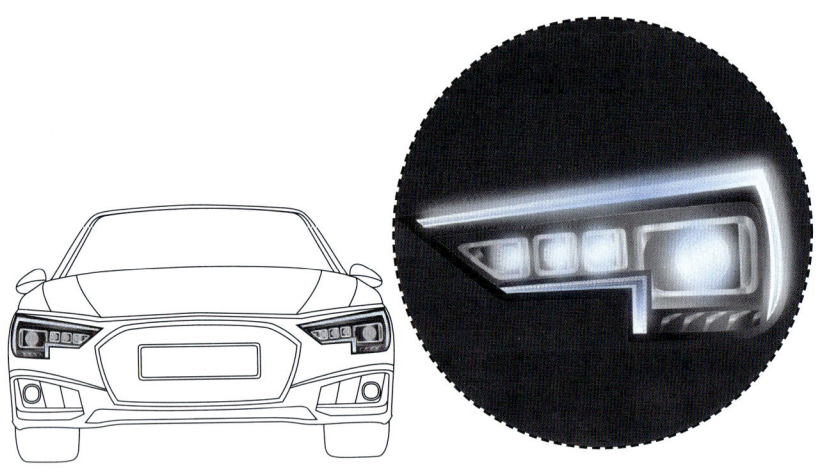

Fig. 527 Matrix led headlight

2. Operation

The system is made up of multiple systems that work together.

A camera is placed behind the windshield to observe oncoming traffic, traffic in front, and pedestrians. The camera also sees where motorists are located on the road. This information is forwarded via CAN bus to the control unit. This will cause part of the light to be dipped or switched off completely at the spot where an oncoming car, driver, or pedestrian is located.

If a pedestrian walks in the direction of the vehicle, the camera will detect this. If the risk of a dangerous situation arises, the pedestrian will be warned with three bright flashes.

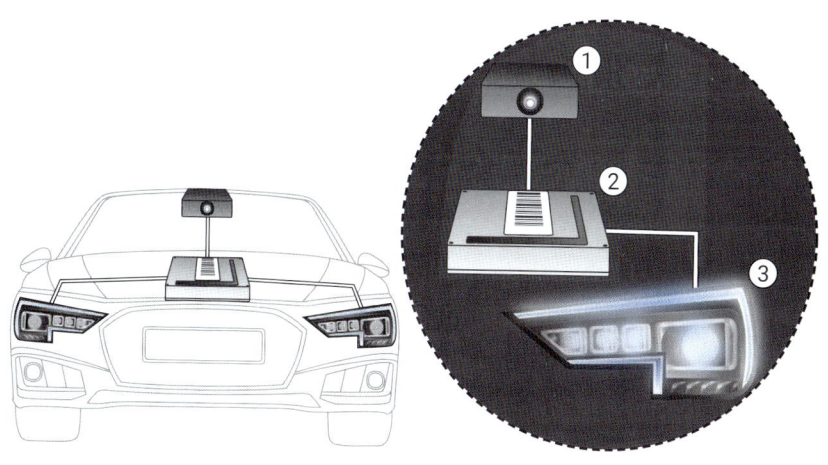

Fig. 528 Matrix LED components: 1. Camera 2. Matrix LED control unit 3. Matrix LED headlight module

Fig. 529 Pedestrian/driver warning in the event of a dangerous situation

3. Advantages

The big advantage of this system is that you can drive with the high beam on constantly without blinding others.

In dangerous situations with pedestrians, both the pedestrian and the driver are warned.

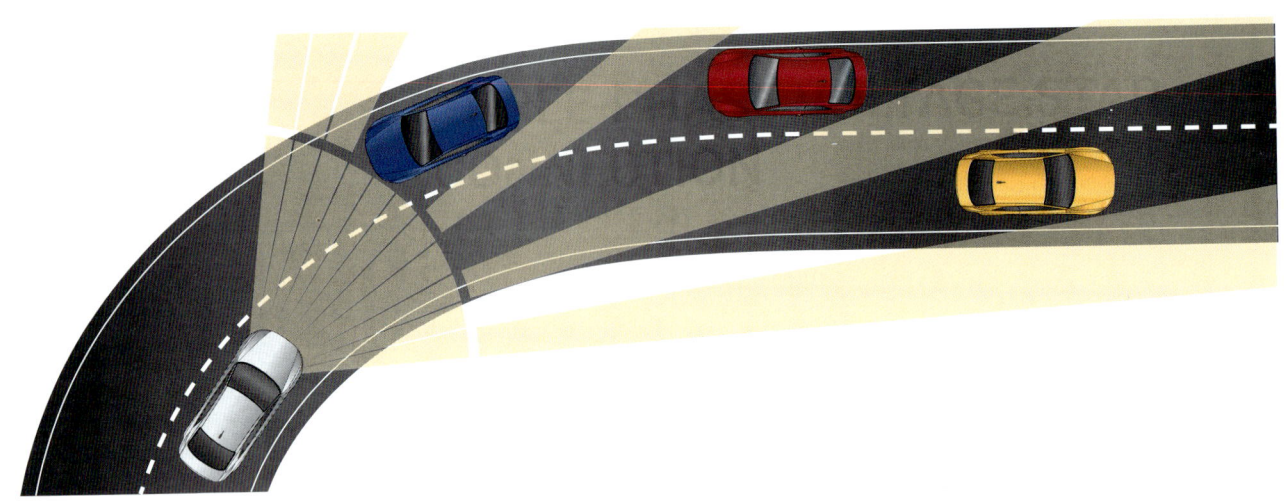

Fig. 530 Driving with high beam

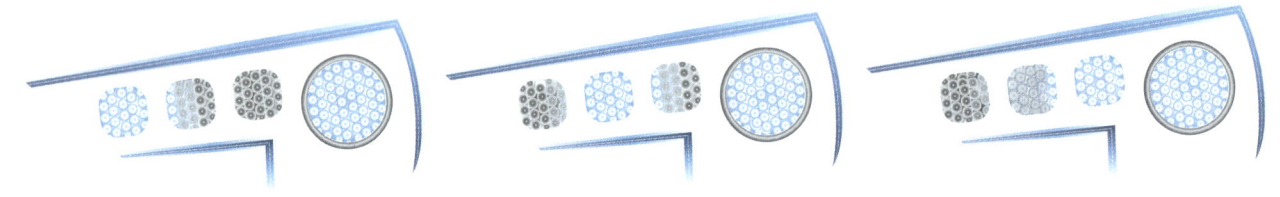

Fig. 531 LED light sections are switched on and off when it's necessary.

Due to the bright LED light, stationary objects along the road are seen much earlier than with a normal light.

There are no moving parts in the headlight unit (less chance of defects).

Fig. 532 Reflectors switch off to prevent glare.

HOW TO: REPLACE AN HID BULB

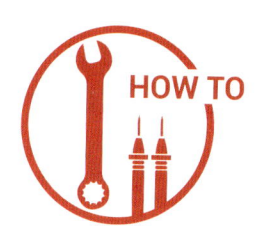

1. Diagnosis

First make a good diagnosis. Switch on the ignition to switch on the lights. Check which bulb is defective.

Fig. 533 Switch on the lights to see which bulb is defective.

Fig. 534 The left low beam is defective. The light color and brightness show that this is an HID bulb.

2. Safety

There are high electrical voltages on HID bulbs. This can be dangerous.

For this reason, make sure you remove the battery voltage from the light system before you start. Then wait a few minutes to make sure the system is electrically discharged.

Fig. 535 Disconnect the battery or remove the headlight fuse.

3. Disassembly

Disassemble the necessary parts to access the HID bulb in the headlight unit. Sometimes it is easier to disassemble the entire headlight unit.

Remove the HID bulb from the headlight unit by turning the bulb counterclockwise. The bulb can also be screwed or clamped.

Fig. 536 Disassemble the necessary parts to access the HID bulb.

Fig. 537 Disconnect the plug and turn the bulb counterclockwise to remove it.

4. Fitting

To install a new bulb, proceed in reverse order.
Do not touch the bulb with bare fingers. This causes the bulb to malfunction faster.

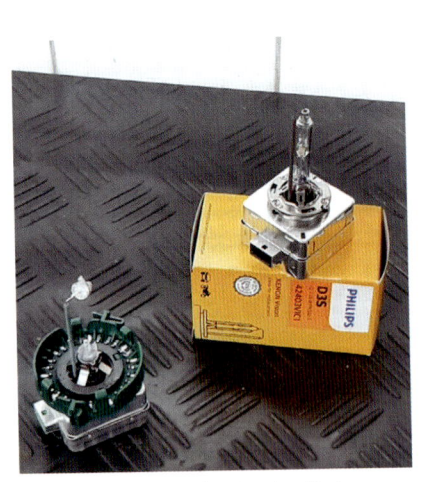

Fig. 538 Transfer the plastic clip to the new bulb.

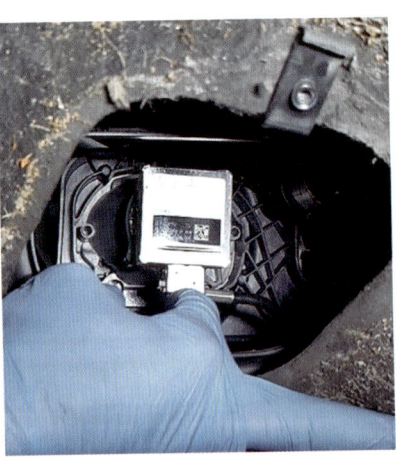

Fig. 539 Turn the bulb clockwise into the headlight and snap the plug in.

Fig. 540 Install the parts that cover the lamp.

5. Check

Reattach the battery terminal or replace the fuse.

Check the low beam for the following:
— Beam pattern.
— Light height.
— Color difference.

If necessary, adjust the light height using a headlight adjustment device. To do this, first place the headlights in the basic position. Consult the workshop manual to see how to do this for a given type of car. Some cars require the engine to be running in order to do this.

If the color difference is too great, the other bulb should also be replaced.

Fig. 541 Check the systems for proper operation.

Fig. 542 Turn the lights off. You have completed the repair.

HEADLIGHT CLEANING SYSTEMS

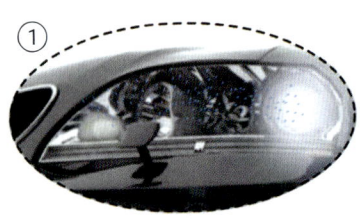

Fig. 544 Different cleaning systems: 1. High-pressure washer. 2. Low-pressure washer and wiper.

1. Introduction

Headlight cleaning systems ensure the lens of the headlight is kept clean to prevent incorrect beam pattern and light diffusion. Unwanted light diffusion can blind oncoming traffic.
A headlight cleaning system is mandatory with vehicles that use gas discharge lamps, also known as High Intensity Discharge (HID) lamps.

There are two types of cleaning systems:
— With low-pressure washers and wipers.
— With high-pressure washers only.

This lesson only discusses the second system, because it's the most commonly used.

In the EU, a headlight cleaning system is mandatory for cars with gas discharge lamps.

2. High pressure system

The high pressure system ensures cleaning liquid is sprayed against the headlight lens for approximately 0.8 seconds under high pressure.

When you operate the windshield washer when the lights are on, the headlight washers are activated.

Fig. 545 The headlight washer only works when the lights are switched on.

3. Telescopic headlight washer

The headlight washer that is used the most is the telescopic one. This washer is integrated in the front bumper of the vehicle's body. When the washer cleans the headlight, it slides out. After cleaning, the washer slides back due to a spring.

The headlight washer system consists of the following parts:
— Windscreen washer switch.
— Reservoir and pump.
— Washers.
— Light switch.
— Control unit.
— Central valve.

Fig. 546 Operation of the telescopic headlight washer.

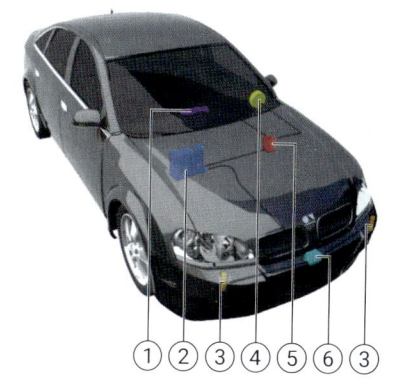

Fig. 547 The headlight washer system: 1. Windscreen washer switch. 2. Reservoir and pump. 3. Washers. 4. Light switch. 5. Control unit. 6. Central valve.

TAIL LIGHTS

Fig. 548 Functions of the rear lights: 1. Reverse light. 2. Turn signal. 3. Rear light/brake light. 4. Rear fog light.

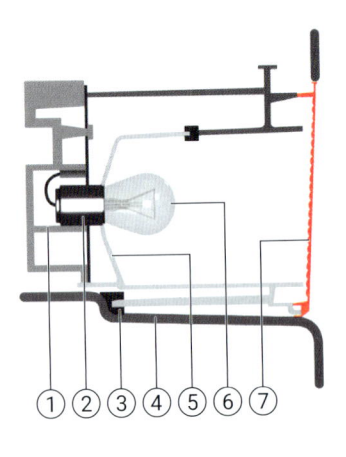

Fig. 549 Rear light, parts: 1. Bulb socket. 2. Fitting. 3. Seal. 4. Bodywork. 5. Reflector. 6. Lamp. 7. Lamp glass with optical profiling.

1. Introduction

Tail lights have multiple functions:
— Turn signal.
— Rear fog light.
— Brake light.
— Reverse light.
— Tail light.

Bulbs are normally used but LED lights are becoming more common.

2. Components

Every light in the taillight has the same components regardless of the function of the light.

3. Systems with Bulbs

Different reflector and lamp glass combinations are possible for a taillight with a bulb. These systems all have their own characteristic light distribution.

Light can be distributed in 3 ways:
— Parallel: the beam of light is only aimed ahead.
— Divergent: the beam of light is spread.
— Convergent: the beam of light comes together at one point.

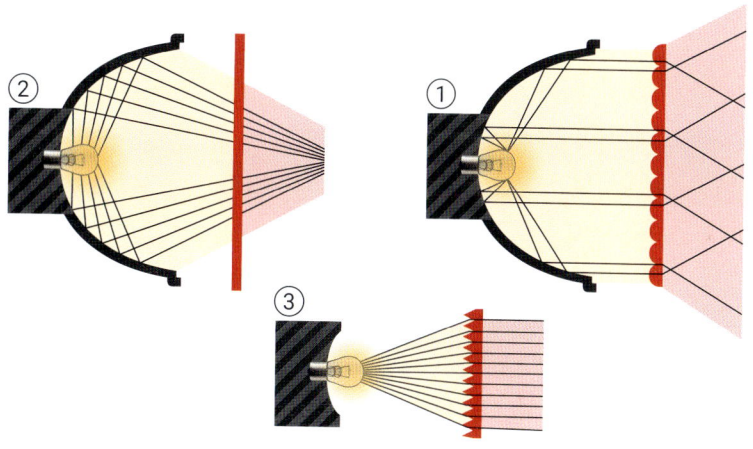

Fig. 550 Rear light, light distribution: 1. Divergent light beam. 2. Convergent light beam. 3. Parallel light beam.

4. Systems with LED Lamps

LED lights are being used more often on today's vehicles.

These lamps have a number of advantages when compared to regular bulbs:
- They consume less energy.
- They have a longer service life.

A disadvantage is that it costs more, because multiple LEDs are required.

Different systems are used for LED lamps; indirect lights via a reflector, the standard reflector and the Fresnel lens. A Fresnel lens can capture more oblique light from a light source, thus allowing the light to be visible over greater distances.

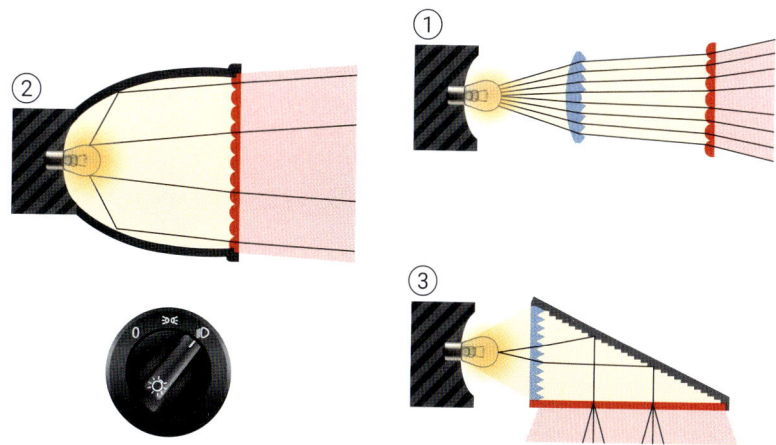

Fig. 551 Rear light, LED: 1. Fresnel lens. 2. Reflector system. 3. Indirect lighting via reflector.

TURN SIGNALS

1. Introduction

All motor vehicles that are in traffic must be equipped with turn signals. These are used to indicate to other road users that the vehicle is changing direction. Turn signals are also called direction indicators.

A number of points have been determined in road traffic law that turn signals must comply with. For example, the turn signals at the front of the vehicle must be white or amber, and those at the rear must be red or amber. The flashing must occur automatically, with a frequency of 90 times per minute, plus or minus 30 times a minute.

Fig. 552 A turn signal in operation

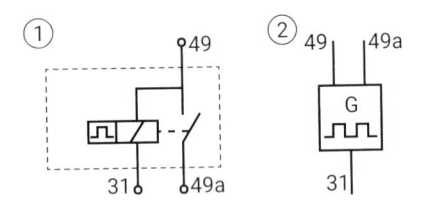

Fig. 553 1. Electrical symbol for the flasher unit showing the internal circuit 2. Electrical symbol for the flasher unit without showing the internal circuit

2. Flasher Unit

A flasher unit is used to make the turn signals flash automatically. It consists of a relay that is operated by the pulse generator. The pulse generator ensures that the flasher unit switches the turn signals on and off 60 to 120 times per minute. If one of the lamps is defective, the frequency with which the turn signals are controlled will be much higher. This informs the driver that one of the lamps is defective and needs to be replaced.

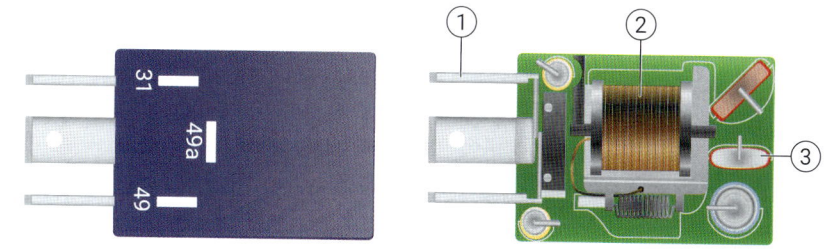

Fig. 554 Flasher unit. 1. plug connection 2. relay. 3. pulse generator

3. Hazard Warning Lights

The turn signal circuit is also used for hazard warning lights. If the hazard warning lights are switched on with a separate switch, all the turn signals on the vehicle will flash. This informs other road users of a dangerous situation and that they must be careful. When the hazard warning lights are switched on, a separate warning light will also be activated to alert the driver that the hazard lights are on.

Fig. 555 Hazard warning light switch

Fig. 556 1. left turn signal control light 2. hazard warning control light 3. right turn signal control light

4. Turn Signals and Hazard Warning Lights

Direction indicators or flashing lights only work when the ignition is on.

When the switch S1 is set to position 1, the internal switch will make contact with terminal 15 (switched positive via contact).

The current will flow from 15 through fuse Fa2 at alarm switch S5 (in position 0) to terminal 15. The current then continues from 49 to terminal 49 of K1.

Flashing unit

The flashing of lamps is obtained by the flashing unit K1. When direction indicator switch S4 is actuated, relay K1 will convert the signal from S5 into a pulse voltage for the left or right direction indicator.

The current will pulse until the connection of the direction indicator switch is interrupted.

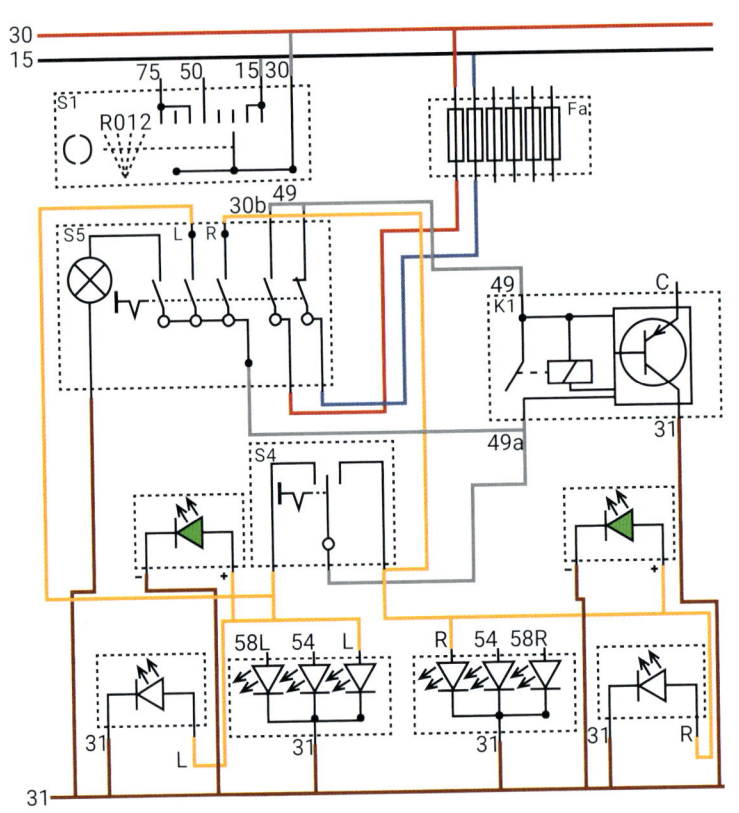

Fig. 557 Diagram for turn signals and hazard warning lights

Turn signals or direction indicators

If the indicator switch S4 is operated to the left, the current through the switch will flow via connection 49a to the indicator lights front left and rear left. The lights will flash.

When the switch is put back to the middle, the power will be switched off and the lights will stop flashing.

Hazard warning lights

The hazard warning lights must be able to operate when the ignition is off. After fuse Fa1, connection 30 will have (constant positive) voltage to operate the hazard lights.

As soon as S5 is operated, the current will run from S5 connection 30b to 49 of K1. In addition, the contacts L and R of switch S4 are bridged. The hazard warning lights will now come on without operating the indicator.

Connection 49 of S5 is interrupted to prevent voltage remaining at 15 when the ignition is switched off.

CORNERING LIGHTS

1. Introduction

Headlights alone do not adequately illuminate the road and obstacles when turning a sharp corner or driving around a curve. Cornering lights solve this problem.

There are two cornering light systems: **static** and **dynamic**.

A static cornering light is an additional light fixed at an angle within the headlight housing.
A dynamic cornering light is able to turn into the corner, providing even greater illumination of the area.

Fig. 558 Static corner lighting: 1. lamp, static corner lighting 2. turn signal switch 3. light switch

Fig. 559 Dynamic corner lighting: 1. rotating headlight 2. light switch 3. steering wheel

2. Static Cornering Lights

A static cornering light means that an additional light is incorporated into the headlight system. This light is switched on when you operate the turn signal. A separate beam of light will then illuminate the corner and surrounding area you'll be turning into. Therefore, obstacles and other motorists can be more easily seen.

The voltage from the turn signal is sent to the cornering control unit, which activates the cornering light.

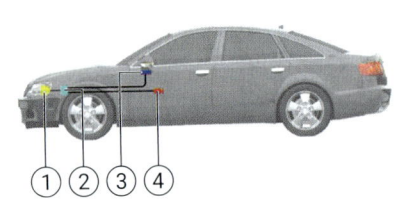

Fig. 560 Parts of the static corner lighting: 1. headlight 2. control unit corner lighting 3. turn signal switch 4. light switch

14. LIGHTING SYSTEMS   303

Fig. 561 Static corner lighting, operating the left turn signal provides corner lighting on the left.

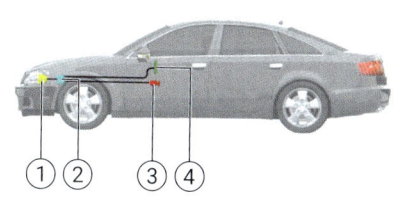

Fig. 562 Parts of the dynamic corner lighting:
1. headlight
2. corner lighting control unit
3. light switch
4. steering angle sensor

3. Dynamic Cornering Light

In regard to the dynamic cornering light, the headlights will turn to follow the curve in the road. The position of the headlight will depend on the position of the steering wheel. When you turn the steering wheel, you will see the beam of light turn as well.

A steering wheel angle sensor will send the position of the steering wheel to the cornering light control unit.
This control unit will then activate the servo motor in the headlight.

GPS

Dynamic corner lighting can be optimized with the help of the GPS. The dynamic corner lighting control unit receives information from the GPS system.

Based on the position of the vehicle, determined by the GPS system and the roadmap of the GPS system, the dynamic corner lighting is able to shine further and earlier into the corner. The system knows when a corner is coming, its direction, and its course.
The information from the GPS system is communicated via CAN bus to the corner lighting control unit.

304 ELECTRICAL SYSTEMS

Fig. 563 Light beam when driving straight ahead

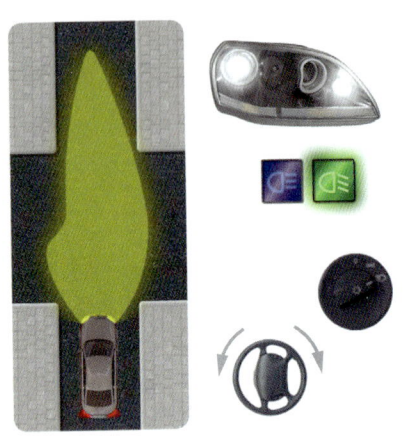

Fig. 564 Light beam when steering to the left

Fig. 565 Light beam when steering to the right

TRAILER LIGHTS

1. Introduction

Any kind of trailer a vehicle tows on public roads needs to be fitted with lights (and reflectors) so that other vehicles will be able to see the trailer at night from the side and the rear, and also to signal to other vehicles when the trailer and the towing vehicle are stopping or turning. The stopping and turning lights are necessary even in the daytime.

These lights require wiring that is connected directly to the vehicle's lighting system. Since a trailer is a discrete vehicle that needs to be disconnected from the towing vehicle most of the time, a multi-pin socket is used to easily make the electrical connection between the vehicle and the trailer, and the trailer plug socket needs to be a standard configuration so that the lights will work properly when towed by other vehicles. All trailer plugs have a ground wire (white); the trailer ball is NOT a sufficiently stable ground to make the trailer "one" with the vehicle in an electrical circuit sense.

A trailer that is only equipped with lights typically uses a flat or round 4-pin plug to feed the rear lights, license plate light, brake lights, and turn signal indicators.
Side marker lamps must also be present on most trailers that are allowed to transport more than 3,000 lbs but side marker lamps are a good idea on any trailer, regardless of transport capacity.

North American trailer plugs come in configurations from 4-pin to 7-pin, depending on how the trailer is equipped.

In this course we will discuss the various different plug configurations.

Two common systems are used in the US.
— 4-pin flat connectors, often used for simpler trailers.
— 7-pin round blade connectors, often used in campers/RVs, etc.

Fig. 566 Trailer Lights

Fig. 567 Female 4-Pin Plug.

2. 7-Pin Plug and Socket

7-pin plug/sockets on light vehicles typically have six blade terminals surrounding one round pin terminal, which is the 7th pin.

There are TRADITIONAL and STANDARD configurations, but they're almost the same, with only few wire color differences. Here's how the TRADITIONAL plug is wired.

The blades on the truck side are MALE, but the connector shell is FEMALE, with a square cutout shape code at the top of the shell for proper indexing. As for the wiring, we'll look at the the truck side, because that's where the power comes from.

The six blades line up with clock face positions, but pin number 1 is the bottom left blade, so that's where we'll start.

The 7 o'clock blade on the truck socket is the white ground wire.
There is no 6 o'clock blade.
The 5 o'clock blade is the blue trailer brake wire.
The 3 o'clock blade is the green wire Right Turn/Stop Lamp feed, and the 1 o'clock blade feeds a black wire reserved for straight battery power. There is no 12 o'clock blade.
The 11 o'clock blade feeds the brown wire that leads out to the trailer Tail Lights and Clearance Lights. The 9 o'clock blade is the Left Turn/Stop Lamp feed. The round pin in the center, when used, is always for reverse (backup) lights, which is, on the TRADITIONAL plug, a purple or violet wire.

On the STANDARD plug, the blade positions are the same but the colors are different. The reverse lights feed will be a yellow wire instead of purple and the Left Turn/Stop wire will be red instead of yellow.

The Tail/Clearance Light feed on the STANDARD plug feed a green wire rather than a brown one, which is used for Right Turn/Stop Lamp.

The STANDARD plug still uses white for ground and blue for brake controller output.

The trailer side plug is a mirror image of the truck side, but with female blade sockets and a male connector shell with a square shape code at the top to match the truck connector shell.

It is important to note that commercial/agriculture trailer plugs with round rather than blade pins have a totally different pinout.

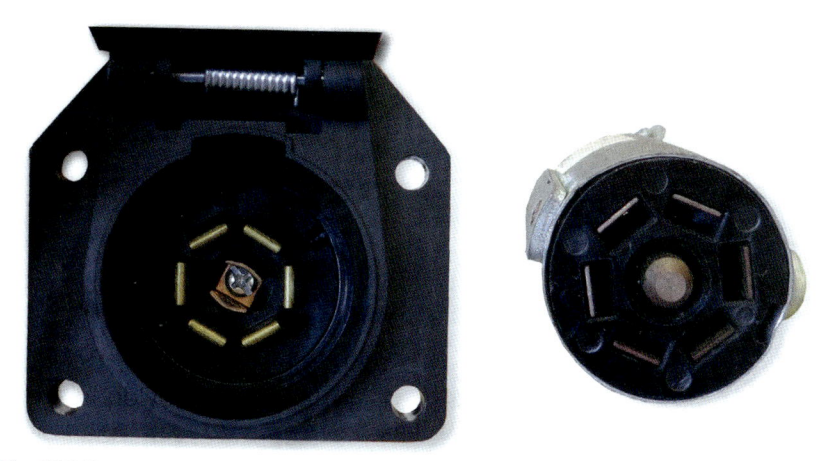

Fig. 568 7-pin plug/socket.

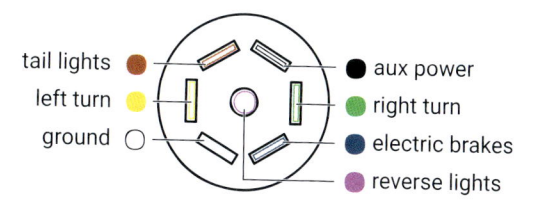

Fig. 569 7-pin plug/socket connection diagram.

3. 6-Pin Connector

The 6-pin connector has the standard four pins common to all trailer feeds, i.e., - ground (white), left turn/stop (yellow), right turn/stop (green), and tail light feed (brown) - but also have two additional pins - trailer brake output (blue) and a feed for auxiliary (red, 12 volt) power to the trailer.

Fig. 570 The 6-pin connector has the four standard wires, plus a feed for auxiliary 12-volt power and electric trailer brakes.

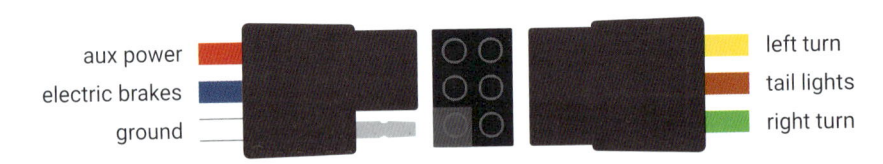

Fig. 571 Wiring diagram for 6-Pin connectors

4. The 5-pin connector has the four standard wires plus a wire for trailer reverse lights.

The 5-pin connector is becoming the new standard for trailers under 3000 lbs. in the United States. This plug design is very similar to the older 4-pin layout, but reverse lights have been added to the 5th pin. This extra pin is often used to temporarily block out the surge brakes when the trailer is backed up.

Fig. 572 5-pin Plug and Socket.

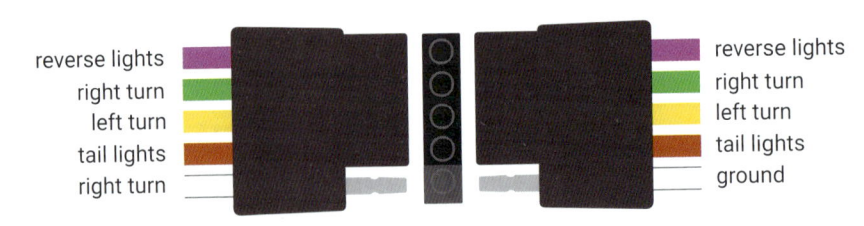

Fig. 573 5-pin plug and socket diagram (flat and round plugs).

Fig. 574 Female 7-Pin Plug

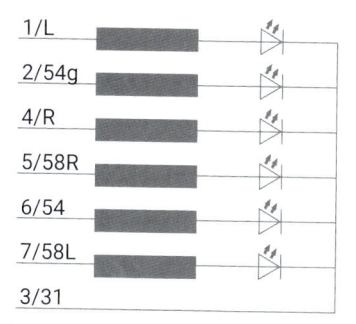

1/L
2/54g
4/R
5/58R
6/54
7/58L
3/31

Fig. 575 Socket tester diagram.

5. Checking the Socket

For diagnosis and testing, the best place to begin testing is on the vehicle side of the plug, because that's the active (origin) side of the circuit.

The most common tool for this is the LED (Light Emitting Diode) tester with a long cable. Think of this as a set of trailer lights you can plug in, but with no trailer. There is an LED tool configured for each pinout so you can plug the tool in and watch the tool's corresponding LEDs while you operate the vehicle lights and controls.

The problem with the LED tester is that it takes almost no voltage to illuminate Light Emitting Diodes. What that means is that, if there's a voltage drop issue, the LED tester might show the circuits operational but the trailer lights - which actually require current to work - might still be inoperative. In that case, it's best to use a light bar with incandescent lamps that actually require the same amount of current as the trailer itself.

Nowadays, a separate trailer tow module is typically used to carry the load of the lights. Vehicles that come with OEM trailer plugs will be wired for this (with dedicated relays) and don't require a separate trailer tow module. Also, vehicle manufacturers sometimes provide a trailer tow module that can be easily installed.

When installing a trailer tow plug on a vehicle that came without one, tapping directly into the vehicle wiring to feed the trailer lights can cause serious damage to the vehicle's electrical lighting system due to the added load from the trailer's Tail Lamps and Clearance Lamps. The OEM wiring is only sufficient to carry the load of the OEM lights on the vehicle and cannot handle the extra load of trailer lights. While the Stop and Turn Lamps always pull more amps than the tail lights while they're operating, they don't operate for as long as the Tail Lamps, which will be illuminated for an entire night time drive. The tail Lamps and Clearance Lamps may remain illuminated for many hours.

The trailer tow module will have three separate internal relays; one relay will be for the tail lights and one relay each for stop/turn lights. A dedicated (fused) power supply connected directly to a live battery circuit feeds the "common" terminals of all three relays so that the tail lamp and stop/turn wires from the vehicle are only required to provide a tiny whisper of current to close the relay coils. When a light circuit from the vehicle triggers its relay to close, the relay feeds dedicated battery power to the trailer lights, effectively carrying the heavy load of the lights without burdening the vehicle's electrical circuits.

Fig. 576 Socket tester LED with cable.

Fig. 577 CAN bus module.

6. Network Function Trailer Lights

With a vehicle where the lights are switched by means of CAN bus, the wiring cannot simply be tapped to the trailer vehicle's trailer connection. These systems have a dedicated Trailer Module "node" connected to the CAN bus. The Trailer Module is connected to the CAN bus of the vehicle and extracts the information from the CAN bus data stream needed to control the lights. For example, when a "brake light on" message appears on the CAN bus, the trailer module will, from its internal circuitry, provide power to the Stop Lamps. The trailer socket is connected to the Trailer Module via the wiring loom and therefore receives voltage on the correct pin.

When connecting this CAN bus "node," the network's Gateway Module must be notified that a trailer is connected. Vehicle Dynamics systems such as ABS and Stability Control Systems will need to operate differently when a trailer is being towed. In addition to the Vehicle Dynamics system changes, if the trailer is heavy, the automatic transmission controls will use a different gear shift program and the engine management system may need to adjust its injection strategy.

This information is also important for the roof control module on convertibles, since the connected trailer or object might, for example, be a bicycle carrier. This is important when folding the convertible top in or out with a bicycle carrier attached, because the tailgate can come into contact with the bicycles.

LIGHT INSPECTION

1. Introduction

A vehicle's lights need to be checked for:
— Correct operation.
  Do the lights work properly when you switch them on?
— Damage to the glass covering the lamps and the reflectors.
  The damage must not negatively affect operation.
— Beam pattern.
  Using a headlight adjustment device.
— Light intensity.
  Using a flux meter.

2. Examples

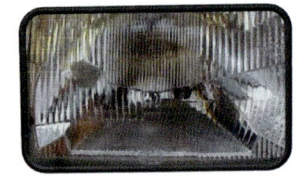

Fig. 578 Shielding lights. The illuminating part of the headlamps (low beam and high beam) is partly shielded by headlight covers. The function of the headlamps must not be affected to a significant degree.

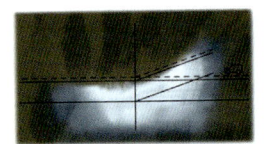

Fig. 579 A repair has been carried out using silicone sealant. The headlamp tester indicates that no clear horizontal dividing line between light and dark is visible; this is not allowed.

14. LIGHTING SYSTEMS   313

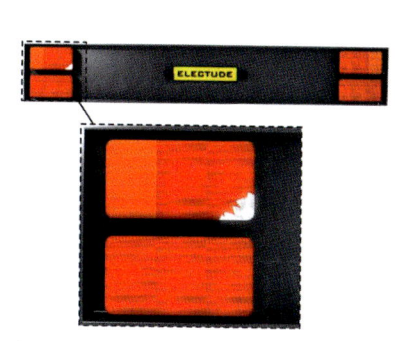

Fig. 580 There is a hole in a rear light cover. A white light shines to the rear as a result. This is only permitted for reversing lights.

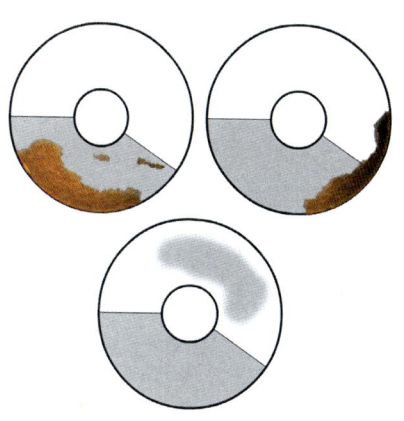

Fig. 581 The low beam section of the reflector is reflective. The projected low beam image in the headlight tester is good. Standards for damage (rust/weathering) in the low beam section of the headlamp reflector vary from state to state.

HOW TO: DIAGNOSE THE DIPPED HEADLIGHTS RELAY

1. Dipped headlights remain on

The dipped headlights in this car remain on when the light switch is turned off. The question is: what is wrong with the electrical circuit?

Fig. 582 Tools Required

Fig. 583 The dipped headlights are turned off using the light switch.

Fig. 584 The dipped headlights remain on.

Find the relay for the dipped headlights in the relay box. To determine which relay the dipped headlights relay is, check the relay box cover or workshop documentation.

Fig. 585 The dipped headlights relay is located in the relay box.

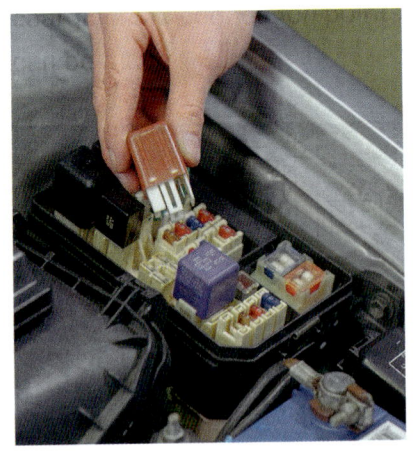

Fig. 586 The dipped headlights turn off when the relay is removed.

Fig. 587 The dipped headlights are off.

2. Check the voltage on the relay pins

To take voltage measurements on the relay, the relay is connected to the relay socket via Y cables. The relay works again and Y cables are used to conduct measurements while the electrical circuit is working properly.

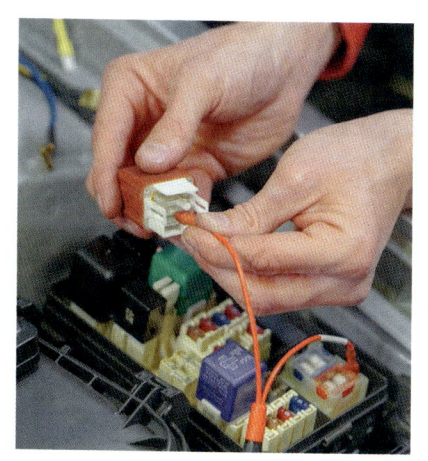

Fig. 588 Connect the relay pins to the Y cables.

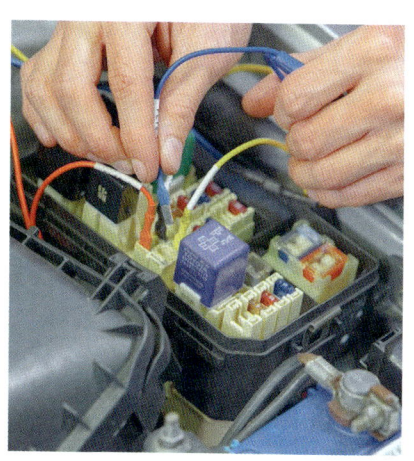

Fig. 589 Connect the other end of the Y cables to the connections in the relay socket.

Fig. 590 The dipped headlights remain on.

3. The electrical diagram for the dipped headlights

The dipped headlights remain on. The following measurements must be performed next in order to find out what is wrong with the circuit.

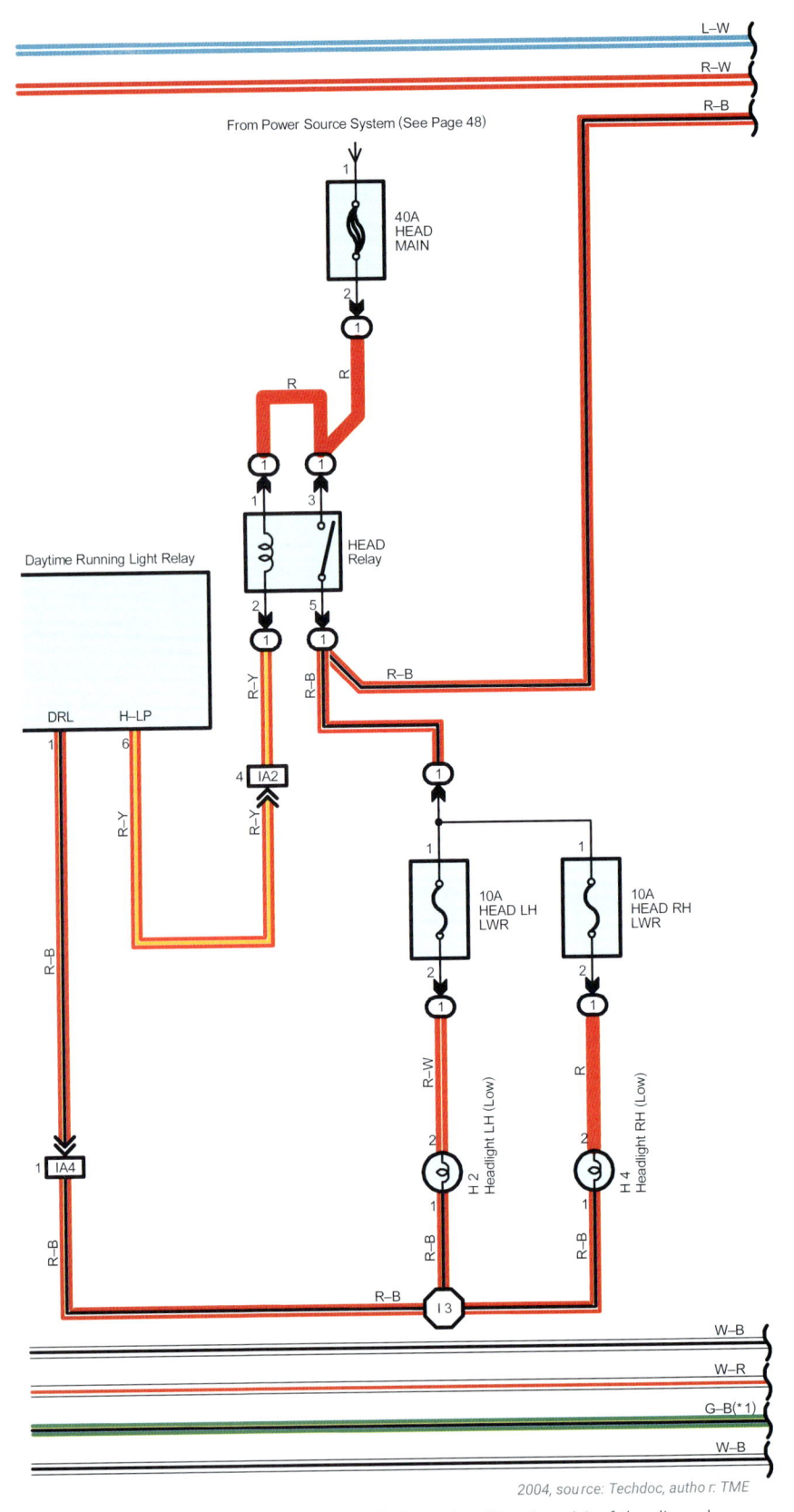

Fig. 591 The diagram of the dipped headlights relay. Pins 1 and 3 of the dipped headlights relay ('HEAD Relay') are directly powered by the battery via the '40A HEAD MAIN' fuse. Pin 2 is controlled via the 'DR Light Relay'. If the light switch is switched on, pin 2 is grounded. The relay switch for the dipped headlights is then closed: the lights are powered and switched on. Pin 5 indicates 12 V if the relay switch for the dipped headlights is closed.

4. Measurements on the dipped headlights relay

The light switch is off, but the lamps are still on. The voltage is measured across the relay switch. Pins 3 and 5 show around 12 V. This means the relay switch is closed. The relay coil is measured next. Both pins indicate around 12 V. The relay is not engaged. Pin 2 is 12 V, but the switch is closed.

Fig. 592 Measured on pins 3 and 5 of the relay: the voltage is 12 V. The lights are on.

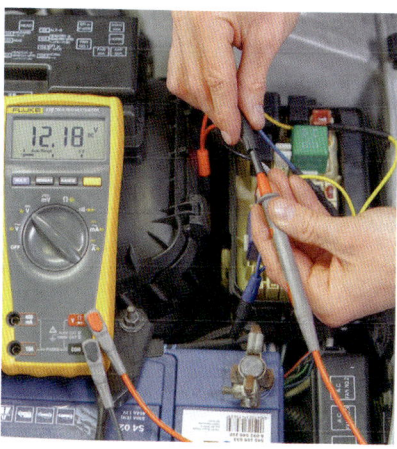

Fig. 593 Measured on pin 2 of the relay: the voltage is 12 V. The relay coil is not engaged, but the switch is closed.

Fig. 594 The lights are switched on. Pin 2 now reads 0 V. The relay control works correctly. The switch in the relay is stuck, which causes the lights to stay on. The relay needs to be replaced.

Replace the relay and check whether the lights switch off now. Now switch the lights on and check whether they work.

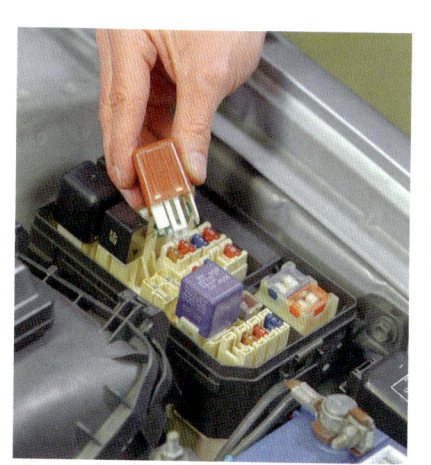

Fig. 595 Install the new relay in the relay box.

Fig. 596 The lights remain off.

Fig. 597 Turn on the lights using the switch. The lights work now.

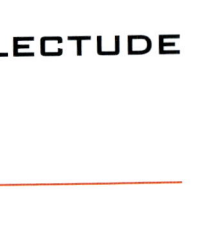

Gasoline Engine Construction and Operation

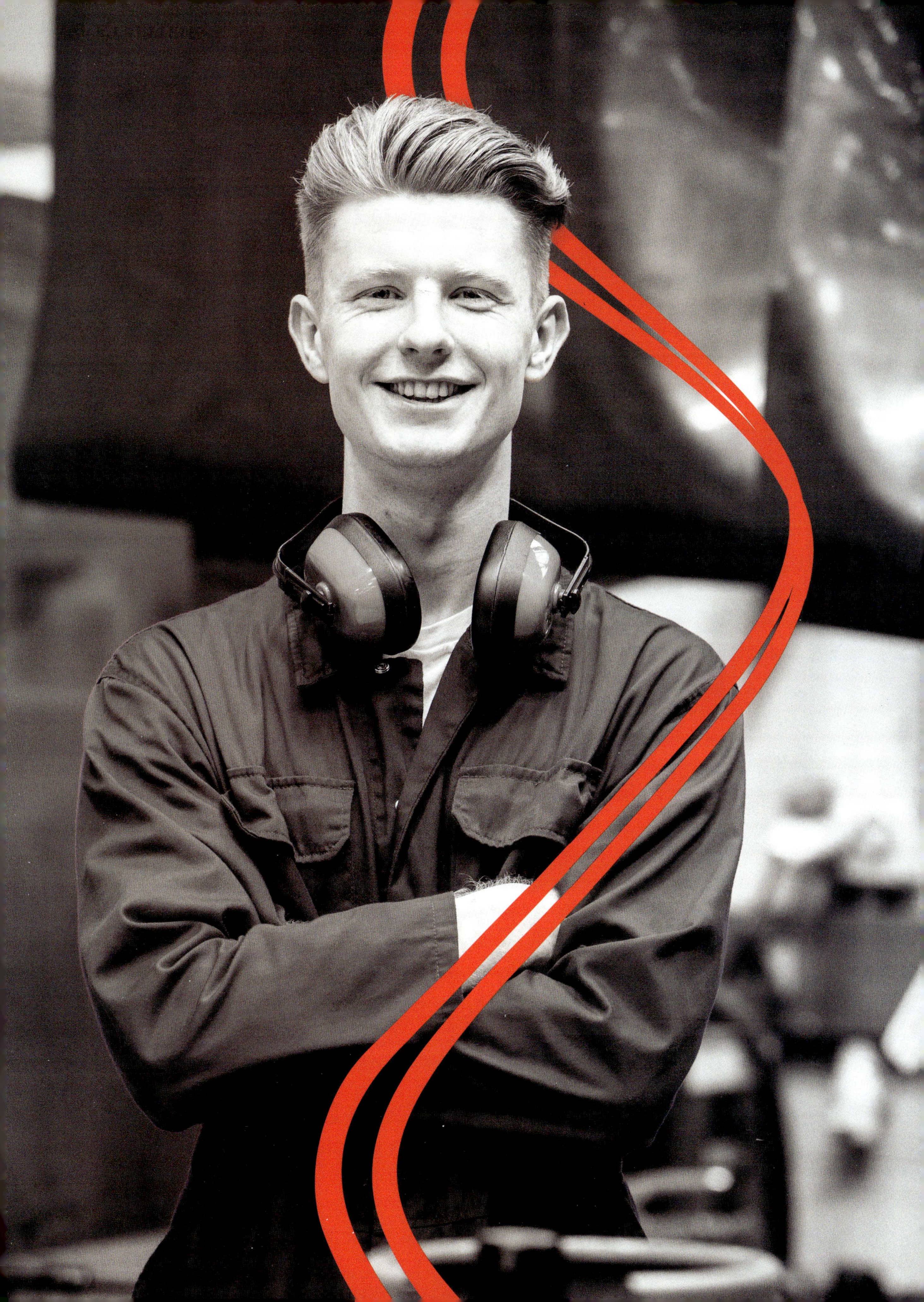

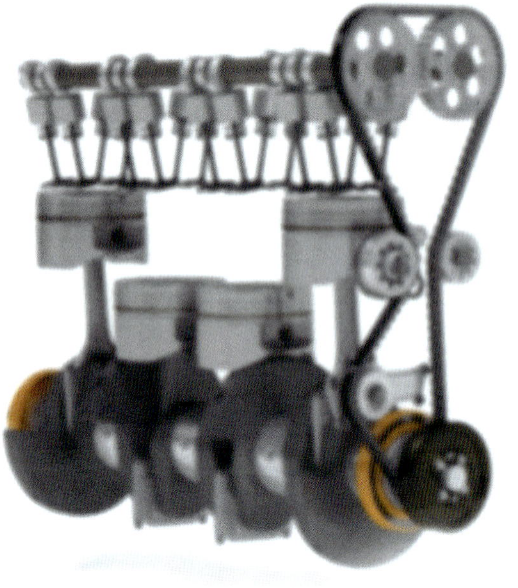

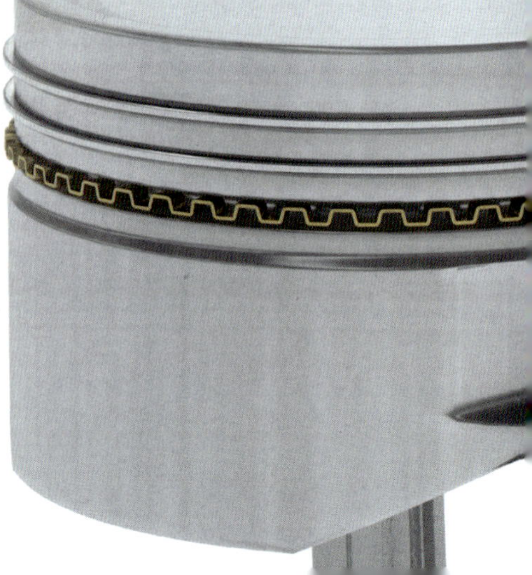

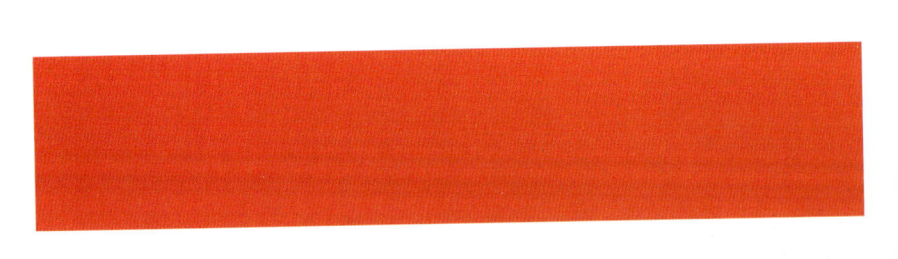

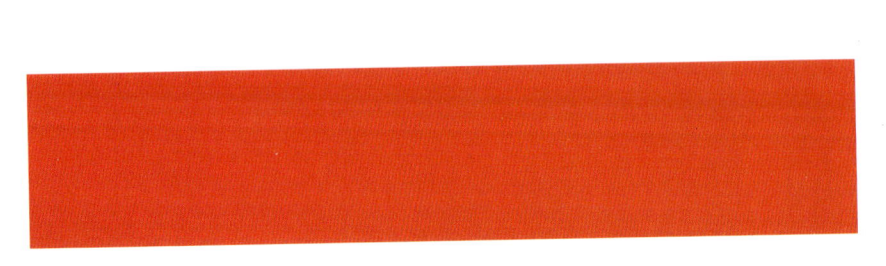

1. Combustion Engine Fundamentals

ENGINE MECHANICAL COMPONENTS

1. Engine

The housing of a piston engine is called the engine block or cylinder block. The engine assembly consists of 3 major components:

1. Cylinder head.
2. Engine block.
3. Oil pan or Crankcase.

- Water jackets, coolant passages, and oil galleries are found in the block and cylinder head. They cool the engine and supply oil to moving parts.
- The cylinders are found in the block and house the pistons.
- The crankshaft is attached to the block with bearing caps and bolts or a bed plate.
- The camshaft and valves are located in the cylinder head in an engine with an overhead camshaft configuration.
- The cylinder head seals the top of the cylinders.
- The oil pan is a reservoir for oil and seals the lower portion of the block.

324 GASOLINE ENGINE CONSTRUCTION AND OPERATION

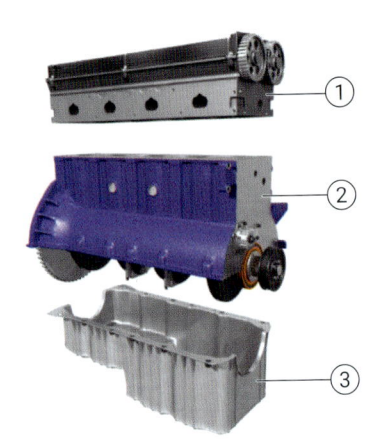

Fig. 1 The three basic engine components: 1. Cylinder Head. 2. Block. 3. Crankcase.

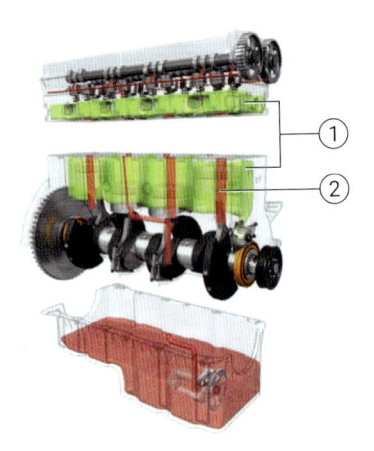

Fig. 2 The internal parts of the engine block: 1. Coolant Channels 2. Oil Channels.

Fig. 3 The Drive: 1. Flywheel. 2. Connecting Rod. 3. Camshaft. 4. Valves. 5. Water Pump. 6. Oil Pump. 7. Crankshaft.

2. Mechanical Components

The mechanical components that provide power to drive the car can be found in the engine block.

— The pistons close off the cylinders from the combustion chambers at the engine deck (top surface of the block) and transfer the power of the combusted gases to the connecting rods.
— The connecting rods convert the reciprocating movement of the pistons to rotational movement of the crankshaft.
— The crankshaft transfers rotating movement to the transmission and drive wheels.
— The camshaft(s) open the intake and exhaust valves. The camshaft(s) is/are driven by the crankshaft.
— The intake and exhaust valves open and close off the intake and exhaust ports.
— The flywheel is a large, heavy wheel attached to the rear of the crankshaft. It stores/releases rotational energy to keep the engine rotating smoothly and provides a ring gear for the starter to engage into for starting the vehicle.
— The vibration dampener (harmonic balancer) is attached to the front of the crankshaft. It removes harmonic vibrations throughout rotational movement of the crankshaft.
— The oil pump supplies pressurized oil to the engine.
— The water pump circulates coolant through the engine and radiator.

PISTON ENGINES

1. Piston Operation

The piston engine is a type of internal combustion engine.
Piston engines convert the upward and downward movement of a piston into rotating movement of the crankshaft.
In other words, reciprocating movement is converted into rotational movement.

When the piston is at the lowest position in the cylinder, this is called Bottom Dead Center or BDC.
When the piston is at the highest position in the cylinder, this called Top Dead Center or TDC.

The combustion of air and fuel above the piston at TDC causes cylinder pressure to rise, forcing the piston downward.

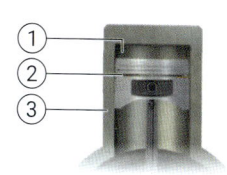

Fig. 4 Three important parts of a piston engine: 1. Combustion chamber. 2. Piston. 3. Cylinder.

Fig. 5 Piston positions: 1. Bottom dead center (BDC). 2. Top dead center (TDC).

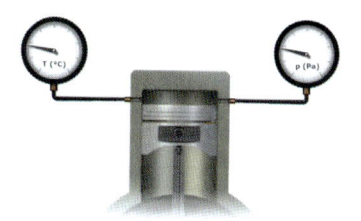

Fig. 6 Pressure and temperature for the combustion, piston can be found in the TDC.

Fig. 7 Pressure and temperature during combustion, piston moves downwards.

2. Crank-Connecting Rod Mechanism

The crank-connecting rod mechanism converts the reciprocating movement of the piston into a rotating movement.

A flywheel has been installed on the crankshaft. This stores energy during the power stroke. The flywheel releases this energy to the crankshaft during the other strokes.

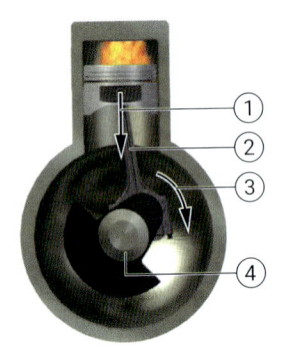

Fig. 8 Movement of the piston and crankshaft: 1. The piston's reciprocating movement. 2. Connecting rod. 3. The crankshaft's rotating movement. 4. Crankshaft.

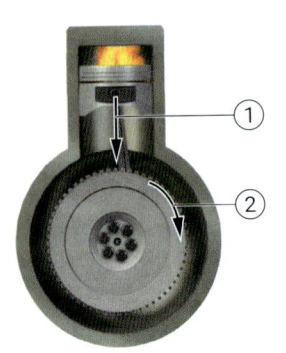

Fig. 9 Power is stored in the flywheel: 1. The piston moves downwards. 2. The crankshaft and the flywheel rotate clockwise.

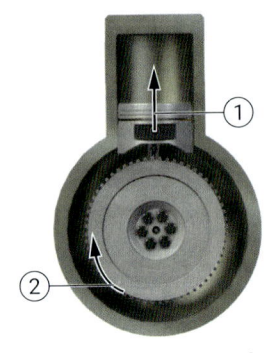

Fig. 10 Power from the flywheel moves the piston upwards: 1. The flywheel rotates clockwise. 2. The piston is moved upwards by the crankshaft.

ENGINE BLOCK TYPES

1. Basic Types

There are different types of engine blocks with multiple cylinders. The type of engine block depends on:
— The number of cylinders
— The installation space
— The powertrain

When there is little space for the engine block, it's often installed in the transverse direction of the vehicle, the crankshaft is at a right angle and is called a transverse engine. This is a space-saving method in combination with front-wheel drive and is used for many cars.

The radial engine is an engine block type that has never been used in cars but has been used in aircraft and some early motorcycles.

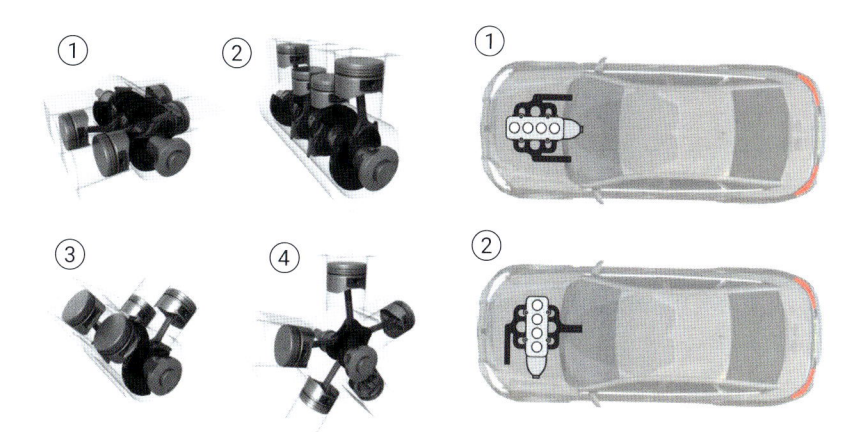

Fig. 11 Various engine block types: 1. Boxer engine. 2. In-line engine. 3. V-engine. 4. Radial engine.

Fig. 12 Different mounting orientations: 1. Engine block mounted in the longitudinal direction. 2. Engine block mounted in the transverse direction.

2. Variants

An inline engine with 4 or more cylinders has the disadvantage of being long. This makes it difficult to install the engine in the transverse direction.

A V-engine, on the other hand, is wider and more difficult to install in the transverse direction.

The solution is to combine both; the VR engine. The VR-engine is used when the number of cylinders is between 5 and 6.

The W-engine consists of two VR engines casted together into a V. This design allows manufacturers to fit more cylinders into a smaller space. Normally this design is used in engines with 8 to 16 cylinders. Sometimes a W-engine design is used instead of a V-engine; because a W-engine with 8 or more cylinders is not as long as a V-engine with the same number of cylinders. W-engines however, are wider than V-engines.

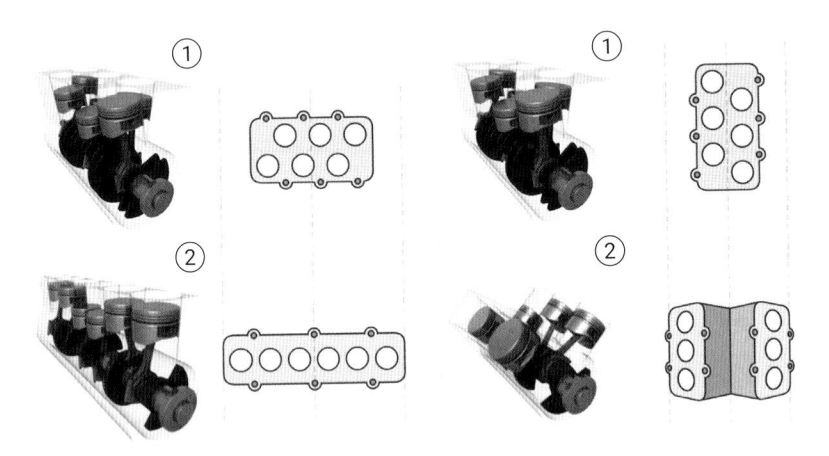

Fig. 13 The difference between an in-line engine and a VR engine: 1. VR engine. 2. In-line engine.

Fig. 14 The difference between a V engine and a VR engine:
1. VR6 engine. 2. V6 engine.

Fig. 15 The difference between an in-line engine, a V engine and a VR engine.

Fig. 16 The difference between a V engine and a W engine:
1. W12 engine. 2. V12 engine

4-STROKE PISTON ENGINE

1. 4-Stroke Process

The 4-stroke cycle repeats over and over again in the internal combustion engine.

1 cycle consists of 4 strokes. A stroke occurs every half revolution of the crankshaft;

1. The intake stroke: the intake valve opens and the fuel/air mixture fills the cylinder.
2. The compression stroke: the intake valve closes and the air/fuel mixture is compressed.
3. The power stroke: the valves are closed; the compressed mixture is ignited and the piston is pushed downward - turning the crankshaft.
4. The exhaust stroke: the exhaust valve opens and the combusted gases are pushed out of the cylinder.

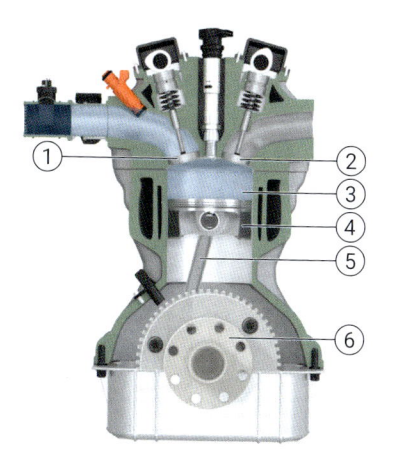

Fig. 17 Four-stroke engine structure: 1. Intake valve. 2. Exhaust valve. 3. Cylinder. 4. Piston. 5. Connecting rod. 6. Crankshaft.

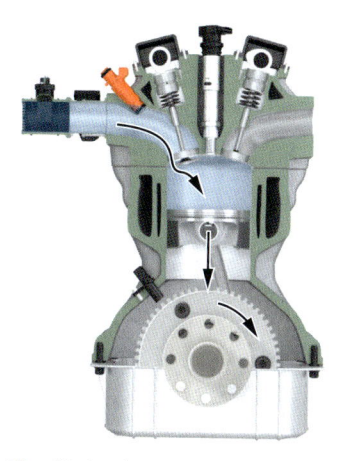

Fig. 18 Intake stroke.

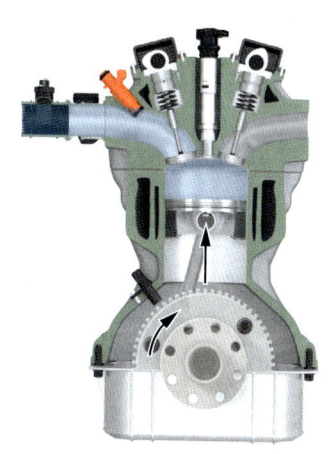

Fig. 19 Compression stroke.

Fig. 20 Power stroke.

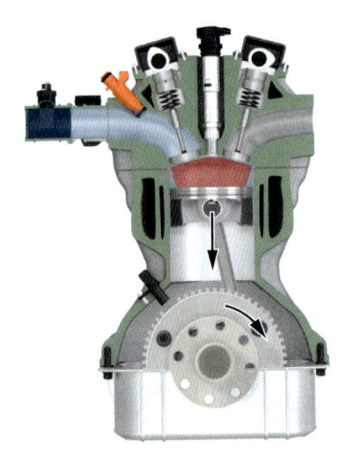

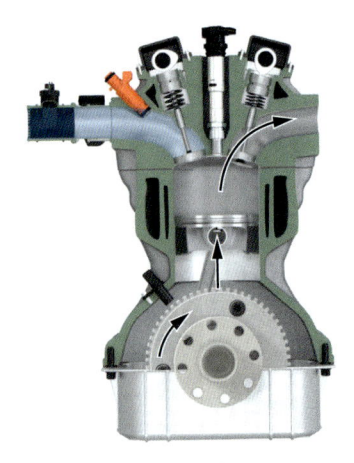

Fig. 21 Exhaust stroke.

2. Energy Conversion

In an internal combustion engine, heat (thermal energy) is converted into movement, also called mechanical energy.

This process is always repeated in the same way:
- Fuel and oxygen (outside air) flow into the cylinder (intake stroke).
- These are mixed in the cylinder into a gas mixture and then compressed (compression stroke).
- The mixture ignites.
- Both the temperature and the pressure in the cylinder rise as a result of the combustion.
- The piston is pushed downwards in the cylinder because of the increased pressure (power stroke).

3. A Rotating Movement from a Linear Movement.

The piston moves in a straight line in the cylinder.
It is converted into a rotating movement with the help of the crank connecting rod mechanism.
The connecting rod revolves around two points:
- The crankshaft at the bottom.
- The piston pin on the top.

The linear movement of the piston can be converted into a rotating movement of the crankshaft because the connecting rod can pivot at both the top and the bottom.

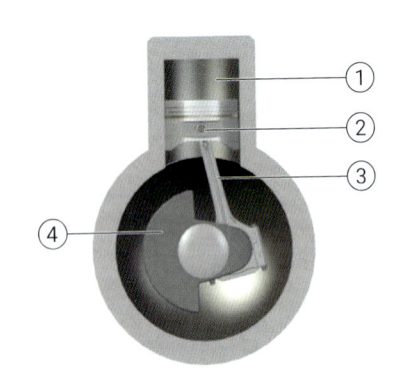

Fig. 22 Cylinder section: 1. Cylinder. 2. Piston pin. 3. Connecting rod. 4. Crankshaft.

2-STROKE PISTON ENGINE

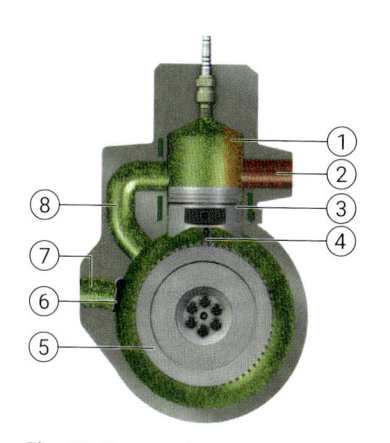

Fig. 23 Two-stroke engine structure:
1. Cylinder. 2. Exhaust port.
3. Piston. 4. Connecting rod.
5. Flywheel. 6. Reed valve. 7. Inlet port. 8. Transfer port.

1. Introduction

The combustion cycle of a 2-stroke or 2-cycle engine consists of two strokes. The 2-stroke engine must go through the same phases in one crankshaft revolution, that the 4-stroke engine takes two crankshaft revolutions to accomplish.

Because the crankcase is used for the 2-stroke process, the 2-stroke engine is lubricated by the fuel.

Lubrication oil is precisely mixed with the fuel, and burned along with it. This is why many 2-stroke engine smoke slightly from the tailpipe during operation.

Two-stroke piston engines use ports instead of intake and exhaust valves. The transfer and exhaust ports are opened and closed by the piston. The inlet port is opened by vacuum in the crankcase. Two-stroke piston engines can still be found in mopeds, old jet skis, and dirt bikes. It is also very common to see outdoor power equipment like chain saws and string trimmers still using the two-stroke engine design. However, this type of engine is being used less and less because of increasingly strict emissions requirements.

2. The 1st Stroke

When the piston moves down the following happens:

1. The air/fuel mixture is ignited and the piston is pushed down.
2. The exhaust gasses flow out of the cylinder via the exhaust port.
3. A fresh air/fuel mixture is pressed into the combustion chamber from the crankcase via the scavenging port.

Fig. 24 The piston is pushed down by the combustion.

Fig. 25 Exhaust gases flow out of the cylinder. At the same time, fresh mixture flows into the cylinder via the crankcase and transfer port.

3. The 2nd Stroke

During the upward movement of the piston the following takes place:

1. The reed valve opens and a fuel/air mixture is drawn in via the inlet port.
2. The air/fuel mixture on top of the piston is compressed.
3. The exhaust gasses of the previous power stroke flow out via the exhaust port.

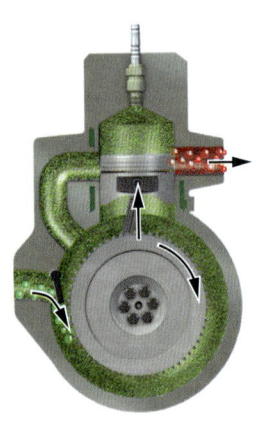

Fig. 26 The last remnants of the exhaust gases flow out and new air/fuel mixture is drawn in via the inlet port.

Fig. 27 The mixture above the piston is compressed.

OTTO ENGINE

1. Introduction

The Otto engine is a 4-stroke internal combustion engine where the air/fuel mixture is ignited by a spark. The best known fuel for the Otto engine is gasoline, but LPG (liquefied propane gas), CNG (compressed natural gas), and ethanol can also be used. The name of the Otto engine comes from Nikolaus Otto, the inventor of this engine.

Chemical energy is converted into mechanical energy in the engine. This engine operates by compressing an air/fuel mixture, and igniting the compressed gasses with a spark.

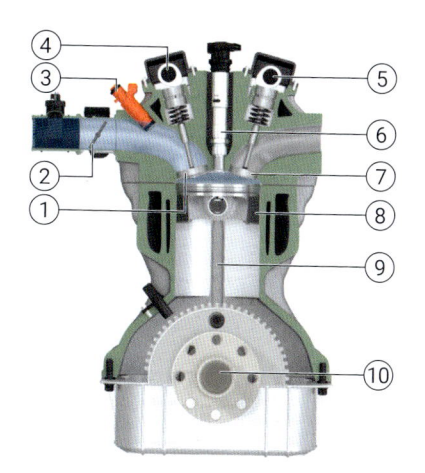

Fig. 28 Construction of the Otto engine: 1. Intake valve. 2. Throttle valve. 3. Injector. 4. Intake camshaft. 5. Exhaust camshaft. 6. Spark plug. 7. Exhaust valve. 8. Piston. 9. Connecting rod. 10. Crankshaft.

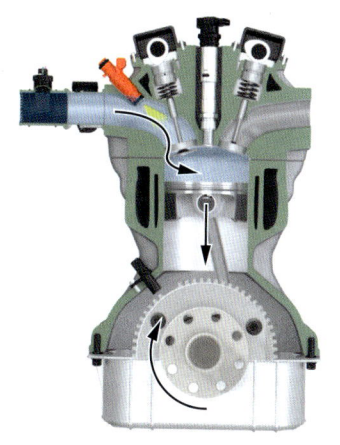

Fig. 29 Intake stroke.

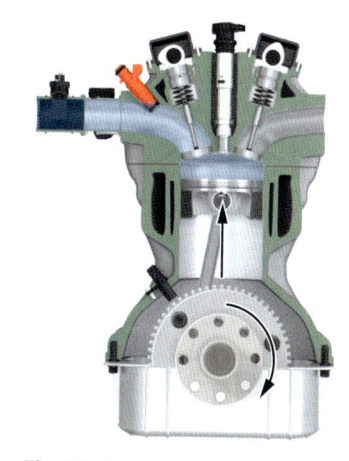

Fig. 30 Compression stroke.

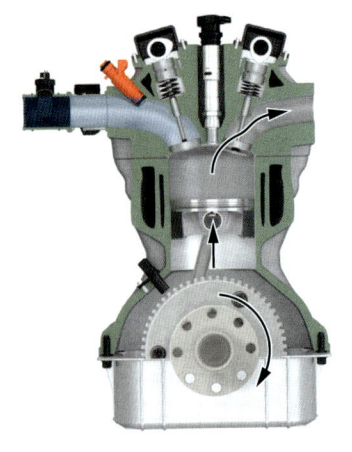

Fig. 31 Power stroke.

Fig. 32 Exhaust stroke.

2. Forming the Mixture

The camshaft(s) control the valves that open and close the intake and exhaust ports of the engine.
Air flows into the engine through the intake port during the intake stroke.

Fuel is then injected according to the quantity of air.
The fuel is injected into the intake port or cylinder. The fuel must be atomized (converted into very small droplets) to ensure it mixes well with air.

There are 2 different injection systems:
— *Indirect* injection: found in the intake port.
— *Direct* injection: found in the combustion chamber.

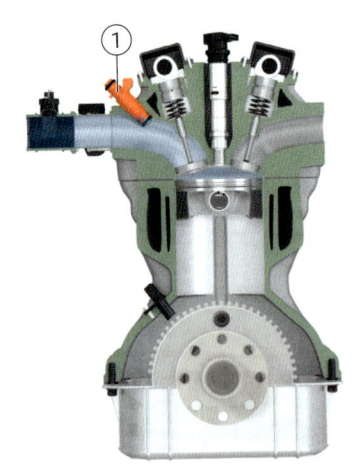

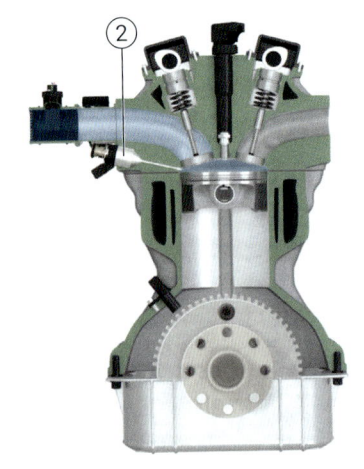

Fig. 33 Fuel Injection: 1. Indirect injection. 2. Direct injection.

Fig. 34 A spark from the spark plug ignites the mixture.

3. Ignition

The spark from the spark plug ignites the air/fuel mixture at the end of the compression stroke.

This ensures that the compressed air/fuel mixture ignites and the temperature increases. The fuel is vaporized at this time, so it can be ignited. The pressure in the cylinder increases following ignition.

4. Identification

The Otto engine closely resembles the diesel engine. You can tell them apart by their specific components.

The figure shows you a 4-stroke Otto engine. It contains intake and exhaust valves and may be identified by the use of spark plugs as the ignition source.

NOTE Do not confuse the spark plugs of an Otto engine with the glow plugs of a diesel engine.

Fig. 35 An Otto engine can be recognized by the spark plugs (1).

DIESEL ENGINE

1. Introduction

The diesel engine in a passenger car is a 4-stroke engine. The diesel engine is named after the inventor, Rudolf Diesel.

In a diesel engine, chemical energy is converted into mechanical energy. A fuel-air mixture is required for this. The best known fuels for this engine are diesel fuel and biodiesels such as vegetable oils.

Diesel engines do not have spark plugs, but rather rely on high combustion chamber temperatures, around 600 °F (300° C) and very high fuel injection pressures, 36,000 psi (2500 bar) to ignite the mixture. Diesel fuel has low volatility, so the fuel ignites on its own when the temperature of the compressed air in the combustion chamber is sufficiently high.

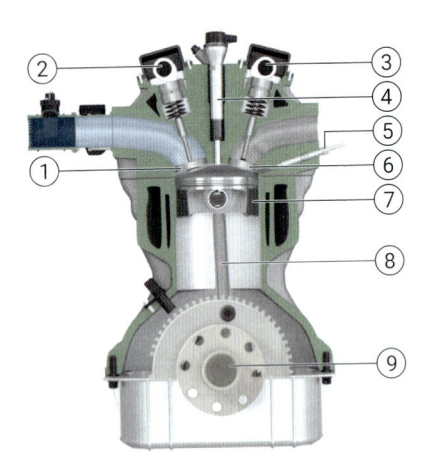

Fig. 36 The Structure of a Diesel Engine: 1. Intake valve 2. Camshaft 3. Camshaft 4. Mechanical injector 5. Glow plug 6. Exhaust valve 7. Piston 8. Connecting rod 9. Crankshaft

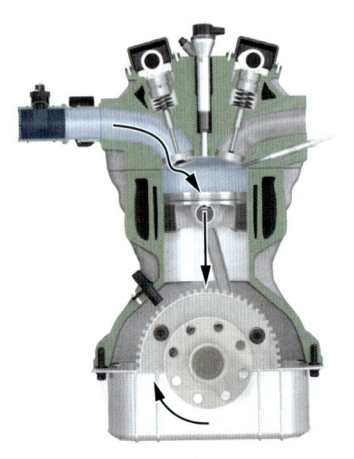

Fig. 37 Intake stroke.

Fig. 38 Compression stroke.

Fig. 39 Power stroke.

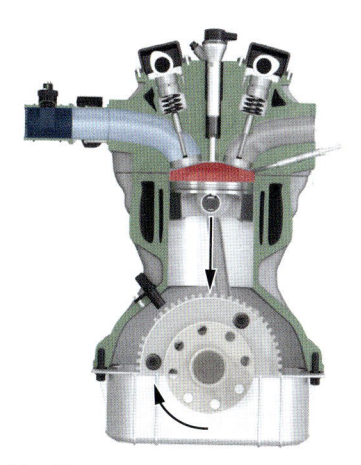

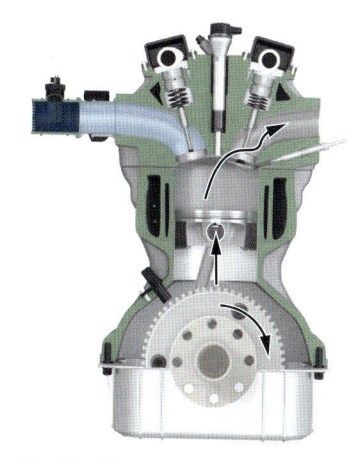

Fig. 40 Exhaust stroke.

2. Mixture Formation

Unlike a gasoline engine, many diesel engines do not have a restrictive throttle valve. However, if a throttle valve is used, it is typically placed at wide open throttle. It is only closed or partially closed to eliminate run on (run on is when an engine keeps running for a short time after being shut off), or to help with controlling NOx emissions.

The camshafts and valves operate the intake and exhaust ports of the engine.
During the intake stroke, the piston descends from the top to the bottom. The intake valve is open, and the exhaust valve is closed. When the piston reaches the bottom of the cylinder, both valves close, and the piston travels back to the top on the compression stroke.

Diesel engines have a long compression stroke, thus compressing a volume of air into a very small space. This causes the air molecules to rub against each other, generating heat in excess of 600°F (300°C).
Compression ratios on Diesel engines are 15:1 to 17:1.

Modern diesel fuel systems inject fuel into the superheated air at very high pressure. High fuel injection pressure and electronically controlled nozzles control fuel injection. An injector atomizes the fuel directly into the combustion chamber or cylinder. The quantity of fuel injected depends on the position of the acceleration pedal.

Fig. 41 Injection.

Fig. 42 1. Injectors.

3. Self-Ignition

Diesel engines have the property of self-ignition at high temperature. This high temperature is attained by compressing the air volume.

Diesel engines can be hard to start in cold weather. Various techniques are used to heat either the entire engine or the air in the combustion chamber. The most common way to start a diesel engine is to heat the air in the combustion area using the glow plugs.

The diesel engine is referred to as a **compression ignition** engine because it uses the heat of the compression stroke to burn the fuel.

Fig. 43 Self-Ignition

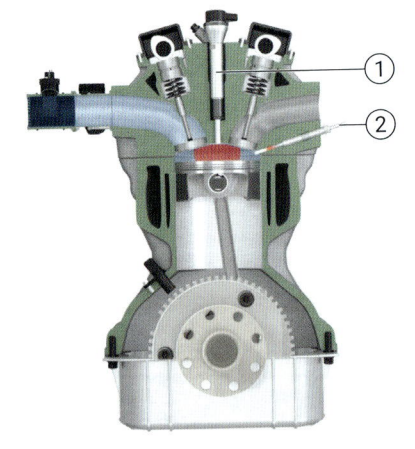

Fig. 44 A glow plug heats the air in the front combustion chamber.
1. Mechanical injector. 2. Glow plug.

4. Features

Diesel engines are more powerful and produce more torque than gasoline engines. Diesel engines also achieve superior fuel economy and operate at lower RPMs.

Older diesel engines were very noisy and produced a lot of smoke and harmful emissions. Modern diesels inject a small "pilot injection" to initiate combustion prior to adding the main fuel charge. This improves emissions and reduces that annoying noise typically associated with older diesel engines.

Fig. 45 1. Glow plugs.

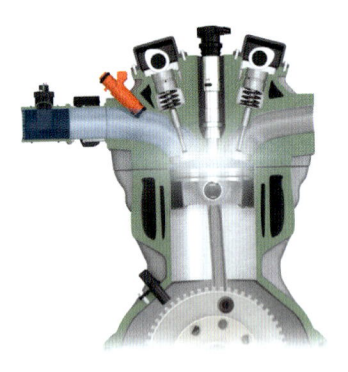

POWER DIAGRAM

1. Creating a Power Diagram

A power diagram is an overview of the strokes of the 4-stroke cycle process.

The diagram is called a power diagram because it begins with the power stroke.

Once all the strokes are added together, a degrees scale is created, from 0 to 720°.

A widely used engine type is the four-cylinder engine. With this type of engine, two pistons move upward simultaneously, and two pistons move downward simultaneously. A power stroke occurs every 180 degrees of crankshaft rotation; this means that a piston will have completed all four strokes. This construction allows four-cylinder engines to use a smaller flywheel than those that are used for two and three-cylinder engines.

Fig. 46 The power diagram of a four-stroke engine: 1. Power stroke. 2. Exhaust stroke. 3. Intake stroke. 4. Compression stroke.

2. 4-cylinder Power Diagram

You can create a power diagram for all 4-stroke engines.

When you arrange a power diagram for a multi-cylinder engine, you can easily determine the firing order.

On most 4-cylinder engines, the #1 cylinder is usually closest to the timing chain or belt.

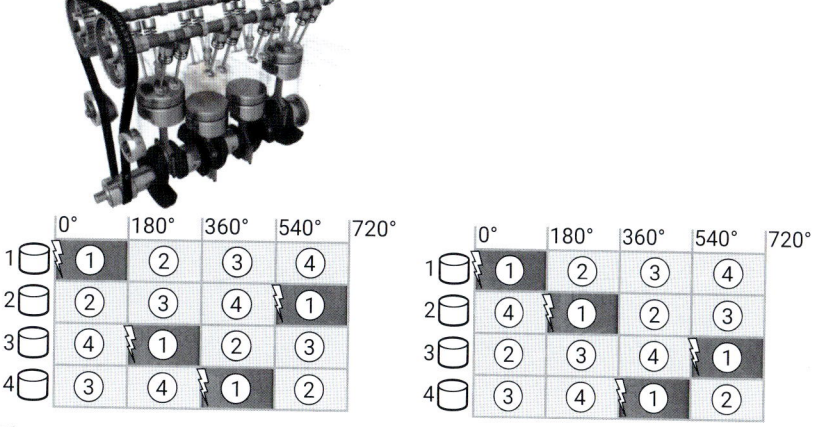

Fig. 47 The power diagram of a four-cylinder four-stroke engine with the firing order 1-3-4-2.

Fig. 48 The power diagram of a four-cylinder four-stroke engine with th firing order 1-2-4-3.

3. Power Diagram of a Two-Cylinder Engine

On the basis of the power diagram, we can recognize the construction of the engine. The construction of many two-cylinder engines includes inline engines with opposite running pistons, inline engines with synchronous pistons, and boxer style engines. In the case of inline engines with opposite running pistons, one piston moves upwards while the other moves downwards. In the power diagram, you can clearly see that the two power strokes take place immediately after each other. Then there are two strokes where no work takes place. This type of engine will have a lot of vibration and run roughly but does have a favorable mechanical load. Synchronous pistons in inline engines will move up and down simultaneously. This type of engine has an alternating power and intake stroke which makes it relatively quiet despite its large mechanical imbalance.

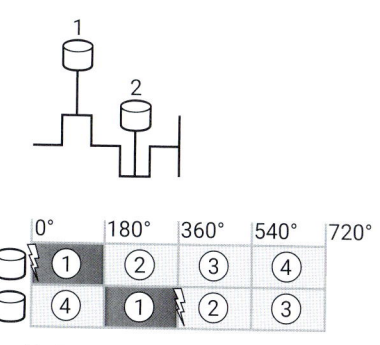

Fig. 49 Power diagram of an inline engine with opposite running pistons.

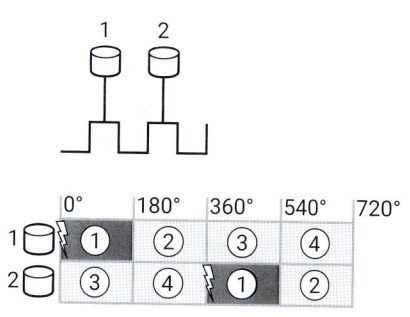

Fig. 50 Power diagram of an inline engine with synchronous pistons.

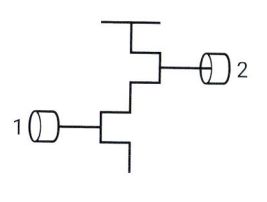

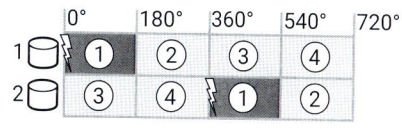

Fig. 51 Power diagram of a boxer engine.

The most favorable engine shape for a two-cylinder engine is the boxer version. Here the pistons are horizontal and move simultaneously toward and away from each other. The power stroke and intake stroke follow each other alternately. This form combines the best characteristics of the two previously discussed forms without the disadvantages.

4. Power Diagram of a Three-Cylinder Engine

With a three-cylinder engine, the pistons move 120 degrees in relation to each other. This means that there is a power stroke every 240 degrees. This type of engine runs turbulently when compared to the four-cylinder inline engine. Despite its rough running characteristics, the three-cylinder is still often used in modern vehicles. Advantages are its compact construction, which makes it lighter, warm up faster, and experience fewer friction losses. Balancing shafts help keep the turbulent loop of this design under control.

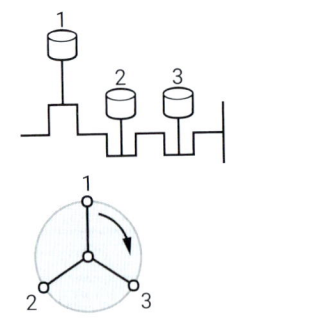

Fig. 52 Three-cylinder inline engine.

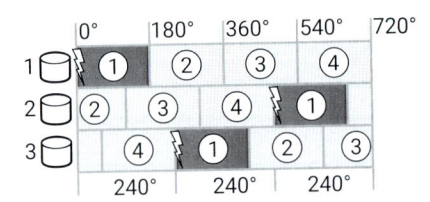

Fig. 53 Power diagram of a three-cylinder inline engine.

5. Power Diagram of a Four-Cylinder Boxer Engine

A four-cylinder boxer engine has two opposing cylinder rows. The opposing pistons make an opposite movement. As a result, the boxer engine has a quiet loop. The power strokes follow each other after 180 degrees and are evenly distributed over the two revolutions of the crankshaft.

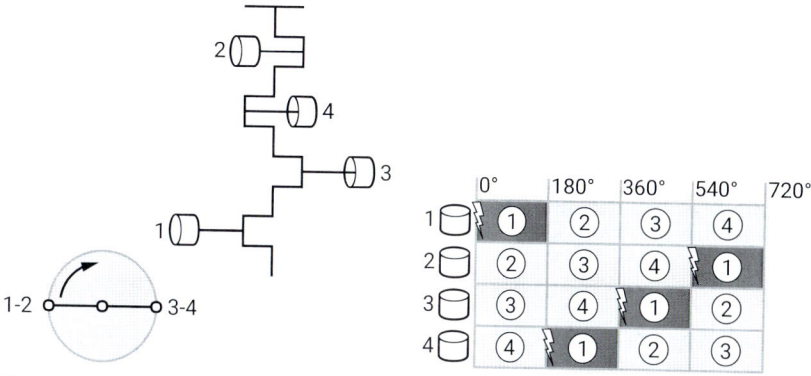

Fig. 54 Four-cylinder boxer engine.

Fig. 55 Power diagram of a four-cylinder boxer engine.

6. Power Diagram of a Six-Cylinder Engine

In a six-cylinder engine design, a power stroke takes place every 120 degrees of crankshaft rotation. Due to overlap of the power strokes, these engines are virtually free of vibration. There is also a small flywheel used as a result of there being no intake stroke that has to be overcome.

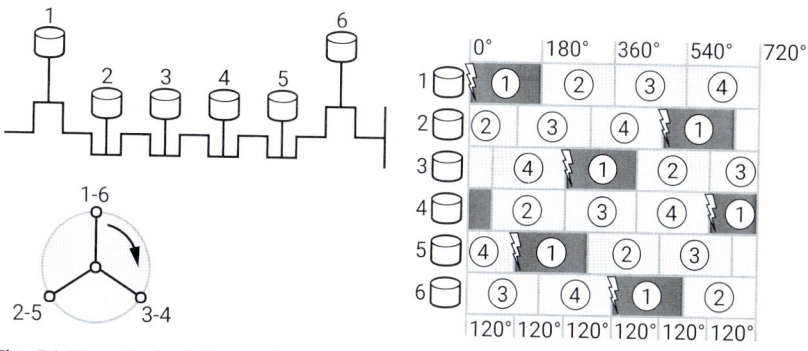

Fig. 56 Six-cylinder inline engine.

Fig. 57 Power diagram of a six-cylinder inline engine.

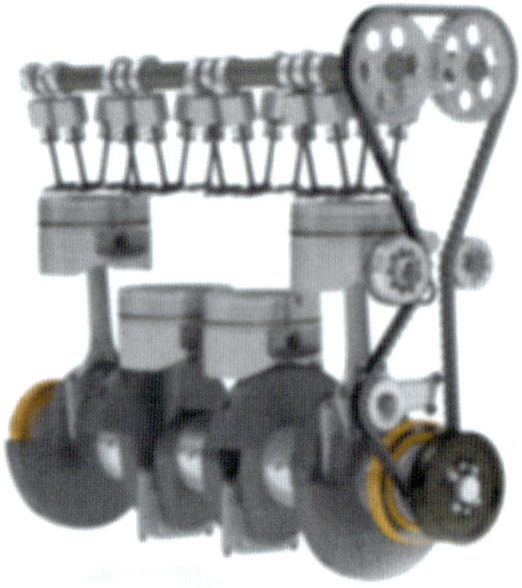

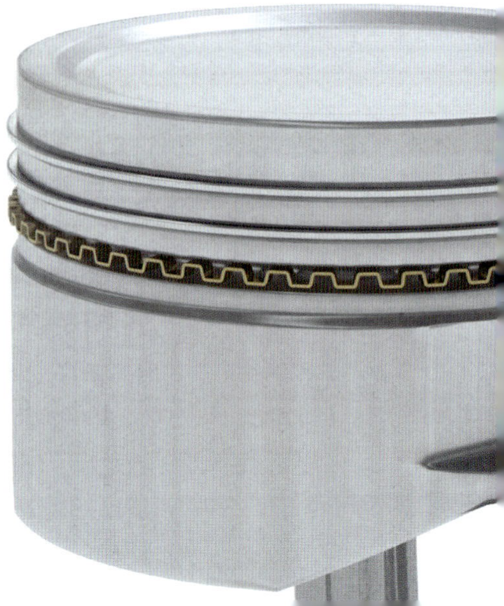

2. Engine Main Parts

ENGINE BLOCK

1. Introduction

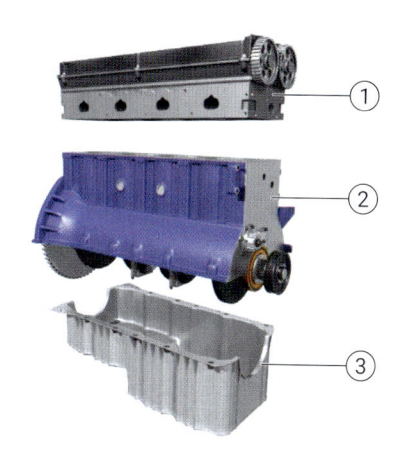

Fig. 58 Engine block structure:
1. Cylinder head. 2. Block. 3. Crankcase.

Together with the cylinder head, the block forms the main structure of the engine. The block is enclosed by the cylinder head at the top and by the oil pan at the bottom.

In the block there are passages for coolant and oil. These passages provide engine cooling and they transport oil to moving parts of the engine.

The crankshaft is mounted in the center of the engine block and held in place by bearing shells and main bearing caps. The caps are secured to the block with large bolts.

NOTE The area below the cylinders, (where the crankshaft is mounted) is sometimes referred to as the crankcase.

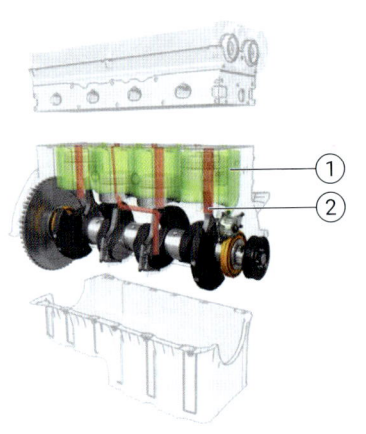

Fig. 59 Passages in the block: 1. Coolant passages. 2. Oil passages.

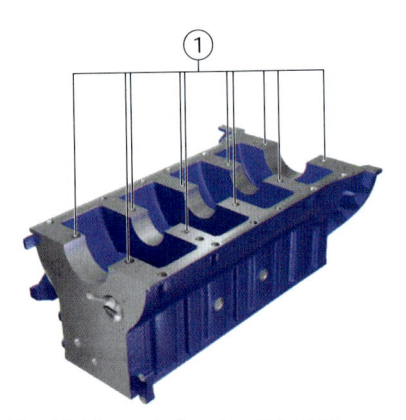

Fig. 60 The main bearing caps are attached to the block (1).

2. Cast Iron

If the block is made from cast iron, the cylinders are bored into the block. Cast iron can possess good oil retaining properties; therefore it's not necessary to install cylinder liners of another material.

After boring, the cast iron cylinder walls are "cross hatched" using a honing tool. This further enhances oil retention, providing an even lower friction coefficient between the cylinder and the piston.

The biggest disadvantage of cast iron compared to aluminum is that engine blocks made from cast iron are heavier.

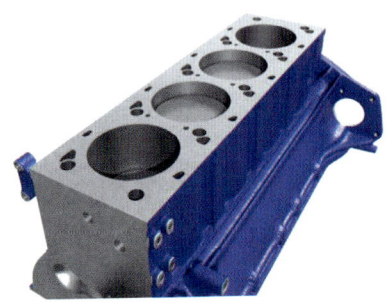

Fig. 61 Cast iron block.

3. Dry Cylinder Lining

If the block is made of a light metal (such as aluminum), cylinder liners of another material need to be installed. As a rule, light metals do not possess the same low frictional properties as cast iron.

This can be resolved however by pressing cast iron liners into the cylinders. This type of lining is called a dry cylinder lining, because the liner is not in direct contact with the coolant.

The main advantages of making blocks from aluminum verses cast iron is aluminum is lighter and a better conductor of heat.

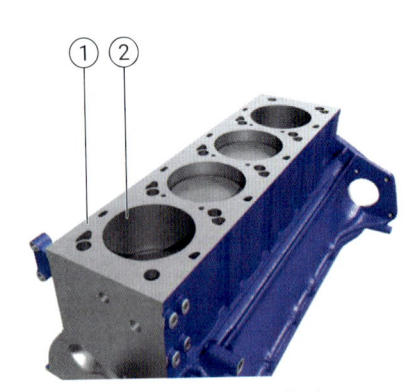

Fig. 62 Block (1) with dry cylinder liners (2).

Properties of a dry liner are:

- The cooling is not as effective because the coolant is not in direct contact with the cylinder liner.
- Repairs are more complex because special tools are necessary.
- Ensuring a seal between the coolant passages and the cylinder lining is unproblematic.
- The block is very rigid.

4. Wet Cylinder Liner

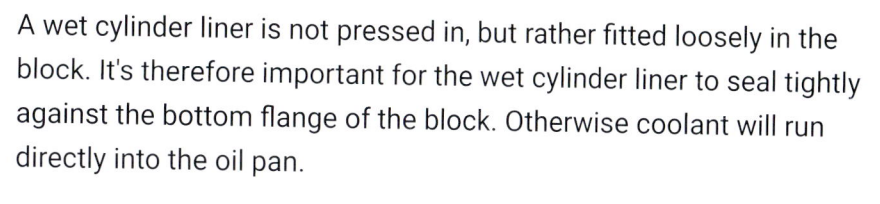

A wet cylinder liner is not pressed in, but rather fitted loosely in the block. It's therefore important for the wet cylinder liner to seal tightly against the bottom flange of the block. Otherwise coolant will run directly into the oil pan.

The wet cylinder liner always projects a little above the top of the engine block. When you fit the cylinder head, the wet cylinder liner is pressed down against the bottom gasket and flange.

The cylinder liner is called wet, because it comes in direct contact with the coolant. Because of this, heat dissipation is better than a block with a dry cylinder liner. Also, because the liner is not pressed into the bore, it's also easier to replace.

The cylinder base gasket can be made of rubber (o-ring) or copper.

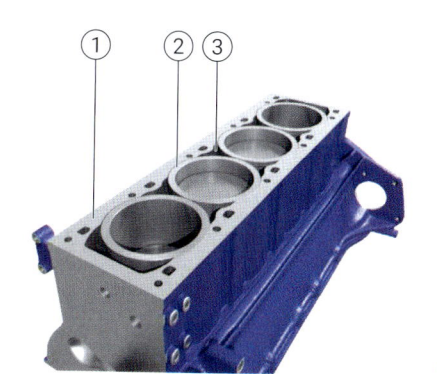

Fig. 63 Wet Cylinder Liner

Fig. 64 Block with wet cylinder liners: 1. Block. 2. Cylinder liner. 3. Coolant.

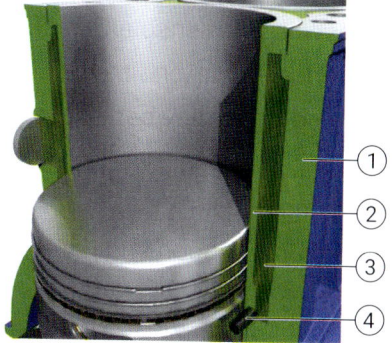

Fig. 65 Block with wet cylinder liners: 1. Block. 2. Cylinder liner. 3. Space for coolant. 4. Cylinder base gasket.

Properties of a wet liner are:
— Effective cooling because the coolant is in direct contact with the cylinder lining.
— It is easy to perform repairs on the cylinder liner.
— It is necessary to have a seal between the coolant passages and the cylinder lining. There is therefore a greater risk of leakage.
— The block is not very rigid.

Fig. 66 Bolts and rings retain the cylinder liner after the cylinder head is removed. This keeps the cylinder liner in place and prevents leakage from the gaskets.

CYLINDER

The cylinder is the hole bored in the block in which the pistons travel up and down. There are two types:

— Integral cylinders.
— Cylinder liners.

1. Integral Cylinder

Integral cylinders are part of the engine block. This type is often found in cast iron blocks. The cylinder is cast in one piece, together with the block, and machined to create a smooth cylinder wall. Cast iron cylinder walls are extremely resistant to wear caused by the piston rings.

Integral cylinders (usually) cannot be replaced as a separate item. If an integral cylinder is damaged, a decision needs to be made as to whether the damage can be repaired by machining the cylinder wall.

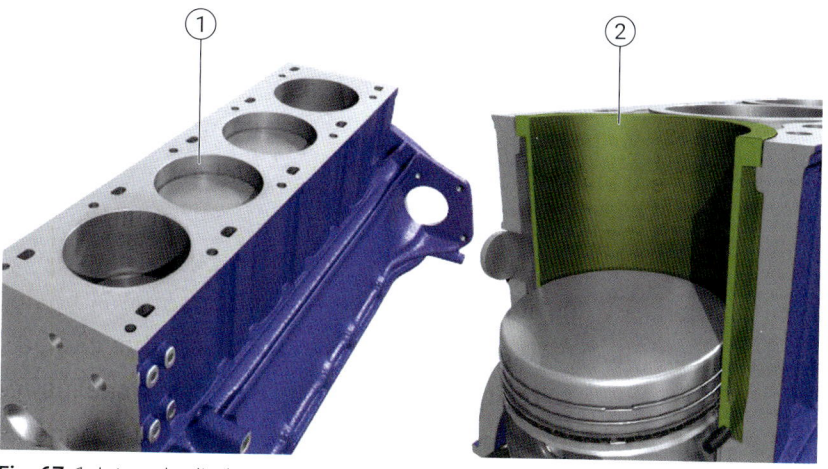

Fig. 67 1. Integral cylinder. 2. Cylinder liner.

The following work is commonly performed on a cylinder:

— Measuring cylinder wear.
— Boring and honing the cylinder.

2. Cylinder Liner

Cylinder liners are often used in aluminum blocks. Separate cylinder liners made of forged steel are pressed into the aluminum block. This is because steel has much better wear resistance than aluminum.

In some cases, the iron is applied as a galvanized coating on the aluminum instead of pressing in a liner.

A distinction is made between dry and wet cylinder liners. Dry cylinder liners are thin iron sleeves pressed into an oversized hole in the block. The liner is supported by the engine block when it absorbs the combustion forces.

Wet cylinder liners are thick-walled cylinders surrounded by coolant. These liners have to be able to withstand combustion forces on their own.
Both dry and wet cylinder liners can be replaced separately.

The following work is commonly performed on a cylinder:

— Measuring cylinder wear.
— Boring and honing the cylinder.

CYLINDER HEAD

1. Introduction

The cylinder head houses the valve mechanism. It is fastened to the engine block, sealing the top of the cylinders.

The cylinder head is usually made from aluminum alloy or cast iron, but you may find cylinder heads made from magnesium alloy.

The lobes on the camshaft open the valves, and valve springs force the valves closed.

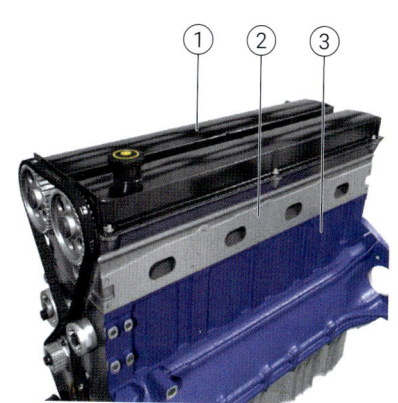

Fig. 68 Engine block structure: 1. Valve cover. 2. Cylinder head. 3. Block.

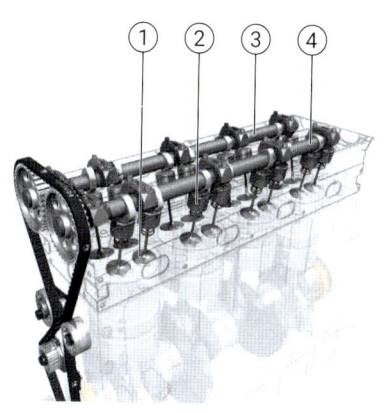

Fig. 69 Valve control in the cylinder head: 1. Valve. 2. Tappet. 3. Intake camshaft. 4. Exhaust camshaft.

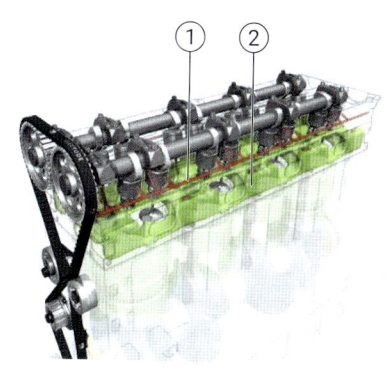

Fig. 70 Oil passages (1) and coolant passages (2) in the cylinder head.

2. Cooling and Lubrication

Combustion of air and fuel cause the cylinder head to become hot; therefore cooling is required.
Passages are machined into the cylinder head to facilitate the flow of coolant to carry away the heat.

Oil passages are also machined into the cylinder head to facilitate lubrication of the valve mechanism.

3. Cylinder Head Gasket

The cylinder head gasket or head gasket is fitted between the top of the block and the cylinder head, forming a seal between the two parts. The head gasket seals in combustion gasses, as well as coolant and oil that pass between the block and cylinder head.

The sealing surface on the cylinder head must be perfectly flat in order for the head gasket to seal properly. The flatness of the cylinder head can be checked using a straight-edge and feeler gauge.

The number of punched holes or notches at the edge of the gasket are an indication of the thickness of the gasket.

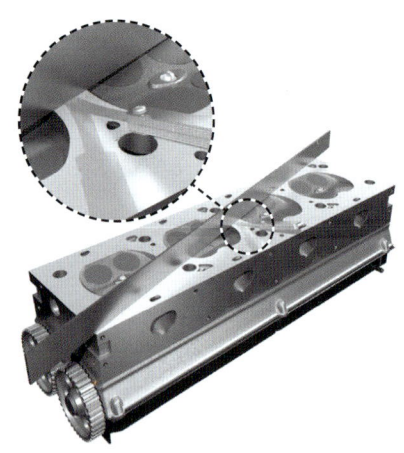

Fig. 71 Checking the cylinder head for flatness.

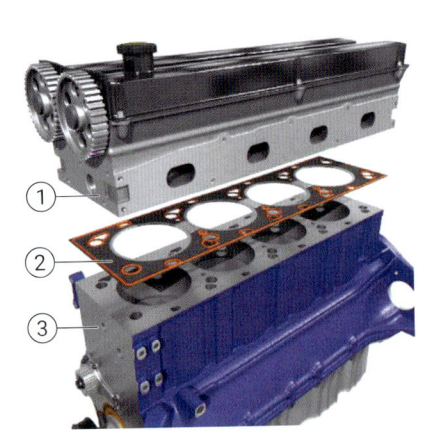

Fig. 72 Cylinder head gasket: 1. Cylinder head. 2. Head gasket. 3. Block.

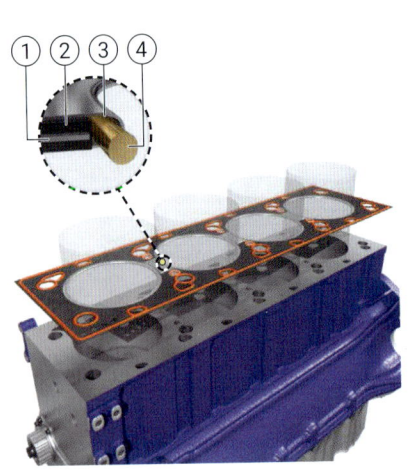

Fig. 73 Cylinder ring: 1. Metal core. 2. Graphite-based gasket material. 3. Steel edge. 4. Wire core.

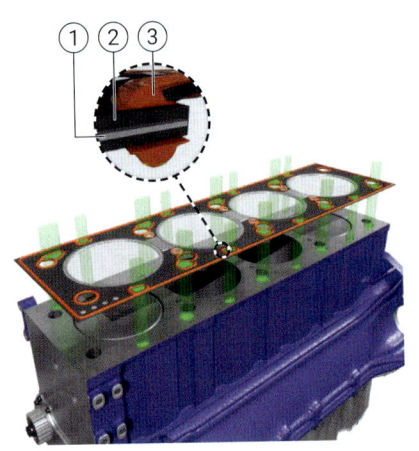

Fig. 74 Coolant passage seal: 1. Metal core. 2. Graphite-based gasket material. 3. Rubber ring.

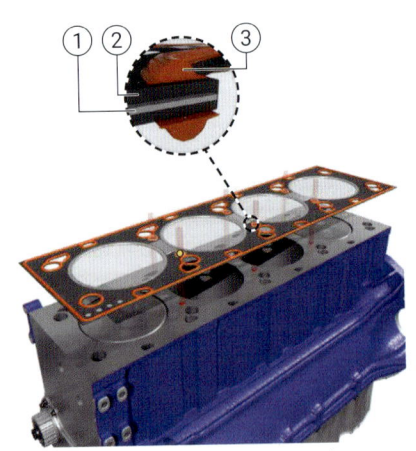

Fig. 75 Oil passage seal: 1. Steel core. 2. Graphite-based gasket material. 3. Silicone ring.

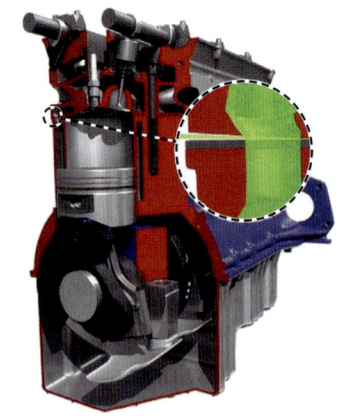

Fig. 76 Leak near the head gasket caused by a damaged or warped cylinder head.

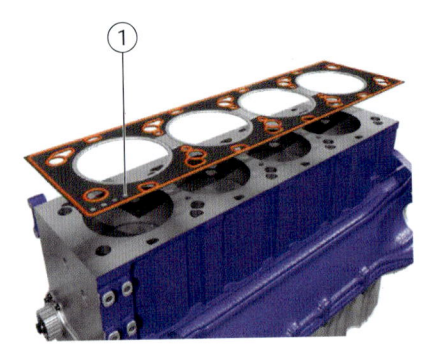

Fig. 77 Head gasket thickness indicator: 1. Number of holes indicates the thickness.

Fig. 78 Metal cylinder head gaskets are made up of multiple layers.

4. Head Gasket Materials

In addition to graphite-based gasket materials with metal and rubber rings, there are also metal gaskets. These consist of several plates with a coating. The profiling in the layers forms rings around the openings to be sealed. When installed, this profiling is compressed to create a tight seal. As with other types of gaskets, this type of gasket can only be used once.

5. Cylinder Head Bolts

Special cylinder head bolts are used to fasten the cylinder head to the engine block. The clamping force used to secure the head to the block is very important, because these bolts are heavily loaded during the power strokes.

In many cases, "torque to yield" bolts are used. After tightening the bolts to a specified torque, the bolts are then turned a certain number of degrees (angle) to the specified yield point.

The cylinder head bolts must be tightened using the correct sequence to avoid warping the head, which would cause a poor seal. The tightening procedure is usually carried out in multiple phases, to ensure the mutual difference between bolts is minimized.

This method of tightening also prevents the head gasket from getting damaged.

In the first stages, the bolts are tightened using a torque wrench, for example in phase 1: 22 ft-lb, phase 2: 44 ft-lb. In the final phase, the bolts are tightened a few degrees further using the torque angle meter, for example in phase 3: +120°.

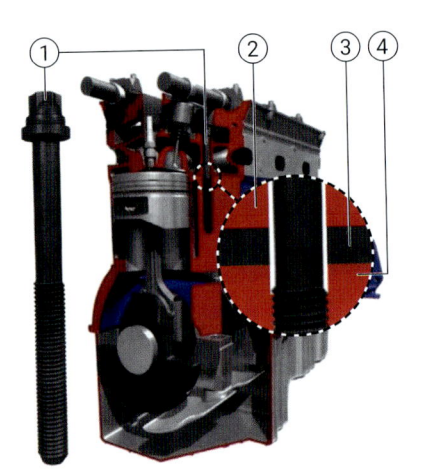

Fig. 79 Cylinder head bolts:
1. Cylinder head bolt. 2. Cylinder head. 3. Head gasket. 4. Block.

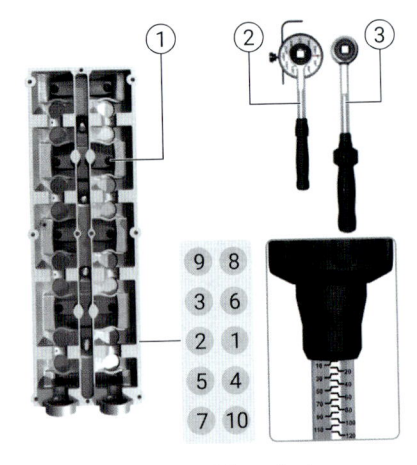

Fig. 80 Tightening of the cylinder head bolts: 1. Cylinder head bolt. 2. Torque angle meter. 3. Torque wrench.

6. Stretch Bolts

Cylinder head bolts may take the form of stretch bolts. A stretch bolt has a stretch section between the head and the thread, where the diameter is smaller than a "normal" bolt. This stretch section elongates (stretches) during the final phase of tightening. This means the bolt is put under maximum preload and the cylinder head gasket is clamped as firmly as possible between the cylinder head and the block.

The elongation of used stretch bolts is permanent; used stretch bolts are longer than new ones. Once a stretch bolt has been used, it must not be stretched again. The stretch bolt itself may even break. For this reason, stretch bolts always need to be replaced after disassembly.

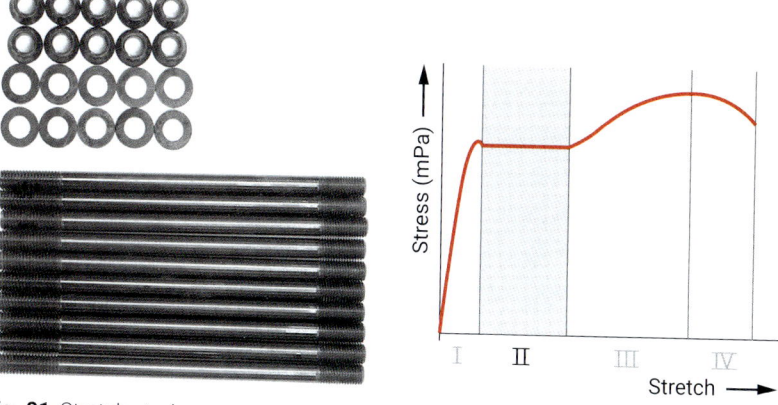

Fig. 81 Stretch studs.

Fig. 82 Stress-strain diagram: II shows the stress after tightening: constant pressure of the bolt on the material as its length changes.

7. Combustion Chamber

There are several different combustion chamber designs, including: flat, wedge-shaped, hemispherical and pent-roof.

Each shape has its own characteristics:
— Flat: large cooling surface which causes a lot of heat loss.
— Wedge: similar to flat, but with the valves behind each other and therefore only one camshaft.
— Hemispherical: small surface, low heat loss.
— Pent-roof: similar to hemispherical, but with larger valves.

In many situations, more than 2 valves are used per cylinder. This creates a larger flow area, which has the advantage of improved filling and transfer flow. The valves themselves can also be smaller, which has the advantage of enabling higher engine speeds (rpm).

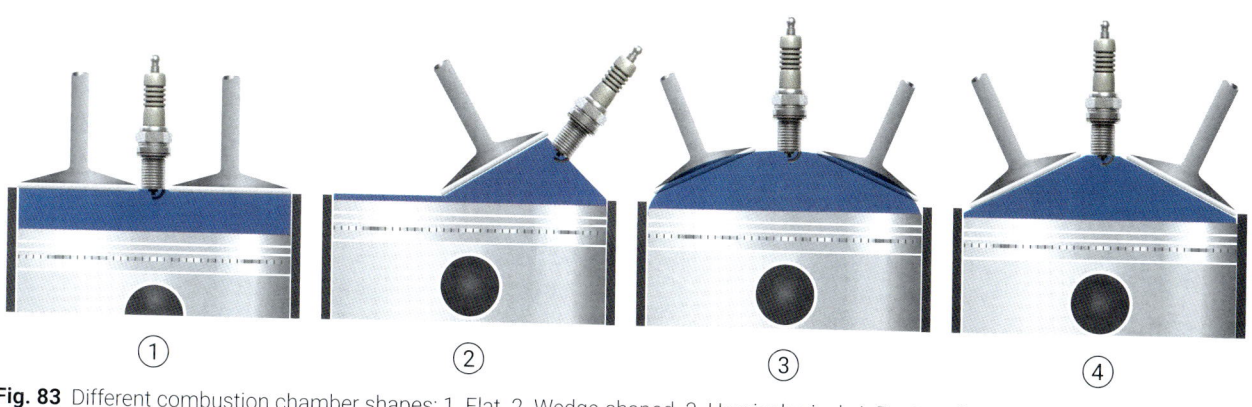

Fig. 83 Different combustion chamber shapes: 1. Flat. 2. Wedge-shaped. 3. Hemispherical. 4. Pent-roof.

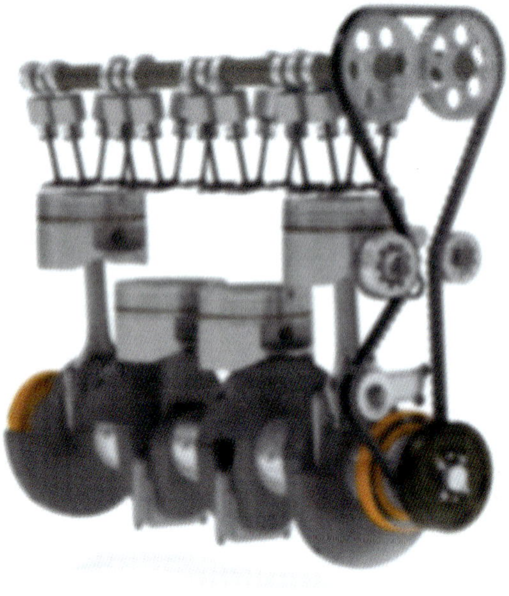

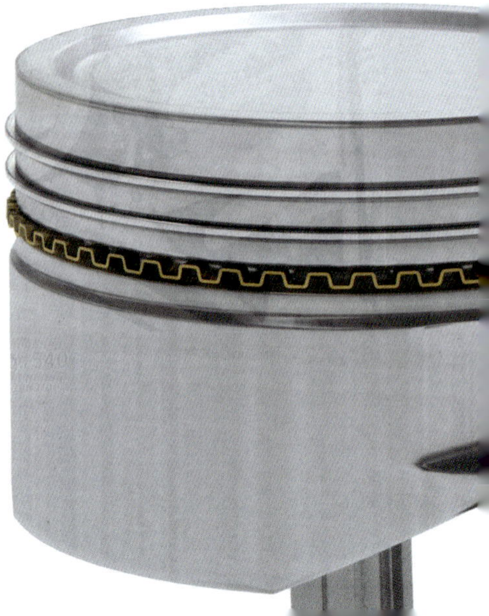

3. Piston and Connecting Rod

PISTONS

1. Introduction

Pistons take up the forces released by combustion. The piston pin and connecting rod transmit those forces to the crankshaft. The piston also ensures that the intake gases are pulled in, compressed and that exhaust gasses are forced out of the cylinder after combustion takes place.

Pistons for use in automobiles are mostly made from aluminum alloy. Details of the installation clearance, diameter and fitting direction can be found on the piston (see figure 187). The piston must be installed with the arrow pointing towards the front of the engine (timing chain/belt side).

Pistons are required to withstand high speed, rapid acceleration/deceleration, high pressure and intense heat. That's why requirements for pistons are extremely stringent.

Requirements:
— Light weight; which translates to less inertia.
— Low expansion when heated.

Fig. 84 Piston markings:
1. Assembly direction. 2. Assembly clearance. 3. Diameter.

- Able to withstand high temperatures.
- Effective heat conduction in order to prevent temperature differences.
- Good sliding properties.
- Extremely strong.

2. Construction

A piston consists of the following parts:

- **Piston Crown**
  This forms the top of the piston and can be either flat or domed as shown in the example.
- **Top Land**
  This is the side of the piston head above the piston rings. This area provides added strength and reduces heat flow to the rings.
- **Piston Ring Grooves**
  These are the recesses for the piston rings.
- **Piston Rings**
  These seal the space between the piston and the cylinder wall; preventing oil from entering the combustion chamber and combustion gasses from entering the crankcase. They also help channel away heat from the piston to the cylinder wall. The gap in the piston ring is known as the piston ring gap.
- **Piston Pin Aperture**
  The piston pin or wrist pin, which connects the piston to the connecting rod, sticks through this aperture (hole).
- **Piston Skirt**
  This guides the piston in the cylinder and conducts heat away from the piston to the cylinder wall.

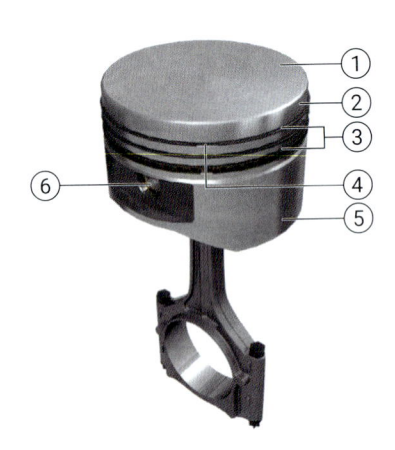

Fig. 85 Piston structure: 1. Piston crown. 2. Combustion ring. 3. Piston rings. 4. Piston ring groove. 5. Piston skirt. 6. Piston pin hole.

3. Types

There are different types of pistons with combinations of each.

The four most common types include:
- **Two-part piston** *(upper left)*
  The piston base is made from strong metal and is therefore able to withstand high combustion forces. The piston skirt is made of lightweight aluminum alloy, which helps to reduce mass.
- **Piston with combustion chamber** *(upper right)*
  The combustion chamber in many diesel engines is actually in the top of the piston rather than the cylinder head. As the piston

comes up on compression, air is swirled and compressed within the hollow of the piston. This design also works to increase compression.

— **Domed piston** *(lower left)*
Domed pistons are most commonly used in high performance gasoline engines. The domed area takes up space within the combustion chamber, effectively increasing the compression ratio. Valve recesses are cut in the top of the piston to allow space for the valves to open.

— **Dished piston** *(lower right)*
This design is frequently used in gasoline direct injected engines. The dish helps to direct the mixture for a more efficient burn.

Fig. 86 Various pistons: 1. Two-part piston. 2. Piston with combustion chamber. 3. Piston with valve cavities. 4. Piston with dish.

4. Heat Expansion

The cylinder expands as a result of the high temperatures in the engine.

In order to prevent the piston from sticking in the cylinder, pistons have a special shape when cold.

When the engine is cold, the piston is tapered and oval-shaped. As a result of its mass and distribution of the temperature, the piston acquires a cylindrical and round form as it warms up.

In some cases, compensation segments are used in order to evenly distribute the heat absorbed by the piston. Compensation segments take the form of steel pieces cast into the piston that are able to conduct the heat effectively.

If the cylinder is made from aluminum-silicon, the play between the piston and the cylinder can be kept small, as both expand by approximately the same amount.

Fig. 87 Cold piston.

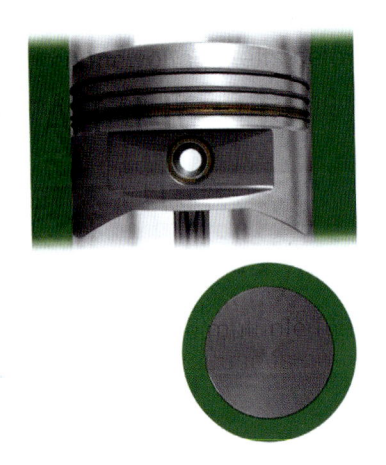

Fig. 88 Hot piston.

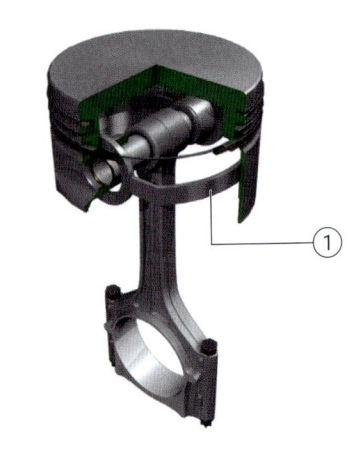

Fig. 89 Piston with compensation segment (1).

5. Compression Rings

Piston rings are highly important components of the piston.

We can distinguish between compression rings and bevelled-edge oil rings. Compression rings work with the lubrication oil to form an effective seal between the piston and the cylinder wall. Oil-control rings have two bevelled edges that scrape the oil from the cylinder wall. Compression rings are positioned in the upper two grooves. The oil control ring is positioned in the bottom groove.

There are different types of piston compression rings.
— Rectangular piston ring: simple and cheap to produce.
— Taper-faced ring: improves the in-flow process.
— Semi-keystone ring: combats the formation of a carbon layer.
— Napier ring: scrapes oil from the cylinder wall in addition to sealing compression.

When fitting compression rings, it is important to ensure that the ring gaps are not inline with one another. If this occurs, combustion gases will escape into the crankcase.

Fig. 90 Compression ring in the piston ring groove.

Fig. 91 Various types of piston ring: 1. Rectangular piston ring. 2. Taper-faced ring. 3. Semi-keystone ring. 4. Napier ring.

6. Bevelled-Edge Oil Rings

Bevelled-edge oil rings are responsible for wiping away excess oil from the cylinder wall, in order to prevent oil from entering the combustion chamber.

The following are two types of oil rings, together with their benefits:
— **Bevelled-edge oil rings**
   These scrape oil from the cylinder wall, resulting in lower oil consumption.
— **Bevelled-edge oil ring with expander ring**
   The expander ring provides increased contact pressure, enabling this piston ring to provide better performance than a conventional bevelled-edge oil ring.

As with compression rings, it's important not to align the ring gaps on oil control rings or oil could find its way into the combustion chamber.

Fig. 92 Beveled-edge oil control ring.

Fig. 93 Different shapes of beveled-edge oil control rings: 1. Beveled-edge oil control ring. 2. Beveled-edge oil control ring with expansion spring.

7. Piston Temperature

The piston is cooled in order to control its temperature. Cooling occurs by way of a lubricant film towards the cylinder wall. Splash lubrication from the crankshaft is also used. An oil spray nozzle can also be fitted. This sprays engine oil against the underside of the piston to cool the piston head.
This is known as piston cooling.

Fig. 94 Piston cooling: 1. Piston. 2. Oil spray nozzle.

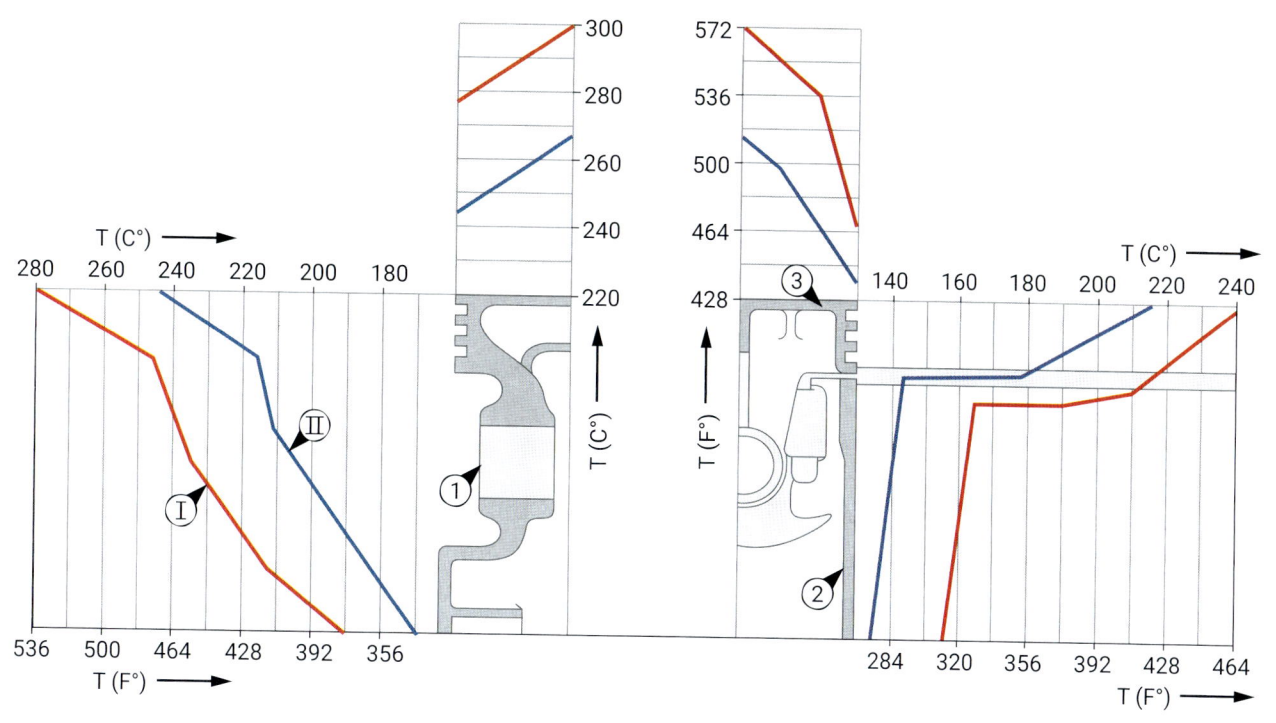

Fig. 95 I. Piston temperature profile without oil cooling. II. Piston temperature profile with oil cooling. 1. Temperature at piston pin hole. 2. Temperature at sliding surface side. 3. Temperature at piston head.

The piston temperature is lowered by means of piston cooling. The part of the piston located closest to the combustion gets the hottest. The temperature decreases as you move farther away from the combustion.

8. Piston Construction

The goal is to keep the weight of the piston as low as possible in order to achieve higher piston speeds.
This can be done by reducing the size of the piston skirt as much as possible or removing sections of it.

The piston has a graphite layer on it in order to optimize the sliding properties of the piston.
Graphite has excellent sliding characteristics and penetrates the surface layer of the piston.
The clearance between the piston and the cylinder wall is approximately 0.002 inches (0.05 mm), excluding the graphite layer. The graphite layer itself is around 0.0008 inches (0.02 mm) thick.

Fig. 96 Piston with graphite layer on the piston skirt.

MEASURING PISTON WEAR

The piston diameter can be measured to determine the degree of piston wear. Over time, the piston diameter reduces slightly due to friction between the cylinder wall and piston. Piston wear is measured as follows:

Fig. 97 Measuring piston diameter.

1. Measure the piston diameter with a micrometer. Consult the vehicle service information for the relevant vehicle for the correct location to measure the diameter. Usually, the diameter is measured at the bottom of the piston, just under the piston pin. Some manufacturers, however, also specify that the diameter needs to be measured at the level of the pin.

2. Compare the measured value with the specification in the vehicle service information and determine the difference between these two values.

3. The difference between the measured and specified values is the degree of wear. Consult the vehicle service information to determine whether the wear is still within specifications.

If the wear is exceeds the specifications, then the piston needs to be replaced.

MEASURING PISTON PIN WEAR AND CLEARANCE

The piston pin is inspected for wear by measuring the outer diameter of the piston pin. This is done as follows:

1. Use a micrometer to measure the piston pin diameter in the center of the pin and at both ends. It is not necessary to measure both ends of a piston pin that is pressed into the piston.
2. Compare the measured value with the specification in the vehicle service information and determine the difference between these two values.
3. The difference between the measured and specified values is the degree of wear. Consult the vehicle service information to determine whether the wear is still within specifications.

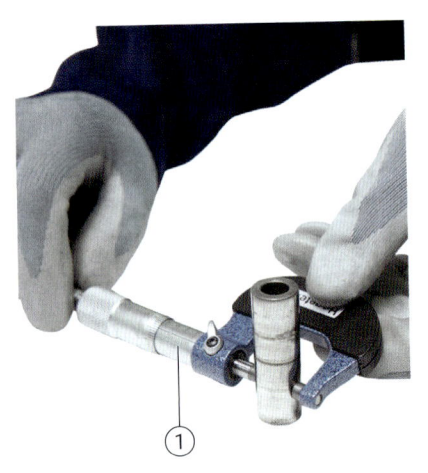

Fig. 98 1. Micrometer.

Fig. 99 Inner diameter of the piston pin journal.

With a floating piston pin, the piston pin clearance also needs to be established. This can be determined as follows:

1. Use a telescopic gauge or bore gauge to measure the inner diameter of the piston journal.
2. Use a micrometer to measure the outer diameter of the piston pin.
3. Piston pin clearance is the difference between the inner diameter of the piston journal and the outer diameter of the piston pin.

4. Compare the measured value against the information specified in the vehicle service information.

XYZ Engine	Piston pin diameter			Radial clearance		
	24 mm			max 0.09		
			Measured value			
			Left	Middle	Right	Conclusion
Cylinder 1	Piston pin diameter	Measurement 1	23.98	23.95	23.98	OK
		Measurement 2	23.97	23.95	23.95	OK
	Small-end	Measurement 1	24.05	24.07	24.07	
		Measurement 2	24.06	24.05	24.04	
	Radial clearance		0.09	0.12	0.12	not OK

Fig. 100 Measurement table of axial piston pin clearances.

Replace the piston if the piston pin clearance is greater than specified.

In some cases, it is also possible to bore out the piston journal. An oversize piston pin can then be used in this case.

DETERMINING PISTON CLEARANCE

Piston clearance is determined by measuring the difference between the inner diameter of the cylinder and the piston diameter. The steps below describe how this is done:

- Set a micrometer to the reference cylinder diameter. The reference diameter is the cylinder diameter given in the technical specifications.
- If necessary, carefully place the micrometer in a bench vice. Make sure that you only tighten the bench vice gently - just tight enough to hold the micrometer.
- With the bore gauge, select a measuring pin and shims as required to make up the reference cylinder diameter. Consult the operating instructions for the bore gauge if necessary.
- Place the bore gauge in the micrometer, which is set to the reference cylinder diameter. Move the bore gauge up and down, noting where the bore gauge needle changes direction.

Fig. 101 Reference cylinder diameter.

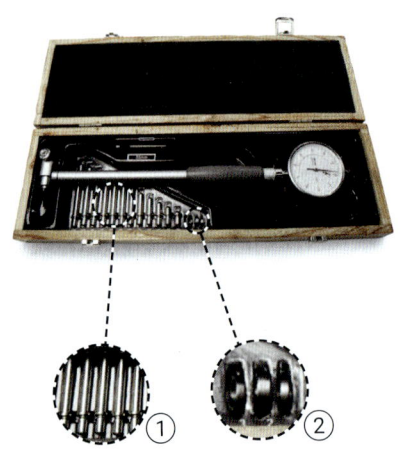

Fig. 102 Bore gauge: 1. Measuring pin. 2. Shims.

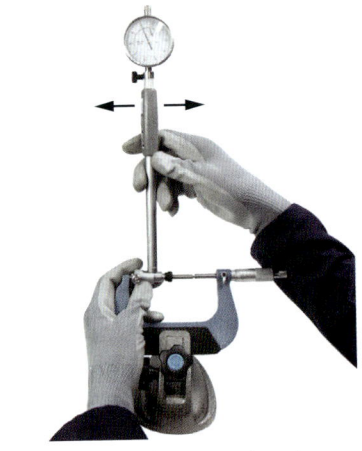

Fig. 103 Use the micrometer to set the bore gauge.

- Set the dial gauge to 0 at the exact point where the needle changes direction. Consult the operating instructions for the bore gauge if necessary.
- The 0 point now corresponds to the reference diameter.
- Everything measured by the bore gauge is compared with the 0 point, i.e. the reference cylinder diameter. The measured value

can therefore be smaller or larger than the reference cylinder diameter.
— Place the bore gauge in the bottom of the cylinder, where there is the least wear.
— Move the bore gauge back and forth, noting where the bore gauge needle changes direction.
— Now read off the value. Consult the operating instructions for the bore gauge if necessary.
— Depending on the measurement, the measured value is added to or subtracted from the reference value.

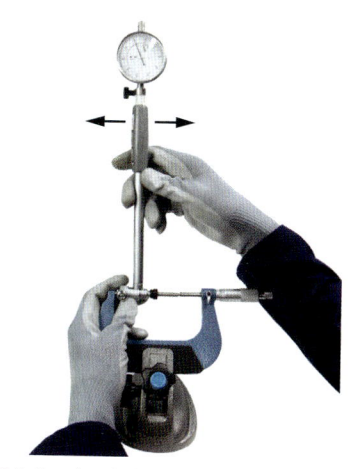

Fig. 104 Set the dial gauge to 0.

Fig. 105 Measure the inner diameter of the cylinder.

Fig. 106 Measure the diameter of the piston.

— Then use a micrometer to measure the piston diameter. Consult the vehicle service information for the relevant vehicle for the correct location to measure the diameter. Usually, the diameter is measured at the bottom of the piston, just under the piston pin. Some manufacturers, however, also specify that the diameter needs to be measured at the level of the pin.
— Determine the difference between the inner diameter of the cylinder and the diameter of the piston.
— The difference between the measured and specified values is the clearance. Consult the vehicle service information to determine whether the clearance is within specifications.

If the cylinder clearance is too great, this can be solved by:
— Installing a new standard size piston. This can only be done if the cylinder diameter is still within the specifications.
— Boring out all of the cylinders and installing oversized pistons.

PISTON RING GAP AND PISTON RING CLEARANCE

1. Piston Ring Gap

Piston ring gap is the clearance between the two ends of the piston ring when the piston is in the cylinder. The following steps describe how ring gap is measured:

— Place a single piston ring in the cylinder.
— Push the piston ring into the cylinder with the piston crown. This ensures that the piston ring "hangs" straight in the cylinder.
— Take a feeler gauge and measure the size of the gap between the two ends of the piston ring.

If the ring gap is too small, a bit of material can be removed from both ends of the piston ring using a file.
If the ring gap is too large, the piston rings may be too worn. If there is excessive end clearance when new piston rings are used, it may mean that the diameter of the cylinder has become too large.

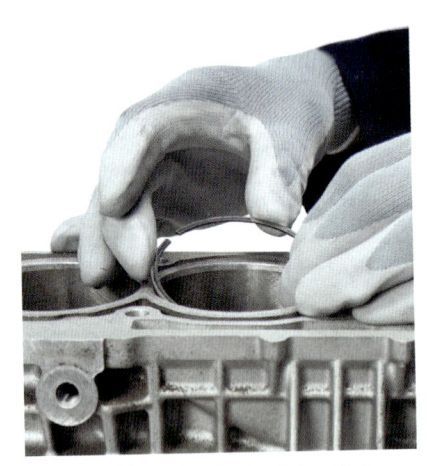

Fig. 107 Place the single piston ring in the cylinder.

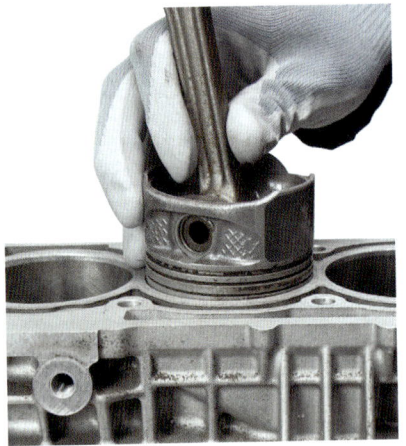

Fig. 108 Push the piston ring into the cylinder with the piston.

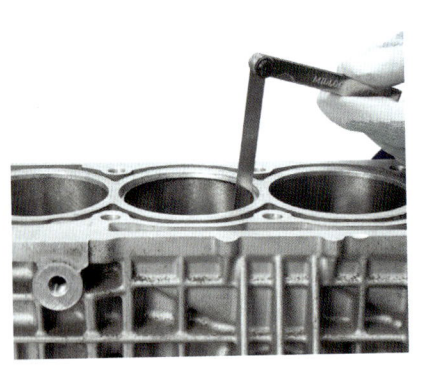

Fig. 109 Measure the piston ring gap.

2. Piston Ring Installation

When installing new piston rings in the old piston, the piston ring groove needs to be cleaned thoroughly.

The piston rings are bent carefully into the grooves of the piston by hand. Special tools are also available to make the fitting of piston rings easier.

When installing piston rings, make sure that the openings or spring gaps are not positioned above one other. If these openings are installed above one other, then the rings will not seal as efficiently and result in a loss of compression.

3. Piston Ring Clearance

Inspect the piston ring clearance before the piston rings are installed.

Piston ring clearance is determined as follows:

— Use a new piston ring and a feeler gauge.
— Place the new piston ring in the groove and measure the vertical clearance using the feeler gauge.
— Determine whether the piston ring clearance is within the specifications stated in the vehicle service information .

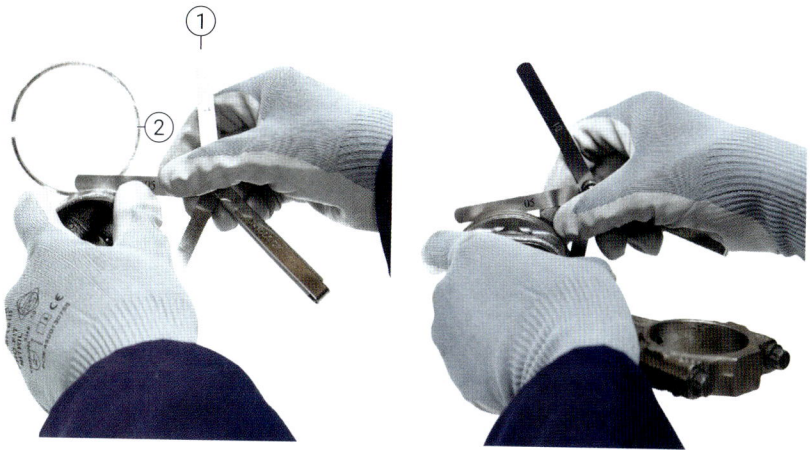

Fig. 110 1. Feeler gauge. 2. New piston ring.

Fig. 111 Measure the groove clearance for all grooves.

CONNECTING ROD

1. Introduction

The connecting rod connects the piston to the crankshaft. The function of the connecting rod is:
- To work together with the crankshaft and convert the up and down movement of the piston into a rotating movement
- To transfer force from the piston to the crankshaft

The cross-section of the connecting rod is usually I-shaped but can also be H-shaped. These shapes make the connecting rod strong while keeping the mass low.

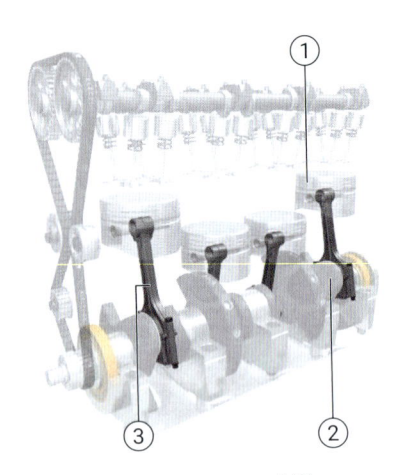

Fig. 112 The connecting rod (3) connects the piston (1) with the crankshaft (2).

2. Construction

Most connecting rods are made of alloy steel or light metal.

The top end of a connecting rod is called the small end. The piston is fitted to the small end with a piston pin.

The bottom or big end of the connecting rod is fitted to the crankshaft and secured by a bearing cap.

Two friction bearing shells are positioned between the crankshaft and connecting rod. A thin film of oil provides lubrication to the bearing when the engine is running.

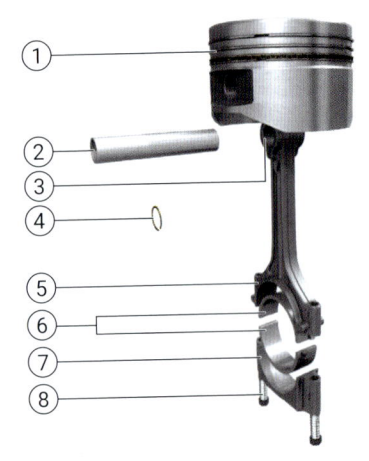

Fig. 113 Connecting rod structure: 1. Piston. 2. Piston pin or wrist pin. 3. Small end. 4. Circlip. 5. Big end. 6. Bearing shells. 7. Connecting rod bearing cap. 8. Bolt.

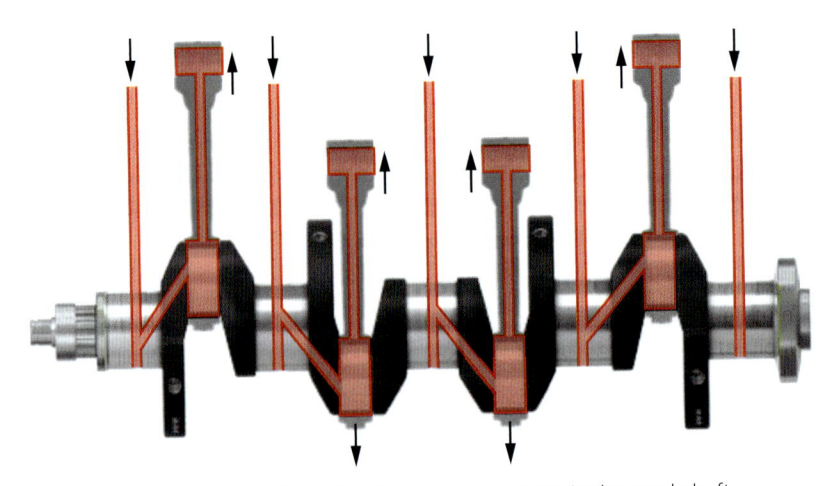

Fig. 114 The connecting rods are lubricated via passages in the crankshaft.

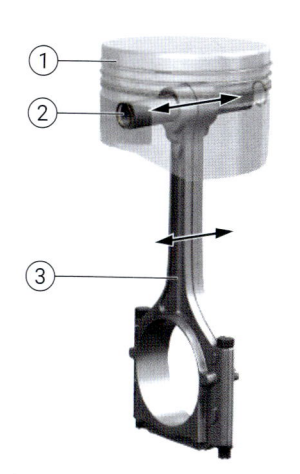

Fig. 115 Piston pin movement:
1. Piston. 2. Piston pin.
3. Connecting rod.

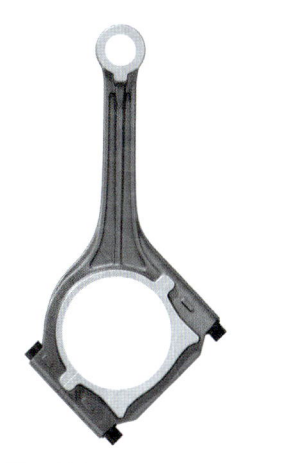

Fig. 116 Diagonally split connecting rod.

3. Piston Pin

The piston pin forms a "pivot" connection with the connecting rod. This is accomplished in 3 ways:

— **Fixed (stationary) piston pin**

This piston pin is rigidly fastened to the piston. The piston pin can turn in the connecting rod.

— **Semi-floating pin**

This piston pin is fixed to the connecting rod. The piston pin can turn in the piston.

— **Full-floating pin**

This piston pin can turn in the connecting rod and in the piston. The pin is secured on both ends by spring clips.

4. Construction

If the big end of a rod is large enough, it is possible to split it diagonally. This allows a connecting rod to be removed from the cylinder.

The connecting rod shank is between the small end and the big end. It is loaded by tensile, bending and buckling forces.

The connecting rod shank must be strong and rigid because of the strong centrifugal and compressive forces (forces resulting from the piston weight and the engine speed) acting on it. For this reason, the connecting rod is forged in a high-grade steel alloy. Materials used include molybdenum, manganese and chromium.

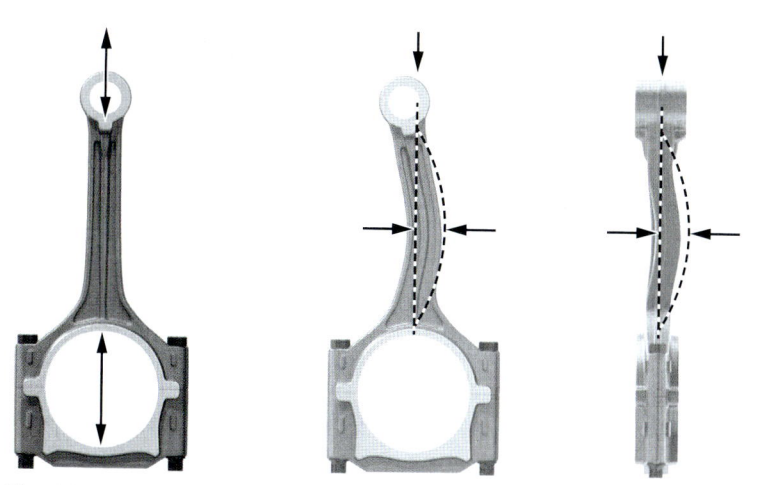

Fig. 117 Forces acting on a connecting rod.

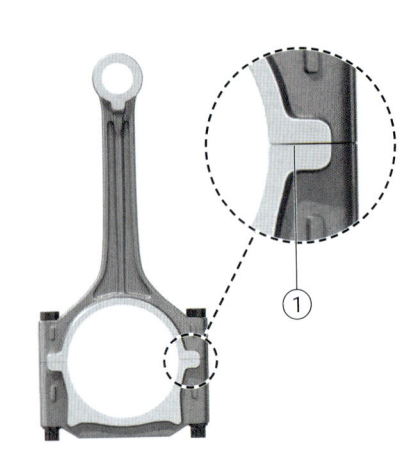

Fig. 118 Fracture line as part of a scoured surface (1).

Because of the forces acting on the connecting rod bearings, the fit between the connecting rod and bearing cap needs to be perfect. This is why connecting rod bearing caps are often fractured from the connecting rod, which ensures the bearing cap fits precisely.

With this method, the connecting rod and bearing caps are produced as a complete unit. The surface between the connecting rod and bearing cap is then scored with a laser. After this, the connecting rod and the connecting rod bearing caps are broken apart at the scoured line. Fractured-cap connecting rods and bearing caps must never be interchanged because every fracture is unique.

PLEASE NOTE It is important to install the connecting rod bearing caps back onto the respective connecting rod immediately after disassembly. This is to prevent dirt from getting into the precisely fitted area.

MEASURING CONNECTING ROD BEARING CLEARANCE

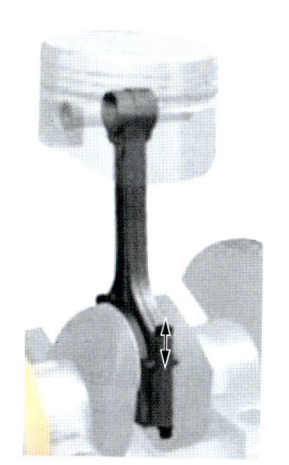

Fig. 119 Radial connecting rod bearing clearance.

1. Introduction

Radial connecting rod bearing clearance is the clearance between the bearing shells and the crankpin. There always needs to be a minimum clearance between the bearing shell and the crankpin so that the oil film can pass between these two components.

If there is too much radial clearance, the connecting rod has excessive space to move up and down. This can cause serious vibration and knocking in the engine. Oil will also run out from between the bearings, causing a loss of proper lubrication.

If there is not enough radial clearance it will result in too much friction during the rotation of the engine. This can cause excessive wear and heating of the bearing shells.

Radial bearing clearance is determined by the thickness of the bearing shell. The bearing shell can be adjusted by installing a bearing shell of a different thickness. Radial bearing clearance depends on the make and model of the vehicle. Therefore, the correct clearance always needs to be taken from the vehicle service information of the relevant vehicle.

Measuring the radial connecting rod bearing clearance is basically the same as measuring the radial crankshaft main bearing clearance. There are two methods of measuring radial bearing clearance:

1. Using a micrometer and bore gauge.
2. With Plastigauge.

2. Micrometer and Bore Gauge

Measuring the bearing clearance using a micrometer and bore gauge is a precise method consisting of the following steps:

- Use a micrometer to measure the outer diameter of the crankpin. Measure the diameter at several different positions to make sure that the crankpin is round.
- Lock the micrometer as soon as you have measured the diameter.
- Use the micrometer as a reference for the bore gauge.
- Put the internal micrometer inside the bore gauge and set the bore gauge dial to 0. Consult the operating instructions for the bore gauge if necessary.

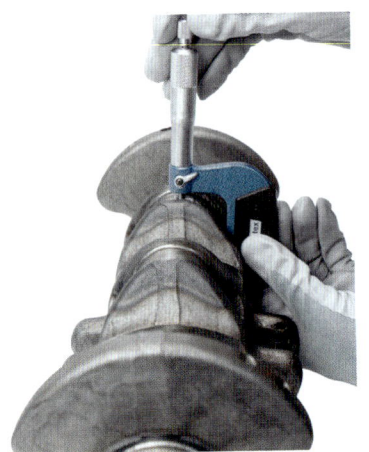

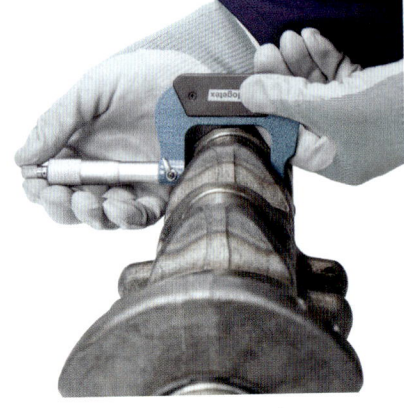

Fig. 120 Measure the diameter of the crankpin with the micrometer.

Fig. 121 Measure at several positions.

- Consult the vehicle service information for the vehicle you are working on. Review the installation instructions for the connecting rod bearing cap carefully. Take particular note of the following points:
    - Bearing cap reference marks.
    - Lubrication of the bearing cap bolts before installation.
    - Torque for tightening the bearing cap bolts.
- Next, install the bearing shells in the big end of the connecting rod according to the specifications for the vehicle you are working on. When doing so, pay attention to any reference marks on the bearing shells, connecting rod and bearing cap which indicate the proper installation locations.
- Tighten the bearing cap to the torque specified in the vehicle service information for the vehicle you are working on.
- Then place the bore gauge in the big end hole with the bearing shells installed inside and measure the inner diameter.
- Now subtract the measured inner diameter from the outer diameter of the crankpin. The difference is the bearing clearance.
- Check this value against the value specified in the vehicle service information.

— Repeat the process for the other connecting rod bearings.

Fig. 122 Use the micrometer to set the bore gauge.

Fig. 123 Measure the inner diameter of the big end.

Fig. 124 Measure at several positions.

XYZ Engine	Axial connecting rod bearing clearance	Radial connecting rod bearing clearance	Diameter crank pin				
	0.37	0.08	47.8 -0.022/ -0.042				
				Measured value			
				Left	Middle	Right	Conclusion
Cilinder1	Crank pin		Measurement 1	47.772	47.771	47.768	OK
			Measurement 2	47.773	47.77	47.765	OK
	Big-end		Measurement 1	47.92	47.917	47.92	
			Measurement 2	47.921	47.915	47.922	
	Radial clearance			0.149	0.147	0.157	Not OK
	Axial play					0.35	OK

Fig. 125 Measurement table of connecting rod clearances (values in mm).

3. Plastigauge

Plastigauge is a plastic thread developed especially for measuring radial bearing clearances. The advantage of Plastigauge is that no expensive measuring tools are required to be able to measure the radial clearance. The disadvantage, however, is that the measuring method with Plastigauge is less precise than the measuring method using a micrometer and bore gauge.

There are three different Plastigauge sizes because the radial connecting rod bearing clearance can vary according to the vehicle's make and model:

1. Green Plastigauge, designed for bearing clearances of 0.001 to 0.003 inches (0.025 to 0.076 mm).
2. Red Plastigauge, designed for bearing clearances of 0.002 to 0.006 inches (0.051 to 0.152 mm).
3. Blue Plastigauge, designed for bearing clearances of 0.004 to 0.009 inches (0.102 to 0.229 mm).

Fig. 126 Select the correct Plastigauge and cut off a piece.

Fig. 127 Place the strip on the connecting rod bearing, in the longitudinal direction of the crankshaft.

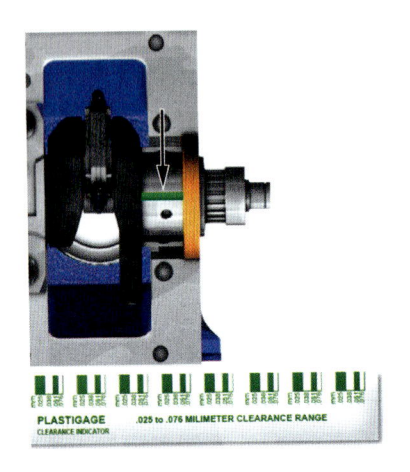

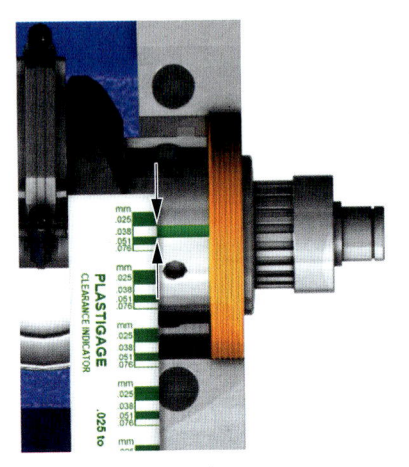

Fig. 128 Based on the measurement strip, determine the measured clearance.

Measuring the connecting rod bearing clearance using Plastigauge consists of the following steps:
— Place a piece of Plastigauge on the crankpin in the longitudinal direction of the crankshaft.
— Install the connecting rod with bearing shells onto the crankpin according to the specifications for the vehicle you are working on.
— Tighten the connecting rod bearing caps to the torque specified in the vehicle service information of the vehicle you are working on.
— Then remove the connecting rod.
— Check the radial clearance using the measuring scale on the Plastigauge packaging.
— Check the measured value against the value specified in the vehicle service information.
— Repeat the measurement for the other connecting rod bearings. Carefully remove any residual Plastigauge.

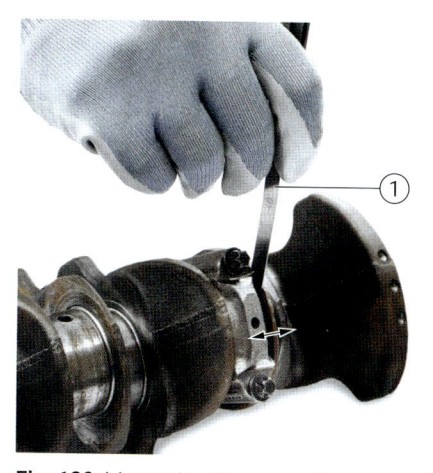

Fig. 129 Measuring the connecting rod side clearance. 1. Feeler gauge.

4. Measuring the Connecting Rod Side Clearance.

Side clearance of the connecting rod is the distance between the side of the connecting rod and the crankshaft web or another connecting rod.

Side clearance is determined using a feeler gauge between the connecting rod and crank web or from connecting rod to connecting rod. After taking the measurement, compare the measured value with the value specified in the vehicle service information of the relevant vehicle.

If the side clearance is not within specifications, the connecting rod needs to be replaced or the crank web ground to fit.

5. Measuring the Small End

The diameter of the small end can be measured to determine the degree of wear. If the wear exceeds specifications, the bushing in the small end needs to be replaced with a new bushing.

The small end diameter is measured as follows:
— Use a telescopic gauge or bore gauge to measure the inner diameter of the small end.
— Take at least two measurements at 90° to measure the ovality of the small end.
— Also take at least two measurements at different depths in the small end to check whether it is parallel.
— Compare the measured values against the values specified in the vehicle service information.

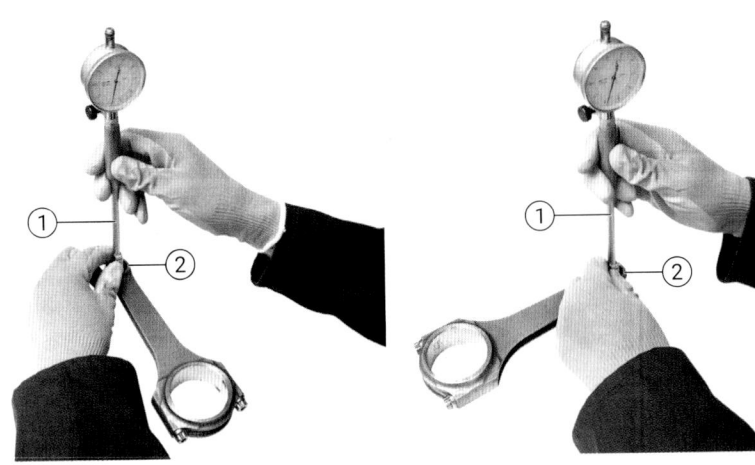

Fig. 130 1. Telescopic gauge.
2. Small end.

Fig. 131 Take several measurements.

POLISHING THE CONNECTING ROD

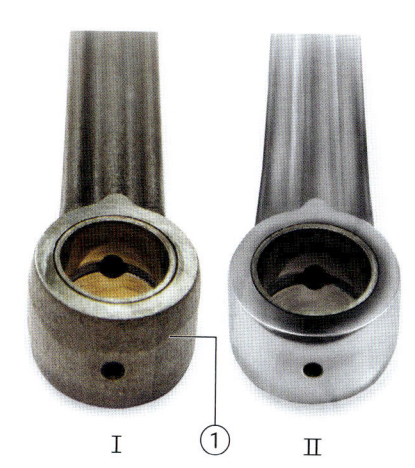

Fig. 132 I. Unpolished connecting rod. II. Polished connecting rod. 1. Casting edge.

Connecting rods are often polished to prevent them from fracturing and breaking when they are installed in engines that run at high speeds and have a high compression ratio. In this type of engine, the connecting rod is exposed to high axial loading; i.e. the connecting rod is continuously being subjected to a strong pushing and pulling forces.

This load is not evenly distributed over the connecting rod; the load is concentrated at specific points. The loading at these points is very high and the connecting rod could potentially break at such a point.

The load is concentrated at the sharp corners, such as in the casting edges of cast iron connecting rods. Once a crack has formed in this location, the crack will increase in size and can ultimately result in the connecting rod breaking.

In general, rounded corners spread the load better over a larger surface than sharp corners. That is why the sharper edges on connecting rods are rounded off to make them stronger.
The illustration shows an example of a standard connecting rod and a polished connecting rod with the casting edges removed.

PISTON BORE OFFSET

1. Introduction

Offset of the piston pin means that the pin is not located at mid width of the piston.

If the piston pin is not located in the middle of the piston, you must fit the piston in a specific direction. On the piston there is an arrow indicating the mounting direction of the piston.
The arrow must point in the direction of the timing chain or belt.

If there is an arrow on the piston, it does not always mean that the piston bore is offset. There are also other reasons for fitting a piston in a particular direction.

Fig. 133 The piston pin is positioned off-center.

Fig. 134 The arrow indicates how the piston is to be installed.

Fig. 135 It is also sometimes possible to see the piston bore offset on the underside of the piston.

2. Without piston bore offset

In an engine that runs clockwise, the connecting rod pushes the piston against the right cylinder wall when it moves up. When the connecting rod is standing vertically at TDC, the connecting rod pulls the piston down. At this moment the piston switches sides and pushes the piston against the left cylinder wall.

Fig. 136 Without piston bore offset

During the power stroke, powerful forces act on the piston, and it changes sides with great force. This causes considerable noise and wear of the cylinder wall and the piston.

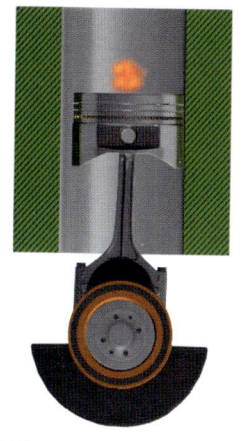

Fig. 137 The piston is about to switch sides at TDC.

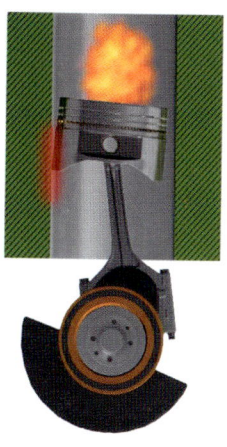

Fig. 138 The piston tilts and is pushed against the left cylinder wall by the pressure of the power stroke.

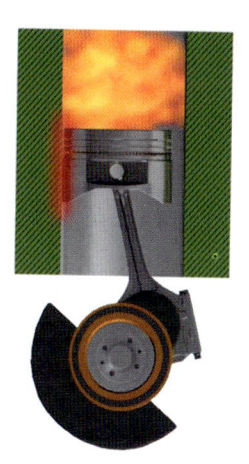

Fig. 139 The piston is now positioned entirely on the left cylinder wall.

3. With piston bore offset

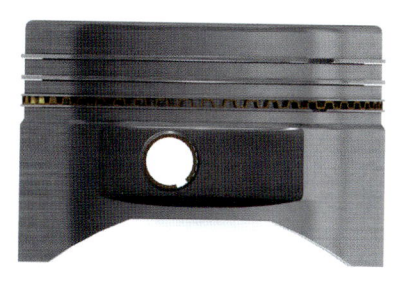

Fig. 140 With piston bore offset

If the piston pin is not located in the middle of the piston, the connecting rod will already be standing vertically before TDC. The piston then already changes sides before TDC. This ensures that the piston does not change sides with great force during the power stroke. There is less noise, and the piston and cylinder suffer less wear.

Fig. 141 The piston is about to switch sides, even before TDC.

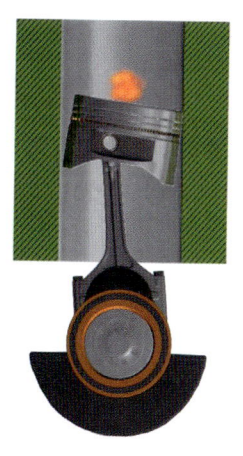

Fig. 142 The piston switches sides at TDC.

Fig. 143 The piston is now positioned entirely on the left cylinder wall as the power stroke begins.

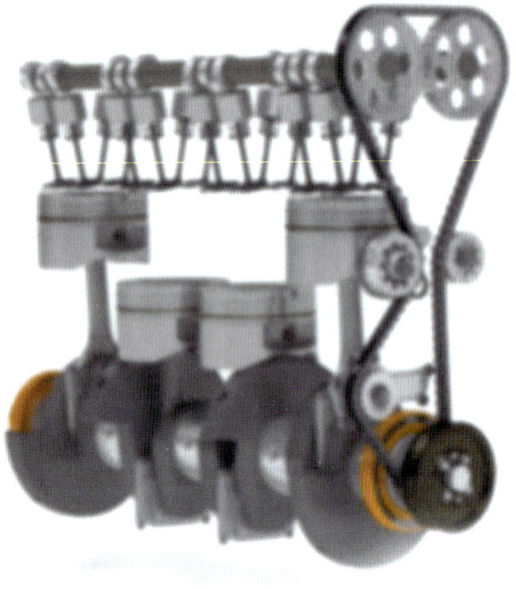

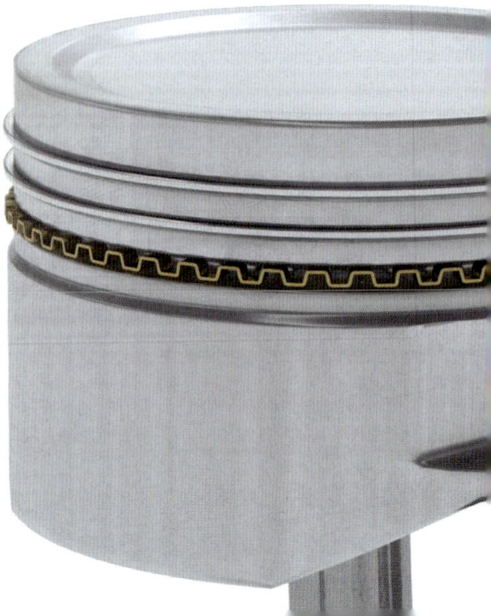

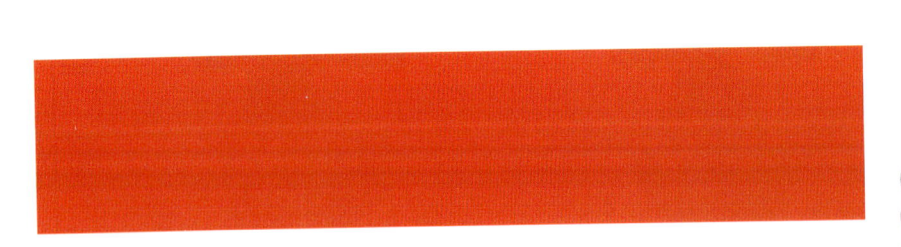

4. Crankshaft

CRANKSHAFT

1. Introduction

The crankshaft is the main shaft of the engine. Its primary task is to drive the wheels via the drivetrain as well as the camshaft(s) by means of a timing belt or chain.

The crankshaft is made from a single piece of cast iron or steel.

The crankshaft consists of:
- crankshaft main journals - these connect the crankshaft to the engine block.
- connecting rod journals; the connecting rods are connected with the crankshaft at this point.
- counter weights - these ensure that the crankshaft is balanced.

A crankshaft must be balanced in order to operate with minimum vibration.

Fig. 144 The crankshaft:
1. Connecting rod bearing journal. 2. Main bearing cap. 3. Main bearing journal. 4. Counterweight.

2. Crank Angle

The connecting rod journals are at a certain angle to one another. This angle is known as the crank angle. This angle is selected in such a way so that the power strokes of the engine are equally distributed.

In a 4-stroke engine, there is 1 power stroke for every 2 revolutions. Two revolutions is the equivalent of 720° of rotation. You can calculate the crank angle if you divide 720° by the number of cylinders the engine has. One or more connecting rods may be attached to a single connecting rod bearing journal. This primarily depends on the type of engine block.

Fig. 145 The crankshafts for various engine block types: 1. V engine. 2. Boxer engine. 3. In-line engine.

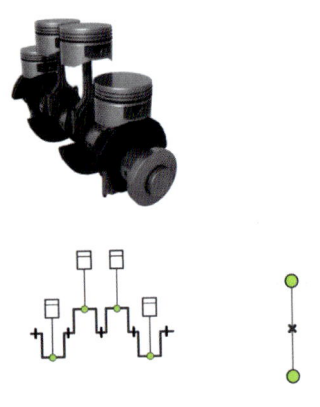

Fig. 146 The crank angle for a four-cylinder in-line engine is 180°.

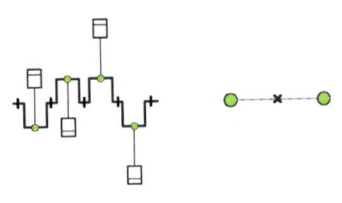

Fig. 147 The crank angle for a four-cylinder boxer engine is 180°.

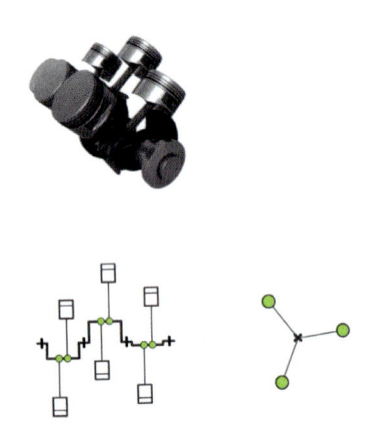

Fig. 148 The crank angle for a six-cylinder V engine is 120°.

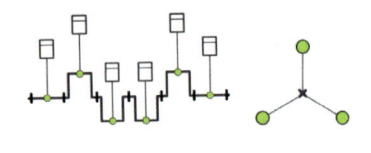

Fig. 149 The crank angle for a six-cylinder in-line engine is 120°.

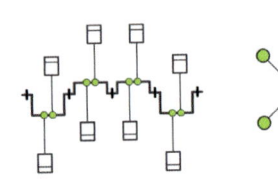

Fig. 150 The crank angle for an eight-cylinder V engine is 90°.

3. Lubrication

The crankshaft is a moving part and requires lubrication. The oil is directed to the bearing journals.

The crankshaft main journals have a direct oil supply from the engine block. The connecting rod journals have supply passages via the crankshaft journals.

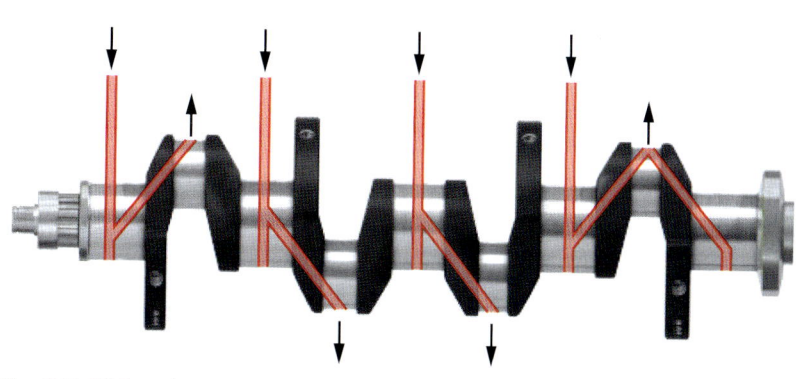

Fig. 151 Oil flow through the crankshaft.

4. Bearings

The crankshaft rotates and therefore requires bearings. It is able to revolve thanks to main bearings. Each crank journal is enclosed by a main bearing assembly. A main bearing consists of two bearing shells. Each bearing shell has a recess so that it is only able to fit in the bearing cap one way.

The crankshaft also includes bearings in an axial direction. Axial means along its length. Thrust bearings can be found on one or both sides of the crankshaft.

The main bearings are made of a softer material than the crankshaft itself. That way, only the bearing shells need to be replaced in the event of wear and tear.

Between the bearing shells and bearing journals is a film of oil, the purpose of which is to keep wear and heat accumulation to a minimum.

Fig. 152 Axial and radial crankshaft bearings.

Fig. 153 Crankshaft main bearings: 1. Radial bearing shell. 2. Axial bearing.

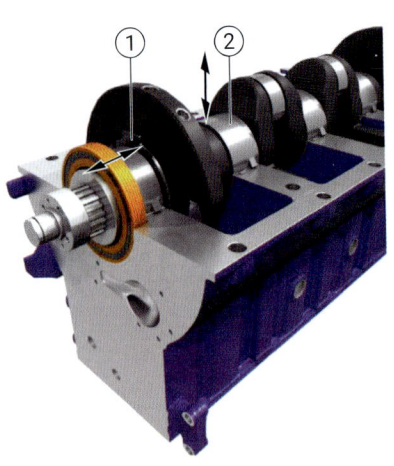

Fig. 154 Radial and axial bearings of the crankshaft: 1. Axial bearing. 2. Radial bearing shell.

5. Construction

Crankshafts may be made of forged or cast steel. The bearing journal surfaces are hardened to make them resistant to wear and ensure that they remain tough.

Bearings

A bearing shell can be made of various materials.

The innermost layer is the running surface. This is where the shaft rotates. It is made of a very soft alloy of lead-indium or white metal. Any hard particles released through wear are captured and therefore do not travel any further.

There may be a layer of nickel between the running surface and lead-bronze layer to ensure that the running surface does not come into contact with the lead-bronze.

The lead-bronze layer is attached to the steel shell. It consists of 75% copper, 23.5% lead and 1.5% tin.

The steel shell forms the carrier and provides the mechanical strength.

Fig. 155 Crankshaft: 1. Hardened layer on crankpins.

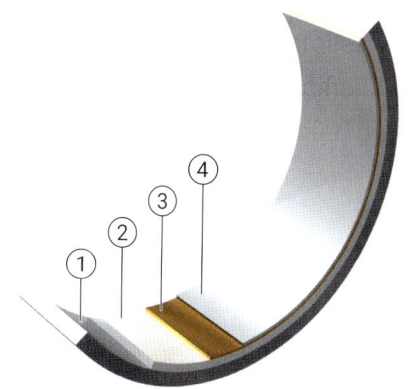

Fig. 156 Bearing shell structure: 1. Steel shell. 2. Lead-bronze layer. 3. Protective layer. 4. Running surface.

MEASURING RADIAL MAIN BEARING WEAR

1. Introduction

Radial main bearing clearance is the clearance between the bearing shells and the crankshaft bearings. There must always be a minimum clearance between these two components to allow the oil film to pass between the bearing shell and the crankshaft bearing.

The crankshaft may start to vibrate and shake with excessive radial clearance. This can cause bearing shells and bearing caps to get damaged. If there is not enough radial clearance, there will be too much friction during the rotation of the crankshaft. This can cause excessive wear and heating of the bearing shells.

Fig. 157 Radial clearance of the crankshaft.

Radial bearing clearance is determined by the thickness of the bearing shell. The bearing shell can be adjusted by installing a bearing shell of a different thickness.

Radial bearing clearance depends on the make and model of the vehicle. Therefore, the correct clearance always needs to be taken from the vehicle service information of the relevant vehicle.

A rule of thumb for correct bearing clearance is:
— 0.0001 inch (0.025 mm) of bearing clearance per 1 inch (25 mm) crankshaft diameter.

There are two methods of measuring radial bearing clearance:

1. Using a micrometer and bore gauge.
2. With Plastigauge.

2. Micrometer and Bore Gauge

Measuring the bearing clearance using a micrometer and bore gauge is a precise method consisting of the following steps:
- Install the bearing shells and bearing caps according to the specifications for the vehicle you are working on.
- Tighten the bearing caps to the torque specified in the vehicle service information of the vehicle you are working on.
- Use a micrometer to measure the diameter of the crankshaft main bearing. Measure the diameter at several points to make sure that the bearing is round.
- Lock the micrometer as soon as you have measured the diameter.
- Use the micrometer as a reference for the bore gauge:
  - Put the internal micrometer inside the bore gauge and set the bore gauge dial to 0.
- Put the bore gauge between the installed bearing shells and measure the difference between the inner diameter of the bearing shells and the outer diameter of the main bearing.
- The difference is the bearing clearance.
- Check the measured value against the value specified in the vehicle service information.
- Repeat the process for the other main bearings.

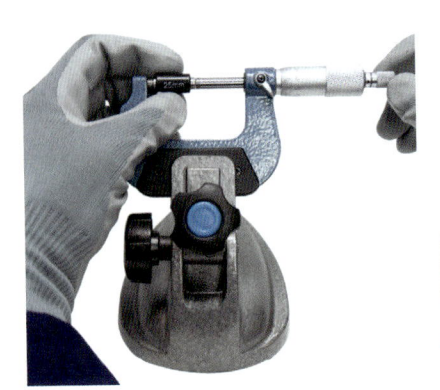

392 GASOLINE ENGINE CONSTRUCTION AND OPERATION

Fig. 158 Check the zero level setting of the micrometer.

Fig. 159 Measure the diameter of the main bearing with the micrometer.

Fig. 160 Measure at several points.

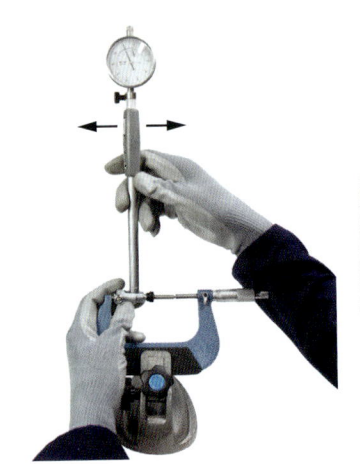

Fig. 161 Use the micrometer as a reference for the bore gauge.

Fig. 162 Measure the inner diameter of the bearing shell at several points.

XYZ Engine	Axial play	Radial clearance	Main bearing journal			Crank pin diameter
	0.07-0.17	0.03-0.08 warelimit 0.17	54 -0.022/-0.042			47.8 -0.022/-0.042
			Measured value			
			Left	Middle	Right	Conclusion
Bearing 1	Bearing	Measurement 1	53.965	53.97	53.963	OK
		Measurement 2	53.965	53.97	53.969	OK
	Crankshaft	Measurement 1	53.915	53.87	53.923	OK
		Measurement 2	53.915	53.87	53.925	OK
	Play		0.05	0.1	0.046	OK

Fig. 163 Measurement table of radial crankshaft clearances (values in mm).

3. Plastigauge

Plastigauge is a plastic thread developed especially for measuring radial bearing clearances. The advantage of Plastigauge is that no expensive measuring tools are required to be able to measure the radial clearance. The disadvantage, however, is that the measuring method with Plastigauge is less precise than the measuring method using a micrometer and bore gauge. There are three different Plastigauge sizes because the radial main bearing clearance can vary according to the vehicle's make and model:

1. Green Plastigauge for bearing clearances of 0.001 to 0.003" (0.025 to 0.076 mm).
2. Red Plastigauge for bearing clearances of 0.002 to 0.006" (0.051 to 0.152 mm).
3. Blue Plastigauge for bearing clearances of 0.004 to 0.009" (0.102 to 0.229 mm).

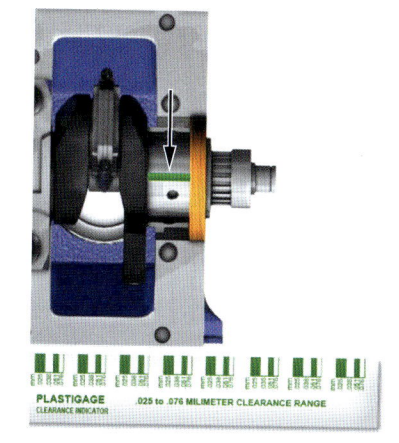

Fig. 164 Select the correct type of Plastigauge according to the manufacturer's information.

Fig. 165 Place the strip on the main bearing, in the longitudinal direction of the crankshaft.

Measuring the main bearing clearance using Plastigauge consists of the following steps:

— Place a piece of Plastigauge on the main bearing in the longitudinal direction of the crankshaft.
— Install the bearing shells and bearing caps according to the specifications for the vehicle you are working on.
— Tighten the bearing caps to the torque specified in the vehicle service information of the vehicle you are working on.
— Then remove the bearing shells and bearing caps.

- Compare the compressed thread with the measuring scale on the Plastigauge packaging to determine the radial clearance.
- Compare the measured value against the value specified in the vehicle service information.
- Repeat the measurement for the other main bearings.
- Remove any residual Plastigauge carefully from the main bearings and bearing shells.

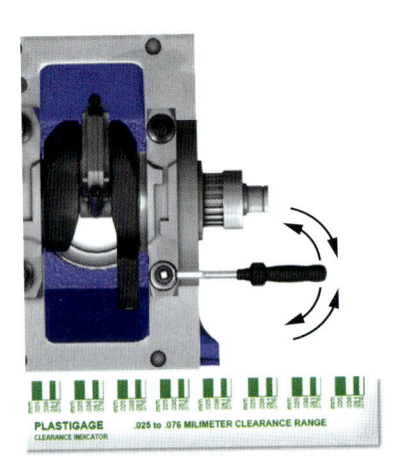

Fig. 166 Tighten the bearing caps to the specified torque.

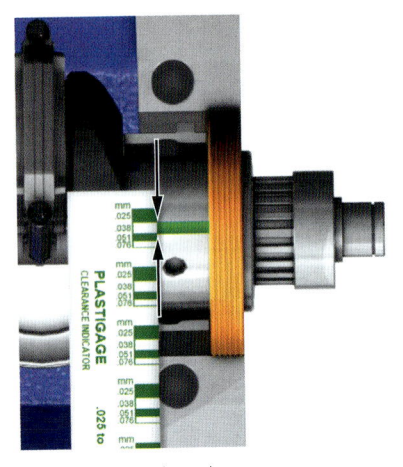

Fig. 167 Based on the measurement strip, determine the measured clearance.

MEASURING AXIAL CRANKSHAFT WEAR

Axial clearance is determined by the thickness of the axial washers. These washers or shims are often fitted with a main bearing. The rings are either integrated into a bearing shell or take the form of separate shims. The clearance can be adjusted by installing axial washers of varying thicknesses.

The axial washers are fitted to accommodate the axial forces caused by operation of the clutch.

Axial crankshaft clearance is measured using a dial gauge and a magnetic stand:

— Position the magnetic stand on a stable location against the block.
— Make sure that the measuring probe of the dial gauge presses against the crankshaft while under a small preload.
— Fix the hinge points of the stand.

Fig. 168 Axial clearance of the crankshaft.

Fig. 169 Thrust bearing shells on the crankshaft.

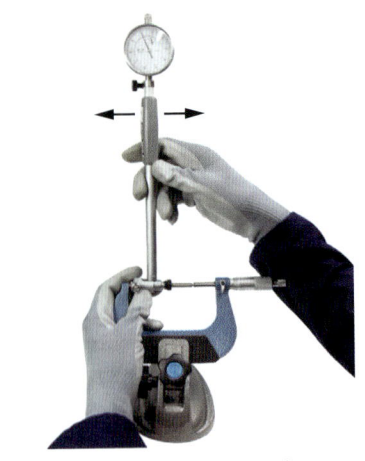

Fig. 170 The dial gauge needs to be under a slight preload.

- Push the crankshaft in the longitudinal direction to one side and set the dial gauge to 0.
- Push the camshaft in the opposite longitudinal direction and read off the dial gauge. This is the axial clearance.
- Compare the measured clearance with the specified value.

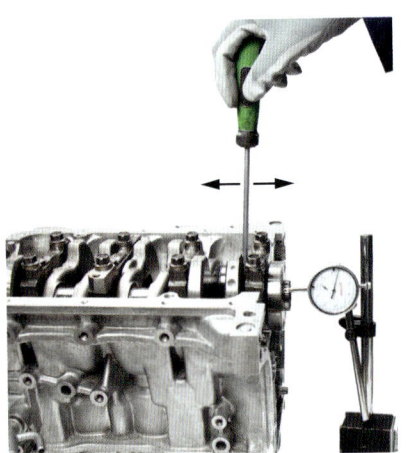

Fig. 171 Push the crankshaft to the left and set the dial gauge to 0.

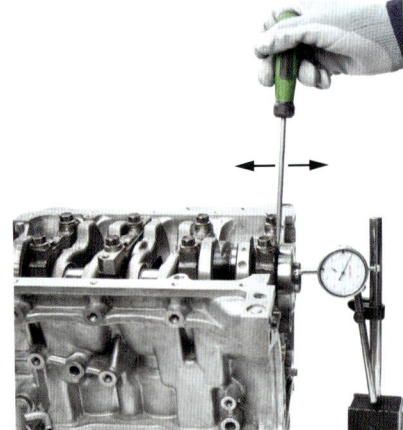

Fig. 172 Then push the crankshaft to the right and read off the clearance.

CRANKSHAFT RUNOUT INSPECTION

1. Measuring the Runout

It is possible to check whether the crankshaft is bent by measuring the crankshaft runout. The runout is measured using a dial gauge and a stand. The outermost main bearings rest on the stand, while the dial gauge is mounted on the central main bearing while under a small preload.

- Set the dial gauge to 0.
- Rotate the crankshaft.
- Read the change on the dial gauge.
- Compare the measured value against the value specified in the vehicle service information for the car you are working on.
- Repeat the measurement as required (and where possible) at other points on the crankshaft.

Fig. 173 Runout of the crankshaft.

2. Straightening the Crankshaft

If the crankshaft is bent, it will need to be replaced. In some cases, however, it may be possible to straighten the crankshaft:
- Place the crankshaft with its outermost main bearing in a stand.
- Use the dial gauge to measure the maximum displacement.
- Use a copper hammer and a chisel.
- Place the chisel next to the bearing surface with the maximum runout.
- Hit the chisel with the hammer.
- Then measure the result and repeat the processes above until the crankshaft is straight.

Caution! This work is very specialized and requires an understanding of the materials. This is not a job for a technician.

Fig. 174 Measuring the crankshaft runout.

Fig. 175 Sometimes a crankshaft can be straightened.

LINE BORING

Line boring is used to make sure that all bearing caps are "in line." If a cylinder block has become too hot, for example, the bearings may no longer be correctly aligned. It is possible to check whether they are "in line" by placing a straight edge across the main bearing beds and measuring the clearance between the straight edge and bed.

To position the main bearings of a crankshaft precisely along a straight line, all bearing caps are installed and torqued to specifications. Then the diameter is enlarged using a line boring machine so that the beds of all the main bearings are in line once again.

After line boring, oversized or thicker bearing shells are used to achieve the correct bearing clearance.

Line boring is performed by an engine machine shop.

After line boring, the crankshaft can be installed back into the block.

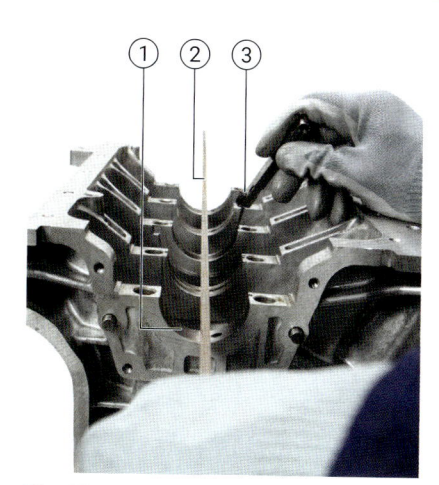

Fig. 176 1. Main bearing bed. 2. Straight edge. 3. Feeler gauge.

CRANKSHAFT DAMAGE AND CAUSES

1. Damaged Crankshaft and Bearing Shells

Determining the exact cause of a damaged crankshaft or crankshaft bearing shell requires a lot of experience. The damage can usually be attributed to one of the following causes:

1. Weakening of the main bearings from previous bearing damage or as a result of poor machining.
2. Installing the wrong type of bearing shells, for example, made out of the wrong material or with a missing oil feed hole.
3. Not achieving the specified bearing clearance due to, for example, a deformed crankshaft, main bearing diameters that are too large or too small or because of oval main bearings.
4. Insufficient lubrication when the engine is stated for the first time after a crankshaft repair; components not being sufficiently lubricated during assembly; lubrication system not being sufficiently filled and/or pressurized before starting.
5. Failing to replace an oil filter or oil cooler after a crankshaft repair.
6. Interchanging the main bearing shells and the connecting rod bearing shells.
7. Tightening bearing caps to an incorrect torque or installing them with the old fasteners.
8. Failure to follow manufacturer specifications during the reassembly of the engine.

Fig. 177 Damaged crankshaft.

2. Broken Crankshaft

A broken crankshaft may be caused by the following:

1. Mechanical overload caused by incorrect combustion or hydraulic shock (fluid hammer).
2. Sudden and rapid deceleration of the crankshaft caused by selecting an incorrect (too low) gear or a component breaking and jamming it.
3. Extreme vibrations caused by incorrect or damaged vibration dampers and/or by the flywheel.

4. Damage on the crankshaft which was not identified when the crankshaft was installed.
5. Poorly executed crankshaft repairs or modifications.

Fig. 178 Broken Crankshaft

3. Assembling Damage

PLEASE NOTE

Crankshaft damage can be caused by incorrect assembly. A short summary of how to correctly install a crankshaft is given below. This method assumes that the crankshaft has been checked for the following:
— Runout.
— Radial bearing clearance.

Crankshaft assembly method:

1. Before assembly, check the crankshaft for existing damage.
2. Install the bearing shells. When doing so, always take into account the condition of the oil feed holes and oil grooves. These must not be blocked or damaged. In addition, always check the correct assembly method given in the vehicle service information.
3. Use an air gun to carefully blow out the oil holes in the crankshaft.
4. Apply the oil specified in the vehicle service information to the sliding surfaces of the bearing shells and crankshaft.
5. Place the crankshaft in the main bearing beds of the engine block.
6. Install the bearing caps. When doing so, note the bearing cap numbers or codes.
7. Apply a small amount of the specified oil to the bearing cap screws and tighten them to the predetermined torque.
8. Check whether the crankshaft rotates freely.
9. Check the axial clearance and adjust it if necessary.

FLYWHEEL

1. Flywheel Mass

Attached to the crankshaft of engines using a dry plate clutch is a heavy cast iron flywheel. It takes energy to get a flywheel moving. Once the flywheel is moving, it's difficult to slow it down. This ensures that the engine runs smoothly.

A 4-stroke piston engine transfers energy to the crankshaft once every four strokes. The crankshaft has to keep rotating for the other three strokes. During these three strokes the flywheel releases stored energy to keep the engine rotating smoothly.

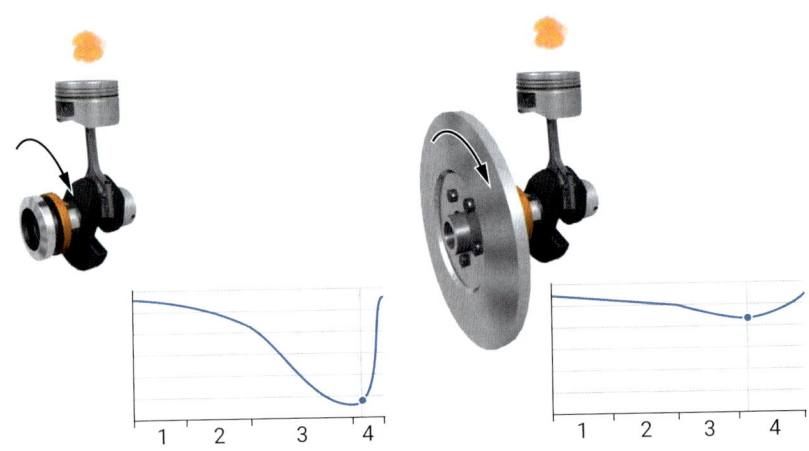

Fig. 179 The speed of the crankshaft is shown on the graph for one working cycle.

Fig. 180 A flywheel provides a more constant crankshaft speed.

2. Multiple Cylinders

In engines with more cylinders the flywheel is smaller. This is because there are more power strokes per revolution of the crankshaft.

The more cylinders, the smoother the engine runs.

Fig. 181 A smaller flywheel for an engine with more cylinders.

Fig. 182 The flywheel: 1. Ring gear. 2. Reluctor ring. 3. Bore hole. 4. Pressure plate installation location. 5. Dowel pin.

3. Crankshaft to Flywheel Connection

The flywheel and crankshaft are always balanced together. For this reason the flywheel and crankshaft must be accurately fitted together; a small error and the flywheel will vibrate.

The flywheel is balanced by drilling small wells in it to remove metal from the heavier spots. Therefore the flywheel has to always be installed on the crankshaft in the same way.

Not every hole in the flywheel is a drilled well. Some holes are threaded. These holes are used to attach the pressure plate. The positioning pins on the flywheel make sure that the pressure plate is correctly installed.

Flywheels are often fitted with a :
- ring gear; the pinion of the starter engages into the ring gear, and causes the crankshaft to rotate when the engine is starting.
- timing ring: The control unit can determine the position of the crankshaft from the teeth on the timing ring.

4. Dual-Mass Flywheel.

Irregular movements of the crankshaft occur in the engine during the four-stroke process. These irregularities are to be avoided, which is why a dual-mass flywheel is installed in some cars. This reduces noise and vibrations in the drivetrain and chassis.

A dual-mass flywheel is a flywheel which is divided into two parts. One part is fixed to the crankshaft. The other part is connected to the pressure plate. The clutch plate also engages with this second part. The two parts are connected via several long torsional damping springs. These springs absorb the vibrations.
As soon as the crankshaft speeds up, the springs absorb the pressure and transfer it to the second disc. Conversely, the second disc absorbs the pressure as the transmission slows.

Fig. 183 The principle of the dual-mass flywheel: 1. Primary flywheel, connected to the crankshaft. 2. Torsion springs. 3. Secondary flywheel, connected to the pressure plate.

The flywheel is also fitted with a damper. This damper can take the form of a hydraulic damper or a friction damper.
The dual-mass flywheel works so well that torsional damping springs in the clutch are no longer needed.

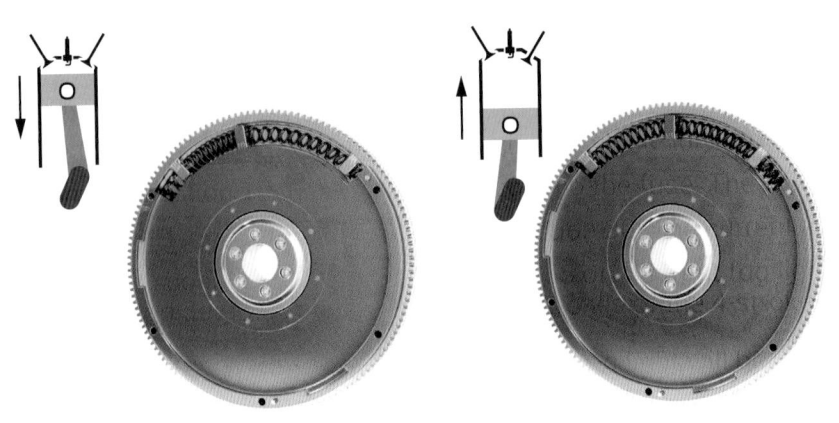

Fig. 184 The springs absorb acceleration or deceleration.

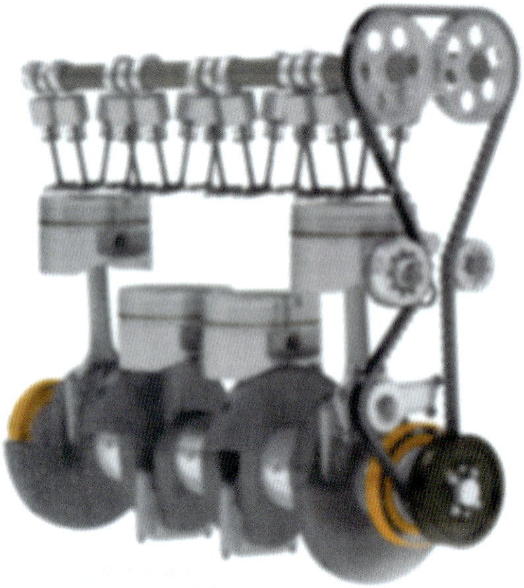

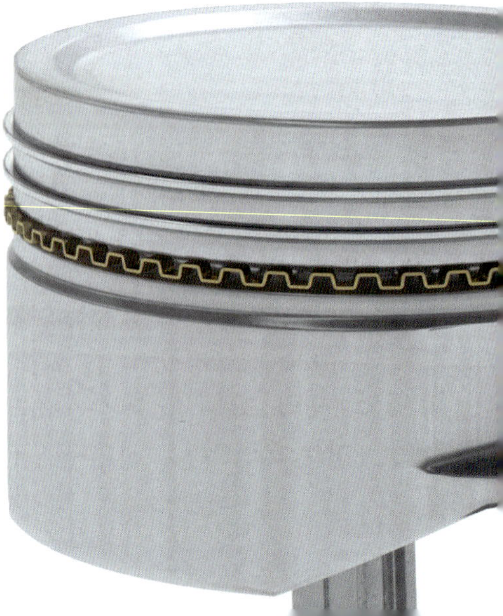

5. Valves and Camshaft

VALVES

1. Introduction

Valves open or close off cylinder access. The intake valve opens during the intake stroke so that the air/fuel mixture or air can flow into the cylinder. During the other strokes of the four-stroke cycle, the intake valve is mostly closed so that pressure can build up in the cylinder.

The exhaust valve opens during the exhaust stroke so that all of the combustion gases can flow out of the cylinder. This valve is also closed during the remaining part of the four-stroke cycle in order to allow pressure to build up in the cylinder.

The valves are fitted with a valve head, which moves down into the valve seat of the cylinder head. These two components create a gas-tight seal when the valve is closed. The valve stem is installed in the cylinder head valve guide in such a way that it can travel up and down.

The lobe of the camshaft opens the valve by pushing the tappet downwards against the spring force. Ultimately, the spring pressure ensures that the valve closes when it is not acted upon by the cam lobe.

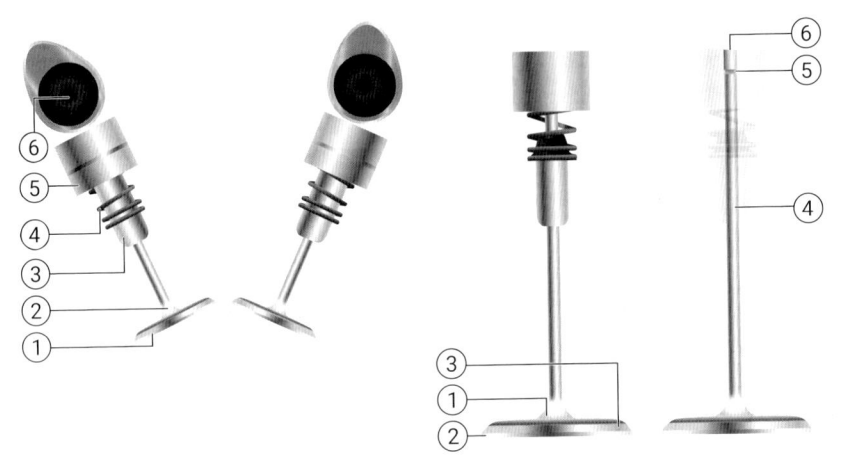

Fig. 185 1. Valve seat. 2. Valve. 3. Valve guide. 4. Valve spring. 5. Tappet. 6. Camshaft.

Fig. 186 1. Valve head. 2. Valve head seat. 3. Valve sealing surface. 4. Valve stem. 5. Valve key groove. 6. Valve stem end.

The valve itself consists of the following components:
— Valve head.
— Valve head seat.
— Valve sealing surface.
— Valve stem.
— Valve key groove.
— Valve stem end.

The valve head is the part of the valve that is exposed to the combustion gases in the cylinder. The outer diameter of the valve head is the same as the valve size.

The valve head is extra thick to ensure that the valve is not burned by the hot combustion gases. This is easy to see at the valve head seat. The height of this edge shows how much additional material is added to the valve head to protect it from burning and melting.

The valve sealing surface is the surface that creates a gas-tight seal together with the valve seat.

The valve stem is a long shaft that runs through the cylinder head and ultimately comes in contact with the camshaft. The stem is often polished or chrome-plated so that it moves up and down in the valve guide with as little friction as possible.

A valve key groove is ground at the end of the stem. This groove encloses the valve spring.

The end of the valve stem is the part which directly contacts the tappet. In some cases, the end is covered with a hard alloy to limit wear.

2. Dimensions

The most important valve dimensions are:
— Valve head diameter.
— Sealing surface angle.
— Valve length.
— Stem diameter.

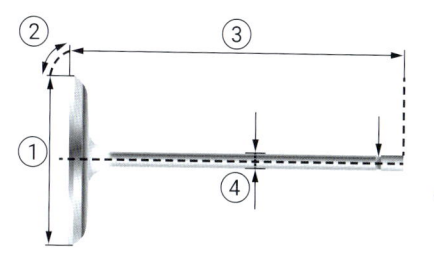

Fig. 187 1. Valve head diameter. 2. Sealing surface angle. 3. Valve length. 4. Stem diameter.

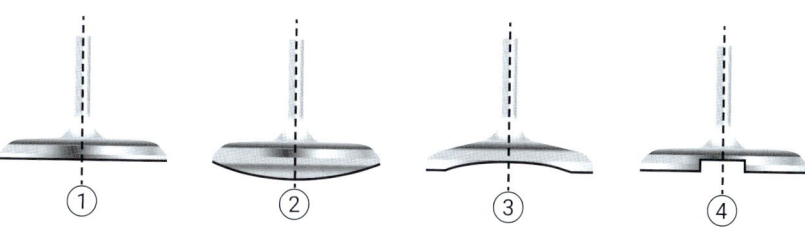

Fig. 188 1. Flat head. 2. Oval head. 3. Tulip-shaped head. 4. Hollow head.

There are different types of valve heads. A distinction can be made between the following valve head shapes:
— Flat head.
— Oval head.
— Tulip-shaped or hollow head.

Flat and oval heads are often used for engines that run at low speeds. The advantage of these heads is that they have considerable resistance to high combustion temperatures.

Hollow or tulip-shaped heads are very flexible. That means this type of head does not bounce on the valve seat when closing at high speeds.

3. Cooling Systems

In some cases the valve stem is filled with sodium. This has two advantages:

1. Additional cooling.
2. Reduced weight.

Sodium is a material that melts when the engine reaches normal operating temperature. The molten sodium "sloshes" up and down in the valve stem. While sloshing around, the sodium extracts heat from the hot valve head and transfers it upwards via the valve stem and valve guide to then release it to the coolant.

There is a reduction in weight because the valve stem is hollow and because sodium is lighter than steel.

Fig. 189 1. Hollow valve stem. 2. Sodium.

Fig. 190 Valve Seal

Proper lubrication of the valve stem is completely reliant on the rubber valve stem seal working correctly. This valve seal is installed over the valve guide.

The valve seal ensures that the correct quantity of oil needed for valve stem lubrication can seep into the valve guide.

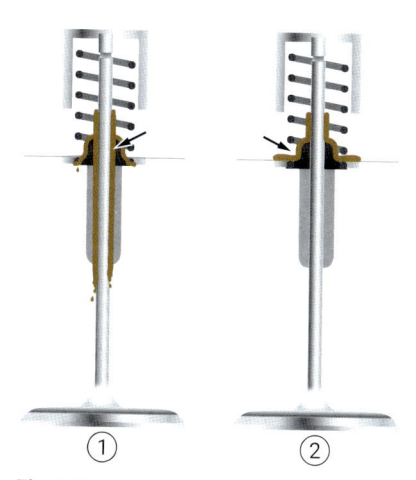

Fig. 191 1. Valve seal letting too much oil through. 2. Valve seal letting too little oil through.

4. Valve Seal

If the valve seal allows too much oil to pass, then too much oil will be drawn into the cylinder. This causes higher oil consumption and the engine may emit blue smoke from the exhaust. Conversely, if the valve seal does not allow enough oil to flow through, then the valve stem could wear excessively.

The most important valve service work that is carried out in a repair facility is:
- Replacing valve seals.
- Checking valve length, valve head thickness and valve head diameter.
- Checking valve guides and valve stems.
- Visually inspecting valves and valve seats.

CAMSHAFT

1. Introduction

Camshafts ensure that the intake and exhaust valves open and close at just the right moment. Most modern engines use one or more overhead camshafts driven by a belt or a chain.

Bottom-mounted camshafts are still used in some cases. These camshafts are located in the engine block and are generally driven by a chain or gearwheels.

Camshafts rotate at half the speed of the crankshaft. This means that camshafts complete one full revolution for every two full revolutions of the crankshaft.

Camshafts are made of cast iron or forged steel and consist of the following main components:
— The bearings.
— The cams.

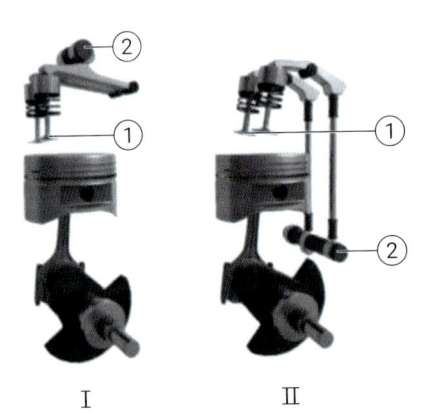

Fig. 192 I. Overhead camshaft. II. Bottom-mounted camshaft. 1. Valve. 2. Camshaft.

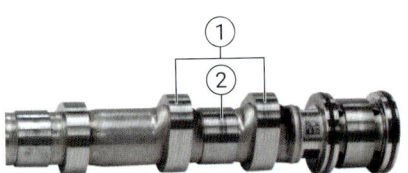

Fig. 193 Hollow camshaft with separate cams connected by expansion of the camshaft. 1. Cams. 2. Bearing.

2. Bearings

Camshaft bearings are comparable to main and connecting rod bearings. They consist of:
— The sliding bearing part on the camshaft.
— A bearing shell.
— A bearing cap.

The bearing shell can be made up of one or two separate bearing shells. Both are equipped with oil feed holes, which are supplied with oil from the cylinder head through oil holes.

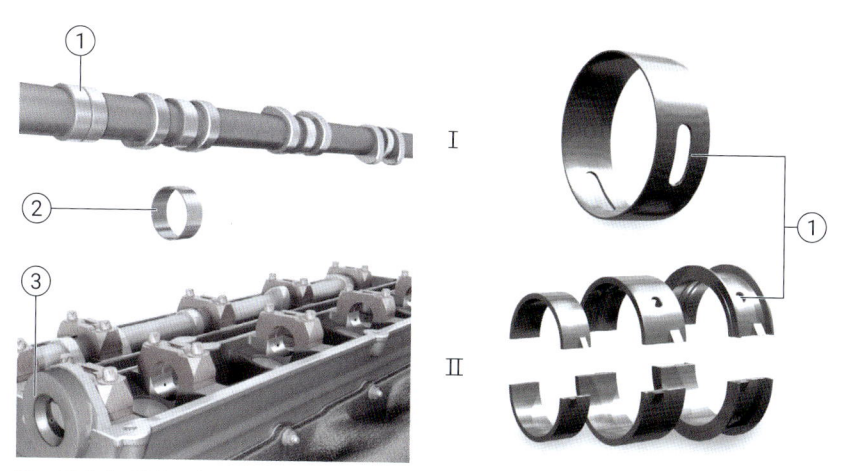

Fig. 194 1. Sliding bearing part on the camshaft. 2. Bearing shell. 3. Bearing cap.

Fig. 195 I. One-piece bearing shell. II. Two-piece bearing shell. 1. Oil supply hole.

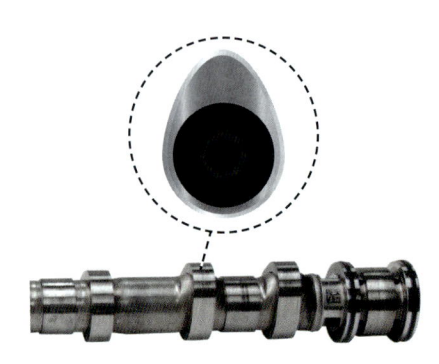

Fig. 196 Oval camshaft cam.

3. Cam Lobes

Cam lobes are the oval structures on the camshaft which convert the circular motion of the shaft into the up and down movement of the valves. The camshaft and cam lobes are usually cast or forged as a single component and then machined afterwards. There are also camshafts where the cam lobes are crimped onto the shaft. Another alternative involves placing the cam lobes on a hollow shaft that is then expanded using fluid pressure. This fixes the cams onto the shaft.

The shape and position of the cam lobe determines:
— The valve timing: when the valve opens and closes with respect to the piston position.
— The opening time of the valve: how long the valve stays open.
— The valve opening or valve lift: how far the valve opens.
— The valve overlap: the time during which the intake and exhaust valves are open at the same time.

The most common types of inspections needed while working on the camshaft involves:
— Measuring camshaft wear.
— Inspecting camshaft runout.
— Measuring radial clearance.
— Measuring axial clearance.

VALVE OPERATION

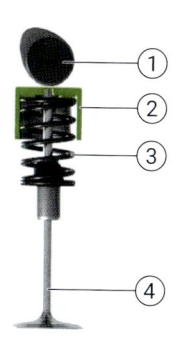

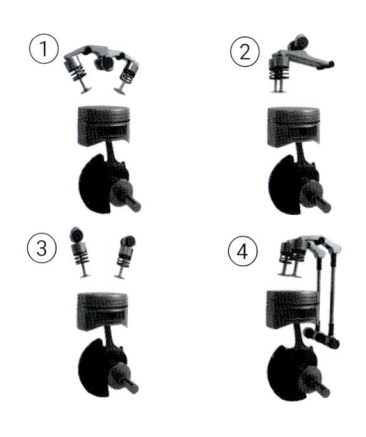

1. Types

In a piston engine, the valves are opened and closed mechanically. This type of valve operation exists in a variety of forms.

In passenger car and light truck engines, the camshafts are often located in the cylinder head. In heavy-duty/commercial vehicle engines, the camshaft is often located in the engine block.

2. Floating valve

The function of a valve spring is to enable the valve to follow the profile of the cam.
A floating valve is a valve that is **no longer** able to follow the profile of a cam. Floating valves can cause engine damage.
If the camshaft operates the valve spring too quickly, the valve stays open.

Methods of preventing floating valves include:

1. Altering the design of the valve spring
2. A stronger valve spring

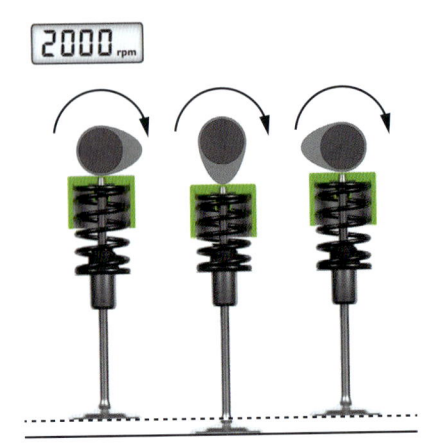

3. Valve Spring Types

In order to keep the valve from floating, the following different configurations are used:

1. Valve spring with unequal rate
2. Trapezoidal valve spring
3. Double valve spring

The strongest part of the valve spring is fitted against the cylinder head, because the moving mass must be kept as small as possible. If the moving mass is smaller, then the forces that operate the valves are also kept smaller.

4. Valve Clearance

Engine components expand and contract as a result of temperature changes. Wear and tear, expansion and contraction of the camshaft operation can be compensated for by:

1. Set valve clearance (lash)
2. Hydraulic valve lash compensator (hydraulic valve lash limiter)

If there is insufficient valve clearance in a cold engine, the valves will no longer close properly when the engine is hot. This causes a loss of power. The valves may also burn, as they cannot transmit their heat to the cylinder head.

Therefore, a technician must properly set the valve clearance to compensate for temperature changes and wear. However, if the engine is equipped with hydraulic lash compensators, there's no need for manual adjustment.

Manual valve adjustment is accomplished by either turning an adjustment nut or by installing a shim, which is held in place by a recess in the top of the valve lifter.

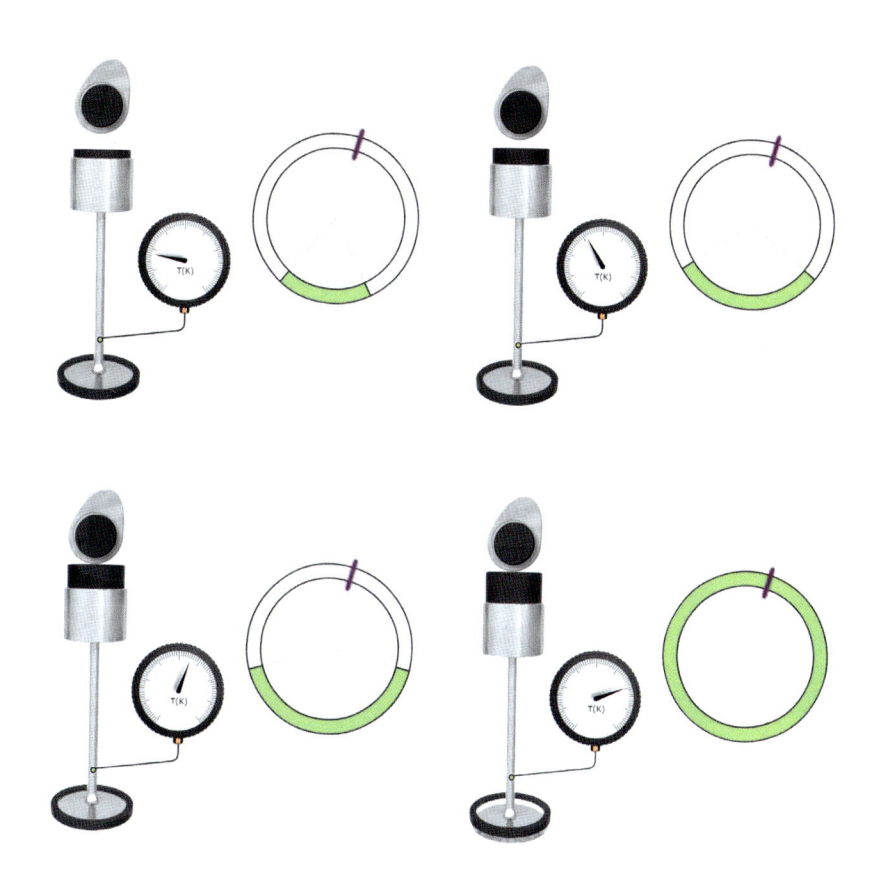

5. Hydraulic Valve Lash Compensator

The hydraulic valve lash compensator (sometimes referred to as a hydraulic clearance limiter) ensures that neither valve clearance nor the need to set it by hand is required.

A hydraulic lash compensator works as follows:

1. The engine is started.
2. The hydraulic lash compensator is pumped full of oil.
3. The oil pressure forces the check-ball in the cylinder away from its seat and the compensator fills completely with oil.
4. After the compensator is filled, the check-ball reseats. As the engine warms to operating temperature and parts begin to expand, the plunger is forced downward against spring

418 GASOLINE ENGINE CONSTRUCTION AND OPERATION

pressure. Because oil cannot be compressed, some oil is forced out of the compensator between the cylinder wall and plunger.

Note: in other applications, the lash compensator mechanism is built into the valve lifter.

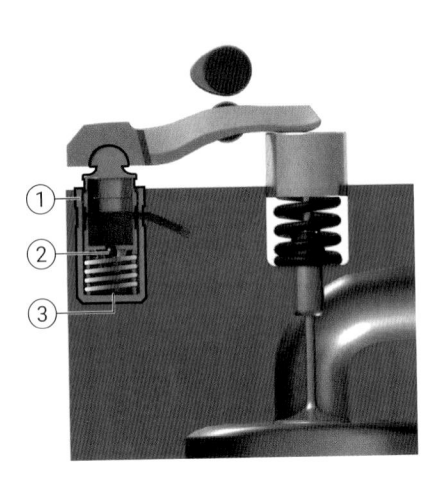

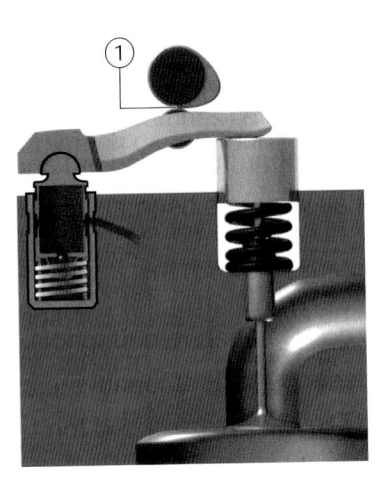

TIMING SYSTEM

1. Introduction

The intake and exhaust valves are opened by the camshafts against spring pressure, and it is important that the valves are opened and closed at the right time. The crankshaft drives the camshaft(s) gear(s) using a toothed belt, a chain, or other gears.

2. Timing

The timing system of a 4-stroke engine makes the connection between the crankshaft and the camshaft. The camshaft operates the intake and exhaust valves and rotates at half the speed (revolutions per minute) of the crankshaft.

The crankshaft and the camshafts must be positioned in exact relationship to each other. If the engine is not properly timed, the valves may come in contact with the tops of the pistons on some engines (called "interference engines") causing major damage.

Before the timing belt is installed, you need to make sure the cams and crankshaft are positioned correctly. The easiest method is as follows:

1. Position the #1 piston in the top dead center (TDC) position of the compression stroke. Some engines require a special tool to locate the crankshaft in this position.
2. Position the intake camshaft in the manufacturer's instructed position, which is usually indicated by specific timing markings or with a special tool.
3. Position the exhaust camshaft in the manufacturer's instructed position, which is usually indicated by specific timing markings or with a special tool. Some engines use a timing belt with marks that align with the mark on the crankshaft and the camshaft sprocket. Most times you don't have to remove the valve cover to install the timing belt.

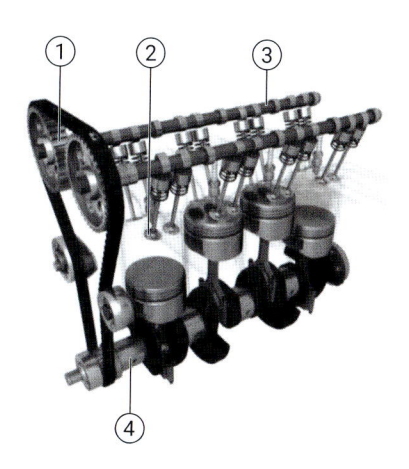

Fig. 213 The crankshaft drives the camshaft: 1. Camshaft sprocket. 2. Valves. 3. Camshaft. 4. Crankshaft.

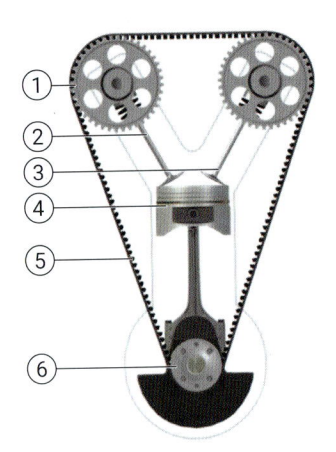

Fig. 214 Camshafts driven by a timing belt: 1. Camshaft sprocket. 2. Intake valve. 3. Exhaust valve. 4. Piston. 5. Timing belt. 6. Crankshaft gear.

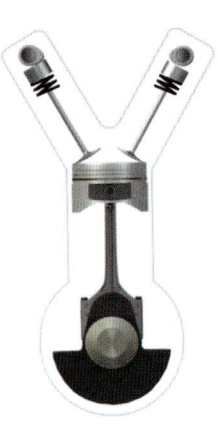

Fig. 215 The correct position of the crankshaft and camshafts relative to each other.

Always follow the manufacturer's instructions when setting the engine timing.

3. Components

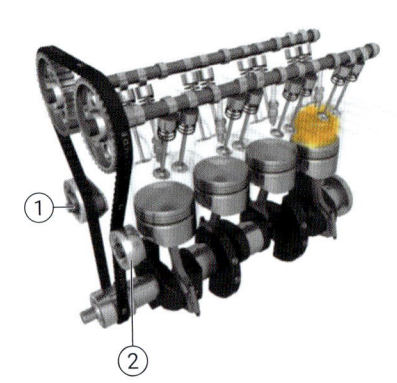

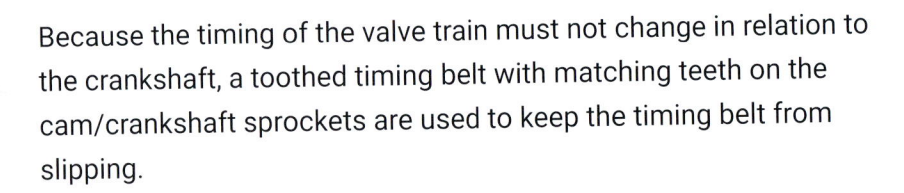

Because the timing of the valve train must not change in relation to the crankshaft, a toothed timing belt with matching teeth on the cam/crankshaft sprockets are used to keep the timing belt from slipping.

However, if the timing belt is not properly tensioned, it could easily jump teeth or come off the cam/crankshaft sprockets completely. The belt tensioner and idler pulley maintain the correct belt tension to prevent this from happening. Note: Tighter isn't better – a timing belt can make a howling noise if it's too tight.

On some engines, the crankshaft indirectly drives the diesel fuel injection pump and/or water pump via the timing belt. Some Toyota engines drive the oil pump with the timing belt.

Fig. 216 Tensioning the timing belt: 1. Idler. 2. Idler pulley.

Fig. 217 Different versions of valve train types: 1. Timing gears. 2. Timing chain. 3. Timing belt.

4. Types

Timing gears are most often used in heavy-duty commercial vehicles.

A timing belt or chain is used in most passenger vehicles and light trucks, although today a chain is most commonly used, due to the added strength.

Motorcycles typically use timing chains.

VALVE TIMING

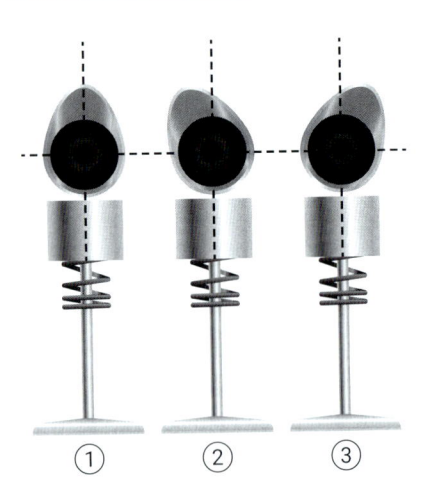

Fig. 218 1. Intake valve starting point. 2. Intake valve delayed. 3. Intake valve advanced.

1. Introduction

Valve timing determines when the valve opens and closes with respect to the position of the piston. The valve timing is mainly determined by the position of the cam in relation to the crankshaft.

For an engine that rotates clockwise, the following applies:
— If the cam is moved opposite to the direction of rotation (counterclockwise), the valve will open later.
— If the cam is moved in the direction of rotation (clockwise), the valve will open earlier.

The ideal valve timing depends on the speed and load of the engine. As a general statement, we can say that the following applies at low engine speeds:
— Open intake valve late and close it early.
— Open exhaust valve late and close it early.

At higher rpm:
— Open intake valve early and close it late.
— Open exhaust valve early and close it late.

The valve timing cannot be varied with a fixed camshaft. In this case, the engine designer must choose between a camshaft design that is ideal for high rpm or one that is ideal for low rpm.

2. Variable Valve Timing

Variable valve timing is a system that changes the valve timing according to the speed and load of the engine. Essentially, there are two variable valve timing designs:

1. Two different cam lobes that operate one valve.
2. One camshaft that can alter its position in respect to the camshaft drive.

In the first case, there are two cam lobes and two rockers which operate a single valve:

1. One cam lobe for low rpm, which operates the low rpm rocker, and
2. One cam lobe for high rpm, which operates the high rpm rocker.

At low rpm, the high rpm rocker "idles". Only once the engine reaches a high speed is the high rpm rocker connected to the low rpm rocker by means of an actuator. This means that the opening and closing points and the lift height of the valve are then determined by the high rpm rocker.

In the second case, the camshaft drive consist of two parts. One part is connected to the timing drive and the other part is connected to the camshaft. An actuator causes both parts to turn slightly with respect to each other if the camshaft timing needs to be adjusted.

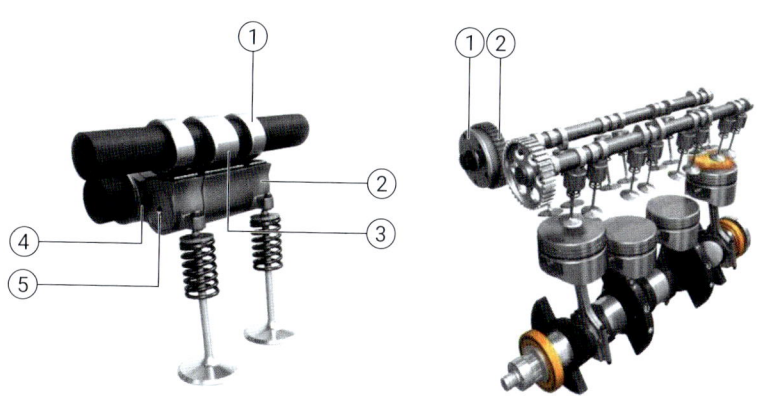

Fig. 219 1. Low rpm cam lobe. 2. Low rpm rocker. 3. High rpm cam lobe. 4. High rpm rocker. 5. Connecting lever.

Fig. 220 1. Camshaft gearwheel. 2. Adjusting device.

Fig. 221 Left: pointed cam lobe, short opening time. Right: wide cam lobe, long opening time.

3. Opening Time and Cam Lobe Shape

The opening time of the valve has an effect on the charge rate of the cylinder and is determined by the width of the cam. A pointed cam lobe has a short opening time, whereas a wider, more rounded cam lobe has a long opening time.

The opening time is expressed in crankshaft degrees. For example: a cam lobe has an opening time of 250°. This means that during a crankshaft revolution of 250°, the valve will be partially open in any case.

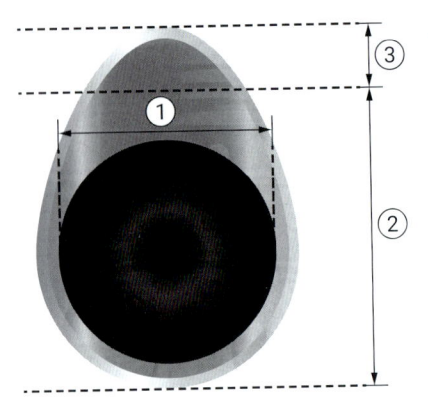

Fig. 222 1. Camshaft diameter.
2. Valve lift provided by cam lobe.
3. Valve lift height.

4. Valve Lift Height

The valve lift also affects the charge rate of the cylinder and is determined by the cam lobe height. The valve lift height can be calculated by subtracting the cam lobe travel from the total height of the cam.

The valve lift height is limited by the distance between the valve and the piston, the valve timing and the opening time of the valve.

VALVE OVERLAP

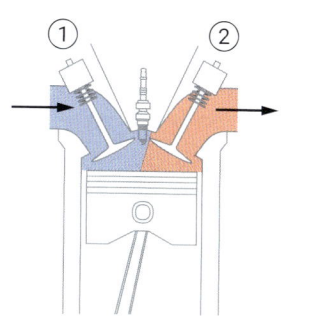

Fig. 223 1. Intake. 2. Exhaust. Exhaust gases flowing out create a vacuum.

Valve overlap is the point when the intake and exhaust valves are open at the same time. Because both valves are open, the rapid flow of exhaust gases is used to fill the cylinder. The exhaust gases leaving the cylinder create a vacuum in the cylinder which then draws in the intake gases.

Valve overlap is achieved by adjusting the distance or degrees between the intake and exhaust cam. The more degrees that separate the intake and exhaust cams, the bigger the valve overlap.

The valve overlap depends to a large extent on the valve timing. Also applicable here is the fact that the ideal valve overlap is determined by the engine speed and load. In general, we can say:

At low rpm:
— A small valve overlap.

At high rpm:
— A large valve overlap.

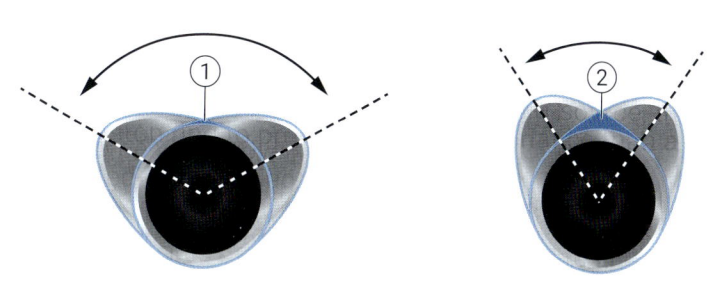

Fig. 224 1. Small valve overlap. 2. Large valve overlap.

CAMSHAFT ADJUSTMENT

1. Introduction

Valve timing, valve lift, and valve opening duration are all interlinked. Engine designers select the ideal combination of these, to ensure the engine provides maximum performance across the entire rpm range.

By using variable valve timing, valve lift, and valve opening duration, it's possible to coordinate the opening of the valves according to driving conditions. This can be done by adjusting the camshaft(s).

Variable valve timing, valve lift, and stroke duration take place on the intake camshafts. However, many of today's engines feature control over the exhaust camshaft(s) as well.

Fig. 225 Variable valve timing for intake camshaft: 1. Camshaft phaser. 2. Camshaft sprocket. 3. Intake camshaft.

2. Variable Valve Timing

In an engine with variable valve timing, the camshaft turns around its own longitudinal axis. In this way you can adjust the valve overlap.

The camshaft phaser (adjuster) is operated by means of engine oil pressure. Oil pressure is controlled by the ECU through a control solenoid (oil control valve) that regulates the oil supply to the camshaft phaser.

When engine rpm is high, an increase in valve overlap is required to achieve optimum cylinder filling. When engine rpm is low, less or no valve overlap is required.

Fig. 226 Camshaft phaser/adjuster: 1. Camshaft rotation. 2. Phaser housing. 3. Adjustment mechanism. 4. Advance adjustment direction. 5. 'Normal' valve timing. 6. Advance valve timing.

Fig. 227
Camshaft solenoid valve.

Fig. 228
Camshaft solenoid valve in the valve cover.

3. Variable Valve Opening Duration

In the case of a variable valve opening duration, two camshaft profiles can be used. In this way, you can adjust the amount of time the valve is open based on operating conditions.

The camshaft has three lobes for each pair of intake valves. The two outermost cam lobes have the same profile, while the center lobe has more valve lift and different durations for opening and closing.

The rockers contain a locking pin that allows all three rockers to be linked together. This means that it is possible to choose between cam outer lobes or center lobe operation. The locking pin is operated by means of engine oil pressure. An electronic control solenoid operates the oil supply to push the piston pin and lock all rockers together.

When the rpm is high, the valves open according to the center cam lobe, which increases the valve opening duration.

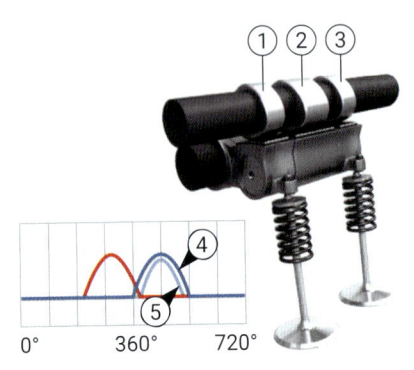

Fig. 229
Variable valve opening time: 1. Cam low speeds. 2. Cam high speeds. 3. Cam low speeds. 4. Valve open high speeds. 5. Valve open low speeds.

Fig. 230
Variable valve timing mechanism: 1. Locking pin. 2. Slip rocker low speeds. 3. Slip rocker high speeds. 4. Slip rocker low speeds.

4. Variable Valve Lift

During changes in valve lift, the camshaft and lobes shift along the shafts longitudinal axis. The longitudinal axis is the line drawn through the center of the camshaft from front to back. The fact that the cam lobes are tapered means that by shifting the camshaft, the valves are opened further.

The camshaft adjuster is operated by means of engine oil pressure. An electronic solenoid oil control valve operates the oil supply to the camshaft adjuster.

When the rpm is high, a large valve opening is required to achieve optimum cylinder filling. When rpm is low, a smaller valve opening is required.

Fig. 231 Mechanism variable valve lift: 1. Camshaft adjustment housing. 2. Adjustment piston. 3. Adjustment direction bigger lift.

Fig. 232 Variable valve height due to the axial movement of the camshaft.

5. Possible Adjustments

Three elements of the camshaft can be adjusted:
- Timing
- Opening duration
- Lift

In practice we can observe a combination of these adjustments. Benefits of a variable valve timing are as follows:
- Higher power
- Higher torque at low rpm
- Lower emissions
- Low idling rpm

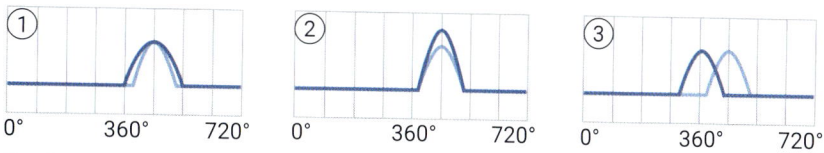

Fig. 233 Different adjustment options: 1. Variable opening duration. 2. Variable lift. 3. Variable timing.

6. Valvetronic System

In some engine designs, a 'valvetronic' system is applied. This means the engine has variable intake valve lift and timing control. This is how the amount of air to the cylinders is regulated which in turn affects the power generated. Even though this system will eliminate the throttle plate function, one is still installed in case the valvetronic system fails. Unless it is needed, the throttle plate will remain in the fully open position. The valvetronic system consists of an actuator (stepper motor), an eccentric shaft, a roller follower, a rocker arm, a spring, and a lever.

At low speeds the lever must travel a great distance before the slip rocker is operated, which in turn presses the valve. As a result, the valve opening is minimal, and little air flows into the engine. If we want the engine to deliver more power, the actuator is controlled. This causes the eccentric shaft to rotate clockwise. Due to the leverage, the lever moves to the right. This brings the lower part of the lever closer to the slip rocker. If the camshaft now operates the lever, the lever will press the slip rocker, and thus the valve. Because the underside of the lever has a curvature, the valve will also be pressed in deeper. More air now flows into the engine.

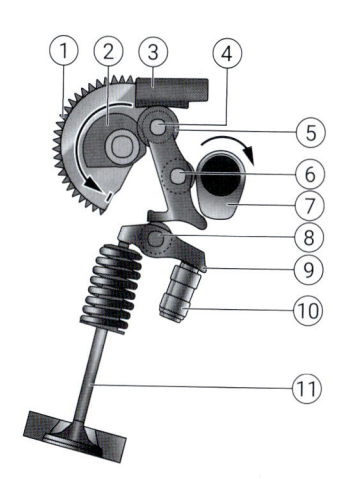

Fig. 234 Valvetronic valve operation system: 1. Tooth segment. 2. Eccentric shaft. 3. Fixed support. 4. roller. 5. Adjustment lever. 6. Roller. 7. Camshaft. 8. Roller. 9. Slip rocker. 10. Hydraulic lifter. 11. Valve.

The advantage of the valvetronic system, compared to the conventional system with throttle plate, is that the throttle plate can remain fully open. As a result, no flow losses occur from the engine.

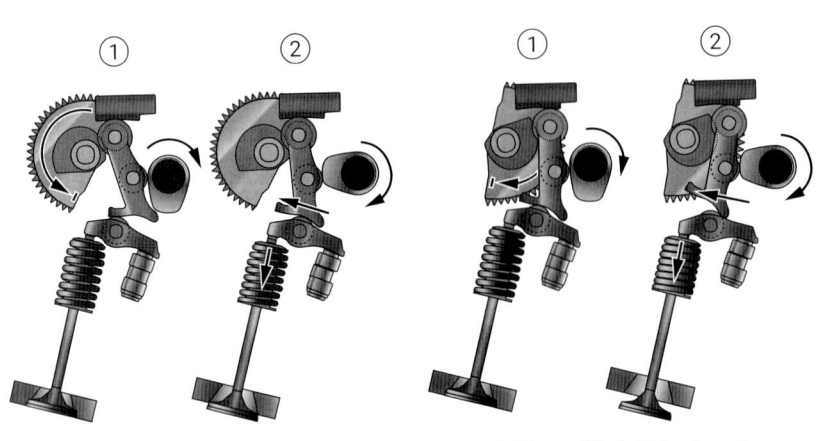

Fig. 235 Small lift: 1. Valve is not operated. 2. Valve is operated by the camshaft.

Fig. 236 Bigger lift: 1. Valve is not operated. 2. Valve is operated by the camshaft.

MEASURING CAM LOBE WEAR

1. Introduction

If one or more of the cam lobes on the camshaft are worn, the intake or exhaust valve can no longer be opened sufficiently. Naturally this has negative consequences for the charge rate of the engine.

The degree of cam lobe wear can be inspected in two ways:

1. Checking the cam lobe wear with the camshaft installed.
2. Checking the cam wear with the camshaft removed.

2. Measuring Cam Lobe Wear With the Camshaft Installed

If the camshaft is still installed in the cylinder head, cam lobe wear can be measured as follows:

— Position the cam lobe to be measured so that it pushes the valve in, i.e. with the cam lobe pointing down.
— Take a dial gauge (with a magnetic stand) and place it on the top of the cam lobe.
— Set the dial gauge to 0.
— Turn the camshaft one full revolution while observing the maximum displacement on the dial gauge.
— The difference between the minimum and maximum displacement is the "lift" of the cam lobe.
— Refer to the technical documentation for the specified value for the lift.
— Now calculate the difference between the prescribed lift and the measured lift. The calculated difference is the cam lobe wear.

Fig. 237 The displacement of the dial gauge is the "lift" of the cam lobe.

3. Measuring Cam Lobe Wear with the Camshaft Removed

If the camshaft has been removed, cam lobe wear can be measured as follows:

- Use a micrometer to measure the cam lobe height as shown in the illustration.
- Refer to the vehicle service information for the specified value for the cam lobe height.
- Now calculate the difference between the specified cam lobe height and the measured cam lobe height. The calculated difference is the cam lobe wear.

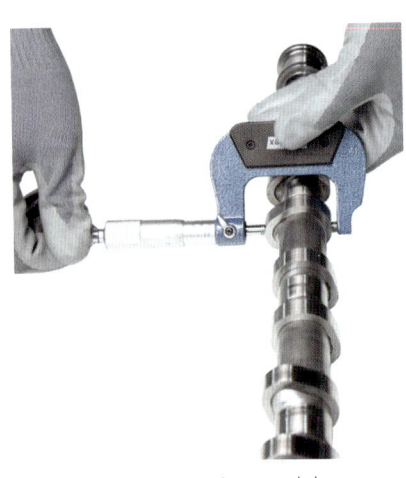

Fig. 238 Measuring the cam lobe height.

CAMSHAFT RUNOUT INSPECTION

By measuring the camshaft runout, it is possible to check whether or not the camshaft is bent. The runout is measured using a dial gauge and a stand. The outermost camshaft bearings rest on the stand, while the dial gauge is mounted on the central camshaft bearing under a small preload.

The steps to determine the runout are given below:
— Set the dial gauge to 0.
— Rotate the camshaft.
— Read the displacement on the dial gauge.
— Compare the measured value against the value specified in the technical documentation for the car you are working on.
— Repeat the measurement as required (and where possible) at other points on the camshaft.

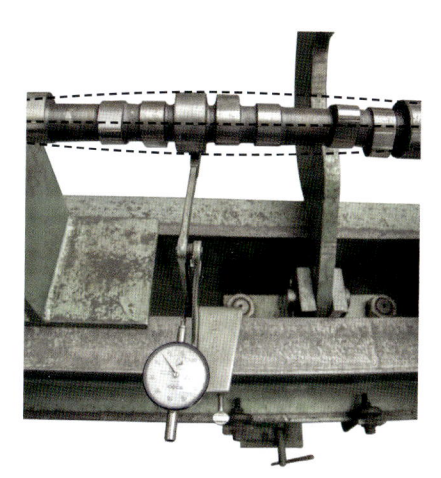

Fig. 239 Camshaft runout is measured at the center camshaft bearing.

CAMSHAFT RADIAL AND AXIAL BEARING CLEARANCE

1. Introduction

The camshaft's radial clearance is the distance between the bearing shells and the camshaft bearings. There must always be a minimum clearance between these two components so that the oil film can pass between the bearing shell and the bearing.

If there is excessive radial clearance, the camshaft may start to vibrate and shake. This can cause bearing shells and bearing caps to get damaged.

If there is not enough radial clearance, too much friction will be created during the rotation of the camshaft. This can cause excessive wear and heating of the bearing shells.

Radial bearing clearance is determined by the thickness of the bearing shell. The bearing shell can be adjusted by installing a bearing shell of a different thickness.

Fig. 240 Radial camshaft clearance.

There are two methods of measuring radial bearing clearance:

1. With a micrometer and bore gauge or telescopic gauge. This method is used for one-piece bearing shells in particular.
2. With Plastigauge. This method is used for two-piece bearing shells in particular.

2. Micrometer and Bore Gauge

Measuring the bearing clearance using a micrometer and bore gauge is a precise method consisting of the following steps:
— Install the bearing shells and bearing caps according to the specifications for the vehicle you are working on.

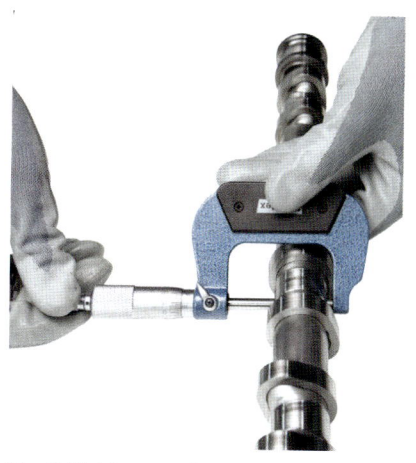

Fig. 241 Measure the outer diameter of the camshaft bearing.

- Tighten the bearing caps to the torque specified in the technical documentation of the vehicle.
- Use a micrometer to measure the outer diameter of the camshaft bearing. Measure the diameter at several different locations to make sure that the bearing is round.
- Lock the micrometer as soon as you have measured the diameter.
- Use the micrometer as a reference for the bore gauge:
  - Put the internal micrometer inside the bore gauge and set the bore gauge dial to 0.
- Position the bore gauge between the installed bearing shells and measure the internal diameter.
- The difference between the outer diameter of the camshaft bearing and the inner diameter of the bearing shell is the bearing clearance.
- Check the measured value against the value specified in the technical documentation.
- Repeat the process for the other camshaft bearings.

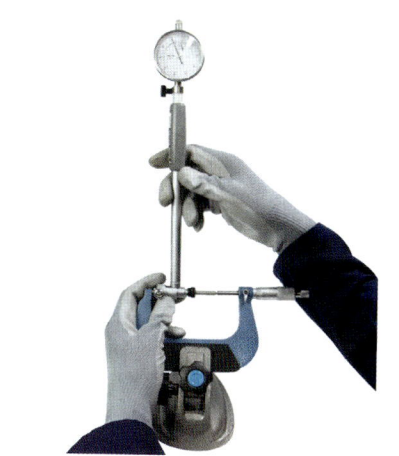

Fig. 242 Use the micrometer to set the bore gauge.

Fig. 243 Measure the internal diameter of the camshaft bearing.

Fig. 244 Cut off a small piece of Plastigauge.

3. Plastigauge

Plastigauge is a plastic thread developed especially for measuring radial bearing clearances. The advantage of Plastigauge is that no expensive measuring tools are required to be able to measure the radial clearance. The disadvantage is that the Plastigauge measuring method is not as precise than the measuring method with micrometer and bore gauge.

There are three different Plastigauge sizes because the radial main bearing clearance can vary according to the vehicle's make and model:

1. Green Plastigauge, designed for bearing clearances of 0.001 to 0.003 inches (0.025 to 0.076 mm).
2. Red Plastigauge, designed for bearing clearances of 0.002 to 0.006 inches (0.051 to 0.152 mm).
3. Blue Plastigauge, designed for bearing clearances of 0.004 to 0.009 inches (0.102 to 0.229 mm).

Measuring the camshaft bearing clearance using Plastigauge consists of the following steps:
— Place a piece of Plastigauge on the bearing in the longitudinal direction of the camshaft.
— Install the bearing shells and bearing caps according to the specifications for the vehicle you are working on.
— Tighten the bearing caps to the torque specified in the technical documentation of the vehicle you are working on.
— Then remove the bearing shells and bearing caps.
— Check the radial clearance using the measuring scale on the Plastigauge packaging.
— Compare the measured value against the value specified in the technical documentation.
— Repeat the measurement for the other camshaft bearings. Carefully remove any residual Plastigauge from the bearings and bearing shells.

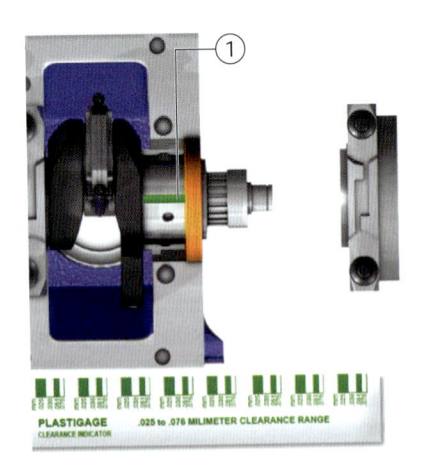

Fig. 245 Place the strip on the bearing in the longitudinal direction of the camshaft.

Fig. 246 Tighten the bearing shell properly and to the correct torque.

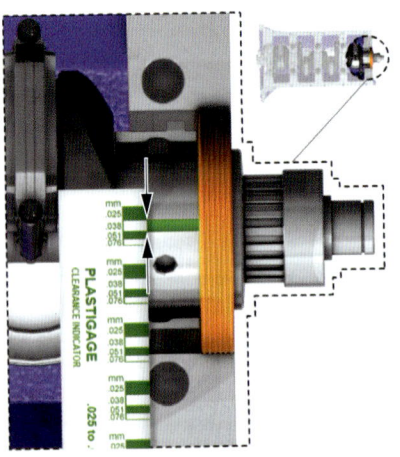

Fig. 247 Determine the bearing clearance using the measuring scale on the ruler.

Fig. 248 Measuring the axial clearance.

4. Measuring Axial Camshaft Clearance

Axial clearance is the clearance in the longitudinal direction of the camshaft. In most cases, this clearance is measured using a dial gauge with a magnetic base according to the following steps:

— Position the magnetic stand on a stable location against the block.
— Make sure that the measuring probe of the dial gauge presses against the camshaft while under a small preload.
— Fix the hinge points of the stand.
— Push the camshaft in the longitudinal direction to one side and set the dial gauge to 0.
— Push the camshaft in the opposite longitudinal direction and read off the dial gauge. This is the axial clearance.
— Compare the measured clearance with the specified value.

REPLACING A VALVE SEAL

1. Replacement

In most cases, valve seals can be replaced without having to remove the cylinder head or the valves. The procedure is as follows:

1. Remove the valve cover and the spark plug or glow plug.
2. Turn the crankshaft so that both the exhaust and intake valves are closed on the cylinder on which the valve seal will be replaced.
3. Attach an air hose to the (glow) spark plug hole using an adapter set.
4. Connect the air hose to the compressed air system and pressurize the cylinder to a maximum of 72.5 psi. The air pressure will ensure that the valves remain closed when the valve springs are pushed in.
5. Use a valve spring lifter to push the valve spring in.
6. Remove the valve spring retainers using a magnet.
7. Remove the valve spring.
8. Replace the valve seal. When doing so, it may be necessary to use a special tool such as valve seal pliers.

Caution! If the piston is at TDC when the valve spring is removed, there is a chance that the valves will contact the piston, resulting in bent valves.

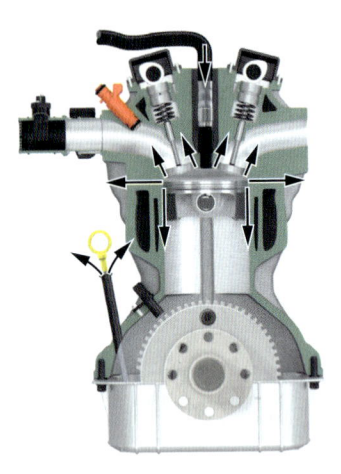

Fig. 249 The pressure in the cylinder holds the valves closed.

Fig. 250 Tools for pressing in the valve spring.

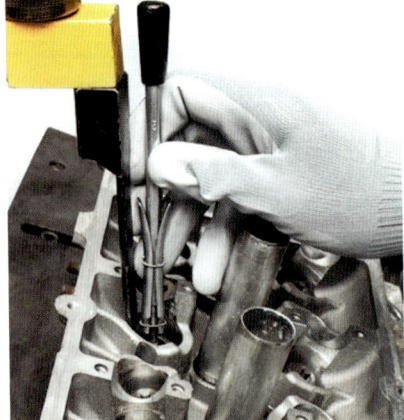

Fig. 251 It is easier to assemble the valve spring retainers with the use of a special pair of pliers with magnet.

CHECKING VALVE LENGTH, VALVE HEAD THICKNESS AND VALVE HEAD DIAMETER

Valve length and valve head thickness give an indication of the valve wear. Valve length can be inspected by measuring the distance from the underside of the valve head to the end of the valve stem using a vernier caliper.

The valve needs to be replaced if the measured length is shorter or larger than the length specified in the technical documentation. The valve head thickness and diameter are measured using a vernier caliper at the locations shown in the illustration.

Replace the valve if one of the two measured values is less than the value specified in the technical documentation.

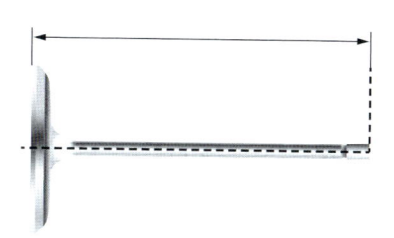

Fig. 252 Valve length.

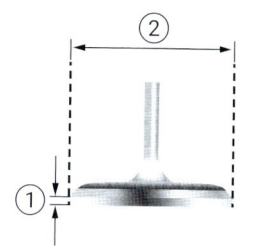

Fig. 253 1. Valve head thickness. 2. Valve head diameter.

CHECKING THE WEAR AND CLEARANCE OF VALVE GUIDES AND VALVE STEMS

1. Valve Guide

Excessive wear on the valve guide causes the valve stem to move sideways. These sideways movements can result in:

- Wear and damage on the valve stem.
- Wear and damage on the valve seal.
- Excessive oil consumption.
- Burned valve.
- Knocking noises.

Valve guide wear is determined by measuring the inner diameter at three points using a dial gauge.

To measure the roundness of the valve guide, the dial gauge is turned through 90° and the same measurements are repeated again.

Replace the valve guide if the measured values are larger than the values specified in the technical documentation. Also replace the valve guide if it is oval-shaped.

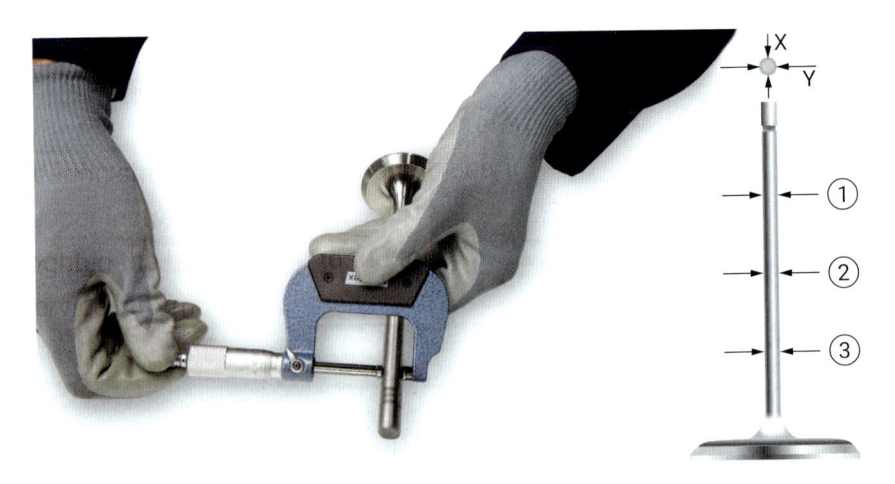

Fig. 254 Measure the outer diameter of the valve stem at several points.

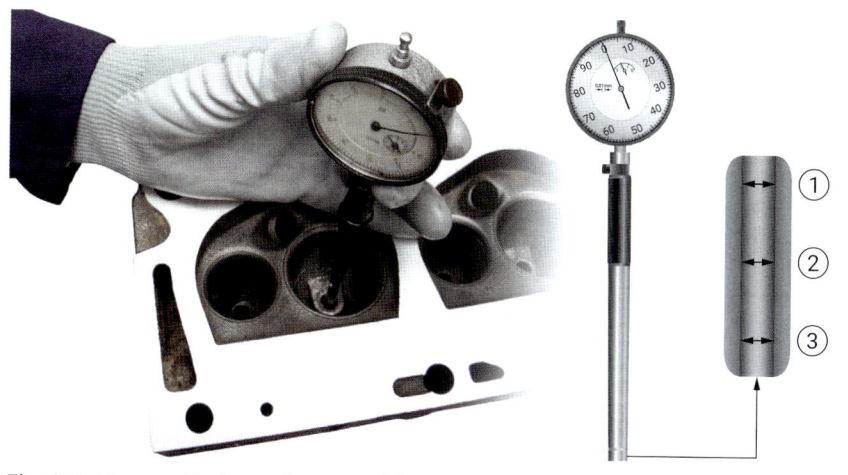

Fig. 255 Measure the inner diameter of the valve guide at several points.

2. Measuring Wear

Valve stem wear is measured by measuring the outer diameter of the stem at three points with a micrometer.

Here we also check for roundness by rotating the micrometer 90° and repeating the same measurements again.

Replace the valve if the measured values are smaller than the values specified in the technical documentation. Also replace the valve if the valve stem is oval-shaped.

The clearance between the valve guide and valve stem is determined by calculating the difference between the inner diameter of the valve guide and the outer diameter of the valve stem.

Replace the valve and/or valve guide if the clearance does not meet the specifications.

Fig. 256 1. Inner diameter of valve guide. 2. Outer diameter of valve stem. 3. Clearance valve guide/valve stem.

HOW TO: CHECKING VALVE CLEARANCES

1. Look for Information

First look for the technical information such as the valve clearance, tightening torques and the work description. Also read the safety warnings which apply for this car.

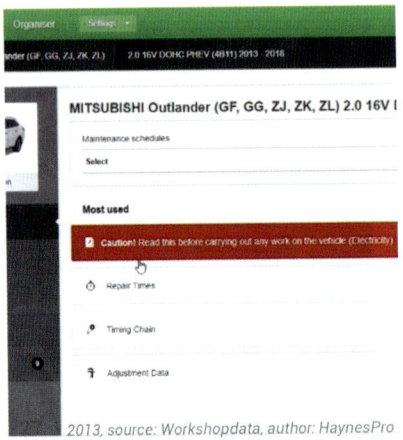

Fig. 257 Go through the safety warning.

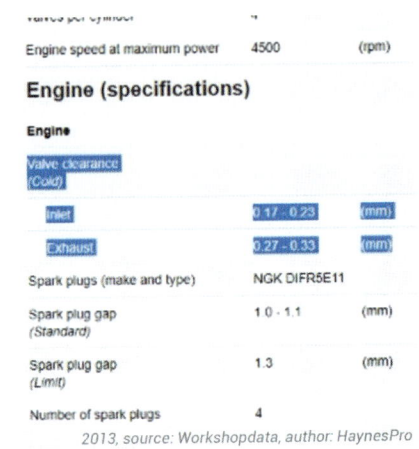

Fig. 258 Look for the valve clearance.

2. Preparation

Always measure the valve clearance with the engine cold. Remove the parts to access the valves.

Fig. 259 Remove the air filter housing.

Fig. 260 Diconnect the plugs of the ignition coils and remove the ignition coils.

Fig. 261 Blow the valve cover edge clean with compressed air.

Fig. 262 Remove the cable harness from the ignition coils.

Fig. 263 Remove the bolts and the valve cover.

Fig. 264 Remove the valve cover gasket.

3. Setting Cylinder 4 to Rocking

The engine is a 4 cylinder 4 stroke engine with the firing order: 1-3-4-2.

To adjust the valves of cylinder 1, the valves of cylinder 4 must be set to rocking. To set the valves to rocking, the crankshaft is rotated.

The valves are rocking when the exhaust valve is not moving down yet and the inlet valve is just closed.

Fig. 265 Only turn the crankshaft clockwise.

Fig. 266 When cylinder 4 is at the rocking point, cylinder 1 can be set.

Only turn the crankshaft clockwise. If it is turned counterclockwise, the central bolt of the crankshaft can become loose. The timing chain tension can also be lost and the chain may jump over the gear.

4. Checking cylinder 1 valve clearance

The valve clearance is checked using a feeler gauge. The valve clearance of the inlet valve must be between 0.17 mm and 0.23 mm. A 0.20 mm feeler gauge must slip through quite easily, but must not be loose or stick. Next take a feeler gauge which is 0.05 mm thicker; this should not fit in the gap. Then continue with the exhaust valves. The exhaust valves are checked in the same way but in this case the prescribed clearance is 0.27-0.33 mm.

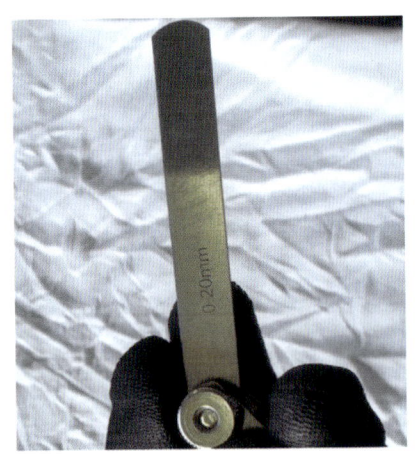

Fig. 267 Feeler gauge thickness of 0.20 mm.

Fig. 268 Check the intake valve of cylinder 1.

5. Checking cylinder 3 valve clearance

The firing order of this engine is: 1-3-4-2. This means that turning the engine half a crankshaft revolution further will set cylinder 2 to rocking. When cylinder 2 is at the rocking point, this means that cylinder 3 can be set.

1 on rocking = set 4

2 on rocking = set 3

3 on rocking = set 2

4 on rocking = set 1

Fig. 269 Turn the crankshaft exactly half a revolution clockwise.

Fig. 270 Check the exhaust and inlet valves of cylinder 3 and repeat this action for cylinders 2 and 4.

6. Completion

Carefully replace everything as it was. Make sure that you place all hoses and plugs neatly back into position. Finally, always go on a test drive and bring the engine up to temperature. Afterwards, check whether the valve cover seal is still sealing properly.

Fig. 271 Install the valve cover. Tighten the bolts with the prescribed torque. Work from the middle towards the outside.

Fig. 272 Install the ignition coils and connect them again.

Fig. 273 Install the air filter housing.

VISUAL INSPECTION OF VALVE SEAT AND VALVE

Special tools that are not typically available in the average shop are required to measure the valve seat and, in particular, the sealing surface. These measurements are therefore often left to overhaul specialists. In any case, work on the valve seat, such as grinding and replacing, is no longer carried out in the shop. Vehicle technicians can still visually inspect the valve seat to identify problems.

Vehicle technicians will look for the following points in particular when carrying out a visual inspection of the valve seat:

— Burned spots.
— Cracks.
— The general condition of the valve seat.

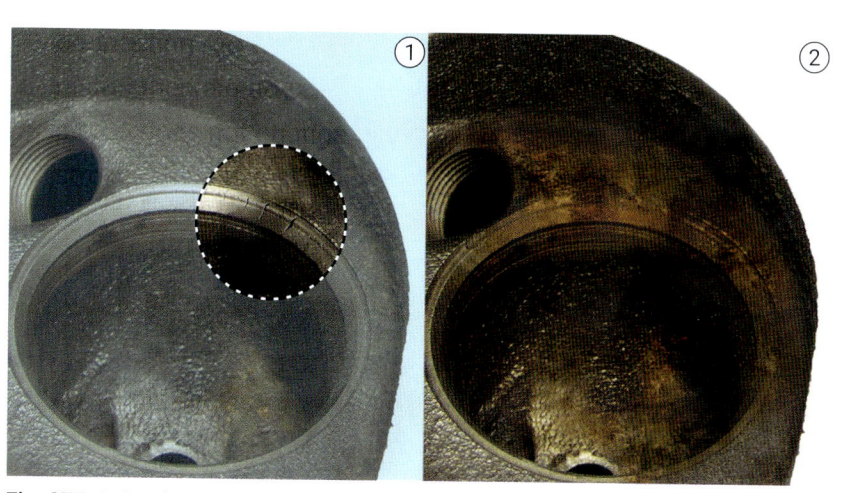

Fig. 275 1. Crack in the valve seat. 2. Deposits on the valve seat.

Vehicle technicians will look for the following when carrying out a visual inspection of the valve itself:

— Burned valve.
— Damaged valve sealing surface.
— Bent valve stem.
— Cracked valve head.
— Split valve head.
— Edge too sharp or too thin.

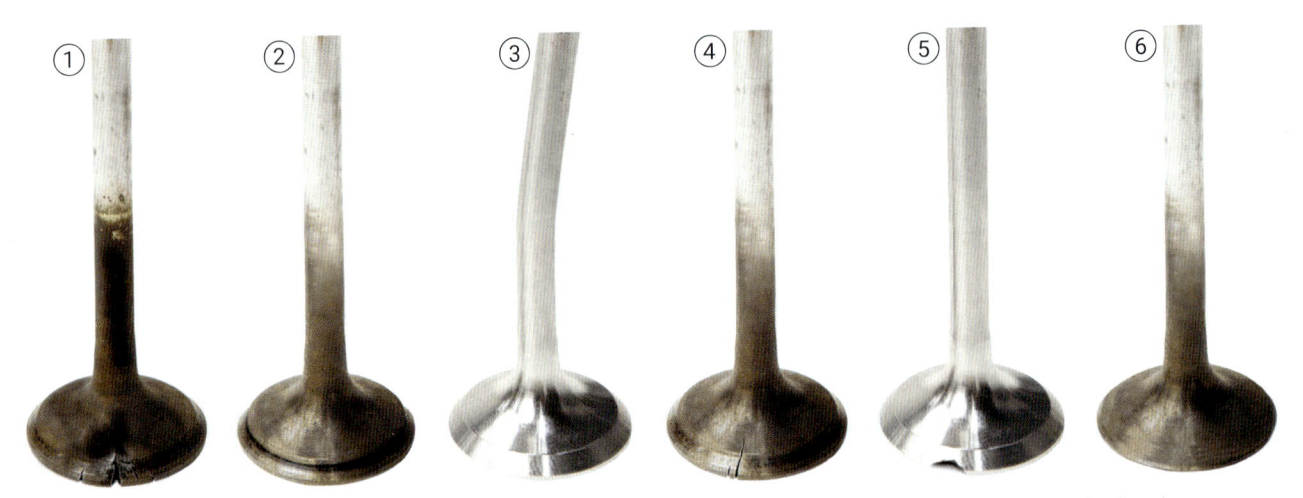

448 GASOLINE ENGINE CONSTRUCTION AND OPERATION

Fig. 276 1. Burned valve. 2. Damaged valve sealing surface. 3. Bent valve stem. 4. Cracked valve head. 5. Split valve head. 6. Edge too sharp or too thin.

HOW TO: REPLACE VALVE COVER GASKET

1. Look for Information

Before starting the job first look for the technical information such as tightening torques and work description.

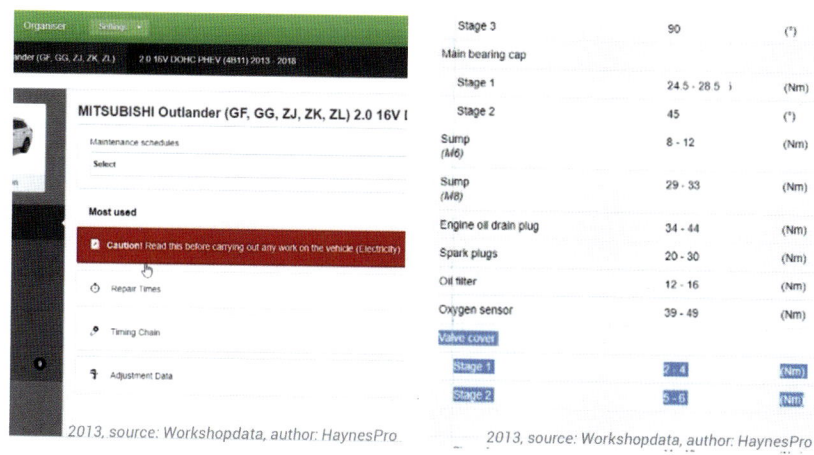

Fig. 277 Go through the safety warning.

Fig. 278 Look for the torque figures: Step 1: 2-4 Nm; Step 2: 5-6 Nm.

2. Preparation

First remove the components which get in the way of disassembling the valve cover. In this case, these are the air filter housing, the air filter housing support and the ignition coils.

Fig. 279 Remove the air filter housing.

Fig. 280 Diconnect the plugs of the ignition coils and remove the ignition coils.

Fig. 281 Remove the air filter housing support.

3. Cleaning

When disassembling the valve cover, dust and grit can enter the engine. To prevent this, the edge around the valve cover is cleaned with compressed air. Push a wad of paper into the inlet pipe so that the dust flying around cannot enter the engine.

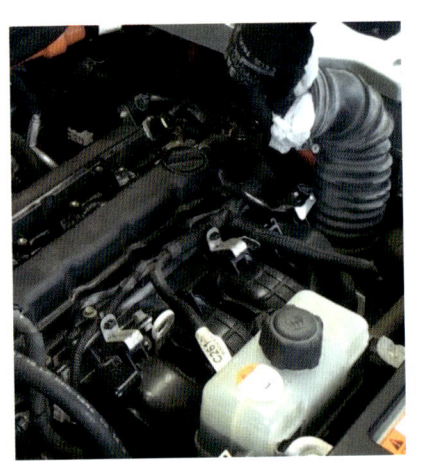

Fig. 282 Close off the intake pipe.

Fig. 283 Blow the valve cover edge clean with compressed air.

4. Removing the Valve Cover

The valve cover is fixed in place with bolts. The bolts might be of different lengths. Make sure the bolts are installed in the same order in which they were removed.

Fig. 284 Remove the cable harness from the ignition coils.

Fig. 285 Remove the bolts and the valve cover.

Fig. 286 Take away the valve cover gasket.

5. Gasket Replacement

Compare the new gasket with the old gasket. If it is the correct gasket, place it on the cover as it should be installed.

Push the corners into the ridge. As soon as you see it fits, push the rubber completely into the cover. If the gasket does not stay in place, you can stick down the gasket using a small amount of grease or liquid gasket.

Fig. 287 Press the gasket into the ridge of the cover.

6. Cleaning the Gasket Surface

Clean the gasket surface on the cylinder head using a piece of paper. Remove liquid gasket with a sealant scraper and sandpaper. If there are irregularities in the gasket surface, apply new liquid gasket to the gasket surface.

Fig. 288 Remove the old liquid gasket with a sealant scraper.

Fig. 289 Dress the surface with a piece of sandpaper.

Fig. 290 Apply liquid gasket when necessary.

7. Installing the Valve Cover

Place the valve cover down in the correct position in one movement. Hand-tighten all bolts in the correct sequence and in the correct position. Do this evenly and work from inside to outside.

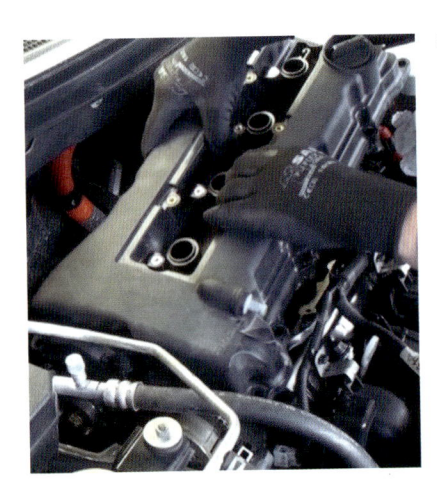

Fig. 291 Try to position the valve cover correctly first time round.

Fig. 292 Install the bolts.

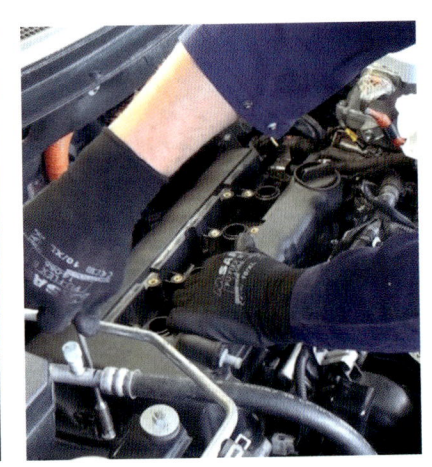

Fig. 293 Work from the middle towards the outside.

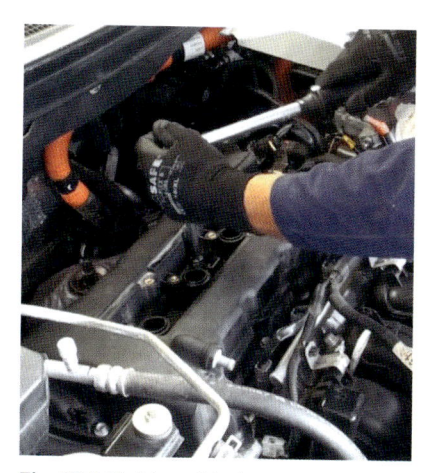

Fig. 294 Tighten all bolts with a torque wrench.

8. Tightening the valve cover

Tighten the valve cover as indicated in the specifications of the manufacturer. In this case it must be done in 2 steps.

Step 1: 2-4 Nm.
Step 2: 5-6 Nm.

Work from the middle towards the outside again.

9. Completion

Carefully replace everything as it was. Make sure that the intake pipe is free again. Place all hoses and plugs back neatly in place.

Finally, always go on a test drive and bring the engine up to temperature. Afterwards, check whether the new valve cover seal is still sealing properly.

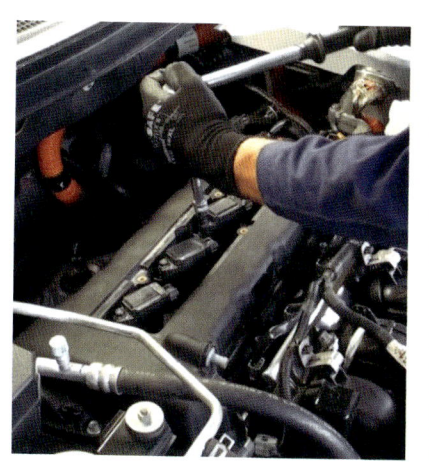

Fig. 295 Install the ignition coils.

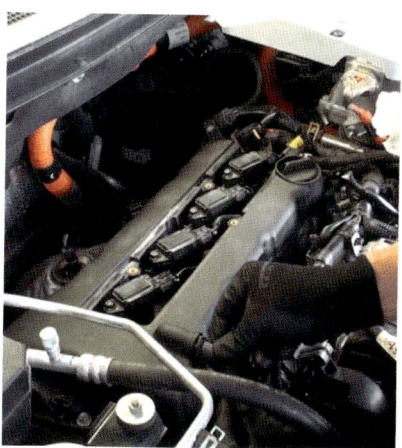

Fig. 296 Install the hoses of the crankcase breather.

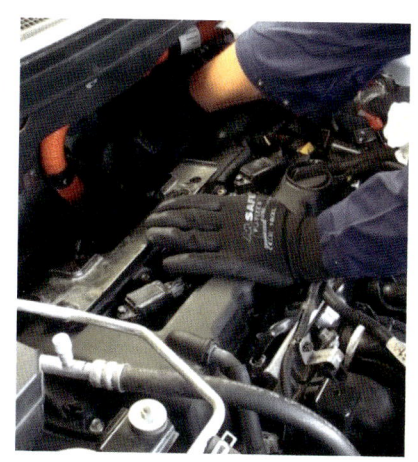

Fig. 297 Install the air filter support.

Fig. 298 Install the air filter housing.

Fig. 299 Make sure that the intake pipe is free again.

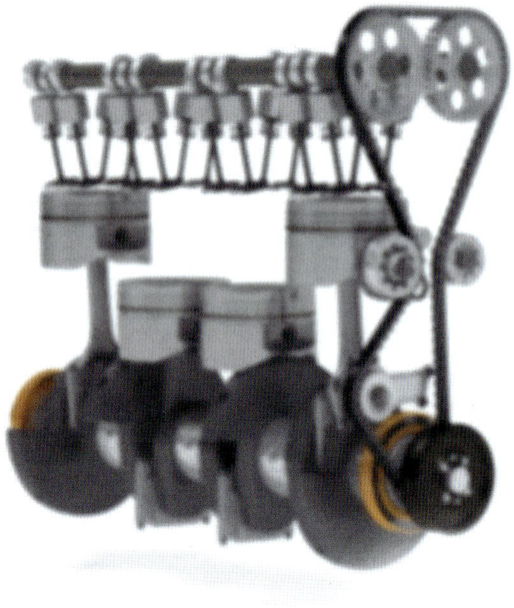

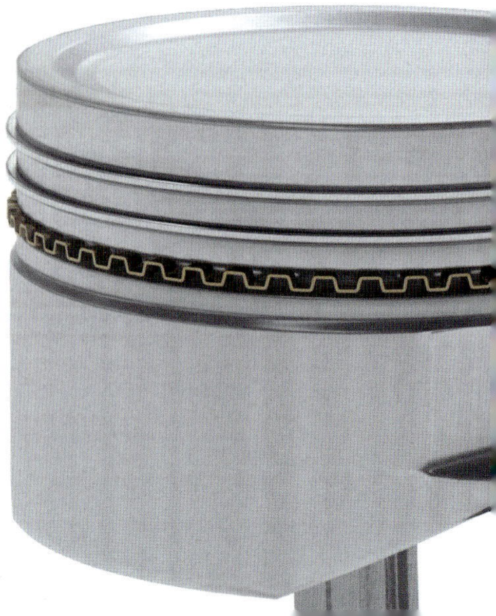

6. Engine Mechanical Principles

STROKE VOLUME

1. Stroke Volume

The main dimensions of an engine are its bore and its stroke. These two dimensions determine the characteristics of the engine.
- The bore is the diameter of the cylinder. This dimension is also used for the diameter of the piston.

- The stroke is the distance travelled by the piston between Bottom Dead Center (BDC) and Top Dead Center (TDC).

You can calculate the stroke volume of one cylinder by multiplying the area of the piston by the stroke.

Piston area $= {}^1/_4 * \pi * d^2$

$d =$ piston diameter in millimetres.

$\pi =$ approximately 3.14

2. Bore to Stroke Ratio

Combustion engines can be divided into three categories by looking at the bore diameter and the stroke length.

1. If the stroke length is smaller than the bore diameter, this is called a short-stroke engine, or it is sometimes referred to as an over-square engine.
2. If the stroke length is greater than the bore diameter, this is called a long-stroke engine.
3. If the stroke length is equal to the bore diameter, this is called a square engine.

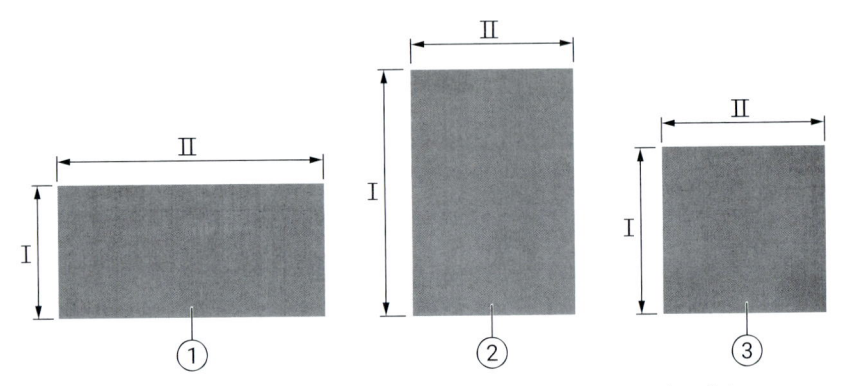

Fig. 301 Types of engines: 1. Short-stroke engine or over-square engine. 2. Long-stroke engine. 3. Square engine. I. Stroke. II. Bore.

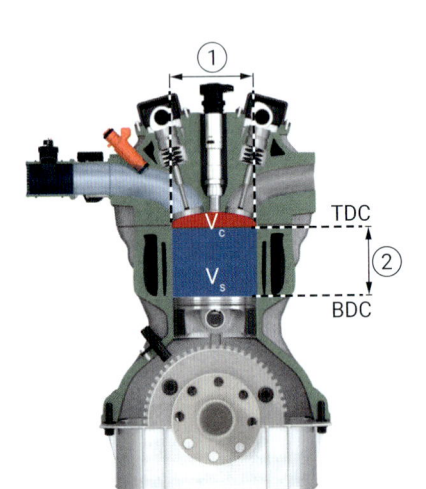

Fig. 302 The stroke length and the compression volume: 1. Bore. 2. Stroke.

3. Calculating Stroke Volume and Engine Displacement

The engine displacement and compression ratio of an engine can be found in the engine specifications.

The total engine displacement of the complete engine is the stroke volume of a cylinder multiplied by the number of cylinders.

Engine displacement = stroke volume × number of cylinders

The stroke volume of a cylinder is calculated by multiplying the cylinder area by the stroke length. As a formula, this is:

$$V_s = {}^1/_4 \pi * d^2 * s$$

$d =$ diameter of the cylinder (bore).
$s =$ stroke.
A calculation is given below.
An engine has 4 cylinders.

The bore (d) of the cylinders is 2.5 inches.
The stroke length is (s) is 3 inches.
The objective is to find the stroke volume (V_s) and the total engine displacement (V_{cyl}).

First V_s:
$V_s = {}^1/_4 \pi * d^2 * s =$
$V_s = {}^1/_4 \pi * 2.5^2 * 3$
$V_s = 0.785 * 2.5^2 * 3$
$V_s = 0.785 * 6.25 * 3$
$V_s = 14.7 in^3 = 240 cm^3 = 240 cc$
$(1 cm^3 = 1 cc)$

Then the engine displacement:
$V_{cyl} = number of cylinders * V_s$
$V_{cyl} = 4 * 14.7 in^3 (or 240 cc)$
$V_{cyl} = 58.8 in^3 (or 960 cc)$

COMPRESSION RATIO

1. Introduction

During the compression stroke the air/fuel mixture is compressed. The compression ratio is a measurement indicating how strongly the air in the cylinder is compressed during the compression stroke.

Inside the cylinder the piston creates two different chambers.
— The space above the piston at top dead center (TDC) is the combustion chamber volume.
— The space above the piston at bottom dead center (BDC) is the stroke volume plus the combustion chamber volume.

The stroke volume is the space between the TDC and the BDC.

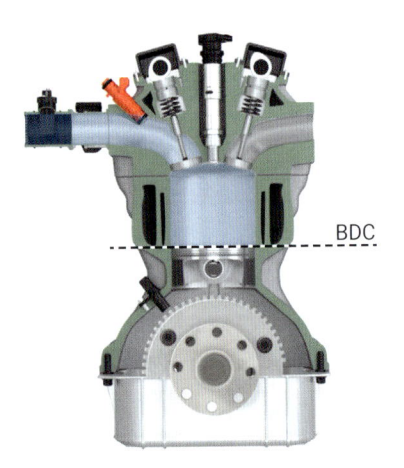

Fig. 303 Piston at Bottom Dead Center (BDC).

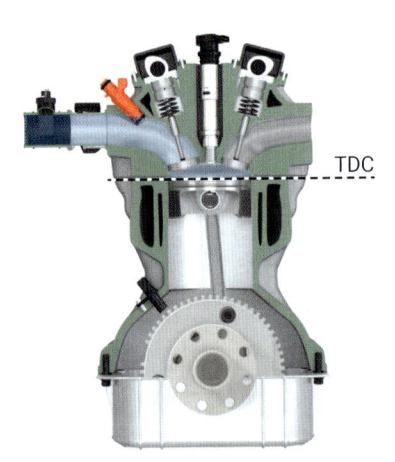

Fig. 304 Piston at Top Dead Center (TDC).

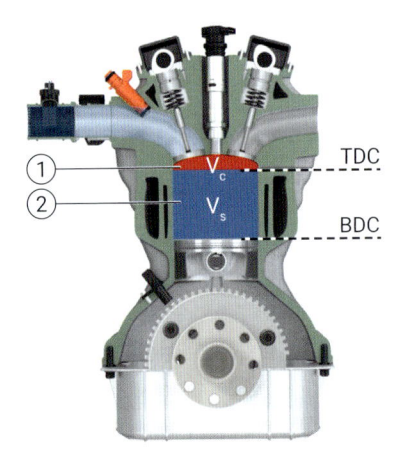

Fig. 305 Combustion space (1) and stroke volume (2).

Even when the piston is at TDC, there is still space at the top. The space between the top of the piston and the cylinder head is called the combustion space or the clearance volume.

During the compression stroke, the piston starts at BDC. The total volume above the piston is compressed to the volume of the combustion space.

The ratio between the total volume above the piston at BDC and the volume of the combustion space is called the compression ratio.

2. Compression Ratio

The compression ratio is the ratio between the volume above the piston in BDC (stroke volume plus combustion chamber volume) and the volume above the piston in TDC (combustion chamber volume).

Formula:

$$\varepsilon = \frac{(V_s + V_c)}{V_c}$$

ε = compression ratio (epsilon)
V_s = Stroke volume (cm³)
V_c = Combustion chamber volume (cm³)

The compression ratio is often expressed in a figure related to 1. For example 8:1. This means that the stroke volume and the combustion chamber volume combined are eight times as large as the combustion chamber volume itself.

3. Calculating the Compression Ratio

To calculate the compression ratio of a cylinder, you will need the stroke length and the compression volume.

A calculation is given below.

An engine has a combustion chamber space (Vc) of 20 cubic Inches (50 cm³). The stroke volume (Vs) is 140 cubic Inches (350 cm³).

$$\varepsilon = \frac{(V_s + V_c)}{V_c}$$

$$\varepsilon = \frac{(140 + 20)}{20}$$

$$\varepsilon = 8 : 1$$

A ratio of 14 to 20 : 1 is acceptable for diesel engines. For four-stroke engines a ratio of 7 to 12: 1 is an acceptable range.

ENGINE PERFORMANCE GRAPH

1. Dynamometer

A dynamometer measures engine torque through a braking mechanism that provides resistance. Once torque is determined, power can be calculated.

To perform a power test, you need to input specific vehicle data into the dyno computer:
— enter the vehicle specifications
— warm up the engine to operating temperature
— secure the vehicle
— shift into top gear (or one gear lower)
— switch on the dyno blower fan

Fig. 306 Dynamometer

Power is measured in two ways:
— At the flywheel, using an engine dynamometer.
  This way, there is no significant loss through a drivetrain.
— At the wheels, using a chassis dynamometer.
  Loss through the drivetrain can be significant: up to 30%.

Some chassis dynamometer programs can measure drivetrain losses by allowing the dynamometer to drive the vehicle wheels while coasting.

2. Calculating Power

Now that you have determined the torque with the dynamometer, you can calculate the power. You do this with the following formula:

$$P = M * 2 * \pi * n$$

P = power (HP or W)
M = torque (Ft Lbs or Nm)
π = 3.14
n = speed (rev/sec)

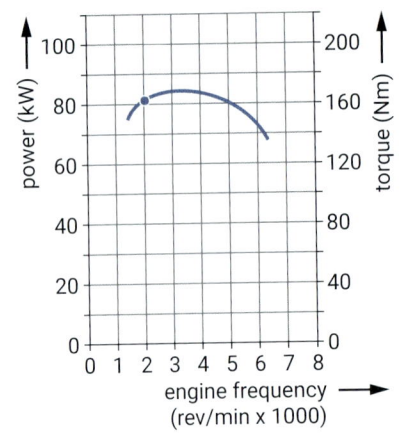

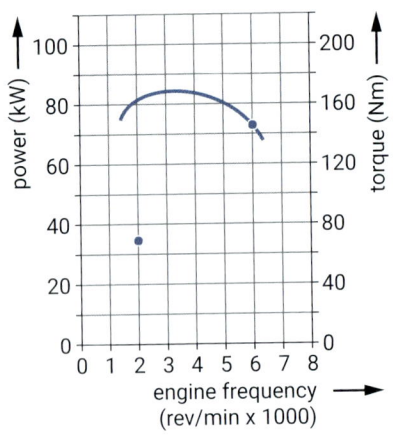

464 GASOLINE ENGINE CONSTRUCTION AND OPERATION

Fig. 307 Choose a speed that you can easily read: 2000 rpm.

Fig. 308 Plot the result of your first calculation on the graph.

EXAMPLE Use the torque curve in the graph to calculate the power. To do so, carry out the following steps:

1. Choose a speed that you can easily read: 2000 rpm.
2. The torque (M) at 2000 rpm is 163.
3. Calculate the speed from rpm to rps (revs/sec): 33.33 rps.
4. Apply the formula:
$$P = M * 2 * \pi * n$$
$$P = 163 * 2 * 3.14 * 33.33$$
$$P = 34118 W =$$
5. Calculate the power from watts to kilowatts (kW): 34.1 kW.
6. Plot the result of your calculation on the graph.
7. Apply the same calculation at every 100 rpm and also plot these points on the graph.
8. Draw a line between the points you plotted on the graph.

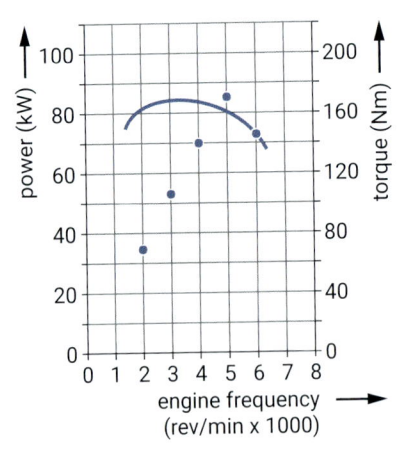

Fig. 309 Apply the same calculation at every 1000 rpm and also plot these points on the graph.

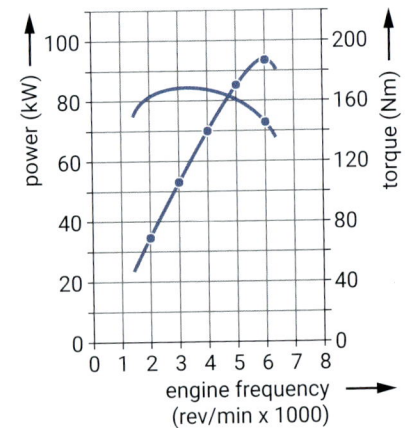

Fig. 310 Draw a line between the points that you plotted on the graph.

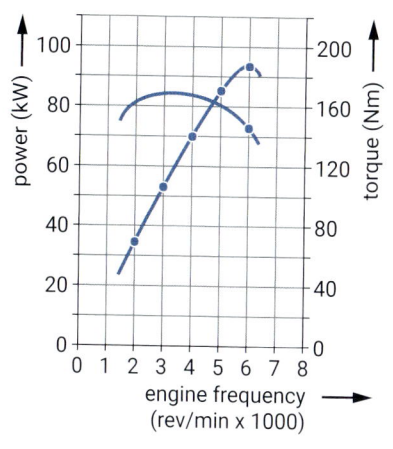

Fig. 311 Engine Performance Graph

3. Engine Performance Graph

A characteristic curve indicates the amount of *power* a combustion engine can deliver at a certain *engine speed*.

The engine's power largely depends on the cylinder's degree of filling. This in turn is determined by the throttle position.

The power increases up to a certain rpm, after that it begins to drop off.

A transmission with selectable gear ratios is used to keep the engine in the rpm range that makes the most power. If a transmission with only one ratio were used, the engine would rev too high or stall when accelerating .

INTERNAL COMBUSTION ENGINE EFFICIENCY

1. Efficiency

Fuel is required to operate an engine. In the combustion process, the fuel is partly transformed into mechanical energy. Due to phenomena such as friction and heat generation, which create thermal energy, 100% efficiency in producing mechanical energy cannot be achieved.

The fuel that is supplied to the engine represents a certain value of power called P_{in}. Due to the combustion of the fuel, the engine is running, causing the flywheel to turn. The power available at the flywheel is P_{out} called output power. The higher the efficiency of an engine, the more efficiently power is produced. However, there will always be losses between P_{in} and P_{out}.

Causes of power loss:
- Friction loss - friction generates heat (thermal energy), causing power loss in engine.
- Heat loss - heat transfer by the cooling system and heat that leaves through the exhaust system.
- Radiation from the engine - the engine gets warm and radiates.
- Due to incomplete combustion, the fuel particles don't burn completely.

The ratio between P_{in} and P_{out} is called efficiency.
The efficiency is expressed as a percentage or with the Greek letter η (èta).

In formula form it looks like this:

$$\eta = \frac{P_{out}}{P_{in}} * 100\%$$

η = efficiency (èta)
P_{in} = power supplied (HP or kW)
P_{out} = power output (HP or kW)

2. Comparison Between the Efficiency of an Otto Engine and a Diesel Engine

To make it visible where losses occur, we use a Sankey diagram, named for the inventor of this kind of flow diagrams. Here we can read energy flow from engines and what energy losses there are.

In the diagrams shown below we see:
— The 100% power/energy contained in the fuel.
— Losses in the drive train from exhaust-gas heat loss, cooling loss, mechanical loss, and radiation loss.
— Losses to heat and cooling.

Here are a Sankey diagram of an Otto engine and a Sankey diagram of a diesel engine. The Otto engine has an efficiency (effective power) of 28%. The diesel engine has an efficiency (effective power) of 36%.

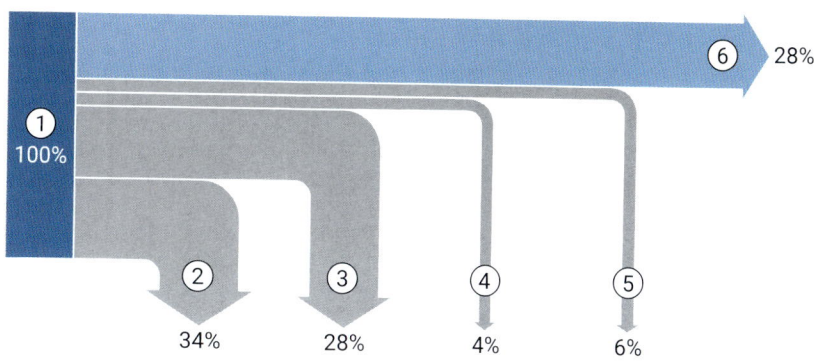

Fig. 312 Sankey diagram Otto engine: 1. Energy from fuel. 2. Exhaust gas heat loss. 3. Cooling loss. 4. Mechanical loss. 5. Radiation loss. 6. Effective power.

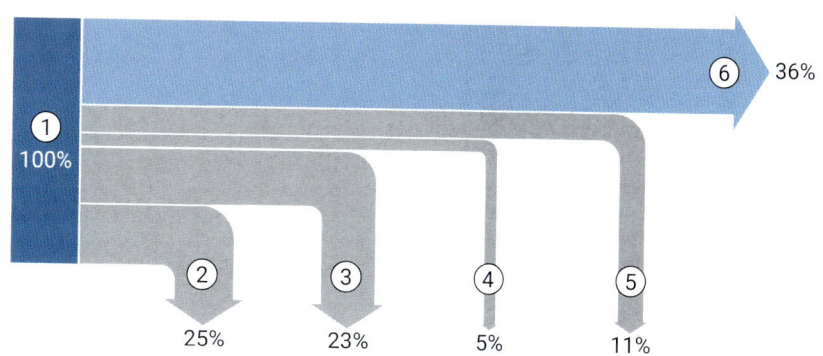

Fig. 313 Sankey diagram diesel engine: 1. Energy from fuel. 2. Exhaust gas loss. 3. Cooling loss. 4. Mechanical loss. 5. Radiation loss. 6. Effective power.

Exhaust and cooling losses are the largest and therefore most important factors contributing to the efficiency of an engine.

In the examples, combined exhaust and cooling losses are:
- 62% with the Otto engine.
- 48% with the diesel engine.

By a more effective combustion of the fuel in a diesel engine, the generated heat is better utilized. Less heat escapes through the exhaust and the cooling system.

The radiant heat coming from the engine is also lost; therefore, we call it radiation loss.
In the examples, this is the radiation loss:
- 6% with the Otto engine.
- 11% with the diesel engine.

The mechanical losses are smaller with an Otto engine than with a diesel engine. This is why:
- In an Otto engine, the pressures and thus the capacities are smaller. This creates less friction.
- A diesel engine has a mechanical high-pressure pump which causes extra loss.

In the examples given, the mechanical losses are as follows: 4% with the Otto engine; 5% with the diesel engine.

A diesel engine has a higher efficiency because there is a more complete combustion of the fuel. In addition, the diesel engine has a higher compression ratio, and the diesel engine has no restrictive throttle valve in most cases.

3. Example

An engine is supplied with 225 kW of energy from the fuel. 78 kW remains at the flywheel of the engine.

Use this data to calculate the efficiency of this engine.

Given:
$P_{in} = 225 kW$
$P_{out} = 78 kW$
Asked: η

Answer:

$$\eta = \frac{P_{out}}{P_{in}} * 100\%$$

$$\eta = \frac{78kW}{225kW} * 100\% = 34.66\%$$

This efficiency is the ratio between these:
– The power from the fuel.
– The power at the flywheel.

You could say the difference between the energy that goes in compared to the amount of energy that goes out is the engine's efficiency, which in this example is 34%. This efficiency is also called 'effective efficiency' or 'total efficiency'.

470

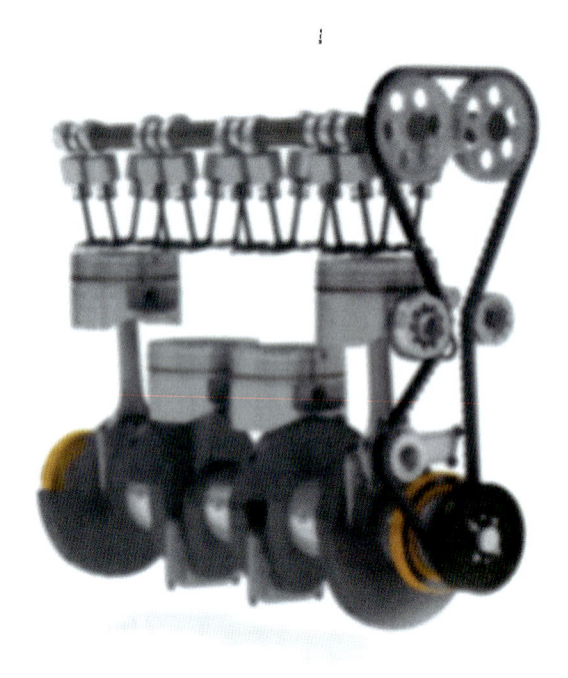

7. Load on Engine Components

LOAD ON ENGINE COMPONENTS

1. Introduction

The gas pressure and piston force generated during ignition of the air/fuel mixture produces loads on various engine components. To visualize the load, the gas pressure can be converted into piston force and then broken down into:

- Side thrust.
- Connecting rod forces.
- Radial forces.

During the four-stroke process, the gas pressure above the piston varies continuously. Take, for example, the difference in gas pressure between the power stroke and intake stroke. This fluctuating gas pressure creates a variable or uneven load on the various engine components. For an automotive technician, it is important to have an understanding of irregular loading and the resulting negative effect on the crankshaft and the drivetrain.

The gas pressure in the cylinder is also affected by the driver. For example, if a driver applies full throttle while at a low engine speed, high gas pressure is generated within the cylinder. This high gas pressure results in a high load on certain engine components. This is why it is important for automotive technicians to understand these effects so they can advise the customer about driving techniques that will help to extend the service life of the engine.

2. Load From Side Thrust, Connecting Rod Force and Radial Force

As mentioned earlier, the piston force can be broken down into forces within the crank/connecting rod mechanism. These forces vary depending on the position of the crankshaft.

At the position of the piston pin, the piston force (F_1) can be broken down into 2 forces: the connecting rod force (F_2) and the side thrust (F_3). The connecting rod force is the force that is "pushing on" the connecting rod. The side thrust is the force which presses the piston against the cylinder wall.

At the position of the crankpin, the connecting rod force can be broken down into 2 forces: the tangential force (F_4) and the radial force (F_5). You can calculate the engine torque using the tangential force. The radial force is the force which needs to be absorbed by the crankshaft.

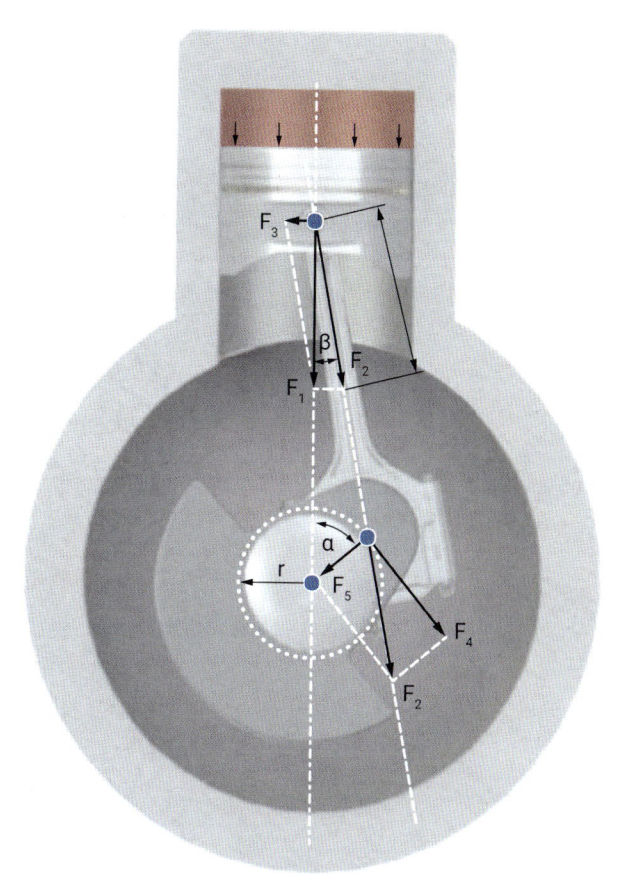

Fig. 314 Piston force at a crankshaft angle of 45°: F1 = piston force, F2 = connecting rod force, F3 = side thrust, F4 = tangential force, F5 = radial force.

The illustration shows an exploded view of the components of the crank/connecting rod mechanism. From this illustration, it is clear which components are loaded by the side thrust, connecting rod force and radial force:

- Piston.
- Piston rings.
- Piston pin.
- Connecting rod.
- Connecting rod bearing.
- Connecting rod bolt.
- Crankshaft.

The cylinder wall is also loaded by the piston force, namely by the side thrust.

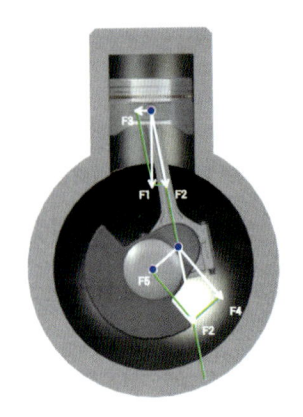

Fig. 315 Loading of engine components at 45°: 1. Piston. 2. Piston rings. 3. Piston pin. 4. Connecting rod. 5. Connecting rod bearing. 6. Connecting rod bolt. 7. Crankshaft.

3. Loading at a Crankshaft Angle of 0° and 180°

The illustration below shows the components of the crank/connecting rod mechanism at a crankshaft angle of 0°. This also applies at a crankshaft angle of 180°.

From the illustration, it is clear that the following components are particularly loaded by the strong connecting rod and radial forces:

— Piston pin.
— Connecting rod.
— Connecting rod bearing.
— Connecting rod bolt.
— Crankshaft + bearings.

The piston rings and the cylinder wall do not experience as high a load in this crankshaft position.

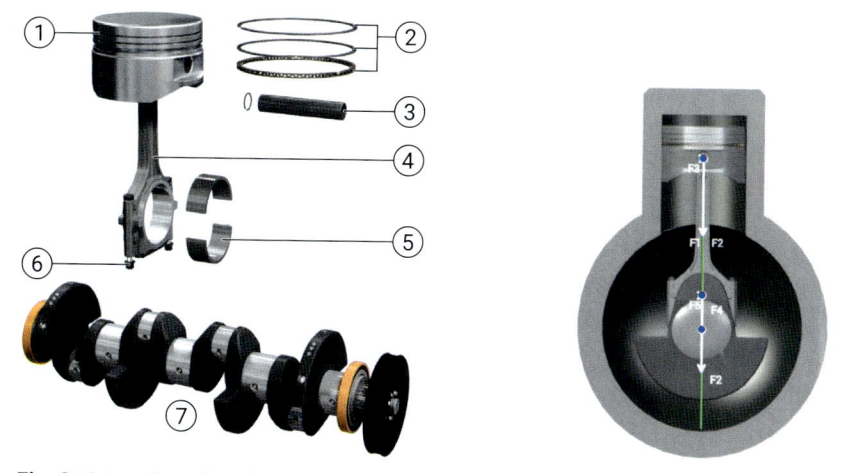

Fig. 316 Loading of engine components at 0°: 1. Piston. 2. Piston rings. 3. Piston pin. 4. Connecting rod. 5. Connecting rod bearing. 6. Connecting rod bolt. 7. Crankshaft.

4. Loading at a Crankshaft Angle of 90°

At a crankshaft angle of 90°, it is clear that the piston rings and the cylinder wall are particularly loaded due to the strong side thrust.

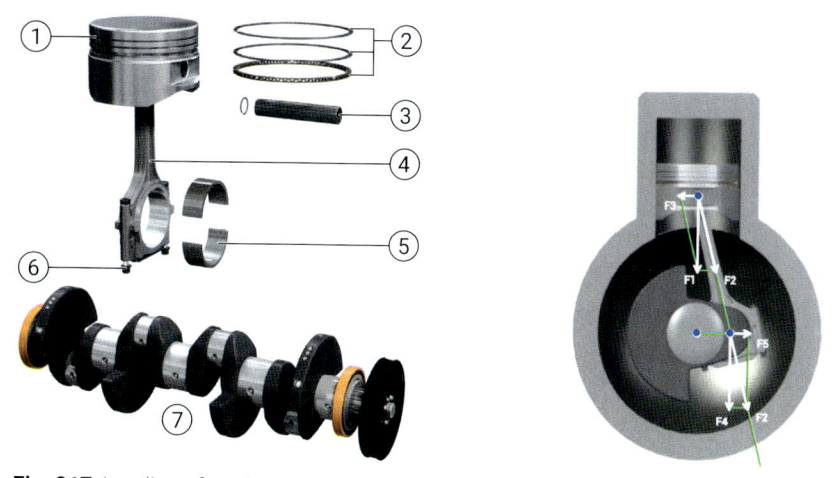

Fig. 317 Loading of engine components at 90°: 1. Piston. 2. Piston rings. 3. Piston pin. 4. Connecting rod. 5. Connecting rod bearing. 6. Connecting rod bolt. 7. Crankshaft.

IRREGULAR LOADING

1. Introduction

Irregular loading means uneven or variable loading. This type of loading is the result of the variable load transfer on the crankshaft. During the two crankshaft revolutions covered by the four-stroke cycle, the crankshaft does not rotate at the same constant speed. The crankshaft is decelerated significantly during the compression stroke, whereas it undergoes extreme acceleration in the power stroke.

At an average speed of 800 rpm, the minimum speed may be around 640 rpm during the compression stroke, while it can be around 960 rpm during the power stroke.

Some effects caused by this irregular crankshaft motion include:

— Twisting of the crankshaft and vibrations in the drivetrain.
— Undesirable vibrations and belt tension when driving auxiliary equipment.

2. Crankshaft Torsion and Vibrations

Crankshaft torsion is a result of irregular loading during the power stroke and the differences in mass inertia of the various mechanical engine components.

During the power stroke, the piston force pushes the piston and connecting rod downwards, causing the crankshaft to turn. This accelerates the crankshaft almost instantly.

However, the flywheel is located at the end of the crankshaft. This flywheel has a large mass and does not accelerate easily. In other words, the crankshaft effectively sits between the flywheel, which is difficult to start moving, and the piston, which wants to accelerate the crankshaft. This causes the crankshaft to twist slightly.

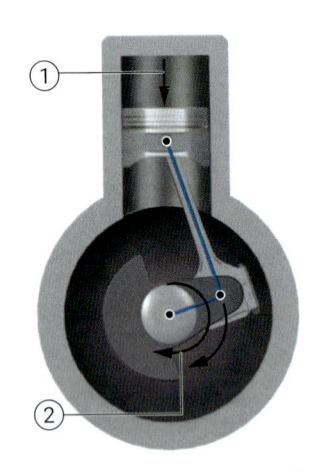

Fig. 318 1. Piston force. 2. Torsion.

The opposite situation occurs at the end of the power stroke. At one end of the crankshaft is a heavy flywheel, while at the other end, the piston force accelerating the crankshaft drops off. This causes the crankshaft to return to its original condition, which can result in vibrations.

The longer the crankshaft, the greater the effect of torsion in the crankshaft. This is one of the reasons why designers choose a V6 instead of a six-cylinder in-line configuration.

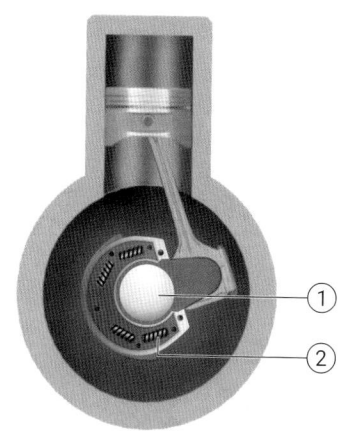

Fig. 319 1. Rotating mass. 2. Damping springs.

Fig. 320 Dual-Mass Flywheel.

An internal vibration damper is one of the solutions used to neutralize this torsion in the crankshaft. This kind of damper is incorporated into the crank web and consists of a rotating mass connected to the crankshaft by springs. The torsional resistance of the springs, together with the mass inertia of the damper, provides the correct damping frequencies on the crankshaft.
A second flywheel in the form of a heavy crankshaft pulley distributes the torsion over the length of the crankshaft.

The dual-mass flywheel is also a good example of a damper that reduces crankshaft torsion and vibrations in the drivetrain.

Fig. 321 1. Overrunning alternator pulley.

3. Vibrations When Powering Auxiliary Equipment

When driving auxiliary equipment - like the alternator, for example, assemblies are added to reduce the impact of irregular loading. For example, the overrunning alternator pulley.

Overrunning alternator pulleys "decouple" the alternator from the rotational irregularities of the crankshaft. This application reduces stresses and vibrations on the serpentine belt.

LOAD AND DRIVING BEHAVIOR

1. Introduction

Driving behavior can also have an effect on the loading of mechanical engine components. This is best illustrated using the following two extreme situations as examples:
- Low rpm and high load.
- High rpm and low load.

2. Low RPM and High Load

A good example of low rpm and high load is driving up a hill in too high of a gear at full throttle.

The extreme loading that occurs in this situation can be explained using the following observations:
- The more the cylinder fills with air/fuel mixture, the higher the charge rate.
- The higher the charge rate, the higher the gas pressure.
- The higher the gas pressure, the stronger the piston force.

At full throttle, there is a high charge rate. There is no restriction preventing air or the air/fuel mixture from flowing into the cylinder. (The throttle valve is fully open.)

At low engine speeds, there is plenty of time to fill the cylinder. Low engine speeds therefore enable a high charge rate. That is why the combination of a low engine speed with a fully opened throttle valve ensures an especially high charge rate.

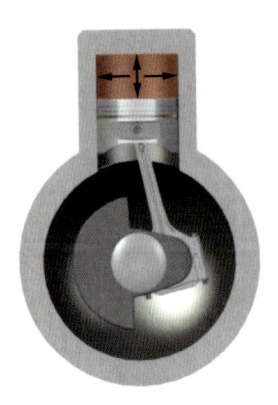

Fig. 322 A high load and low rpm = high gas pressure.

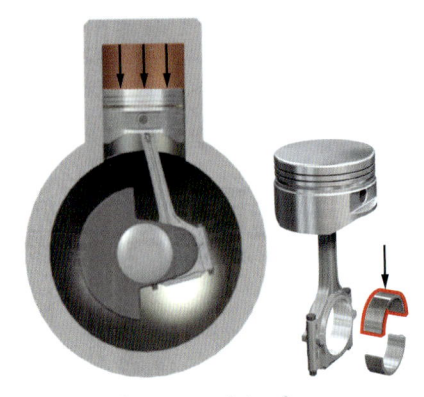

Fig. 323 The strong piston force creates a high load on the top connecting rod bearings.

The high charge rate produces high gas pressure during the compression and power strokes.

The high gas pressure causes very strong piston forces, which cause wear on the top connecting rod and main bearing shells in particular.

3. High RPM and Low Load

An example of high rpm and low load is when revving the engine powerfully while idling. The engine does not have any work to perform and so it quickly shoots up through the rpm range.

The throttle valve is open in this situation, which can potentially cause a high charge rate. However, the limiting factor for the charge rate is the high engine speed. At a high engine speed there is only just barely enough time to fill the cylinder sufficiently. This then results in a relatively low charge rate.

Fig. 324 A low load and high engine speed = strong centrifugal forces.

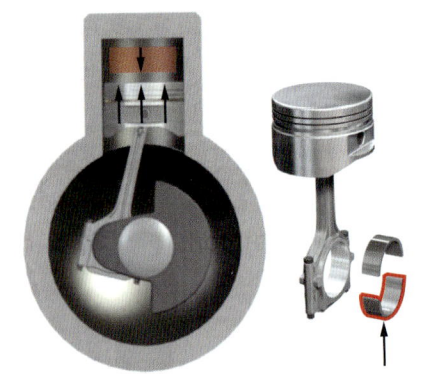

Fig. 325 The strong centrifugal forces exert a high load on the lower connecting rod bearings.

The relatively low charge rate results in low gas pressure. During the compression stroke, the piston is only decelerated slightly as a result of the low gas pressure.

However, at high engine speeds, there are strong centrifugal forces. The piston is launched upwards, as it were, by the strong centrifugal forces, and is decelerated only slightly by the weak piston forces. This situation also places additional load on the lower bearings shells.

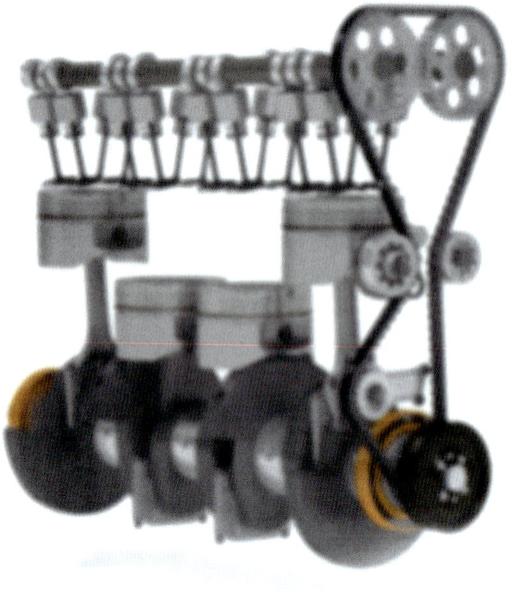

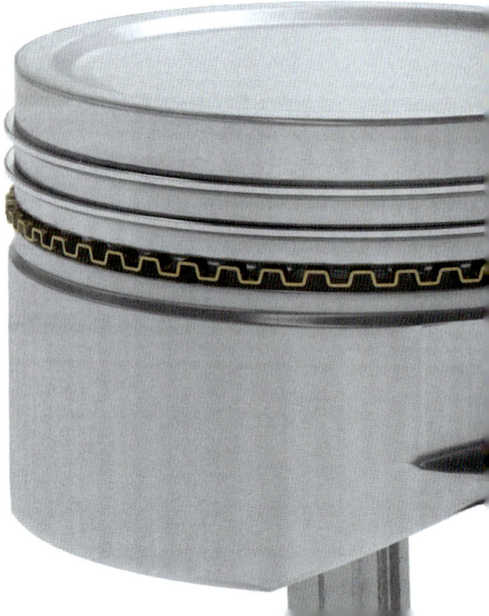

8. Engine Vibrations

ENGINE VIBRATIONS

1. Introduction

Gas pressure and the resulting piston force causes the crank/connecting rod mechanism to move. The pistons rise and fall, which is converted into rotational movement by the crankshaft.

The up and down movement is also known as reciprocating motion. The rotational movement is often referred to as rotary motion.

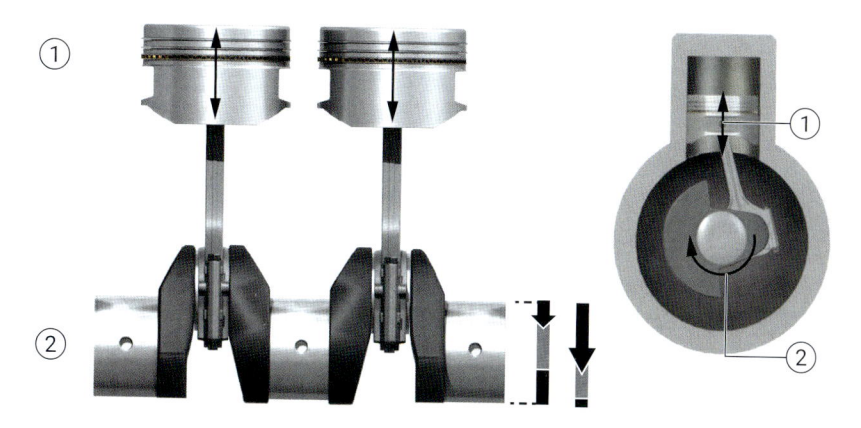

Fig. 326 1. Reciprocating mass. 2. Rotating mass.

2. Reciprocating and Rotating Mass

The mass of the components moving up and down is also called reciprocating mass. This applies to the piston, and in part, to the connecting rod.

The mass of the components with rotating movement is called rotating mass. The crankshaft is the most important example of this.

Reciprocating mass and rotating mass are the two main causes of engine vibrations. In order for an engine to be free of vibrations, a literal counterweight needs to be provided for both of these masses.

A third major cause of engine vibrations is the rapid and sudden creation of gas pressure - explosion - when the air/fuel mixture is ignited.

This sudden gas pressure causes ignition forces which are felt as vibrations or sometimes even as shaking.
The best way to eliminate vibrations caused by ignition forces is to time the ignition to occur at regular intervals.

Fig. 327 Vibrations caused by ignition forces.

BALANCING RECIPROCATING MASSES

1. Introduction

The piston is the largest reciprocating mass in an engine. It is also the main cause of engine vibrations.

In the course of one crankshaft revolution, the piston moves from TDC to BDC. At BDC the piston decelerates and changes direction. However, due to mass inertia, the piston wants to continue moving in the same direction at the same speed. This results in a force in the direction TDC -> BDC.

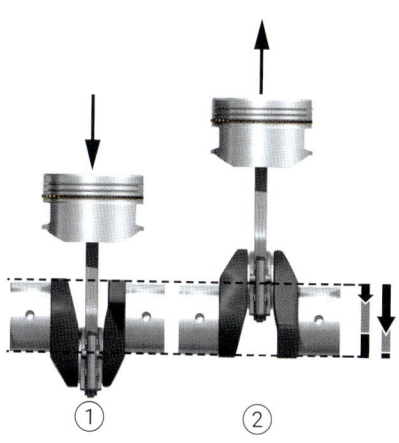

Fig. 328 1. Force in the direction TDC -> BDC. 2. Force in the direction BDC -> TDC.

From BDC, the piston moves back to TDC, where the same phenomenon occurs but in the opposite direction:
- Piston decelerates.
- Piston changes direction.
- Mass inertia results in a force in the direction BDC -> TDC.

2. Primary Force

Together, the force in the direction TDC -> BDC and the force in the direction BDC -> TDC cause a vibration which occurs once per crankshaft revolution. This force is also called primary force.

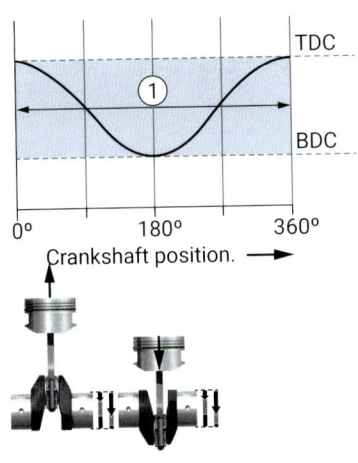

Fig. 329 X-axis: crankshaft position, Y-axis: primary force, black line = primary force, 1 = a vibration.

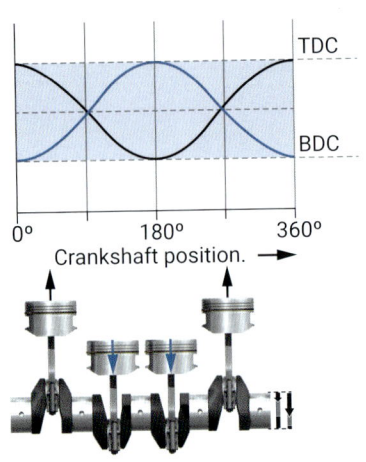

Fig. 330 Balancing primary forces in a 4-cylinder in-line engine: X-axis: crankshaft position, Y-axis: forces, black line = primary forces, pistons 1 and 4, blue line = primary forces, pistons 2 and 3.

3. Balancing Primary Force

It is easy to balance the primary forces in a 4-cylinder in-line engine. By ensuring that the pistons move in opposing directions, the primary forces cancel each other out.

Even in a 1-cylinder engine, these primary forces can be easily managed by fitting a counterweight on the crankshaft, which moves opposite to the piston.

4. Secondary Force

The construction of the crank/connecting rod mechanism is such that the piston also accelerates and decelerates at other locations, not only at TDC and BDC. This happens because, in a revolution of the crankshaft, the connecting rod moves not only up and down but also back and forth.

The back and forth movement occurs as a result of the crankshaft rotation.

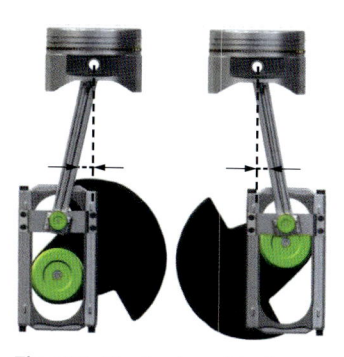

Fig. 331 The back and forth movement of the connecting rod.

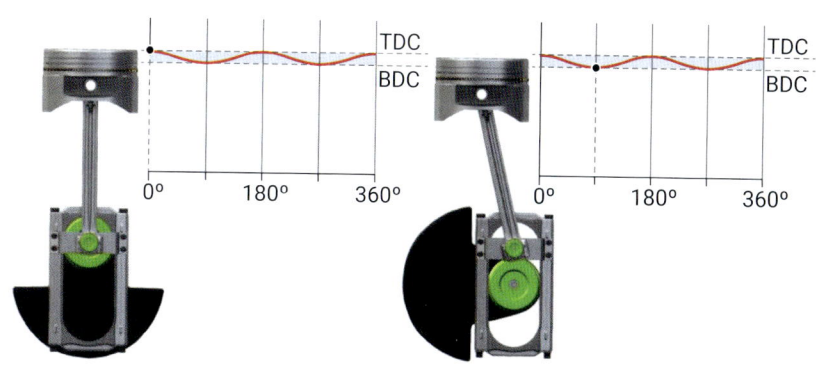

Fig. 332 TDC -> 90°, piston movement is accelerated.

During a revolution of the crankshaft, the back and forth movement of the connecting rod causes additional piston accelerations and decelerations during the following crankshaft position changes:

TDC -> 90°
90° -> BDC
BDC -> 270°
270° -> TDC

The piston movement caused by the connecting rod is also known as secondary piston movement.

Secondary Piston Movement TDC -> 90°
From TDC to a crankshaft position of 90°, the connecting rod moves outwards. During this movement, the connecting rod pulls the piston even further in the direction of BDC, which causes the piston to accelerate even more.

Secondary Piston Movement 90° -> BDC
From a crankshaft position of 90° to BDC, the connecting rod moves inwards. This movement pushes the piston back in the direction of TDC. However, the primary piston movement is in the direction TDC -> BDC. In this case, the piston movement, which is caused by the connecting rod, opposes the primary piston movement and the piston is decelerated.

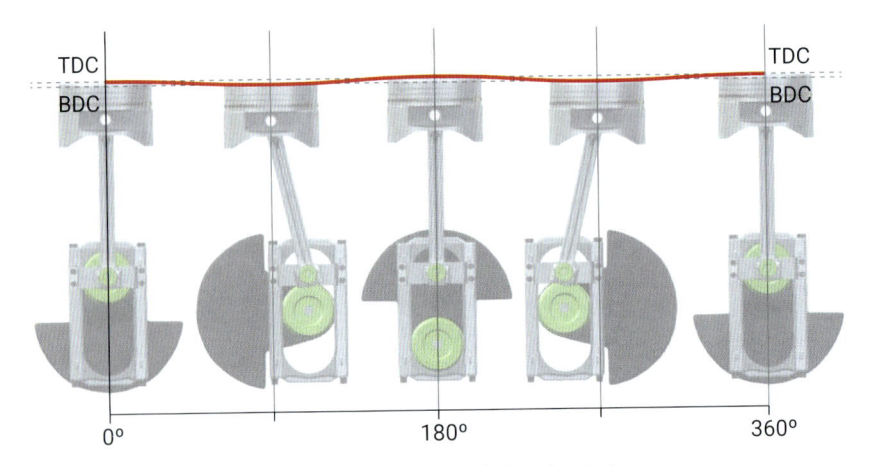

Fig. 333 90° -> BDC -> 270°, piston movement is decelerated.

Secondary Piston Movement BDC -> 270°

From BDC to a crankshaft position of 270°, the connecting rod moves outwards again. During this movement, the connecting rod pulls the piston back towards BDC again. However, the primary piston movement is now from BDC to TDC. Here too, the secondary piston movement is opposite to the primary piston movement. This results in deceleration of the piston.

Secondary Piston Movement 270° -> TDC

From a crankshaft position of 270° to TDC, the connecting rod moves inwards. Due to this secondary piston movement, the piston is pushed even further in the direction of TDC. The primary piston movement is also in the direction of TDC. The two movements reinforce each other, which causes the piston to accelerate faster.

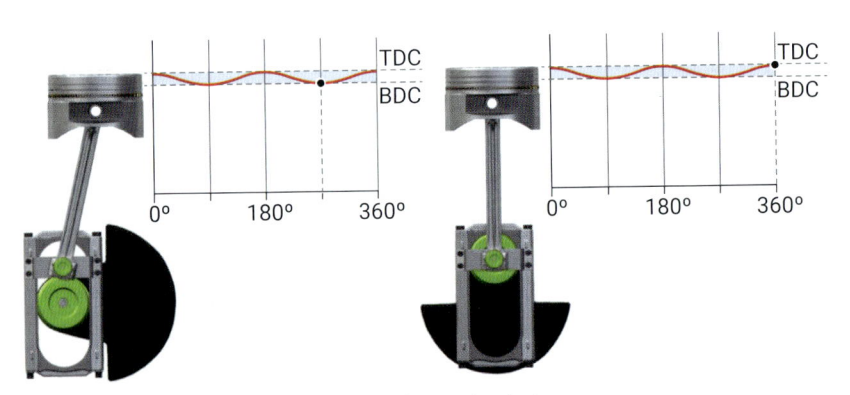

Fig. 334 270° -> TDC, piston movement is accelerated.

The additional accelerations and decelerations generate extra forces which cause two vibrations per crankshaft revolution. These forces are therefore called secondary forces.

The primary and secondary forces reinforce each other in the crankshaft position changes:

TDC -> 90°

270° -> TDC

The primary and secondary forces counteract each other in the crankshaft position changes:

90° -> BDC

BDC -> 270°

The sum of the primary and secondary forces is shown in the graph.

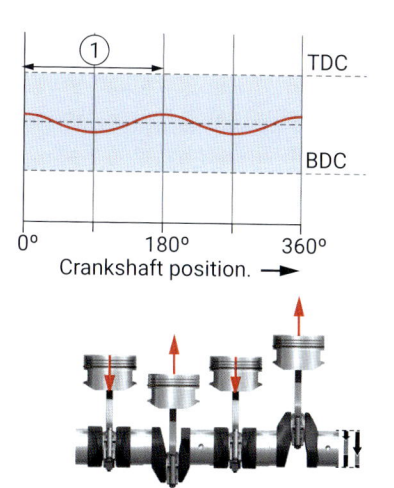

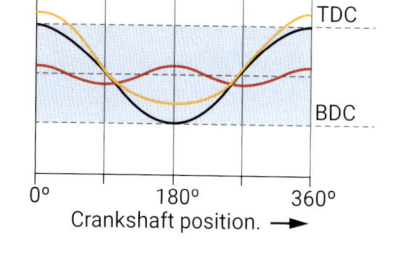

Fig. 335 X-axis: crankshaft position, Y-axis: primary force, 1. one vibration, red = secondary force.

Fig. 336 X-axis: crankshaft position, Y-axis: primary force, blue = primary force, red = secondary force, yellow = sum of the forces.

5. Balancing Secondary Forces

Secondary forces are mainly balanced by installing balancing shafts.

In a 4-cylinder engine, two balancing shafts are often installed, which are driven by the crankshaft. The balancing shafts have a weight on one side of the shaft. Both shafts rotate twice as fast as the crankshaft and rotate in opposing directions.

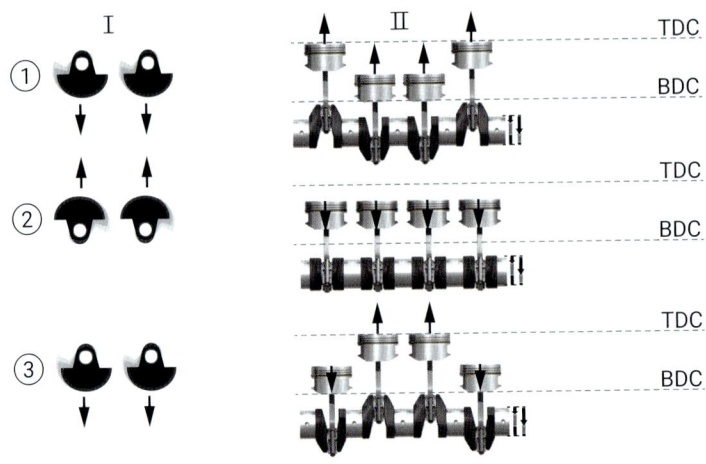

Fig. 337 I. Balancing shaft position. II. Crankshaft position. 1. TDC 1 and 4, BDC 2 and 3. 2. Crankshaft position 90° and 270°. 3. BDC 1 and 4, TDC 2 and 3.

At TDC and BDC, the secondary force is directed upwards. This is caused by the inward movement of the connecting rod. The balancing shafts provide force in the opposite direction.

At crankshaft positions 90° and 270°, the secondary force is directed towards BDC. This is caused by the outward motion of the connecting rod. The balancing shafts also provide force in the opposite direction here.

The graph above is a graphical representation of the balancing of the secondary forces by the balancing shafts.

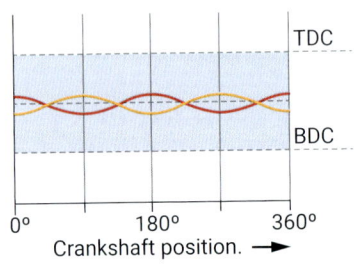

Fig. 338 X-axis: crankshaft position Y-axis: forces Red = secondary force Orange = balancing shaft counter-force.

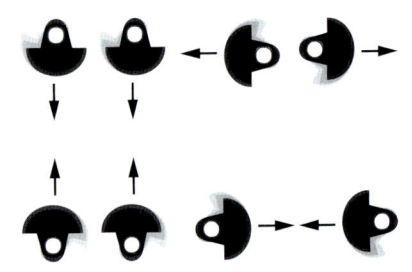

Fig. 339 The balancing shafts rotate in opposite directions.

There are always two balancing shafts installed, which rotate in opposing directions, so that the balancing shafts serve as counterweights for each other in the other crankshaft positions.

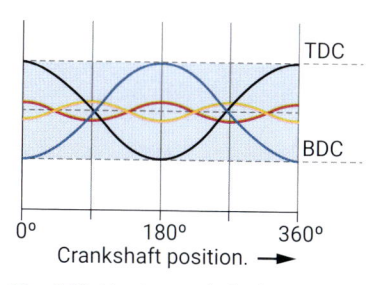

Fig. 340 X-axis: crankshaft position Y-axis: forces Blue = primary forces pistons 1 and 4 Brown = primary forces pistons 2 and 3 Red = secondary force Orange = balancing shaft counter-force.

6. Summary: Balancing Reciprocating Masses

The graph provides an overview of the balancing of the reciprocating masses in a 4-cylinder in-line engine. It shows the following:

— Primary forces are balanced by allowing the pistons to move in opposite directions.
— Secondary forces are balanced using balancing shafts.

BALANCING ROTATING MASSES

1. Introduction

The primary rotating mass in an engine is the crankshaft. Forces and torque are caused by the rotation of the crankshaft, which leads to vibrations. For this reason, the rotating masses of the crankshaft need to have a counterweight in order for the engine to rotate without vibrations.

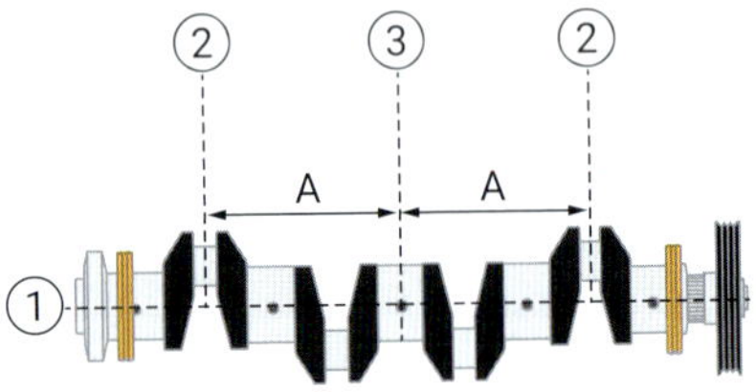

2. Crankshaft: Components and Dimensions

Essentially, a crankshaft consists of the following components:

— The crankshaft.
— The crankpins where the connecting rods are mounted.

Fig. 341 1. Crankshaft centerline. 2. Crankpin perpendicular. 3. Center bearing cap perpendicular A. Distance between the crankpin perpendicular and the bearing cap perpendicular.

The crankshaft is suspended in the main bearing caps of the engine block so that it can rotate around its own axis.

The illustration shows the most important dimensions of the crankshaft. These are:

— The crankshaft centerline: the axis around which the crankshaft rotates.
— The crankpin perpendicular: this is a line extending perpendicular to the axis of the crankpin. This line extends from the center of the piston (pin) downwards. This is also the line along which the piston forces act on the crankpin.
— The bearing cap perpendicular: this is the support point of the crankshaft.
— The distance between the crankpin perpendicular and the bearing cap perpendicular.

These dimensions are used in the following steps to explain how the crankshaft is balanced.

3. Vibrations Caused by Mass Forces

When a crankshaft turns, the masses of the crankpins swing outwards. This phenomenon is better known as centrifugal force.

In the crankshaft shown in the illustration, both crankpins are mounted on the same side. This construction can be found in parallel twin motorcycles and in "big bang" MotoGP motorcycles.

This kind of crankshaft design can also be found in the middle two cylinders of a 4-cylinder in-line engine.

The illustration shows that the centrifugal forces of both crankpins reinforce each other. Therefore, the forces of this crankshaft are unbalanced and would cause substantial vibrations in the engine block.

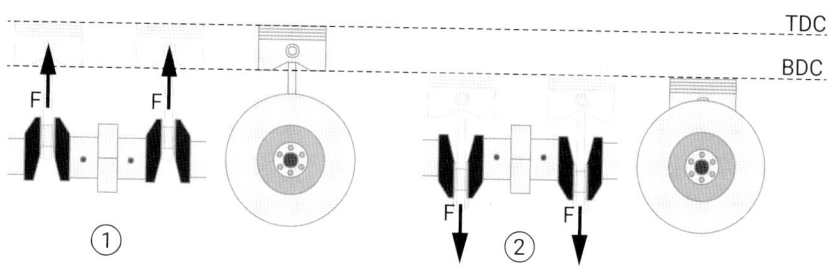

Fig. 342 F. Centrifugal force. 1. TDC. 2. BDC.

Both centrifugal forces primarily act on the crankpin perpendicular. Through the crankpin, the forces act on the support point of the crankshaft: the bearing cap perpendicular.

In this case, the distance between the crankpin perpendicular and the bearing cap perpendicular works as a kind of lever and, together with the centrifugal forces, creates a torque.

The (simplified) formula below clearly shows the relationship between:
— torque,
— force, and
— lever or lever arm.

Torque = force x lever arm

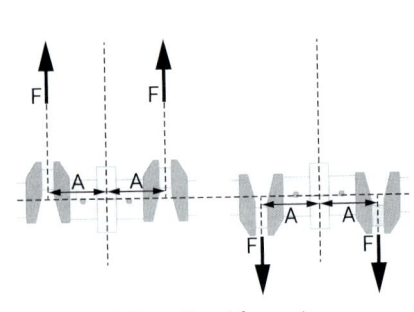

Fig. 343 F. Centrifugal force. A. Length of the lever arm.

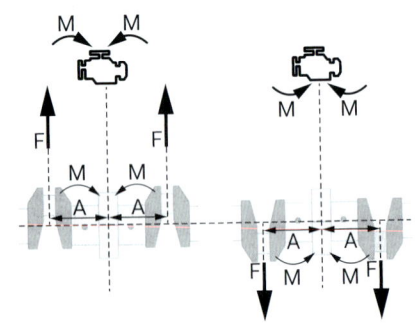

Fig. 344 F. Centrifugal force. A. Length of the lever arm. M. Torque. 1. TDC. 2. BDC.

$$M = F * r$$

M = Torque in foot-pounds $[ft/lb]$
F = Force in pounds force $[lbf]$
r = Length of the lever arm in feet $[f]$

The illustration shows the torque caused by the centrifugal forces.

At TDC, the torque on the left side of the main bearing journal rotates clockwise. Of course, this direction of rotation is caused by the direction of the centrifugal force and the position of the force with respect to the support point, the main bearing journal.

The torque on the right side of the main bearing journal rotates counterclockwise at TDC. Therefore, the directions of rotation of both torques cancel each other out and do not give rise to vibrations.

Conclusion:
For this crankshaft, the following applies:

— The forces reinforce each other and give rise to vibrations.
— The torques are in equilibrium and do not give rise to vibrations.

4. Vibrations Caused by Torque

In the crankshaft below, the crankpins are positioned on opposite sides of the crank centerline. This means that the centrifugal forces act in opposition and cancel each other out.

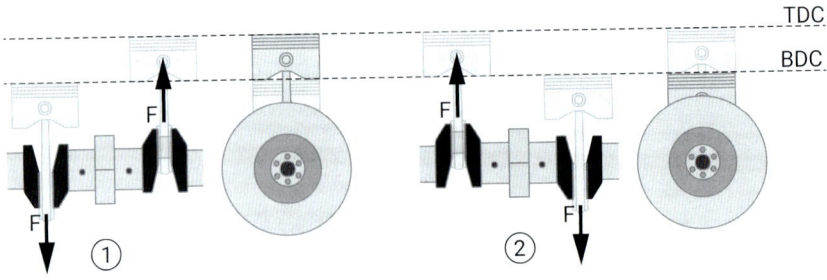

Fig. 345 F. Centrifugal force. 1. TDC. 2. BDC.

In this crankshaft, however, the torque forces reinforce each other. At TDC, both torques rotate counterclockwise, while at BDC they

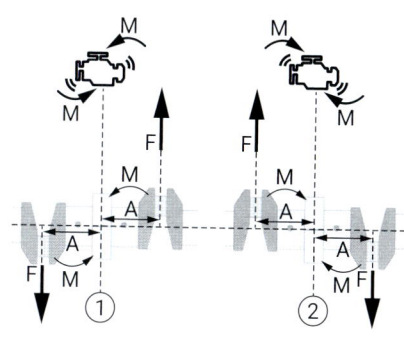

Fig. 346 F. Centrifugal force. M. Torque. 1. TDC. 2. BDC.

both rotate clockwise. This causes substantial engine vibration in the longitudinal engine axis.

Conclusion:

For this crankshaft, the following applies:

— The forces are in equilibrium.
— The torque forces reinforce each other.

5. Balancing the Crankshaft

Counterweights are set opposite both crankpins in order to achieve equilibrium of both the forces and torque.

Positioning these counterweights balances the crankshaft completely and the engine rotates more or less free of vibrations.

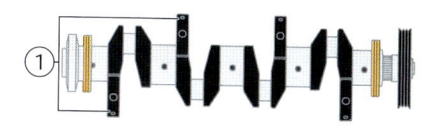

Fig. 347 1. Counterweights.

Conclusion:

For this crankshaft, the following applies:

— The forces are in equilibrium.
— The torque forces are in equilibrium.

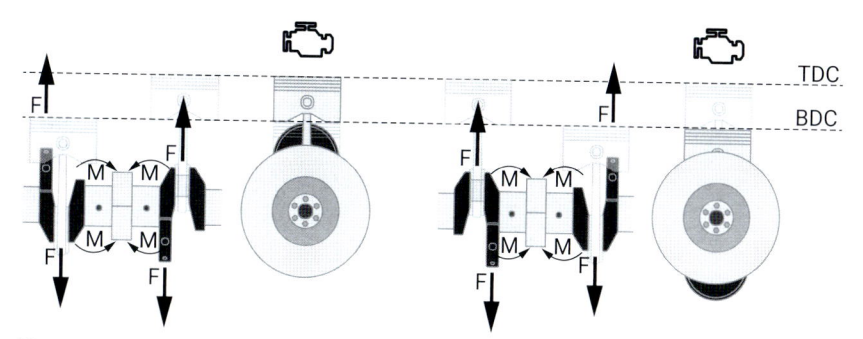

Fig. 348 F. Forces and torque forces cancel each other out.

BALANCING IGNITION FORCES

Vibrations caused by ignition forces arise from the sudden build-up of gas pressure when the cylinder fires in the power stroke. The best way to deal with these vibrations is to allow the ignition of each cylinder to take place at regular intervals.

In a 4-stroke engine, the duration of the work cycle is 4 piston strokes. One piston stroke covers 180°. Four strokes therefore cover 4 x 180° = 720°. The cylinder fires only once per 720° work cycle.

The more often ignition can occur during a 720° crankshaft rotation, the less the vibrations from the ignition forces will be felt.

Firing can only occur more often if there are additional cylinders.

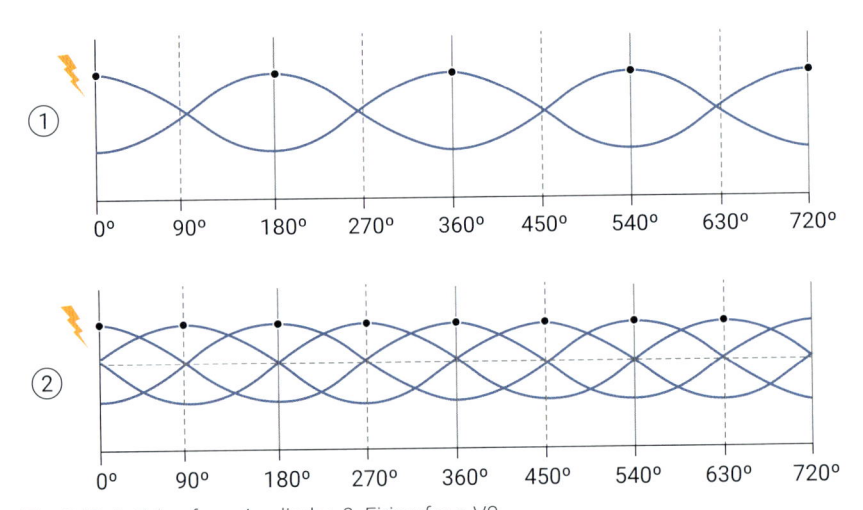

Fig. 349 1. Firing for a 4-cylinder. 2. Firing for a V8.

FOR EXAMPLE In a 4-cylinder in-line engine, it is possible to fire once per 180° crankshaft rotation:

$$720°/4 = 180°$$

In a V6 engine, it is possible to fire once per 120° crankshaft rotation:

$$720°/6 = 120°$$

In a V8 engine, it is possible to fire once per 90° crankshaft rotation:

$$720°/8 = 90°$$

HARMONIC VIBRATION DAMPENER

1. Torsional Vibrations

The crankshaft is attached to the flywheel. The flywheel is heavy and has a high inertia.

At every power stroke, great force is exerted on the crankshaft. Since the flywheel has a high inertia, the crankshaft is twisted. After the power stroke the force exerted on the crankshaft decreases.

The crankshaft wants to return to its original shape and springs back. This causes torsional vibrations in the engine and transmission. This also places significant tension on the cam-belt and accessory drive belt, which stresses the driven components.

Fig. 350 1. Crankshaft. 2. Flywheel.

Fig. 351 Generation of torsional vibrations during the power stroke.

2. Harmonic Vibration Dampener

A harmonic vibration dampener must absorb the torsional vibrations in the crankshaft. Besides these vibrations, the harmonic vibration dampener must also dampen the vibrations from the serpentine belt, which are caused by uneven rotation of the engine.

The vibration dampener is installed at the crankshaft pulley.

Fig. 352 Torsional vibration damper: 1. Torsional vibration damper. 2. Outer ring. 3. Inner ring. 4. Rubber damping layer.

It consists of two separate parts:
— the part into which the crankshaft fits: (the inner ring);
— the part on which the belt runs: (the outer ring).

The inner and outer rings are separated by a layer of rubber damping material.

3. Higher Revolutions

At higher revolutions the crankshaft rotates evenly. The vibration damper then rotates evenly along with the crankshaft. At low revolutions, for example when starting, the vibration damper does not rotate evenly along with the crankshaft.

During the power stroke, the crankshaft accelerates, and the inner ring accelerates with it. Because of inertia, the outer ring does not accelerate at the same speed. The rubber damping layer accommodates for this difference in speed by deforming. This dampens the torsional vibration. The rubber damping layer can twist to a maximum of 20°.

When the air conditioning is switched on, for example, the belt (and the outer ring with it) rotate more slowly. The rubber damping layer accommodates this difference in speed by deforming.

Fig. 353 Torsional vibrations (1) are reduced at higher engine speeds.

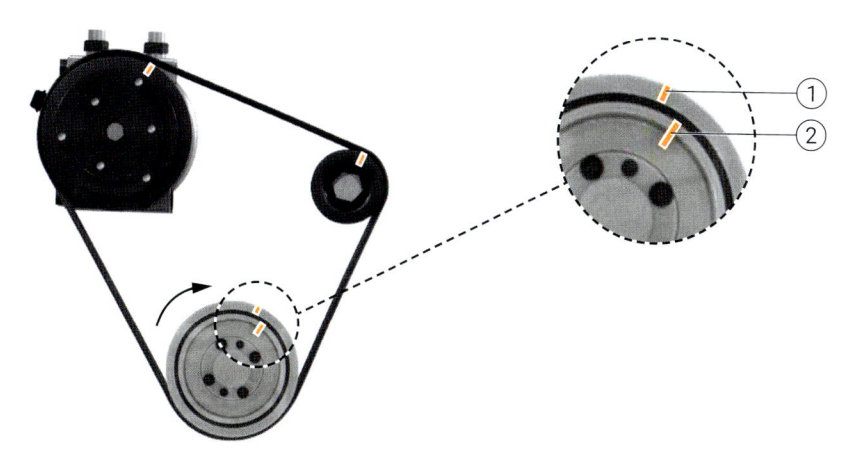

Fig. 354 When the air conditioning is switched on, the torsional vibration damper absorbs the speed difference: 1. Outer ring is very slightly delayed. 2. Inner ring continues to rotate normally.

4. Built-in Torsional Vibration Damper

If there is a built-in torsional vibration damper, it will be integrated within the crankshaft.

In this case, springs will be used instead of a rubber core. Because the housing of this vibration damper is connected to the crankshaft, advancing and retarding movements can be absorbed by the springs.
— When the crankshaft speeds up, the damping mass retards.
— When the crankshaft slows down, the damping mass advances.

5. Balancing Shafts

Balancing shafts are often used to reduce engine vibrations. They absorb imbalanced forces.

There are two causes of imbalance:
— A primary piston movement.
— A secondary piston movement.

Primary Piston Movement
When a piston moves vertically up and down from TDC or BDC, it is referred to as a primary piston movement. The big end makes the same movement. Every revolution of the crankshaft means that this movement occurs twice: at TDC and at BDC.

An imbalance can occur at this point. This imbalance can be absorbed by a balancing shaft. This shaft needs to revolve at the same rotational speed, parallel to the crankshaft and in opposing directions.

The crankshaft and balancing shaft are connected by two gearwheels that have the same number of teeth. The balancing shaft also needs to rotate in the same position relative to the crankshaft, which can be recognized by reference marks on the gearwheels.

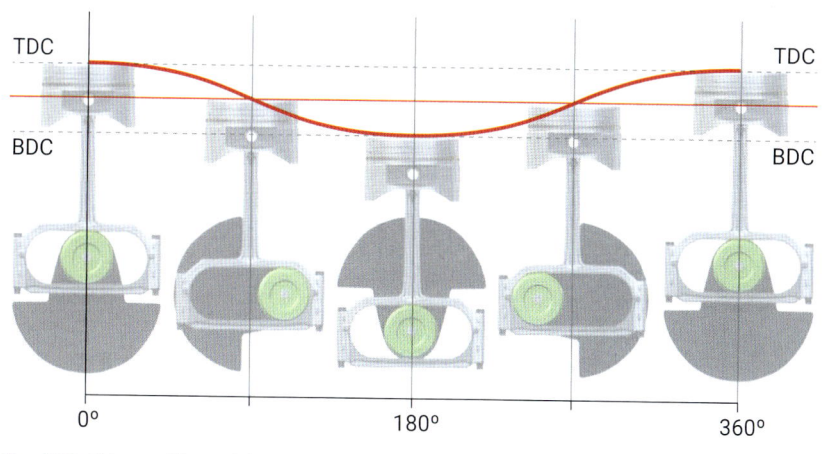

Fig. 355 Primary Piston Movement

Secondary Piston Movement

Secondary piston movement is caused by the horizontal movement of the big end.

This improves acceleration and deceleration of the piston. Viewed from TDC, this movement takes place four times: twice to the left and twice to the right.
The balancing shaft needs to rotate twice as fast to absorb this imbalance. This is why its gearwheel has half the number of teeth, resulting in a gearing effect.

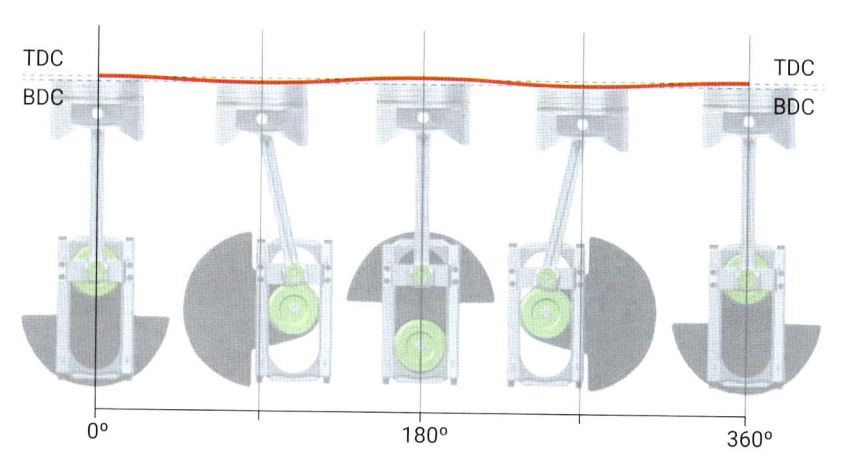

Fig. 356 Secondary Piston Movement

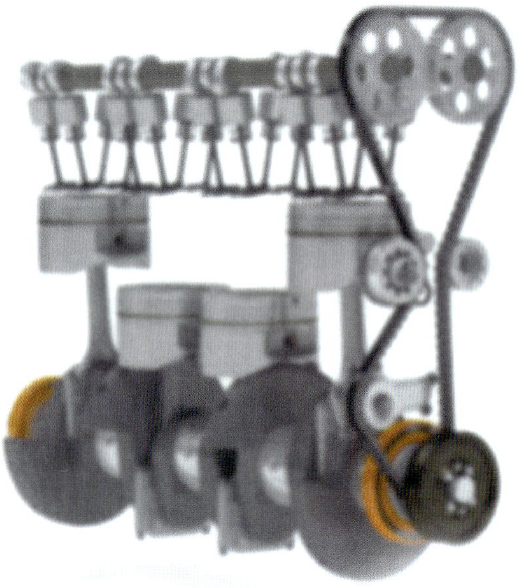

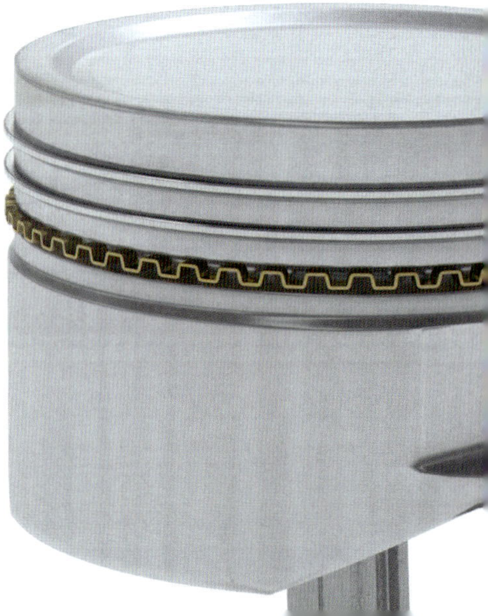

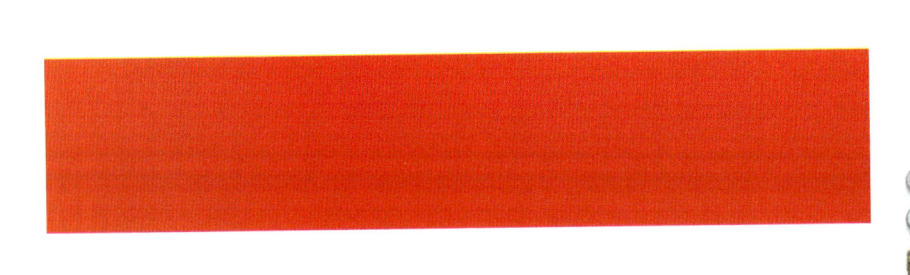

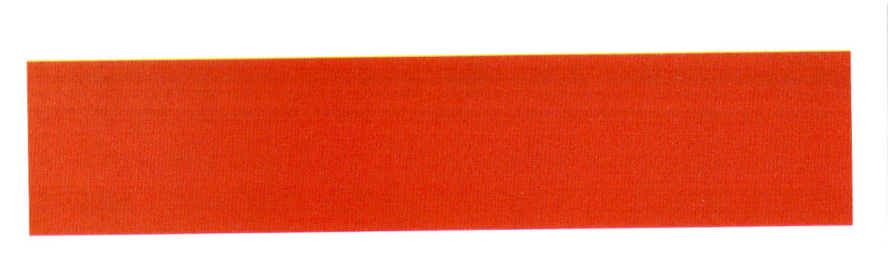

9. Measuring Engine Condition

MEASURING COMPRESSION

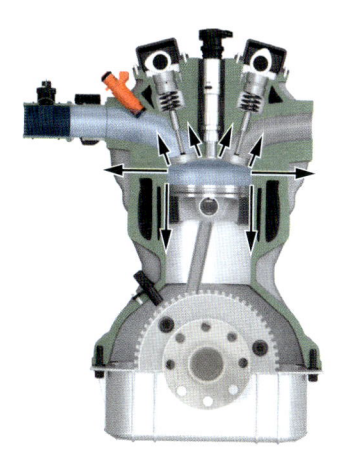

Fig. 357 Places where pressure loss can occur.

1. Introduction

If the performance of an engine is not satisfactory, it may be due to many different factors. For example:
— Mechanical problems: valves, piston rings, or head gaskets.
— Malfunctions in the fuel system.
— Malfunctions is the ignition system.

If the fuel and ignition systems are operating properly, you can adjust the valve clearance (valve lash) according to the vehicle service information for some engines. Most hydraulic lifter engines have an automatic valve lash adjustment. If all of these (valve lash, ignition, and fuel system) are working correctly and the engine still displays problems, then the next step is to perform an engine compression test.

If the engine is worn the compression pressure may be too low, which will result in poor engine performance.

Possible causes:
— Worn piston rings - Rings do not seal the gap between piston and cylinder wall.

- Head gasket problem - Gasket does not seal the combustion chamber.
- Leaking valves - Valves do not seal the combustion chamber properly.

2. Compression Tester

To perform an engine cylinder compression test, you have to use a compression gauge. There is a difference between doing a compression test for Otto engines and for diesel engines.
- With diesel engines, the injectors or glow plugs are removed, and the compression gauge is connected to the location of the injectors or glow plugs. The fuel supply is also shut off.
- With Otto engines, the spark plugs are removed. The ignition is also switched off, and the fuel supply interrupted.

The compression test can then be started. All cylinders can be tested one at a time in this way.

3. Performing a Compression Test

A compression test is effective for determining engine condition. It is important to follow the correct procedure, so each cylinder can be compared with each other and properly evaluated.

To conduct a compression test, always follow the sequence as stated in the service manual. Failure to do so will result in bad readings.
Before performing a compression test the following engine conditions must be met:
- The fuel and ignition systems are disabled.
- The engine is at operating temperature. (Use extreme caution when working on a hot engine!)
- The air filter must be clean.
- The throttle valve must be fully open.
- The engine must crank at a correct speed during the test. That means the battery should be fully charged and the starter in good condition. A low cranking speed gives more time for leakage and therefore a low compression. A high cranking speed, on the other hand, causes little leakage and results in high compression.
- All spark plugs should be removed to help maintain correct starter speed and reduce battery drain.

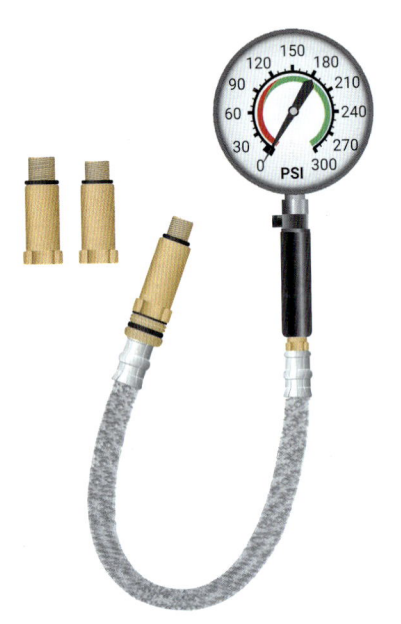

Fig. 358 Compression tester for the Otto engine with adapters for different spark plug holes.

Information on engine temperature, cranking speed, and adjustments can be found in the vehicle service information; this will help to set up a perfect condition for the compression test.

Fig. 359 The compression test must be carried out for all cylinders under the same conditions.

4. Compression Test Results

If a compression test has been done, the outcome must be assessed.
Important to note:
— The difference between the readings from each cylinder may not exceed 10% of the highest measured value.
— The final compression pressure value must at least be within vehicle manufacturer's specifications.

The image shows a result of a compression test. The measurement is done on a 4-cylinder Otto engine.

After all the cylinders have been tested, a comparison of cylinders can be made. A good engine will have no more than 10% of the highest reading variation between cylinders. The calculation is as follows: The measurement shows that the highest measured value is 140 psi (960 kPa).
The lowest measured value is 128 psi (880 kPa).

All the compression readings of the cylinders should be above the 10% of the maximum reading. 140 − 14 = 136 psi (960 − 96 = 864 kPa).

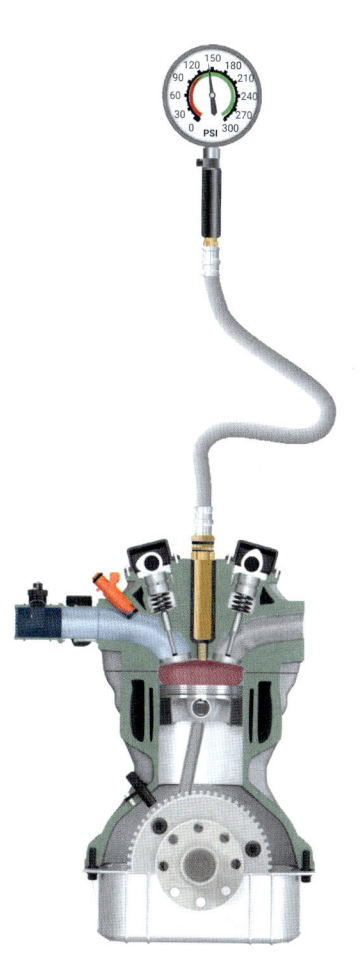

Fig. 360 Select the correct adapter and place it in the spark plug hole.

The lowest value is 127 psi (880 kPa), and thus this result meets the requirements.

In addition, there are the specified factory values as well. According to the specification, this engine may have a final compression pressure between 123 and 145 psi (850 and 1000 kPa).
The final compression pressure must be at least 123 psi (850 kPa). The result also meets this requirement.

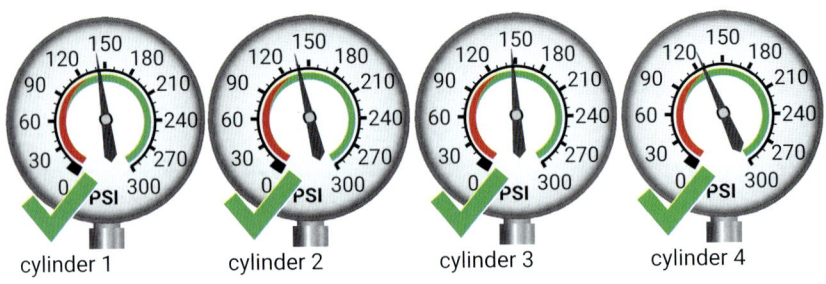

Fig. 361 The outcome of the compression test (100 kPa=14.5 psi).

5. Different Measurement Results

Various results can be obtained from the compression test.

- The final compression pressure of the cylinders in relation to each other is virtually the same, and the minimum final pressure indicated by the manufacturer is met; this engine is working properly.
- The final compression pressure of one cylinder is lower than that of the other cylinders. Possible causes: - a leaking intake valve - a leaking exhaust valve, stuck piston ring, or damaged piston.
- The final compression pressure of two adjacent cylinders is too low. Possible cause: - a crack in the engine block or the cylinder head - a leaking head gasket.
- None of the cylinders achieves the specified minimum final compression pressure. The most common cause of this is stuck or worn piston rings.

Whether the piston rings are the cause of the compression loss can be checked as follows:
- Squirt a small amount of oil (0.34 oz or 10 ml) into the weak cylinder(s). Crank the engine a few times. This way the oil is distributed across the cylinder wall and takes over the task of the piston rings.

— Reinstall the compression gauge into that cylinder and conduct the test.

If the compression gauge shows much higher values, it can be assumed that the leakage between piston and cylinder is caused by worn piston rings.

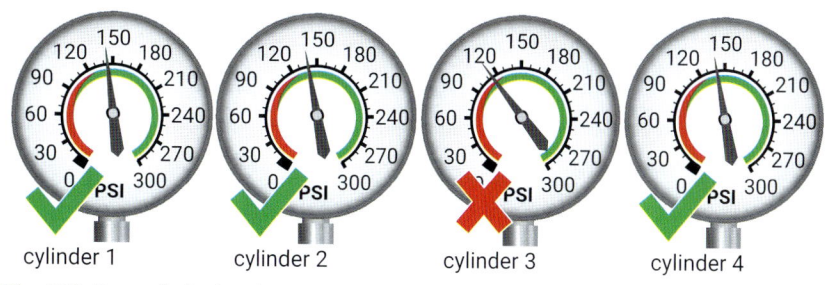

Fig. 362 One cylinder has low compression.

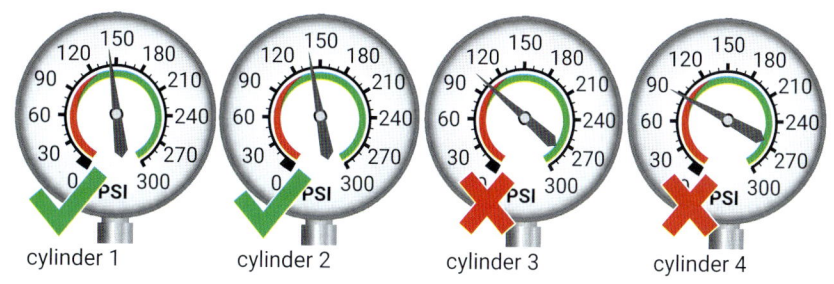

Fig. 363 Two cylinders have low compression.

HOW TO: CYLINDER COMPRESSION TEST OTTO ENGINE

1. Tools Required

Fig. 364 Tools Required

2. Remove the Ignition Coil and Spark Plug.

Fig. 365 Remove the connector from the ignition coil and remove the ignition coil. Loosen (turn) the ignition coil carefully to avoid damaging it.

Fig. 366 Loosen the spark plug and remove it. To ensure that the engine does not start, remove the relay and/or fuse from the fuel pump. With diesel engines, the fuel supply must be shut off.

3. Install the Compression Gauge and Measure Compression.

Fig. 367 Screw the compression gauge into the spark plug hole. Start the engine and read the gauge.

Fig. 368 The gauge indicates almost 188 psi (13 bar); in the specifications of this car, 145 to 188 psi (10 -13 bar) is sufficient. By doing the same measurement for the other cylinders, you can see if these cylinders are also okay.

Fig. 369 After the measurement, install the spark plug and tighten it to the specified torque with a torque wrench. Install the ignition coil and connect the connector. Start the car to check that it is working properly again.

HOW TO: RELATIVE CYLINDER COMPRESSION TEST

1. Connect the Amp Clamp.

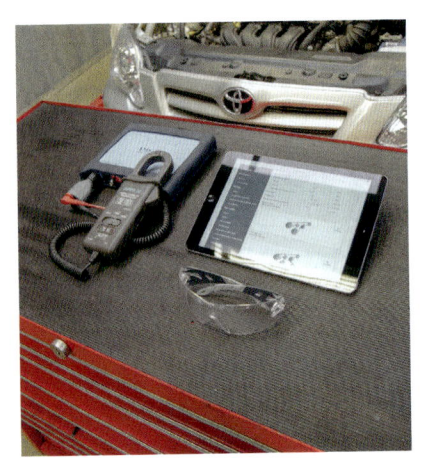

Fig. 372 Tools Required

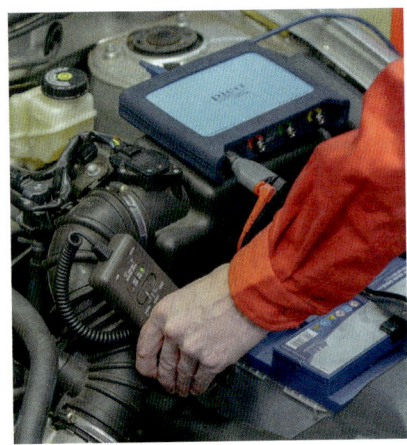

Fig. 373 Connect the amp clamp to the + cable of the battery. To ensure that the engine does not start, remove the relay and/or the fuse from the fuel pump. The fuel supply must be shut off for diesel engines.

2. Connect the Amp Clamp to the Oscilloscope.

Fig. 374 Connect the amp clamp to the oscilloscope. Start the engine and save the oscilloscope image.

Fig. 375 To show the difference between good and bad compression, we removed a spark plug from on of the cylinders. First, remove the ignition coil.

Fig. 376 Then remove the spark plug. Start the engine and save the oscilloscope image.

3. Compare the Oscilloscope Images.

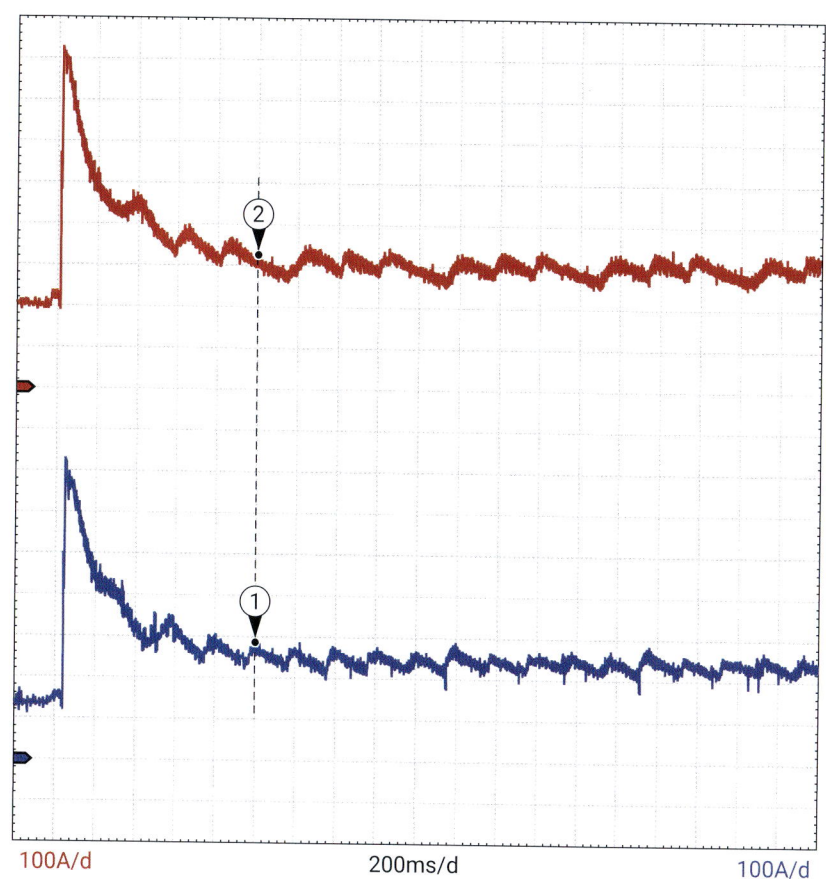

Fig. 377 The bottom scope image is of the engine working properly, the small peaks in current (1) being the peaks of the compression strokes. The increase in compression causes the increase in power consumption of the starter motor. The top scope image is the image of the engine from which the spark plug has been removed. At (2) you can see that a peak is missing; this is the cylinder that no longer builds up compression.

Fig. 378 Install the spark plug and the ignition coil according to the service manual. Reconnect the ignition coil and install the fuel pump relay and/or fuse. Start the car and see if everything works properly.

MEASURE CYLINDER LEAKAGE

1. Introduction

To determine the cause of low compression you must search further. With the aforementioned method of adding 0.33 fl oz (10 ml) of oil per cylinder, it is possible to rule out whether the piston rings are a cause.

Another option is to disassemble the cylinder head and look for valve problems. This is always a time-consuming and expensive job. The best option is to do a cylinder leakage test using a special tool - a cylinder leak tester. A cylinder leak test will allow the pressure loss location to be determined with some accuracy.

To perform a leak down or cylinder leakage test, the following conditions must be met.
— The engine must be at operating temperature.
— The piston must be at top dead center (TDC) so that the intake and exhaust valves are closed.
— The car must be in the highest gear if it is a manual transmission, and the parking brake must be on to prevent the engine from turning when air is compressed into the cylinder.
— The cylinder leak tester must be calibrated.
— The cylinder leak tester is connected to the compressed air system of the shop.
— On the other side, the gauge is connected to the location of the spark plug (Otto engines), glow plug, or injector (diesel engines).

When these conditions are met you can take the measurement. The gauge shows the difference between the supplied pressure and the residual pressure in the cylinder.

Fig. 380 Cylinder leak tester in operation.

Fig. 381 Cylinder leak tester.

2. Calibration

The tester must be calibrated to compensate for the influence of the compressed air network of the workshop. The tester's instruction manual tells you how to do this.

Fig. 382 Place the calibration pin in the cylinder leak gauge.

Fig. 383 With the adjustment knob, you adjust the indicator until the position 'Cal' has been reached. Now the gauge has been calibrated.

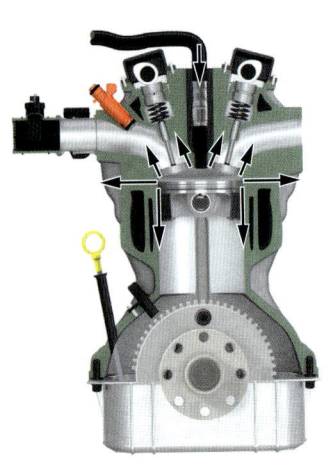

Fig. 384 Possible leakage locations.

3. Leakage Losses

The 'leaking' of a cylinder is normal but must, of course, be within certain margins. Normally, this should not be more than 25% unless the manufacturer of an engine specifies otherwise.
A result of a leakage measurement is shown as leakage loss or efficiency depending on the execution of the gauge, but always in percentages.
Leakage losses of 15% are normal.

For example, if the leakage loss is 18%, the efficiency is 100 - 18 = 82%.
The leakage loss between the cylinders must not exceed 20% of the average value of the highest and lowest measured value.

Suppose a leakage measurement gives the following result:
— Cylinder 1: 15%
— Cylinder 2: 16%
— Cylinder 3: 19%
— Cylinder 4: 12%

The measurement meets the set standard if none of the cylinders has more than 25% leakage.

The average value of the highest and lowest measured value:
19% + 12% = 31% : 2 = 15.5%

The difference between the highest and lowest measured value may not exceed 20% of the average value.
In this case, this means that it may be 20% of 15.5%:
0.2 x 15.5 = 3.1%
With that, the highest measured value may be this: 15.5% + 3.1% = 18.6%
The lowest measured value may be this: 15.5% - 3.1% = 12.4%

This means that this engine does not meet the requirements as the highest and lowest measured values are higher (19%) and lower (12%).

If the leakage losses are too great, you can trace the leakage at the indicated locations by listening carefully.

- In the event of a leaking head gasket, leakage will occur via the adjacent cylinder or the cooling system.
- If the piston rings are leaking or the cylinder wall has wear, whistling or hissing will come out of the oil filler cap hole, dipstick tube, or positive crankcase ventilation (PCV) valve.
- If there is air hissing out of the exhaust manifold or turbocharger, there is a leakage through the exhaust valve.
- If air is heard whistling from inside the intake manifold an intake valve is likely leaking.

POWER BALANCE TEST

1. Power Balance Test Explanation

Because the pressure above the piston increases considerably, the crankshaft accelerates at the moment of a power stroke. This acceleration of the crankshaft is measured during a power balance test. The greater the acceleration of the crankshaft, the greater the contribution of the combustion. If combustion is less effective, the crankshaft will also accelerate less at that moment.
During the power balance test, each power stroke can be associated with the corresponding cylinder.

The measurement results are stored in the corresponding computer module. You can assess the measurement results after the test using a scan tool. Cylinders that function less well provide less acceleration and can be recognized in this process.

MEASURING CYLINDER WEAR

Cylinder wear is measured as follows:

- First, ensure that the cylinder does not have any scratches or deep wear marks.
- Then set the micrometer using the reference cylinder diameter. This can be the cylinder diameter shown in the technical specification or the measured cylinder diameter.
- If necessary, carefully place the micrometer in a bench vice. Make sure that you only tighten the bench vice gently - just tight enough to hold the micrometer.
- With the bore gauge, select a measuring pin and shims as required to make up the reference cylinder diameter. Consult the operating instructions for the bore gauge if necessary.

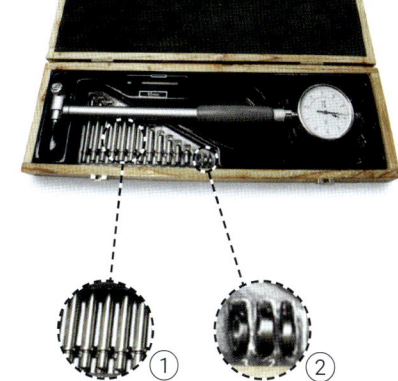

Fig. 385 Reference cylinder diameter.

Fig. 386 1. Measuring pin. 2. Shims.

- Place the bore gauge in the micrometer, which is set to the reference cylinder diameter. Move the bore gauge up and down, noting where the bore gauge needle changes direction.

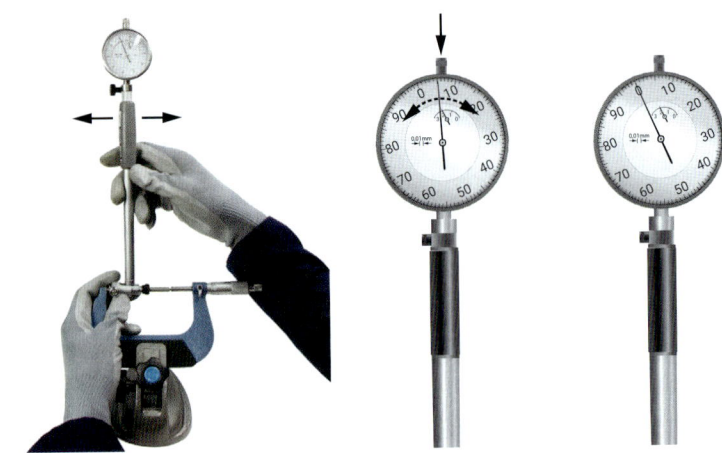

Fig. 387 Place the bore gauge in the micrometer set to the reference diameter.

Fig. 388 Set the dial gauge to 0.

- Set the dial gauge to 0 at the exact point where the needle changes direction. Consult the operating instructions for the bore gauge if necessary.
- The 0 point now corresponds to the reference diameter.
- Everything measured by the bore gauge is compared with the 0 point, i.e. the reference cylinder diameter. The measured value can therefore be smaller or larger than the reference cylinder diameter.
- Place the bore gauge in the cylinder, about 0.4 to 0.8 inches (1 to 2 cm) from the top edge of the cylinder.
- Move the bore gauge back and forth, noting where the bore gauge needle changes direction.
- Now read off the value. Consult the operating instructions for the bore gauge if necessary.
- Depending on the measurement, the measured value is added to or subtracted from the reference value.

Fig. 389 Place the bore gauge in the cylinder.

Fig. 390 Measure in different directions.

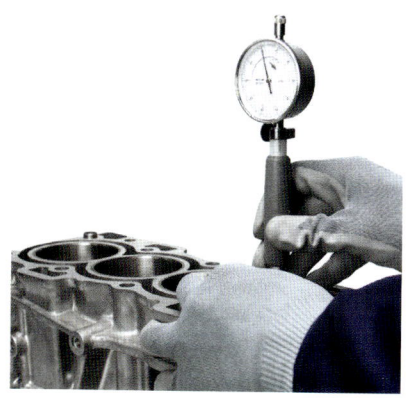

Fig. 391 Measure at different depths.

- To measure how oval the cylinder is, take several measurements at the same height turning the bore gauge a quarter turn each time.
- To measure how parallel the cylinder is, measure at the top, middle and bottom of the cylinder and compare the values.
- Compare the measured values with the values specified in the vehicle service information and decide whether additional work is needed on the cylinder.

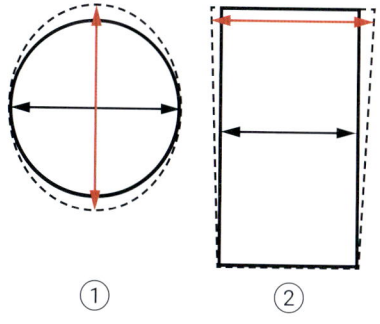

Fig. 392 1. Measuring cylinder ovality. 2. Measuring cylinder parallelism.

XYZ Engine	Cylinder Diameter	Ovality			
	79.51	max 0.1			
		Measured value			
		Top	Middle	Bottom	Conclusion
Cylinder 1	Measurement 1	79.48	79.49	79.5	OK
	Measurement 2	79.35	79.45	79.5	OK
	Ovality	0.13	0.04	0	Not OK

Fig. 393 Measuring table for cylinder ovality (mm).

BORING AND HONING THE CYLINDER

1. Introduction

The terms boring and honing are often used interchangeably. Boring and honing can indeed be done for the same thing - repairing a cylinder by removing material. However, it is useful to make the following distinction:

- **Boring:** boring removes much more material from the cylinder wall so that scratches disappear and the cylinder is once again perfectly round and parallel, with the same cylinder diameter at the top and the bottom. The tip of the boring head can remove material from a cylinder wall in larger quantities and faster than honing stones.
- **Honing:** it is also possible to remove material by honing. However, honing is intended as a surface treatment process to slightly "roughen" the cylinder wall so that the cylinder wall and piston rings can "bed in" better.

2. Boring

Cylinders are bored if they have major scratches or damage or if the cylinder is too oval or not parallel enough.

Boring out a worn or damaged cylinder ensures that the piston rings seal properly again and that no compression pressure or oil can leak past the rings.

Cylinders are usually bored out in increments of 0.010 inches (0.25 mm) until all of the damage and irregularities have been removed. There is a final limit for this: the oversize limit.

The oversize limit is specified by the factory to prevent the cylinder walls from becoming too thin as a result of too much material being removed. This is because cylinder walls that are too thin can crack easily from the combustion pressure.

Fig. 394 Machine for boring cylinders.

After boring, it is important to install an oversized piston and piston rings.

Boring is generally performed by machinist who would have the proper equipment.

3. Honing

Honing a cylinder can be done to restore the correct roughness of the cylinder wall. Honing is often done after cylinders are bored in order to make the cylinder walls smoother. Honing can also be used to slightly roughen the cylinder wall of a used cylinder before installing a new piston and piston rings.

This is because the surface of a cylinder wall needs to have exactly the right structure and roughness. If the cylinder wall is too rough, it can cause notches and damage on the piston rings. If the cylinder wall is too smooth, then the piston ring will transport a small amount of oil upwards every time the piston moves up. This oil enters the combustion chamber, resulting in oil consumption. During a cold start with a cylinder wall which is too smooth, there will be no oil between the piston ring and the cylinder wall, causing additional wear.

Honing creates a precise structure of small crosswise scratches in the cylinder wall. This cross-hatch pattern ensures that the piston ring and the cylinder wall bed in correctly. This, in turn, guarantees a good seal between the piston ring and cylinder wall. The engine only needs to run for just a few minutes for this bedding to happen. Honing is generally performed by machine shop.

Fig. 395 Cross-hatch pattern after honing.

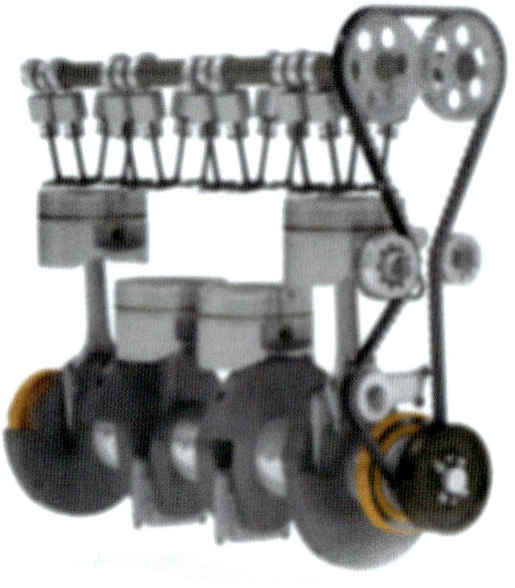

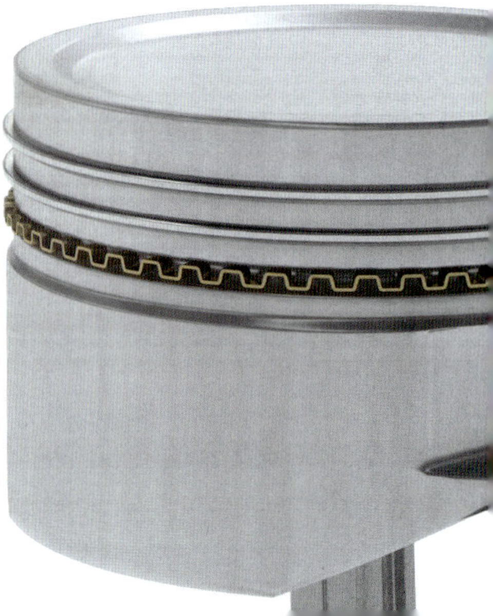

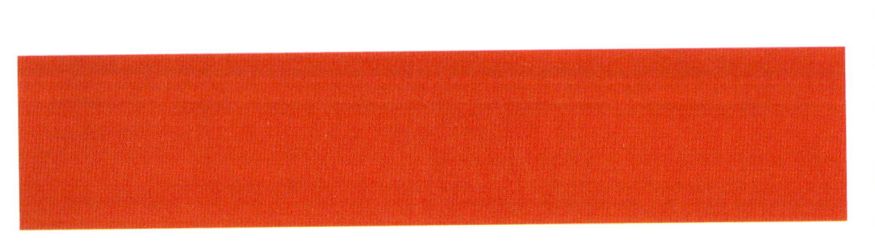

10. Lubrication System: Fundamentals

LUBRICATION

1. Requirement

There are many moving parts inside an internal combustion engine. Friction occurs when moving parts rub against each other. Friction creates heat and causes parts to wear. The heat from friction transfers to engine components. The piston may even seize and destroy the engine.

It's therefore necessary to reduce the friction as much as possible. For this purpose, a lubricant is used.

Fig. 396 As the moving parts slide against each other, they are subject to wear, which will result in higher temperatures.

Fig. 397 Warm parts may expand to such an extent that they seize.

2. Full Lubrication

During full lubrication, the friction is considerably reduced.

The space between the two surfaces is filled with oil so they do not touch.

The layer of oil between the surfaces is called oil film.

Fig. 398 With full lubrication, there is a layer of oil between the piston and the cylinder wall.

3. Residual Lubrication

If the oil film is very thin, it can cause parts to contact each other and wear prematurely. It is important that the system has some lubrication available in the form of a thin film. This thin film of oil is called residual lubrication.

Residual lubrication occurs when the engine is being started and the oil pump has not had enough time to distribute oil to the engine.

4. Tasks

Besides lubrication to reducing friction, oil has other important roles:
— Cooling
  Splash lubrication or oil jets cool the piston head and cylinder wall.

Fig. 399 Splashed oil cools the cylinder wall.

- Sealing

  The oil film between piston ring and cylinder wall helps to seal the combustion chamber.

- Cleaning

  Dirty engine oil is transported to the oil filter.

- Sound dampening

  The oil film ensures that moving parts do not touch, reducing engine noise and wear.

- Power transfer

  With hydraulic tappets the power of the cam lobe is transferred to the rocker through the oil pressure in the tappet and a constant valve clearance is maintained.

Fig. 400 A lubrication film creates a seal between the piston ring and the cylinder wall.

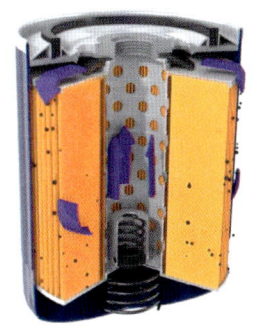

Fig. 401 Oil loosens dirt and carries this dirt to the oil filter.

Fig. 402 The engine will make a lot of noise on ignition if there isn't any oil.

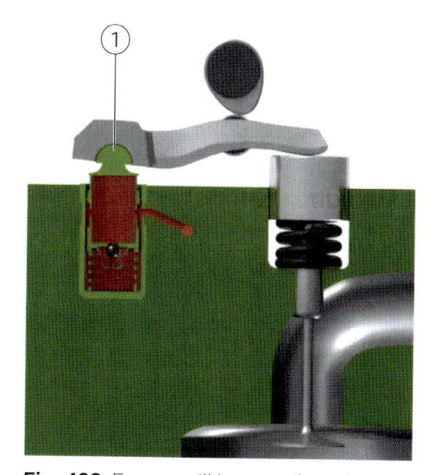

Fig. 403 Forces will be transferred. The hydraulic valve rocker (1) uses oil pressure to open the valve.

LUBRICATION TYPES

1. Types

Motor vehicles have many moving parts that require lubrication.

Moving parts can be lubricated in several ways:
— lubricating with an oil and fuel mixture
— forced lubrication
— splash lubrication
— greasing

Fig. 404 Different types of lubrication: 1. Fuel/oil mixture lubrication. 2. Pressure lubrication. 3. Grease lubrication. 4. Splash lubrication.

2. Lubrication with a Fuel and Oil Mixture

Lubrication with a fuel and oil mixture is used in two-stroke engines. The oil lubricant is added to the fuel. The mixture flows along moving parts that need lubricating.

The oil may be stored in a separate tank and can then be mixed with fuel during operation. In many cases, the oil and fuel lubrication is pre-mixed.

However, the oil must be well mixed with the fuel so that it does not leave behind carbon residue after combustion.

Fig. 405 This two-stroke piston engine uses a fuel/oil mixture lubricant.

3. Forced Lubrication

Four stroke engines use forced lubrication. Oil is stored in a reservoir (the oil pan) and transported to engine parts through a separate system.

Because the oil is pressurized, all passages between the reservoir and the engine parts are completely filled with oil.

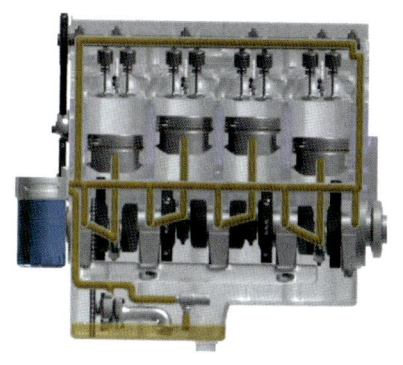

Fig. 406 The four-stroke piston engine uses pressure lubrication.

Fig. 407 The oil is transported to the bearings when the engine is started.

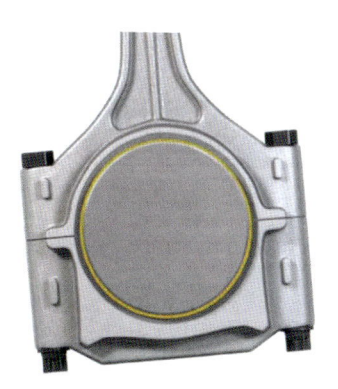

Fig. 408 The revolutions disperse the oil across the crankshaft bearing.

4. Splash Lubrication

In splash lubrication, oil is propelled or squirted against the parts that require lubrication.

In a four-stroke combustion engine, the oil can be squirted against the piston and cylinder wall by oil nozzles. The parts are both lubricated and cooled this way.

Fig. 409 Splash lubrication: The oil is splashed against the piston and the cylinder wall.

5. Grease

Greasing is often used where there is no continuous oil application. Oil lubrication is often better, but greasing can be sufficient if temperatures are lower.

Greasing is often used in roller bearings, such as wheel bearings. Grease is applied during assembly or during maintenance.

Fig. 410 Grease lubrication is used in a roller bearing in a steering knuckle.

LUBRICATING OIL: PROPERTIES

1. Characteristics

In order to guarantee good lubrication, lubricating oil must have a number of properties.

The following properties meet stringent requirements:
— viscosity
— flash point
— pour point
— adherence

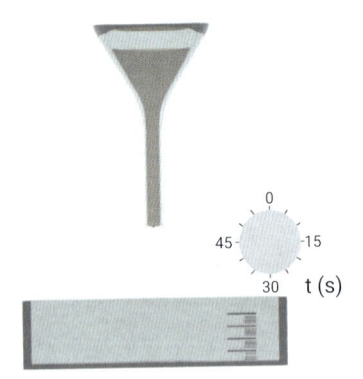

Fig. 411 We can determine the viscosity using this funnel which has been filled with oil.

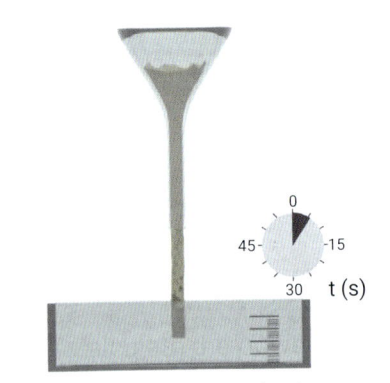

Fig. 412 We will determine the time it takes for the funnel to empty.

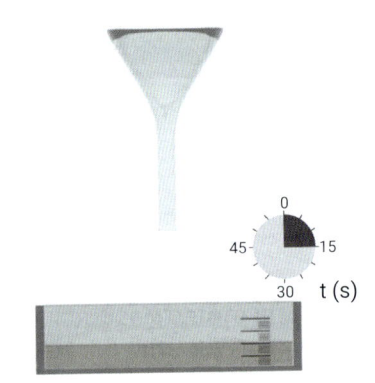

Fig. 413 It took 15 seconds for the funnel to empty.

2. Viscosity

Viscosity is a measure of the lubricating oil thickness.

Thick lubricating oil has a high viscosity and thin lubricating oil has a low viscosity.

If oil is too thick, it will be difficult to supply sufficient oil to all parts that require lubrication. Also the resistance between moving surfaces becomes greater. On the other hand, if oil is too thin, there won't be an adequate oil film barrier between moving parts. In both cases (whether too thick or thin) lubrication is not optimal.

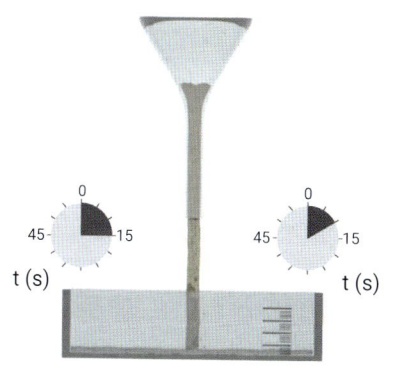

Fig. 414 High viscosity oil is more viscous than low viscosity oil. The time it takes for a funnel to empty depends on the viscosity.

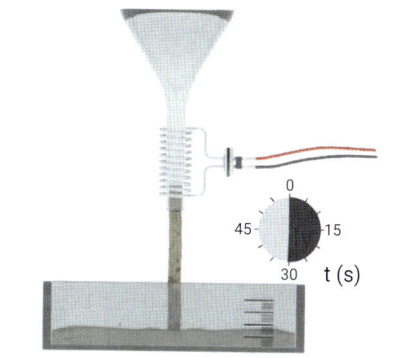

Fig. 415 Oil type X has high viscosity when it is cold. It will take longer for the funnel to empty.

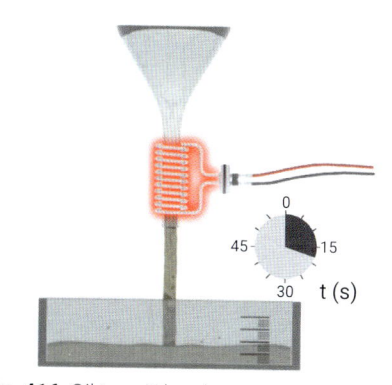

Fig. 416 Oil type X has lower viscosity when it is hot. It will not take as long for the funnel to empty.

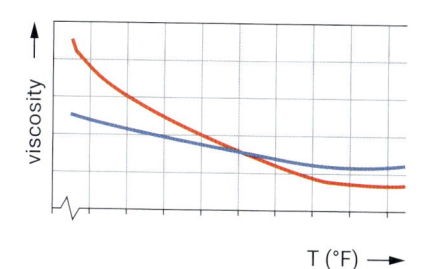

Fig. 417 Viscosity index. This graph indicates the difference between two different oil types. The height of the red line changes dramatically as the temperature rises. The blue line is nearly horizontal.

3. Viscosity Index

The lubricating oil viscosity depends on the temperature. At a higher temperature, oil is thinner than at a lower temperature.

To what extent viscosity is temperature dependent is shown by the viscosity index.

The viscosity of lubricating oil with a low viscosity index is highly dependent on the temperature. The viscosity of lubricating oil with a high viscosity index is not so dependent on the temperature.

A perfect lubricating oil has a constant viscosity at any temperature.

4. Adherence

The adherence indicates to what extent lubricating oil adheres to a surface.

A high adherence is advantageous for lubrication and reduces the occurrence of boundary lubrication (moving parts that are not totally separated by a film of oil).

Fig. 418 Lubricating oil with strong adhesion.

Fig. 419 Lubrication oil with lower adhesion.

5. Flash Point

The flash point of lubricating oil is the temperature at which the lubricating oil vapor can briefly combust.

To prevent overheating of lubricated parts, the flash point must be high enough to prevent combustion.

6. Pour Point

The pour point of lubricating oil is the temperature at which the liquid state of oil turns to a solid state.

The oil should not congeal too quickly, so the lubricating oil can still be used even in the winter.

7. Other Properties

Besides these important properties the following properties are also important:
— carbon content
  Indicates how fast the oil is contaminated by combustion deposits.
— hygroscopic
  To what extent the oil is able to absorb water.
— density
  The specific density of the lubricating oil. This also defines how well the oil allows mixing with other oil types.

Fig. 420 Flash point check for lubricating oil.

Fig. 421 Solidification point check for lubricating oil.

8. Additives

By adding additives to the lubricating oil, various properties can be improved.

The following additives are often used:
- viscosity index improving additives
- adherence improving additives
- pour point lowering additives
- anti-foaming additives
- anti-oxidant additives:
  Protects the oil against negative influences of oxygen.
- anti-wear additives:
  Ensures a better oil film.

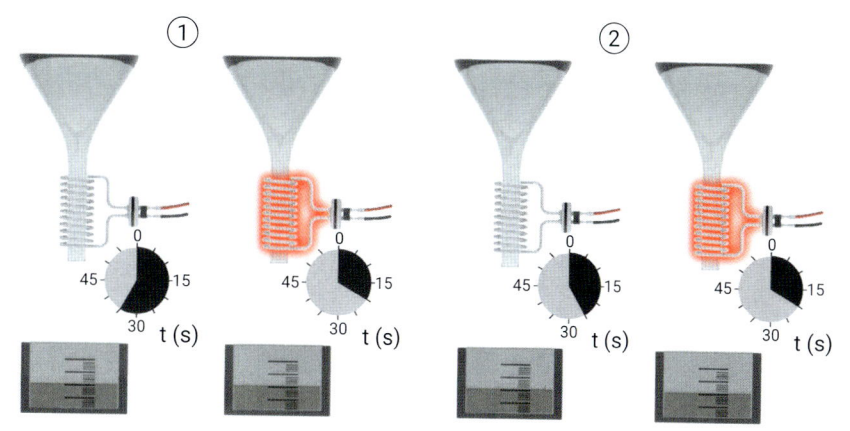

Fig. 422 Additives may improve the properties of the oil. The illustration features a test with (1) and without (2) a viscosity-improving additive in both hot and cold states.

Fig. 423 Example of contamination. The oil is black and caked. Thickened oil prevents proper cooling and lubrication.

Fig. 424 Varnish deposits (1) have created brown deposits on the metal parts.

LUBRICATING OIL: TYPES

1. Lubricating Oil

Lubricating oil is used to reduce friction between moving parts. Lowering friction translates to less heat and wear.

There are many types of lubricating oil:
- Mineral-based lubricating oil
- Vegetable-based lubricating oil
- Animal-based lubricating oil
- Synthetic lubricating oil
- Semi-synthetic or synthetic blend lubricating oil
- Compound lubricating oil

2. Mineral-Based Lubricating Oil

Mineral oil is made in a refinery, processed from crude oil extracted from the earth.

Advantages:
- Long service life
- Inexpensive

Disadvantage:
- Does not adhere well to surfaces without additives

Application:
- Engine lubricants
- Transmission lubricants

Fig. 425 Crude oil is pumped up from the earth.

3. Vegetable-Based Lubricating Oil

Vegetable oil is made by pressing seeds of plants.
Coleseed, cotton seed, and castor seed are most often used to make vegetable oil.

Advantages:
- Very good lubrication properties
- Adheres well to surfaces

Disadvantage:
— Short service life

Application:
— Vegetable lubricating oil is added to mineral oil to improve its properties.

4. Animal-Based Lubricating Oil

Animal-based lubricating oil is made through a process of boiling down and pressing out the bones and fat from animals, such as fish.

Advantages:
— Very good lubrication qualities
— Adheres well to surfaces
— Consistent viscosity at different temperatures

Disadvantage:
— Short service life

Application:
— Animal lubricating oil is added to mineral oil to improve its properties.

Fig. 426 Different sources of vegetable oil.

Fig. 427 A source of animal oil.

5. Synthetic Lubricating Oil

Synthetic lubricating oil is made in a laboratory.

Advantages:
— Very good lubrication qualities
— Adheres well to surfaces
— Almost constant viscosity at different temperatures
— Extended service life when compared to mineral oil
— Resistant to high temperatures

Disadvantage:
— Expensive

Application:

— Engine lubricants
— Transmission lubricants
— Synthetic oil can be added to mineral oil to improve its properties.

Fig. 428 The source of synthetic lubricating oil is the laboratory.

Fig. 429 Semi-synthetic lubricating oil has mineral lubricating oil as a source.

6. Semi-Synthetic Lubricating Oil

Mineral oil is processed in a laboratory until it is made into semi-synthetic oil.

Advantages:
− Lubricates very well
− Adheres well to surfaces
− Maintains a more constant viscosity at different temperatures than mineral oil
− Can be used for longer periods

Disadvantage:

− More expensive than mineral oil

Application:

− Lubrication of combustion engines
− Lubrication of transmissions

Fig. 430 Compound lubricating oil is a mix of oils.

7. Compound Lubricating Oil

Compound lubricating oil is made by mixing mineral lubricating oil with vegetable and/or animal lubricating oil.

Advantage:
− Combination of the positive properties of mineral, vegetable, and animal lubricating oil

Disadvantage:
− Absorbs water

Application:

− Transmissions that are heavily loaded
− Lubrication of parts affected by other lubricating oil

ENGINE OIL CLASSIFICATIONS AND RATINGS

1. Properties and Standards

There are specific properties and standards for lubricants approved for use in automobile engines. The recommended oil for a specific engine application may be found in the vehicle owner's manual or manufacturer's service information.

The most important qualities of a lubricant are:
- viscosity
- viscosity index
- flash point
- adhesion properties

There are various standards for the type and quality of a lubricant:
- SAE
- API
- ACEA

2. SAE

The SAE (Society of Automotive Engineers) specification indicates the viscosity (thickness) of the oil. The oil viscosity depends greatly on temperature.

A single grade (straight weight) oil viscosity is rated at either a high or low temperature. It's important that you recognize the oil's viscosity rating, otherwise you may choose the wrong oil for the engine operating conditions (high or low temperatures).

If the oil is tested at low temperatures (i.e. approx. 0°F (-18°C)), the viscosity index is indicated with a number followed by the letter 'W' for winter.

FOR EXAMPLE SAE 10W.

If the oil is tested at high temperatures (i.e. approx. 212°F (100°C)) the index is just a number, for example: SAE 40.

3. Multigrade

With a multigrade oil, the viscosity is specified for both low and at high temperatures (multi-viscosity rating). For example: SAE 10W 40

This multigrade oil has a viscosity comparable to (single grade) SAE 10W at low temperatures and a viscosity comparable of SAE 40 at high temperatures.

Fig. 431 Indication of a single grade oil low temperature tested.

Fig. 432 Indication of a single grade oil high temperature tested.

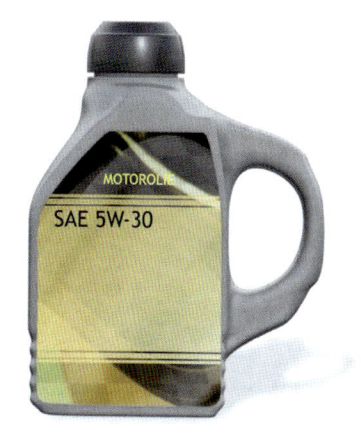

Fig. 433 Indication of a multi-grade oil low and high temperature tested.

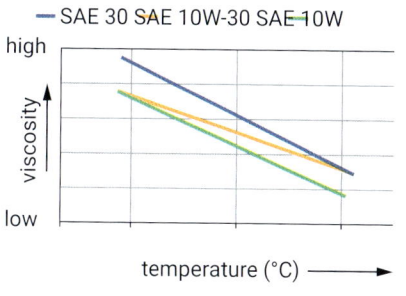

Fig. 434 Graphic of a multi-grade oil.

4. API Rating

The API (American Petroleum Institute) specification provides an overview of the uses and quality of the oil.
The first letter indicates which type of engine the oil is compatible with:
— S - gasoline engine.
— C and F - diesel engine.

Fig. 435 Designation API oil specification for gasoline engines manufactured after 1997.

A letter with a quality designation can be found after the letter indicating the type of engine. The successive letters are indicative of higher quality.

Gasoline:
- SA - SH.

  These are outdated specifications.
- SJ - SP.

  SJ is the lowest quality and SP is the highest quality.

Diesel:

The coding for diesel may include the number 2 or number 4 which indicate if the oil is intended for a two-stroke or a four-stroke engine. (i.e. CJ-4)

- CA - CG.

  These are outdated specifications.
- CH - CK.

  CH is the lowest quality and CK is the highest quality.

- FA.

  This oil has been specially developed for diesel engines manufactured after 2017 with advanced exhaust gas treatment.

Attention!
This oil (FA) may only be used if the manufacturer has specified it. This oil is not compatible with C-category oil.

5. ACEA

The ACEA (European Automobile Manufacturers Association) specification indicates the quality of the oil.

A letter indicates for which type of engine the oil is suitable:
- A - otto engine
- B - light diesel engine
- A/B - otto- and light diesel engine
- C - for engines equipped with exhaust gas after-treatment equipment.
- E - heavy-duty diesel engine

Fig. 436 ACEA designation on the packaging: 1+2 Otto and light diesel engines. 3+4 Heavy diesel engines.

After the letter for the type of engine is a number that indicates the properties of the oil.

A higher number refers to a more recently developed type of oil, not necessarily a higher quality.

The properties of the oil are determined by the base oil used and the additives added.

The list below provides a global overview of the ACEA designations for engine oil.
The number refers to specific applications and characteristics, such as:
— Fuel savings.
— Long service life.
— Wear-preventing properties.
— Compatibility with vehicles with exhaust gas treatment.

This is why the manufacturer's instructions must be followed when determining which type of oil to use.
The replacement interval is always dependent on the manufacturer's instructions.

A/B specification:
The A/B specifications are suitable for gasoline and diesel engines in passenger vehicles and light commercial vehicles.

A3/B3
— Not suitable for direct injection diesel engines.
— High internal friction (high HTHS).

A3/B4
— Suitable for direct injection diesel engines.
— High internal friction (high HTHS).

A5/B5
— Oil for high performance engines.
— Low internal friction (low HTHS).
— Not suitable for certain engines - consult the vehicle information.

C specification:
The C specifications are suitable for high performance gasoline and diesel engines in passenger vehicles and light commercial vehicles. Additionally, the oils are suitable for engines with particle filters, three-way catalytic converters and NO_x catalytic converters.

C1 and C2
- Low internal friction (low HTHS).
- Low SAPS.
- Not suitable for certain engines - consult the vehicle information.

C3 and C4
- High internal friction (high HTHS).
- Low SAPS.
- Not suitable for certain engines - consult the vehicle information.

C5
- Oil with extremely low viscosity to help reduce CO_2 emissions.
- Extremely low internal friction (low HTHS).
- Low SAPS.

E specification:
The E specification is intended for diesel engines with or without turbo installed in heavy commercial vehicles under medium to heavy operating conditions.

E4
- For diesel engines which meet Euro 1, 2, 3, 4 or 5 emission standards.
- Engines without a particle filter.
- Some engines with EGR (consult the manufacturer's instructions).
- Some engines with SCR NO_x catalytic converter (check the manufacturer's instructions).

E6
- For diesel engines which meet Euro 1, 2, 3, 4, 5 or 6 emission standards.
- Engines with EGR.
- Engines with particle filter and SCR NO_x catalytic converter.
- Engines that run on fuel with a low sulfur level.

E7
- For diesel engines which meet Euro 1, 2, 3, 4 or 5 emission standards.
- Engines without a particle filter.
- Engines with EGR.
- Some engines with SCR NO_x catalytic converter. (check the manufacturer's instructions).

E9
- For diesel engines which meet Euro 1, 2, 3, 4, 5 or 6 emission standards.
- For engines with particle filter and SCR NO_x catalytic converter.
- Engines that run on fuel with a low sulfur level.

6. HTHS and SAPS

The terms HTHS and SAPS partially determine the oil's application. The values for this are determined by means of an HTHS test and an SAPS test.

HTHS

HTHS stands for "High Temperature High Shear." During the HTHS test, oil with high shear is subjected to high temperatures. The result of this test yields information about the robustness of the oil. The internal friction of the oil is another way of putting this. In other words, how easy is it for the particles to move against each other. Oil with a low HTHS value has low internal friction. The drawback is that the lubrication film is more likely to break down.
Oil with low internal friction and a low HTHS value saves on fuel. This oil may only be used in engines that have been specially developed for it.

SAPS

The term SAPS stands for "Sulfated Ash, Phosphorus and Sulfur". The SAPS value provides information about the creation of ash and the phosphorus and sulfur levels. A low ash value indicates that very little ash is formed during combustion.
It is important that as few ash particles as possible find their way into the exhaust gases; this is especially the case for engines with exhaust gas treatment.

7. OEM Recommendations

The Original Equipment Manufacturer of an engine is likely to have quality requirements in place for the oil to be used in an engine. Usually, these are specified tighter than the standard requirements.

The OEM's intention is to warrant the reliability of an engine, and the extension of its ALE (Average Lifetime Expectancy).

You may find the following designations listed on engine oil packaging in addition to the ACEA and API standards. These standards have been created by vehicle manufacturers or other bodies.
For example, packaging designations may include:

5W30.
ACEA C3.
API SP.
VW 504.00/507.00.
BMW long-life-04.
MB-approval 229.51.

This oil meets all the demands made by the above-listed specifications; this includes the specifications created by Volkswagen, BMW and Mercedes.

Always check the manufacturer's specifications when replacing the oil. Using the wrong type of oil to fill or top up the oil levels may result in engine damage.

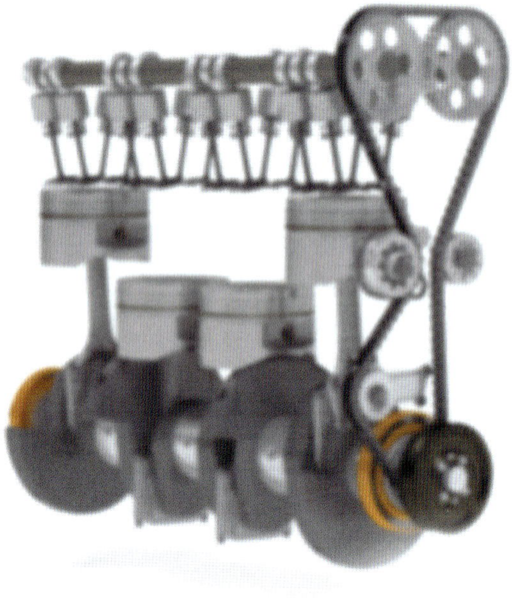

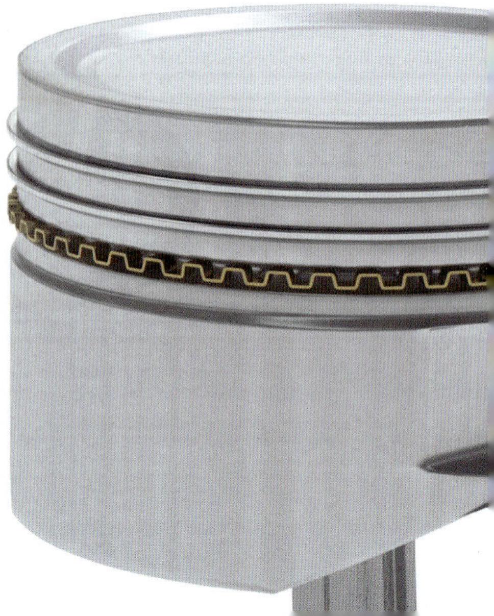

11. Lubrication System: Components

LUBRICATION SYSTEM

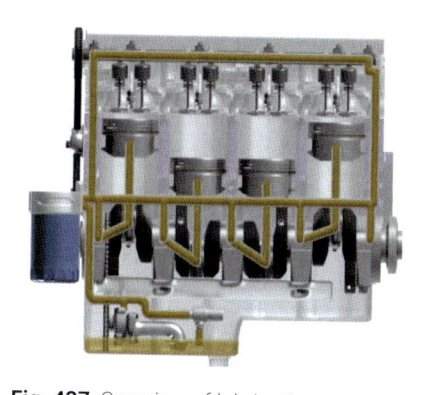

Fig. 437 Overview of lubrication system. The brown colors are the oil galleries that flow in bores through the crankshaft to enable the supply of oil to the bearings.

In an engine, different parts move alongside each other. Here are some examples:
— The piston rings move along the cylinder wall.
— The crankshaft and camshafts rotate on a film of oil between the bearings and inserts.
— The lifters (tappets) slide across the lobes of the camshaft.
— The teeth of gears slide past each other.

1. Task of the Lubrication System

The most important task of the lubrication system is to ensure all moving engine components are lubricated under all operating conditions.

The lubrication system also ensures clean oil is transported, under pressure, to engine components.

Not all the engine components are lubricated under pressure; some engine parts receive oil by splash lubrication.

2. Lubrication Circuit

The oil pump draws oil from the oil pan sump and delivers it through the filter to the oil galleries (passages) in the block. These galleries supply oil to crankshaft and cylinder head.

Oil that's channeled to the crankshaft bearings is then channeled to the connecting rod bearings. From there, oil is channeled through a passage in the connecting rods and on to the wrist pins and pistons.

Oil is supplied to the camshaft, valves, and lifters through passages in the cylinder head.

Oil returns in a repetitive cycle to the oil pan by gravity through return holes in the corners of the cylinder heads.

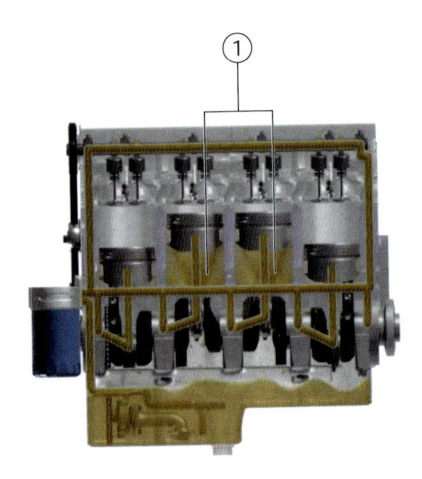

Fig. 438 In the engine, there is pressure lubrication and (1) splash lubrication. The oil sprays between the bearings of the crankshaft against the cylinder wall.

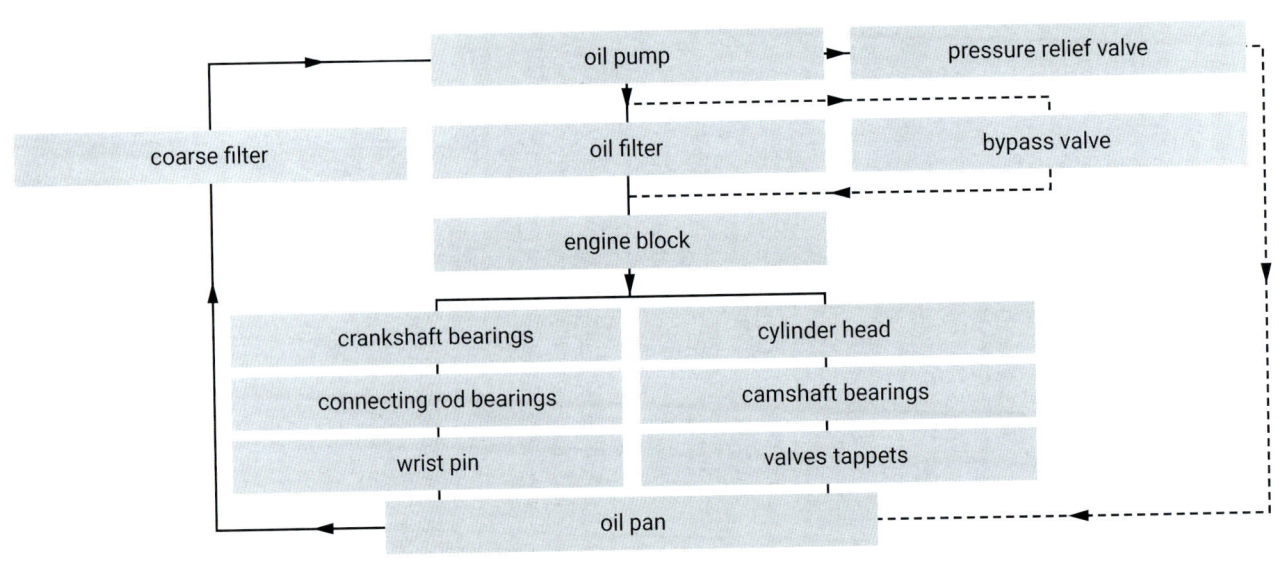

Fig. 439 Schematic representation of a simple lubrication system.

3. Components

The lubrication system contains the following components:
- **Oil pan:**
  storage for the oil supply
- **Strainer:**
  screen that keeps large debris from entering and damaging the oil pump
- **Oil pump:**
  forces the oil under pressure through the lubrication system

- **Oil filter:**

  filters contaminants from the oil

- **Bypass valve:**

  If the filter becomes plugged, the bypass valve, which is part of the oil filter, opens and oil is pumped to the engine parts unfiltered.

- **Oil galleries:**

  passages like blood vessels in the engine block and other engine parts that enable oil transportation

- **Pressure relief valve:**

  acts as an oil pressure regulator so the oil pump can consistently provide sufficient oil pressure to the gallery

- **Seals:**

  Lip-seals, retainer rings, and gaskets prevent oil leaks.

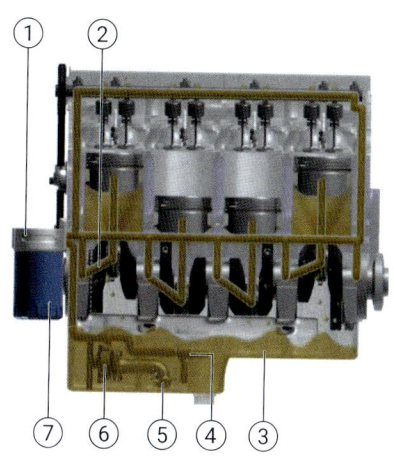

Fig. 440 Components of a lubrication system: 1. Bypass valve. 2. Oil galleries. 3. Oil pan. 4. Pressure relief valve. 5. Oil strainer. 6. Oil pump. 7. Oil filter.

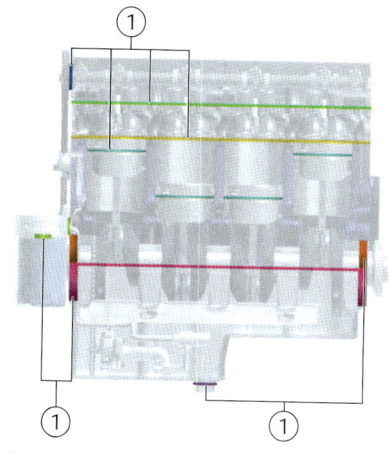

Fig. 441 1. Sealing the lubrication system with a front timing chain seal, rear main crankshaft seal, oil filter seal, oil drain plug gasket, oil rings, valve cover gasket, camshaft gasket, and head gasket.

4. Other Tasks

The most important task for lubrication is to reduce friction. Other tasks include the following:

- Cooling
- Sealing
- Cleaning
- Muting sound

DRY SUMP LUBRICATION SYSTEM

Fig. 442 Some motorcycles have a dry oil pan.

1. Task

The lubrication system ensures correct lubrication of all moving engine parts under all circumstances.

Lubrication systems can be divided into two types:
— wet sump
   The lubrication oil is stored in the engine sump (oil pan).
— dry sump
   The lubrication oil is stored in a separate reservoir.

Wet sump is often used in:

— cars
— light trucks
— large trucks and tractors

Dry sump is used in:

— four-stroke motorcycles
— racing cars
— marine engines
— aircraft engines

2. Characteristics

If you compare both lubrication systems, the following differences stand out:
— separate oil reservoir
   The oil supply is not in the sump (oil pan).
— flat sump
   The sump collects the oil and ensures its transportation to the reservoir.
— multiple oil pumps
   The oil pumps are not mounted in the sump, but rather placed outside the engine. The pumps are belt driven by the crankshaft.

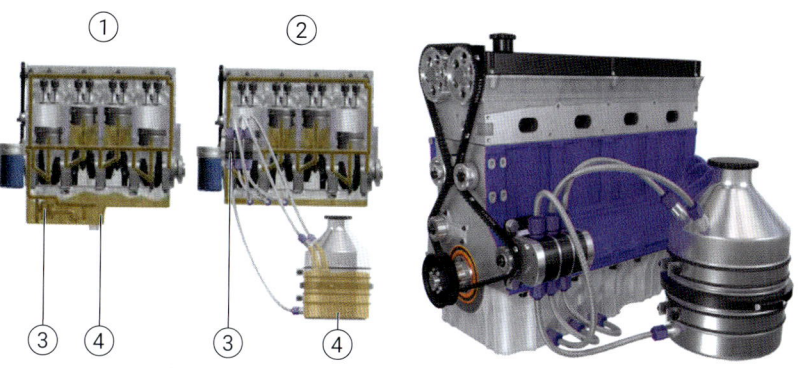

Fig. 443 1. Engine block wet oil pan. 2. Engine block dry oil pan. 3. Oil pumps. 4. Oil reserves.

Fig. 444 Parts of a dry sump lubrication system.

3. Operation

The lubricating oil is drawn out of a reservoir and force fed to engine parts that require lubrication.

After lubrication of the engine parts, the oil is returned by gravity, into the flat and shallow sump. There the oil is pumped back to the reservoir by means of scavenger pumps. Often several scavenger pumps are used to lower the chance of getting air in the lubrication system.

A dry sump lubrication system has an oil filter and a pressure relief valve (just as a wet sump lubrication system). If the oil supply is small, an oil cooler can be mounted to maintain the correct oil temperature.

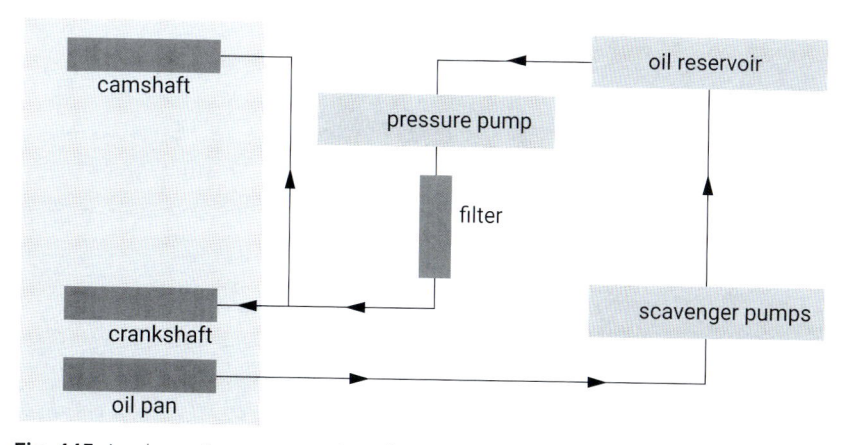

Fig. 445 A schematic representation of a dry sump lubrication system.

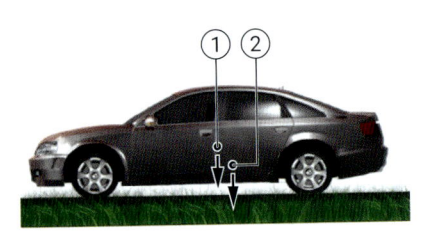

Fig. 446 1. The location of the center of gravity when a wet sump lubrication system has been used. 2. The location of the center of gravity when a dry sump lubrication system has been used.

4. Advantages and Disadvantages

The advantages of a dry sump lubrication system are:
— Larger oil capacity is possible due to an external oil reservoir.
— The engine can be mounted lower in the chassis; achieving a lower center of gravity.
— The oil reservoir can be placed anywhere; this also has a positive effect on the weight distribution.
— G-forces have no effect on oil supply and oil pressure.

A dry sump system has the following disadvantages:

— more expensive
  More oil pumps, extra pipes and hoses, etc.
— More components that require service.
— Greater chance of air in the system, which can cause bearing damage.
— The capacity must be larger than a wet sump system; therefore it takes longer for the oil to reach operating temperature.

Fig. 447 The low center of gravity in cars with a dry sump lubrication system means they are less likely to roll over.

Fig. 448 The oil in cars with a wet sump lubrication system moves during a sharp turn.

OIL PUMP

1. Task

The oil pump ensures sufficient oil supply under all operating conditions.

The oil pump draws in oil from the oil pan and forces it, under pressure, to engine parts that require lubrication.

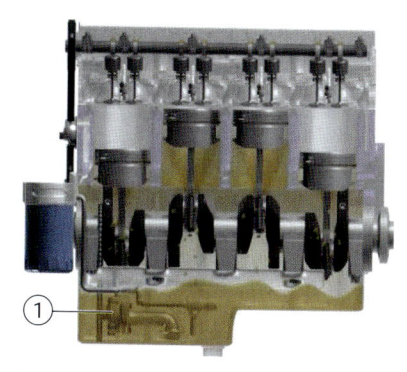

Fig. 449 In a wet oil pan system you will find the oil pump in the oil pan:
1. Oil pump.

2. Types

There are different types of oil pumps available. The types listed below are the most common ones:
— Gear pump.
— Rotor pump.
— Crescent pump.
— Vane pump.

All these types of pumps draw in oil by means of volume increase. Oil pressure is built up by means of a volume decrease.

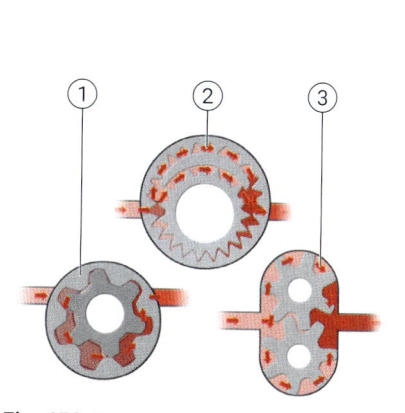

Fig. 450 Types of oil pumps:
1. Rotor pump. 2. Crescent pump. 3. Gear pump.

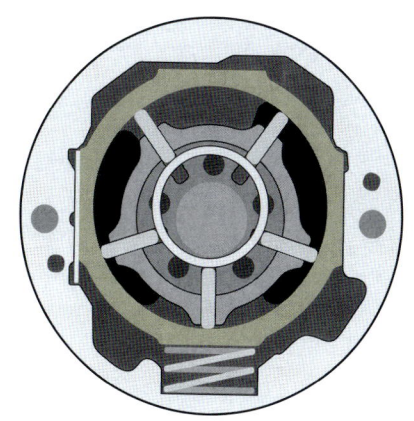

Fig. 451 Vane pump with variable output.

There are oil pumps where the volume increase on the inlet side and the volume decrease on the pressure side both vary. As a result, these oil pumps have a variable yield.

3. Powertrain

The engine drives the oil pump.

The rotation of the crankshaft, camshaft or balancer shaft is transferred to the oil pump via one of these frequently used methods:
- gear chain drive
  A gear on the crankshaft is chain-connected to a gear on the oil pump.
- worm drive
  The gear wheel on the oil pump shaft acts on a balancer shaft or camshaft worm gear.
- directly on the crankshaft
  The oil pump is slid over the crankshaft. Two flat sides on the crankshaft fit into the oil pump.

Fig. 452 Oil pump with shaft drive.

Fig. 453 Oil pump located directly on the crankshaft.

Fig. 454 Oil pump with gear chain drive.

4. Gear Pump

In the oil pump housing, two gears are mounted. These gears are fitted precisely in the housing.

On this pump, the engine drives the right-hand gear. The left-hand gear engages with the right-hand gear and is also driven. The space between the teeth is filled with oil. Oil is transferred from the inlet side to the pressure side.

At the inlet side, the volume increases slightly. Due to the drop in pressure, oil is drawn out of the oil pan.

At the pressure side, the volume decreases, so oil pressure is built up and pumped to the engine parts.

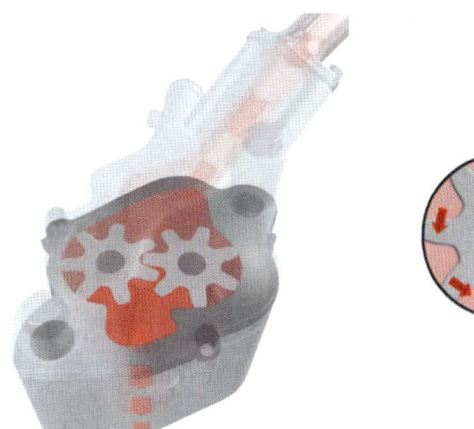

Fig. 455 Oil pump with two gears. The suction side is on top and the pressure side is on the bottom.

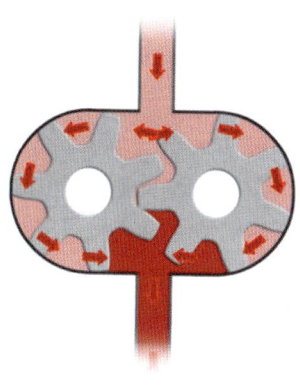

Fig. 456 Operating principle of a gear pump. The inlet side is on the top. Oil is transported externally and compressed during transit.

5. Rotor Pump

The rotor pump consists of a housing, a inner rotor and an outer rotor ring.

The engine drives the rotor. The outer rotor is driven by the inner rotor.

The pump housing is divided into an inlet side and a pressure side. The rotor pump draws oil out of the oil pan due to a low pressure that occurs from the increase in volume between the inner and outer rotors.

The oil is forced to the engine parts on the pressure side, because the volume decreases.

Fig. 457 Rotor pump. The inlet side is on the bottom and the pressure side is on top.

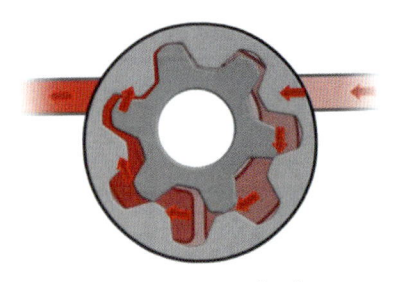

Fig. 458 Operating principle of a rotor pump. The inlet side is on the right. Oil is transported by the gear teeth and is pushed out to the left.

6. Crescent Pump

The crescent pump, sometimes called a sickle crescent pump, consists of a housing, two gears and a crescent. The engine drives the inner gear. The outer gear is driven by the inner.

The space between the gears and the crescent is filled with oil. The oil moves from the inlet side to the pressure side. From the pressure side, the oil is pumped to engine parts that require lubrication.

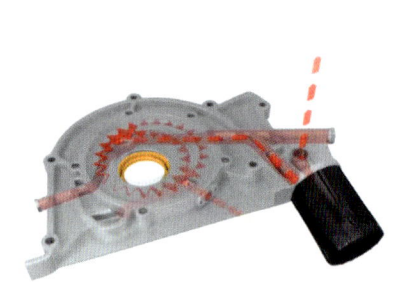

Fig. 459 Crescent pump. The inlet side is on the bottom and the pressure side is on the right.

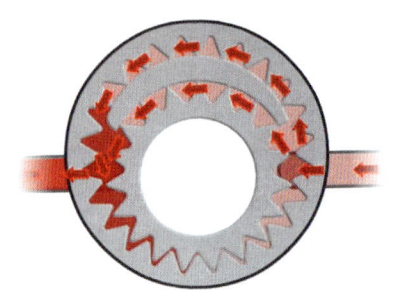

Fig. 460 Operating principle of a crescent pump. The inlet side is on the right. The oil is transported by the gear teeth via the crescent shape and is pressed towards the oil filter to the left.

7. Vane pump.

The vane pump consists of a housing with a pump shaft in the middle. There are vanes in the pump shaft which can move in the pump shaft grooves. The principle of increasing the volume on the inlet side and decreasing the volume on the pressure side also applies here. Oil is sucked in and pumped to the parts which need lubricating under pressure.

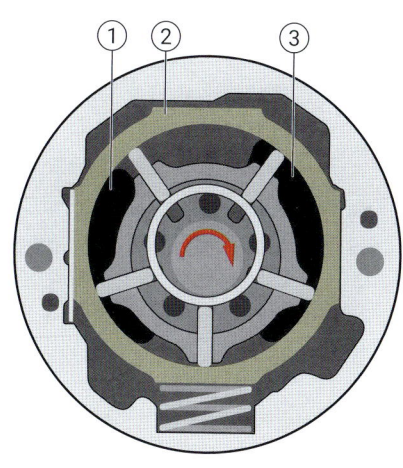

Fig. 461 Vane pump: 1. Inlet side. 2. Pump element. 3. Pressure side.

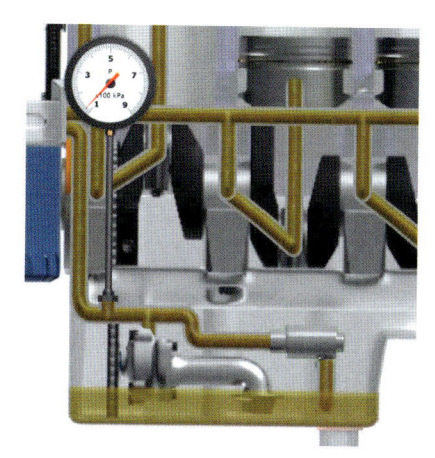

Fig. 462 Oil pressure gauge connected to the oil pump. Some engines have been equipped with a plug for this purpose. An oil pressure gauge can also be fitted instead of an oil pressure sensor.

8. Oil Pressure

The oil pressure must be high enough to ensure adequate lubrication of critical engine parts.

The oil pressure depends on:
- oil pump capacity
- type of oil
  For example, the oil should not be too thin.
- oil level
  There must be sufficient oil in the oil pan.
- condition of the oil pump
  A worn oil pump delivers a lower pressure than a new one.
- condition of the engine
  For instance: due to leakages from worn bearings the oil pressure may not build up enough.
- the condition of the oil filter

In the vehicle service information you will find the exact specifications for the oil pressure. For example 36 PSI (250 kPa) at 2000 rpm and 72 PSI (500 kPa) at 5000 rpm.

9. Capacity

The capacity of an oil pump indicates the amount of oil which can be transferred in a given time.

The capacity of an oil pump depends on:

- the oil pump construction
  A large volume oil pump can transfer more oil than an oil pump rated at a smaller volume.
- the engine speed
  The higher the engine speed, the greater the oil transfer in a given time.

10. Theoretical Yield

The yield (capacity) of a gear pump depends on the contents of a gear tooth and the number of teeth the gear has. As a result, the total yield for a gear pump can be calculated by multiplying the contents of a gear tooth by the number of teeth. A gear pump has two gears so we need to double this value. All the gear teeth in a gear will have transported their oil volume when the gears have rotated once. This is the yield per rotation. If we multiply this amount by the rotational speed of the oil pump (rotations per second) we get the yield per second. This is a theoretical yield as it does not account for things like losses resulting from leakage and oil being caught in the gear teeth.

11. Determining the Theoretical Yield

Consequently, the theoretical yield can be calculated as follows:

Yield $= n_{oilpump} * z * 2 * V_{th}$

$n =$ rotational frequency
$z =$ number of teeth per gear
$V_{th} =$ gear tooth volume

The unit of volume for the gear tooth is expressed in inches³ and the rotational frequency in Hz. The unit for the calculated yield is therefore in³/s.

Calculation example:
A gear pump has gears with 13 teeth and a gear tooth volume of 0.01 in³. The oil pump is directly driven by the crank shaft. The engine's rotational frequency is 15 Hz. Calculate the oil pump's theoretical yield once the engine has been running for 10 minutes.

Assume:
$n_{engine} = 15 Hz$
$z = 13 teeth$
$V_{th} = 0.01 in^3$
$t = 10 min.$

Find:
Yield at t.

Solution:
Yield per second is:
$n_{oilpump} * z * 2 * V_{th}$

$15 Hz * 13 * 2 * 0.01 in^3 = 3.9 in^3$

Yield after 600 seconds is: $600s * 3.9 in^3 = 2340 in^3 = 1.35 ft^3$

Practical yield:

If an oil pump has leakage losses amounting to 5%, this means that 5% of the theoretical yield will be lost. The yield of the oil pump will be limited to 95%. When we apply this to the oil pump in the calculation example, we can see that the practical yield of the oil pump can be calculated as follows:

$0.95 * 1.35 ft^3 = 1.2825 ft^3$.

12. Checking the Oil Pump

The oil pump is always exposed to oil. However, this does not mean it is not subject to wear.

Checking a Gear Pump

A gear pump can be inspected for wear at two points: radial and axial. This is done using a set of feeler gauges and a steel edge.

You need to measure the distance between the top of the gear and the pump housing wall for the radial clearance. The axial clearance is the distance between the gear and the edge of the pump housing.

Fig. 463 Measuring the radial clearance. The feeler gauge is placed between the top of the tooth and the pump housing wall: 1. Feeler gauge. 2. Driven gear. 3. Pump housing. 4. Driving gear.

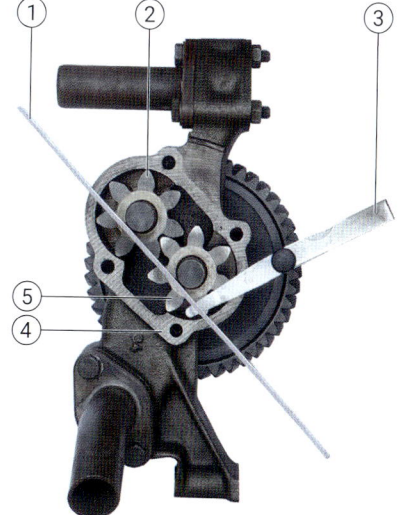

Fig. 464 Measuring the axial clearance. The feeler gauge is placed between the gear and the steel edge: 1. Steel edge. 2. Driven gear. 3. Feeler gauge. 4. Pump housing. 5. Driving gear.

Checking a Crescent Pump

The axial and radial clearance are measured in a similar fashion for crescent pumps.

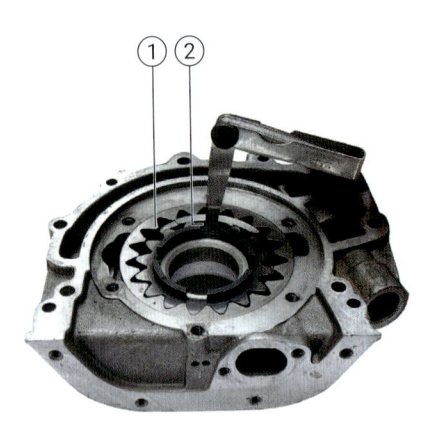

Fig. 465 Measuring the radial clearance. The feeler gauge is placed between the top of the tooth and the crescent wall:
1. Determining the radial clearance of the outer gear. 2. Determining the radial clearance of the inner gear.

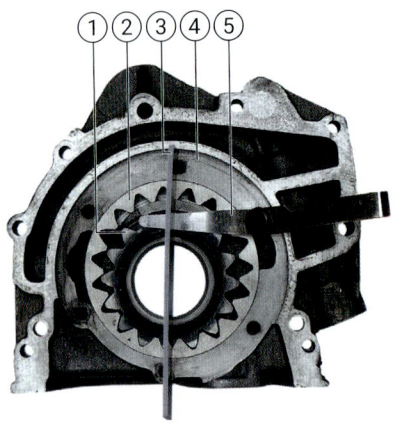

Fig. 466 Measuring the axial clearance. The feeler gauge is placed between the gear and the steel edge: 1. Inner gear. 2. Outer gear. 3. Steel edge. 4. Pump housing. 5. Feeler gauge.

13. Oil Pump with Variable Output

Powering an oil pump requires energy. This energy is provided by fuel and will be transferred via the piston, the connecting rod and the crankshaft to the oil pump's drive via combustion pressure. As the oil pump reaches maximum pressure, even at a low rotational speed, it will result in excess capacity. This excess capacity is at the expense of fuel consumption. As car manufacturers need to reduce consumption, oil pumps with a variable yield are used. The amount of oil that can be transported between the teeth or baffles is adapted to meet the demand in this type of oil pump.

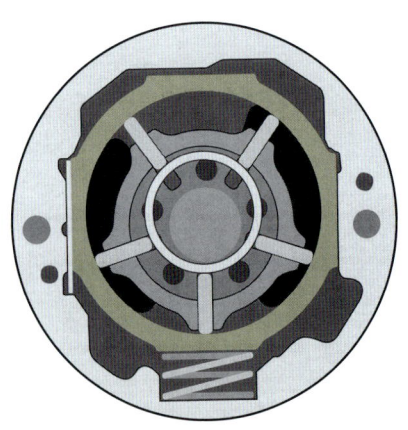

Fig. 467 Position of the oil pump during low oil pressure.

Position During Low Pressure

If the pressure is low, the maximum amount of oil is transported between the baffles on the intake side to the pressure side.

Position During High Pressure

This oil pressure will press against the top of the pump element if the oil pressure is high. The pump element counteracts the spring pressure. This means the volume increase is lower and less oil is drawn in. As a result, less oil is pushed out, which reduces the yield of the oil pump.

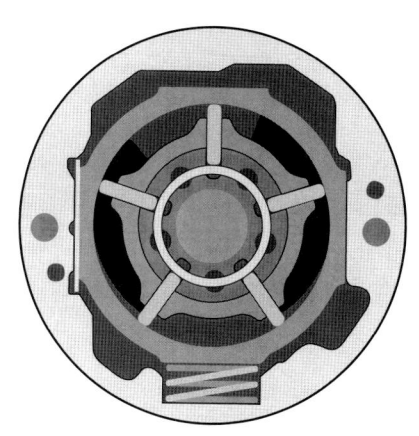

Fig. 468 Position of the oil pump during high pressure.

The oil pressure created by the oil pump changes its position, which means the yield is variable.

LUBRICATION SYSTEM: PRESSURE RELIEF VALVE

1. Task and Location

The oil pump in a lubrication system runs at an overcapacity, able to deliver a higher oil pressure than necessary. The oil pressure relief valve prevents the oil pressure from becoming too high.

The oil pressure relief valve is located in either the oil pump or the high pressure pipe, leaving the oil pump.

Possible consequences of excess oil pressure include:
- oil leakage
  Leakages via gaskets and oil seals.
- oil consumption
  Oil can enter the combustion chamber.
- Valves with hydraulic tappets / lifters can remain open too long.

Fig. 469 Location in the lubrication system: 1. Oil pump. 2. Pressure relief valve.

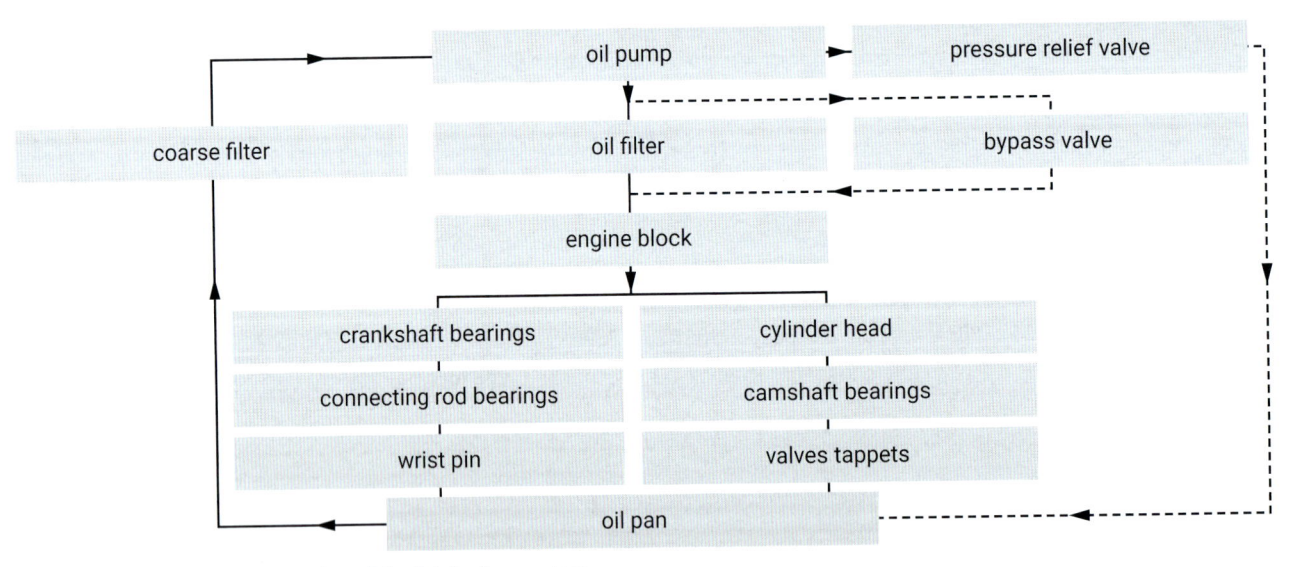

Fig. 470 Schematic representation of the lubrication system.

2. Oil Return

If oil pressure becomes too high, the pressure relief valve opens; limiting the oil pressure.

11. LUBRICATION SYSTEM: COMPONENTS

Depending on the design of the relief valve, lubricating oil may flow into the oil pan or be returned to the intake side of the oil pump.

3. Ball Check-Valve Operation

The pressure relief valve can be designed as a ball check-valve.

The ball check-valve consists of:
— housing
— ball
— spring

The lubricating oil presses against the ball. If the oil pressure exceeds the spring force, the ball lifts from its seat. The oil flows back to the oil pan via the oil pressure relief valve.

By changing the spring force, the maximum oil pressure can be adjusted.

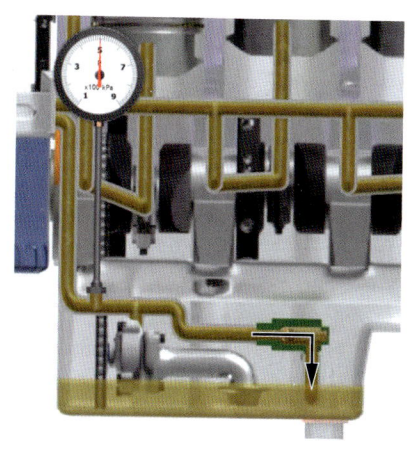

Fig. 471 The oil pressure valve drains excess oil to the oil pan.

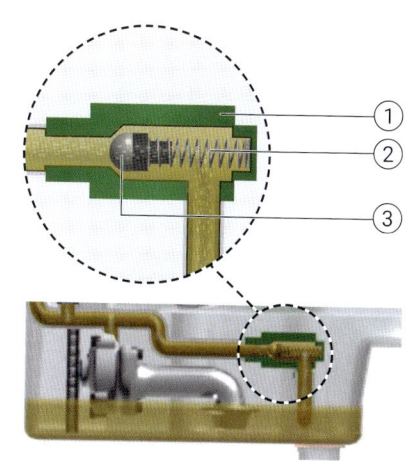

Fig. 472 The ball valve: 1. Housing. 2. Spring. 3. Ball.

4. Plunger Valve Operation

The pressure relief valve can also be designed as a plunger valve.

A plunger valve consists of:
— casing
— plunger
— spring

The lubricating oil is forced against the plunger. When the oil pressure exceeds the spring force, the pressure side is connected to the intake side.

As with the ball valve type, the maximum oil pressure also depends on the spring force.

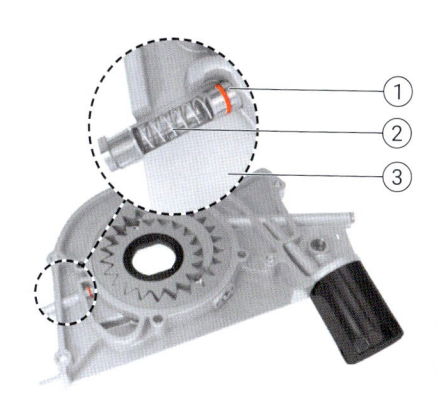

Fig. 473 The plunger valve drains excess oil to the suction side of the oil pump or back to the oil pan: 1. Plunger. 2. Spring. 3. Housing.

OIL FILTER

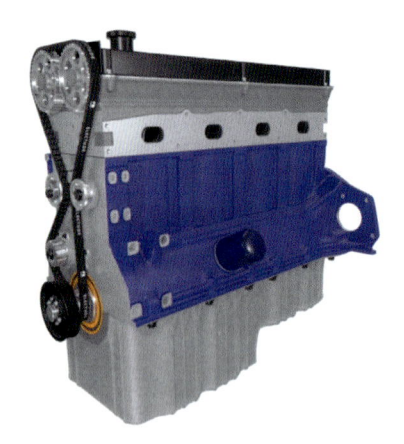

Fig. 474 Oil filter installed on the side of the block.

1. Task

The oil filter is designed to remove debris from the lubricating oil. Friction and wear on moving parts cause carbon and metal particles to enter the lubrication system.

A filter is used to reduce wear on engine parts by removing carbon and metal particles from the oil. This action also helps to increase the oil's life.

The oil filter is usually mounted on the side or bottom of the engine block.

Fig. 475 Oil filter with double seal ring.

Fig. 476 Oil filter with single seal ring.

2. Construction

Oil filters can be divided into two categories:
— Screw-on oil filters.
— Oil filters with interchangeable filter element.

The illustration depicts what is known as a screw-on oil filter. The other illustration depicts what is known as an oil module with an interchangeable filter element.

An oil filter is made up of different parts:
— The *seal* ensures no oil can leak out from between the engine block and the oil filter.
— A screw thread connects the *base plate* to the engine block.

- A *check valve* ensures oil does not flow back into the engine block if the oil pressure drops.
- The *filter element* ensures the oil is filtered.
- The *central mesh tube* reinforces the filter element and prevents creasing in it.
- The *bypass valve* ensures that a clogged filter is not blocked.
- The *spring* determines the pressure in the bypass valve and makes sure components stay put.
- The *housing* ensures a seal is created and is resistant to oil pressure.

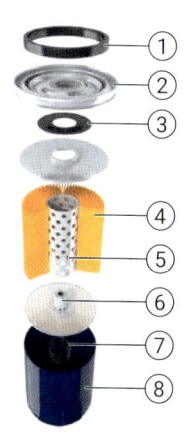

Fig. 477 Structure of the oil filter: 1. Rubber grommet. 2. Base plate. 3. Check valve. 4. Filter element. 5. Central mesh tube. 6. Bypass valve. 7. Spring. 8. Housing.

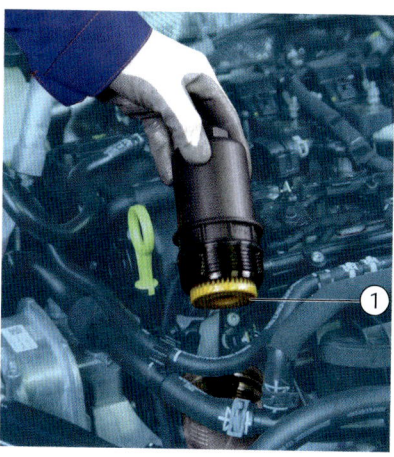

Fig. 478 Oil module with interchangeable filter element (1).

Fig. 479 A cross-section of an oil filter.

3. Operation

An oil pump forces oil from the oil pan through the outer holes in the filter's base plate.

Oil then passes through the filter element and via the base plate, back into the block.

Debris is trapped in the filter element. The oil filter should be replaced regularly to avoid becoming clogged with debris.

4. Types

There are two types of filter systems:

Full flow: The oil flowing into the engine block always goes through the oil filter. In this system, during normal operation, unfiltered oil cannot be pumped around.

Bypass: In this filter system, the oil that is pumped through the engine block is separate from the oil filter. Filtered oil is returned directly to the oil pan. In this system, it is possible for unfiltered oil to be pumped around.

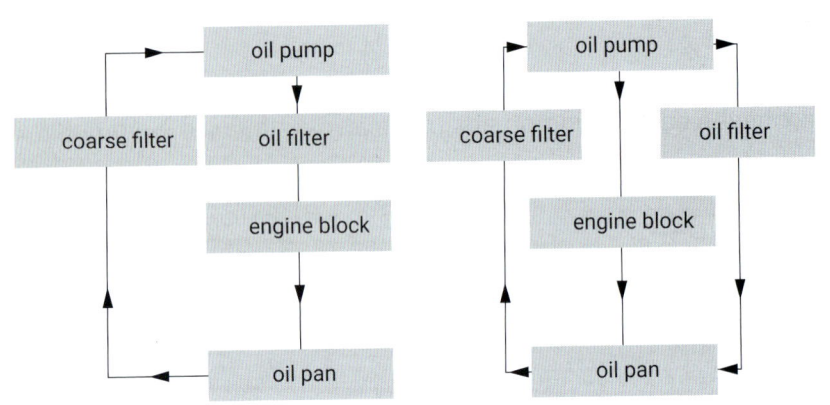

Fig. 480 Schematic depiction of the oil flow through a full-flow filter system.

Fig. 481 Schematic depiction of the oil flow through a bypass filter system.

Fig. 482 Contaminated oil filter with an open bypass valve. The unfiltered oil flows to the components which need to be lubricated.

5. Bypass Valve

In a full flow oil filter, there's a bypass valve.

The bypass valve opens if the filter element becomes clogged with debris. Oil is then directly forced through the lubrication system, no longer passing through the filter element.

Contaminated oil is allowed to circulate through the system; but this is better than no oil being circulated at all.

6. One-way Check Valve

An oil filter contains a non-return valve. This valve ensures that oil can not run out of the filter after the engine is shut off.

Oil remains in the filter, so oil pressure is immediately available when starting the engine.

Fig. 483 Oil filter without a check valve. The oil flows out of the filter if the pressure drops.

Fig. 484 Oil filter with check valve. The oil remains in the filter if the pressure drops.

7. Oil Filter with Heat Exchanger

Controlling the oil temperature is very important. Oil coolers are used for this purpose. The heat exchanger is an oil cooler which cools (or heats) the oil using coolant. The heat exchanger may be integrated in the oil module but it can also be a separate component which has been assembled on the engine block. In the latter case, the oil filter is often screwed onto the heat exchanger. First the oil will flow through the filter, then it will flow through the heat exchanger and it will then flow into the main oil channel.

The advantage of a heat exchanger is that the coolant will heat the oil while the engine is heating up. After all, the coolant heats up quicker than the oil in the lubrication system. If the temperature of the oil exceeds that of the coolant, then the heat from the oil will be discharged to the coolant.

Fig. 485 The heat exchanger is located between the engine block and the oil filter.

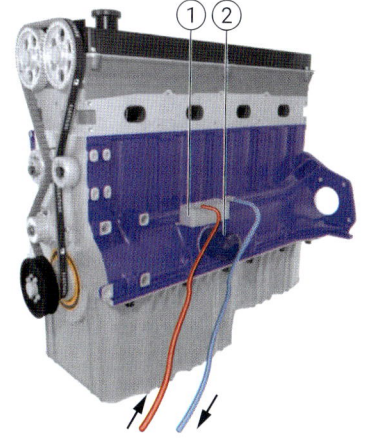

Fig. 486 1. Heat exchanger on the engine block. 2. Oil filter.

8. Replacing a Screw-on Oil Filter

Both the oil and the oil filter need to be replaced at regular intervals. The manufacturer will specify when the oil filter needs to be replaced as this interval differs by each vehicle.

As the filter slowly becomes clogged with dirt and wear particles, it becomes harder and harder to pump oil through it. At a certain point the filter no longer functions sufficiently.

You need to use the right tools to remove a screw-on filter. The use of incorrect tools may damage the filter which will make it even harder to remove.

Fig. 487 Tools for removing oil filters.

The fitting surface needs to be cleaned to ensure no dirt becomes trapped in the seal before a new screw-on filter can be installed.

PLEASE NOTE The seal ring needs to be lubricated using a bit of oil. This prevents the rubber rolling up during the assembly of the oil filter, which in turn prevents any leaks.

Fig. 488 Cleaning the fitting surface.

Fig. 489 Lubricating the seal ring.

9. Replacing an Interchangeable Filter Element.

The filter module usually consists of an aluminum filter housing with a black plastic cap.

The filter housing cap needs to be loosened before the filter element can be removed. The removable filter element, also known as the oil filter insert, can be replaced once the cap has been removed.

The rubber ring needs to be replaced at the same time as the filter element. This ring is included and needs to be lubricated.

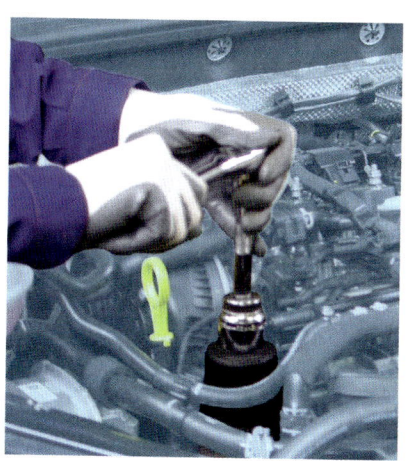

Fig. 490 The right tools need to be used when removing the filter housing. The filter housing is made of plastic.

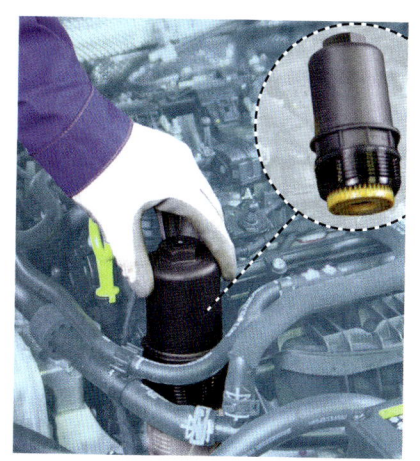

Fig. 491 Partially loosen the housing and then wait a short time. This will give air access and allows the oil to sink. You can then continue the removal process.

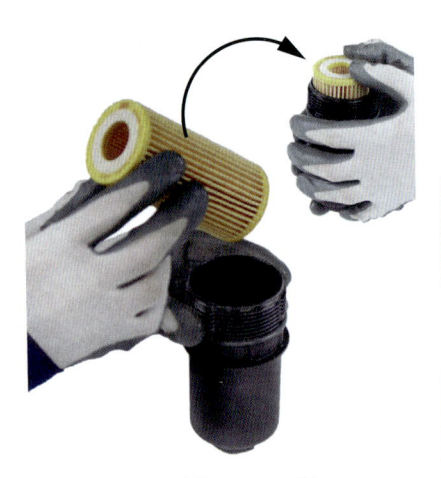

568 GASOLINE ENGINE CONSTRUCTION AND OPERATION

Fig. 492 Assembling a new filter.

Fig. 493 Fitting a new seal ring.

Fig. 494 Tighten it to the correct torque specification following assembly.

OIL COOLER

1. Task

An oil cooler ensures that the correct engine oil temperature is maintained.

Engine oil at the correct temperature has the best lubricating properties; increasing the life of the oil and engine.

If the oil becomes too hot, it can lead to accelerated wear of components; possibly resulting in engine seizure.

An oil cooler is a form of:
— heat exchanger
— radiator

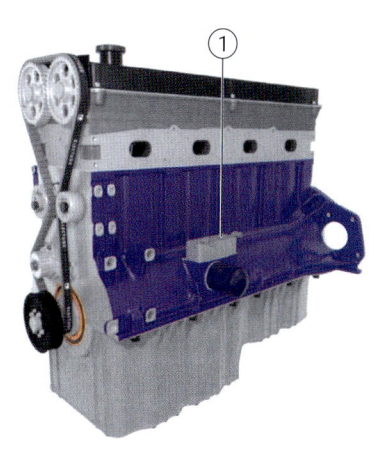

Fig. 495 Coolant cooled oil cooler: 1. Heat exchanger.

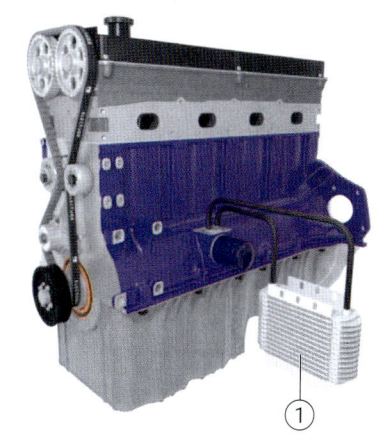

Fig. 496 Air-cooled oil cooler: 1. Oil cooler in the form of a radiator.

2. Construction

Here you can see an oil cooler in the form of a heat exchanger.

There are four connections: two for the coolant and two for the engine oil.

The oil cooler consists of a top and a base plate, separated by cooling plates.

The plates have special grooves to guide the flow and improve heat transfer capability.

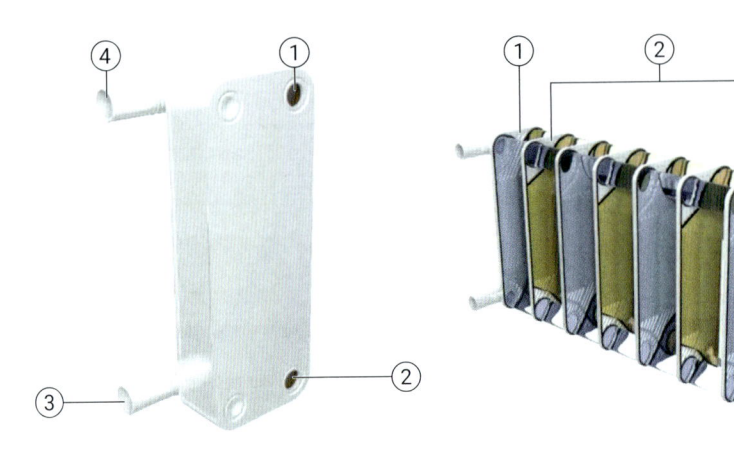

Fig. 497 Heat exchanger connections: 1. Oil return. 2. Oil supply. 3. Coolant return. 4. Coolant supply.

Fig. 498 Heat exchanger structure: 1. Top plate. 2. Cooling plates. 3. Base plate.

3. Operation

Heat from the oil is transferred to the cooling system. Engine oil and coolant flow in the opposite direction to increase efficiency.

When the engine is cold the engine coolant heats up the oil. When the engine is hot, then coolant cools the engine oil.

If there is an internal coolant leak, then oil may mix with the coolant, and vice versa.

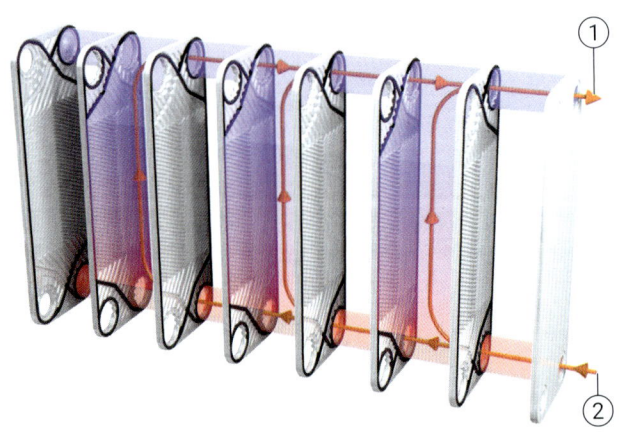

Fig. 499 Heat exchanger. Hot oil runs from bottom to top via the exchanger: 1. Oil return. 2. Oil supply.

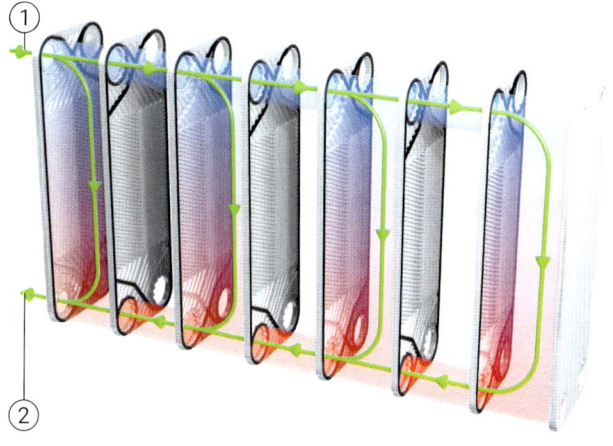

Fig. 500 Heat exchanger. Coolant runs from top to bottom via the exchanger: 1. Coolant supply. 2. Coolant return.

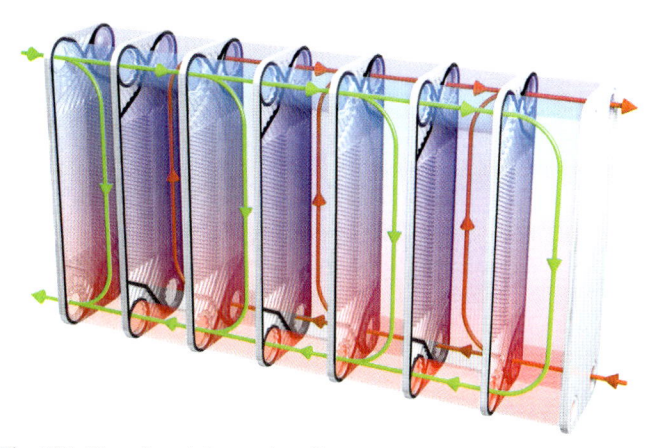

Fig. 501 The oil and the coolant flows are separated from each other by the plates and therefore release heat.

4. Radiator Oil Cooler

This is a radiator type oil cooler. Between the block and the oil filter is a branch in the lubrication system. Oil runs from here to the radiator type cooler.

The oil cooler is placed in the airflow. Heat from the oil is released into the air; the temperature of the oil is reduced by 77-122°F (25-50°C).

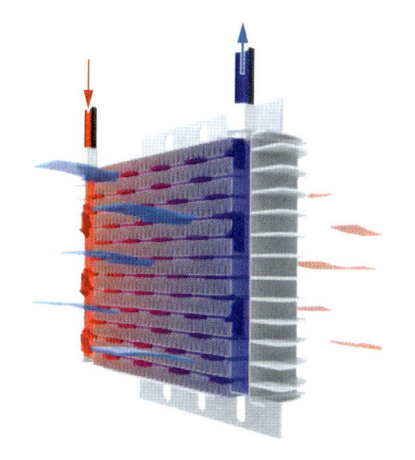

Fig. 502 Oil cooler. The oil's heat is released into the colder air flowing past.

OIL PRESSURE SENSOR

1. Function and Location

Loss of oil pressure can damage an engine permanently. Therefore, a low oil pressure warning lamp is used to alert the driver if oil pressure becomes too low.

Oil pressure is monitored in two ways:

— oil pressure switch
— oil pressure sensor

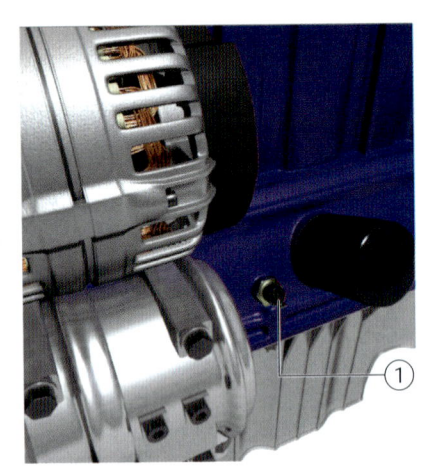

Fig. 503 Oil pressure sensor or oil pressure switch (1): the oil pressure sensor is often located near the oil filter or in the cylinder head.

The oil pressure switch or sensor is usually mounted on the side of the engine block; however sometimes a second switch or sensor is mounted on the cylinder head.

An oil pressure switch is able to control the warning lamp directly, by providing a switched ground connection through the engine block when oil pressure is too low. An oil pressure sensor provides a signal to the ECU and the ECU controls the operation of the warning lamp when oil pressure is too low.

2. Oil Pressure Switch

An oil pressure switch is either in the electrically open or closed state.
Oil pressure exerts force against a membrane.

A spring located on the other side of the membrane ensuring the electrical contact is held in the electrically closed position when the engine is not running or when oil pressure is too low.

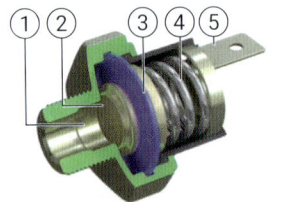

Fig. 504 Oil pressure sensor design: 1. Oil channel. 2. Engine block ignition. 3. Diaphragm. 4. Spring. 5. Connection.

When the engine is running and there's adequate pressure, the oil exerts force against the membrane, causing the spring to compress. This action opens the ground contact within the switch.

The oil pressure switch is typically grounded through the engine block.

Fig. 505 1. Ignition switch. 2. Oil pressure switch.

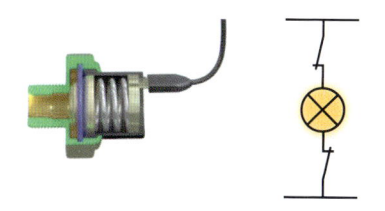

Fig. 506 Oil pressure switch with engine off and ignition on: a connection is made when the oil pressure is too low. The oil pressure light will switch on.

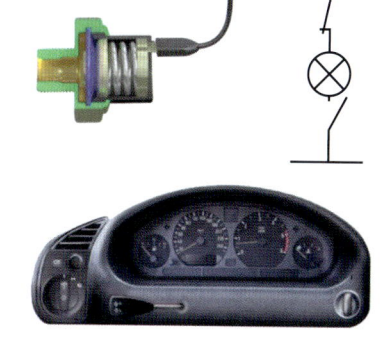

Fig. 507 Oil pressure switch with engine running: the connection is broken if the oil pressure is sufficient. The oil pressure light will switch off.

3. Oil Pressure Sensor

Unlike an oil pressure switch that's either in the open or closed position; an oil pressure sensor measures the actual pressure of the oil.

Oil pressure sensors are connected to the ECU and have a positive, ground and signal wire connection.

There are two types of oil pressure sensors:

- **Piezo-pressure sensor:**
  A measuring element is placed on a membrane. Membrane pressure deforms the measuring element, which changes the element's resistance value.
- **Capacitive pressure sensor:**
  This sensor has both a fixed and movable plate. Pressure alters the distance between the two plates and changes the capacitor's capacitance.

All pressure sensors have an amplification circuit that convert measured values to a signal the ECU can interpret.

574 GASOLINE ENGINE CONSTRUCTION AND OPERATION

Fig. 508 Oil pressure sensor housing.

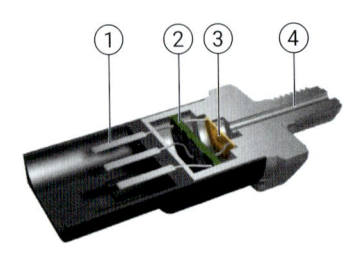

Fig. 509 Piezoelectric oil pressure sensor: 1. Connections. 2. Amplifier switches. 3. Diaphragm with measuring element. 4. Measuring tube.

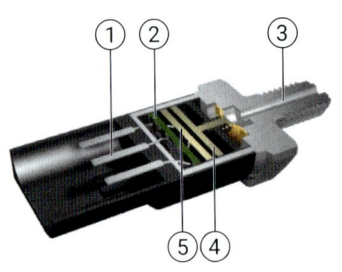

Fig. 510 Capacitive oil pressure sensor: 1. Connections. 2. Amplifier switches. 3. Measuring tube. 4. Moving plate. 5. Fixed plate.

LUBRICATION SYSTEM: OIL SEALS

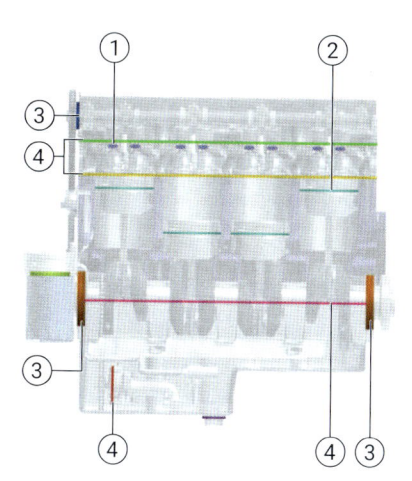

Fig. 511 Seals: 1. Valve stem seals. 2. Piston oil ring. 3. Oil seals. 4. Gaskets.

1. Task

Oil leaks and consumption are prevented by installing gaskets and seals between critical engine parts.

In an engine you will find (among others) the following seals:
— gaskets
— oil seals
— valve stem seals
— oil scraper rings
— sealing washers

2. Requirement

When fitting the oil pan to the engine block, it may appear that the surfaces are completely flat. However, by closer inspection, you'll notice that both the oil pan and the engine block mounting surfaces are not completely flat. Lubrication oil could then leak between these two surfaces.

The mounting surface between the oil pan and engine block must be sealed by means of a gasket, to prevent oil from leaking out.

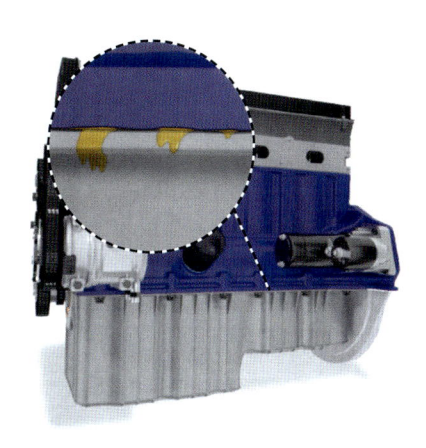

Fig. 512 Leaking oil pan.

3. Gaskets

Gaskets are clamped between two stationary surfaces. For example, between the valve cover and the cylinder head.

Gaskets can be made from different materials, for example:
— rubber
— cork
— paper

Liquid sealants are also available. A liquid sealant is usually silicone-based. There are different types with a variety of properties, for example: sealants which offer resistance to certain liquids or high temperatures.

Fig. 513 Liquid gaskets.

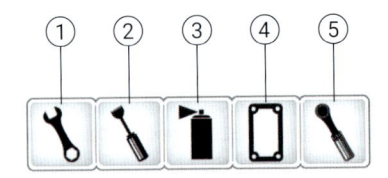

Fig. 514 Step-by-step replacement plan: 1. Remove the part. 2. Clean the fitting surfaces. 3. Scour the fitting surfaces. 4. Refit the gasket. 5. Refit the part and use the correct torque specifications and sequence to tighten it.

4. Gasket Replacement

If you're replacing a valve cover gasket, you should follow these steps:

— remove the valve cover
— remove the gasket
— carefully clean the surfaces, removing remnants of the old gasket and oil residue
— fit a new gasket
— install the valve cover bolts and tighten evenly, according to manufacture's specified torque

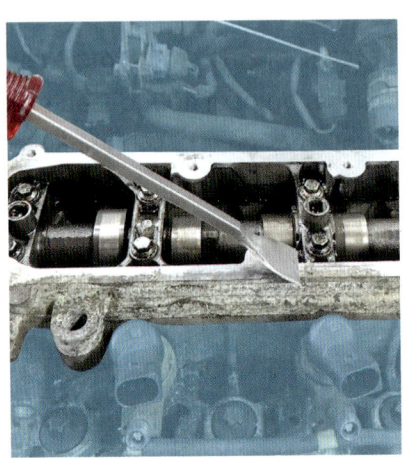

Fig. 515 Gasket residue must be removed using a gasket scraper. Make sure you do not damage the aluminum contact surface.

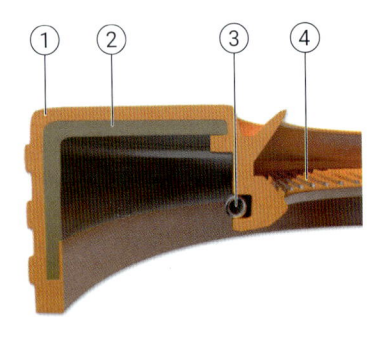

Fig. 516 Oil seal cross-section: 1. Outer casing. 2. Reinforcement ring. 3. Coil spring. 4. Seal joints.

5. Oil Seal

Oil seals are always mounted between a rotating and a stationary part. For example between a crankshaft and the engine block.

A oil seal is made up of the following parts:

— outer seal
— metal reinforcement ring
— sealing lip
— spiral spring (expander). This pushes the sealing lip onto the shaft.

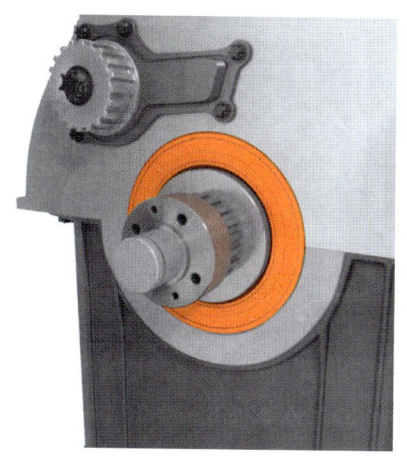

Fig. 517 An assembled crankshaft oil seal.

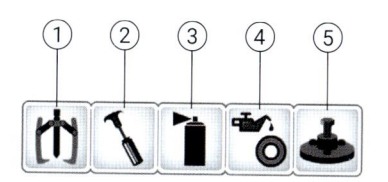

Fig. 518 Steps when replacing an oil seal: 1. Remove the pulley. 2. Pull the oil seal. 3. Clean the fitting surface. 4. Lubricate the oil seal. 5. Replace the oil seal using special tools.

6. Oil Seal Replacement

If, for example, you replace the front crankshaft oil seal (timing chain end), you should follow these steps:
- remove the crank pulley with special puller
- remove the oil seal, with the aid of a special tool, to prevent damage to the crankshaft journal and housing.
- carefully clean all surfaces which are in contact with the oil seal
- lubricate the new seal with clean oil
- fit the new oil seal

   The oil seal must be fitted with the sealing lip in the oil flow direction. To prevent install damage and leaks from skewed mounting, the seal must be evenly tapped into place with the appropriate sized seal installer (driver) tool.

Fig. 519 The oil seal lips must be lubricated according vehicle service information.

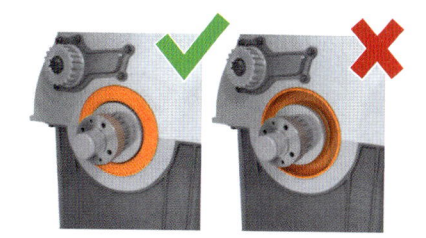

Fig. 520 Left: a correctly fitted oil seal; right: an incorrectly fitted oil seal.

Do not damage the seal lip when fitting a new oil seal. Some oil seals are prone to damage. These need to be fitted using a mounting ring. The oil seal is first slid onto the mounting ring backwards. The mounting ring is then placed against the axle and the oil seal can then be slid onto the axle.

No oil or grease may be used during the installation if the seal lip is made of Teflon (PTFE).

Fig. 521 Fitting an oil seal using a mounting ring.

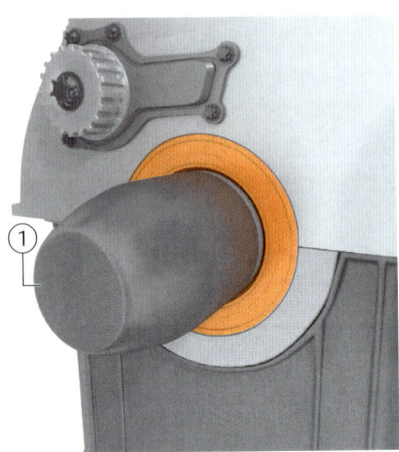

Fig. 522 Fitted using a mounting ring (1). In some cases, a mounting punch is used in addition to the mounting ring to spread the load across the oil seal.

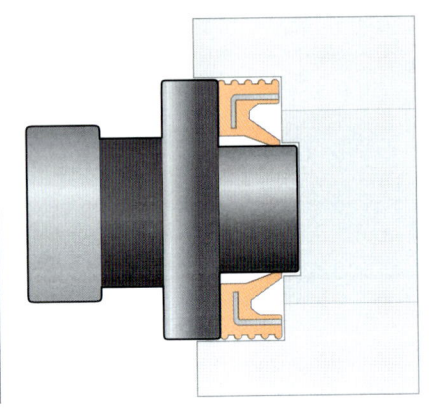

Fig. 523 Oil seal mounting punch.

7. Other Seals

Besides these oil gaskets and seals, the following seals are also important in preventing oil leaks and consumption:

- valve stem seals
  Restricts oil from passing from the cylinder head down the valve stems and into the combustion chamber.
- oil scraper ring
  Limits the amount of oil that gets past the piston and into the combustion chamber.
- drain plug sealing washer
  Prevents leaks from around the drain plug. During oil changing, the sealing washer should be replaced.
- oil filter
  A rubber square cut ring ensures sealing between the oil filter and engine block.

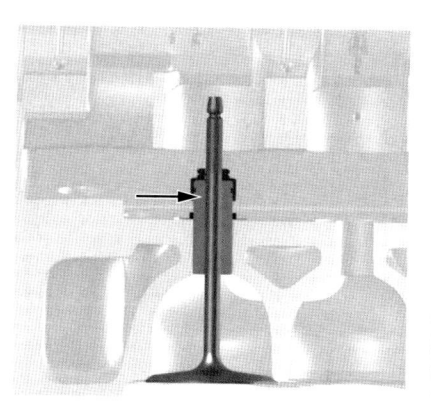

Fig. 524 Valve stem seal with a proper fitting seal: the valve stem seal is soft and flexible; there is barely any leakage near the valve stem.

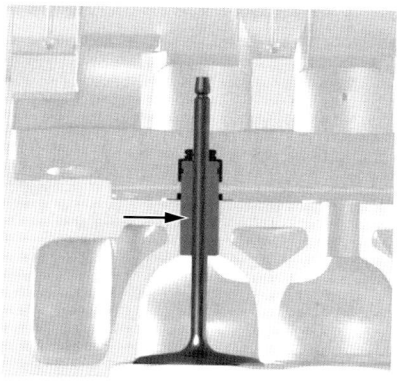

Fig. 525 Valve stem seal with a poor seal: the valve stem seal is hard and rigid; allowing leakage near the valve stem.

CRANKCASE VENTILATION

1. Introduction

Positive crankcase ventilation (PCV) is a system that vents crankcase vapors to the intake manifold.
These positive crankcase vapors, more commonly referred to as "blow-by gases", escape past the piston rings, and into the crankcase (area below the cylinders) during the combustion process.

A crankcase ventilation system may include:
- cyclone oil separator
- labyrinth oil separator
- pressure regulating valve

Blow-by gases mix with crankcase oil, causing eventual harm to the engine; as well as the environment, if ventilated to the outside air. Blow-by gases contain water vapor, gasoline vapor and combustion residues.

Fig. 526 Crankcase ventilation system: 1. Pressure control valve. 2. Labyrinth oil separator. 3. Cyclone oil separator.

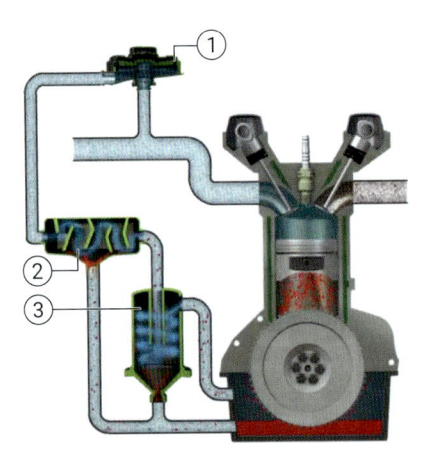

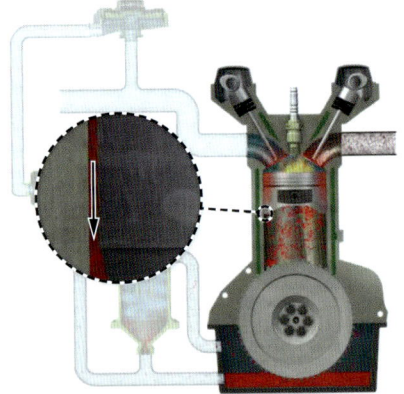

Fig. 527 Gases escape into the crankcase from between the piston and the cylinder walls.

2. Operation

A complete seal between cylinder wall and piston is impossible. The same goes for the valve guide seals. This causes combustion gases to escape into the crankcase while the engine is running.

Gases are drawn from the crankcase by a low pressure (vacuum) in the intake manifold.

If crankcase vapors are not vented, they can cause excess pressure in the crankcase. As a result, gaskets and seals will leak oil. This could even lead to a crankcase explosion.

Crankcase vapors flow through the *cyclone oil separator* to the *labyrinth oil separator.* After this, the crankcase vapors flow through the *pressure regulating valve (or) positive crankcase ventilation (PCV) valve* to the intake manifold.

3. Oil Separator

The oil separator prevents oil from being drawn into the intake duct through the crankcase ventilation system.

When the oil mist flows in the intake duct through the ventilation, the following parts can be contaminated or damaged:
- mass air flow sensor
- supercharger or turbo
- intake air cooler
- valves
- combustion chamber
- exhaust system including catalytic converter
- in diesel engines: the particulate filter

There are two types of oil separators, separate and combined:

- Cyclone separator
  The air is brought into a vortex, and oil is projected against the wall.
- Labyrinth separator
  Oil drops splash against the walls by the directional changes in the labyrinth.

Oil is then returned to the oil pan. Water and fuel vapors are allowed to pass into the intake duct.

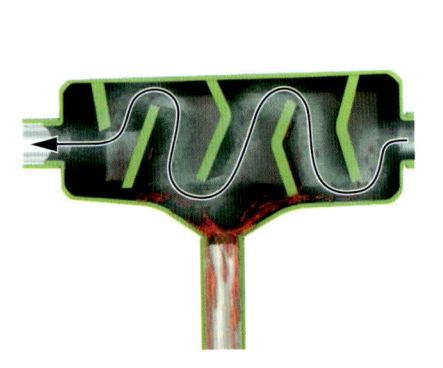

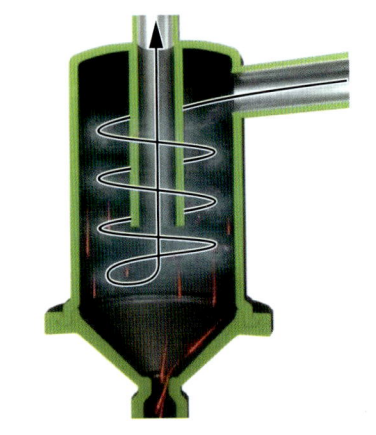

Fig. 528 Labyrinth oil separator.

Fig. 529 Cyclone oil separator.

4. Pressure Regulating Valve

The pressure regulating valve (or) positive crankcase ventilation (PCV) valve ensures a constant, low pressure (slight vacuum) in the crankcase. This is 0.29-0.44 PSI (0.02 - 0.03 bar) below the atmospheric pressure. The crankcase vapors flow towards the intake manifold.

There are two chambers in a pressure regulating valve:
— one chamber connected to the outside air
— one connected to the intake manifold

A pressure spring controls the pressure of the crankcase ventilation.

The valve closes when the pressure in the intake manifold decreases.

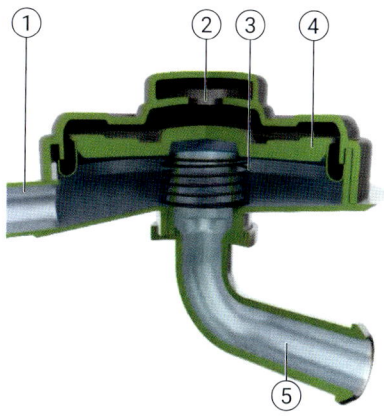

Fig. 530 Pressure control valve:
1. Oil separator connection.
2. Exterior air connection. 3. Spring.
4. Diaphragm. 5. Inlet manifold connection.

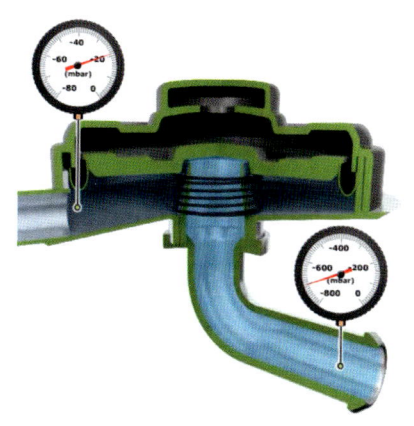

Fig. 531 Low pressure in the inlet manifold. The valve is closed.

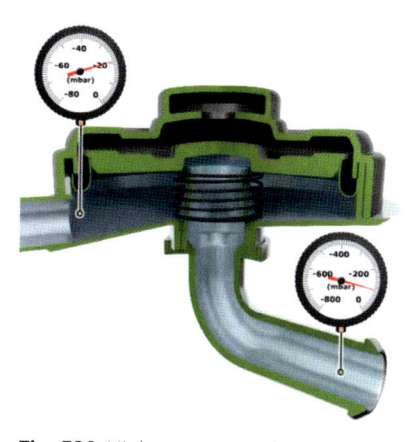

Fig. 532 High pressure in the inlet manifold. The valve is open.

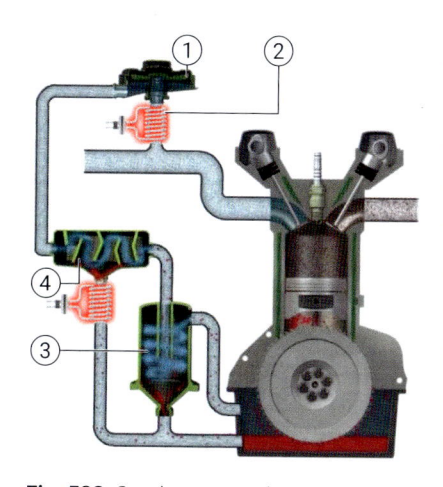

Fig. 533 Crankcase ventilation with possible locations for crankcase ventilation heating: 1. Pressure control valve. 2. Heating element. 3. Cyclone oil separator. 4. Labyrinth oil separator.

5. Heating Element Crankcase Ventilation

A limited amount of the combustion gases will end up in the crankcase blow-by gases. This includes moisture which may form condensation when it comes into contact with colder parts of the crankcase and in the crankcase ventilation system. This moisture may freeze during the winter, which may result in blockage. A heating element has been added to the crankcase ventilation system to prevent this. This electrical heating system is turned on based on the exterior temperature.

6. Crankcase Ventilation System Maintenance

Just like other parts of the engine, the crankcase ventilation system needs to be regularly maintained. The manufacturer's maintenance recommendations will contain information about when it needs to be inspected or cleaned.
The following items need to be inspected during servicing:
Blockages of the hoses and connections.
— Kinked or pinched hoses.
— Damaged or leaking hoses.
— The function of the system's valves.
— Flow and sealing in the right direction.
— Pollution of the strainers and filters.

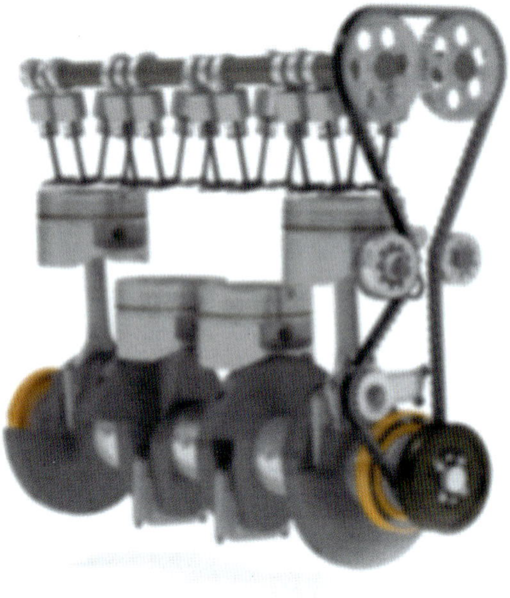

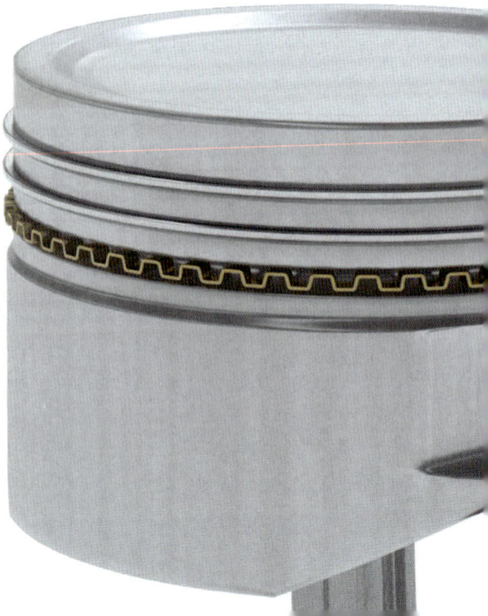

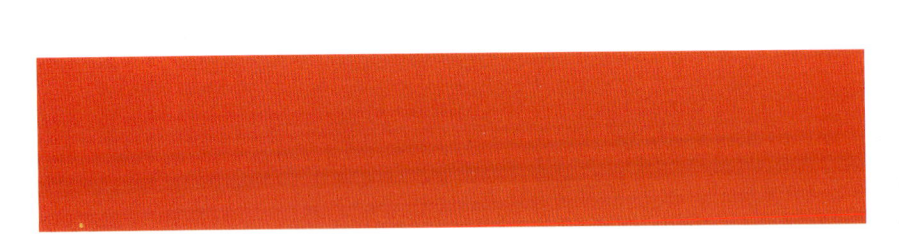

12. Lubrication System: Maintenance

CONTAMINATION OF THE LUBRICATION SYSTEM

1. Combustion Gases and Combustion Residues

Combustion gases which are formed in the combustion chamber are usually emitted via the exhaust valve. However, the seal between the piston and the cylinder is never optimal. This means that some of these gases also end up in the crankcase via the cylinder walls. These gases are known as blow-by gases.

The various components of blow-by gases can then pollute or degrade the oil. Examples include:

— Moisture.
— Hydrocarbons (unburned fuel).
— Soot, ash and carbon particles.
— Nitrogen oxides.

The hydrocarbons in blow-by gases may condense in the crankcase and become mixed with the oil. These unburned fuel residues may result in oil thinning. This reduces viscosity and may reduce the lubricating capacity.

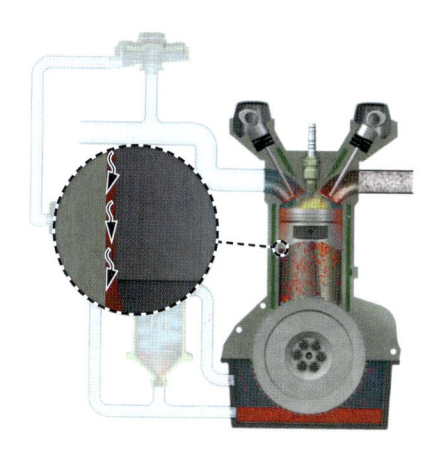

Fig. 534 Blow-by gases may leak between the piston and the cylinder walls.

2. White Sludge.

Another important component of combustion gases is moisture. This means that blow-by gases also contain moisture. Moisture which condenses as it comes into contact with the cold parts of the crankcase will become water (condensation). The water will remain in the crankcase and may become mixed with the oil if the engine does not reach operating temperature. When oil mixes with water a white substance is created which is known as "white sludge". It is also known as "mayonnaise". The first place white sludge is often encountered is on the bottom of the oil cap. This is often a sign there is more in the engine itself. Parts of the crankcase ventilation may become contaminated and clogged as a result.

The water in the white sludge may also result in parts of the engine starting to rust.

3. Black Sludge

Another type of engine oil pollution is caused by long-term exposure to high temperatures. The oil may start to oxidize as a result, which can result in extreme thickening. The thick black substance which forms deposits in the crankcase and the cylinder head are known as "black sludge".

The risk of black sludge increases if oil is not changed at regular intervals. The oil will age, and absorbed soot and ash particles will result in the oil not being able to absorb any other fine particles. The oil is saturated and its lubricating properties are reduced.

Oil channels may become blocked due to the build-up of black sludge, which means that oil cannot access all the engine parts. The oil strainer in the oil pump may also become clogged. This means the oil pump is not able to draw in enough oil, which will result in the oil pressure being too low.

Minor pollution can be resolved by cleaning the engine using a special cleanser which is added to the oil before it is drained. In more serious cases, the crankcase and the cylinder head cover will need to be addressed. The engine internals will then need to be cleaned thoroughly.

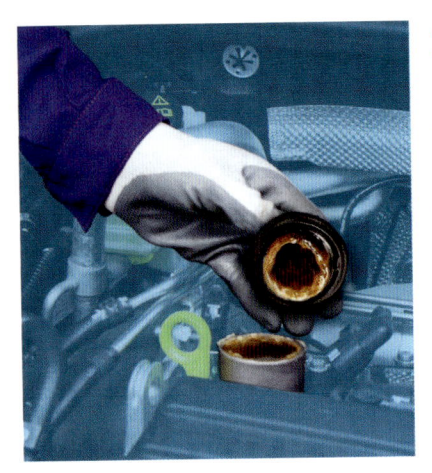

Fig. 535 White Sludge.

Fig. 536 Black Sludge

CHANGING OIL

1. Introduction

The engine oil change interval is specified by the vehicle manufacturer. In between changes, you should check the oil level regularly.

Before beginning an oil change, check to ensure that you have all necessary parts and tools to complete the job.

When draining the engine oil, it's important that the car remain level. This is so the used oil can quickly and completely drain out of the engine.
Used oil can cause serious harm to the environment; therefore, never dump used oil down the drain, or onto the ground. Used oil must be properly stored in an above ground waste container and processed by waste oil recycler.

Oil filling is done via the oil filler cap. You can usually recognize the filler cap by the "oil can" symbol. When you're finished filling the engine with new oil, check the lubrication system for external leaks.

Fig. 537 Combustion engine

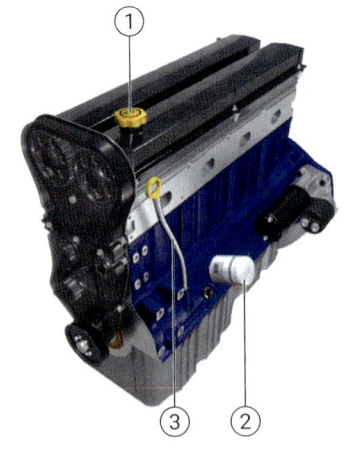

Fig. 538 Oil change components: 1. Oil cap. 2. Oil filter. 3. Dipstick.

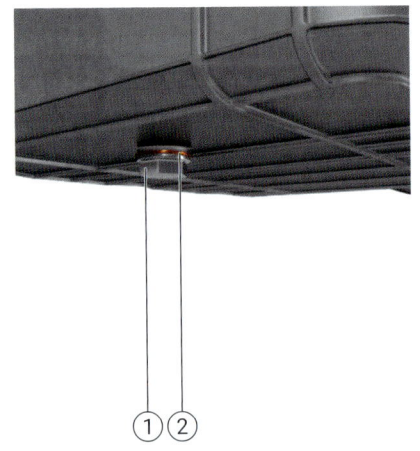

Fig. 539 Oil pan: 1. Oil pan plug. 2. Oil pan plug ring.

2. Step-by-Step Plan

Changing the oil is accomplished most efficiently by following a step-by-step plan. Following a plan helps to avoid costly mistakes.

Follow these steps in order:

1. Remove
2. Install
3. Fill-up

Removing
1. Warm up the engine.
2. Switch off the engine.
3. Remove the oil cap.
4. Position the oil drain pan.
5. Remove the oil pan plug.
6. Remove the oil filter with a special tool.
Installing
7. Replace the oil filter.
8. Lubricate the oil filter ring.
9. Fit and tighten the oil filter by hand.
10. Replace the oil pan plug sealing washer.
11. Refit the oil pan plug with a torque wrench.
Fill-up
12. Top up the oil.
13. Refit the oil cap.
14. Leave the engine idling.
15. Check the oil level.
16. Remove the oil drain pan.

Fig. 540 Step-by-step oil change procedures.

3. Removing

Begin with draining the used oil.

First warm-up the engine.

- Oil gets thinner as it warms-up; allowing it to quickly and completely drain out of the engine.
- Dirt dissolves in oil and will be removed from the engine along with the used oil.

Before draining oil, take measures to ensure used oil won't get onto your hands or run down your arm. Always wear safety glasses to protect your eyes!

After taking the appropriate safety measures, you may remove the oil filler cap, drain the used oil and remove the oil filter.

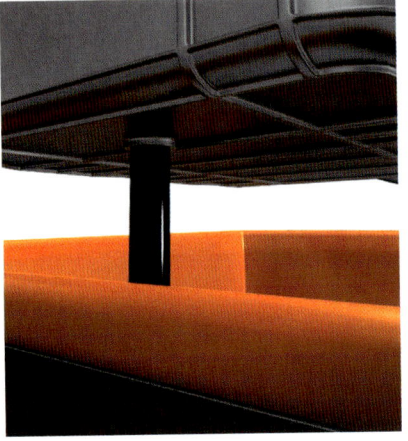

Fig. 541 Remove the oil cap.

Fig. 542 Remove the oil pan plug.

4. Installing

Now that you've disassembled everything, you can reinstall the drain plug and install a new oil filter. You should also replace the drain plug gasket to prevent leakage.

You must install the drain plug using the specified torque, to avoid damaging the screw threads.

Lubricate the rubber sealing ring of the new filter with clean engine oil. Use a clean rag to wipe away used oil and debris from the oil filter adapter sealing surface. Then install and tighten the new filter by hand. Don't use an oil filter wrench to tighten the new filter. This can cause over-tightening, making the filter difficult to remove at the next service.

12. LUBRICATION SYSTEM: MAINTENANCE

Fig. 543 Install the oil filter. Lubricate the rubber ring with oil.

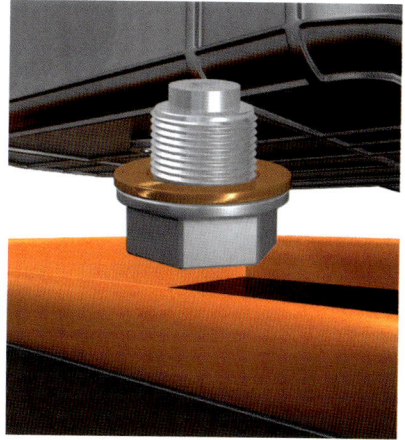

Fig. 544 New oil pan plug ring installed.

5. Fill-up

Next, you need to refill the oil and to check the oil level. Too much engine oil can lead to permanent engine damage.

To know how much oil the engine needs, check the vehicle service information. Below are the details of this engine.

Vehicle Service Information:
- Oil without filter: 4 Quarts (3.75 liters)
- Oil with filter: 4.5 Quarts (4.25 liters)
- Oil viscosity: SAE 5W-30
- Oil pressure at 2000 rpm: 36 PSI (2.5 bar)

Fig. 545 Add oil until the amount specified by the manufacturer has been reached.

Fig. 546 Check the oil level using the dipstick. The oil should reach the upper line.

Oil level lower than the maximum level.

Engine oil is primarily intended for lubrication, however it also has a cooling function. The oil flows through the engine and absorbs heat. Most of this heat is released into the ambient air:
— Via the air which flows past the oil pan.
— Via an oil cooler if one is present.

As an example, a total of 4 quarts of oil may be present if the oil level is at its maximum level. And a total of 3 quarts of oil may be present, for example, if the oil level is at its minimum level.

Oil spends less time in the oil pan if the oil level is low. This means that the oil will not be able to emit as much heat. The oil may overheat if the engine load is heavy. This is why oil levels should be checked more often if there is a heavy load on the engine. Make sure that the oil level remains at its maximum level if this is the case. The oil will absorb less engine heat if the oil cannot release its own heat. The engine temperature may increase as a result.

Oil level higher than the maximum level.
Attention!
Never add too much engine oil!

An excessively high oil level can also have negative effects, like:
— Foaming caused by the crankshaft churning the oil. Foam contains air, which weakens the oil film.
— More oil is splattered against the cylinder walls. This increases oil consumption.
— Power is also lost because of the crankshaft churning the oil.
— Oil leakage may occur because more oil comes into contact with the oil seal.
— Oil may flow into the intake sector via the crankcase ventilation. This results in contamination in both the intake ports and the intake valves.
— Diesel engines, where oil flows into the combustion chambers via the intake ports and crankcase ventilation, may run out of control. This is then used as additional fuel. The engine's rotational speed will run at an uncontrolled rate and will no longer be able to be turned off normally. This may result in irreparable engine damage.

Fig. 547 The use of long life oil is identified using a sticker.

6. Replacement Interval

The oil replacement interval depends on a number of things.

First, aging of the oil needs to be taken into consideration. Oil quality decreases due to oxidation. This process takes place even if a car is not used very often or if it is never used. Aging can be slowed down by the use of oil additives, like anti-oxidants, but it can never be completely halted.

The other factors are self-explanatory and depend on how a vehicle is used:
— The amount of mileage put on the vehicle in a year.
— Whether or not the engine regularly reaches operating temperature when in use.

The vehicle manufacturer will specify a replacement interval for each type of vehicle. It is based on standard usage. Example: Approximately 7,000 miles per year when the engine regularly reaches normal operating temperature.

The replacement interval needs to be adjusted if the car usage differs. If only a couple of thousand miles are driven each year, for example. The oil will need to be changed once a year if this is the case.

Long Life Oil

Long life oil is a special type of oil which is becoming more prevalent. The composition of this oil means that it does not need to be replaced as often. Long life oil does not age as quickly and does not become contaminated with dirt and wear particles as quickly either. A sticker in the engine area is often used to indicate whether or not long life oil has been used. Make sure the oil filter can also be used for longer periods of time if long life oil is being used. The reason being that the oil filter will need to store and filter dirt and wear particles for longer.

CHECKING OIL LEVEL

1. Task

It's important to check the oil level on a regular basis.

An insufficient amount of oil can lead to permanent engine damage. The lubricating, cooling and cleaning qualities of oil diminish over time; even more so if the oil level remains low.

Too much oil can also lead to problems, such as foaming. Foaming results when the oil level reaches or surpasses the level of the crankshaft in the block. When this happens the throws of the crankshaft beat against the oil like an egg beater, causing aeration of the oil. This action raises pressure in the crankcase and may even force oil past seals and gaskets.

Overfilling can also lead to extra oil being drawn into the intake manifold through the crankcase breather tube. Diesel engines are especially prone to what is referred to as 'stampeding' or 'runaway'. This is when oil drawn into the engine acts as fuel, causing the engine to rev uncontrollably.

When adding oil, it is important to use the right grade of oil. The owners manual or vehicle service information specifies the correct grade of oil for the specific application.

2. Dipstick

The dipstick is easily identified by a bright color; also it usually has a ring-like grip.

A dipstick has two marks on it:
— a 'minimum' mark
— a 'maximum' mark

The correct level of oil is anywhere between these two marks. When adding oil, aim for a level just beneath the 'maximum' mark.

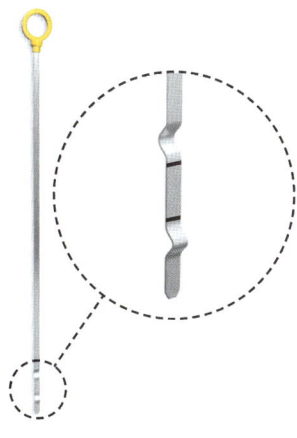

Fig. 548 Dipstick. The top line indicates the maximum level and the bottom line indicates the minimum level.

Usually, the difference in volume between the two marks is 1 quart/liter.

3. Checking Oil Level

There are a few guidelines you must follow when checking the oil level:
— Shut the engine off and wait at least 10 minutes, so the oil can fully drain into the oil pan.
— The car should be parked on a level surface.

Checking the oil level should be done this way:
— Take out the dipstick.
— Clean the dipstick.
— Insert the dipstick fully.
— Take the dipstick out.
— Read the level.

If there's an insufficient amount of oil, more should be added. Before you take another reading, wait a couple minutes to allow the newly added oil to fully drain into the oil pan.

Avoid spilling oil, as high temperatures might cause the spilled oil to smoke or even catch fire. Also, spilled oil can cause certain rubber parts and hoses to swell and disintegrate over time.

Fig. 549 Remove the dipstick.

Fig. 550 Wipe the dipstick clean.

Fig. 551 Read the dipstick and determine the oil level. The oil level is halfway along the dipstick. This means that at least 0.5 quarts of oil needs to be added.

OIL LEVEL SENSOR

Fig. 552 1. Oil level sensor.

1. Task

An oil level indicator is used to warn the driver when the oil level is too low.

The device for monitoring oil level is located at the bottom or side of the oil pan.

There are two ways that the oil level can be monitored:
— oil level switch
— oil level sensor

2. Oil Level Switch

An oil level switch has two positions:
— Open: oil level OK.
— Closed: oil level is too low.

There are two types of level switches:

— **Reed contact**
  If the oil level is below the minimum level, a magnet activates the reed contact; the electric circuit is closed.

— **Electrical conductivity**
  The operation of this switch is based on the electrical conductivity of a liquid.

Two electrodes are fixed at minimum oil level. When the oil level drops below the electrodes, then the resistance between the contacts becomes infinitely high. This is because air is a poor electrical conductor.

An amplifier circuit within the switch assembly generates an identifiable signal for the ECU.

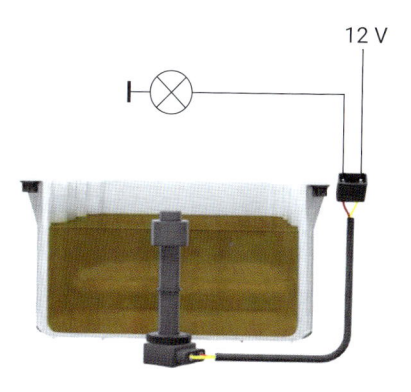

Fig. 553 Oil level sensor with reed switch: the float with the magnet floats on the oil and is at a sufficient level. The reed switch is not operational; therefore the warning light is switched off.

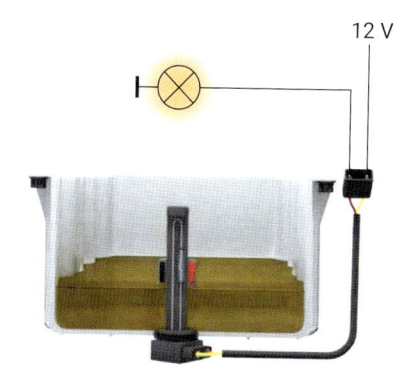

Fig. 554 Oil level sensor with reed switch: the oil level is low; the magnet comes into contact with the reed switch. The reed switch is now operational and the warning light is switched on.

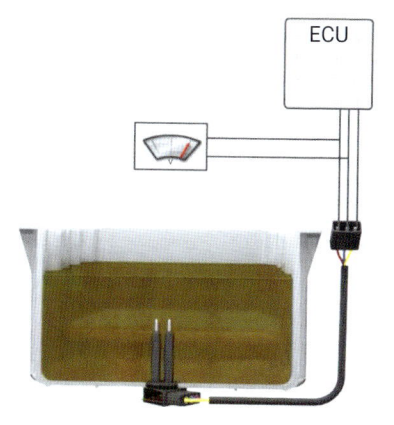

Fig. 555 Oil level sensor, electrical conductors: the oil level is high, the resistance between the electrodes is low.

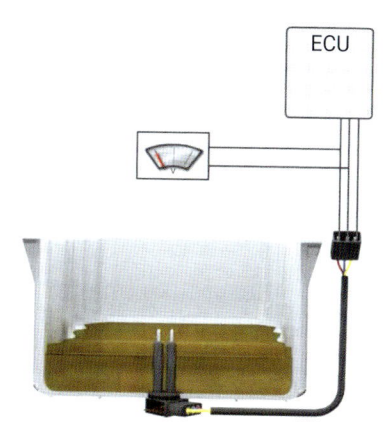

Fig. 556 Oil level sensor, electrical conductors: the oil level is low, the resistance between the electrodes is high.

3. Oil Level Sensor

An oil level sensor not only detects when the level is too low; it can determine the actual oil level.

The oil level can be determined with the following types of sensor:
- potentiometer
- inductive
- capacitive
- electro-thermal

OIL QUALITY SENSOR

Fig. 562 Oil Quality Sensor

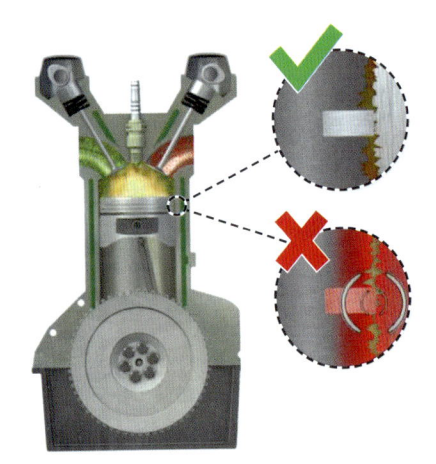

Fig. 563 Difference between friction in moving parts with good and poor oil quality.

1. Task

An oil quality sensor measures the oil quality. The engine control unit uses this information to help determine the service interval. The driver receives this information via the instrument panel display.

Oil temperature and oil level are often determined via this sensor.

This sensor is usually mounted at the bottom of the oil pan.

2. Oil Quality

Poor oil quality results in more friction between moving parts. This leads to the generation of heat and wear, eventually leading to permanent engine damage.

Poor quality oil does not seal as well between the piston and cylinder wall, resulting in more oil entering the combustion chamber; contributing to greater oil consumption. Because of the poor seal, more combustion gases enter the crankcase. Increased friction between moving parts can also result in mechanical noise.

Advantages of having an oil quality sensor are:
- Less risk of engine damage.
- You get the maximum service life out of the oil.
- Lower maintenance costs.
- Less waste oil to deal with is better for the environment.

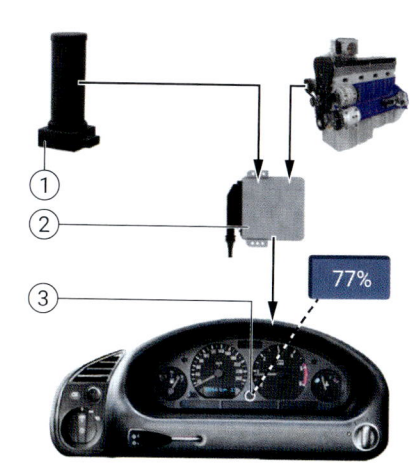

Fig. 564 Information processing oil quality monitoring: 1. Oil quality sensor. 2. Control unit. 3. Information display.

3. Information

An oil quality sensor determines the following data:
- oil level.
- oil temperature.
- viscosity.

Additional factors that influence the oil quality:
- engine load.
- engine speed.
- number of cold starts.
- amount of driving time.

The data is processed by the engine control unit, so that the oil quality can be calculated.

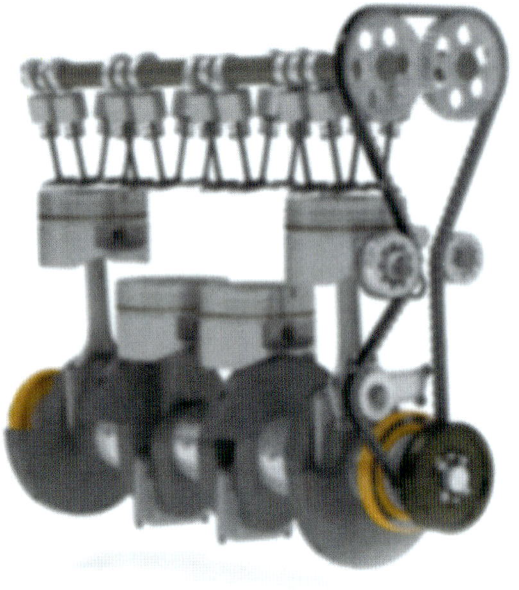

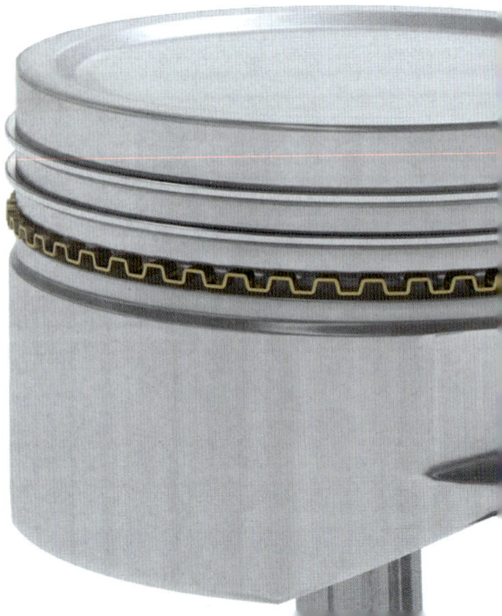

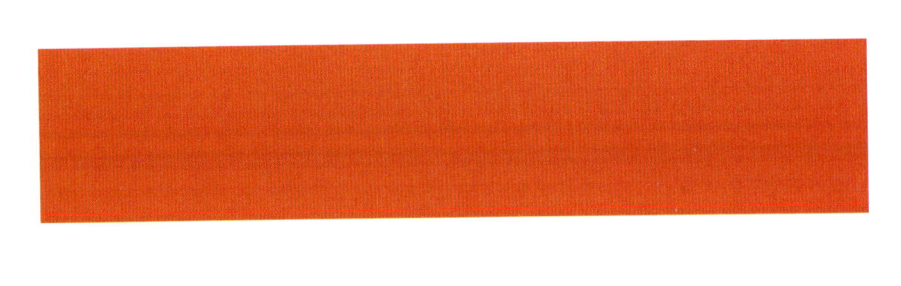

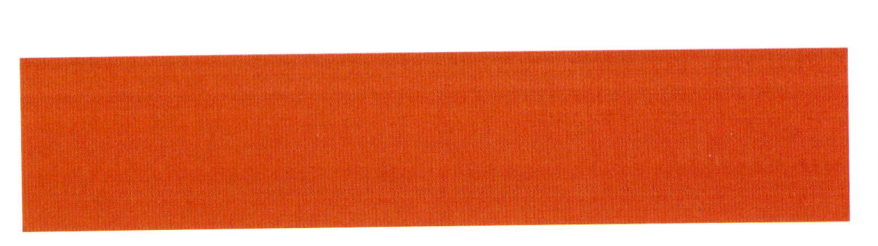

13. Lubrication System: Diagnostics

OIL LOSS

Fig. 567 Oil Loss

1. Oil Loss

An internal combustion engine will always use a slight amount of lubricating oil. In fact, up to one quart for every 3,000 miles is considered normal by some manufacturers like Ford, GM, and BMW. They actually consider a quart every 1000 miles not to be a problem.

Substantial oil loss can occur due to external leaks or when too much oil finds its way into the combustion chamber where it is burned, causing the exhaust to appear blue at times.

2. Oil Leakage

If there's a problem with either a gasket or oil seal, the engine will leak oil.

Common places where oil leaks can occur:
— The oil drain plug
— Valve cover and oil pan gaskets
— Piston oil rings

- The oil filter
- The oil pressure sensor

Leakage occurs in the following situations:

- When gaskets or seals become hard and brittle from age
- When sealing surfaces become warped or damaged
- When gaskets and oil seals are improperly installed
- When gaskets are reused

External oil leaks are often clearly visible; they can be found accumulating on the outside of the engine or dripping from the engine onto the ground. Serious leaks, of course, will cause the oil level to drop.

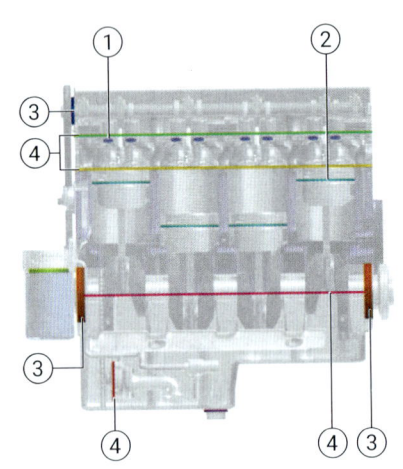

Fig. 568 Seals: 1. Valve stem seals. 2. Piston oil ring. 3. Oil seals. 4. Gaskets.

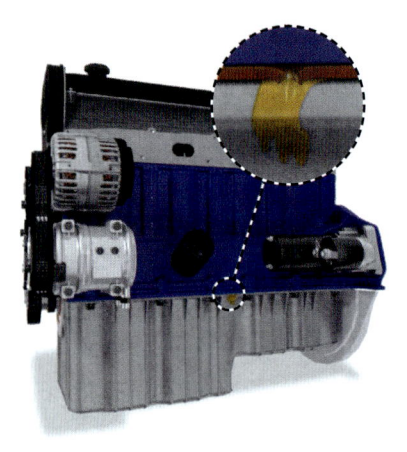

Fig. 569 Example of external oil loss: oil leakage between oil pan and engine block.

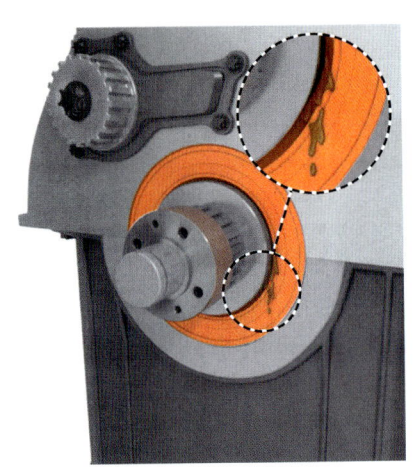

Fig. 570 Example of external oil loss: oil leakage at the crankshaft oil seal.

3. Internal Leakage

Examples of hard to find internal oil leaks:
- A small crack or tear in the head gasket between lubricating oil and coolant passage
- Oil finding its way into the coolant via a leaking oil cooler in the radiator tank

In these cases lubricating oil will be found mixed with the coolant.

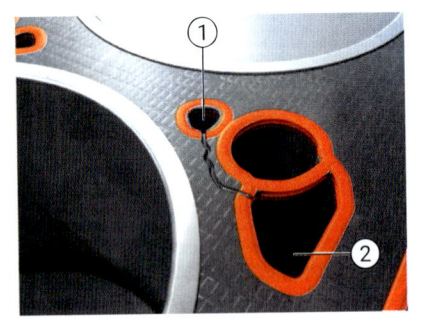

Fig. 571 Example of internal oil loss oil leakage between. 1. Oil gallery and. 2. Coolant passages.

4. Oil Consumption

Sometimes the engine oil is lost in spite of having no visible signs of leakage. This is because oil can enter the combustion chamber where it is burned and lost through the exhaust.

When oil finds its way into the combustion chamber, the source is usually one of the following:
- Worn valve stem seals:
  Lubricating oil enters the combustion chamber through the valve stems.
- Worn piston oil rings:
  Lubricating oil can enter the combustion chamber along the sides of the pistons.
- Defective head gasket:
  There's a small crack in the gasket around the oil passages.
- Crankcase ventilation:
  PCV valve is defective, and oil is drawn into the intake manifold.

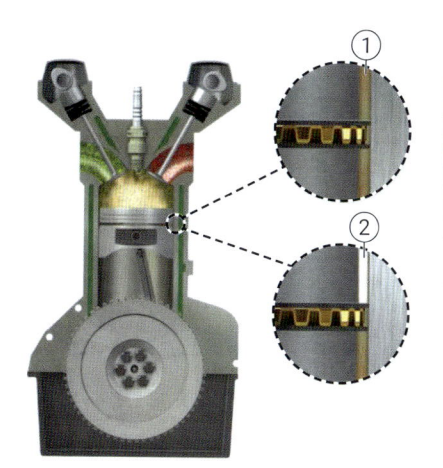

Fig. 572 Internal oil loss: 1. Worn out piston rings cause a lot of leakage of lubricating oil. The lubricating oil then burns in the combustion chamber. 2. There's a normal amount of oil along the piston oil ring; this allows normal oil consumption.

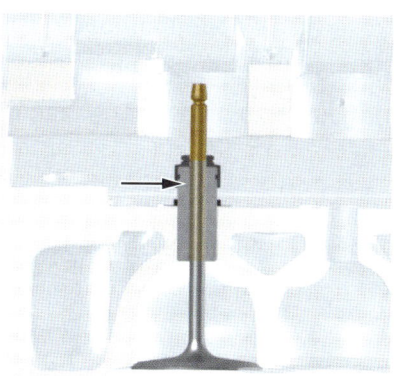

Fig. 573 Valve stem seal with a proper seal: valve stem seal is soft and smooth; there's little leakage along the valve stem.

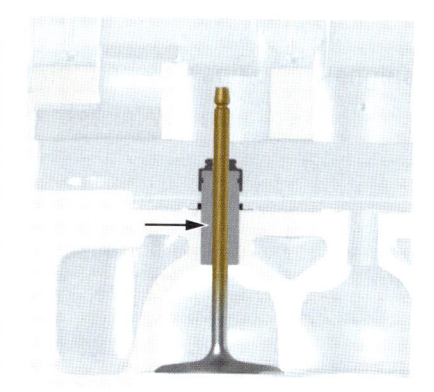

Fig. 574 Valve stem seal with a worn seal: valve stem seal is hard and rigid; there's a lot of leakage along the valve stem.

Another cause of oil consumption may lie with the crankcase ventilation.

When it is clogged, the pressure in the crankcase may rise too high. Oil can then be forced out through oil seals and gaskets.

If the crankcase ventilation is too easy to pass through, there is a risk that too much oil mist will enter the intake manifold. An improperly closing pressure regulating valve or a defective PCV valve could be the cause of this. If the PCV valve is clogged, crankcase pressure will force-feed oil mist through the closure/vent tube into the intake system between the air filter and the throttle body. The oil mist is drawn in by the intake manifold vacuum and then burned in the combustion chamber.

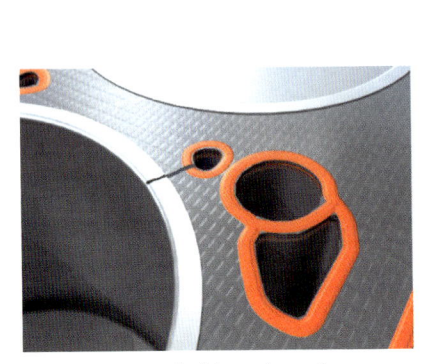

Fig. 575 Internal oil loss: from the oil passages to the combustion chamber.

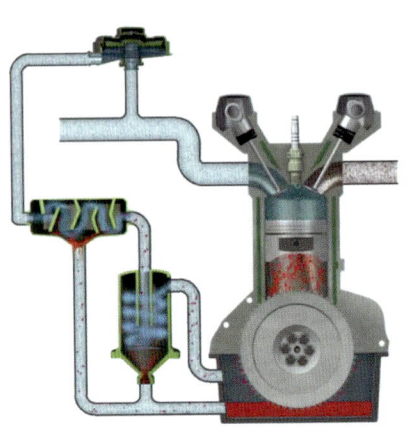

Fig. 576 A defect in the crankcase ventilation system can also cause oil consumption or leakage.

5. Worn Piston Rings

When cylinder walls and piston rings wear, this can lead to increased oil consumption. The piston oil ring normally removes the excess oil from the cylinder wall. When the piston rings wear, they typically wear where they contact the cylinder wall, which affects compression. This kind of wear increases the "end gap" measurement.

When the piston itself wears, the piston rings will become loose in their grooves, which allows the rings to move up and down in the piston ring grooves. This causes a pumping effect. The oil then moves upwards along the piston rings to the combustion chamber.

Fig. 577 The pumping action of piston rings that have too much play.

6. Seized Piston Rings

Piston rings can also get stuck in the piston ring grooves for various reasons. When this happens, they are not pressing firmly enough against the cylinder walls. This will allow too much oil to remain behind after the piston has completed a stroke. This results in oil entering the combustion chambers where it is lost in the burning of the fuel mixture.

7. Worn Crankshaft or Connecting Rod Bearings

When wear causes the clearance between the crankshaft journals and the bearings to become too great, oil will flow out between them. This will cause a loss of oil pressure, and this lost oil will also spray against the cylinder wall. The piston oil rings cannot handle this extra oil, so they do not properly remove it from the cylinder walls. This oil may now enter the combustion chamber and be lost during the combustion. The cam bearings can wear and cause oil pressure loss as well.

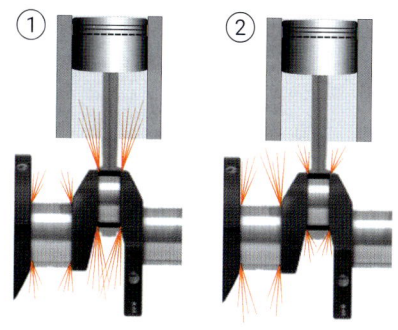

Fig. 578 Excessive play of the crankshaft (2) and connecting rod bearings (1) can result in increased oil consumption.

OIL PRESSURE

1. Excessively Low Oil Pressure

The engine's lubrication system is controlled by the oil pump. The oil pressure may become excessively low due to a variety of reasons and may even be lost entirely. In many cases, the oil pressure warning light on the instrument panel will only light up once it is too late. This means oil pressure has been lost or nearly completely lost. An oil pressure gauge is needed to keep a better eye on the oil pressure. It is possible to connect an external oil pressure gauge to check the oil pressure value if you have any concerns.

Some components may not receive sufficient lubrication if the oil pressure is too low. Insufficient lubrication may result in engine damage.

Oil Level Too Low

There is insufficient oil near the suction inlet pipe when the oil level is too low; this means the oil pump is not able to draw in sufficient oil. The oil pump will also draw in air; oil pressure will drop and there will not be sufficient lubrication.

Contaminated Oil Strainer

The oil pump draws in oil from the oil pan via a strainer. A contaminated strainer will result in insufficient oil being drawn in; as a result, the oil pump will not be able to build up enough pressure.

Worn Out Oil Pump

The oil pump's gears can also wear out; this may, for example, result in there being too much room between the gears and the housing. This will cause internal leakage in the oil pump. The oil pump's yield will drop as a result and insufficient pressure will build up.

Pressure Relief Valve

The pressure relief valve ensures the oil pressure in the lubrication system does not get too high. The valve will open when the predetermined maximum pressure level has been reached and the

Fig. 579 A worn out oil pump will have internal leakage, and as a result, a lower yield.

excess oil will be drained into the oil pan. The oil pressure can also remain too low if this valve is malfunctioning.

- If the resilience of the spring in the valve is too low, then the valve will open even when the pressure is low.
- The valve spring may be broken; this will result in the valve opening even when the pressure is low.
- Contamination may result in the valve not closing properly or even remaining fully open.

Oil Filter

Resistance is increased if the oil filter is excessively contaminated. It becomes increasingly difficult for the oil pump to pump oil through the filter. The bypass valve will be opened and unfiltered oil will be pumped through the engine if the pressure in the oil filter becomes too high. The oil pressure in the section located between the pump and the filter will be adjusted to the maximum level by the pressure relief valve if it fails to open.

However, the rest of the lubrication system, located behind the oil filter, will receive too little oil and the oil pressure in this area will also be too low.

Worn Bearings

Worn bearings may be one of the causes of excessively low oil pressure. The bearings in the crankshaft and the connecting rods are lubricated by the oil pump. Excessive clearance between the bearings may result in the oil passing through the bearings too easily. As a result, the oil pump is not able to build up sufficient pressure.

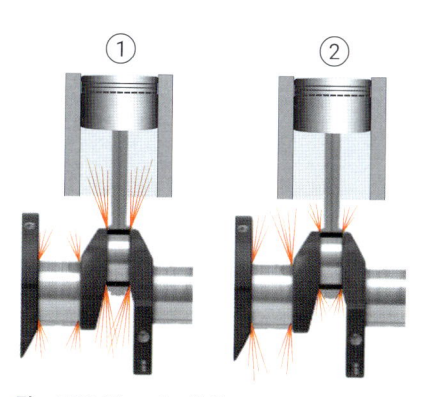

Fig. 580 The oil will flow out from between the bearings if they are worn: 1. Connecting rod bearings with excessive clearance. 2. Crankshaft bearings with excessive clearance.

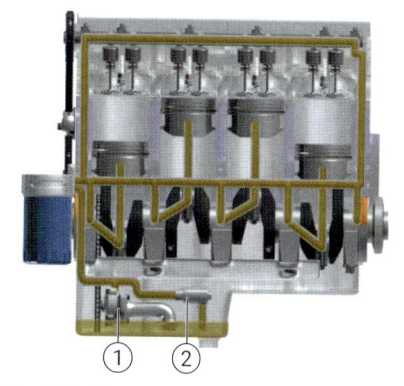

Fig. 581 The pressure relief valve (2) controls the oil pressure in the oil pump (1). The lubrication system will not receive sufficient oil if it does not close.

Excessively Thin Oil

An engine is designed to be compatible with a certain type of oil. If the oil is too thin, it can flow between the bearings too easily, which means too little pressure is built up in the lubrication system.

2. Excessively High Oil Pressure

The pressure in the lubrication system may also become too high. However, the oil pressure warning light in the instrument panel will not indicate this. The only way to see if the oil pressure is too high is to use an oil pressure gauge.

Pressure Relief Valve

The pressure relief valve is intended to ensure the oil pressure cannot become excessively high. The excess oil which has been drawn in will be released back into the oil pan via this valve. Oil pressure may become too high if this valve is stuck. In particular, the oil pump will pump too much oil into the lubrication system at high rotational speeds. This results in excessively high oil pressure if the excess oil is not drained back into the oil pan.

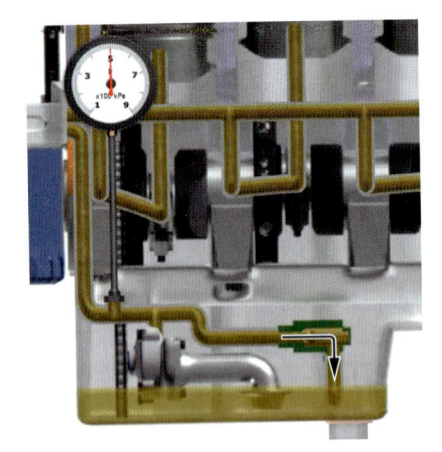

Fig. 582 The pressure relief valve draws the excess oil back into the oil pan so that the pressure does not become excessively high.

OIL TEMPERATURE

1. Excessively High Temperature

The temperature of the lubricating oil may become excessively high for a number of different reasons. As a result, the oil's viscosity may become excessively low. Oil which is too hot will result in an excessively thin film which is not able to sufficiently lubricate the bearings. The metal components will come into contact with each other if the lubricating film breaks down; this will result in extra wear and may even result in damage.
Consistently high oil temperatures will result in premature oil aging which means it will oxidize and thicken more rapidly.

Excessively High Engine Load

A lot of heat is produced by certain parts, like the pistons and the cylinder head, if the engine is exposed to high loads. Some of this heat is absorbed by the oil. The oil will not be able to sufficiently dispose of the heat, and the oil temperature will rise if the engine is exposed to excessively high loads for a long period of time.

Oil Cooler

A poorly functioning oil cooler may result in excessively high oil temperatures.
In an air-cooled oil cooler the fins may become contaminated, which will cause insufficient air to be passed through them.
A heat exchanger cools the oil using a coolant. Contamination or a blockage of the cooling system may result in insufficient coolant being able to pass through it. This means insufficient amounts of heat from the oil will be absorbed, which will result in increasingly high oil temperatures.

Oil Level Too Low

The oil in the oil pan is circulated by the lubrication system. The oil absorbs heat from the various parts it passes through during this process. Oil is cooled in the oil pan once it flows back into it. The oil pan is cooled by the air which passes underneath the engine while it is running. The oil will receive additional cooling if an oil cooler has been installed.

The lower the level of oil in the oil pan, the more often the entire contents will pass through the lubrication system. As a result, the oil will receive less time to cool down in the oil pan. The oil temperature may become excessively high if the oil level is lower than the maximum recommended amount. This is especially the case if the engine is exposed to a heavy load and when the exterior temperature is high.

Fig. 583 Make sure the oil level is at the maximum recommended amount to prevent high oil temperatures.

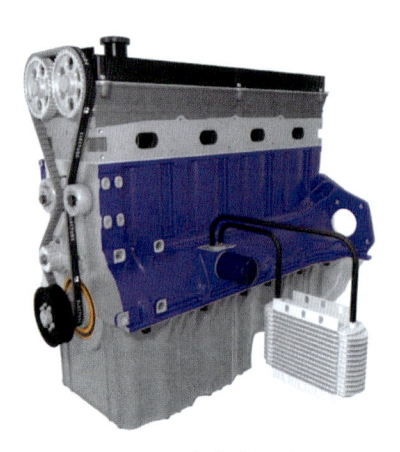

Fig. 584 An air-cooled oil cooler may become contaminated; as a result, it may not be able to dispose of sufficient amounts of heat.

2. Excessively Low Oil Temperature

It is important to ensure the oil regularly reaches operating temperature. Cold oil has higher viscosity and is therefore harder to circulate. There is also a risk that cold oil will not be able to sufficiently lubricate all the different components. This is why you should not immediately put a heavy load on a cold engine.

A cold engine may also result in condensation forming in the crankcase. This is moisture from the blow-by gases which condenses against the cold parts of the engine block. This water may become mixed with the lubricating oil. Once the engine reaches operating temperature, this moisture will disappear from the oil. The engine and the oil will not reach operating levels if the vehicle is frequently used for short trips. This will result in higher water levels in the oil, which will in turn reduce the oil's lubricating capacity. It may also result in white sludge. White sludge can often be found on the bottom of the oil cap. White sludge may cause blockages in, for example, the crankcase ventilation system.

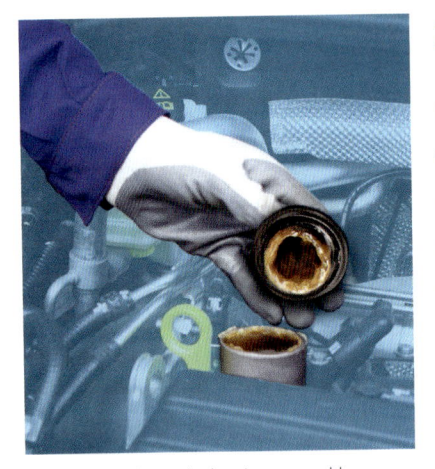

Fig. 585 White sludge is caused by water in the lubricating oil.

Additionally, the water in the oil may result in engine parts becoming rusty.

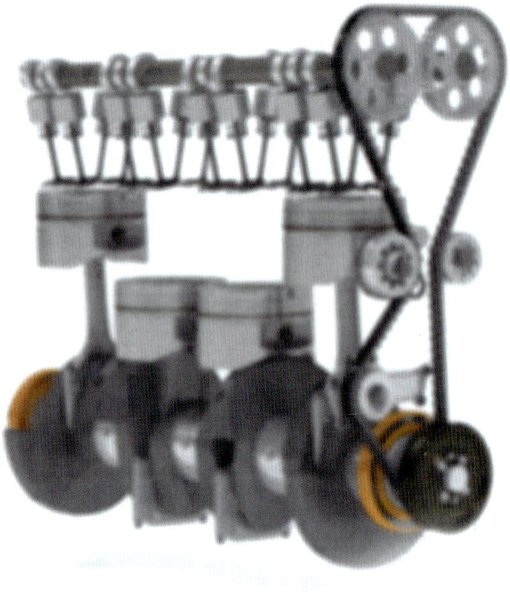

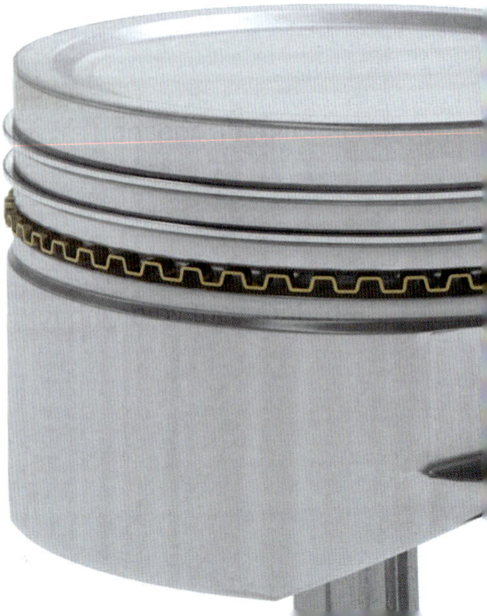

14. Cooling System: Fundamentals

HEAT BALANCE

1. Introduction

Fuel is burned in the engine. This creates a lot of heat. The cooling system dissipates this heat.

The optimum temperature for an engine is called the operating temperature. The cooling system ensures that the engine reaches this temperature as quickly as possible and remains at this temperature during operation.

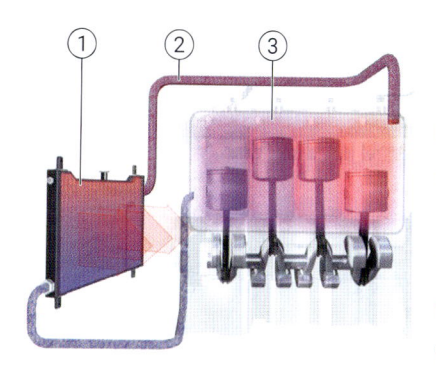

Fig. 586 Cooling system: 1. Radiator. 2. Coolant. 3. Engine block.

2. Necessary Cooling

Cooling is necessary:
— to prevent the engine from overheating
— to achieve proper combustion
— to guarantee proper lubrication at all times

If there is excessive cooling, the engine will not reach operating temperature.

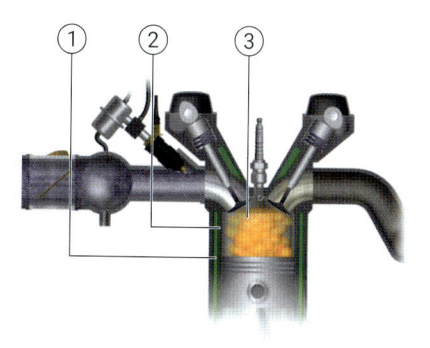

Fig. 587 Engine cooling: 1. Coolant. 2. Cylinder wall. 3. Combustion.

Excessive cooling causes:
- higher fuel consumption
- condensation of fuel
- engine oil contamination

SANKEY DIAGRAM: POWER LOSS

There are many losses in an engine. Only a small portion of the energy of the fuel goes toward driving the vehicle.

The Sankey diagram shows that only a fraction of the total (100%) energy is used to drive the vehicle.

There is namely:
- 33% exhaust loss
- 29% cooling loss
- 5% radiation loss
- 5% mechanical loss

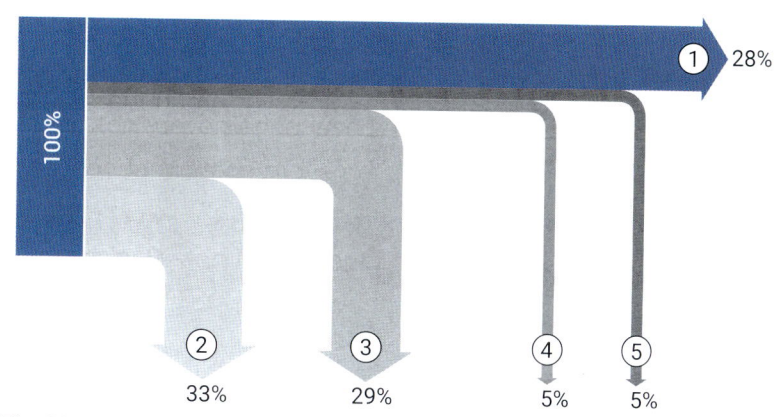

Fig. 588 Causes of energy loss: 1. Propelling the vehicle. 2. Exhaust heat loss. 3. Cooling system heat loss. 4. Radiation heat loss. 5. Mechanical losses.

The exhaust, cooling, and radiation losses are in the form of heat energy. Mechanical energy loss is caused by friction between mechanical parts. The output will then be used for propulsion.

COOLING SYSTEMS

Fig. 589 Air Cooling

1. Air Cooling

Outside air flows around the engine. Engine heat is carried away by the air stream.

The cylinder block and cylinder head have thin metal fins to help transfer heat to the air.
This improves the cooling efficiency of the engine.

For cooling airflow to properly carry the engine heat away, the spaces between the cooling fins must be free of dust, dirt, grease, grass, or any other obstruction.

Advantages of air cooling:
— Less maintenance on the engine is required.
— Engine reaches operating temperature faster than liquid cooling.

2. Forced Air Cooling

The hot engine is cooled by the air flow of an electric fan or blower.

Advantages of air cooling:
— Less engine maintenance is required.
— The engine quickly warms to operating temperature. Direct cooling transfers heat from the engine directly to the outside air flow.

Forced air cooling has more cooling ability when there is no outside air flow.

Fig. 590 Forced Air Cooling

3. Oil Cooling

Oil is also used to help cool the engine. This system is often used alongside the air cooling or liquid cooling system. Placing the oil cooler in the outside air flow causes the oil temperature to drop by 77-122°F (25-50°C).
This ensures that the oil doesn't heat up beyond its temperature threshold and that it remains a good lubricant.

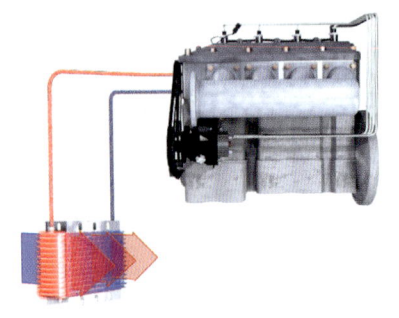

Fig. 591 Oil Cooling

If the oil temperature becomes too high, the quality/viscosity and lubricating effect of the oil will greatly decrease, resulting in oil consumption. Oil coolers are also commonly used on transmissions.

4. Liquid Cooling System

Liquid cooling is the most common method of cooling an engine.

Advantages of liquid cooling:
- The engine cools more uniformly. The flow of liquid coolant can be better controlled than outside air flow.
- Less engine noise: The liquid around the cylinders dampens noise.
- When the engine is switched off after a road trip, it remains warm longer. This helps the engine reach normal operating temperature more rapidly after a pause in driving.

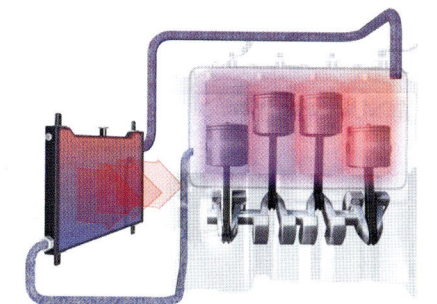

Fig. 592 Liquid cooling system

5. Internal Passages

Engines with liquid cooling systems have internal passages called water jackets inside the cylinder block and cylinder head. The coolant is pumped through these water jackets.

The liquid cooling system consists of the following components:
- Water pump: this provides the coolant flow as long as the engine is running.
- Thermostat: regulates the coolant flow through the radiator and engine.
- Radiator fan: provides needed airflow at low vehicle speed, high engine temperature, or when the A/C is in use.
- Radiator: transfers coolant heat to the outside air flow.
- Pressure cap: controls the pressure in the cooling system and increases the boiling point of the coolant by three degrees per pound of pressure.
- Hoses: connect the components of the cooling system.

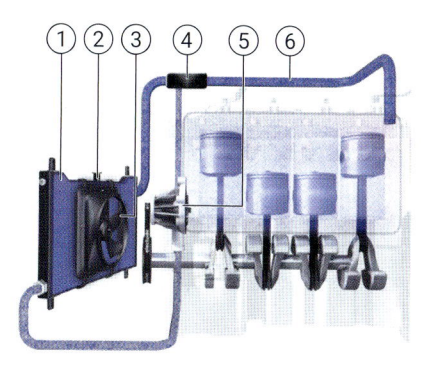

Fig. 593 Liquid cooling system components: 1. Radiator. 2. Pressure cap. 3. Fan. 4. Thermostat. 5. Water pump. 6. Hose.

Always check the cooling system for leaks. The coolant level should be full. Hoses must not be damaged, bulging, or have visible cracks. Also check the connection at the hose clamps.

ELECTRONIC CONTROLS OF MODERN COOLING SYSTEMS

1. Introduction

In simple cooling systems, you will find a number of electrical components in addition to the mechanical components.
— Engine coolant temperature sensors for the engine temperature gauge on the instrument panel.
— Thermal switch for controlling the operation of the cooling fan.
— Electric cooling fan.

Modern cars must meet increasingly stringent environmental requirements. The engine's operating temperature is very important for its ability to meet these requirements. This is why the engine temperature must be accurately monitored and controlled.

Some examples of this are:
— Rapid warm up of a cold engine.
— Adjusting the operating temperature to match the engine load.

2. Electronic Controls

To be able to accurately control the coolant temperature of a modern engine, a number of parts are electronically controlled by the engine control unit.
These actuators, such as the electric thermostat, affect the operating temperature of the engine.
To be able to properly control all of this, the control unit must receive correct information from a number of sensors.

Some sensors are specifically contained in the cooling system, but information from the sensors of other systems, such as the engine speed sensor, is also used.

14. COOLING SYSTEM: FUNDAMENTALS

Engine Control Unit

- Engine speed sensor.
- MAF: Mass Air Flow Sensor
- Coolant level sensor
- Engine coolant temperature sensor
- Radiator coolant temperature sensor
- Interior temperature control CAN
- Information trailer module CAN
- Speed signal CAN

- Auxiliary heater
- Electric water pump
- Electric Thermostat
- Electric cooling fans control unit
- Electric cooling fan 1
- Electric cooling fan 2
- Data link connector (DLC)

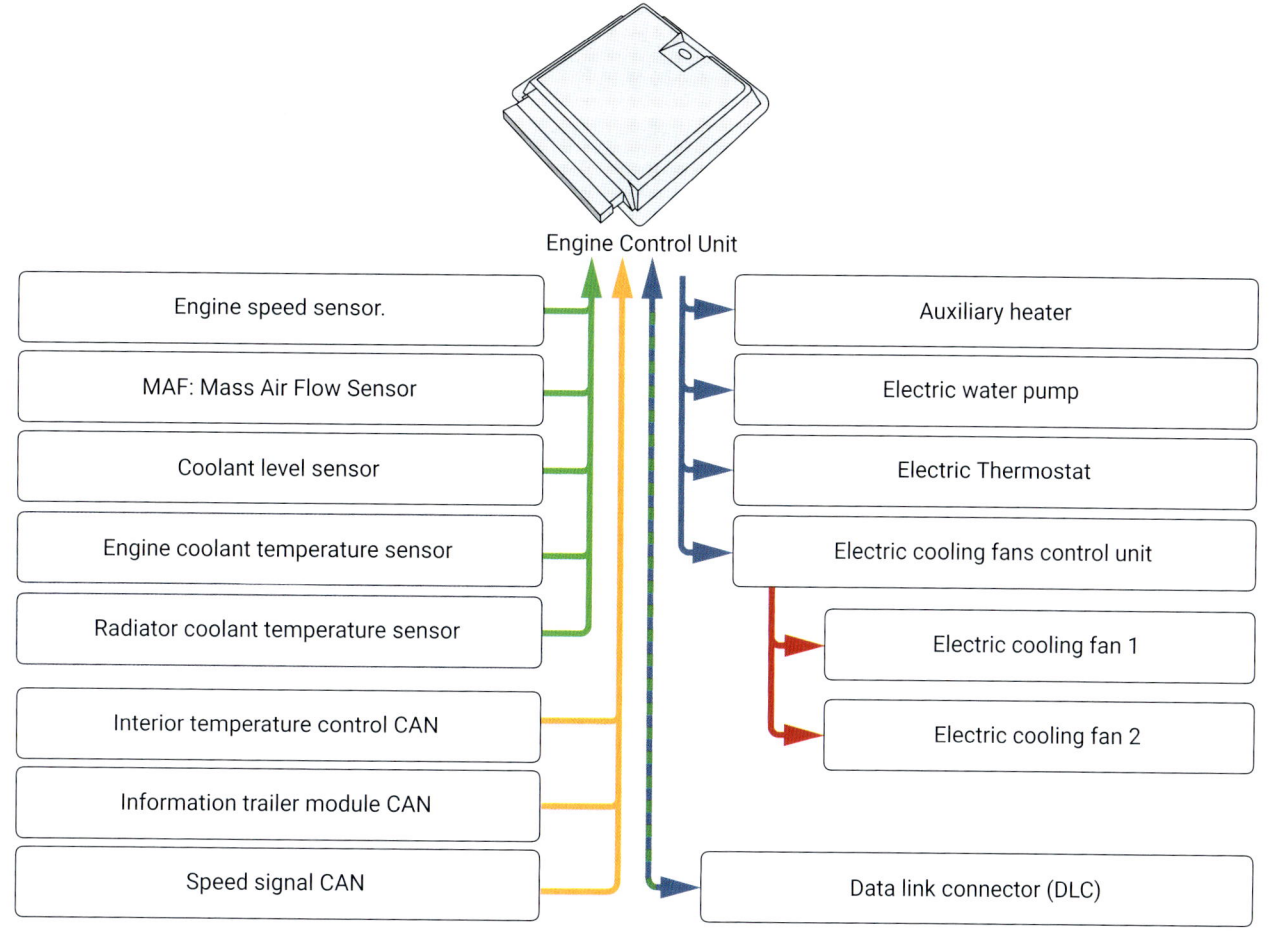

Fig. 594 Block diagram of the electronic control of a modern cooling system.

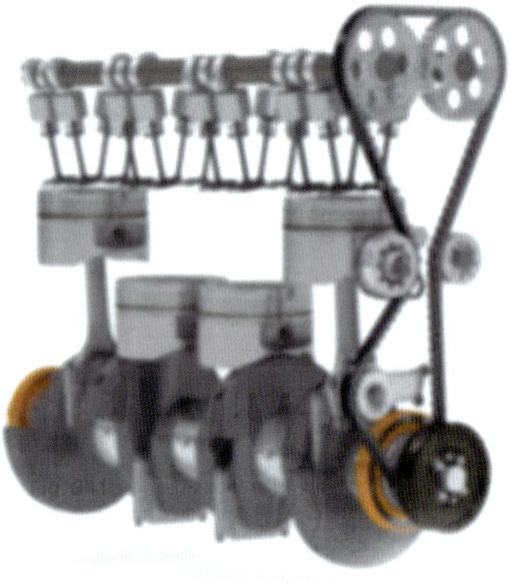

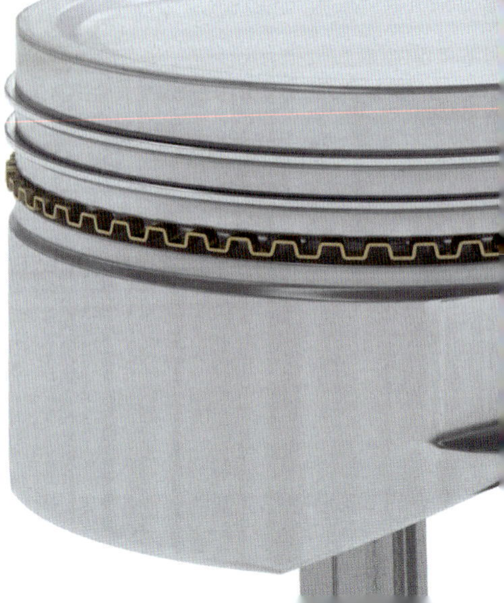

15. Cooling System: Components

ENGINE COOLANT

1. Engine Coolant

Engine coolant is a specially formulated mixture of water, glycol (antifreeze), and various additives. Engine coolant needs to withstand temperatures below zero without freezing and above several hundred degrees in heat without boiling. Engine coolant is poisonous and should be handled with care.

2. Engine Coolant Components

Water

Demineralized/distilled water (with calcium and other elements removed) should always be used when mixing coolant to prevent cooling system clogging and damage.

Glycol

Glycol is one type of antifreeze/coolant. The level of glycol determines the freezing point of the coolant. This is approximately around -13 to -40°F. Mono Ethylene Glycol (MEG) or Mono-Propylene Glycol (MPG), which is less toxic, can be used as an engine coolant.

MEG coolant has a greater ability to absorb heat than other coolant types, so it is more widely used.

A 60% glycol/40% water mix provides the best protection against freezing. Pure coolant turns to jelly at about -8°F, but the 60/40 mix is good to -40°F.

Additives

A mix of additives are used in coolant:
- Antifoam:
  This additive prevents foaming of the coolant. Foam absorbs less heat and impedes circulation.
- Anticorrosion:
  The parts of the engine and the cooling system consist of different metals, which can result in electrolytic corrosion. Anticorrosion additives prevent this by stopping conduction, which is a chemically created electrical current flow that erodes the different metals in the cooling system.
- Lubricating properties:
  A carbon ring is used to seal the water pump shaft to the housing, and has to be lubricated to prevent squeaking and premature failure.

Colors

There are different types of coolant. Coolants can generally be distinguished from each other by their color.
- Blue or green (G11): This is a simple composition that contains silicates (salts). It is commonly used in older engines.
- Red or yellow (G12): This is suitable for aluminum engines. The silicates have been replaced by Organic Acid Technology (OAT).
- Purple or colorless (G12 +). This is a universal coolant that contains improved additives compared to the red coolant.
- Red/pink G13 (G12++): This coolant contains silicate additives. The coolant has extra aluminum protection for modern engines and long-life applications.

The term G is a standard classification for engine coolants that was developed by Volkswagen.
It is not recommended to mix coolants together. Always check the manufacturer's specifications before adding coolant to a system!

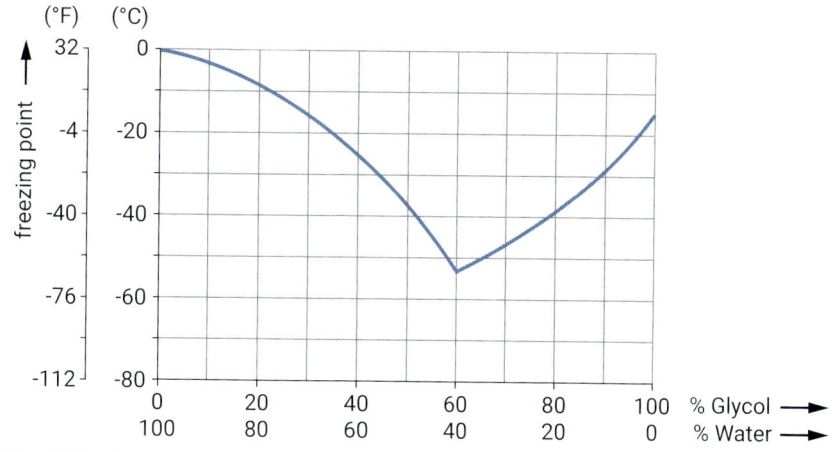

Fig. 595 Mixing ratio determines the freezing point (0°C=32°F, -50°C=-58°F).

3. Changing Coolant

Coolant breaks down over time and becomes very acidic, which causes the additives in the coolant and the materials in the engine to deteriorate. As the quality decreases, coolant must be replaced according to the manufacturer's instructions.

Some car manufacturers use Long Life coolants, which sometimes last for the entire service life of the vehicle.

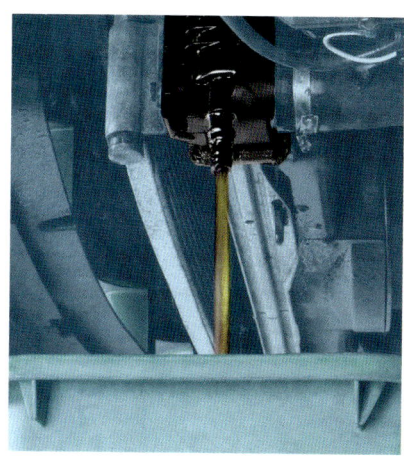

Fig. 596 Old coolant shows oxidation.

MECHANICAL WATER PUMP

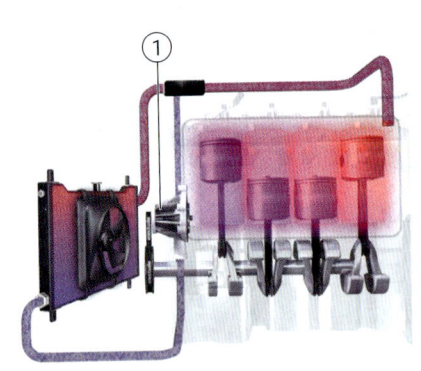

Fig. 597 The cooling system with a mechanical coolant pump (1).

1. System

The water pump (coolant pump) ensures the coolant flows through the engine and radiator.

The pump draws in 'cooled' antifreeze/coolant from the bottom of the radiator and pumps it through cooling passages of the engine.

'Hot' coolant flows from the top of the engine to the radiator.

A serpentine, V belt or timing belt is responsible for driving the water pump.

2. Mechanical Water Pump

The water pump is a centrifugal pump. The pump consists of a housing containing an impeller.

The liquid flows from the middle of the pump between the rotating blades of the impeller.

The speed of the rotating blades throws the coolant outward. This is called centrifugal force.

Advantages of a centrifugal pump:
— simple construction
— small size
— high liquid displacement

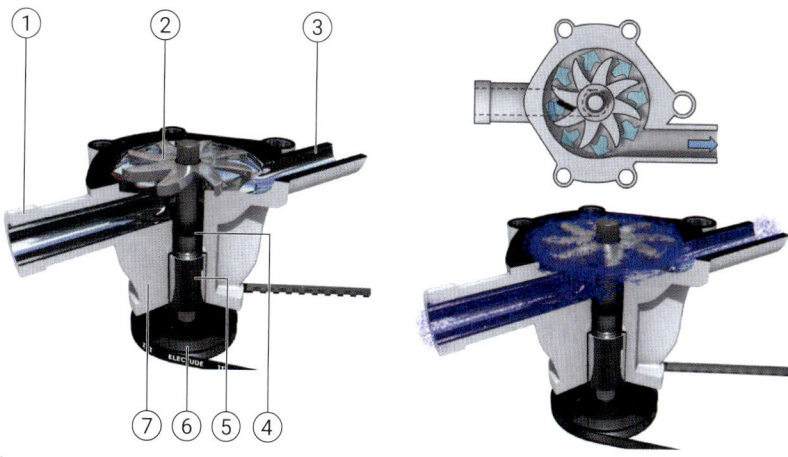

Fig. 598 Construction of a coolant pump: 1. Suction side. 2. Rotor. 3. Discharge side. 4. Sealant. 5. Bearing. 6. Pulley. 7. Pump housing.

Fig. 599 Coolant flow through the coolant pump.

The engine block often makes up part of the housing. The housing has a rotor and is bolted to the engine block. A gasket or rubber O-ring is installed between the pump and the engine block as a method of sealing the system.

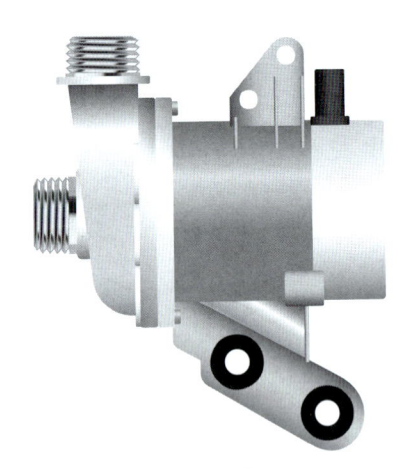

ELECTRIC WATER PUMP

The electric water pump is a centrifugal-type pump. The pump consists of a housing containing a rotor that is driven by an electric motor. The operating principle is the same as that of the mechanical water pump; only the drive mechanism is different.

Electric water pumps have a number of important advantages over a mechanical water pump:

1. Its placement in the cooling system no longer has to be located on the belt side of the engine.
2. The pump can be installed to the side or at a low out-of-the-way location. Due to this, there is a better utilization of available space.
3. The water pump no longer has to be driven by the serpentine belt or the timing belt. Therefore, the water pump does not affect these drive systems.
4. The power required to operate the water pump no longer needs to be supplied by the crankshaft. This results in less parasitic power loss.
5. The electric water pump does not operate when the engine is cold. Because of this, the engine warms up faster and emits less hazardous emissions during its warm-up phase.

Always refer to the vehicle service information when bleeding the cooling system with an electric coolant pump. The pump must be running in order to bleed the system.
The pump must be activated through a special procedure setting.

Fig. 600 Electric Water Pump

THERMOSTAT

1. Introduction

The thermostat regulates the flow of coolant through the radiator. The thermostat ensures that the engine reaches operating temperature quickly and remains at this temperature.

If the normal engine operating temperature is reached quickly, this translates to:

— less engine wear.
— improved fuel economy.
— lower emission of harmful exhaust gases.

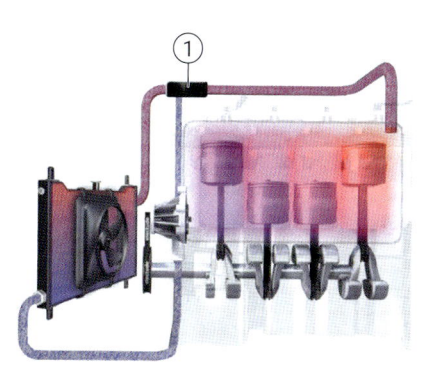

Fig. 601 Cooling system with a thermostat (1).

2. Principle

In the picture a cylinder containing wax is shown. The cylinder is sealed by a membrane.

When the temperature increases, the wax in the sealed cylinder expands.
Due to the expansion of the wax, the membrane moves upward.

When the temperature falls, the wax contracts.
Due to the contraction of the wax, the membrane moves downward.

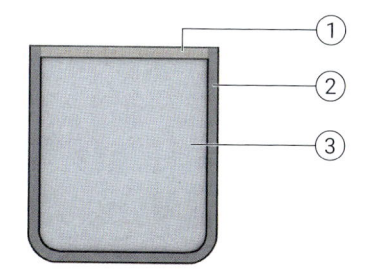

Fig. 602 Cylinder with wax: 1. Membrane. 2. Cylinder. 3. Wax.

Fig. 603 The wax expands and the membrane moves upwards.

Fig. 604 The wax contracts and the membrane moves downwards.

3. Operation

The thermostat consists of a sealed cylinder filled with wax.
When the engine is cold, the wax is solid.
When the engine becomes hot, the wax melts.
This melting causes the wax to expand.

Due to the expansion of the wax, the plunger is forced out of the cylinder.

When the engine cools down, the wax solidifies again.
The spring forces the plunger back into the cylinder.

Fig. 605 Construction of the thermostat: 1. Spring. 2. Plunger. 3. Cylinder. 4. Wax.

Fig. 606 The plunger is pressed outward.

Fig. 607 The spring retracts the plunger.

4. Operation of a Closed Cylinder

This closed cylinder is also filled with wax.
In this example, the plunger is fixed and the cylinder is able to move.

When the engine becomes hot, the wax pushes the cylinder downward.

When the wax cools, the spring pushes the cylinder upward.

Fig. 608 The cylinder is pressed downward.

Fig. 609 The spring retracts the cylinder.

5. Single-Action Thermostat

The thermostat regulates the coolant flow from the engine to the radiator. This is achieved by making the opening to the radiator larger or smaller.

When the engine is cold, no coolant flows through the radiator. The coolant then flows through the bypass.

When the coolant becomes hot, the thermostat opens. Coolant then flows through the radiator.

In a single-action thermostat, the bypass is always open.

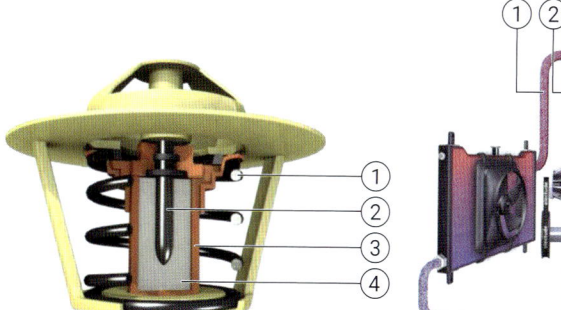

Fig. 610 Construction of the thermostat: 1. Spring. 2. Plunger. 3. Cylinder. 4. Wax.

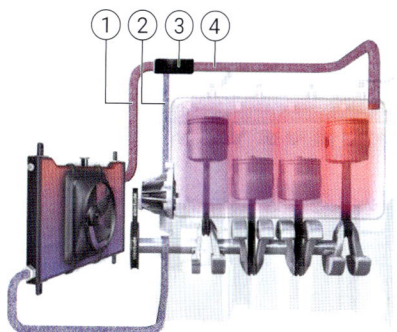

Fig. 611 Cooling system: 1. Pipe to the radiator. 2. Pipe to the bypass. 3. Thermostat. 4. Pipe from the engine.

If the engine is cold, no coolant will be flowing through the radiator. If that is the case, the coolant flows through the bypass.

As the coolant warms, the thermostat opens. Coolant will then flow through the radiator. With a single-action thermostat, the bypass is always open.

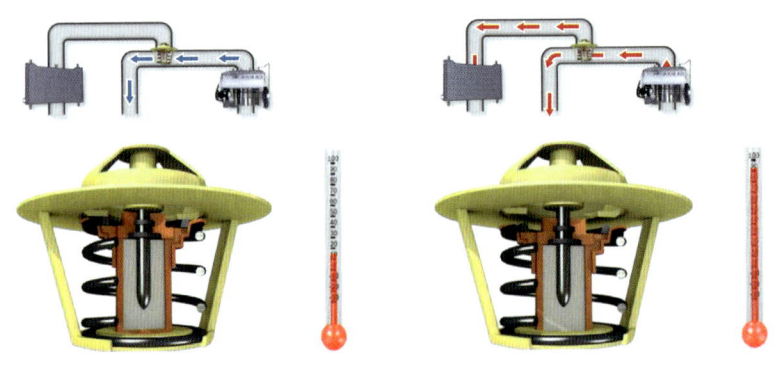

Fig. 612 Flow of coolant, cold.

Fig. 613 Flow of coolant, warm.

6. Double-Action Thermostat

A double-action thermostat has two valves, a main valve and a bypass valve.

In their initial positions, the main valve is closed and the bypass valve is open.

If the engine becomes hotter, the main valve opens the opening to the radiator.
The bypass valve then closes the opening to the bypass.

Fig. 614 Double-action thermostat: 1. Main valve. 2. Plunger. 3. Wax element. 4. Spring. 5. Bypass valve.

Fig. 615 Flow of coolant, cold.

Fig. 616 Flow of coolant, warm.

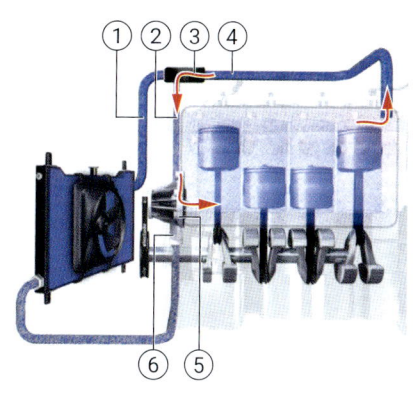

Fig. 617 Cooling system: 1. Pipe to the radiator. 2. Bypass pipe. 3. Thermostat. 4. Pipe from the engine. 5. Coolant pump. 6. Suction side of coolant pump.

Fig. 618 Venting outlet with valve.

7. Bypass

In a system with a double-action thermostat, the coolant will flow back to the engine through the bypass when the engine is cold, rather than flowing through the radiator. Therefore, the bypass is a connection between the pipe coming from the engine to the thermostat and the suction side of the coolant pump. In this way, the coolant is circulated without flowing through the radiator. This means that the engine can warm up gradually.

If coolant is not circulated, some areas in the engine may become warmer than other areas. This leads to thermal stresses placed on the engine, which can crack or warp the engine block and heads.

8. Venting

To ensure that air can leave the cooling system, there is a small venting valve in the thermostat. The venting valve is located in the wide flange.

To prevent this small hole from clogging, it is fitted with a small valve. Due to the flow of the coolant, this remains continuously in motion, ensuring that the hole stays open.

When replacing the thermostat, be sure to position the new thermostat so that the hole is in the same (top) position.

9. Temperature Cycle

There is a way to regulate the engine temperature more precisely. To do so, two thermostats are used that open sequentially.
One thermostat opens at a low temperature. Once this has fully opened, the other will also open.

The heat is dissipated over a wider temperature range, ensuring that the engine warms up more evenly.

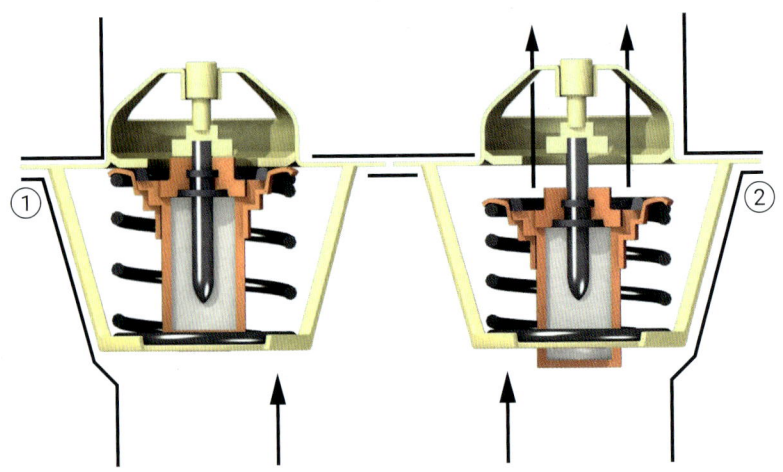

Fig. 619 Thermostat (1) is still closed, while thermostat (2) is almost completely open.

10. Thermostat Testing

Thermostats can be tested to ensure they work properly.

The most important values are the temperature at which the thermostat begins to open and the temperature at which the thermostat has opened completely.

Place the thermostat and a thermometer into a container of water. Gradually heat up the water and note the temperature at which the thermostat opens. Next, note the temperature at which the thermostat has opened fully.

Compare this data to that supplied by the manufacturer. They should be the same.

Fig. 620 Setup for thermostat testing.

ELECTRIC THERMOSTAT

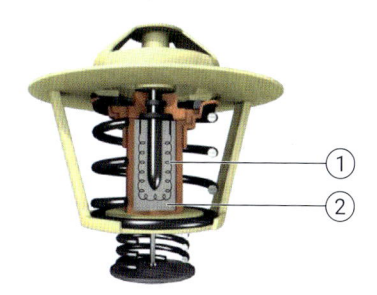

Fig. 621 Electric thermostat:
1. Thermostat wire. 2. Wax.

1. Introduction

The higher the coolant temperature, the more the wax in a thermostat expands. An electric thermostat has a filament inside the wax element.

The wax rapidly expands when an electric current is passed through the filament. This allows the thermostat to respond better to varying operating conditions.

An electric thermostat can be controlled much more accurately than a mechanical thermostat. The motor always operates at the ideal temperature.

2. Operation of the Thermostat

Temperature below 176°F (80°C):
The filament is not heated.
The coolant flows through the bypass.
No coolant flows through the radiator.

Temperature between 176-208°F (80-98°C):
The filament is heated and the wax expands. The main valve opens the passage to the radiator.
The bypass valve then closes the opening to the bypass.

Temperature above 208°F (98°C):
The filament is heated further.
The main valve opens the passage to the radiator further.

If the filament does not function, then the electric thermostat functions as a conventional thermostat.

634 GASOLINE ENGINE CONSTRUCTION AND OPERATION

Fig. 622 Main valve closed, thermostat wire not heated.

Fig. 623 Main valve is starting to open, thermostat wire is heated.

Fig. 624 Main valve is open, thermostat wire is heated even more.

HOW TO: REPLACING THE THERMOSTAT

1. Detecting a Faulty Thermostat

The thermostat regulates the coolant flow through the radiator. This keeps the engine at the correct operating temperature. A thermostat can fail in different ways.
The thermostat no longer opens, remains open or randomly opens and closes. This causes the engine to become too warm, to remain cold or causes rapid temperature fluctuations.

Take the time to make a proper diagnosis. If the engine temperature is too high, feel the radiator hoses. Also check the function of the water pump(s), control valves, sensors, radiator and cooling fan. Check the condition of the head gasket, for example by using a sniffer. Read out any fault codes in the engine management unit. Some thermostats are controlled electronically. The thermostat is usually screwed into or onto the cylinder head. The amount of work required to replace the thermostat differs depending on the type of engine and car.

Fig. 625 The driver of this car receives a dashboard notification that the engine is overheating.

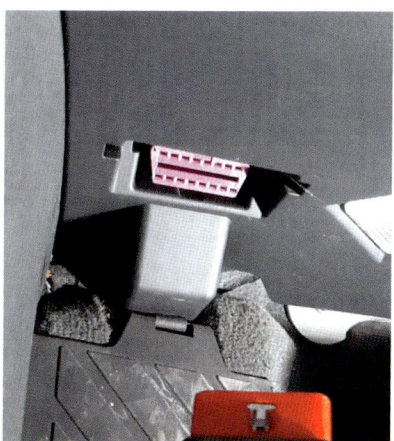

Fig. 626 Read out the fault memory of the engine management system. There are no fault codes.

Fig. 627 While the engine indicates a temperature that is too high, the top radiator hose feels hot. The bottom one feels cold.
These symptoms indicate a blocked radiator, defective water pump or permanently closed thermostat. Considering that the car is quite new and that the coolant is clean, first look at the thermostat.

2. Preparation for Removal

The thermostat is located in the cooling system. Therefore, the coolant must be drained before removal.
Prepare a large drain pan to catch the coolant.

Fig. 628 Let the engine cool down and drain off the coolant.

Fig. 629 On this type of engine, the thermostat is located underneath the air compressor, between the two cylinder banks (V6 engine).
Using compressed air, blow away dirt and dust from the engine before removing the air compressor. This prevents dirt or dust from entering the engine during removal.

Fig. 630 Disconnect air hoses and plugs from the throttle valve housing and the inlet.

Fig. 631 Undo the air compressor and lift it off the engine.

Fig. 632 Seal off the openings with tape. This prevents anything from falling into the engine.

3. Removing the Old Thermostat

Remove the old thermostat. The thermostat can be checked by placing it in a pan of water. Heat the water and use a thermometer to measure the temperature at which it opens.

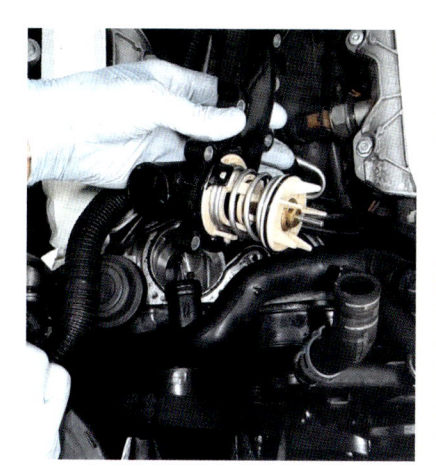

Fig. 633 Release the attachment bolts and remove the old thermostat from the cylinder block.

Fig. 634 The thermostat is removed from the engine.

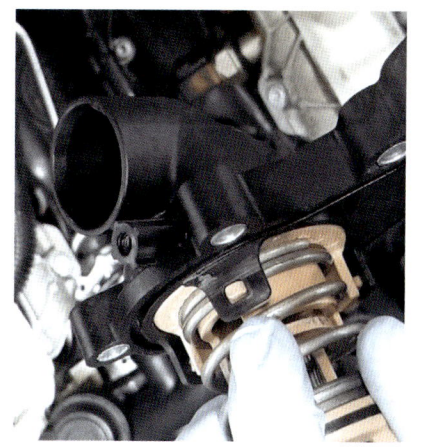

Fig. 635
The attachment between the thermostat and the plastic housing is cracked.
This crack is not necessarily the cause of the thermostat failing to open. In general, nothing unusual can be seen when looking at a faulty thermostat.

4. Installing a New Thermostat

There may be different opening temperatures available for a single type of thermostat. In this case consult the manufacturer's specifications for the correct value.
Replace at least all the seals which have been undone when replacing the thermostat.
Clean the surface of the seal carefully before installation.

Fig. 636 Clean the surface of the seal carefully.

Fig. 637 Replace all seals which have been undone.
It is sensible to also replace seals which you can easily access now.

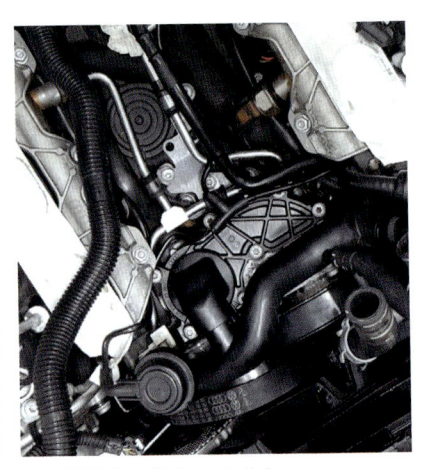

Fig. 638 Carefully install the new thermostat and tighten it to the prescribed tightening torque.
Use special assembly grease for rubber seals. This makes assembly easier and prevents the seal from drying out.
Be careful with the type of grease, because some greases affect rubber.

Fig. 639 Install the air compressor. Tighten the bolts in the prescribed sequence. Use the correct tightening torque.

Fig. 640 Reconnect all air hoses and plugs.

5. Tasks After the Replacement

Refill the cooling system, ideally using a special filling device. Always use the correct coolant type.

Then allow the engine to reach operating temperature. Check the engine temperature and (after cooling down) adjust the coolant level to the correct level.

Fig. 641 Fill the cooling system using a special filling device.

Fig. 642 Start the engine and allow it to reach operating temperature. The engine no longer goes above 90°C.

Fig. 643 To be absolutely sure, check the seals for leaks.

RADIATOR

1. Task

A lot of outside air can flow through the radiator because the radiator is at the front of the vehicle.

The radiator transfers the heat from the coolant to the outside air flow.

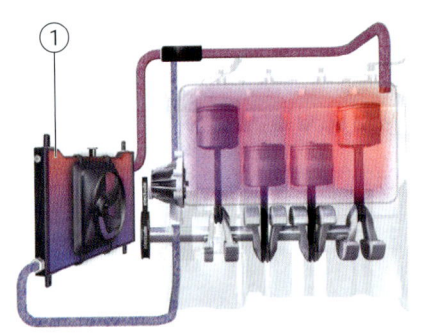

Fig. 645 The cooling system with radiator (1).

2. Components

The radiator consists of:
- radiator core
- water tank(s)

The radiator core consists of small pipes through which the coolant flows. There are cooling fins around the pipes. These increase the cooling surface area of the radiator.

The radiator core is often made of aluminum. The advantage of aluminum is that it is light.

The water tanks seal the pipes on the lower and upper sides. The water tanks are often made of plastic.

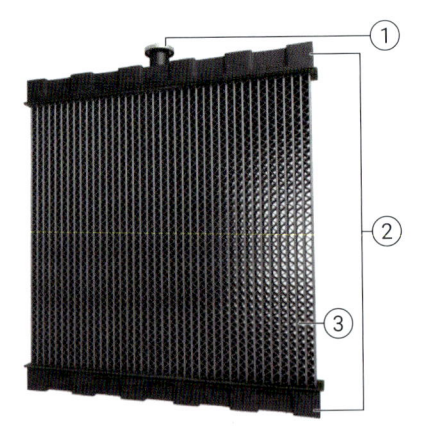

Fig. 646 Construction of the radiator: 1. Radiator cap/pressure cap. 2. Water tanks. 3. Radiator core.

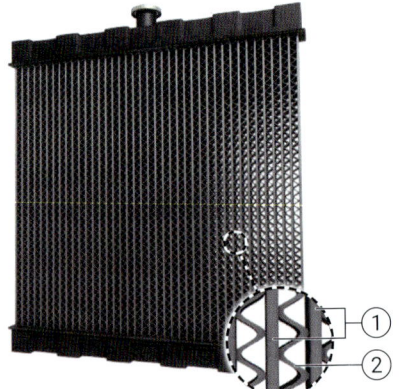

Fig. 647 Construction of the radiator core: 1. Tubes. 2. Fins.

3. Types

There are two different types of radiator:
- Downflow radiators:
  The coolant flows from top to bottom.
- Crossflow radiators:
  The coolant flows horizontally.

Crossflow radiators have a smaller overall height. They are therefore more suitable for streamlined cars with lower/sloping fronts.

Crossflow radiators are positioned low in the car. The top of the radiator is not the highest point of the cooling system.
The filler cap for the coolant is therefore not fitted on the radiator, but on an expansion tank that is placed high under the hood.

Fig. 648 Downflow radiator

Fig. 649 Crossflow radiator

When checking a cooling system, watch out for corrosion. Often, leakage begins from the connection of the tubes to the water tank(s). The fins between the tubes may also become detached due to corrosion. This will cause a decrease in cooling capacity. Often, this process will start at the bottom of the radiator first, where it is affected by road salt and debris.

Fig. 650 Radiator corrosion caused by road salt and debris.

EXPANSION TANK

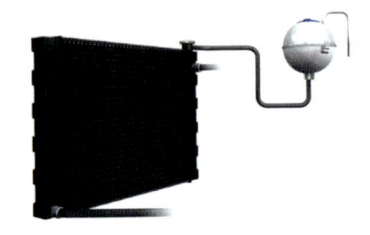

Fig. 651 The expansion tank connected to the radiator.

1. Operation

The expansion tank is a storage tank that contains liquid for the cooling system. When the coolant becomes hot, it expands and enters into the expansion tank. When the coolant cools down and contracts, it generates a suction that draws coolant back into the system. In this way, the system is replenished by the fluid stored in the expansion tank.

It's important that the fluid level inside the expansion tank remain between the minimum and maximum lines. This ensures the coolant has room to expand without overflowing and can contract without pulling air into the radiator.

The expansion tank can be connected to the cooling system in two ways:

- systems in which the coolant does **not** flow through the expansion tank
- systems in which the coolant **does** flow through the expansion tank

2. Systems in which the coolant does not flow through the expansion tank

A hose connects the expansion tank to the overflow of the pressure cap. When the coolant becomes hot, it expands. The excess coolant passes via the pressure cap and the overflow to the expansion tank.

When the coolant cools down, it contracts again. Due to the vacuum in the cooling system, the coolant flows from the expansion tank back to the cooling system. This is called a cooling system with a cold expansion tank.

NOTE Never loosen the pressure cap of the radiator when the engine is hot. The rapid release of pressure will cause the coolant to boil over.

Fig. 652 Coolant level when the engine is cold: 1. Pressure cap. 2. Expansion tank. 3. Coolant level.

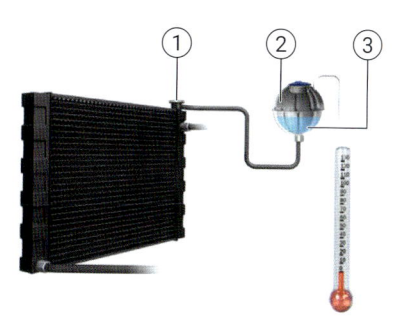

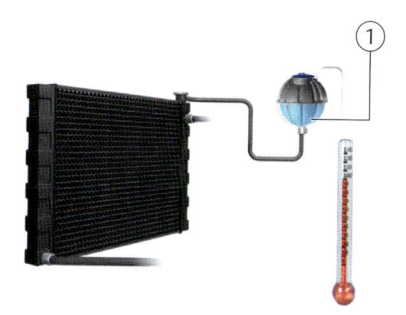

Fig. 653 Coolant level when the engine is warm: 1. Coolant level.

3. Systems in which the coolant does flow through the expansion tank

In this system, the expansion tank is included in the cooling system. Because the coolant flows through the expansion tank, this is called a cooling system with a hot expansion tank.

The expansion tank is positioned higher than the radiator. Consequently, the radiator is always full and there is maximum removal of heat.

In cooling systems with a hot expansion tank, the pressure cap is mounted on the expansion tank.

NOTE Never loosen the pressure cap on the expansion tank when the engine is hot.

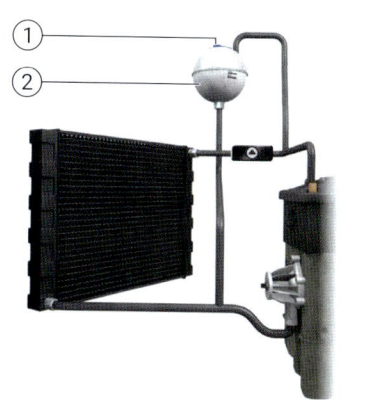

Fig. 654 Expansion tank included in the cooling system: 1. Pressure cap. 2. Expansion tank.

Fig. 655 Coolant level when the engine is cold: 1. Coolant level.

Fig. 656 Coolant level when the engine is warm: 1. Coolant level.

PRESSURE CAP

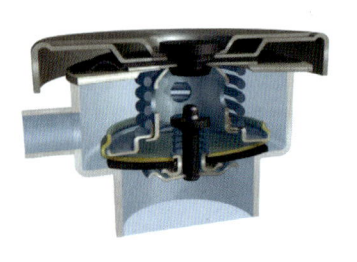

Fig. 657 Cross section of a cooling system pressure cap.

1. Pressure

The cooling system pressure cap is positioned on the expansion tank or on the radiator itself.

The pressure cap ensures there is higher pressure in the cooling system. This pressurizing of the cooling system raises the boiling point of the engine coolant.

2. Operating Temperature

The operating temperature of an engine is approximately 212°F. Under atmospheric pressure alone, the coolant would begin to boil at this temperature.
Boiling is very detrimental to effective engine cooling. If the engine coolant boils, the coolant will evaporate. Additionally, boiling coolant will seriously affect the efficiency of the cooling system, as it will not cool as well due to the formation of air bubbles during the boiling phase.

The cooling system pressure cap allows the cooling system to safely become pressurized. This raises the boiling point of the engine coolant.

Caution: Never remove the cooling system pressure cap from the radiator or the expansion tank when the engine is warm. This will cause the pressure of the coolant to drop rapidly and flash boil. This will create steam and may result in severe burns

Fig. 658 If no pressure cap is installed, the coolant may boil over.

Fig. 659 The operating temperature is higher than 212°F deg. The cooling system is under pressure, which raises the boiling point and prevents the coolant from boiling over.

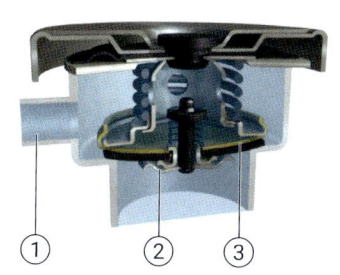

Fig. 660 Cross section of the cooling system pressure cap: 1. Overflow. 2. Vacuum valve. 3. Relief valve.

3. Operation

The pressure cap is made up of:
— Relief valve.
— Vacuum valve.

When the temperature of the engine coolant rises, it expands. This causes the pressure inside the system to rise.

When the pressure reaches a certain value, the relief valve pushes against the relief valve spring and opens, maintaining the cooling system pressure at a predetermined level.
When this occurs, liquid or vapor can escape from the system towards the overflow container.
Excessive engine cooling system pressure can cause leakage and/or damage to the cooling system components.

As the liquid engine coolant cools down, it contracts. This causes a negative pressure to be developed inside the cooling system.
The vacuum valve will open at a specific negative pressure, and this allows coolant from the expansion reservoir to be drawn back into the cooling system.

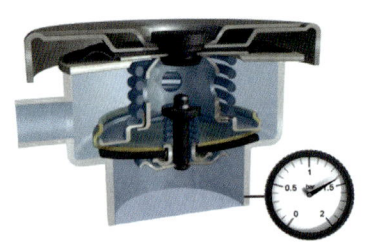

Fig. 661 The cooling system pressure cap ensures that the pressure inside the cooling system can rise to a predetermined level.

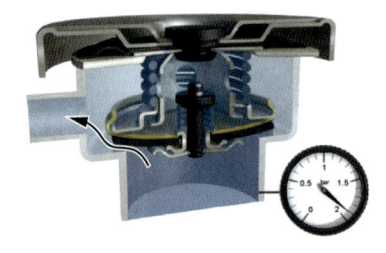

Fig. 662 When the pressure gets too high, the relief valve opens and the pressure is maintained at that level.

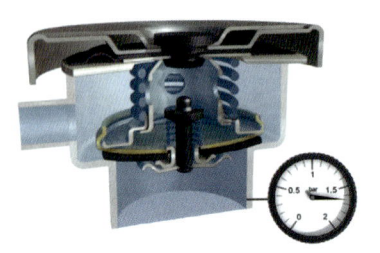

Fig. 663 When the pressure falls below the maximum threshold, the relief valve will close again.

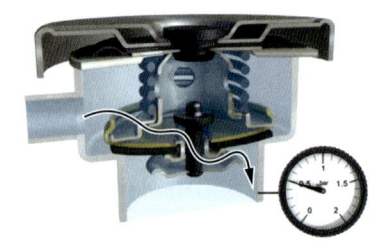

Fig. 664 When the engine cools down, a negative pressure develops, and the vacuum valve will open.

HEATER CORE

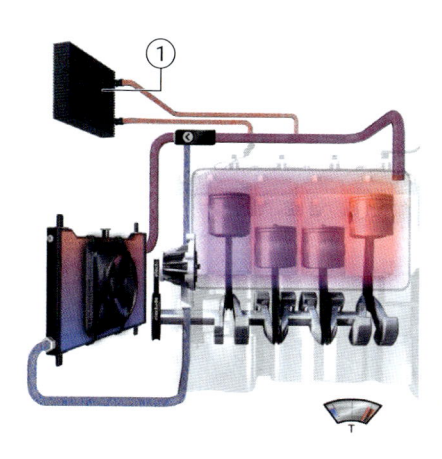

Fig. 665 1. Heater core.

1. Location

The heater core is part of the engine cooling system and provides heat for the vehicle interior.

The heater core is located behind the instrument panel, enclosed within a heater case. Hot engine coolant flows through the heater core. The heater blower fan directs air over the heater core, warming the air, thus heating the vehicle interior.

The temperature of the air can be regulated in two ways:
— air mixing system
— liquid control system.

Just like the coolant radiator, the heater core consists of a radiator core and water tanks.

2. Air Blending System

In the case of the air mixing system, the temperature of the air is controlled by mixing hot and cold air.

The heater case contains a blend door that controls the amount of cold and hot air.
The more air that's allowed to flow through the heater core, the hotter the air becomes that warms the interior.

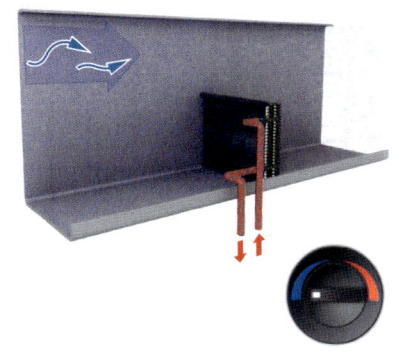

Fig. 666 Flap closed, no warm air added.

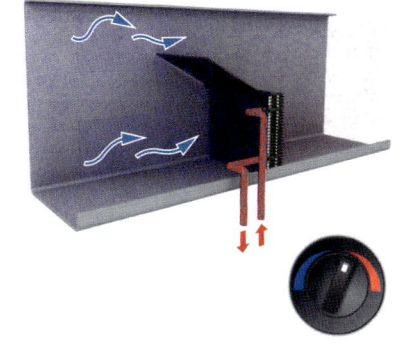

Fig. 667 Flap open, air is flowing through the heater core.

3. Liquid Control System

This system controls the temperature of the air by changing the flow of liquid through the heater core.

The supply line of the heater core contains an adjustable valve. Rotating the valve allows more or less coolant to flow through the heater core, adjusting the air temperature accordingly.

Fig. 668 Valve closed, no coolant flowing through the heater core.

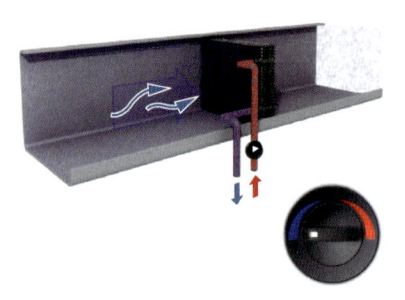

Fig. 669 Valve open, coolant is flowing through the heater core.

4. Heater Modes

In a vehicle, there are usually several ways to control the modes of airflow. Usually, these are: onto the windshield, at vents, or into the floorboard. In many vehicles, the airflow can also be directed backward towards the passengers in the rear seat.
To do so, a system with mode doors is used. By moving the doors into a certain position, the airflow can be directed as needed.

There are tubes coming from the heater assembly through which air is routed. The air flows out of the airflow outlets into the car. Air vents are installed in the dashboard which are used to direct the airflow in the desired direction.

For example, by directing (part of) the airflow towards the windscreen, it can be defrosted or demisted.

The doors are controlled with sliders, rotary knobs, or buttons. In the past, this was usually mechanical, using a cable or vacuum system. Today, the doors are driven by electric motors.

The airflow is created by the heater motor as it sucks exterior air through the interior filter.

Fig. 670 The airflow in the heating installation.

In the recirculation position, the air is not drawn from the exterior, but from the interior. This way pulling in strange smells from outside can be avoided.

The doors can all be combined so that it is always possible to have the desired airflow.

ENGINE COOLANT HOSES

1. Hoses and Tools

Various parts of the engine cooling system are connected by hoses. As the engine vibrates and rotates, there need to be flexible connections made between the different parts of the system. Coolant hose is made out of rubber, with a braided ply layer inside for strength.

The hoses are installed with hose clamps.

These hose clamps can be attached and removed with a screwdriver, a socket wrench, or special pliers.

Fig. 671 Hose clamps.

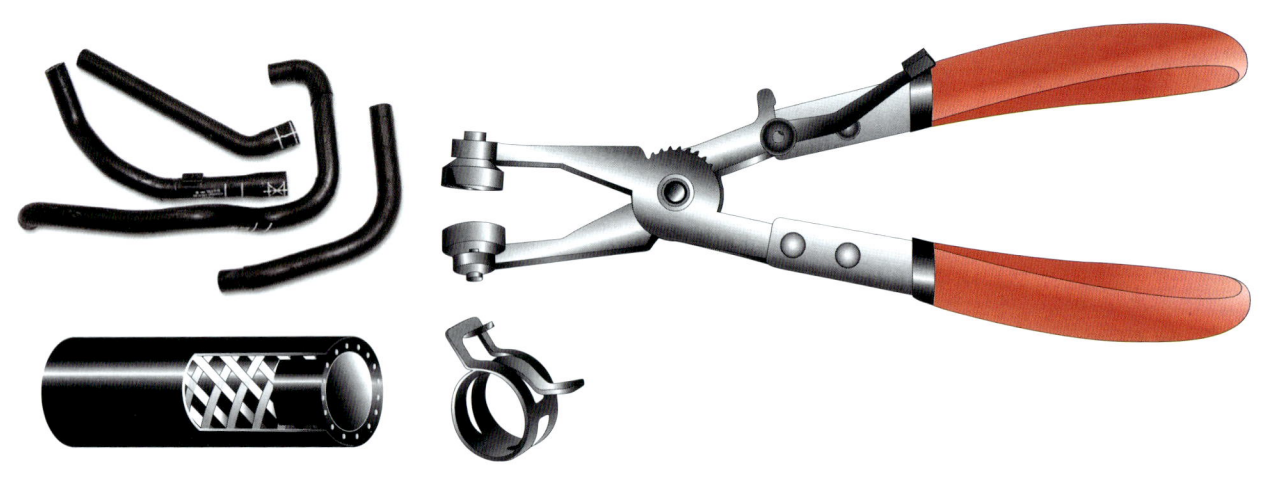

Fig. 672 Hoses with inner braided ply layer.

Fig. 673 Hose clamp pliers.

THERMOSTATICALLY CONTROLLED FAN

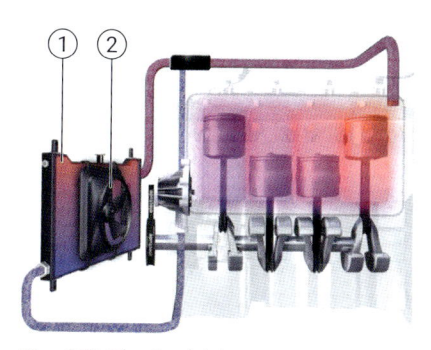

Fig. 674 The fan (2) located behind the radiator (1).

1. Introduction

A thermostatically controlled fan switches on when cooling from the outside air flow is inadequate. For example:
— when driving slowly in heavy traffic
— when the engine is idling
— at high engine loads

The fan can be located either in front of or behind the radiator.

2. Types

A thermostatically controlled fan switches-on when the engine temperature becomes too high.
Thermostatically controlled fans can be:
— an electric motor with a thermal switch
— an electromagnetic coupling
— viscous coupling

These fans have two types of drive.
— electric motor
— serpentine belt

3. Electric Motor with Thermal Switch

An electric motor drives the fan.
This motor is switched on and off by the thermal switch.
The switch is fitted in the radiator.

When the engine is cold, the thermal switch is open and the electric motor is switched off.
When the coolant gets too hot, the thermal switch closes.
The thermal switch switches on the fan via a relay.

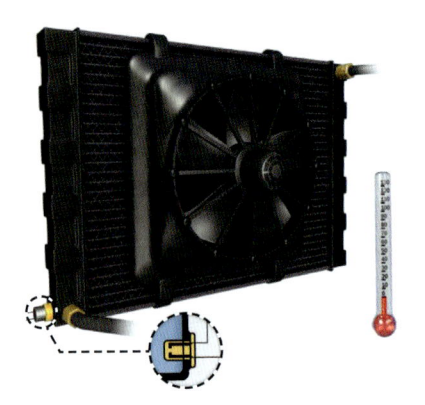

Fig. 675 Electrically powered fan and thermal switch, turned off.

Fig. 676 Electrically powered fan and thermal switch, turned on.

Caution: For some car brands, the fan may still turn on if the engine is warm, even if the car's electrical system has been turned off.

4. Electromagnetic Coupling

The fan is mounted to the shaft of the water pump though a magnetic coupling.
The shaft of the water pump is driven by the serpentine belt.

If the coolant becomes too hot, the thermal switch closes.
The coil of the electromagnetic coupling is energized. As a result, the armature is drawn in and connects with the hub.

The armature and the fan will then rotate with the pump shaft.

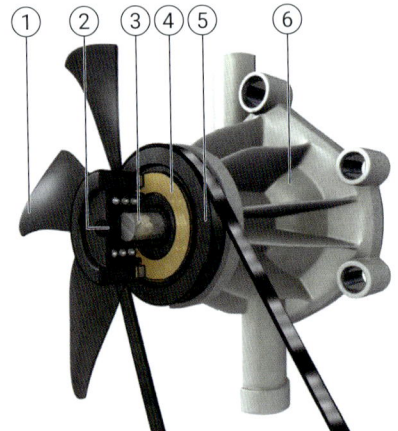

Fig. 677 Fan with electromagnetic coupling: 1. Fan. 2. Anchor. 3. Water pump shaft. 4. Coil. 5. Pulley. 6. Water pump.

5. Viscous Fan

The viscous fan is a temperature-dependent fan coupling. This responds to the air temperature behind the radiator.

The fan is coupled to the shaft of the water pump via a viscous coupling.
When the air temperature behind the radiator is low, the viscous coupling does not connect the water pump with the fan.

When the air temperature behind the radiator is high, the viscous coupling the water pump shaft with the fan.

This connection takes place gradually as the viscous fan clutch heats up.

Fig. 678 Viscous Fan

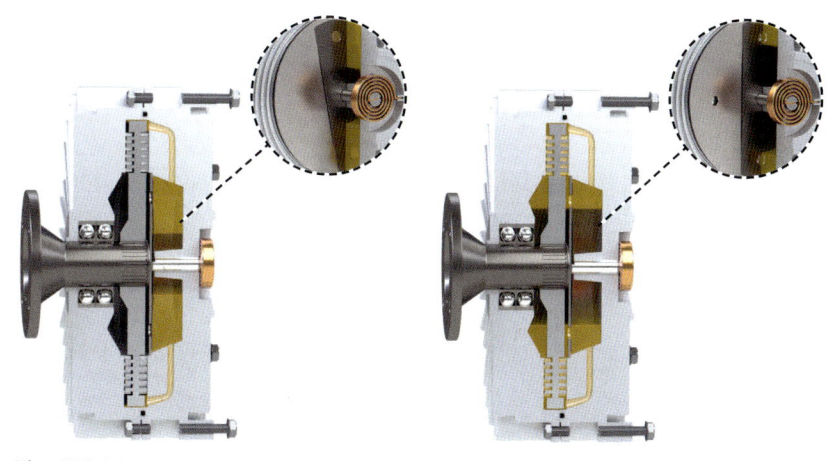

Fig. 679 Viscous coupling with a cold engine.

Fig. 680 Viscous coupling with a warm engine.

The input axle with disc is continuously driven by the water pump. This disc is not connected to the fan housing. As the valved leaf spring is opened by way of a bimetallic strip, more and more silicone fluid flows into the chamber of the disc. As a result, the disc takes the fan housing with it and will rotate faster and faster.

When the temperature behind the radiator decreases, the bimetallic strip will close the outlet once more. The silicone fluid will flow back through the return valve. Slippage between the disc and the housing will occur. Fan speed will decrease.

6. Fan Control

An electrically driven fan should rotate smoothly. The bearings must not make any noises. Also, the fan must not be damaged or be unbalanced. This will cause the fan to vibrate.

If it is driven by a serpentine belt or a V-belt, pay attention to the following:
- Belt tension
  Refer to the vehicle service information for the manufacturer's specifications.
- Belt condition
  Check the belt for cracks and ensure it is properly engaged with the pulley.

7. Testing the thermal switch

The electrical fan is turned on by the thermal switch. This thermal switch is located in the radiator.

There are two kinds of thermal switches:
- Opened when cold.
- Closed when cold.

Opened when cold

If the temperature of the coolant is below the switching temperature, the circuit remains open. Once the switching temperature has been reached, the thermal switch activates, closing the circuit. The electric motor is turned on by a relay and remains on until the coolant temperature has dropped below that of the switching temperature.

Closed when cold

If the temperature of the coolant is below the switching temperature, the circuit remains closed. Once the switching temperature has been reached, the thermal switch activates the circuit. The electric motor is turned on by a relay and remains on until the coolant temperature has dropped below that of the switching temperature.

Operation testing

Create a circuit between a 12-volt battery, a thermal switch, and a light. Insert the thermal switch into a container filled with water which you are going to heat up. Measure the water temperature with a thermometer.

If you are using a thermal switch that opens when cold, the light will not switch on until the water temperature reaches the switching temperature. Make a note of this temperature. Compare this data with the data supplied by the manufacturer.

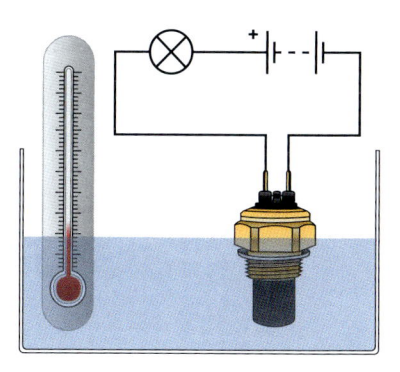

Fig. 681 Test setup for testing a thermal switch that opens when cold.

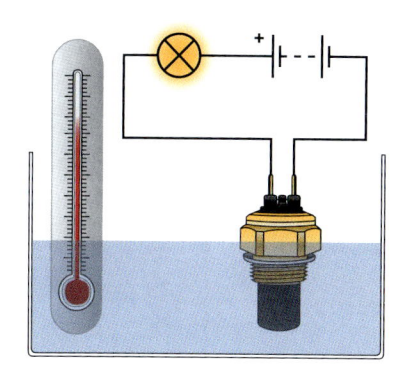

Fig. 682 The switching temperature has been reached; the circuit is now closed.

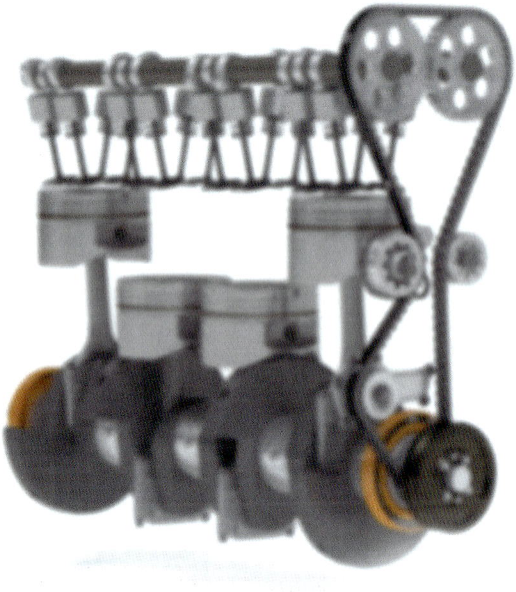

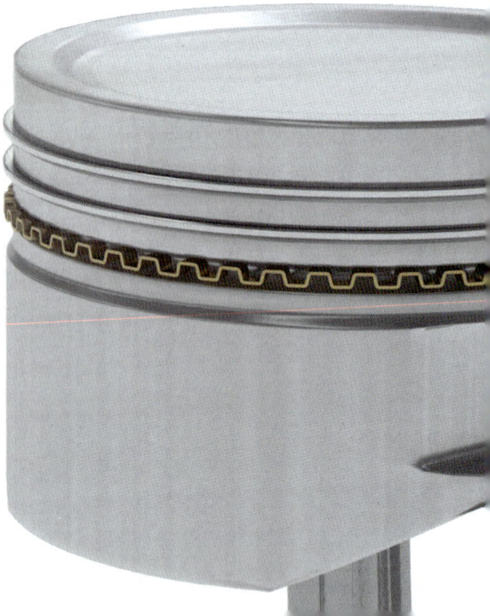

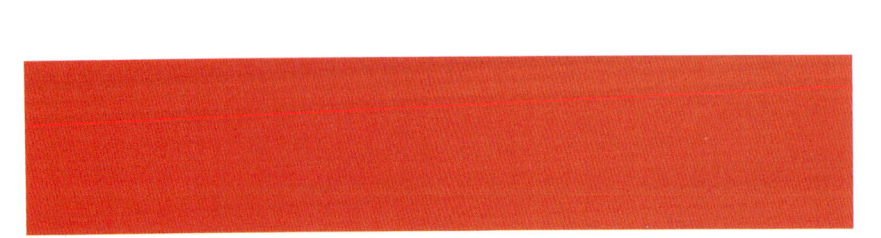

16. Cooling System: Maintenance

COOLING SYSTEM MONITORING: INSTRUMENTATION

1. Introduction

The cooling system must be working properly at all times. If the engine becomes too hot or remains too cold, damage or wear could occur. As part of the maintenance process, the cooling system must be checked. If the cooling system does not function properly, check it to determine the cause. If there is leakage, the coolant will leave green/white traces.

2. Signals

The cooling system can malfunction, causing the engine to run either too hot or cold. This can lead to serious engine damage and/or increased harmful tailpipe emissions if left uncorrected.

In order to prevent engine damage, dashboard instrumentation and warning indicators signal the driver that there's a problem.
The signals relate to the:
— coolant temperature
— coolant level

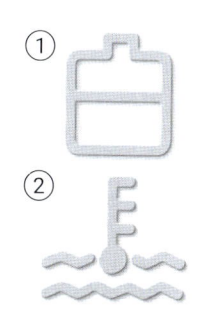

Fig. 683 Warning symbols: 1. Coolant level. 2. Coolant temperature.

3. Engine Coolant Temperature

Coolant temperature

The coolant temperature can be displayed in two ways:
— analog gauge
— digital gauge

The temperature sensor passes the temperature of the coolant to the instrument cluster via data received from the ECU.
The temperature sensor is located in the engine block, thermostat housing or radiator side tank.

There's a warning light on the instrument cluster if not equipped with a temperature gauge.
If the temperature of the coolant becomes too high, the light comes on.

Fig. 684 Possible positions of the temperature sensor: 1. Radiator. 2. Thermostat. 3. Engine block.

NOTE If the coolant level becomes very low, so that the temperature sensor is surrounded by air and not coolant, the temperature gauge may register cooler than actual engine temperature.

Fig. 685 Reading methods: 1. Analog. 2. Digital.

Fig. 686 Coolant temperature warning signal (1).

4. Coolant Level

Level and Temperature

The level control warns the driver if the coolant level becomes too low.

This can be done in two ways:
— warning light
— audible alarm

The level sensor indicates the coolant level by means of a warning light or audible alarm. The sensor is typically mounted in the expansion tank.

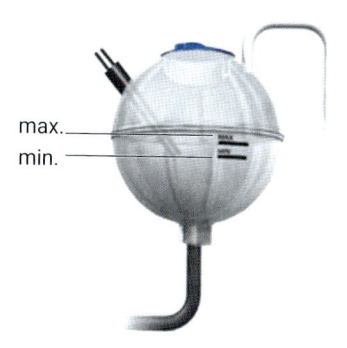

Fig. 687 Expansion tank with coolant level sensor.

Fig. 688 Coolant level sensor.

Operation

The level signal consists of a sensor and a notification system. The level sensor is located in the expansion tank or in the radiator's water tank. If the coolant level becomes too low, the sensor will ensure that a light will turn on or that the display will show a message. A buzzer can also give an alert.

The engine management system of several car manufacturers can store signals so that it is possible to read on which date and at which mileage the warning signal was shown.

5. Mechanical inspection

There are some mechanical parts of the coolant system which must always be inspected. The thermostat is one of these parts.

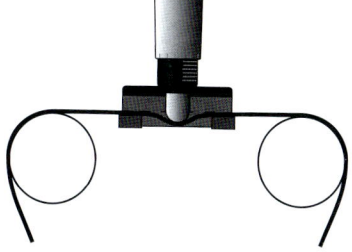

Fig. 689 Belt tension.

Serpentine belt
— Belt tension.
— Cracks in the belt. If there are any cracks in the belt, it must be replaced.
— Damage or detachment of rubber, or unravelling of layers.

Fan
— Check drive.
— Check the point at which it switches on. The engine temperature must not enter the red temperature zone.

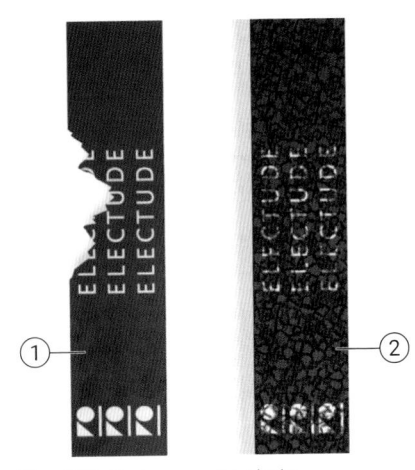

Fig. 690 Bad serpentine belt:
1. Damaged. 2. Dried out.

Thermostat operation
— Switch on the cold engine. The upper hose of the engine to the radiator should not become warm immediately. The main valve must be closed. If it no longer closes properly, water will immediately be pumped from the engine through the radiator. If this is the case, the thermostat must be replaced.
— When the engine heats up to operating temperature, the upper hose between the engine and the radiator should quickly become warm as the thermostat opens.

ANTIFREEZE GAUGE

1. Introduction

Coolant consists of water and an additive. The additive keeps the coolant from freezing.
If there's too little additive in the coolant, it will freeze.

This can cause cracks or ruptures in:
- the engine block
- the cylinder head
- the radiator
- the coolant hoses

In order to prevent cracks, you must check the freeze protection of the coolant before cold weather sets in.

2. Operation

You can determine the freezing point of antifreeze/coolant using an optical gauge.

To measure the freezing point, you must:

1. Remove coolant from the cooling system.
2. Raise the gauge cover.
3. Let a drop of coolant fall on the glass plate.
4. Lower the gauge cover.
5. Read the freezing point on the scale by looking through the site glass.

When you read the freezing point, you'll notice that there are two scales: one for propylene glycol and one for ethylene glycol. The coolant packaging will tell you which type of coolant you're dealing with. Ethylene glycol is most commonly used today.

The freezing point of the coolant needs to be at least -15°F (-25°C), for the cooling system to be considered well protected against freezing.

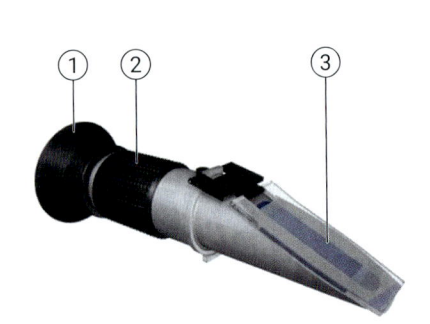

Fig. 691 1. View hole. 2. Optical meter. 3. Lid/glass plate.

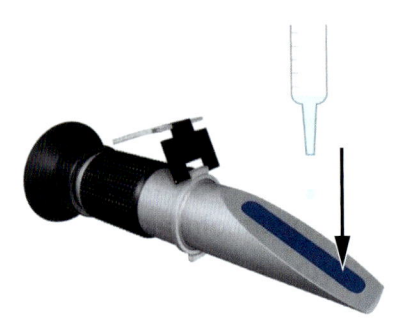

Fig. 692 Placing a drop of coolant onto the glass plate.

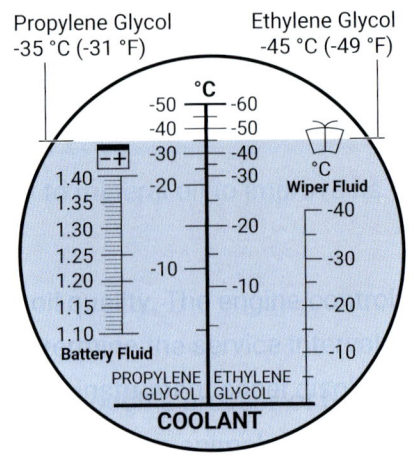

Fig. 693 Reading the freezing point.

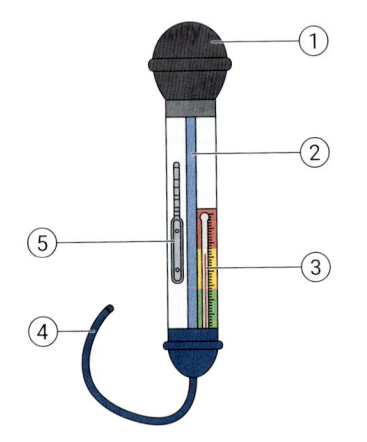

Fig. 694 Antifreeze tester with built-in temperature correction: 1. Rubber ball. 2. Glass tube. 3. Thermometer. 4. Rubber hose. 5. Driver.

3. Specific gravity

Coolant is a mixture of water and ethylene glycol. The mixing ratio determines the specific mass of the mixture.

By measuring the specific mass with an antifreeze tester, the freezing point can be determined.
The temperature of the mixture affects the specific mass.

An automatic temperature correction has been built into the tester. After the coolant is sucked up, the temperature at which the measured mixture will freeze will be displayed.
Generally, a value of at least -15°F is considered safe. Using this tester, you can read the freezing point directly from the position of the driver.

There are also testers that have a thermometer and a driver with a letter code. Using the values measured, the correct freezing point can be found in a table. You cannot read the freezing point directly on these testers.

REPLACING ENGINE COOLANT

1. General

Coolant will break down during the course of its service life. As this occurs, the effectiveness of the additives that are used to improve certain characteristics of the engine coolant is reduced.

To prevent excessive wear and corrosion of the cooling system, the coolant needs to be replaced at the intervals specified by the manufacturer.

There are many different coolants of various types with differing compositions and attributes. This is indicated by the color of the coolant.
Always pay attention to which coolant is specified for use in the engine cooling system.

Some engines have been filled with a "Long life" coolant. This coolant is designed to last for the life of the vehicle under normal operating conditions. These coolants must never be mixed with those of a different color.

Caution: Never mix with or add coolant of a different color, because it may cause electrochemical corrosion in the cooling system.

2. Draining Engine Coolant

Coolant can usually be drained from the radiator or from the engine block. Usually, there is a drain valve or drain plug that is intended for this purpose. However, as the cooling system components age, the drain valve may become corroded of weak. Oftentimes this results in the drain valve breaking. If you have concerns about the integrity of the drain valve, you can remove the lower radiator hose and drain the coolant from here.

The parts to which a drain plug or hose have been attached are often made out of plastic. Therefore, they can be damaged easily or

Fig. 695 Radiator with drain plug:
1. Pressure cap. 2. Expansion tank. 3. Drain plug.

break off. If parts are seized, you can spray penetrating fluid in between them and gently work them apart.

Ensure that the cooling system is no longer under pressure or hot before you start to drain the coolant from it. You can do so by carefully loosening the cap on the radiator or the expansion tank. Failure to remove the pressure cap will prevent air from entering the system, which will cause the coolant to drain very slowly.

You should also ensure that the heater bypass valve is open so that the heater-core will completely drain. Always inspect the color of the drained coolant and check to see if there are any metallic parts which may indicate component wear. The drained coolant can also contain debris and other contaminants such as engine oil or transmission fluid.

Always drain used engine coolant into a labeled container and dispose of it in an environmentally-friendly way. Engine coolant contains hazardous and poisonous materials; take care not to get any coolant in your eyes or on your skin. Should this happen, rinse the exposure site thoroughly with water. Also, be sure not to inhale any vapors generated during the process.

3. Flushing the Cooling System

The cooling system can be flushed if necessary to clean it out during service. If the coolant hasn't been seriously contaminated, tap water can be used for this portion of the service.

If the cooling system is very contaminated, and the coolant is the color of rust, then special cooling system cleaners should be used.

4. Cooling System Filling and Bleeding

When filling, you must always ensure that no air remains inside the cooling system. Always fill a cooling system as specified by the manufacturer in the service information.

PLEASE NOTE Cooling systems with an electric coolant pump may have a different procedure. Consult the vehicle service information!

Air bleeder screws may be installed at several locations. Always unscrew these, so that the air can escape through them. When there is no more air coming through the bleeders, they can be screwed back into place.
It is also possible to carefully detach a hose from a high point in the cooling system while filling, and then re-attach it again once coolant comes out of it.

Consult the vehicle service information in advance to see how many gallons of coolant the cooling system holds. Then, take note of how much coolant you have added. You can then determine how much air is still inside the system.

Let the engine reach operating temperature and depress the accelerator pedal from time to time to increase the engine speed. Check if the cooling fans cycle on. Add coolant to the coolant reservoir and tighten the pressure cap on the expansion tank. Next, let the engine run for a bit until the cooling fan cycle on again. Check the engine temperature gauge, the air bleeder screws, and hose connections that have been detached.

Once the engine has cooled down, check the coolant level and top this up to maximum.

5. Vacuum Filling Cooling System.

Due to the complexity of modern cooling systems, it can be very difficult to purge all of the air from the system. This can create air pockets that will severely compromise the performance of the cooling system.

To prevent this from happening, it is possible to fill the cooling system using a vacuum filling system.

The device is installed on the expansion tank, and contains a main body with a gauge and two hoses. Compressed shop air pressure is applied to one of the hoses, which passes across a venturi and creates a vacuum. This allow all of the air to be evacuated from the cooling system.
The other hose of the device is submerged in clean coolant.

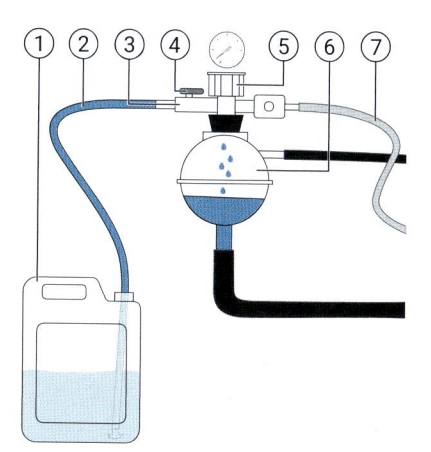

Fig. 696 Vacuum filling system: 1. Container of coolant. 2. Supply hose. 3. Vacuum filling device. 4. Valve. 5. Vacuum gauge. 6. Expansion tank. 7. Air hose.

During this process, a negative pressure will be created inside of the cooling system. You can read the amount of vacuum present on the device's vacuum gauge. Once almost all of the air has been removed from the cooling system, a valve on the device is opened, and the new coolant is sucked into the cooling system, and fills the voids created by the vacuum. This ensures that all areas are filled with coolant. The cooling system is now fully filled with coolant and contains no residual air.

Too much air inside the cooling system stops it from dissipating heat efficiently. The battery pack in hybrid vehicles may be damaged if these cooling systems are not refilled with a vacuum filling device. In combustion engines, this overheating can result in serious engine damage.

6. Complex Cooling Systems

Cooling systems are becoming increasingly complex because new regulations are constantly being enacted that have to be met by modern engines. Engines have a smaller capacity, but they are continuously being improved to offer more and more power. By also meeting the regulations for exhaust emissions, the cooling system can also include a liquid-cooled intercooler(s) in forced-induction-fed engines.

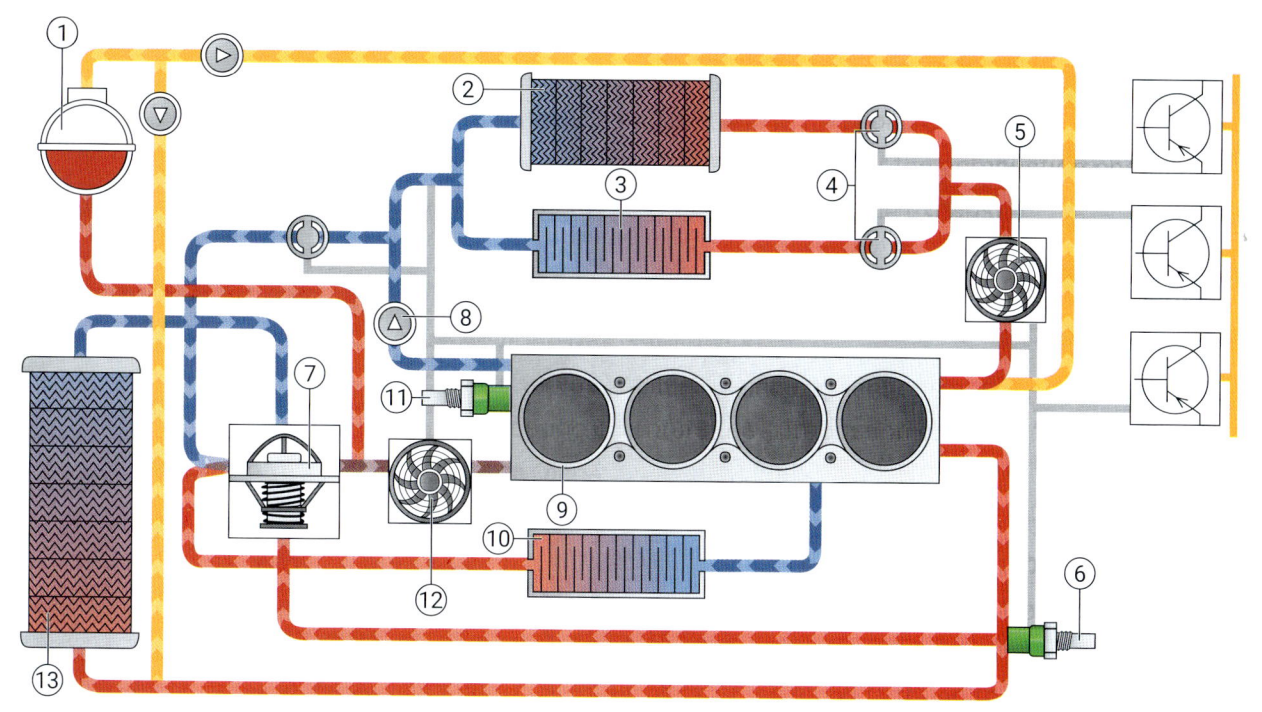

Fig. 697 Modern cooling system: 1. Reservoir. 2. Heater core. 3. Automatic heat exchanger. 4. Shut-off valve. 5. Circulation pump. 6. Coolant temperature sensor. 7. Thermostat. 8. Check valve. 9. Engine block. 10. Oil cooler. 11. Engine temperature sensor. 12. Additional coolant pump. 13. Radiator.

Because there are more stringent regulations that must be met by modern engines, the coolant passages are must be more complex. The engine block and cylinder head are made with very accurate casting processes.

In hybrid cars, the battery pack can also be cooled by a liquid cooling system. There are thin channels surrounding the batteries through which coolant transfers heat from the batteries to the cooling plates.

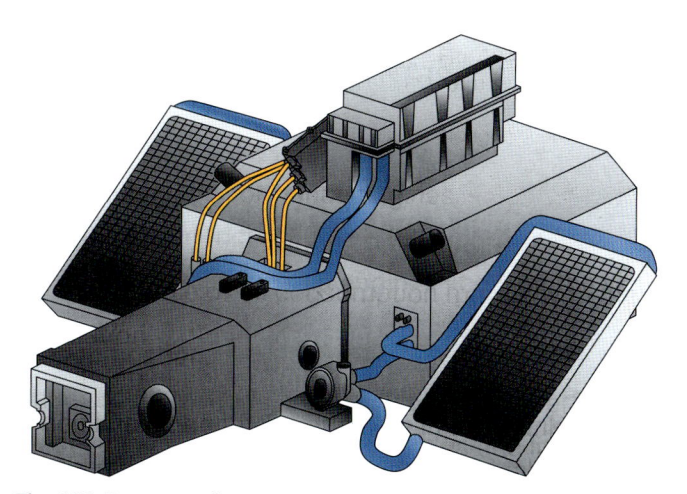

Fig. 698 Battery cooling in an electric Formula E car.

7. Disposing of Used Coolant

Always dispose of coolant in an environmentally-friendly and responsible way. Coolant contains hazardous substances. At the shop, waste should be separated and disposed of properly.

Never mix coolant with other fluids.

Some coolants are biodegradable and are considered to be harmless. Those are coolants based on monopropylene glycol.

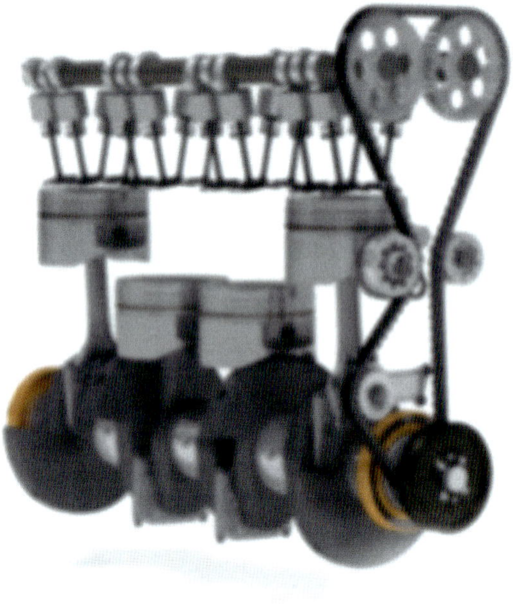

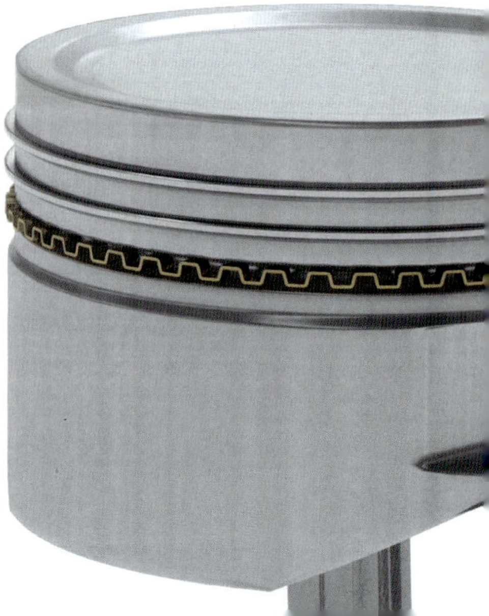

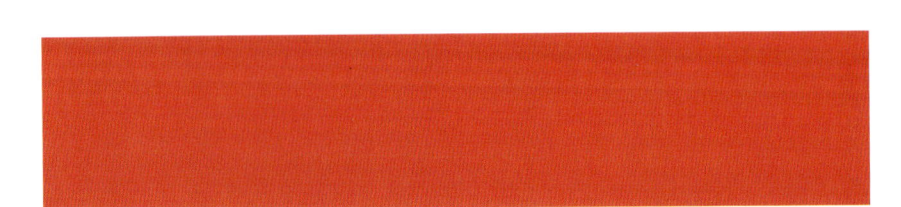

17. Cooling System: Diagnostics

COOLING SYSTEM PRESSURE TESTER

Fig. 699 Corrosion of the radiator.

1. Leakage

Engine cooling systems can develop leaks over time. If the system is losing coolant, you should inspect the following areas for external leaks:

— Coolant hoses and connections
— Radiator tanks
— Water pump
— Core plugs (freeze plugs)
— Intake manifold gasket
— Head gasket
— Engine block

These problems are often identified by performing a careful visual inspection.

To guarantee the proper functioning of the cooling system, the system must be checked during routine maintenance.

Check points

Colored deposits may form from coolant leakage. When this is observed, always check the cooling system to find out what is causing the leak. Spark plugs exhibiting rust deterioration or coolant staining could indicate a coolant leak into that cylinder.

Hoses
— Leakage
— Dry cracks
— Hardening rubber
— Thickening from oil or fluid contamination

Replace hoses if they are not smooth, if they are swollen, or if they are pinched.
Please note that any mineral corrosion/deposits on a hose connection surface should be removed from the metal hose connection before replacing the hose.

Fig. 700 Leaking at the hose clamp

Hose clamps
Check that the hose clamps are correctly positioned and tighten if slight corrosion or deposits are visible on the end of the hose.

Radiator
— Damage to the core
— Corrosion on the core, especially at the bottom
— Look for deposits caused by leaks/seepage
— Damaged rubber bushings at fastening points of the radiator. The radiator's plastic end tanks often crack and leak on high mileage vehicles.

NOTE On modern aluminum/plastic radiators, leaks frequently occur at the seal between the core and the plastic tanks.

Water pump
— A leaking shaft seal is often a sign of worn out water pump bearings. There is a weep hole in the water pump housing through which the leaked coolant can drain. Make sure that there is no visible trace of deposits here. Always replace the water pump if leakage is visible on or around the pump. No leakage should be visible on the gasket or seal.

Coolant
— Check the coolant level in the expansion or recovery tank.

17. COOLING SYSTEM: DIAGNOSTICS   673

— Be sure of proper mixture. Measure the freezing and boiling points of the coolant with a hydrometer or refractometer.

2. Detecting External Leaks

If there are no traces of external leaks, use the pressure tester to help locate the leak.
These are the steps you must follow:

— Remove the pressure cap.

Warning!
Never loosen the pressure cap on the expansion tank or radiator when the engine is hot. Rapid release of pressure will cause hot coolant to rapidly boil over, possibly causing severe burns to your body, hands, or face.

— Ensure the system is full of coolant before beginning the test.
— Install a pressure tester in place of the pressure cap.
— Bring the cooling system up to the prescribed pressure.

If the pressure drops within five minutes, look for a leak somewhere in the cooling system.

Fig. 701 Leaking water pump

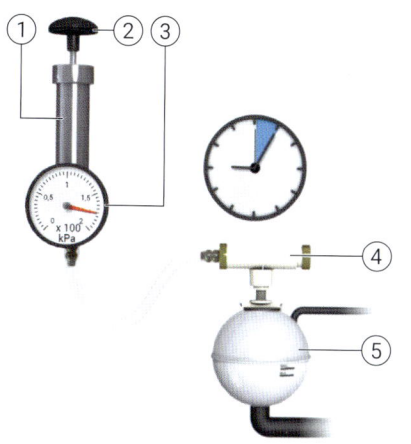

Fig. 702 The cooling system pressure tester: 1. Pressure pump. 2. Handle. 3. Pressure gauge. 4. Adapter. 5. Expansion tank.

cooling system		
opening pressure of the cap	1.5 * 100 kPa	22 psi
thermostat opens at	84 - 98 °C	183.2 - 208.4 °F
cooling system test pressure	1.6 * 100 kPa	23 psi
fan	98 - 102 °C	208.4 - 215.6 °F
electric		
battery	36/44 Ah	36/44 Ah
alternator	70 - 90 A	70 - 90 A
content		
engine sump, including the filter	3.2 L	0.7 gal
cooling system	5.6 L	1.23 gal

Fig. 703 The cooling system operating pressure can be found in the service manual of the car or printed on the pressure cap.

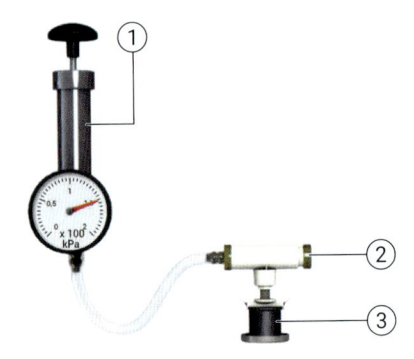

Fig. 704 Testing the pressure cap (3) with the aid of the pressure tester (1) and the correct adapter (2).

3. Testing the Pressure Cap

You can also use the cooling system pressure tester to test the pressure cap.

Mount the pressure tester on the pressure cap using the appropriate adapter.

The system pressure indicated by a manufacturer may vary depending on brand and type. The values are generally between 11 - 18 psi overpressure.
You can find the correct values in the vehicle service information.

COMBUSTION LEAK DETECTOR

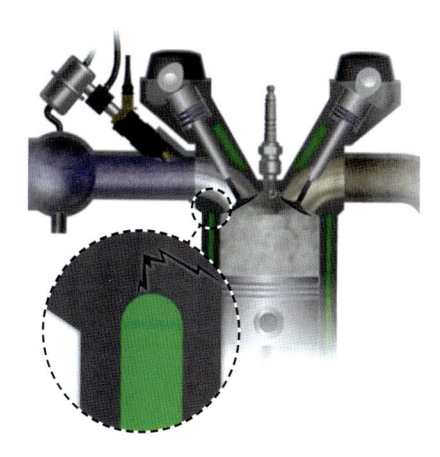

Fig. 705 Combustion Leak Detector

1. Internal Leaks

When the head gasket fire ring fails on one or more cylinders, compression can be forced into the coolant passages. This causes cooling system pressure buildup and overheating concerns.

Larger internal leaks may cause a rapid pressure increase that can be detected by starting the engine cold (coolant full) and running it for a minute or so while feeling the upper radiator hose. A rapid pressure increase indicates a head gasket leak.
Smaller internal leaks of this type can be found with a combustion leak detector kit.

Exhaust gas from a gasoline engine consists mainly of CO_2 gas. The combustion leak tester detects the amount of CO_2 in the cooling system.

2. Combustion Leak Detector

With the combustion leak detector placed at the position of the radiator/expansion tank, the tester can monitor the CO_2 gas in the cooling system.

Before starting the test, you must ensure the following:
- Both reservoirs of the combustion leak detector are filled with blue test liquid.
- The pressure cap is removed.
- The engine is up to operating temperature.

The coolant level should be a few centimeters lower than the pressure cap where the tester is installed, and the rubber ball at the top should be pinched five times.

NOTE Only gas should be drawn up into the tester, not liquid!

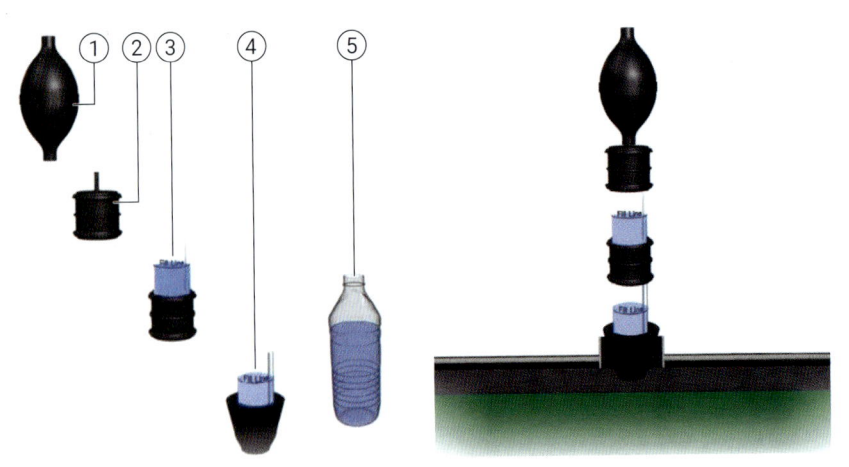

Fig. 706 The combustion leak detector: 1. Rubber ball. 2. Top cap. 3. Upper reservoir. 4. Bottom reservoir. 5. Tester liquid.

Fig. 707 The combustion leak detector at the place of the pressure cap.

3. Operation

If there is CO_2 in the cooling system, the test fluid will change color:
— For a gasoline engine, it will turn yellow.
— For a diesel engine, it will turn green.

If only the lower reservoir changes color, this means you have a minor leak that does not have to be repaired right away.

If the lower and upper reservoirs change color, this means you have a major leak that must be repaired right away.

Fig. 708 The tester fluid in the lower reservoir turns yellow. There is no leakage of the cylinder head gasket.

Fig. 709 The tester fluid in the lower and upper reservoir turns yellow. There is leakage of the cylinder head gasket.

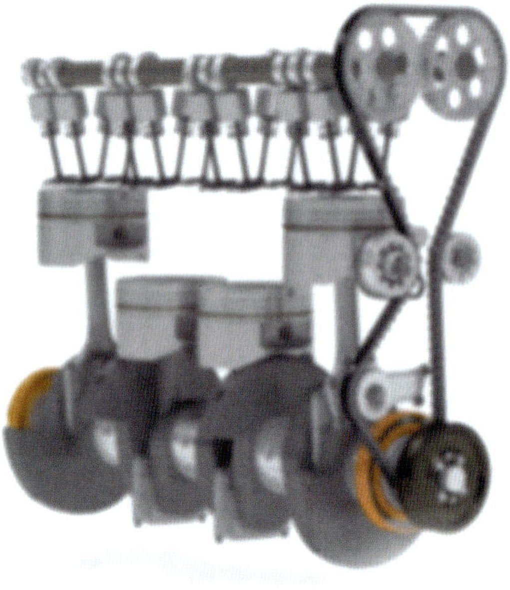

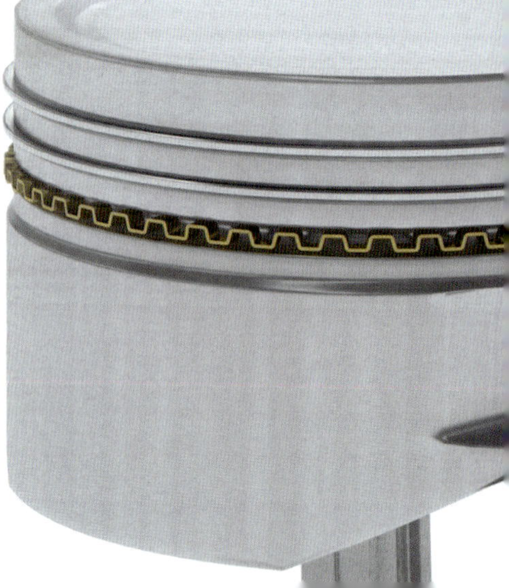

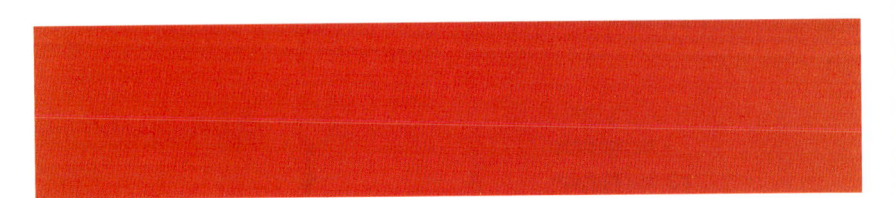

18. Intake System

INTAKE SYSTEM INTRODUCTION

1. Introduction

The intake system provides the supply of air to the engine and ensures that the intake sound is dampened.

The construction and execution of the system depend on the type of engine.

In the image we see the air flow through the various components of the intake system. The air enters through the air filter and flows along the intake path to the cylinders.

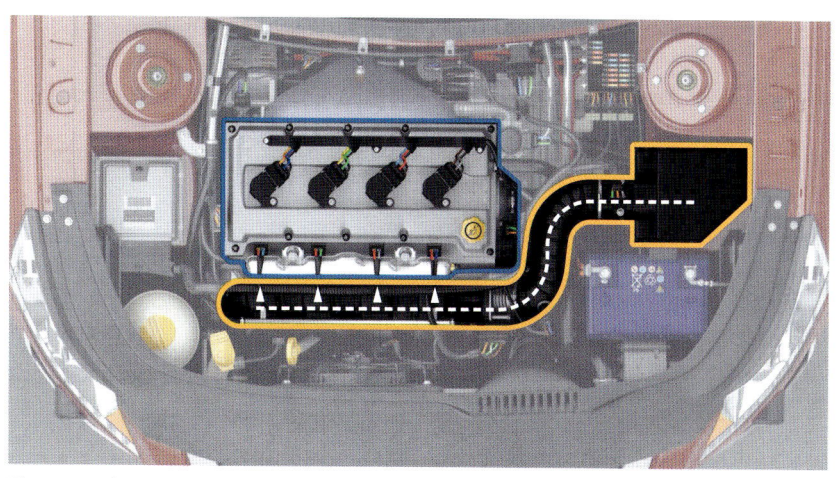

Fig. 710 The intake system: blue = engine l yellow = intake tract.

2. Air filter

The first component in the intake system is the air filter. The air filter element is located in the air filter housing and allows the outside air to flow into the engine. The air filter element catches dust particles so that they do not enter the engine. The ductwork connects the air cleaner housing to the throttle body.

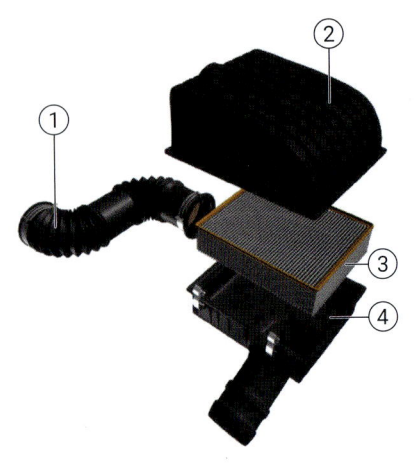

Fig. 711 The air filter: 1. Intake tube. 2. Lid. 3. Filter element. 4. Air cleaner tray.

Fig. 712 Air filter

3. MAF: Mass Air Flow Sensor

The mass air flow (MAF) sensor is usually located near the air filter and measures the air mass that is drawn in by the engine. This information is transmitted by the wiring to the electronic control unit of the engine.

Fig. 713 The mass air flow sensor. 1. Electrical connector 2. Intake 3. Outlet

Fig. 714 The mass air flow sensor mounted to the air cleaner housing.

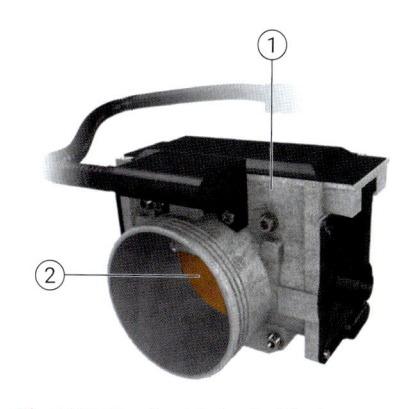

Fig. 715 The throttle body (1), the throttle plate (2).

4. Throttle valve assembly

The throttle body is bolted onto the intake manifold and controls the flow of air into the engine.

In a gasoline engine, the position of the throttle plate depends on the position of the accelerator pedal. The more power required, the more the throttle plate must be opened. In late model vehicles, the throttle plate is operated electrically. In older cars, it is done mechanically by way of a cable.

Fig. 716 The throttle body mounted on the intake manifold.

5. Intake Manifold

The intake manifold ensures the distribution of air across the cylinders. The connection must between the intake manifold and throttle body must be airtight and efficient.

The length and shape of the runners that carry air to the individual cylinders is very important. All cylinders need to receive exactly the same amount of air.

There are also a number of connections and sensors for various systems on the intake manifold.

Fig. 717 Intake Manifold

Fig. 718 The intake manifold mounted on the engine.

6. Accessory Ports

The intake manifold is an important part of some other systems through a network of hoses, sensors, and control valves. For just one example, some of the engine management, sensors are mounted in and on the intake, as is the throttle body. The intake is also used as a source of vacuum for the PCV valve, the brake booster, and other systems.

In addition to the sensors, there are the following connections:
— Vacuum hose for the brake booster
— Crankcase ventilation PCV (positive crankcase ventilation) valve emission control
— EGR (exhaust gas recirculation) connection for adding exhaust gas to the intake manifold to control NO_x by lowering combustion temperatures

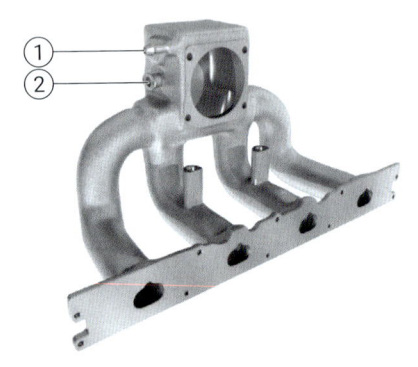

Fig. 719 Connections to the intake manifold. 1. Vacuum connection 2. EGR connection

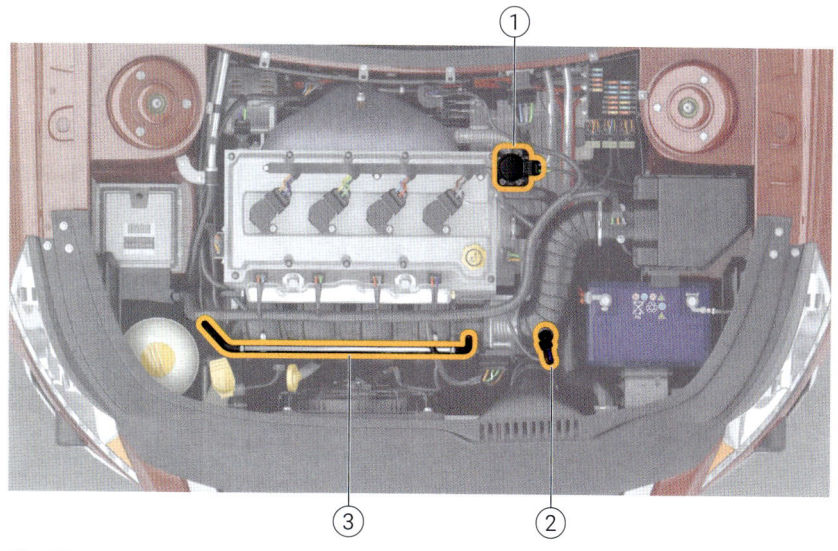

Fig. 720 Connections: 1. EGR valve. 2. Intake air temperature sensor. 3. Vacuum connection (brake booster).

AIR FILTERS

Fig. 721 Air filter

1. Introduction

The air filter supplies the engine with clean air. The abrasiveness of dirt and other fine particles causes engine wear; which leads to poor fuel economy, poor performance, and higher exhaust emissions.

The air filter must stop debris as small as 0.005 mm (0.0002 in.) and store a sufficient amount of debris without restricting air flow. The replacement interval of air filters is usually between 6000 and 20,000 miles (10,000 and 30,000 km), depending on the operational environment and manufacturer recommendations.

Some vehicles are equipped with oil impregnated paper filters. The air filter housing should be replaced if it becomes cracked or damaged. Don't try to patch a cracked filter housing with tape or anything else! Replacing a damaged air filter housing is far less expensive than replacing an entire engine.

Besides cleaning the air, the filter also quiets the suction noise of the intake system.

Because the air is drawn through narrow openings at varying speeds, noise is created (air vibrations). The air filter partially moderates these vibrations. Another task of the air filter is to extinguish flames in the intake system during inductive backfiring events. When the mixture ignites in the intake system due to a defect in the engine, the flame can move through it and possibly set the engine on fire, but the air filter helps prevent this.

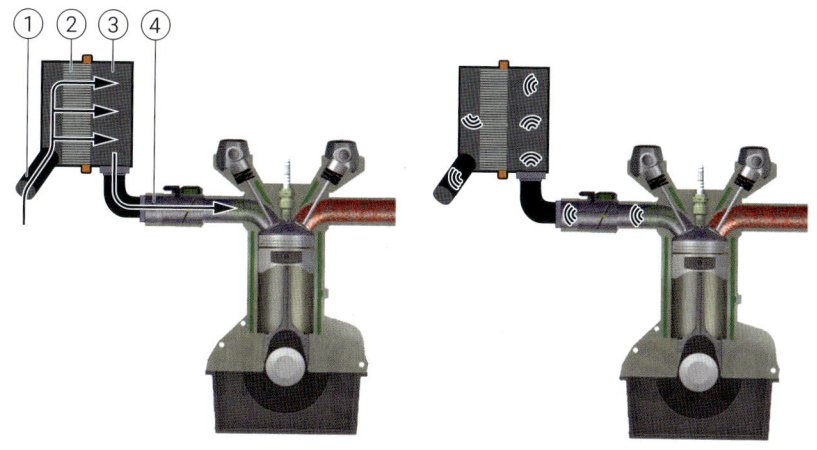

Fig. 722 The air filter in the intake system: 1. Intake tube. 2. Air filter element. 3. Air cleaner housing. 4. Ductwork.

Fig. 723 Sound waves from the intake duct are dampened by the air filter.

2. Dry Air Filter

A dry paper filter is positioned in the middle of an air filter housing. One end of the housing is open to outside air via an inlet tube. A discharge tube on the other side of the filter housing supplies the engine with clean filtered air.

When air flows through the paper filter, dirt and other fine particles are caught in the fibers of the filter element. The paper filter element is pleated (folded) to increase the surface area. This enables the air filter to hold more dirt and debris without restricting air flow.

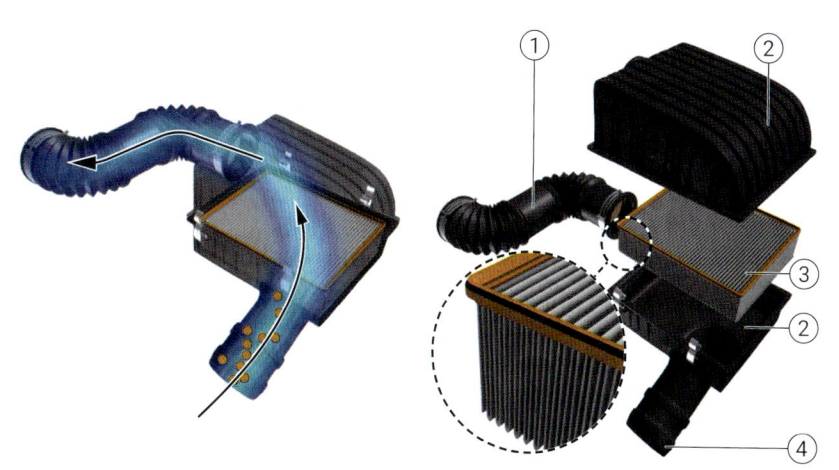

Fig. 724 Air flow through the air filter.

Fig. 725 Components of the air filter: 1. Ductwork. 2. Air cleaner housing. 3. Air filter element. 4. Intake tube.

3. Maintenance of Air Filters

A dirty air filter increases resistance to air flowing to the engine. The resistance in airflow causes the engine to work harder than it should This, in turn, reduces power and fuel economy.

Periodically, the dry air filter's paper filter element needs to be replaced.

When replacing the filter element, consider the following:

— Work according to the manufacturer's maintenance instructions.
— Make sure that dust and dirt cannot enter the mass air flow sensor and the ductwork.
— Use a vacuum to remove dirt from the filter tray.
— Use a cloth and compressed air to clean dust from the filter tray and lid.
— The filter element is mounted in a position that allows filtering of the air in only one direction.
— Make sure the seal around the filter element is connected to the filter tray and cover.
— Make sure the air filter's housing isn't cracked or damaged.

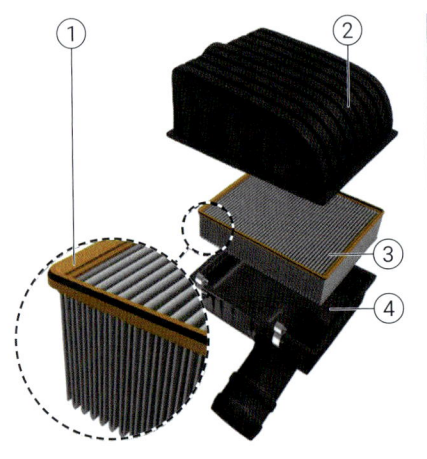

Fig. 726 Replacing an air filter element: 1. Rubber seal. 2. Lid. 3. Filter. element. 4. Air cleaner tray.

Fig. 727 Clean the air filter tray.

HOW TO: USE A SMOKE MACHINE

1. Checking the Ductwork

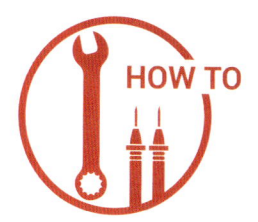

Fig. 735 Tools Required

Fig. 736 Remove the air filter and the mass air flow sensor.

Fig. 737 Place the smoke hose in the intake of the ductwork. Make sure it seals properly so that the smoke ends up in the duct.

Fig. 738 Start the smoke machine and check if smoke is released from the ductwork.

Fig. 739 In this case, there is a leak present; the smoke is released because there is a leak in the connection of the rubber hose. This connection must be repaired.

2. Checking the Exhaust

Fig. 740 Place the smoke hose in the exhaust tail pipe. Make sure it seals properly and that the smoke ends up in the exhaust system.

Fig. 741 Start the smoke machine and check if smoke is released from the exhaust system.

Fig. 742 You can observe in the picture that smoke is being released at the exhaust clamp.

Fig. 743 The exhaust clamp must be tightened or repaired to ensure that the exhaust is perfectly sealed.

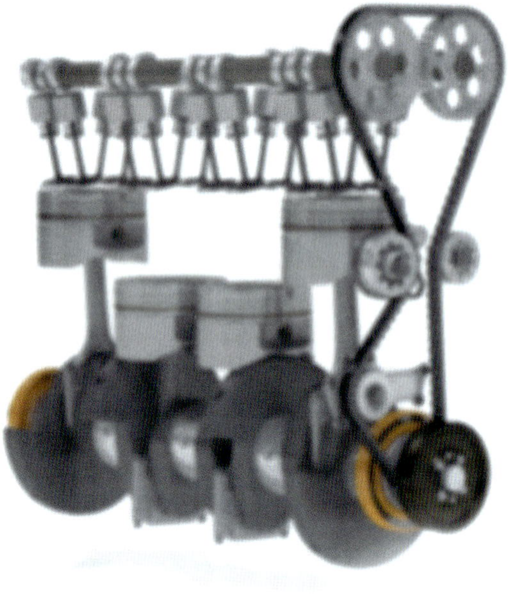

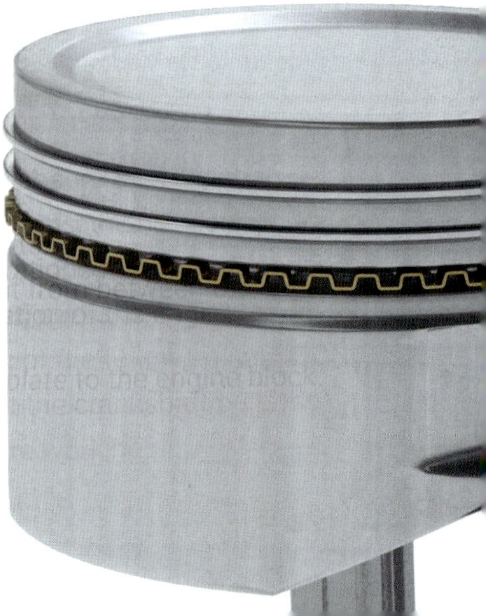

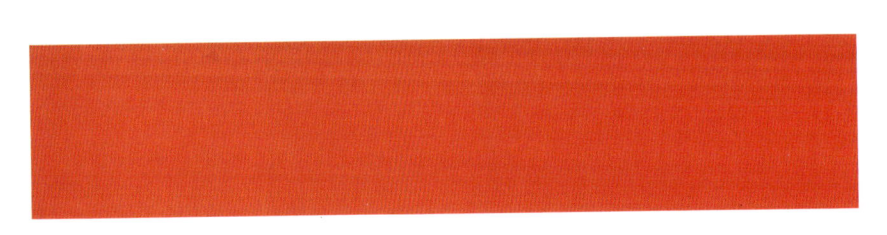

19. Exhaust System

EXHAUST SYSTEM INTRODUCTION

1. Introduction

The exhaust system is usually located underneath the car and runs from the engine to the rear of the car. Components:
- Exhaust manifold
- Exhaust pipes
- Catalytic converter
- Particulate filter
- Resonator
- Muffler

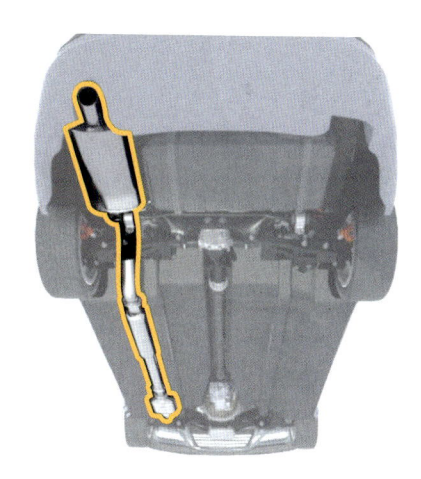

Fig. 745 Under the car view - exhaust system.

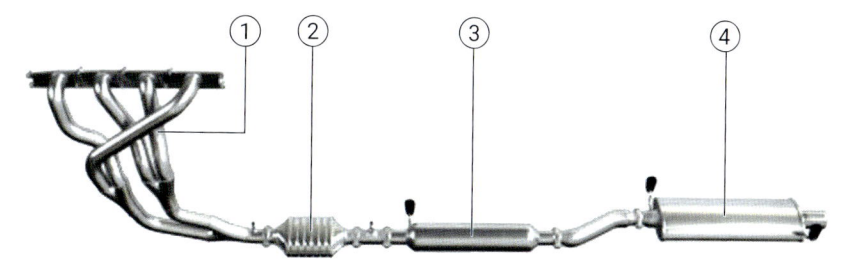

Fig. 746 The exhaust system: 1. Exhaust manifold. 2. Catalytic converter/particulate filter. 3. Resonator. 4. Muffler.

2. Discharge Gases

The most important task of the exhaust system is to guide exhaust gases away from the engine to the outside air. Usually the exhaust system runs under the car from the front to the rear where the gases leave the system. This ensures that the chance of exhaust gases entering the passenger compartment is minimal.
Exhaust gas contains substances that in high concentrations are hazardous to health.
Exhaust system components must be connected in a gas-tight manner to prevent exhaust gas from leaking and being released under the hood, under the car, and into the passenger compartment. The exhaust system must also be able to remove the heat from the exhaust gas. Exhaust gas must have cooled down sufficiently as it flows out of the tail pipe because hot exhaust gases can cause damage or injury.

3. Exhaust Manifold

Fig. 747 Exhaust Manifold

The exhaust manifold collects the burnt gases from the cylinder and directs them to the exhaust pipe. Depending on the engine type, the exhaust manifold may have several passages that blend into a single passage at the end where the manifold is connected to the pipe.

4. Catalytic Converter and Particulate Filter

To reduce harmful emissions (NO_x, CO, HC – nitrogen oxide, carbon monoxide, hydrocarbons) from the exhaust gas, a catalytic converter is incorporated in the exhaust system for gasoline engines. Sometimes the gasoline engine has two catalytic converters, one for NO_x, and the other for CO and HC. Diesel engines have an oxidation catalytic converter and a particulate, filter depending on the system. Sometimes this is extended with an NO_x catalytic converter.

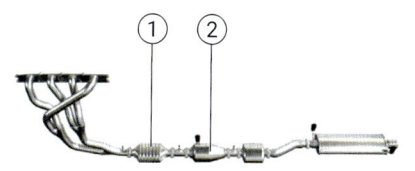

Fig. 748 Exhaust system of a gasoline engine: 1. CO and HC catalytic converter. 2. NO_x catalytic converter.

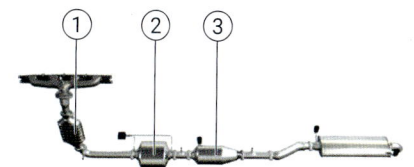

Fig. 749 Exhaust system of a diesel engine: 1. Oxidation catalytic converter. 2. Particulate filter. 3. NO_x catalytic converter.

5. Muffler and Resonator

Another important task of the exhaust system is to muffle the exhaust noise. For this purpose multiple mufflers are often included in the exhaust system. Examples may include a center resonator and a rear muffler. There are different techniques to muffle sound waves in the exhaust system; therefore, you can encounter different shapes and versions of mufflers under a car.

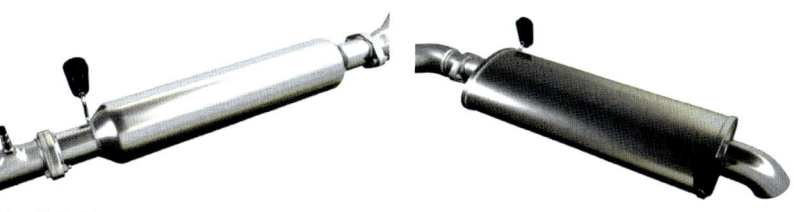

Fig. 750 Resonator.

Fig. 751 Muffler.

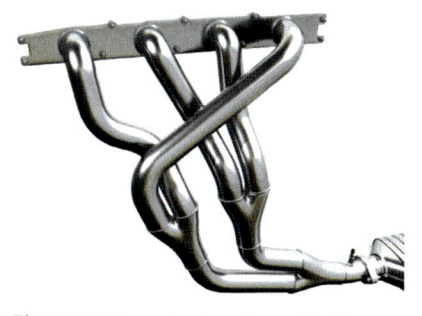

Fig. 752 A tuned exhaust manifold called a header provides a better flow.

6. Types of Exhaust Systems

An exhaust system can be constructed in various ways. To meet all requirements, a manufacturer chooses certain components and a way of construction.

Normal

A normal car has an exhaust system that focuses on low production costs and compliance with environmental requirements. This can sometimes be at the expense of the engine power or the service life of the exhaust.

Sport

In sportier cars you often see a different exhaust system design focused on creating a flow of exhaust gases that enables the engine to deliver more power. A car with such a system must still meet all

Fig. 753 The exhaust manifold with EGR connection (1).

7. Accessory Ports

Both intake and exhaust systems can be fitted with facilities to ensure cleaner exhaust gases. These facilities are also called emission controls.

EGR

The EGR (exhaust gas recirculation) system uses a valve to connect the exhaust system to the intake system. Opening the EGR valve allows the higher pressure from the exhaust to provide its flow into the intake manifold. Every cylinder gets the same amount. This reduces combustion chamber temperatures which reduces NO_x levels.

Secondary Air System

The secondary air system uses an air pump and air valve to introduce extra air into the exhaust system, which provides secondary combustion of the exhaust gases. Due to incomplete combustion during the cold start and warm-up phase, unburned fuel enters the exhaust. The exhaust gases are already hot, so the added air oxidizes the mixture, converting unburned HCs (hydrocarbons) into harmless carbon dioxide and water. An additional advantage is the warm up of the catalytic converter.

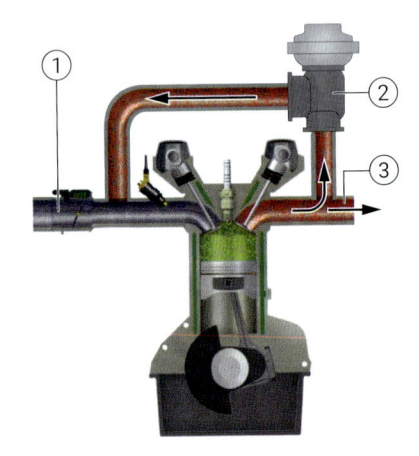

Fig. 754 The EGR system: 1. Intake system. 2. EGR valve. 3. Exhaust system.

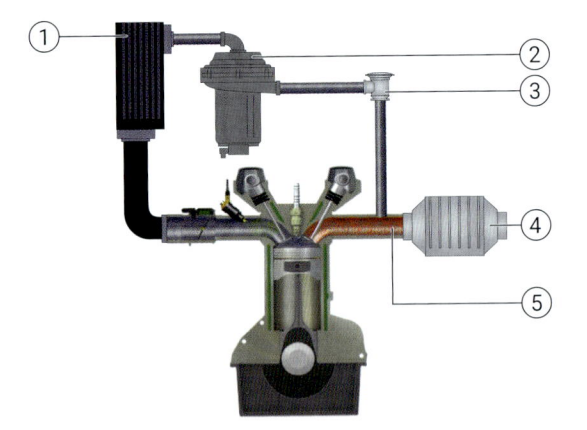

Fig. 755 The secondary air system: 1. Air filter. 2. Secondary air pump. 3. Secondary air valve. 4. Catalytic converter. 5. Exhaust system

EXHAUST PIPES

1. Materials

Most exhaust systems are made of steel with a layer of zinc. The layer of zinc helps prevent rust; however some rust is inevitable. More expensive exhaust systems are made of stainless steel. These exhaust systems can last for the entire life of a car.

2. Attachment

There are different ways to connect exhaust pipes and components. The simplest is the sliding connection where one pipe is pushed into the other. They are then clamped together with an exhaust clamp that squeezes the outer pipe around the inner one.

Fig. 756 Sliding connection with clamp: 1. Pipe with larger diameter. 2. Exhaust clamp. 3. Pipe with smaller diameter.

Flanges at the ends of pipes or components provide another to connect them. Clamping the flanges together with bolts and nuts makes a tight connection. In certain cases a gasket is placed between the flanges for a better seal.

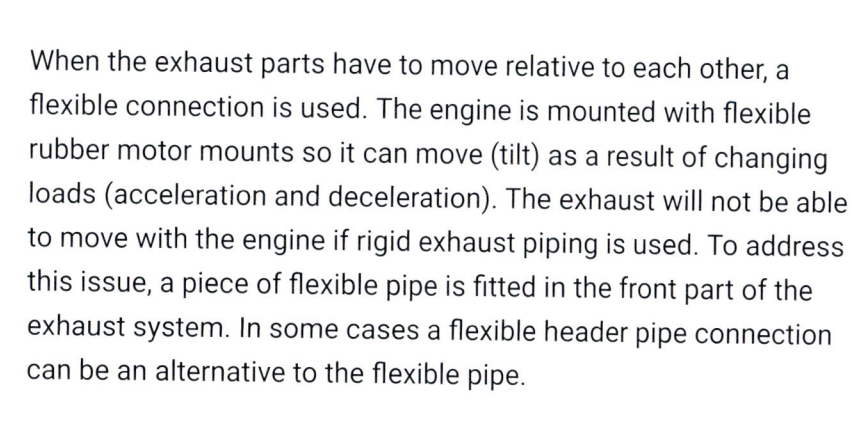

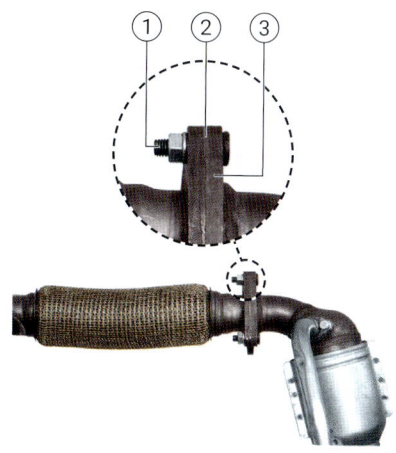

When the exhaust parts have to move relative to each other, a flexible connection is used. The engine is mounted with flexible rubber motor mounts so it can move (tilt) as a result of changing loads (acceleration and deceleration). The exhaust will not be able to move with the engine if rigid exhaust piping is used. To address this issue, a piece of flexible pipe is fitted in the front part of the exhaust system. In some cases a flexible header pipe connection can be an alternative to the flexible pipe.

Fig. 757 Flange connection: 1. Fixing bolt. 2. Gasket. 3. Flange.

Fig. 758 Flexible pipe.

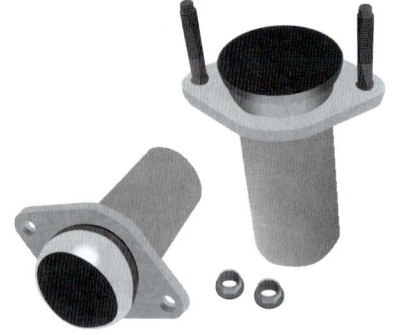

Fig. 759 Flange connection.

Fig. 760 Types of the exhaust clamps.

3. Suspension

Rubber exhaust hangers prevent engine vibrations from being transmitted via the exhaust system into the car body.
Not only vibrations but also changes in length caused by expansion of the exhaust system are absorbed in this way.
The degree of suspension flexibility must be carefully controlled. With too much movement in the suspension, the exhaust system can come into contact with the chassis or other parts. If the suspension is too stiff, unwanted energy can be passed to the exhaust system. This can cause cracks in the pipes and other exhaust parts.

4. Inspection and Maintenance

The exhaust system is exposed to extreme conditions during use. Temperatures can fluctuate from very high during normal use to ambient temperature after the system cools down. Conversely, during short trips the exhaust system does not get hot enough, so water vapor in the system condenses into water. The water vapor that condenses may contain acids that are extra harmful to steel parts and can cause interior rust. Untreated rust eventually creates holes in the system which will prevent it from being gas-tight. The exhaust system can also be externally affected by splashing water and winter road salts. The rear part of the exhaust system is the most vulnerable because its colder temperatures make water vapor slow to evaporate.

Regular checking of the exhaust system should be carried out before submitting the vehicle for safety testing and inspections. A simple and quick test is accomplished by tightly holding a rag over

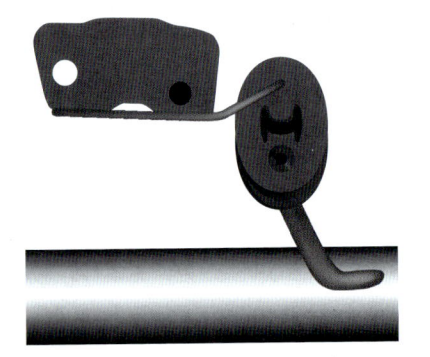

Fig. 761 Rubber hangers must also be checked.

the end of the tailpipe while listening for hissing sounds. If you hear them, then you have a leak that needs further inspection. You can also use a smoke machine to check the exhaust system.

Connectors and attaching bolts are also susceptible to rusting. This can make their removal extremely difficult and can even cause parts to break and come loose.

You can visually check the condition of an exhaust pipe or component. Light surface corrosion does not necessarily mean that the part is in bad condition. If you tap the part carefully with a screwdriver, you can ascertain how deeply the rust has penetrated the steel by the sound it makes. A thoroughly decayed exhaust pipe gives a dull sound.

The rubber hangers that support the exhaust system can dry out or become elongated and must also be checked regularly. Worn or broken rubber hangers/connectors may no longer properly support the exhaust system. This can lead to stress that can damage the pipes and other exhaust parts. The situation can get bad enough that pipes can drop down and be dragged underneath a moving vehicle.

5. Replacing Exhaust Parts

If a part of the exhaust system is worn or damaged, the part must be replaced. Replacement parts are available for all cars. Often these are combinations of mufflers and pipes. These combinations of parts may vary from what was originally installed at the factory. Because of these differences, careful observations must be made before replacing the old parts with new ones.

Removal

Removing exhaust parts can be a tedious task, especially if the fasteners and connections are rusted. Always use suitable tools when removing an exhaust part.

Using twelve-point sockets and wrenches on rusty exhaust fasteners tends to round the fastener off. Exhaust fasteners are best serviced using six-point sockets and wrenches. If the bolt/nut is so rusted that it cannot be loosened by traditional methods, it can help to heat the bolt with a propane or acetylene torch. There are

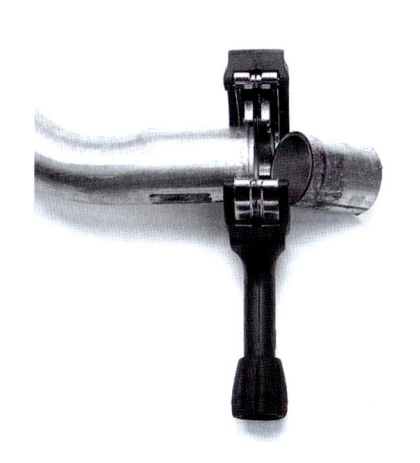

Fig. 762 Tube cutter.

also special electrical tools (induction heaters) on the market that can heat a bolt. Once heat has been applied, cautiously try to loosen the bolt again.

If the bolt can easily be replaced, another option would be to break it intentionally. To remove a piece of pipe or a muffler from the exhaust system, you can also use a pipe cutter. This tool contains cutting discs that work when the tool is placed around the pipe and moved back and forth. As the tool penetrates the pipe, it needs to be slowly tightened until it cuts through.

Installing

When fitting new exhaust parts, attention must be paid to a number of things:
— The connections must be gas-tight. Exhaust assembly paste can be used to create a better seal.
— The entire exhaust system must be suspended free from binding.
— Make sure that the clamps are properly tightened.

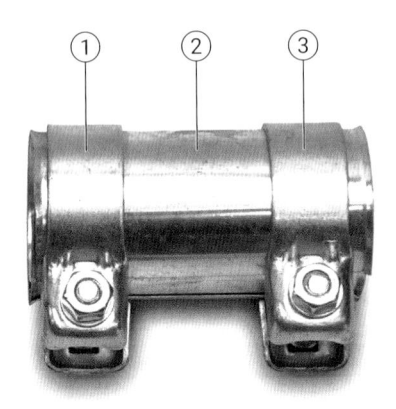

Fig. 763 Coupling piece: 1. Exhaust clamp. 2. Pipe section. 3. Exhaust clamp.

A new gasket must be fitted for flange connections. A sealing ring may also be used with some flexible connections. Make sure that the sealing ring (if reused) and the flexible connection are both in good condition when installing. If a small part of the exhaust system has to be replaced, you can use a coupling piece. This allows you to connect two pieces of pipe with the same diameter.

Fig. 764 Exhaust gaskets.

MUFFLERS

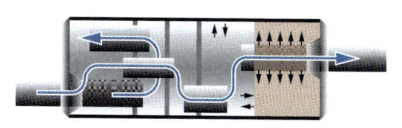

Fig. 765 Different principles can be applied in one muffler.

1. Exhaust Mufflers

Mufflers have been added to the exhaust system to lower the noise to an acceptable level. They muffle the sound waves that exit the exhaust system. Vibrations produce the sound waves that create a lot of noise in the exhaust gases. Below are ways that the muffler can reduce vibrations to achieve sound reduction:
- Absorption
- Reflection
- Expansion
- Interference

Different principles can be applied inside one exhaust muffler. The inner workings of the muffler are not visible from the outside. Some vehicles have an additional muffler known as a resonator or muffler.

Fig. 766 Absorption Muffler.

2. Absorption

In an absorption muffler, the exhaust gases flow through a perforated pipe. A dampening material is fitted around the perforated pipe which absorbs vibrations (sound waves). The vibrations are converted into heat. The dampening material may be steel wool, rock wool, or glass wool.
A single absorption muffler is easy to recognize by looking through one of the openings and seeing the perforated pipe inside.

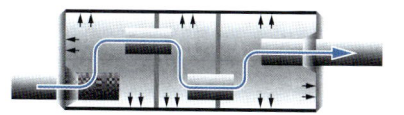

Fig. 767 Reflection muffler.

3. Reflection Muffler

In a reflection muffler, baffles placed on the inside form a resonator chamber that reflects the sound waves. With this arrangement, the sound waves bounce against the baffles and the muffler wall, and are directed back toward their source to disturb other incoming sound waves. This way the sound waves are neutralized and dampened.

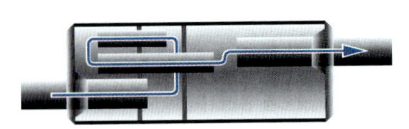

Fig. 768 Expansion muffler.

4. Expansion Muffler

In a muffler that muffles by expansion, the exhaust gas flows through increasingly large pipes and spaces. This allows the exhaust gas to expand and, as a result, the pressure and speed of the gas decrease. This reduces all of the exhaust noise but with better results on the low tones.

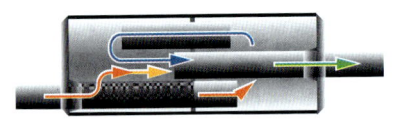

Fig. 769 Interference muffler.

5. Interference Muffler

An interference muffler uses channels of different lengths. The exhaust gas travels a longer distance through one channel than the other. When the gas flows meet again, the sound waves have changed, resulting in a partial canceling effect.

HOW TO: EXHAUST GAS BACK-PRESSURE TEST

1. Check Exhaust Back-pressure Intake Side.

Fig. 770 Tools Required

Fig. 771 Locate a vacuum hose connected to the intake manifold.

Fig. 772 Detach it from the component and connect the vacuum hose to the connection of the vacuum/pressure gauge.

Fig. 773 Start the engine and let it run at idle.

Fig. 774 Read the vacuum in the intake manifold. The vacuum gauge reading should be steady and give a reading of at least 54KPa (16"Hg). For some engines, the intake manifold vacuum could be higher, reaching 74KPa (22"Hg). This vacuum corresponds to the specifications of a properly working engine.

2. Exhaust Back-pressure Test with a Restriction in the Exhaust

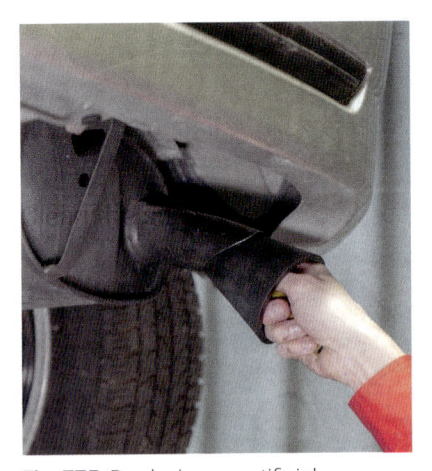

Fig. 775 By placing an artificial restriction in the exhaust, we can see what happens in the intake manifold now.

Fig. 776 Due to the restriction in the exhaust, you can see that the vacuum in the intake manifold decrease, and the needle is not steady. After the test, remove the vacuum gauge and reconnect the vacuum.

3. Measure Exhaust Back-pressure Exhaust Side.

Fig. 777 Tools Required

Fig. 778 Disconnect the oxygen sensor from the exhaust.

Fig. 779 Remove the O_2 sensor from the exhaust.

19. EXHAUST SYSTEM   703

Fig. 780 Mount the test adapter in the thread of the O₂ sensor. Connect the pressure gauge to the adapter.

Fig. 781 Start the car and measure the pressure in the exhaust system. That corresponds to about 9KPa (1.25 psi) at idle and around 14KPa (2psi) at 2,000 rpm. Check for a proper specification in the service manual of the car.

Fig. 782 To show how the pressure develops with a restriction in the exhaust (e.g. a melted catalytic converter), we keep the exhaust artificially closed.

Fig. 783 The exhaust back-pressure is clearly raised when it is a restriction of the exhaust flow or plug in the system.

Fig. 784 With increased rpm, the exhaust back-pressure increases even further. Remove the gauge and the adaptor and mount the O₂ sensor after the test.

Air Conditioning and Electrical Accessories

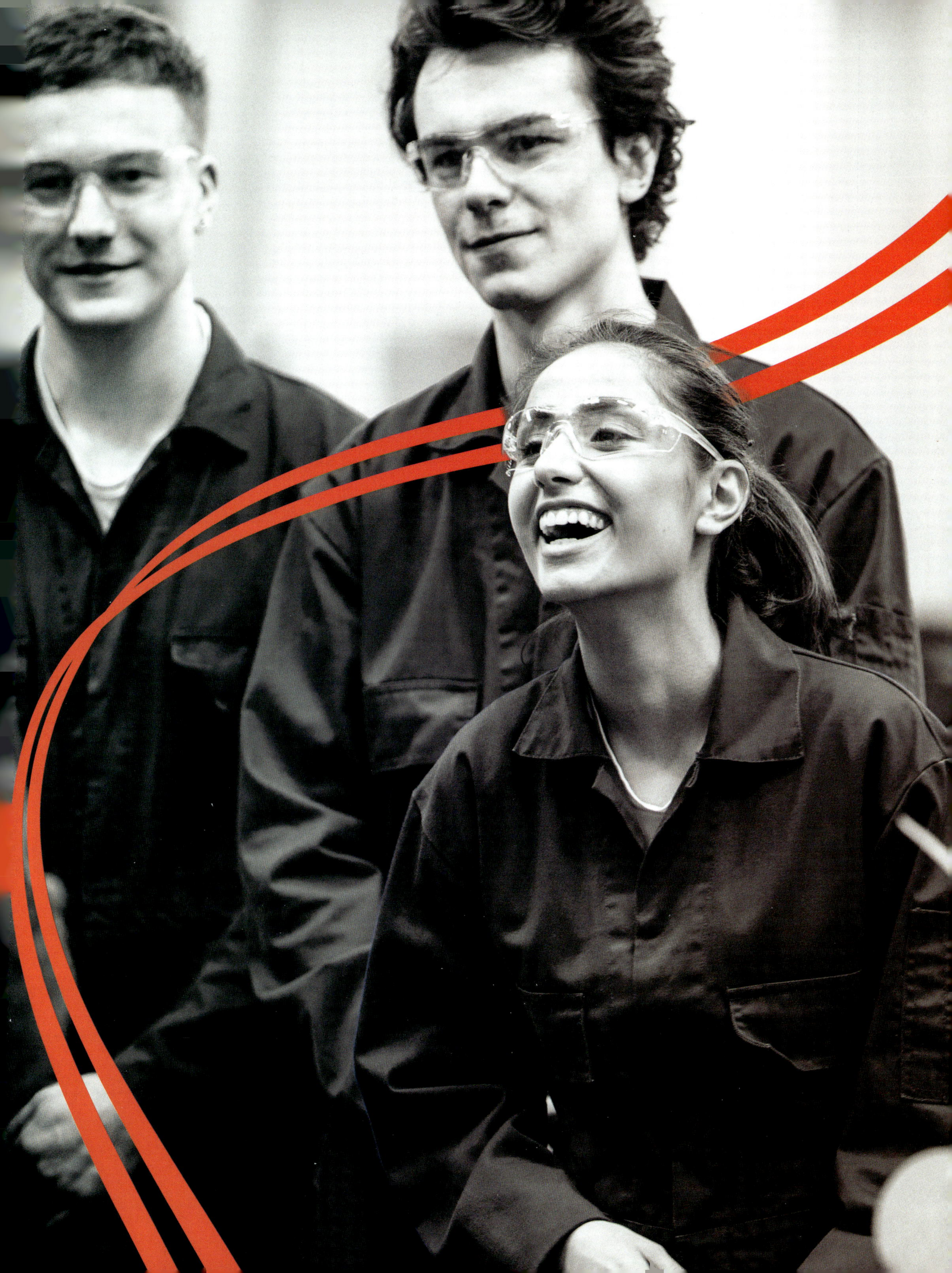

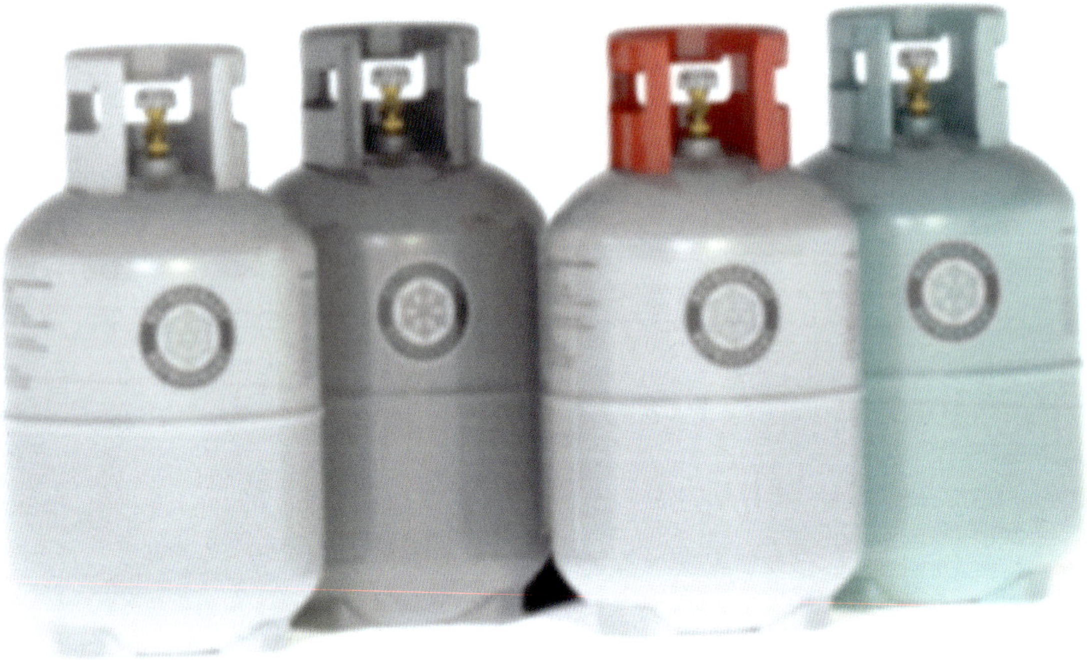

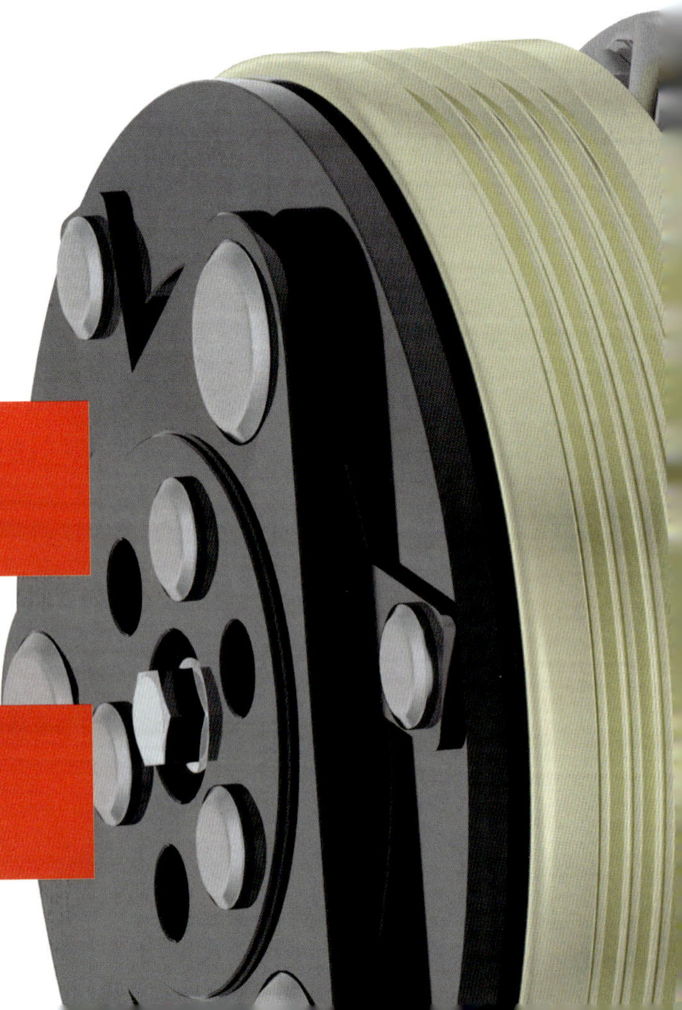

1. Introduction to Air Conditioning Systems

AIR CONDITIONING PRINCIPLES

Fig. 1 Gasoline draws heat away from your hand when it evaporates. This makes your hand feel cold.

Air conditioning systems in cars work in the same way as refrigerators. They produce cold dry air for the passengers, which increases comfort and safety. In order to cool the interior air, a refrigerant is needed to transfer the heat from the interior of the vehicle to its exterior.

During the transition from liquid to gas phase (evaporation), heat is absorbed from the environment. This happens in the evaporator, which cools the interior air. At the same time, heat is emitted outside of the car during the transition from gaseous to liquid phase (condensation). Condensation of the refrigerant happens in the condenser, which is located outside of the vehicle interior. The process of refrigerant evaporation and condensation is repeated continuously.

To gain a better understanding of the processes happening inside an air conditioning system, it is important to properly understand the physical principles (also called the basic physics) of cooling technology. These physical principles will be explained in this chapter. Plus, it is also important to know about the different kinds of refrigerants.

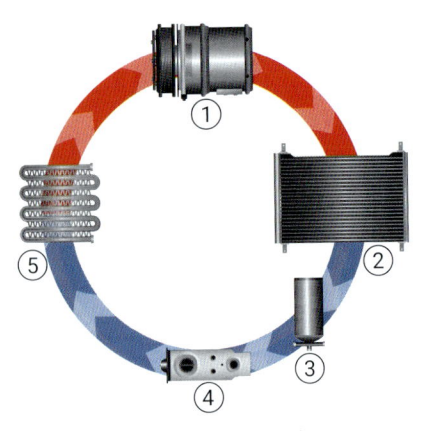

710 AIR CONDITIONING AND ELECTRICAL ACCESSORIES

Fig. 2 Refrigerant circulation in cars:
1. Compressor. 2. Condenser.
3. Receiver drier. 4. Orifice tube.
5. Evaporator.

TYPES OF HEAT

1. Introduction

If ice is heated until it changes into steam, the added heat energy is used in two ways:

Heat energy that causes a change in temperature is called **measurable heat**. The effect of this heat can be observed with a thermometer.

Heat energy that causes a change in state is called **latent heat**. The effect of this heat has no influence on temperature.

Fig. 3 When heating ice until it turns into steam, heat energy is used in two ways.

2. Required Energy

A change in state uses more energy than a change in temperature. During a change in state the temperature of the substance remains constant, because all the absorbed energy is used to change state.

A change of state in either direction uses an equal amount of energy. Condensation uses just as much energy as evaporation.

The change from ice to water uses much less energy than the change from water to steam. Likewise, the change from water to ice uses much less energy than the change from steam to water.

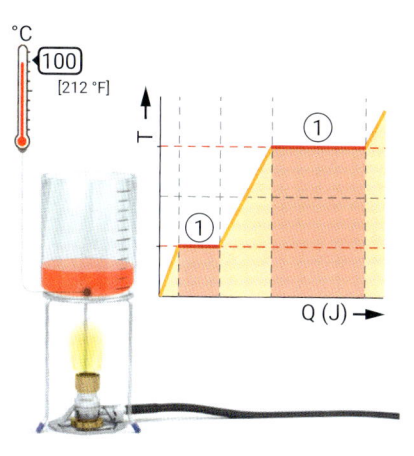

Fig. 4 During phase transitions, energy is added, but the temperature remains constant (1).

3. Superheat

At an atmospheric pressure of 14.7 psi (1 bar), water boils at 212°F (100 °C). At this pressure, water never rises above 212°F (100 °C). However, when all the water changes into steam, the temperature rises further.

If steam is 248°F (120 °C), the temperature is 36°F above the boiling point of water. The temperature above the boiling point is called **superheated**. The moment a substance becomes superheated, it remains in a gaseous state.

Depending on the boiling point of a fluid, the superheat temperature point will also be at a different level.

Suppose that the boiling point of a fluid is at 41°F (5°C). This means that if the steam becomes hotter than 41°F (5°C), this can be called superheat, even though the temperature is not very high.

4. Subcooled

Water boils at 212°F (100 °C) when atmospheric pressure is 14.7 psi (100 kPa). If the temperature falls below 212°F (100 °C), water immediately stops boiling.

Water at 194°F is 18°F below the boiling point. The temperature below the boiling point is called **subcooled.** At this temperature, the substance is always completely liquid.

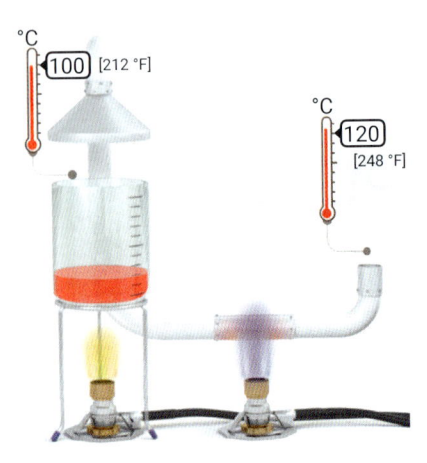

Fig. 5 The steam becomes superheated due to the additional heating. The steam above the liquid is not warmer than the temperature of the boiling point.

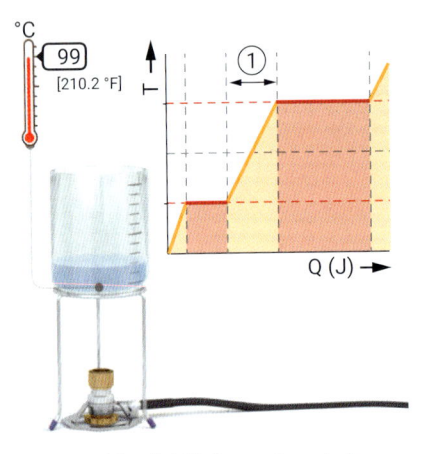

Fig. 6 1. The fluid is in a subcooled condition.

REFRIGERANT: PROPERTIES

1. Introduction

Refrigerant is used as a transportation medium that allows absorbed heat to flow from the evaporator to the condenser. In the condenser, this absorbed heat is then released to the exterior air. In this cycle, the refrigerant undergoes two phase transitions. In the evaporator, the refrigerant changes phases from a liquid to a gas, and in the condenser, it changes from a gas to a liquid.

There are many different kinds of refrigerant used in the automotive industry. The choice of refrigerant depends on many factors.

Important factors to be considered when choosing a refrigerant are:
— Boiling point.
— Cost.
— Environmental impact.
— Regulations.

Fig. 7 Sticker showing the refrigerant used.

2. Water compared with refrigerant: temperature and state

A substance can exist in 3 states. The properties of a substance determine when a substance is solid, liquid or gas.

At a temperature of 32°F (0°C) water turns into ice; at this temperature refrigerant is gaseous. This means that refrigerant boils below 32°F (0°C).

Refrigerant has a low boiling point. This is important in order to allow the refrigerant in the air conditioning system to change state.

The boiling point of the refrigerant will depend on the refrigerant used. Commonly used refrigerants are R134a and R1234yf. The boiling points of these refrigerants are very similar, around -17°F (-27°C).

3. Water: Boiling Point and Pressure

The boiling point is not only dependent on the temperature; the pressure is also important.

At sea level water boils at 212°F (100°C). As the pressure increases, the boiling point rises. If the pressure drops, then the boiling point drops.

Water remains liquid as long as the temperature remains below the boiling point. If the temperature rises above the boiling point, then the water changes state and becomes steam.

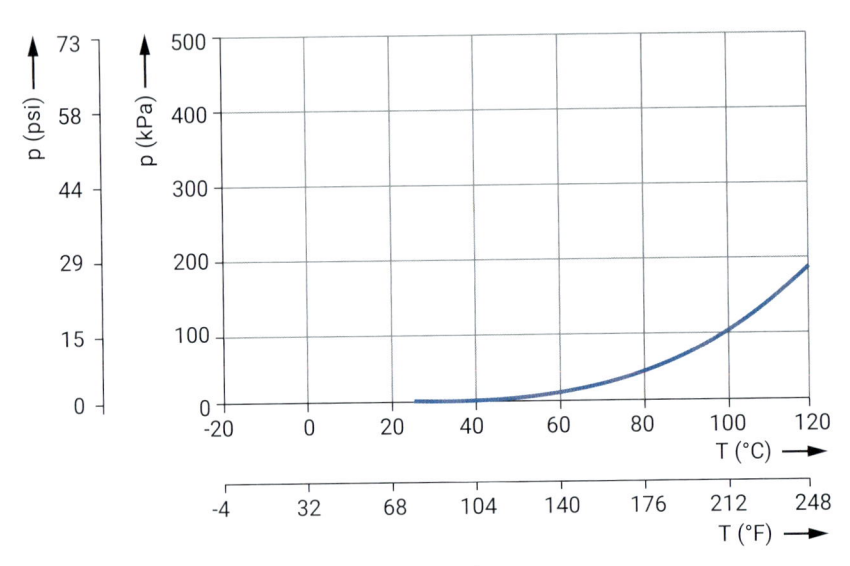

Fig. 8 Relationship between the boiling point and water pressure.

4. Refrigerant: Boiling Point and Pressure

Refrigerant boils at a lower temperature than water. By changing the pressure exerted on the refrigerant, the boiling point changes.

The line of the boiling point can be seen as a dividing line: every point under this line is gaseous, every point above is liquid.

The end of the line is the critical point: above this temperature, the refrigerant is no longer liquid, regardless of the pressure.

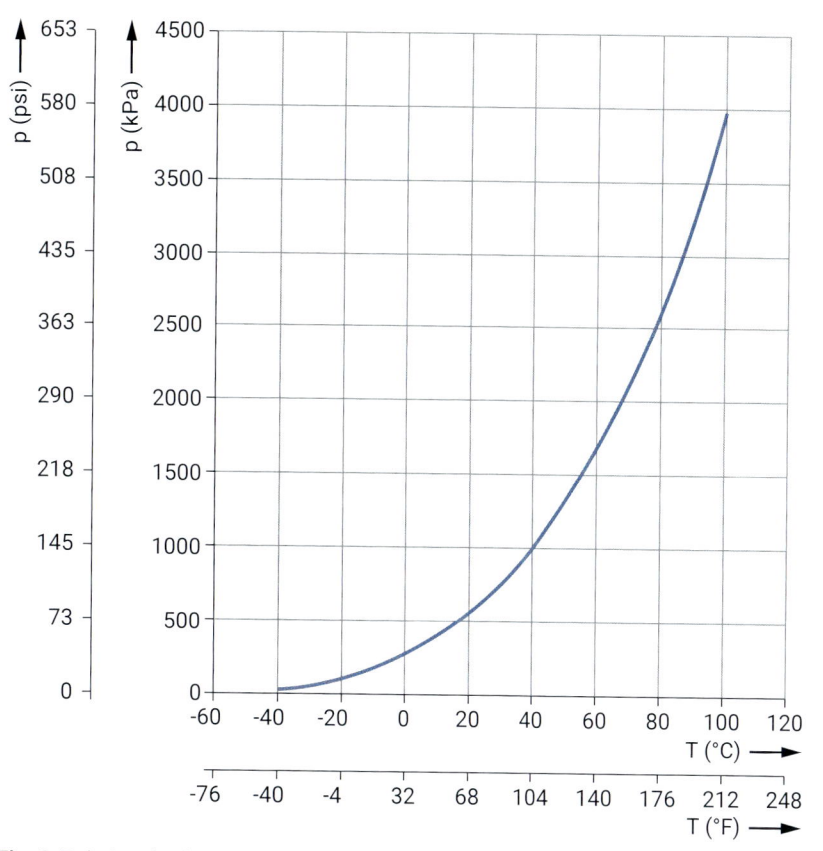

Fig. 9 Relationship between the boiling point and refrigerant pressure.

5. Refrigerant: Types

There are different types of refrigerant. Sometimes the boiling points and corresponding pressures are close to each other, sometimes the differences are large.

R134a and R1234yf look very much alike; air conditioning systems with these types of refrigerant are practically the same.

Some systems use R744, which is the refrigerant term for carbon dioxide. The required pressure for these systems to operate is many times higher than a traditional air conditioning system that operates with a lower pressure.

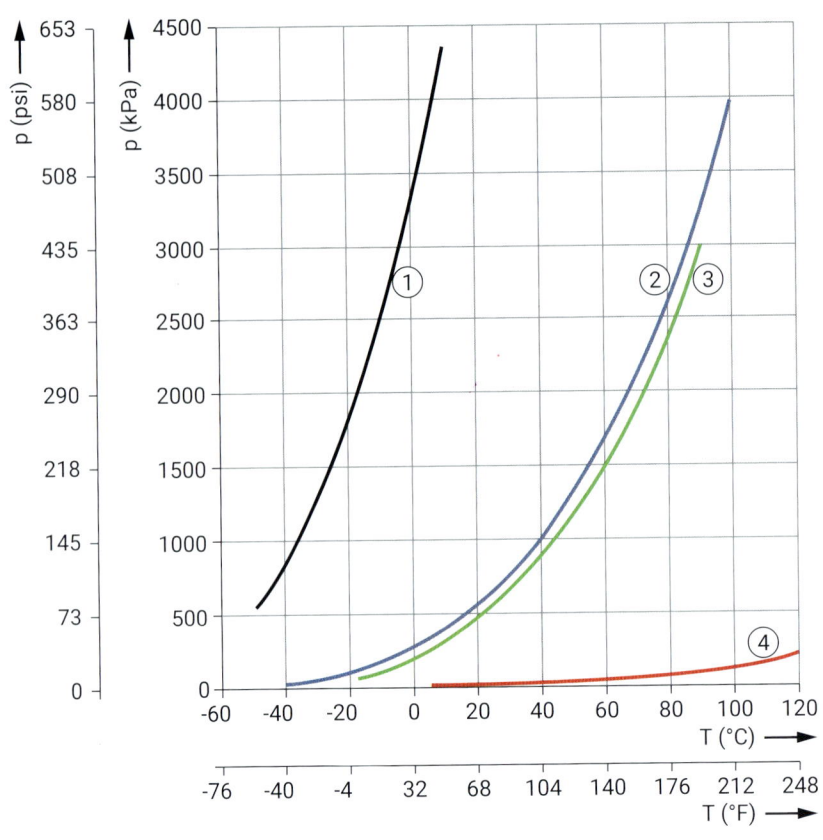

Fig. 10 Relationships between the boiling points and pressures of various kinds of refrigerants and water. 1. R744. 2. R134a. 3. R1234yf. 4. Water.

6. Regulations

There are risks associated with working on systems containing refrigerant. These include personal safety and the safety of your environment. Examples include the risks of frost bite, fire, and suffocation. There are also environmental risks if any hazardous refrigerants would be released into the atmosphere.

Because of this, regulations have been drawn up for work with refrigerants. From 1992 onwards, the EPA-609 certification has been required for a technician to be allowed to purchase more than two pounds of refrigerant at a time.

7. GWP Value

In the Kyoto Protocol, an agreement was made to use refrigerants with a so-called GWP value below 150. GWP stands for Global Warming Potential. The GWP number expresses what the warming potential of a certain gas is relative to CO_2 over the course of 100 years. Therefore, the GWP value of CO_2 is 1.

R134a has a GWP value of 1430. In the United States, starting in July 2015, automakers were to begin phasing out high GWP refrigerants, and have these refrigerants, mainly R134a, phased out of all light-duty vehicle air conditioning systems by 2021.

8. R12

In the past, the car industry used the refrigerant dichlorodifluoromethane. This refrigerant was also referred to as R12 or Freon. R12 is one of the **C**hloro**F**luoro**C**arbon compounds (CFCs for short). R12 is a refrigerant that contains chlorine. When chlorine is combined with ultraviolet radiation, it affects the ozone layer in the atmosphere. The ozone in the atmosphere protects the life on Earth against lethal solar radiation. Because of this, in the Montreal Protocol in 1987, it was agreed that production of CFCs would gradually be phased out.

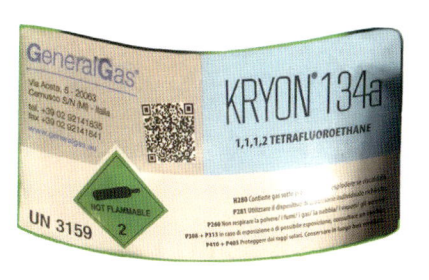

Fig. 11 Different kinds of refrigerant: R12, R744, R1234yf, and R134a.

9. R134a

From 1994 onwards, cars have been equipped with air conditioning systems using R134a refrigerant. This refrigerant is also referred to as tetrafluoroethane. R134a is one of the halogenated hydrochlorofluorocarbon compounds (HFCs for short).

This refrigerant does not contain chlorine and thus does not affect the ozone layer. The thermodynamic properties of R134a are comparable to those of R12. Because of this, an R134a air conditioning system is almost the same as an R12 system. However, R134a did turn out to be a so-called greenhouse gas. The accumulation of greenhouse gases in the atmosphere causes the temperatures on Earth to rise. In the 1997 Kyoto Protocol, it was agreed that the usage of HFC refrigerants would be gradually decreased. According to research, it appears that it takes R134a approximately 13 years to break down in the atmosphere.

Fig. 12 Label of refrigerant R134a.

10. R1234yf

The refrigerant R1234yf was brought to market as an alternative for R134a. This refrigerant is also referred to as tetrafluoropropene and HFO-1234yf.

Fig. 13 Label of refrigerant R1234yf.

The thermodynamic properties of R1234yf are comparable to those of R134a. Therefore, an R1234yf air conditioning system operates in almost the same way as an R134a system.

R1234yf does not affect the ozone layer, breaks down in the atmosphere in 11 days, and its GWP value is 4.

Unfortunately, R1234yf does have some disadvantages. It is much more expensive than R134a and it is flammable.

11. R744

A number of car manufacturers have chosen R744 as an alternative for R134a. R744 is also referred to as carbon dioxide, or CO_2. CO_2 is a natural gas, and therefore a very environmentally-friendly refrigerant. CO_2 is a greenhouse gas, but if it is harvested from the air to be used in the air conditioners, there will be no hazardous effects if the CO_2 escapes back into the air in the case of system leakages.

The use of CO_2 does have a disadvantage, however. The thermodynamic properties of CO_2 are very different from those of R134a. Air conditioners that use CO_2 operate at a much higher pressure, up to approx. 2000 psi.

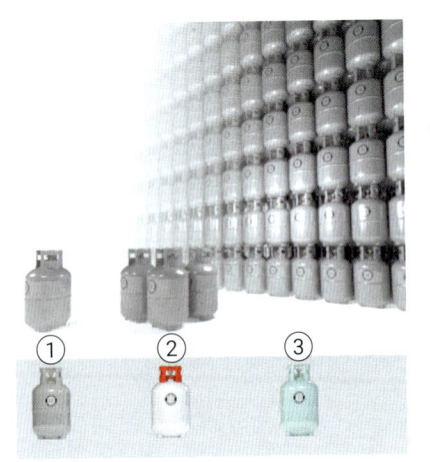

Fig. 14 The GWP value of R744 (1) compared to those of R1234yf (2) and R134a (3).

REFRIGERANT CYCLE

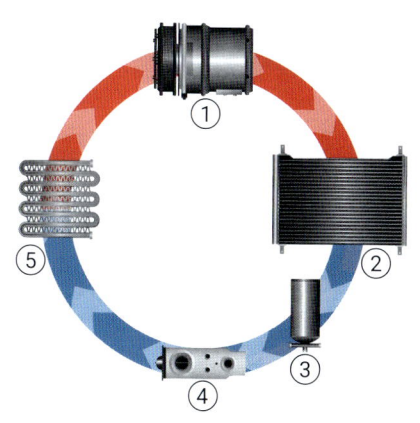

Fig. 15 The refrigerant cycle:
1. Compressor. 2. Condenser.
3. Filter dryer. 4. Orifice.
5. Evaporator.

1. The Refrigerant Cycle

Inside the air conditioning system, the refrigerant undergoes two phase transitions. It changes from a gas to a liquid and then from a liquid to a gas. This is called the refrigerant cycle. The refrigerant cycle can be divided into two pressure areas; one part that is low-pressure, and one part that is high-pressure. The compressor and the orifice divide these two parts.

2. Refrigerant Cycle: Compressor

The refrigerant reaches the compressor as a gas, the temperature and pressure are low.
During compression the pressure increases, causing the temperature and the boiling point of the refrigerant to rise.

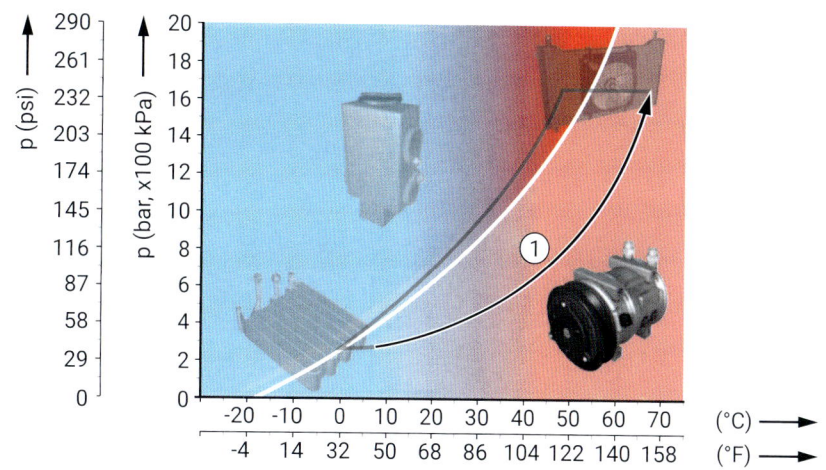

Fig. 16 The refrigerant cycle: 1. Compression stage.

3. Refrigerant Cycle: Condenser

The refrigerant is hot and gaseous when it leaves the compressor. The temperature of the refrigerant drops when it flows through the condenser.
If the temperature drops to below the boiling point, the refrigerant condenses into a liquid.

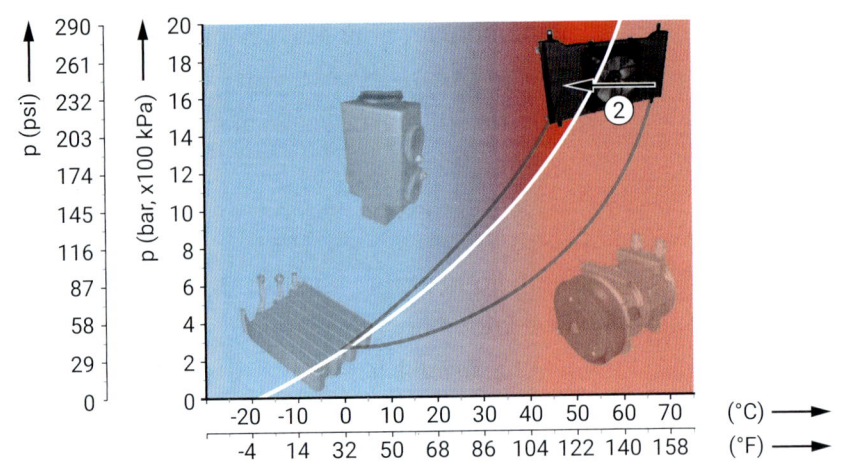

Fig. 17 The refrigerant cycle: 2. Condensation stage.

The condenser is designed to cool and condense the gaseous refrigerant coming from the compressor into the liquid phase.

4. Refrigerant Cycle: Orifice

The refrigerant is fully liquid and the temperature and pressure are high when it reaches the orifice or restriction device.
When the refrigerant flows through the orifice the pressure drops sharply across the restriction, causing the temperature and boiling point to drop rapidly. At this stage the refrigerant is at or near its boiling point.

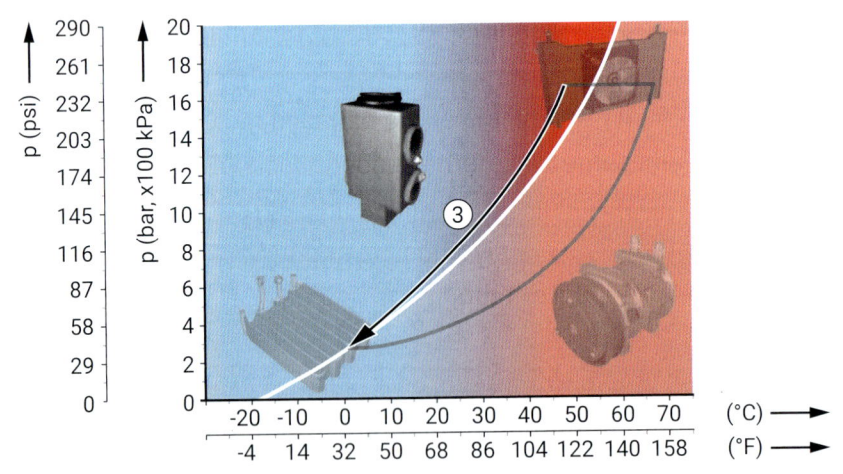

Fig. 18 The refrigerant cycle: 3. Pressure drop stage.

5. Refrigerant Cycle: Evaporator

Once the refrigerant reaches the evaporator, the temperature, pressure and boiling point are low.

The cabin air flowing through the evaporator heats up the refrigerant, causing it to boil immediately and in doing so, absorbing the heat from the air inside of the car.

When the evaporated refrigerant exits the evaporator it takes the heat from inside of the car with it, and the refrigerant cycle begins again.

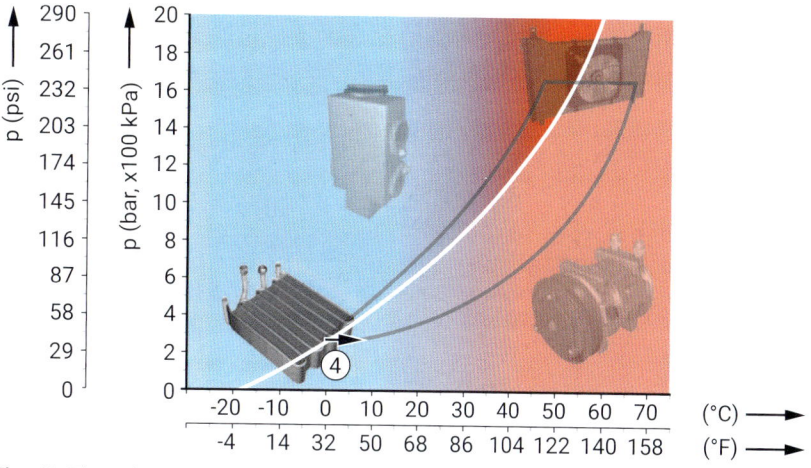

Fig. 19 The refrigerant cycle: 4. Evaporation stage.

6. Refrigerant Cycle: Four Stages

We have discussed the four stages of the refrigerant cycle, through which the heat is removed from the inside of the vehicle. This graph of the refrigerant cycle makes the pressure and temperature of the refrigerant visible. It does not, however, show how much energy is required for evaporation and/or condensation to occur.

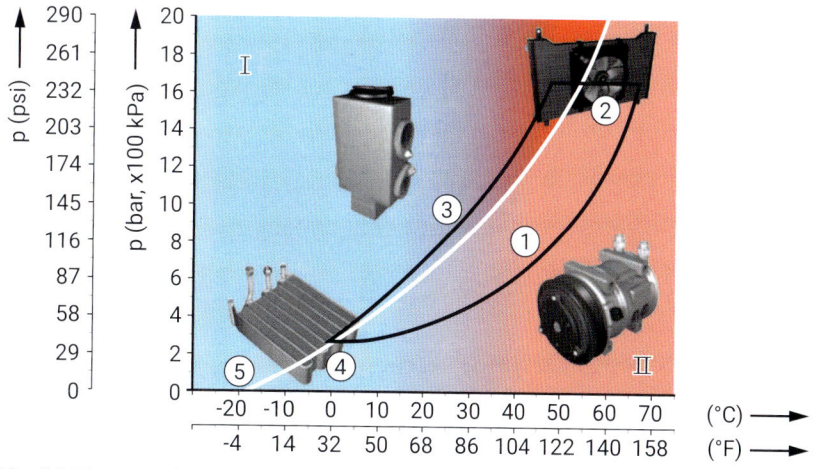

Fig. 20 The complete refrigerant cycle: 1. Compression stage. 2. Condensation stage. 3. Pressure drop stage. 4. Evaporation stage. 5. Refrigerant boiling point line. I. Liquid area. II. Gaseous area.

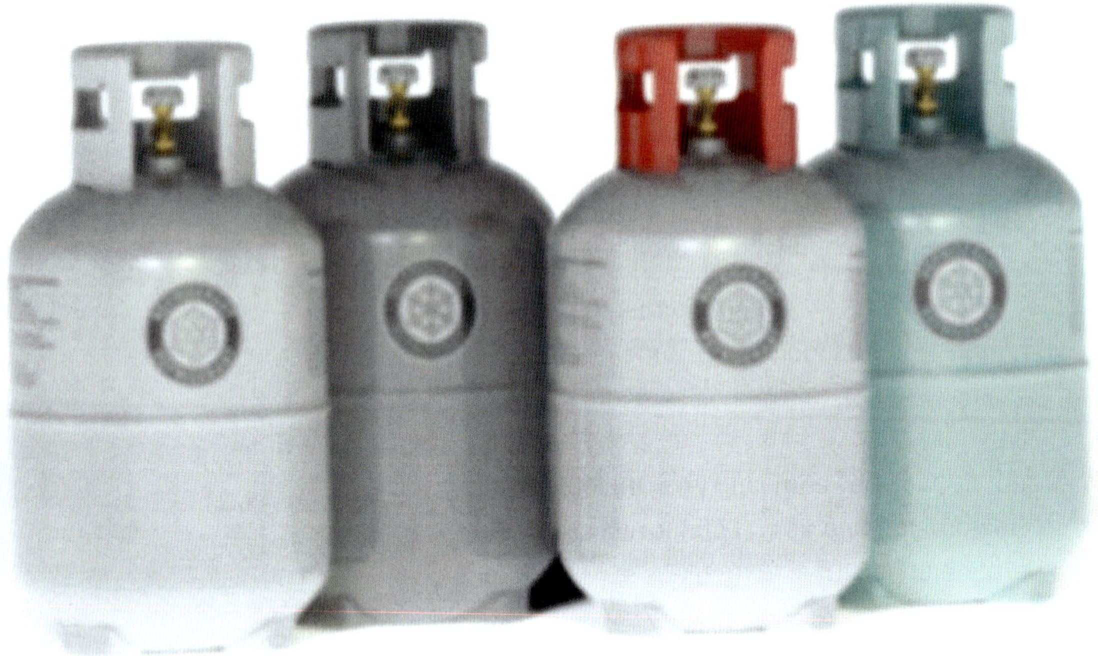

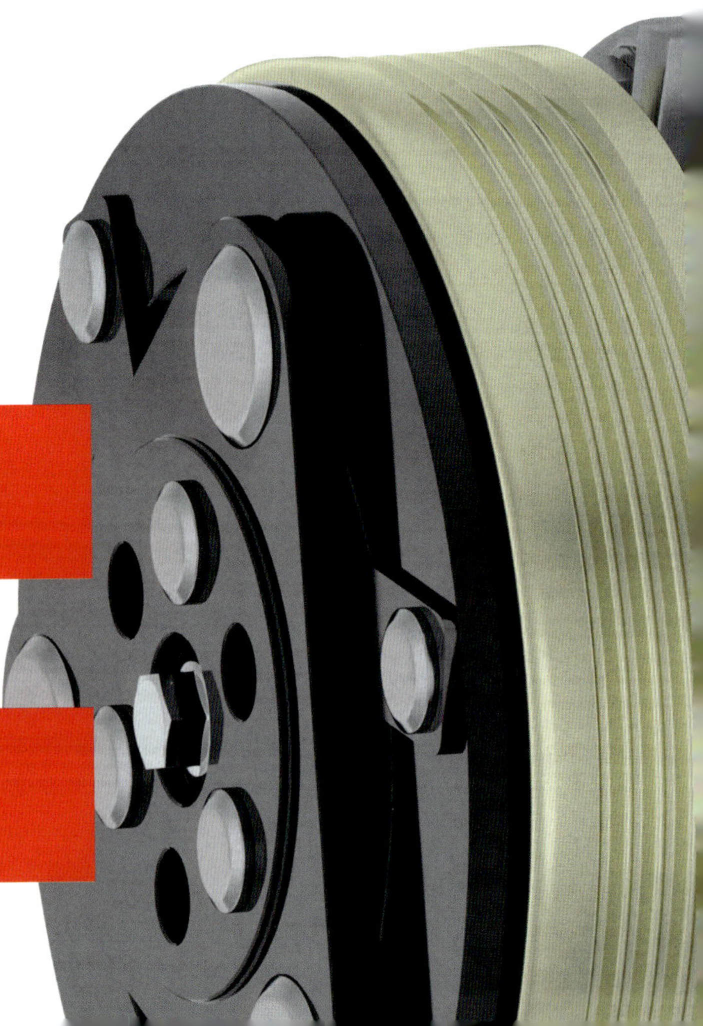

2. Climate Control

CLIMATE CONTROL: OPERATION

1. Introduction

The climate inside a car can be adjusted with the climate control system.

The climate control system has a number of buttons and knobs on the instrument panel. With these buttons and knobs, the climate control system can be operated.

2. Operating Temperature

The climate control system can either cool or heat the air that flows into the interior.

Cooling
If the air conditioning is switched on, the evaporator cools the air flowing through it.

Heating
The air flowing through the heater core is heated.

Fig. 21 Climate control system: 1. Duct for external (fresh) air. 2. Duct for air from inside the car (recirculation mode). 3. Air vents in the car interior. 4. Heater motor speed. 5. Air conditioner controls. 6. Temperature controls. 7. Fresh air/recirculation control. 8. Air vent mode controls.

724 AIR CONDITIONING AND ELECTRICAL ACCESSORIES

Fig. 22 Components of the climate control system: 1. Fan. 2. Recirculation door. 3. Air mode doors. 4. Heater-core. 5. Blend door. 6. Evaporator.

Blend door

The position of the blend door influences the amount of air flowing through the heater core.

3. Control

Outlet airflow flaps

If the position of the climate control mode doors are changed, the direction of the airflow is changed. In this way, you can select from where the air is discharged into the passenger compartment.

Air recirculation

The door at the entrance of the climate control system determines whether outside air is drawn in, or air from the interior is recirculated through the system.

Fig. 23 Air vent directed at the feet.

Fig. 24 Air vent directed at the windscreen.

Fig. 25 Air vent directed at the feet and the windscreen.

Fig. 26 Air drawn from outside.

Fig. 27 Air recirculation: air drawn from the interior.

Fig. 28 To reach the fastest airflow speed, the knob (1) must be set to the highest position. The fan is now rotating in the highest position.

4. Airflow Speed

The fan speed determines the airflow speed through the climate control system.

The temperature inside the car can change quickly with a higher airflow speed.

5. Types

Manual
A manual climate control system needs to be completely set by the user.

Semi-automatic
A climate control system in which the heater door is operated automatically is called semi-automatic. The system tries to keep the interior at the set temperature. If needed, the air conditioning will need to be switched on manually. The airflow speed and location of the outlet airflow must also be selected manually.

Automatic
If all settings of the climate control system are activated automatically, it is called an automatic system. Any adjustment other than setting the temperature will override automatic control (for example, increasing the fan speed manually). To resume automatic control, the "auto" button must be reselected.

Fig. 29 Manual control of the climate control system.

Fig. 30 Semi-automatic control of the climate control system.

Fig. 31 Automatic control of the climate control system.

HEATER

1. Introduction

The outside air temperature is not always ideal. Sometimes it's too cold and other times it's too hot. In order to increase the temperature inside the vehicle, a heater is used.

When the outside air flows through the heater core and into the interior, the air is heated up. This warm air flows through the passenger compartment, increasing the temperature.

Fig. 32 Warm air flowing into the car.

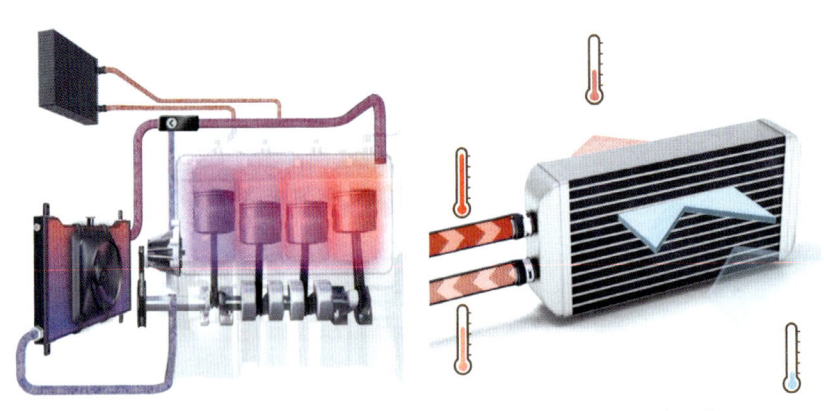

Fig. 33 Heater core at the top-left is heated by the residual heat of the combustion engine.

Fig. 34 Heater core: air that flows past it is heated by the coolant in the channels of the heater-radiator.

The engine provides the heat needed to warm the interior. By burning fuel to power the car, "extra" heat is generated. Usually, this heat is dissipated by the radiator, and through radiation. On cold days, this heat is not entirely dissipated through the radiator; some of it is used to warm the car's interior. The cooler air from outside the car flows through the heater core and is heated by the warm coolant flowing through the heater-core. The heated air then flows into the car's interior.

2. Air Blending System

The amount of heat added to the air flow is adjustable. The position of the blend door determines the amount of air flowing through the heater core. Air flow that does not flow through the heater core does not heat up.

Fig. 35 Hot and cold air are blended.

If the position of the blend door changes, the mixing ratio between the quantity of hot and cold air also changes. As a result, the temperature of the air that flows into the passenger compartment is adjusted.

3. Liquid Control System

Another way to control the temperature of the air flow, is through the use of a heater valve (water valve).

A heater valve controls the amount of coolant that flows through the heater core. If the heater valve is wide open, the air flow heats up a lot. If the heater valve is closed, no coolant is allowed to circulate through the heater core and the air flow does not heat up.

Some systems use both a heater valve and a blend door; these are called combined control systems.

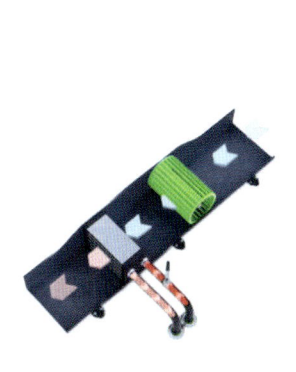

Fig. 36 Fluid mixture system

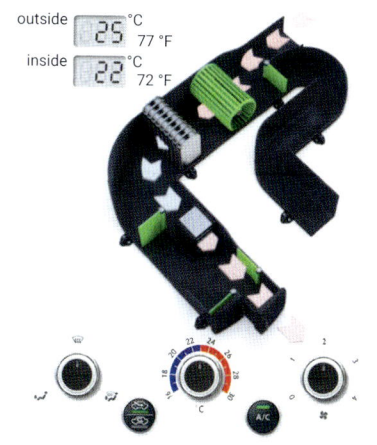

Fig. 37 Combined blended-air heater and air conditioning climate installation.

The degree to which the air flowing in is heated by the heater core depends on the desired climate inside the car.

4. Heating and air conditioning

By placing the air conditioning and the heater core in the system case, the unit becomes more compact. A second advantage is that moist inflowing air can be dehumidified by the evaporator. This is done to prevent the condensation of water vapor onto the windows.

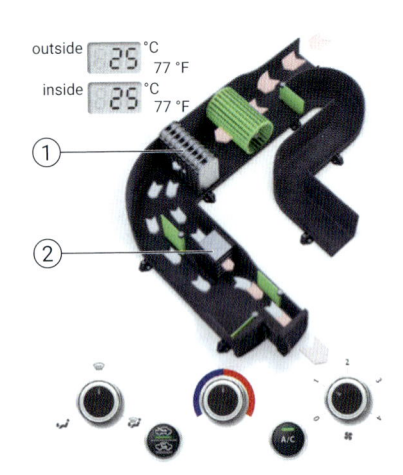

Fig. 38 Air conditioning and heating in a single unit:
1. Evaporator. 2. Heater core.

Fig. 39 Air conditioning evaporator.

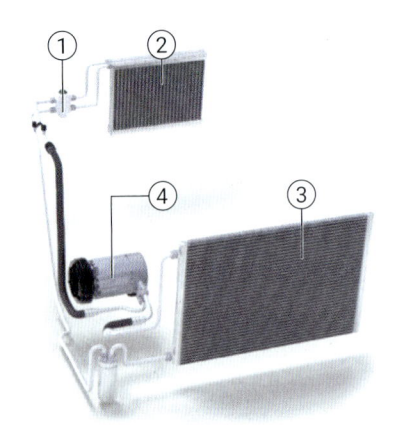

Fig. 40 Air conditioning system: 1. Control valve. 2. Evaporator. 3. Condenser. 4. Air conditioning compressor.

INTERIOR FRAGRANCE DEVICES

1. Fragrance

To ensure that the interior smells nice, some cars are outfitted with a fragrance system.

In simple systems, a single fragrance reservoir is placed next to the air outlet vent, and the fragrance intensity is determined by an adjustment wheel. This adjustment wheel adjusts the opening of the fragrance reservoir.

Fig. 41 Fragrance system:
1. Reservoir. 2. Cover seal.
3. Fragrance pearls.

Fig. 42 Reservoir opening inside the glove compartment.

Fig. 43 Reservoir opening (without foil) snapped into place inside the glove compartment.

More complex systems make use of multiple fragrance reservoirs; it is possible to select the fragrances and their intensities. The fragrance system control blends the smells. A small fan inside the control unit blows the fragrance to the air vents.

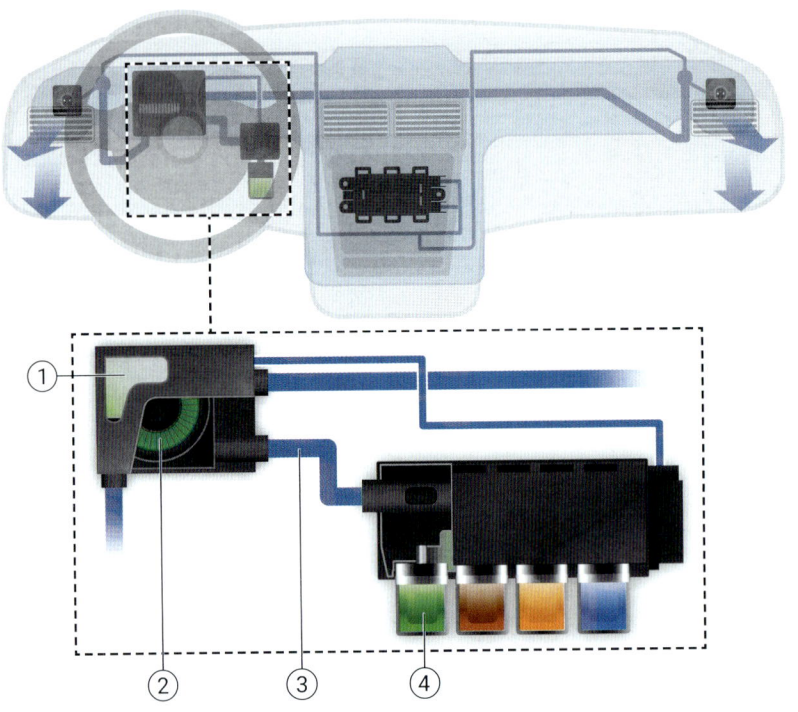

Fig. 44 Fragrance system: 1. Fragrance system control unit. 2. Fragrance system driver. 3. Hose. 4. Fragrance reservoirs.

2. Ionization

An ionizer can be used to further improve interior air quality. Air particles are charged negatively with electrodes. These negative ions in the air reduce hazardous particles in the air. This improves the quality of the air inside the car. The ionizer's electrodes are under high voltage that is provided by a transformer.

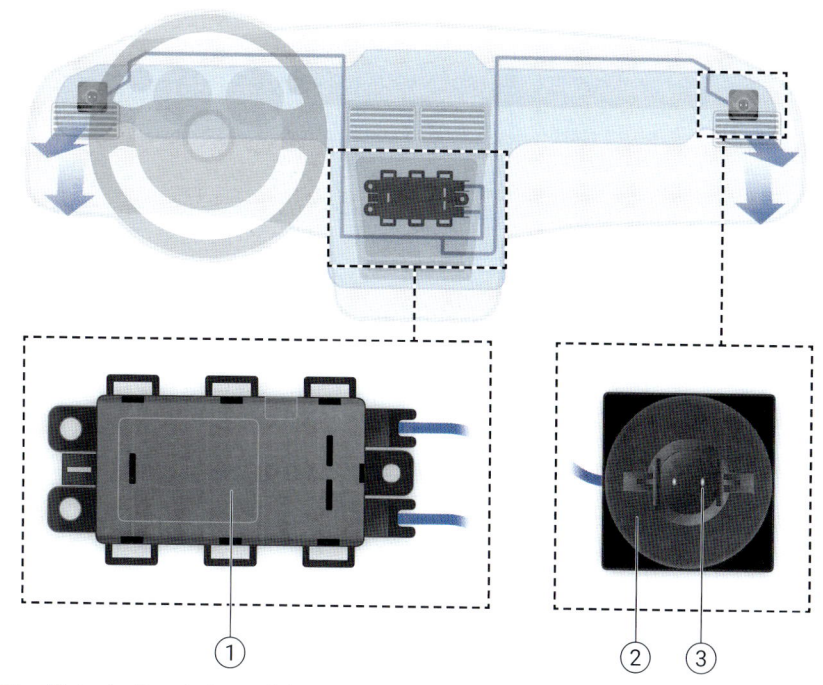

Fig. 45 Ionization: 1. Control device. 2. Ionizer. 3. The electrodes of the ionizer.

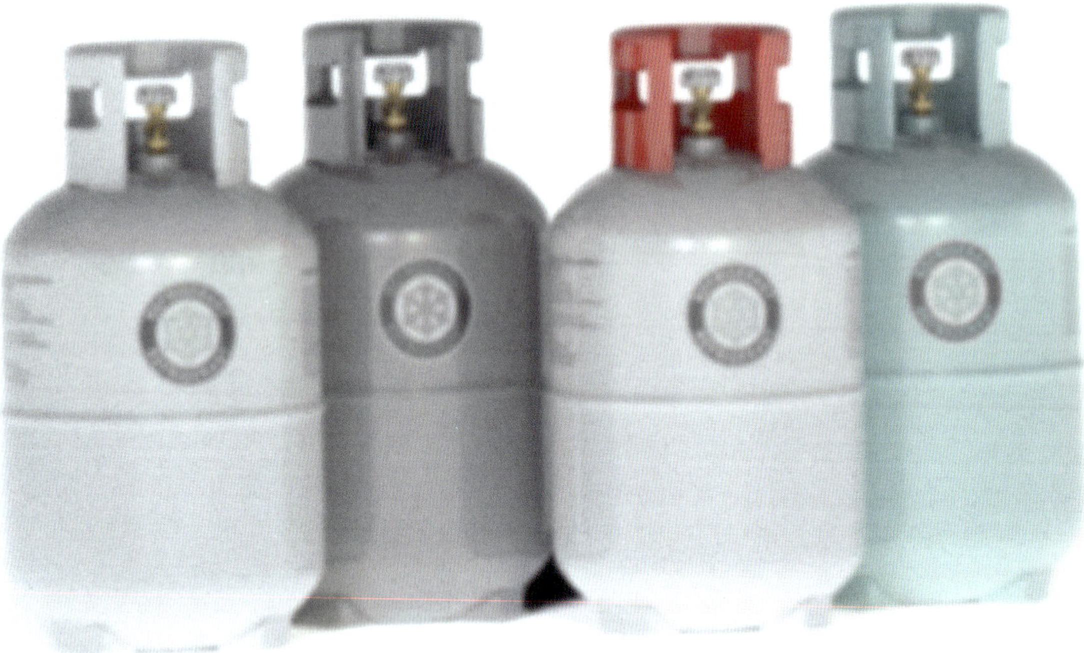

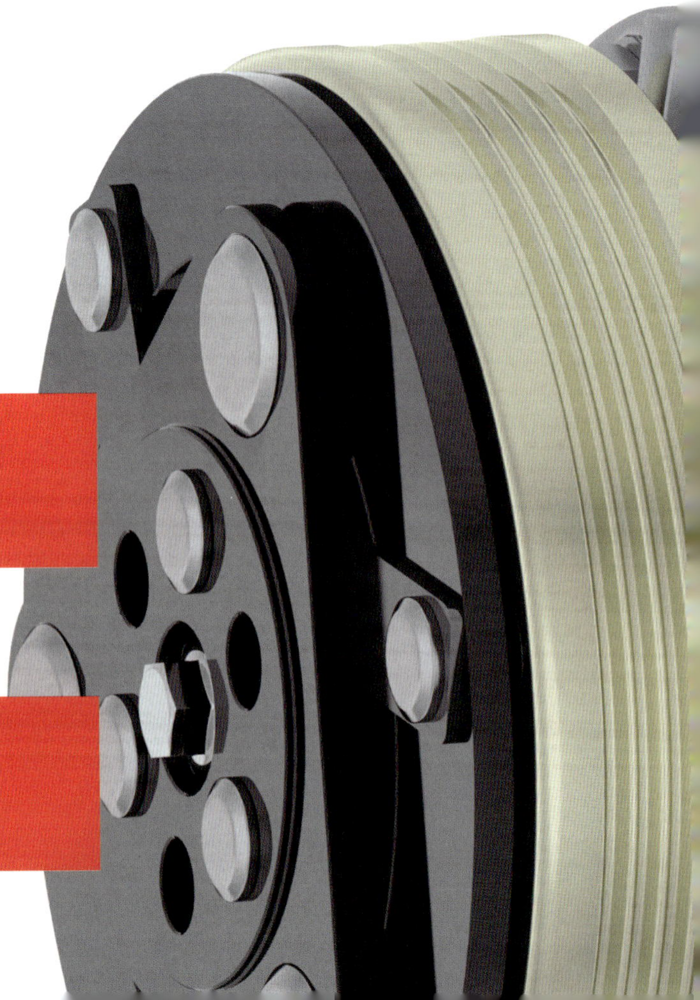

3. Mechanical HVAC Components

COMPRESSOR WITH A FIXED DISPLACEMENT

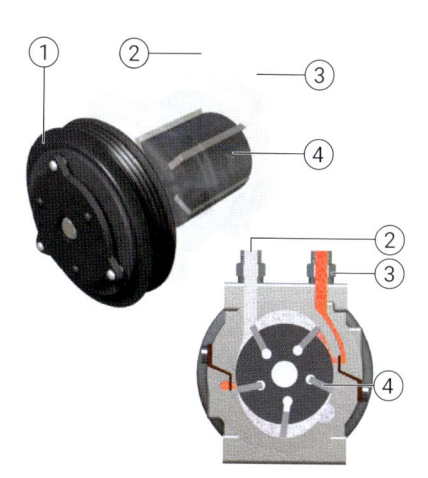

Fig. 46 Vane-type compressor:
1. Magnetic compressor clutch.
2. Suction inlet pipe. 3. Compressed gas discharge pipe. 4. Vane.

This compressor has a fixed displacement. The compressor is driven by the engine. Maintaining system pressure is accomplished by cycling the compressor on and off.

This type of compressor control is easy to recognize. In normal operation, the magnetic compressor clutch will continuously switch on and off. This switching on and off produces an uneven load on the drive belt, compressor, and engine. Additionally, this type of air conditioning system is not easy to adjust in response to cooling loads. Also, since the compressor is directly coupled to the engine, its output fluctuates as engine speed changes.

1. Vane-type Compressor

A vane-type compressor consists of a circular casing that contains a rotor. This rotor has indentations that contain vanes. The vanes create chambers in the compressor casing. While spinning, the size of the chambers will vary. This means that the refrigerant can be sucked in and forced out.

2. Scroll-type Compressor

The scroll compressor consists of a casing that contains a fixed (static) scroll, also referred to as a helix. The driven scroll is located in the open area of the fixed scroll.

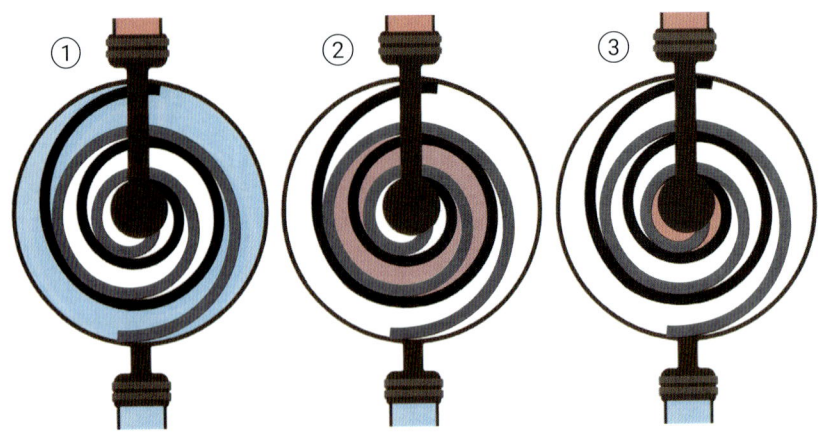

Fig. 47 1. Suction. 2. Compression. 3. Output.

The driven scroll moves in an eccentrically rotating fashion. As this movement happens, the space between both scrolls increases, drawing in refrigerant. As soon as the moving scroll shortens the distance between the scrolls, the pressure of the refrigerant will increase.

The pressure line is connected to the center of the static scroll. From here, the refrigerant exits the scroll compressor under high pressure.

Fig. 48 Electric scroll compressor.

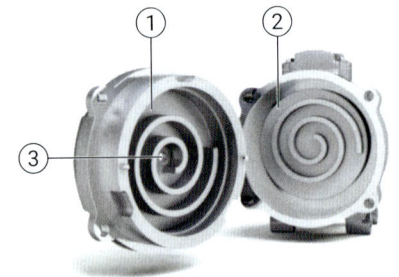

Fig. 49 The center of the scroll compressor: 1. Moving scroll. 2. Static scroll. 3. Discharge port.

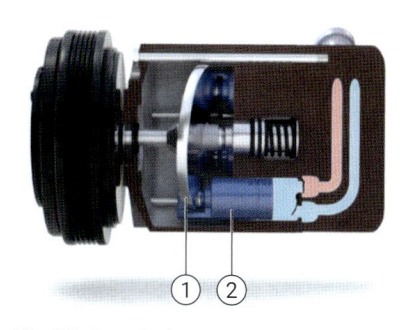

Fig. 50 Swashplate compressor:
1. Swashplate. 2. Piston.

3. Swashplate Compressor

The swashplate compressor is a piston-type compressor. The swashplate converts the pulley rotational motion into the piston reciprocating motion.

By moving the pistons up and down, refrigerant is drawn in and forced out. Valves at the top of the cylinders ensure the refrigerant flows in the correct direction.

VARIABLE DISPLACEMENT COMPRESSOR

In a fixed displacement compressor, its capacity will depend on the engine speed. This type of compressor cannot respond to cooling loads, and cycling on the compressor will put a heavy load on the driving belt and the engine. To make the system more efficient, variable displacement compressors are used.

1. Variable Swashplate Compressor

The variable swashplate compressor is a swashplate-type compressor that has a variable displacement or output. The displacement of the compressor is determined by the angle of the swashplate. This angle will change if the pressure behind the pistons is altered.

If all of the refrigerant is evaporating inside of the evaporator, the compressor output is high. If only a small amount of refrigerant is evaporating in the evaporator, the swashplate adjusts in response to the pressure and reduces the compressor displacement. This allows the compressor to be as efficient as possible, and stops it from pumping more refrigerant through the system than is needed. This increases the efficiency of the air conditioning system.

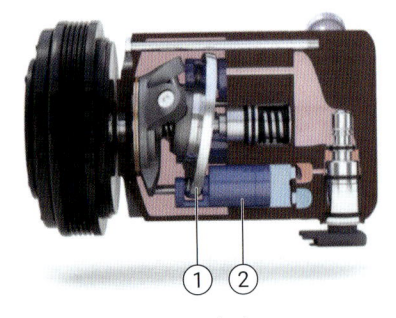

Fig. 51 Variable swashplate compressor: 1. Swashplate. 2. Piston.

Fig. 52 The variable swashplate compressor in a high output state.

Fig. 53 The variable swashplate compressor in a low output state.

Fig. 54 Variable swashplate compressor with internal control valve: 1. Swashplate. 2. Piston. 3. Internal control valve.

2. Variable Displacement Compressor with Internal Control Valve

With the help of a valve inside the compressor housing, the pressure inside the compressor housing can be adjusted. This allows the pressure difference across the pistons and the compressor displacement to be accurately controlled. This valve reacts to the compressor inlet pressure, also called the low-side pressure (maintaining the level of the inlet pressure) and can subsequently change the pressure inside the compressor housing as needed.

By changing the pressure inside the compressor housing, the angle of the swashplate will change, which alters the compressor displacement.

It is also possible to use a scroll-type compressor with an internal control valve. With this type of system, the compressed refrigerant flows back to the suction chamber of the scroll compressor through a bypass valve. This decreases the pumping capacity of the compressor.

By closing the bypass valve, the pump capacity returns to its maximum. The position of the bypass valve is variable, and depends on the pressure inside the compressor.

3. Variable Compressor with External Control Valve

In a compressor with an external control valve, an electromagnetic valve is used to regulate the pressure inside of the compressor housing. The valve is controlled by an ECU, usually by the engine ECU using a pulse width modulated (PWM) signal.

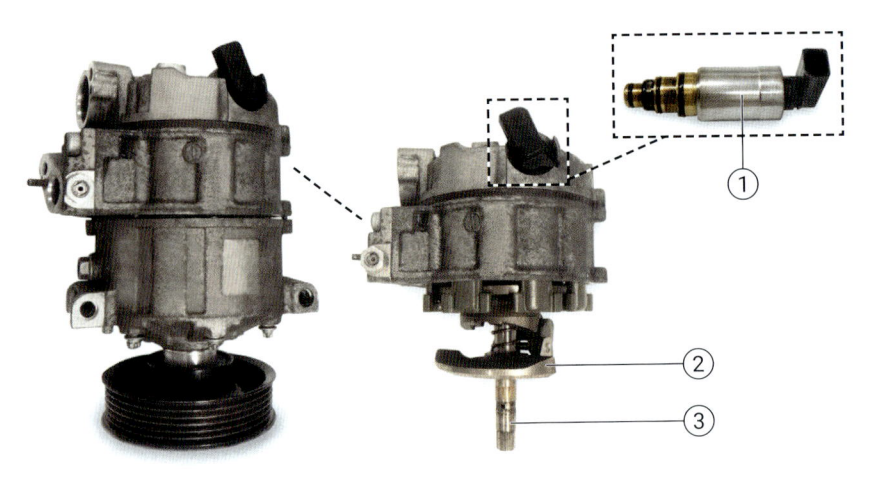

Fig. 55 Variable swashplate compressor with an external control valve:
1. External control valve. 2. Swashplate. 3. Shaft.

External controls can be employed on swashplate-type compressors as well as on scroll-type compressors. By changing the pressure inside the compressor housing of the swashplate compressor, the position of the swashplate will change, and this modifies the stroke of the pistons. In a scroll-type compressor, the electromagnetic valve controls the closing of the bypass channel. Depending on the position of the valve, more or less compressed refrigerant can flow back into the suction chamber of the scroll compressor.

AIR CONDITIONING COMPRESSOR DRIVE

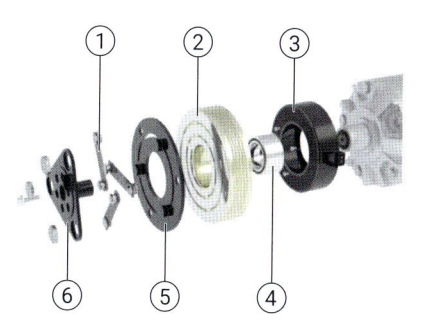

Fig. 56 Construction of the magnetic coupling clutch: 1. Return springs. 2. Pulley. 3. Magnetic coil. 4. Bearing. 5. Ring. 6. Front plate.

1. Magnetic Clutch

The air conditioning compressor is driven by a serpentine belt. During air conditioner operation the compressor must be able to be engaged and disengaged from the drive. To accomplish this, a magnetic coupling clutch is used.

The magnetic coupling clutch consists of three primary components:
— Front plate.
— Pulley.
— Magnetic coil.

The pulley is mounted to the compressor housing with a bearing. When the combustion engine is turned on, the pulley will rotate with the belt. The front plate is connected to the axle of the air conditioning compressor. When the front plate is stationary, the air conditioning compressor is switched off.

The magnetic coil is mounted onto the housing of the air conditioning compressor. When the magnetic coil is energized, the steel ring of the front plate is pulled against the pulley; the air conditioning compressor is switched on. When the coil is powered off, the return springs press the front plate's steel ring back to its resting position.

2. Overpressure Protection

There are several devices designed to protect air conditioning systems from excessively high pressures:
— A high pressure relief valve.
— A thermal protector on the compressor.

High pressure relief valve
In most cases, this valve can be found on the compressor, but it may also have been installed on the receiver drier. The relief valve

ensures that the maximum pressure of the refrigerant is approx. 580 psi (depending on the manufacturer).

Once this pressure is reached, refrigerant is vented from the system. These devices can also be a thermal fuse that melts at approximately 212-230°F, thus draining the entire system.

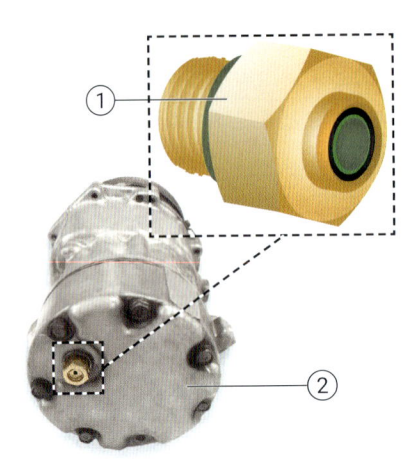

Fig. 57 High pressure relief valve installed in the compressor: 1. High pressure relief valve. 2. Rear of the compressor.

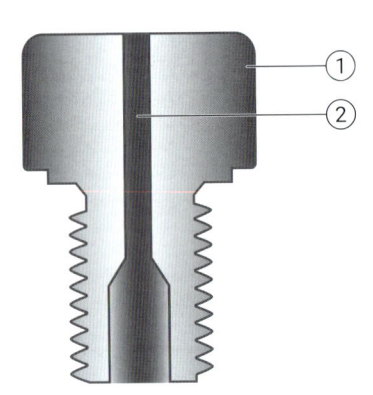

Fig. 58 Thermal fuse: 1. Fuse. 2. Metal with a low melting temperature.

Compressor thermal switch

From an environmental point of view, it is not a good idea to discharge refrigerant at high pressures. Today, we often find a very different type of protection. A thermal switch is installed into the compressor housing. If the pressure in the compressor increases, the temperature will increase as well. At high temperatures, the thermal switch will turn off the power supply to the compressor coupling.

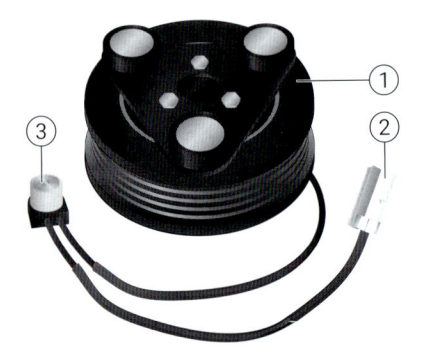

Fig. 59 Thermal switch: 1. Magnetic coupling. 2. Connector. 3. Thermal switch.

Fig. 60 1. Compressor. 2. Compressor with installed thermal switch.

AIR CONDITIONING SYSTEM COMPONENTS

1. Condenser

The condenser is used to cool and condense the gaseous refrigerant that comes from the compressor into a liquid. The refrigerant enters the condenser through the upper connection and should flow in a liquid phase to the accumulator/receiver-drier through the lower connection.

To assist in the dissipation of heat, vehicles are often equipped with one or more additional cooling fans. The fans are turned on when triggered by the high pressure sensor and can usually rotate at varying speeds. These cooling fans can be turned on directly by a pressure switch or remotely by a control unit.

Fig. 61 condenser

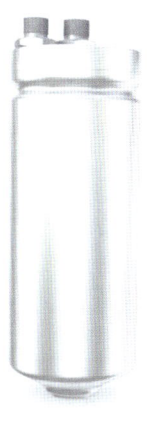

2. Receiver Drier

The refrigerant flows from the condenser into the receiver drier. The receiver drier is used to remove moisture and contamination (solid particles) and to store liquid refrigerant. This ensures a steady flow of clean, liquid refrigerant to the expansion valve. From the condenser, the refrigerant passes through a filter and subsequently through absorbent granules. After that, the refrigerant flows through the outlet through a riser pipe.

Fig. 62 Receiver Drier

Fig. 63 Cross-section of a receiver drier

Fig. 64 Condenser with an integrated receiver drier.

The lubricant (PAG oil) is hygroscopic and may result in water seeping into the system. When the drying material (e.g. silica gel) has become saturated, small water droplets may form, which freeze in/after the expansion valve. This freezing results in a blockage. If the air conditioning system has been open for a while (e.g. due to damage), the receiver drier should always be replaced. Measuring the temperature at the inlet and outlet is a good method for checking if the receiver drier is clogging up. These temperatures should be more or less the same and should not diverge more than approximately 30°F. If this is not the case then the receiver drier is clogged.

In addition to having a filter and drier element, the receiver drier can be equipped with a pressure sensor/pressure switch and/or a service connection. In older cars, the receiver drier may be equipped with a viewing port.

In modern cars, the receiver drier is often integrated into the condenser. In most cases, the receiver drier element is replaced as a detachable insert element.

3. Expansion Valve

The expansion valve is responsible for creating a drop in pressure, which drastically lowers the boiling point of the liquid refrigerant.

There are various designs:
— Thermostatic expansion valve (TXV).
— Block valve (TXV).

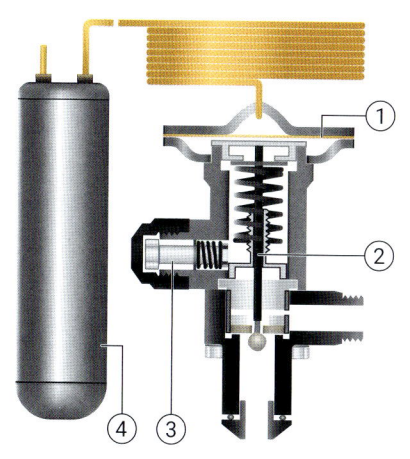

Fig. 65 Thermostatic expansion valve: 1. Membrane. 2. Needle valve. 3. Sealed adjustment screw. 4. Measuring element.

4. Thermostatic expansion valve or TXV valve.

In this expansion body, the size of the orifice is varied in relation to the refrigerant temperature. The refrigerant temperature is measured at the outlet of the evaporator. If the temperature is high, the orifice increases and vice versa. There is a gas in the space above the membrane, in the tube to the measuring element, and inside the measuring element. If the temperature at the evaporator outlet rises, the gas inside the measuring element expands and the orifice size increases with the pressure pins. This way, more refrigerant can flow into the evaporator and the temperature of the evaporator will drop. A drop in temperature will result in the orifice being made smaller again. This way, a balance can be found, and the refrigerant temperature will be kept at a consistent level.

5. Block Valve (TXV).

In modern vehicles, the expansion valve is implemented as a block: the block valve, or TXV. The operation of a TXV is the same as the thermostatic expansion valve.

The evaporator inlet and outlet are both connected to the block valve. The refrigerant enters the block valve from the receiver drier. The refrigerant flows into the evaporator through the orifice. After that, the refrigerant flows through the evaporator, once more through the block valve, and past the measuring element. The temperature of the outflowing refrigerant determines the flow-through rate of the orifice. In other words, refrigerant regulation occurs internally.

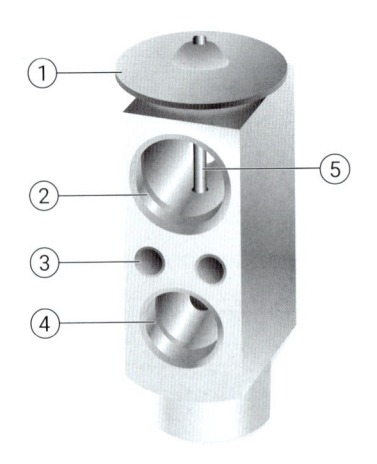

Fig. 66 Block valve (TXV):
1. Membrane. 2. Return from evaporator. 3. Installation bolt holes. 4. High-pressure connection. 5. Flap needle/control pin.

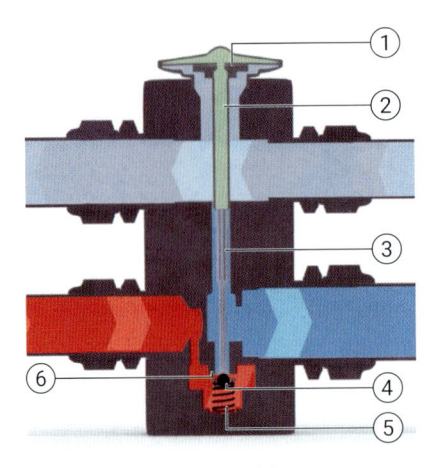

Fig. 67 Cross-section of the TXV:
1. Membrane. 2. Measuring element. 3. Control pin. 4. Ball. 5. Spring. 6. Cavity.

6. Evaporator

The evaporator is placed in the heater/air conditioning case, behind the firewall. The evaporator absorbs heat from the air passing into the interior.

The refrigerant enters the evaporator as a liquid and exits it as a gas. Heat from the air is used to make the refrigerant boil and change phases.

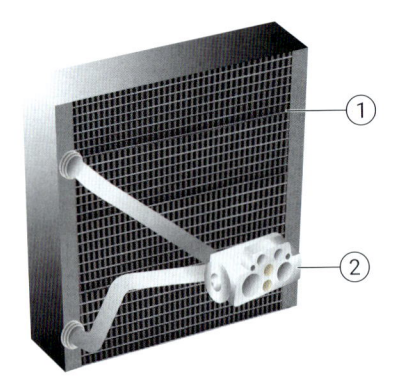

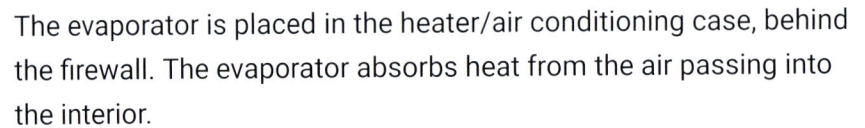

The blower motor is responsible for creating the airflow through the evaporator. During this operation, the air is not only cooled but also dehumidified. Because of the drop in temperature, the moisture in the air condenses onto the evaporator, where the temperature is below the dew point. Floating particles (dust, pollen, etc.) are captured by the moisture on the evaporator. The evaporator case must have good water drainage in order to dissipate this condensation. If the evaporator drain is clogged, this may lead to bacterial growth, foggy windows, and water intrusion onto the floorboard.

If allowed to collect, the moisture and the dust/dirt/pollen particles will result in bacterial growth. This is a leading cause of unpleasant air conditioning system odors. In systems that are not fully automatic, it would be best to turn the air conditioning system off and run the heater for a while before the car (and therefore also the air conditioning system) is turned off. This way, the evaporator and

Fig. 68 1. Evaporator. 2. Block valve (TXV).

the heater assembly are blown dry, and it becomes less probable that bacterial growth will occur.

7. Evaporator Capacity

The evaporator extracts heat from the air inside of the vehicle, and is where the liquid refrigerant evaporates. If a large amount of refrigerant is evaporated in the evaporator, a large amount of heat is also absorbed from inside of the vehicle, and the temperature of the air flow through the air conditioning vents will be greatly reduced. If too little refrigerant evaporates inside of the evaporator, such as the case with a system that is either low on refrigerant or malfunctioning in some way, then the temperature of the air flow though the system will not change very much.

An evaporator with a large capacity is capable of removing a lot of heat from the interior of the vehicle, and thereby producing very low air flow temperatures. Too much refrigerant entering the evaporator will cause its temperature to fall well below 32°F. When this occurs, the moisture condensed on the cool surface of the evaporator will freeze, air flow through the evaporator is no longer possible, and the cooling capacity of the evaporator is greatly reduced. Anytime the evaporator is only capable of creating a very small temperature drop the evaporator capacity has been reduced in some way.

During air conditioner operation, less refrigerant evaporates inside of the evaporator when there is a low cooling load placed on the system, such as when the interior temperature of the vehicle is already low, or if the surface of the evaporator is contaminated, restricting air flow through the evaporator fins.

It is normal that even "leak tight" air conditioning systems loose small amounts of their refrigerant charge over time. This leakage of refrigerant occurs due to the fact that no air conditioning system can be 100% leak proof, even if it is operating correctly. Mechanical movement, extreme temperature environments, and wear all work together to accelerate refrigerant loss. Therefore, an air conditioning system that is low on refrigerant is said to have a reduced capacity, in that the system cannot move as much heat from the passenger compartment when it contains less refrigerant that is was designed to operate with.

Fig. 69 Chiller: 1. Coolant connection. 2. Block valve. 3. Coolant connection. 4. Evaporator (heat exchanger).

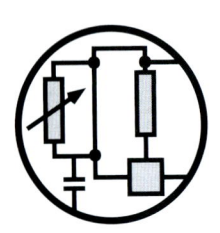

Fig. 70 Interfacing between A/C and the HV battery pack(s).

8. Chiller

In electrical vehicles (BEV) or Plug-in hybrid vehicles (PHEV), it is important that the temperature of the HV battery does not get too high. For these batteries, the ideal operating temperature is between approx. 68°F and 90°F. For hybrid cars, simple air cooling usually suffices. In fully electric cars and Plug-in hybrid vehicles, a liquid-cooled HV battery is usually used. A chiller is used to cool the coolant that circulates through the battery pack. A chiller is connected to the air conditioning system of the car.

In an evaporator, the air that flows into the interior is cooled. In a chiller, the coolant is cooled. The chiller consists of a small evaporator that is surrounded by coolant. This coolant then flows through the HV battery. Just as with an evaporator, the chiller has also been an orifice to create a pressure drop in the refrigerant that passes through it. In this case, it is a block valve (TXV). The supply of refrigerant to the block valve on the chiller can be activated and deactivated electronically via a magnetic flap valve.

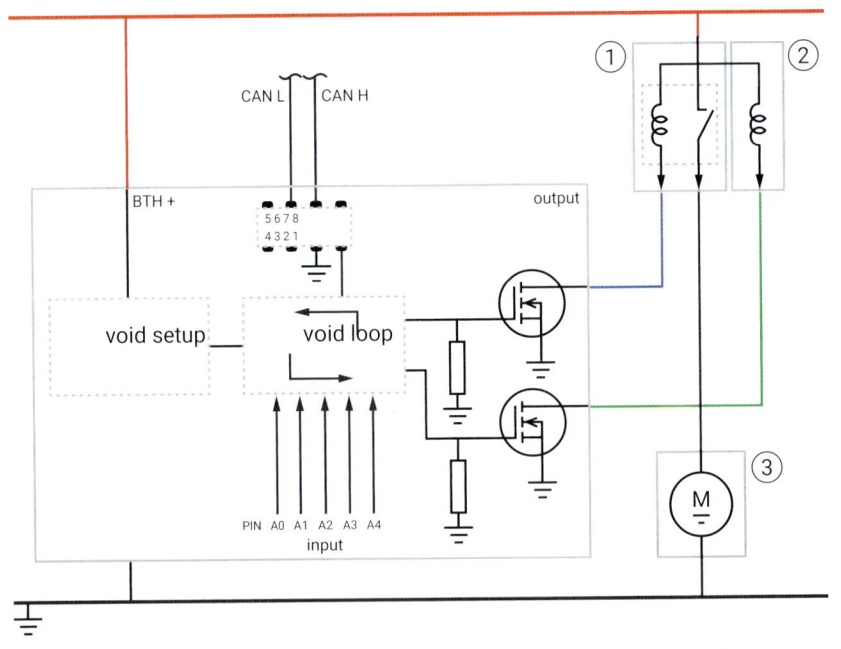

Fig. 71 Temperature control of battery temperature: 1. Fan relay. 2. Magnetic valve for chiller. 3. Fan.

AIR CONDITIONING SYSTEMS WITH FIXED ORIFICE TUBE

In addition to air conditioning systems that use an expansion valve as a variable expansion device, there are air conditioning systems that use a fixed orifice tube as the expansion device. The orifice tube is included in the high-side refrigerant line flowing towards the evaporator and is used in place of an expansion valve. A receiver drier is not used in this type of system. It is replaced by an accumulator. The accumulator is installed on the low-pressure-side of the system between the evaporator outlet and the compressor inlet.

1. Orifice Tube

The orifice tube is an expansion device with a fixed restriction and is located in the line between the condenser and the evaporator. The restriction must be chosen so that, when the system is properly charged, all of the refrigerant will exit the evaporator as a gas. However, since a fixed restriction cannot adjust to cooling loads, it is impossible to ensure that only superheated gaseous refrigerant exits the evaporator without any liquid refrigerant being present under all operating conditions.

The amount of refrigerant that enters the evaporator through the fixed restriction depends partly on the compressor output.
The amount of refrigerant that evaporates in the evaporator depends on the evaporator surface, airflow speed, and temperature inside of the vehicle.
When replacing an orifice tube, the restriction diameter is important. The orifice tube is available in several different colors. The color indicates the diameter of the restriction. Care must also be taken not to damage the o-ring on the orifice tube body when installing an orifice tube. A damaged o-ring will allow refrigerant to leak past the orifice tube unchecked.

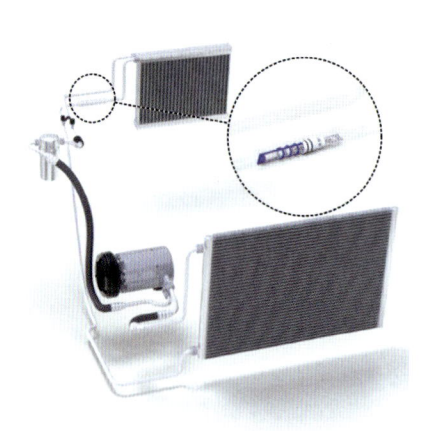

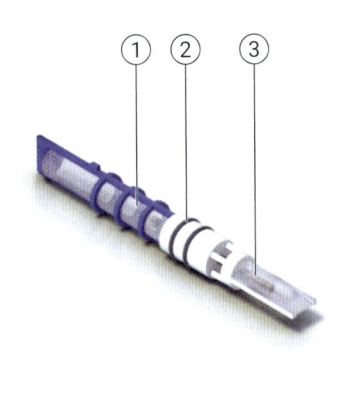

Fig. 72 The orifice tube is located in the high-pressure line between the condenser and the evaporator.

Fig. 73 The color of the orifice tube indicates the diameter of the restrictor: 1. Fine mesh filter. 2. O-rings. 3. Fixed orifice.

In some situations, not all of the refrigerant will be able to evaporate in the evaporator. This is why it is necessary to have an accumulator installed in the suction line after the evaporator. Any liquid refrigerant that may come out of the evaporator will be collected in the accumulator. This stops the liquid refrigerant from reaching the compressor.

2. Accumulator

The accumulator can be found in the low-pressure side of an air conditioning system with a fixed orifice tube. The refrigerant flows from the evaporator, through the accumulator, and then onto the compressor.

Any liquid refrigerant that exits the evaporator will remain in the accumulator, and only gaseous refrigerant can exit the accumulator. The accumulator also filters and dries the refrigerant. Once the refrigerant leaves the accumulator, it does not contain any water or contaminants.

Drying

A pouch of absorbent granules, or desiccant, absorbs water from the refrigerant. Water freezes in parts of the air conditioning system where the temperature is very low. This results in blockages. Water also reacts chemically with refrigerant and its oil, resulting in an acidic solution. This can damage the air conditioning system's components and compromise the operation and lifespan of the system.

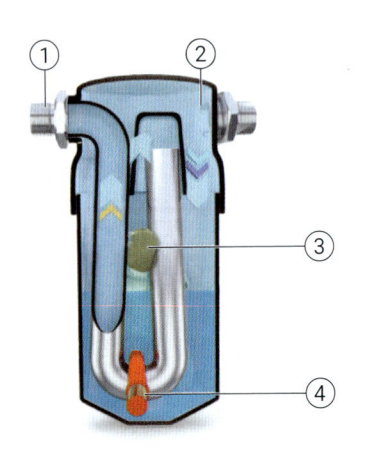

Fig. 74 Cross section of an accumulator: 1. Inlet. 2. Outlet. 3. Absorbent granules. 4. Filter.

Lubrication

The compressor draws gaseous refrigerant through a U-shaped tube. At the bottom of the bend there is a small opening. A very small amount of liquid refrigerant mixed with lubricant is drawn through this hole. A fine mesh filter prevents the outlet from becoming clogged.

Reservoir

The accumulator also functions as a reservoir. Depending on the exterior temperature, the accumulator will store or release liquid refrigerant.

Warm airflow through the evaporator can evaporate more refrigerant than a cold airflow. This has a direct effect on the level of liquid refrigerant stored inside of the accumulator.
Under normal operating conditions, the accumulator is approximately half full of liquid refrigerant.

Replacement interval

Over time a very small amount of moisture seeps in through the couplings and pipes of the air conditioning system, where it mixes with the refrigerant. It will take years before the absorbent granules become saturated due to this moisture exchange.

Manufacturers usually specify the replacement interval for an accumulator. Usually, an accumulator is replaced only when a system becomes less effective. When conducting maintenance on an air conditioning system, always consult the vehicle documentation to prevent causing any damage to the system.

If a part of the air conditioning system is detached, moisture from the surrounding air will reach the absorbent granules. In these circumstances, the absorbent granules will become saturated within three hours. Generally, the accumulator is always replaced if the air conditioning system has been opened.

CLIMATE CONTROL: PIPES, HOSES, AND COUPLINGS

1. Introduction

The components of the air conditioning system are connected to each other by the air conditioning system pipes and hoses. This allows refrigerant to flow through the air conditioning system.

Couplings on the end of the air conditioning pipes and hoses make it possible to disconnect components from the air conditioning system when performing maintenance and repairs.

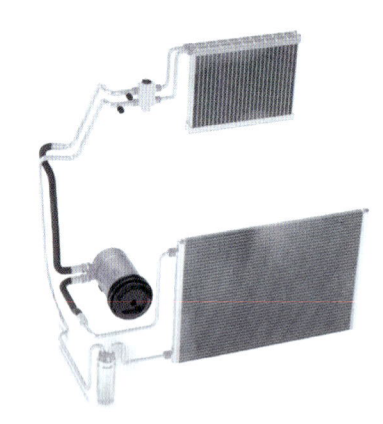

Fig. 75 The hoses and pipes of an air conditioning system.

2. Pipes

Modern air conditioning system pipes are made of aluminum or steel. The diameter of a pipe will depend on where it is located in the air conditioning system.

A pipe on the high-pressure side of the system through which liquid refrigerant flows has a small diameter. On the low-pressure side of the system where the refrigerant is gaseous, the diameter of the pipe is larger.

The pipes must be able to withstand constant exposure to the refrigerant and the lubricant that is dissolved in it. In addition to these requirements, the pipes must be able to withstand the temperature swings, pressure spikes, and phase changes of the refrigerant in the air conditioning system.

3. Internal Heat Exchanger

In some air conditioning systems there may be an internal heat exchanger built into the air conditioner pipe. In these instances, the low-pressure pipe runs partly through the high-pressure pipe. The pipes are joined together one inside of the other, and heat is exchanged between the warm liquid refrigerant and the cold gaseous refrigerant. Due to this heat exchange, the gaseous refrigerant is further superheated, while the liquid refrigerant is further subcooled. This improves the cooling capacity and thus the efficiency of the system.

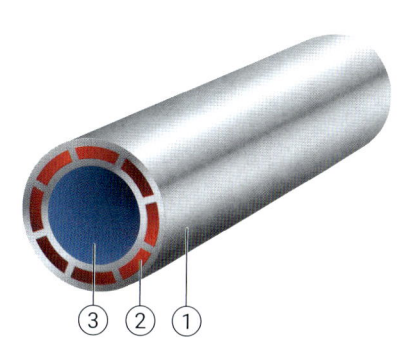

Fig. 76 Cross-section of the heat exchanger: 1. Pipe with heat exchanger. 2. High-pressure pipe. 3. Low-pressure pipe.

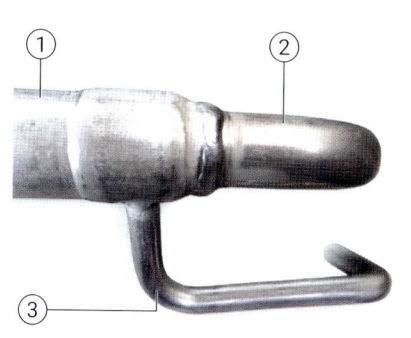

Fig. 77 Pipe with heat exchanger: 1. Heat exchanger. 2. Low-pressure pipe. 3. High-pressure pipe.

4. Hoses

Some parts of the air conditioning system need to move relative to each other. In order for this to be possible, these components are connected with a flexible refrigerant hose.

The hose is constructed of multiple layers. These different layers ensure the hose is sturdy, durable, and resistant against any influence from the refrigerant and the oil that has been dissolved into it.

The lubricating oil in the refrigerant attracts moisture. The composition of the hose(s) ensures as little moisture as possible reaches the refrigerant and the lubricating oil that is dissolved in it.

Fig. 78 Flexible hose.

5. Couplings

Thanks to the use of couplings, it is possible to remove and replace components of the air conditioning system when needed. Depending on the type of coupling used, this can be accomplished with standard tools or in some cases, special tools may be required to release the couplings.

Couplings can be sealed with one or two O-rings, or in some systems gaskets and crush washers are used. The most leak-free type of coupling union using o-rings or gaskets is the pad mounted coupling. Some systems may use compression-type couplings, where a conical metal-to-metal seal is used in place of an o-ring or gasket. Whichever method is used, these sealing elements ensure that no refrigerant can leak out of the union.

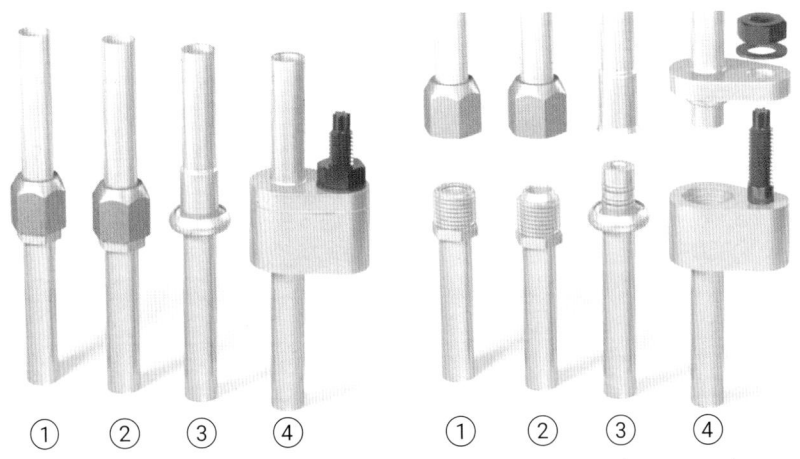

Fig. 79 Various types of couplings: 1. O-ring. 2. Compression coupling. 3. Spring lock coupling. 4. Pad mounted coupling.

Fig. 80 Couplings in their opened condition: 1. Coupling with screw fitting and O-ring. 2. Compression coupling with conical seal. 3. Spring lock coupling. 4. Pad mounted coupling.

Due to requirements regarding air conditioning system leakage reduction, modern cars increasingly use pad mounted couplings in their air conditioning systems.

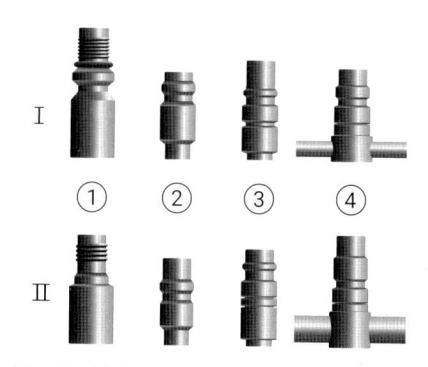

Fig. 81 Various pressure connections: I. High pressure. II. Low pressure. 1. R12. 2. R134a. 3. R1234yf. 4. R744.

6. Service Connections

In order to evacuate and recharge the system, every air conditioning system is equipped with service connections. In almost all cases, one service connection is installed at the low-pressure side and one at the high-pressure side of the system. These two connections have different diameters so that gauges and/or service equipment cannot be hooked up backwards.

Several different refrigerants can be used in air conditioning systems. To prevent the wrong refrigerant from being used in a system, each refrigerant has their own unique type of service connections.

Service connections for R12

R12 service connections have an external screw thread. These allow an R12 system to be recognized immediately, as it is the only system that has service connections with an external screw thread.

Service connections for R134a

R134a service connections have internal screw threads.

Service connections for R1234yf

R1234yf service connections also have internal screw threads. Their diameter and shape are slightly different. You will also notice that the connections of an R134a service station will not fit well on an R1234yf air conditioning system.

In many cases, the protective covers of the service connections are different. They are sometimes green and/or a fire hazard symbol might sometimes be applied. However, this is not always the case. It is important to pay attention to whether a car has an R134a or R1234yf system.

Service connections for R744

The service connections of an R744 system have a different shape and diameter. The protective covers of R744 service connections are pressed into place instead of being screwed on. This prevents the build-up of pressure underneath the protective covers.

7. Servicing Refrigerant

It is relatively easy to mistake the service connections of a R134a and R1234yf systems. If the R134a service station is connected to the service ports of an R1234yf vehicle by mistake, the service connections will not seal correctly, and refrigerant will leak out. Before connecting the service station to a vehicle, be sure to verify that you are using the correct service station for the vehicle.

8. R1234yf Refrigerant Identifier

Since R1234yf refrigerant is much more expensive than R134a, air conditioning installations are sometimes deliberately filled incorrectly. This usually has no direct effect on the operation of the air conditioning system. However, problems will arise when a shop attempts to recover the refrigerant. On the vehicle's identification sticker, it says that the system has been filled with R1234yf and also that the service connections are the R1234yf type. However, if a system has been improperly filled with R134a, during normal service procedures this refrigerant will end up in the R1234yf service machine tank, and contaminate the entire machine.

This mixed refrigerant is unusable and must be disposed of as chemical waste. To prevent this from happening, a refrigerant identifier must be used. By using this device, it is possible to verify if the air conditioning system has been charged with the appropriate refrigerant. The refrigerant identifier can be used as a stand-alone device, but it can also be integrated into the service station in some cases.

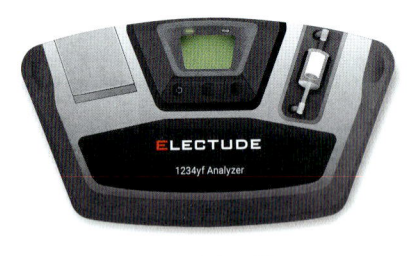

Fig. 82 Refrigerant identifier.

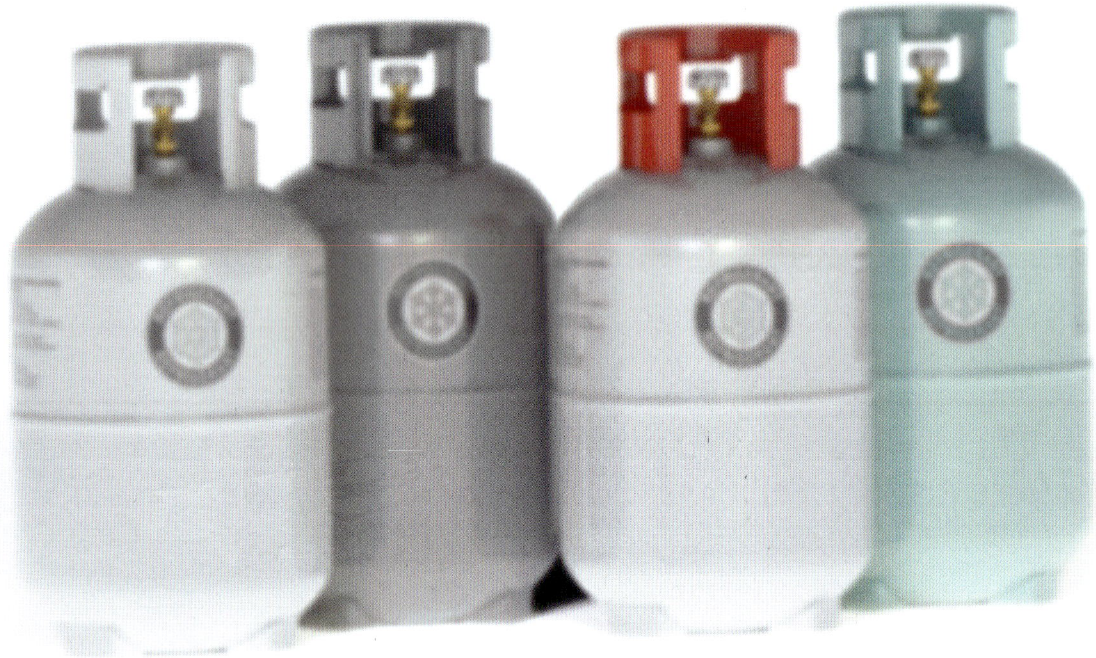
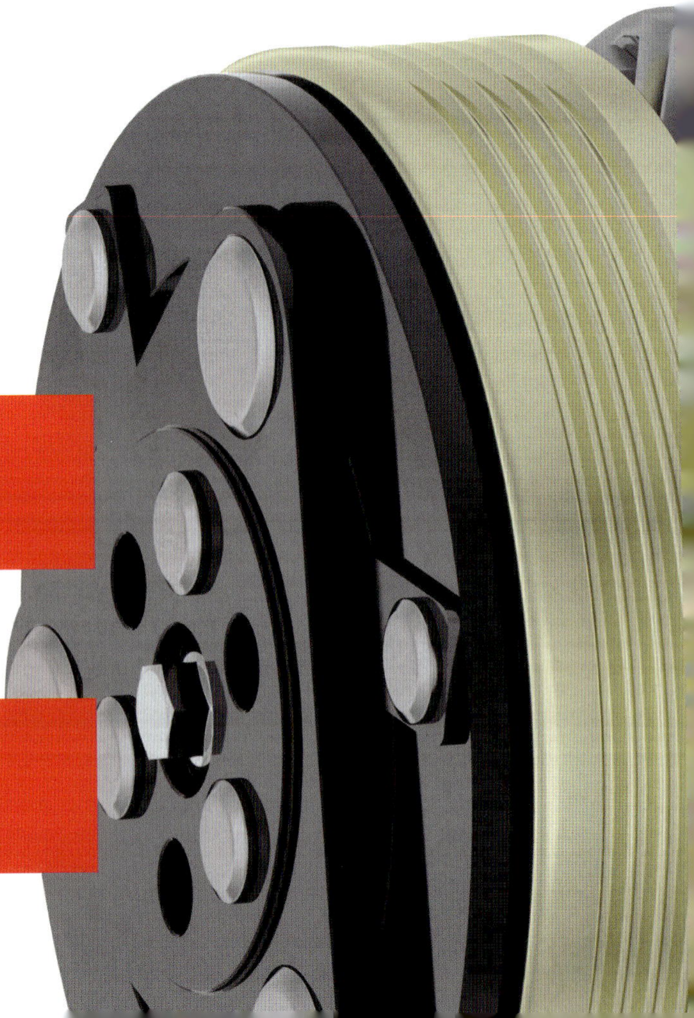

4. Electrical HVAC Components

AIR CONDITIONING ELECTRICAL COMPONENTS

The amount, type, and complexity of the electrical/electronic components used in a particular air conditioning system depend on the desired function of the system and the type of vehicle that it is installed in. In this chapter, we will explain the differences between:
— Manual air conditioning systems, in which the temperature and the air flow are controlled manually.
— Fully automatic air conditioning (climate control) systems, in which the temperature and air flow are controlled automatically, however, with this type of system it is possible to override the automatic control and manually regulate the air flow, blower motor speed, and the recirculation door position.

We will discuss the most commonly used electrical/electronic components of these two systems.

Fig. 83 Manual air conditioning: 1. Fan speed. 2. Temperature control. 3. Air mode door selector. 4. Recirculation on/off. 5. Air conditioning on/off.

Fig. 84 Fully automatic air conditioning: 1. Mode switch. 2. Air conditioning on/off. 3. Recirculation on/off 4. Windshield defogger on/off. 5. Rear window defroster on/off 6. Right temperature control and automatic air conditioning on/off. 7. Fan speed and climate control off. 8. Left temperature control and dual mode on/off.

Fig. 85 Engine Control Unit

1. Engine Control Unit

In most cars, the engine control unit is responsible for activating the air conditioning compressor relay. In a manually operated air conditioning system, a switch on the heater control panel is used to request activation of the air conditioning system. In a fully automatic air conditioning system, various control settings and sensors are used to send a signal to the engine control unit requesting activation of the air conditioning system. This signal is usually sent by the climate control module to the engine control unit through a network (CAN bus). Based on various parameters, the engine control unit decides if the compressor should be turned on or off. Some of these parameters are:

— **Coolant temperature**

Above a certain engine temperature (e.g. 240°F), the compressor is turned off to protect the engine.

— **Engine load**

When a specific engine load has been reached (e.g. 85% throttle valve opening), the compressor is turned off so that compressor drive loss no longer affects the maximum engine power.

— **Fault codes**

If certain (environmental) malfunctions occur, the compressor is turned off to limit the emission of hazardous substances.

— **Evaporator temperature**

If the evaporator temperature is too low, compressor is turned off.

— **Refrigerant pressure**

If the pressure inside the system is too high the compressor is turned off for safety and to prevent damage to the system. If the pressure is too low the compressor is turned off due to the fact that not enough refrigerant and lubricating oil are being circulated, which will damage the compressor.

Fig. 86 1. Three mode refrigerant pressure sensor. 2. Connector with four pins.

COMPRESSOR CONTROLS

If all the requirements for turning on the compressor have been met, the engine control unit will turn on the compressor via a relay.

1. Magnetic Clutch

All air conditioning systems are equipped with a compressor. Depending on the type of compressor used by the system, a magnetic coupling may be used.

In a vehicle with an internal combustion engine, the air conditioning compressor is driven by the crankshaft via a serpentine belt. This means that the serpentine belt is moving when the engine is running.

Fig. 87 Magnetic coupling: 1. Return springs. 2. Pulley. 3. Coil. 4. Bearing. 5. Ring. 6. Triangle bracket.

NOTE The magnetic coupling enables the compressor to remain stationary, even though the belt is moving. It is important to note that conditions such as an overheating engine, or wide open throttle engine operation will cause the ECU to disengage the air conditioning compressor until these conditions change. electric vehicles do not have a crankshaft; in these cases the compressor is driven by an electric motor.

Construction of the magnetic coupling
The magnetic coupling consists of three primary components:
— Front plate.
— Pulley.
— Magnetic coil.

The pulley is mounted to the compressor housing with a bearing. When the combustion engine is turned on, the pulley will follow the motion of the belt.

The front plate is connected to the axle of the air conditioning compressor. When the front plate is stationary, the air conditioning compressor is switched off.

The magnetic coil is mounted onto the housing of the air conditioning compressor. When the magnetic coil is powered on, the steel ring of the front plate is pulled against the pulley; at this point the air conditioning compressor is switched on. If it is no longer powered, then the return springs press the front plate's steel ring back into its resting position, and the compressor is disengaged from the belt.

2. Output Control Valve

The variable swashplate compressor is a compressor with a variable displacement or output.

The output of the compressor is controlled by the angle of the swashplate. This angle changes as the pressure behind the pistons is adjusted. A solenoid valve controls this pressure, according to the requirements of the air conditioning system.

If a lot of refrigerant is evaporating in the evaporator, the output is high; if only a little refrigerant is able to evaporate, the output is low. As a result, the compressor only pumps as much refrigerant as the system needs.

Fig. 88 Compressor with an output control valve: 1. Variable swashplate compressor. 2. Output control valve.

Fig. 89 Output Control Valve

RADIATOR COOLING FAN CONTROL

One or more cooling fans are installed on the radiator/condenser assembly to be able to sufficiently cool the condenser. In most vehicles, the cooling fan will rotate at a low speed when the air conditioning system is turned on. There are also cars in which the cooling fan is activated simultaneously with the air conditioning compressor.

The cooling of the condenser with the cooling fan can be controlled in two ways:
— Stepped control
— Variable control

In both cases, the cooling fan will spin faster when the engine temperature rises and/or there is a higher pressure inside the air conditioning system.

1. Stepped Speed Control

With stepped control of the cooling fan, the cooling fan is activated by relays. In this case, there is a relay for the slow speed of the cooling fan and a relay for the fast speed of the cooling fan. Different circuit configurations are possible with this type of control.

Examples:
— A cooling fan can rotate at a low speed and at a high speed.
— There are two cooling fans, whereby one or two are rotating.
— There are two cooling fans, whereby both rotate slowly in the first position and both rotate quickly in the second position.

Additionally, the two cooling fans may be different sizes.

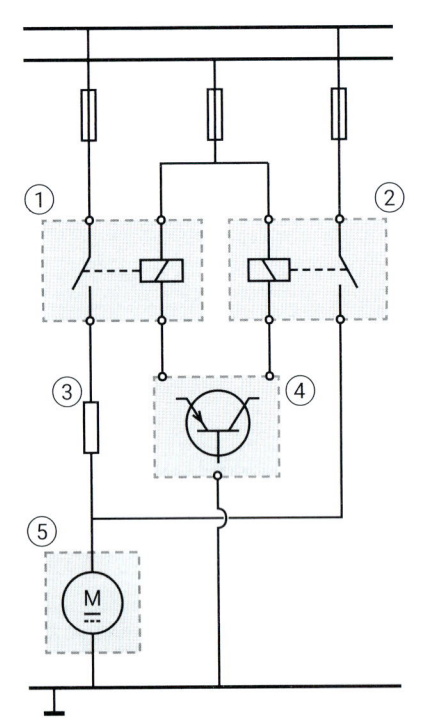

Fig. 90 Stepped control with one motor: 1. Low speed relay 2. High speed relay 3. Resistor 4. Engine control ECU 5. Cooling fan.

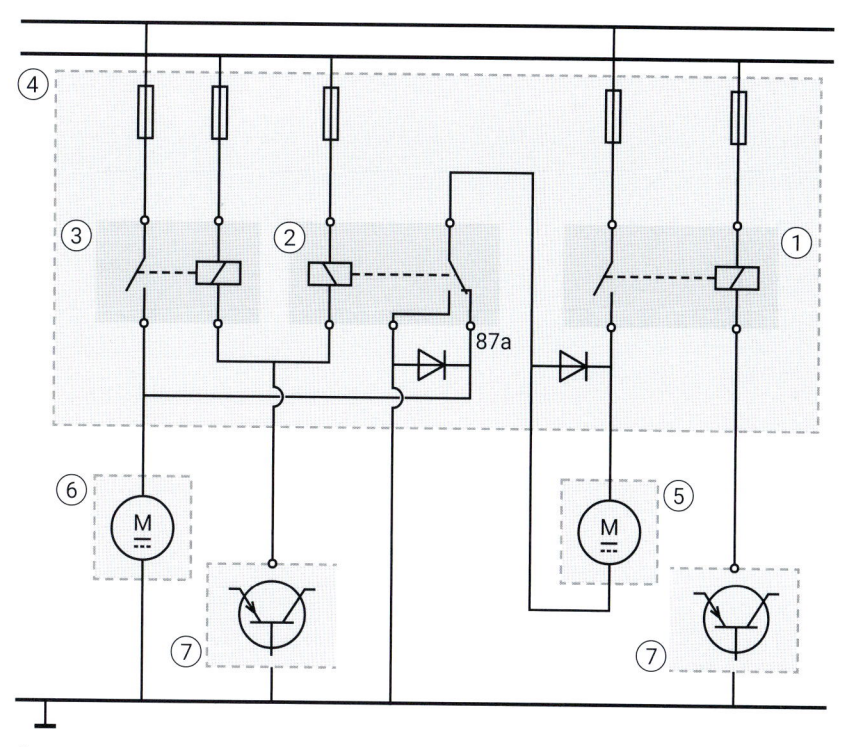

Fig. 91 Stepped control with two motors: 1. Low speed relay 2. Relay. 3. High speed relay. 4. Fuse box. 5. Motor one. 6. Motor two. 7. Engine control ECU.

2. Variable Speed Control

In the case of variable control of the cooling fan, the cooling fan speed is controlled steplessly, or in a smooth linear fashion. This stepless control is achieved by the engine control unit using a pulse width modulated (PWM) control signal to the control unit of the cooling fan. The control unit of the cooling fan controls the electric motor fan and varies its speed.

The control unit of the cooling fan is usually mounted on the cooling fan and it is oriented so it will be cooled by the airflow generated by the fan.

Fig. 92 Cooling fan with variable speed control: 1. Cooling fan control unit. 2. Cooling fan motor.

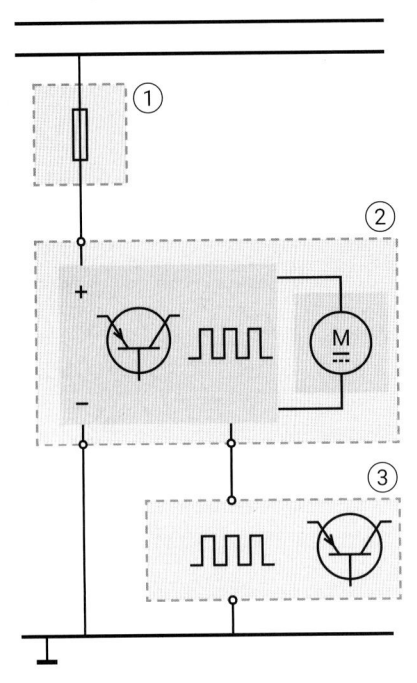

Fig. 93 Diagram of cooling fan with variable speed control: 1. Fuse box. 2. Cooling fan control unit. 3. Engine control ECU.

EVAPORATOR TEMPERATURE

If the evaporator temperature drops below freezing the condensation that forms on the surface of the evaporator coil will freeze. This condensation occurs when the moisture form the air comes into contact with the cooler surface of the evaporator, much in the same way that condensation forms on a cold drinking glass on a warm day.

If the condensation present on the evaporator freezes, air can no longer flow through the evaporator. To prevent the evaporator from freezing, the temperature is monitored by a de-icing switch or an evaporator temperature sensor.

1. De-icing Switch.

The objective of the de-icing switch is to turn the compressor off if the moisture on the evaporator were to freeze. The de-icing switch is installed in older cars with a dynamic thermal expansion valve. A de-icing switch consists of a temperature sensor combined with a tripping relay. The probe of the temperature sensor is placed in between the evaporator fins.

If the evaporator temperature approaches the freezing point, the sensor will activate the relay and turn the compressor off. This allows the temperature of the evaporator to rise as it absorbs the heat from the interior of the vehicle. Once the temperature rises approximately 4 degrees, the switch closes the relay contacts and turns the compressor back on.

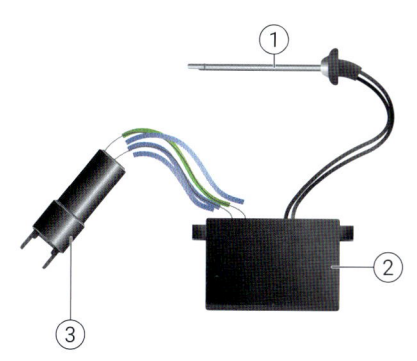

Fig. 94 De-icing switch:
1. Temperature sensor. 2. Relay.
3. Connector.

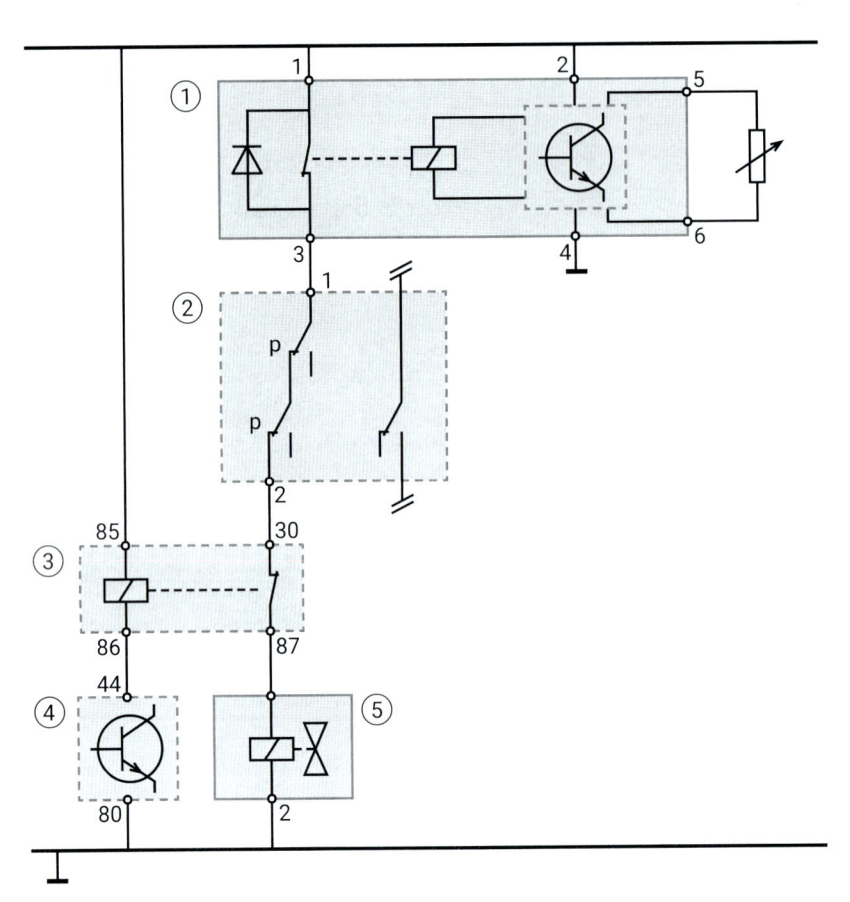

Fig. 95 1. De-icing switch. 2. Refrigerant pressure switch. 3. Compressor clutch relay. 4. Engine control ECU. 5. Magnetic compressor clutch.

2. Evaporator Temperature Sensor

The de-icing switch is no longer used in modern cars. Instead of a de-icing switch, evaporator temperature sensors are used.

The evaporator temperature sensor is installed inside the evaporator. The sensor itself is a Negative Temperature Coefficient (NTC) thermistor. The signal of the evaporator temperature sensor is transmitted to the engine control unit. If the evaporator temperature is too low, the engine control unit will turn off the air conditioning compressor.

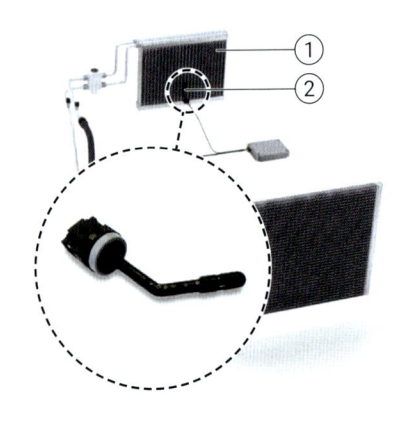

Fig. 96 1. Evaporator. 2. Evaporator temperature sensor.

Fig. 97 Pressure switch

Fig. 98 1. Accumulator. 2. Low-pressure switch.

3. Refrigerant Pressure Switch

The refrigerant pressure switch protects the air conditioning system against pressures which are either too low or too high. A pressure that is too low means that there is a reduced amount of refrigerant and lubricating oil is circulating through the system, which can damage the compressor. Excessively high refrigerant pressures can also cause system damage and pose a safety risk, which is why the compressor is turned off in these instances.

4. Low-pressure Switch

Low-pressure refrigerant pressure switches are only encountered on fixed orifice tube systems. These systems do not use any de-icing switches or evaporator temperature sensors. Since the low-side refrigerant pressure and the evaporator temperature correlate with each other, the compressor cycling can be controlled by the low-side refrigerant pressure. The low pressure switch can be installed on a low pressure pipe or on the accumulator.

At pressures lower than approximately 27 psi, the refrigerant pressure and evaporator temperature are too low and the compressor is switched off. This allows the refrigerant pressure and evaporator temperature to rise. Once the switch senses a pressure of roughly 40 psi in the low-side of the system, the switch closes again and turns the compressor back on. In cases where the refrigerant charge is excessively low or the system is empty, the pressure inside the system will be equal to the pressure outside of the switch, and the compressor will be turned off.

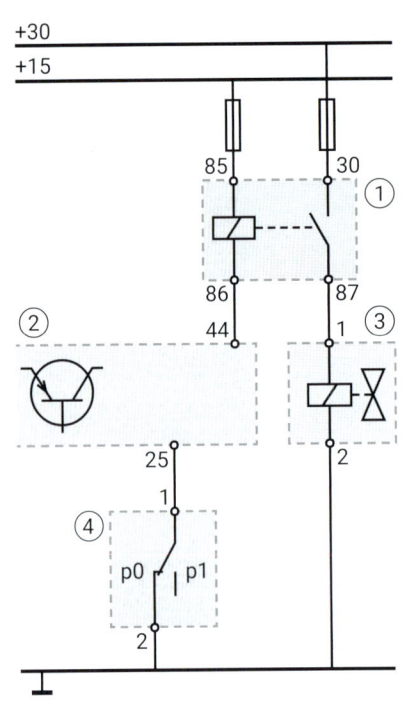

Fig. 99 1. Air conditioning compressor relay. 2. Engine control ECU. 3. Magnetic compressor clutch. 4. Low-pressure refrigerant switch.

Fig. 100 Triple function high pressure switch: 1. Triple function pressure switch. 2. Connector with four pins.

5. High-pressure Switch

The high-pressure switch is mounted onto a high-pressure pipe or onto the receiver drier. Depending on its design, this switch can have two or three functions.

The first function of the high-pressure switch is to protect the system against excessive refrigerant pressure. When the refrigerant pressure spikes to 400 psi and above, the switch turns the compressor off.

The second function of the high-pressure switch is to turn on the high speed cooling fan. This occurs when the pressure switch sees roughly 240 psi. The fans draws air through the condenser, which removes heat from the refrigerant and causes its pressure to drop. Once the pressure reaches approximately 215 psi, the high speed cooling fan is turned off.

An optional third task of the pressure switch is to shut down the system when the refrigerant pressure becomes too low. This applies to vehicles that have an expansion valve.

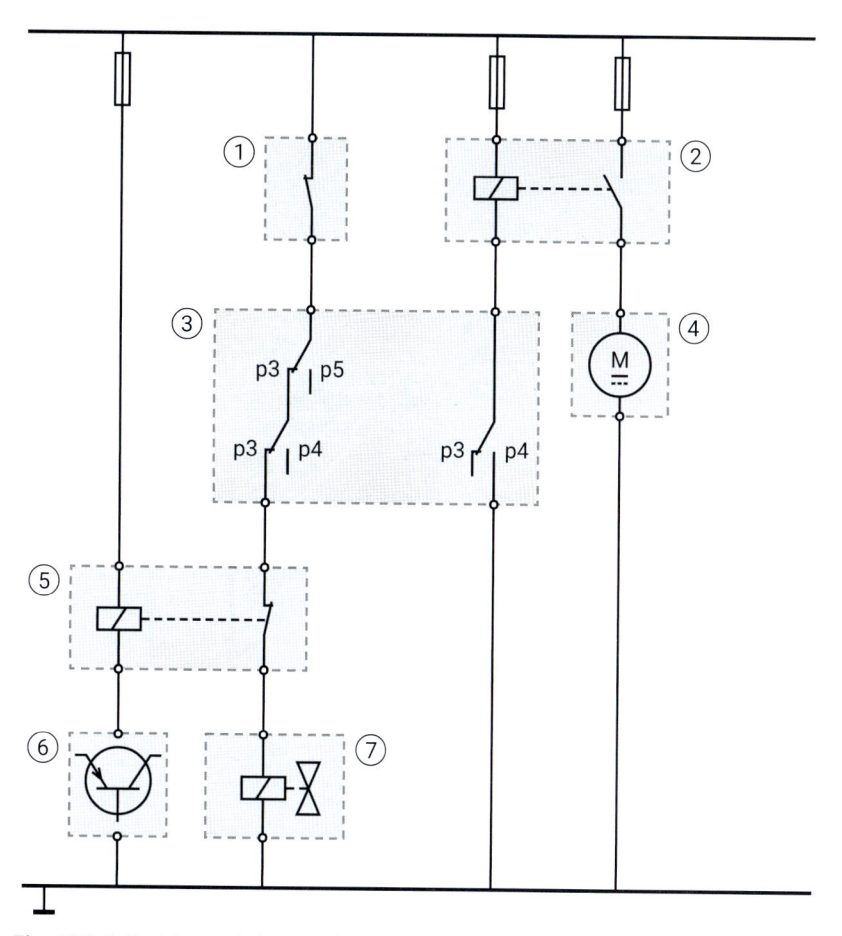

Fig. 101 1. De-icing switch. 2. High speed cooling fan relay. 3. Triple function high pressure switch. 4. High speed cooling fan motor. 5. Air conditioning compressor relay. 6. Engine control ECU. 7. Magnetic air conditioning compressor clutch. Switch states: p3 Normal pressure, p4. High pressure, p5. Low pressure.

6. Refrigerant Pressure Sensors

Refrigerant pressure sensors are used in place of pressure switches in most modern vehicles. The pressure sensor is mounted on the high pressure side of the system, and measures the absolute refrigerant pressure inside of the pipe. If the refrigerant pressure is too low, the compressor will not be turned on. If the refrigerant pressure is too high, the compressor will be turned off. In addition, the engine control unit will turn on the high speed cooling fan if the pressure rises to a predetermined level. In this way, the pressure sensor carries out all of the duties of the triple function high pressure switch.

Fig. 102 Pressure sensor.

The pressure sensor has three connections: a power supply (5 volts), a ground, and a signal wire. The signal voltage lies between 0.5 and 4.5 volts and increases linearly with the refrigerant pressure inside the pipe.

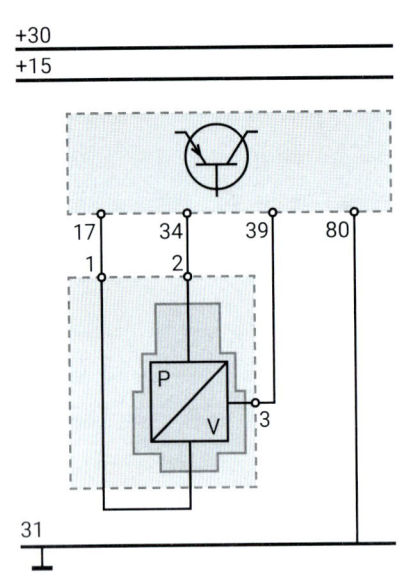

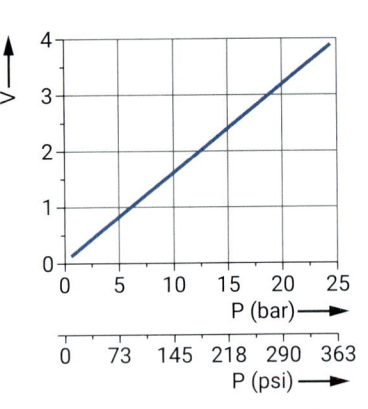

770 AIR CONDITIONING AND ELECTRICAL ACCESSORIES

Fig. 103 Electrical diagram of the pressure sensor.

Fig. 104 Pressure sensor: example of voltage/pressure characteristics.

THE HEATER ASSEMBLY

In most cases, the heater assembly consists of:
- Heater core
- Evaporator
- Cabin air filter
- Heater blend door(s)
- Air distribution (mode) doors
- Recirculation door
- Blower motor
- Air outlet vents

With manually controlled climate control, the doors are adjusted with a strut mechanism and/or with Bowden cables. In fully automatic climate control systems, the doors are adjusted electrically using servo motors.

In manually controlled climate control systems, the blend door function can be implemented as an air mixture valve or as a heater valve.
An air mixture valve mixes the warm air from the heater core with the inflowing exterior air. A heater valve regulates the amount of coolant flowing to the heater core. The heater valve can be controlled manually or electrically.

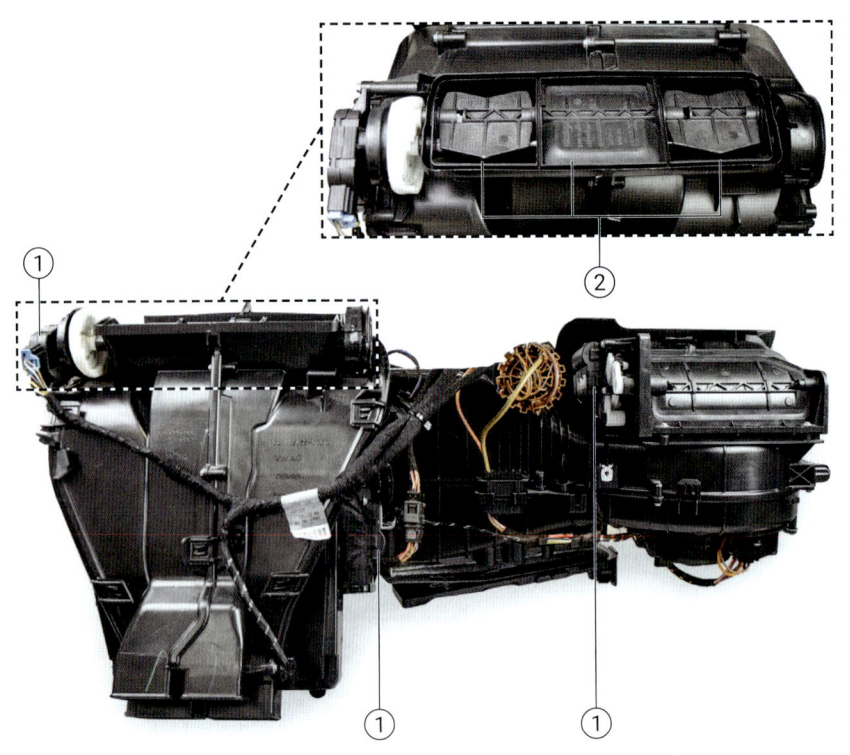

Fig. 105 Complete heater assembly: 1. Adjustment servo motors. 2. Air distribution doors.

1. Electric Heater Valve

The electric heater valve stops the flow of engine coolant through the heater core when maximum cooling is requested. In manually controlled air conditioning systems, the valve is often activated by a switch at the rear of the control unit. The switch is mechanically controlled when the temperature setting is set to maximum coldness. The valve consists of a servo motor with two connections. The valve is opened and closed by changing the polarity of the servo.

2. Electric Water Pump

Some climate control systems are equipped with an electric water pump. This pump ensures that the circulation of the coolant is uniform, even at a low engine speed. Additionally, the pump makes circulation of coolant possible even if the engine has been shut off. This allows the climate control system to use the residual heat of the engine's cooling system to continue to heat the interior after the engine has been shut off, i.e. residual heat utilization.

If the temperature of the coolant drops too much and the requested

Fig. 106 Electric heater valve: 1. Electromagnetic valve. 2. Engine coolant inlet. 3. Engine coolant outlet.

Fig. 107 Electric water pump: 1. Coolant inlet. 2. Connector. 3. 12 volt electric motor. 4. Coolant outlet.

interior temperature can no longer be maintained, then the climate control unit stops using residual heat. Also, if the car battery voltage drops below a certain level, residual heat utilization is stopped.

3. Auxiliary/Parking Heater

The vehicle can also be equipped with an auxiliary/parking heater. This additional heater is often used with diesel engines to heat the cooling system faster and to maintain its heat. This heater can be powered electrical or use fuel as a heat source. The parking heater often uses fuel to heat the coolant and keep it warm. This way, the cooling system can be heated independently from the engine. In that case, the electric water pump ensures circulation of the coolant. These systems are very common in cold climates.

Elaborate parking heater systems use a programmable timer, remote control, or smartphone for activation. The electric water pump can be controlled by the parking heater control unit or by the engine control unit. In both cases, the climate control unit can give the command to activate the water pump via the CAN bus.

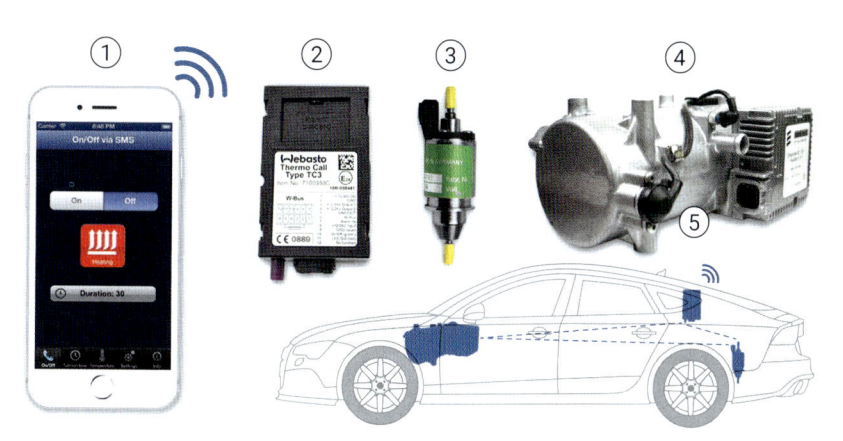

Fig. 108 Parking heater system: 1. Control app. 2. Receiver. 3. Fuel pump. 4. Parking heater unit. 5. Integrated electric water pump.

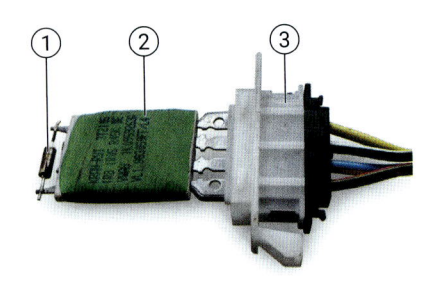

Fig. 109 Blower motor resistor: 1. Thermal fuse. 2. Resistors. 3. Connector.

4. Blower Motor Resistors

Use of series resistors is the standard method for adjusting the blower motor's rotation speed in older vehicles. A resistor switched in series with the heater motor will lower the voltage on the motor (voltage divider), which means that the blower speed will be lower than when the motor is powered directly. The heat generated inside the resistor must be dissipated, which is why these resistors often hang in the stream of the blower motor airflow, within the heater assembly.

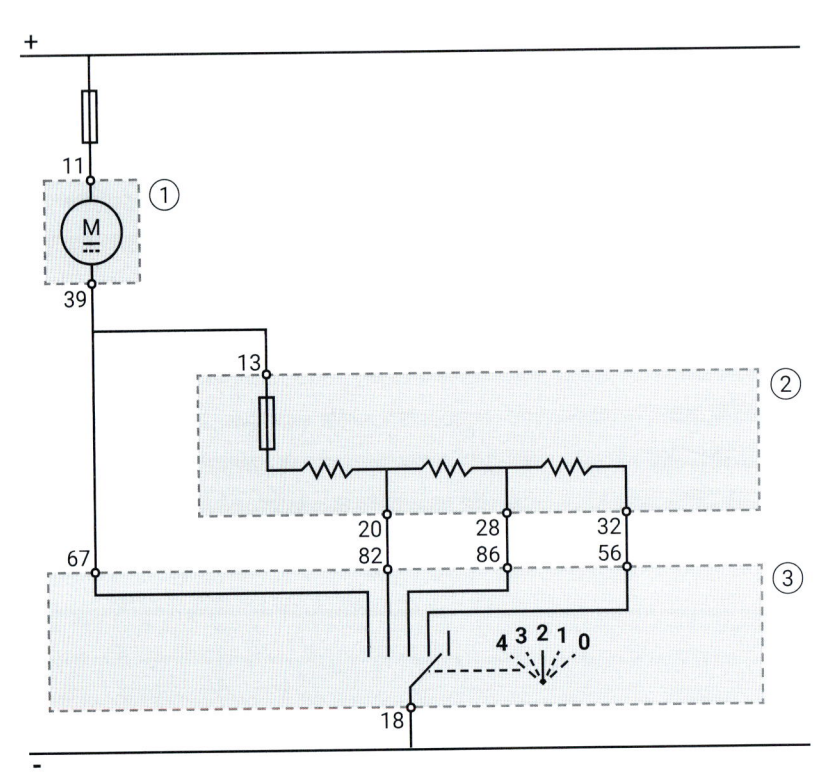

Fig. 110 Diagram of the blower: 1. Blower motor. 2. Series resistors. 3. Switch.

Switch positions: 0. Neutral. 1. Low speed (exterior air). 2. Medium speed (exterior air). 3. High speed (exterior air). 4. Maximum speed.

5. Blower Motor Controls

In modern climate control systems, series resistors are no longer used to control blower motor speed. Instead, the blower motor is equipped with a control unit that controls the blower motor directly. This control unit can be connected directly to the climate control unit or be connected through the climate control bus (LIN). In both cases, the climate control unit determines the desired airflow and converts this into a percentage/blower motor speed.

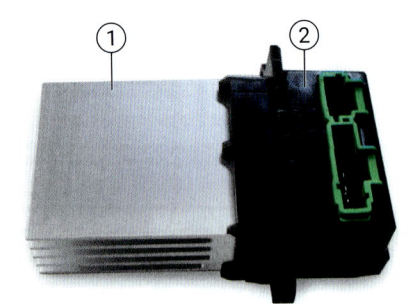

Fig. 111 Blower motor control unit: 1. Heat sink. 2. Electronics with output stage.

The blower motor control unit controls the current through the blower motor, as well as the speed of the motor. If the blower motor experiences a failure, the blower motor control unit reports it to the climate control unit. Failure codes may be stored in the climate control unit.

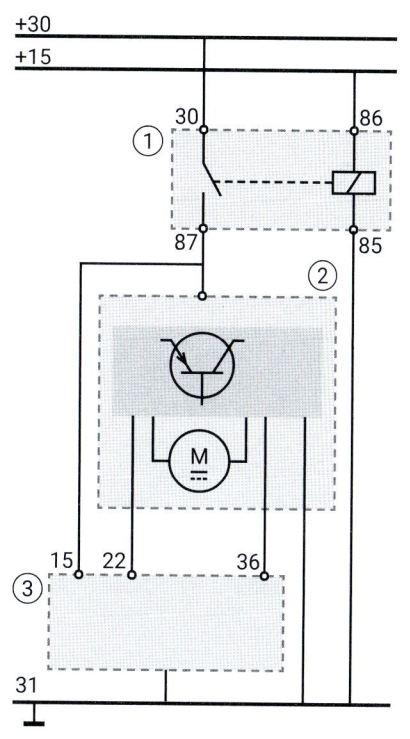

Fig. 112 Diagram of the blower control unit: 1. Blower relay. 2. Fan control unit. 3. Climate control unit. 22. Motor control. 36. Motor feedback.

6. Mode Door Controls

There are various doors (valves) within the heater assembly. Some valves direct airflow to the desired outlet vent. For instance, the windshield, the area around the feet, and the central vent. These valves are called mode doors.

Blend doors are often used to mix the air in order to obtain the desired output temperature. If the vehicle is equipped with a multi-zone climate control system, multiple blend doors are used. Common dual-zone climate control systems can set the temperature for the left and the right side of the vehicle. These systems use two blend doors to accomplish this.

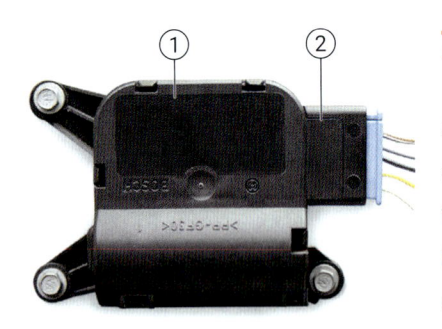

Fig. 113 DC motor: 1. DC motor with sensor. 2. Connector.

A recirculation door is installed to keep out unwanted odors. This door is able to close off the exterior air intake. In contrast with the other control doors, the recirculation door generally has only two positions: open and closed. The climate control module controls the correct positions of the doors automatically. A DC servo motor or a stepper motor is used as an actuator for adjusting these doors.

7. DC Motors

A DC motor (Direct Current motor) is an electric motor that has two connections. The DC motor is controlled with a PWM signal to move the door into the requested position. The ratio between the time that the power is switched on and off determines the position of the door. This control can be accurately compared to controlling the position of the throttle valve with a throttle valve adjustment motor.

A sensor is often integrated into the motor to determine the correct position of the door.

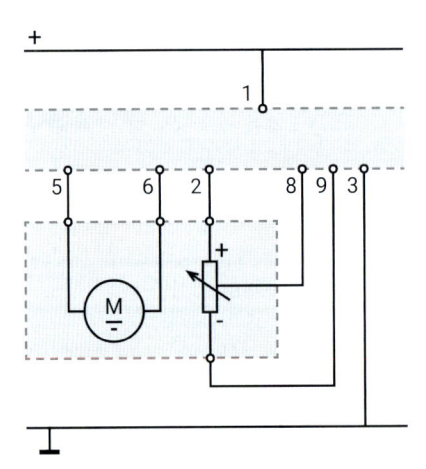

Fig. 114 Diagram of DC motor with feedback.

8. Stepper Motors

Fig. 115 Stepper engine used to control blend door operation:

The doors in the heater assembly can also be controlled with stepper motors. These motors usually have four connections. The stepper motor drives the door with a worm gear construction. Steeper motors can adjust the air doors very accurately. When a stepper motor is replaced, it usually has to be calibrated into the system, as the stepper motor receives feedback from the control unit regarding the door position.

During calibration, the door makes its maximum movement. This way, the maximum positions are determined. With these maximum positions noted, the module calculates the number of steps required to move the door into the desired position.

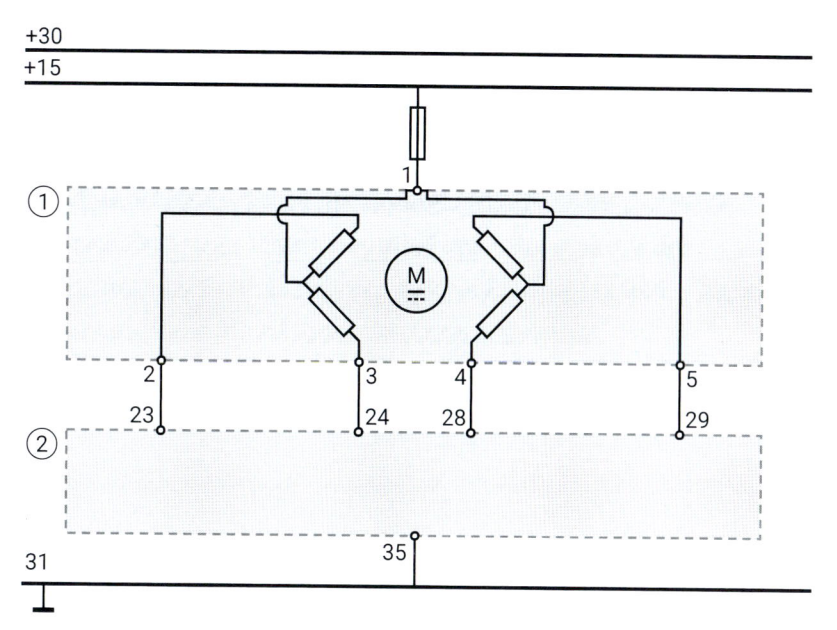

Fig. 116 1. Blend door stepper motor. 2. Climate control module.

9. Intelligent Adjustment Motors

In modern systems, 'intelligent' adjustment motors, also know as servos, are used to control the air doors. These adjustment motors are connected to the climate control unit via a network: the climate bus. Usually, the LIN bus is used for this. This means that the component consists of a servo component and electronics, in which the electronics are used to communicate via the climate bus (LIN), control the servo, and perform self diagnosis.

The component only requires three connections: a communication connection, power, and ground. The climate control unit sets each servo connected to the climate bus (LIN) into the desired position cyclically. The electronics inside each servo determine the rotational direction autonomously, and ensures that it makes the adjustments required for the desired position.

In response to the message from the climate control unit, each servo reports its actual position to the climate bus (LIN) as a message. To check if a desired position has been reached, the climate control unit compares the desired position with the actual position that it has received.

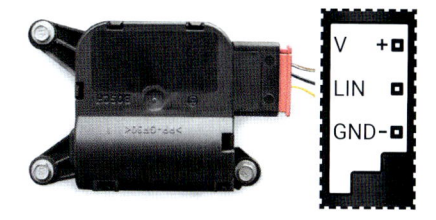

Fig. 117 Servomotor with LIN bus

This is useful in case the ignition is switched off while a servo is rotating. The actual position will now be stored in the climate control unit. In case of under-voltage or over-voltage conditions, the servo will stop moving. If the voltage has returned to a normal level, the servo will complete the movement until the requested position has been reached.

HVAC SYSTEM SENSORS

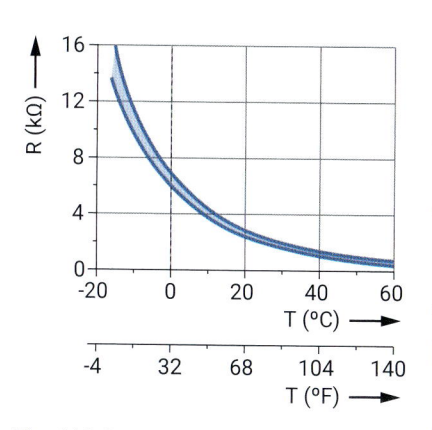

Fig. 118 Properties of an NTC thermistor.

1. Temperature Sensors

All temperature sensors used in the climate control system are Negative Temperature Coefficient (NTC) thermistors. Negative Temperature Coefficient means that when the temperature rises, the resistance decreases. NTC thermistors are chosen because the characteristics of NTC thermistors are more suitable than those of PTC thermistors for climate control sensors.

The sensor is powered by a 5-volt reference voltage that is supplied via a fixed resistor inside of this control unit. The combination of both resistors (voltage divider) creates the 'signal' of the temperature sensor, which range between approximately 0.5 and 4.5 volts.

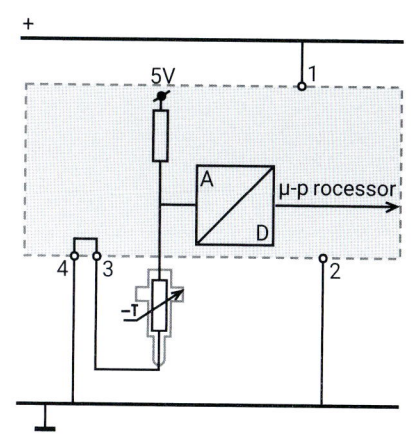

Fig. 119 NTC sensor circuit.

2. Interior Temperature Sensor

As its name implies, this temperature sensor is used to measure the temperature inside the vehicle. The interior temperature is used as the input parameter to control the temperature output of the climate control system. The sensor can be installed in various locations, and may be located near the climate control unit or even built into the climate control unit itself.

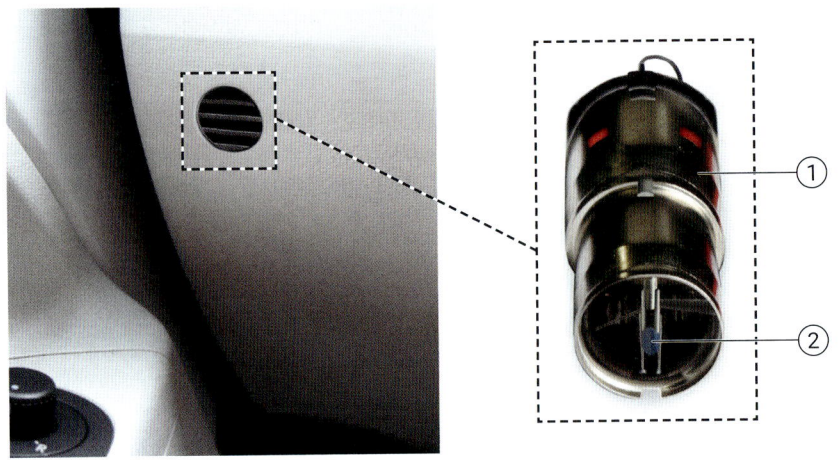

Fig. 120 Interior temperature sensor inside the dashboard: 1. Motor with fan. 2. NTC thermistor

Other manufacturers measure the interior temperature at approximately driver/passenger head height and install the sensor in the vicinity of the rear view mirror. A small fan is integrated into the sensor and ensures that interior air is blown towards the sensor element. If the fan is malfunctioning or the sensor is fouled, the interior temperature will be measured as lower than it actually is. Usually, the occupant experiences this as sharp temperature swings inside the car. The interior temperature sensor contains an NTC thermistor. The interior temperature sensor is used by the climate control system to compare the requested temperature with the temperature measured inside the car.

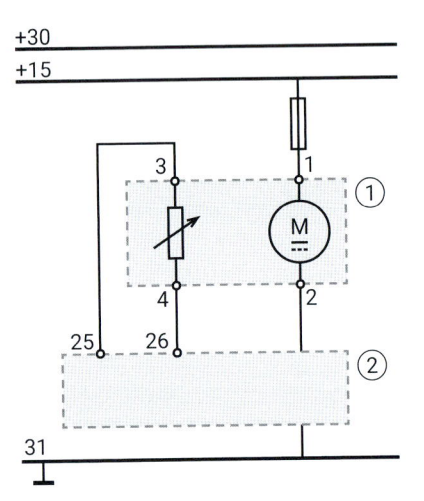

Fig. 121 1. Interior temperature sensor with fan. 2. Climate control unit.

3. Exterior Air Temperature Sensor

The exterior air temperature sensor is an NTC thermistor that measures the temperature outside of the vehicle. The sensor is often installed behind the front bumper, but some manufacturers install it underneath one of the exterior mirrors.

Exterior temperature can be used to:
- Predict the amount of cooling required to reach the desired interior temperature (blower motor speed, the position of the blend doors).
- Recirculation: If the exterior temperature is high and the requested interior temperature is low, the climate control system will close the recirculation door immediately after starting the engine.
- Allows the climate control system to deactivate the compressor below a certain exterior temperature.

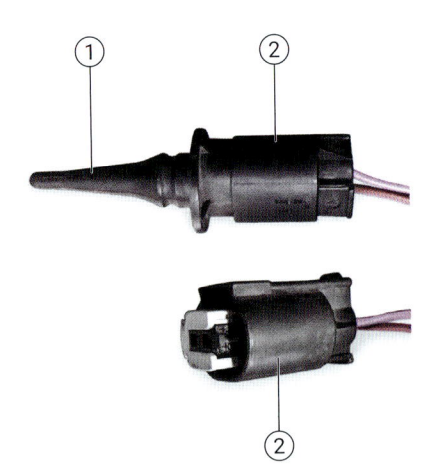

Fig. 122 Exterior temperature sensor: 1. Molded NTC thermistor. 2. Connector.

In vehicles equipped with a network, this NTC temperature sensor is connected to a control unit in the engine compartment that sends the temperature out on the network.

Fig. 123 Exterior air temperature sensor installed into the exterior mirror.

Fig. 124 Exterior air temperature sensor installed behind the front bumper.

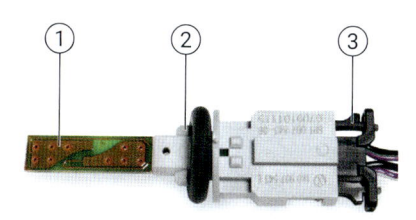

Fig. 125 Air outlet temperature sensor: 1. Sensor element. 2. Mounting bosses (bayonet fitting). 3. Connector.

4. Air Outlet Temperature Sensors

Most systems utilize temperature sensors in the outflowing airways as well as in the vicinity of the outflowing air vents of the heater assembly. They are a component of the temperature regulation system and are used to determine if the requested climate control air temperature has been reached.

In conjunction with the sunlight intensity sensor and the commanded blower motor speed, the outflowing air temperature determines the interior temperature. The outflowing air temperature sensors are directly connected to the climate control unit and contain NTC thermistors.

5. Sunlight Intensity Sensor

The sunlight sensor measures the intensity of the sunlight radiating down on the vehicle. The sunlight sensor accomplishes this by measuring the amount of infrared light shining on the vehicle. This sensor is installed on the top of the dashboard. Some vehicles use more than one sunlight sensor; by installing more than one sensor, the direction of the sunlight can also be determined. This is especially important on multi-zone climate control systems.

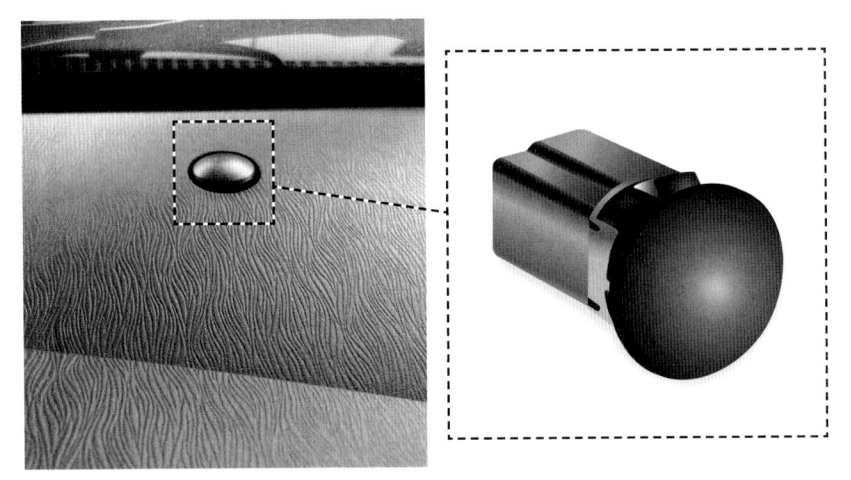

Fig. 126 A sunlight sensor installed on the dashboard.

Each manufacturer uses a slightly different sunlight sensor type, and each produce a unique signal output. One type of sunlight sensor is made with a photovoltaic cell. A photovoltaic cell delivers a voltage signal that gets higher if more light shines onto it. A solar panel is a good example of an array of photovoltaic cells in action.

Sunlight sensors can also be constructed with an infrared light receiver. These devices measure the amount of infrared light present using an optical sensor mounted in an electronic circuit.

The output voltage of the sunlight sensor can be an analog signal that ranges between 1 and 5 volts. It is also possible for the electronics in the sensor to convert the amount of infrared radiation into a digital signal. The electronic sunlight sensors not only detect the amount of sunlight and its angle, but also contains the electronics needed to process the signal (amplification, A/D conversion) and to assess its rationality. This frees up the climate control unit from carrying out these tasks. Vehicles outfitted with a network share the sensor information with other control units, and this information can be used by other control units for carrying out functions such as automatically switching on the car lighting when it becomes dark outside.

Through a phenomenon known as the greenhouse effect, the infrared light of sunlight heats up the interior of the vehicle. Because of this, we can measure the amount of infrared light present, along with the exterior temperature and vehicle speed, and determine the amount of cooling load that is being placed on the system. When the amount of infrared light present changes, adjustments are made to the air output temperature and the blower motor speed so that the desired interior temperature can be reached.

This allows the climate control system to efficiently maintain the interior temperature of the vehicle.

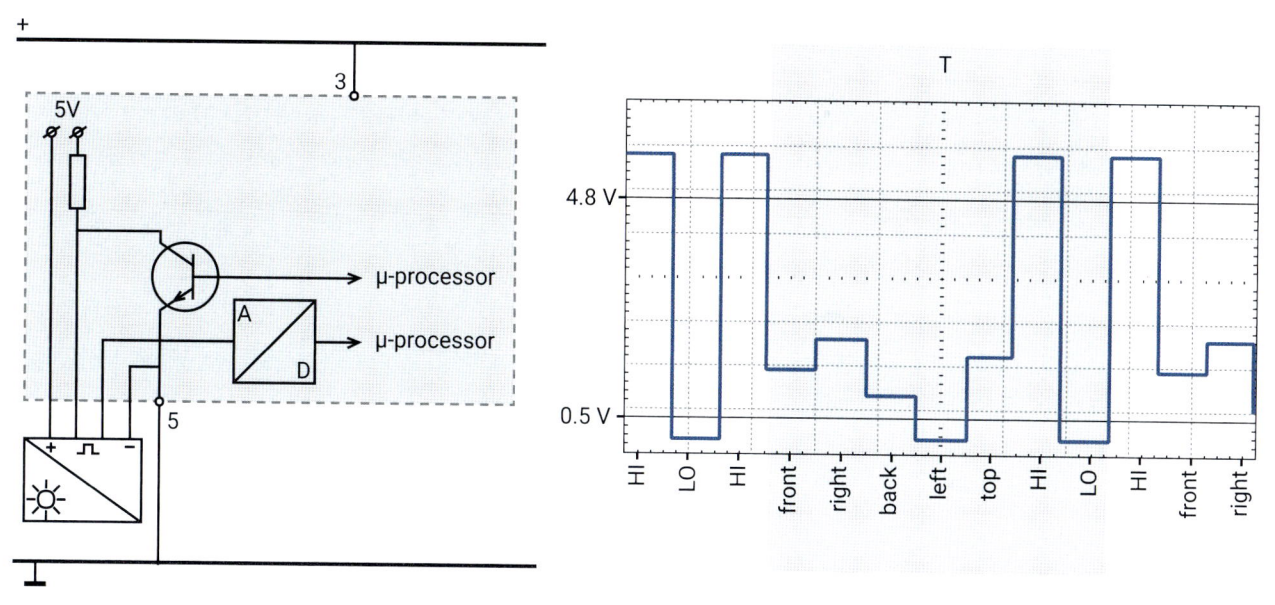

Fig. 127 Main diagram and signal of a five-function sunlight sensor (front, posterior, left, right, on top).

6. Humidity Sensor

Some manufacturers have expanded their climate control systems to include a humidity sensor. This sensor (also known as a dew point sensor) measures the humidity and temperature of the exterior air which is drawn into the system by the blower motor and uses it to calculate the dew point.

The humidity sensor is installed close to the intake opening of the heater assembly, in front of the recirculation door. This sensor can also be combined with the air quality sensor. Additionally, a humidity sensor can also be used to measure the humidity of the air in the vehicle's interior. Depending on application, the humidity sensor can be installed in an air duct or be combined with the interior temperature sensor.

Humidity can be determined in several ways. Some sensors measure humidity through resistance changes. Using this measuring principle, the resistance of the measuring element changes depending on the humidity of the air surrounding the

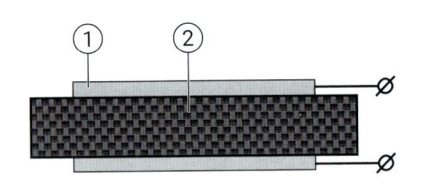

Fig. 128 Humidity sensor: 1. Electrodes. 2. Hygroscopic insulation layer.

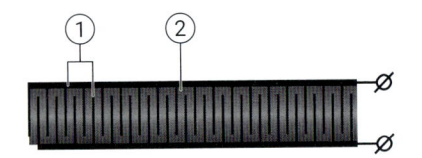

Fig. 129 Humidity sensor with capacitive functionality: 1. Comb-shaped electrodes. 2. Hygroscopic insulation layer.

sensor. In this type of sensor there is an insulation layer between two electrodes with a hygroscopic salt layer (LiCi) on top of it. Depending on the humidity present, this layer attracts a certain amount of moisture, which causes the resistance of the insulation layer to change. The more humidity there is, the lower the resistance of the insulation layer.

Other types of humidity sensors measure the amount of humidity present by way of a capacitive sensor. Using this measuring principle, the capacity of the measuring element changes depending on the humidity present in the air around the sensor. The measuring element has two electrodes with a hygroscopic insulation layer between them. This layer functions as a dielectric. Depending on the humidity present, the dielectric will absorb a certain amount of water, which causes the measuring element to reach a certain capacity. The more water that is absorbed, the higher the capacity of the measuring element will be.

Humidity sensors uses a power supply of 5 or 12 V, and the signal output can be analogue (PWM, 0 - 5 volts) or digital (LIN). It is also possible for the output signal to be a frequency (for instance, between 6100 - 7400 Hz). In this case, higher humidity levels lower the frequency of the signal.

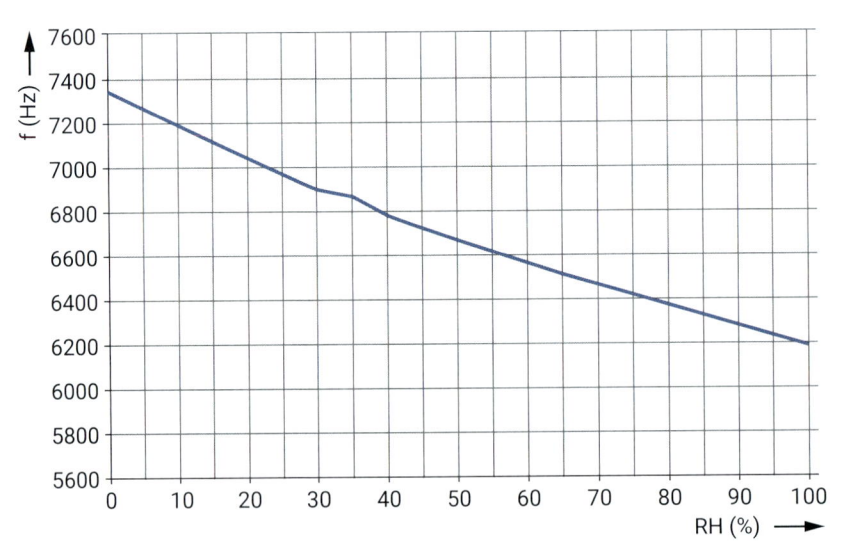

Fig. 130 Properties of a humidity sensor with internal electronic circuit. RH = relative humidity

The humidity sensor is used to determine the relative humidity and the dew point. The relative humidity indicates the correlation between the current moisture and the maximum amount of moisture in the air that can be present at that temperature. This value is expressed in percentages. For the human body, a relative humidity of 60 - 70% is optimal. A lower humidity will cause dehydration symptoms, while a higher humidity makes it more difficult for our bodies to evaporate sweat into the air.

The dew point is the temperature at which the air is saturated with moisture. Cold air can hold less moisture than warm air. Assume that, under certain circumstances, the dew point in an area is at 44°F. If an object with a temperature lower than the dew point is introduced into this area, then part of the moisture in the air will condense onto this object.

If the temperature of the evaporator is lower than the incoming air, then a part of the moisture in the air will condense onto the evaporator. The relative humidity of the air will decrease after it passes the evaporator; in other words, the air is dehumidified. This helps to quickly defog the car windows. A disadvantage, however, is that the air becomes extremely dry after it passes the evaporator, as the relative humidity outside is already very low. The air becomes so dry that occupants will experience this as unpleasant (dry eyes, dry throat, etc.).

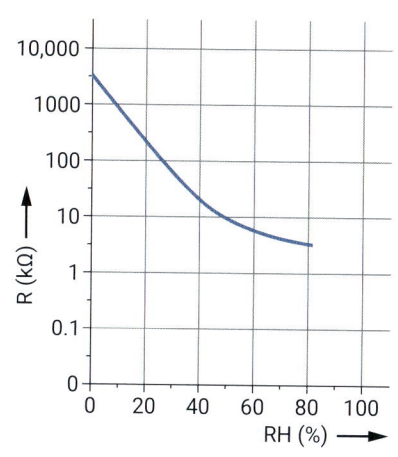

Fig. 131 Properties of a humidity sensor with an insulation layer.

A fully automatic climate control system equipped with a humidity sensor utilizes another control method to maintain a desired humidity level. The air drawn in by the blower motor does not get fully cooled by the evaporator and then reheated by the heater core to the requested temperature. Instead, by regulating the compressor output (using the output control valve), it becomes possible to adjust the capacity of the evaporator.

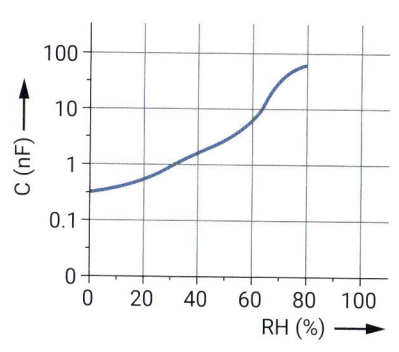

Fig. 132 Properties of a humidity sensor with capacitive functionality.

In this way, it is possible to adjust the amount of cooling, and therefore the amount of drying of the interior air. This allows the system to maintain the relative humidity of the air inside of the vehicle. This means that the evaporator temperature can be run at higher levels to maintain the humidity level. Full evaporator cooling and reheating is only used when the exterior air has a high relative humidity (80% - 100%) in order to ensure that the windows dry rapidly and remain clear.

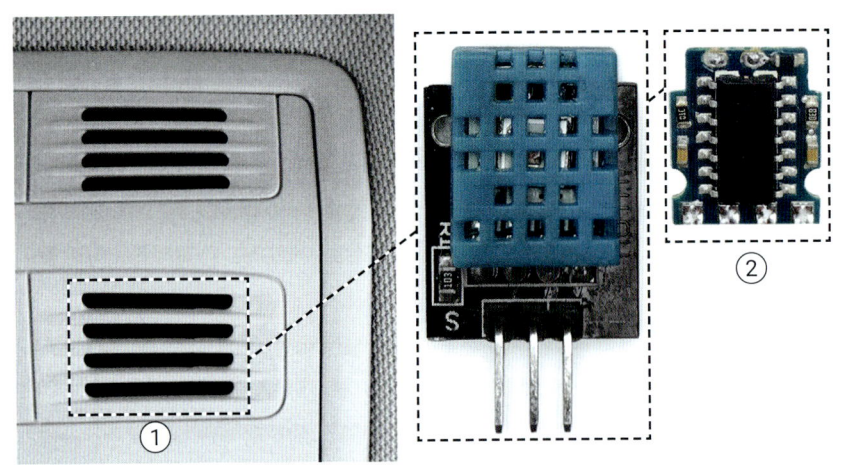

Fig. 133 Humidity sensor: 1. Installation position. 2. Sensor element.

The information from the humidity sensor (dew point) can also be used by a number of different control units. These control units use the information to determine the amount of power required by the mirror and rear window heaters in order to keep these defogged while using as little power as possible (energy conversation).

7. Air Quality Sensor

This sensor determines the proportion of harmful particles in the air that is drawn in. This sensor can determine the concentrations of hydrocarbon (HC), carbon monoxide (CO), and nitrous oxides (NOx) in the air. Just like the humidity sensor, the air quality sensor can be found in the vicinity of the intake opening of the heater assembly. The presence of harmful substances in the air will result in capacity changes in the measuring element of the sensor. The measuring element consists of a film of resistors.

Fig. 134 Air Quality Sensor

The properties of that film are similar to those of an oxidation catalyzer. Oxygen, in a special tin oxide (SnO_2) or zinc oxide (ZnO) surface layer, is used to convert HC into H_2O, CO_2, CO into CO_2, and NOx into NO_2. The chemical process results in a strong resistance change (1 – 100 kΩ) of the film, which is indicative of the concentration of harmful substances.

The sensor uses a power supply of 12 V or 5 V, the signal is analogue (PWM, 0 - 5 volts) or digital (LIN).

Fig. 135 Cross section and chemical process of the air quality sensor: 1. Teflon membrane. 2. Gas-permeable cover. 3. CO/NO$_x$ measuring element. 4. Electrical connections. 5. Housing. 6. Cover with seal. 7. Circuit board. 8. Electrodes. 9. Substrate.

The values obtained from the air quality sensor are used to control recirculation. If too many harmful substances are drawn into the system, the recirculation door is closed off immediately. When the proportion of harmful substances has decreased to acceptable levels, the recirculation door is automatically reopened. The sensor also reacts to a number of volatile organic gasses, which allow the system to respond to unpleasant smells.

Compared to manual control, the benefit of this is that one no longer has to remember to reopen the recirculation door. Forgetting to reopen the recirc door may lead to condensation of the windows and a decrease in interior oxygen content.

8. Multi-functional Sensor

Multiple sensor functions can be combined into a single housing. For instance, the humidity sensor and the air quality sensor can be combined into one single unit. This sensor can then be connected to the climate bus (LIN) and information about the dew point and the proportion of harmful substances present in the air is made available via the network.

The sensor shown here measures CO_2, temperature, and humidity.

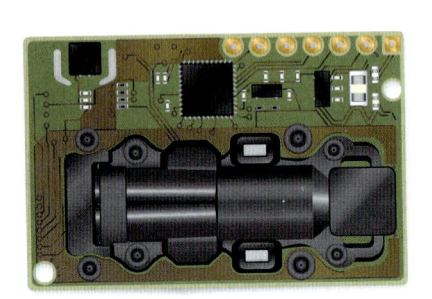

Fig. 136 Multi-functional sensor: CO_2, temperature, and humidity.

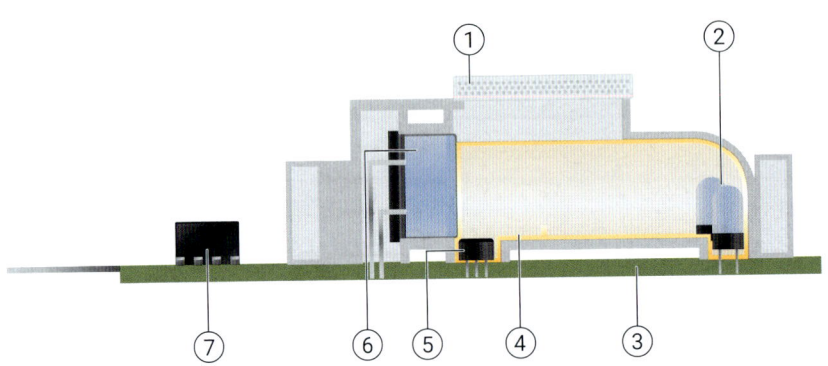

Fig. 137 Assembly of a multi-functional sensor: 1. LEDs. 2. Infrared source. 3. Circuit board. 4. Pipe with evaporated gold layer. 5. Temperature sensor. 6. Pyroelectric sensor with infrared filter. 7. Micro-electromechanical pressure sensor.

9. Carbon Dioxide Sensor

The carbon dioxide level sensor (CO_2) measures the CO_2 concentration in the interior. The sensor is usually installed somewhere in the dashboard near the glove compartment.

The sensor is called a non-dispersive infrared sensor (NDIR). This is a spectroscopic-type of sensor. The basis of this sensor's operating principle is the wavelength-dependent radiation property of CO_2. Infrared light is projected onto a receiver. CO_2 filters a specific wavelength of the infrared light out of it. By measuring the amount of light detected by the receiver, it is possible to measure the amount of CO_2 present in the air.

The signal of this sensor is transmitted to the climate control unit via the climate data bus (LIN).

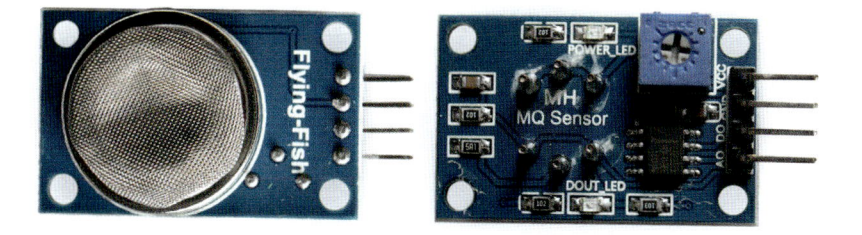

Fig. 138 CO_2 sensor

If the CO_2 value in the interior is too high, the climate control unit can open the recirculation door to allow more fresh air into the interior, thus lowering the concentration of CO_2. If this is not effective enough, the speed of the blower motor can be increased. Depending on the manufacturer, a warning message may be shown on the display if the concentration of carbon dioxide continues to increase. In these cases, the driver may be prompted to lower the windows to let in fresh air.

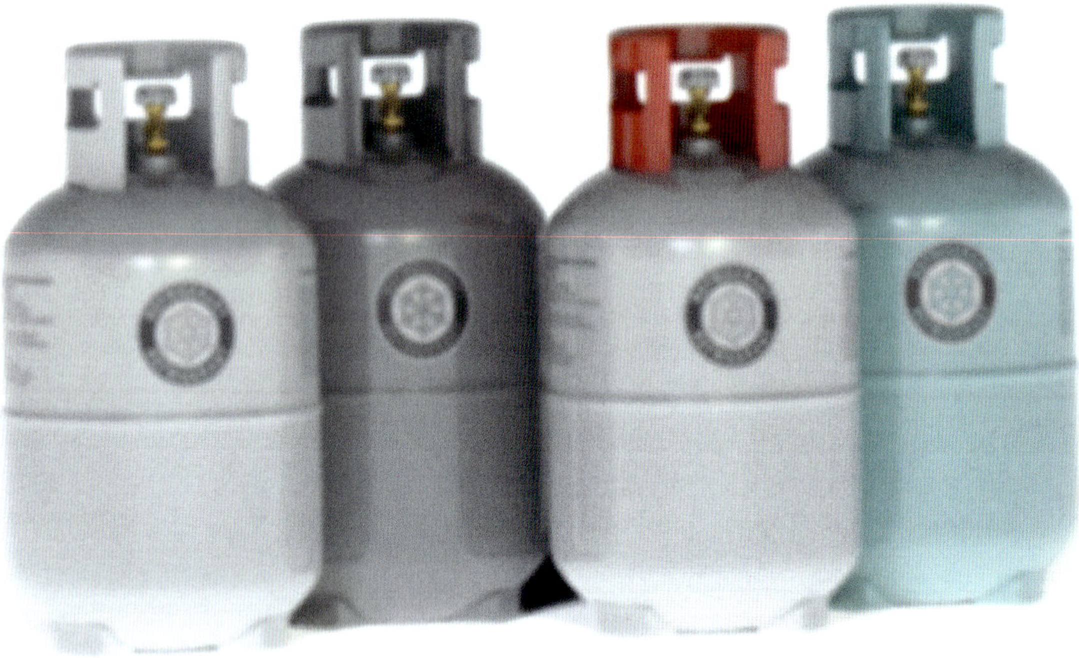

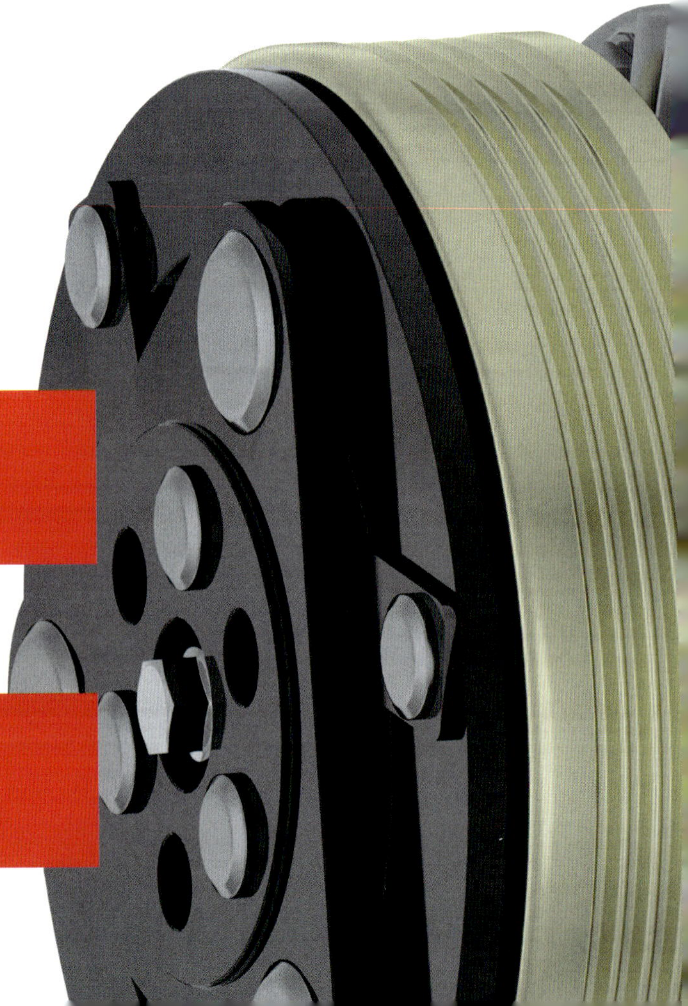

5. HVAC Service and Maintenance

REFRIGERANT RECOVERY AND RECHARGING

1. Introduction

Over time, the refrigerant in the air conditioning system gradually seeps out. This causes the air conditioning system to extract less heat from the airflow; this leads to the customer complaint of poor air conditioning system performance. Even an air conditioning system in perfect condition can lose as much as 10% of the total refrigerant capacity annually.

You can check and recharge the refrigerant amount in the system using a recovery/service machine.

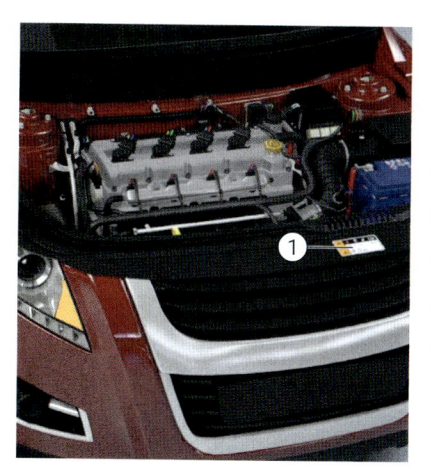

Fig. 139 Specifications for the air conditioning system can be found on the information sticker (1).

NOTE Never perform maintenance and/or repairs on an air conditioning system without the proper equipment.

2. Checking the air conditioning system

Before connecting the recovery/service machine to the vehicle's air conditioning system, a number of things need to be completed.

Information about the type and amount of refrigerant can be found on a sticker in the engine compartment. The sticker also specifies what type of compressor oil the system requires.

Always inspect the service connections of the air conditioning system and ensure they are clean, otherwise dirt can enter the recovery/service machine. To prevent contamination, corrosion, and leakage, the service connections are sealed with screw-on plastic caps.

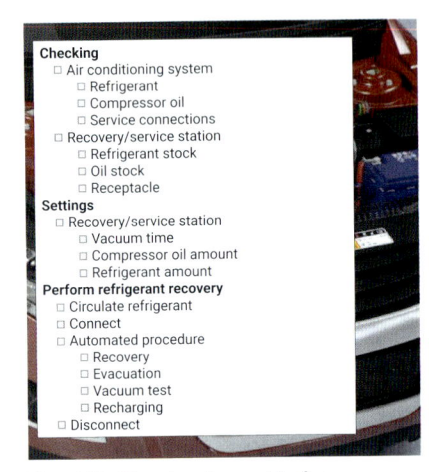

Fig. 140 Step-by-step guide for recovering and recharging refrigerant.

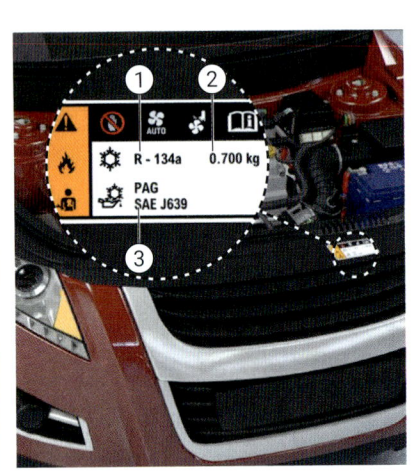

Fig. 141 Information sticker for the air conditioning system: 1. Type of refrigerant. 2. System capacity. 3. Type of compressor oil.

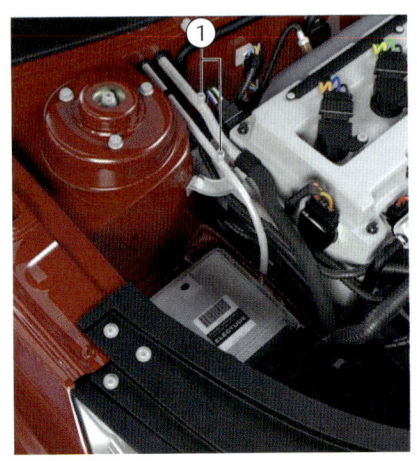

Fig. 142 Service connections (1) of the air conditioning system.

3. Check the recovery/filling machine

First check to ensure there's enough oil and refrigerant in the recovery/service machine. Clean refrigerant is stored in a tank inside of the machine.

New compressor oil, and the used oil and refrigerant dye that is removed from the system during the recovery cycle, is stored in separate bottles on the side of the machine.

Make sure you have enough space in the used oil bottle before you begin the recovery process. If the used oil bottle is nearly full, empty it before beginning the recovery process. Used compressor oil is considered chemical waste, and needs to be disposed of in accordance with environmental regulations.

Fig. 143 Check the containers of oils and dye.

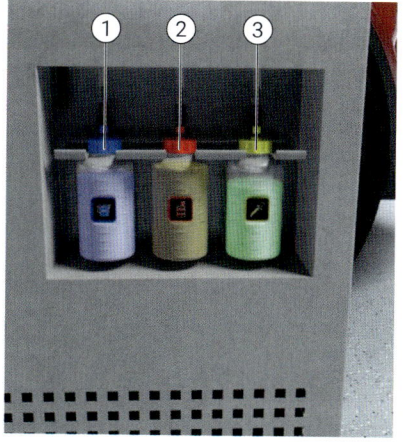

Fig. 144 Contents of the containers: 1. New compressor oil. 2. Recovered compressor oil. 3. UV leak detection fluid.

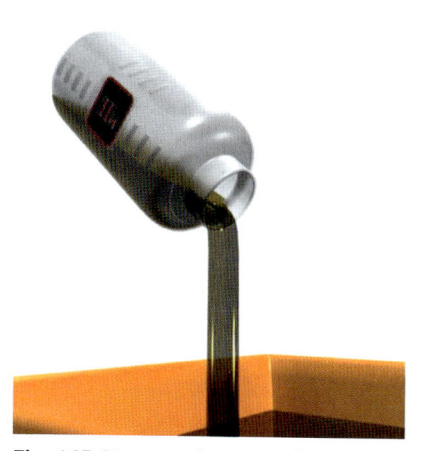

Fig. 145 Dispose of recovered compressor oil; it is chemical waste.

4. Setting-up the recovery/service machine

Vacuum time
After the refrigerant has been recovered the system needs to be placed under a vacuum. Placing the system under a vacuum will lower the boiling point of any water in the system, thereby causing it to boil off and be sucked out, and it will ensure all of the air/refrigerant has been removed from the system. Usually the vacuum time is set to between 25 and 30 minutes. A shorter vacuum time may not remove residual refrigerant and/or moisture from the system.

Amount of compressor oil
You can set the amount of oil that the machine adds. If you choose the automatic setting, the service machine adds the same amount of oil that was removed during the recovery process.

Amount of refrigerant
The refrigerant charge amount can be specified in ounces. This value indicates the total amount of refrigerant to be added to the air conditioning system.

Fig. 146 The service machine.

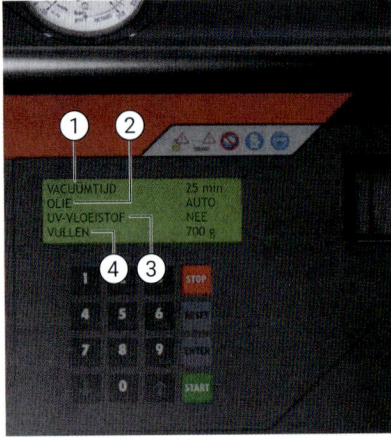

Fig. 147 Service machine display:
1. Time to evacuate the air conditioning system. 2. The amount of oil to be added. 3. Add UV fluid. 4. Amount of refrigerant.

5. Perform refrigerant recovery

Operate
Turn on the air conditioning system and let the system run for 5 minutes. Then turn the system off. The compressor oil is now mixed well with the refrigerant, and more oil will be removed from the air conditioning system during the recovery process.

Connecting
The recovery/service station can now be connected to the air conditioning system. The blue service hose is connected to the low pressure line; the red service hose is connected to the high pressure line.

Push the quick release coupling onto the service connections of the vehicle, then tighten the tap on the quick release coupling; the service machine and the air conditioning system are now one closed circuit.

Fig. 148 Connecting the service machine to the service connections of the air conditioning system.

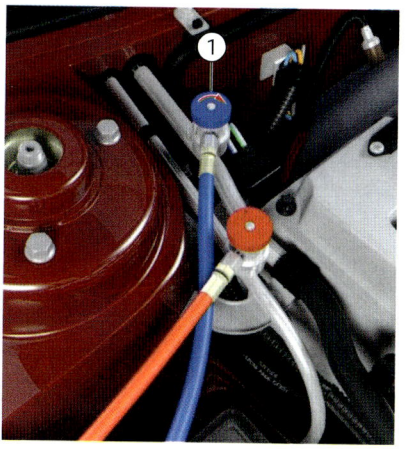

Fig. 149 Lines connected: first, open the low-pressure line (1) by rotating the coupling.

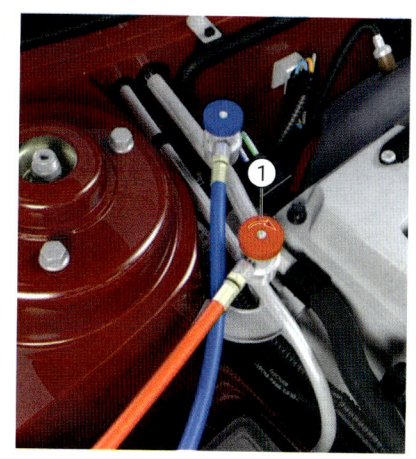

Fig. 150 Next, open the high-pressure line (1) by rotating the coupling.

6. Recovery

After the recovery/service machine instructs you to open the high and low pressure taps, the automatic recovery and filling procedure can begin.

The recovery/service machine passes the recovered refrigerant through a filter and dryer.

The compressor oil removed during recovery is separated; after which, the amount removed is determined.

After it has been filtered, the recovered refrigerant is added to the refrigerant in the tank of the service machine.

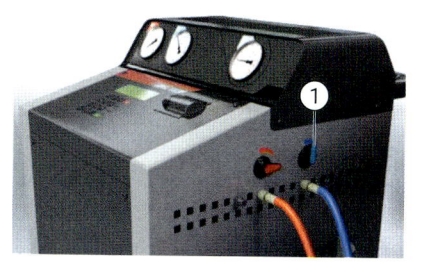

Fig. 151 First, open the low-pressure line (1) on the service machine.

Fig. 152 Next, open the high-pressure line (1) on the service machine.

7. Evacuation

During the evacuation cycle, the remaining refrigerant and moisture is removed from the air conditioning system.

When the set vacuum time has elapsed, the service machine performs a vacuum test: the filling station stops the vacuum pump and checks to see if vacuum is maintained for a period of time.

8. Recharging

After the vacuum test is complete the recovery/service machine recharges the air conditioning system with the specified amount of refrigerant and compressor oil.

As the air conditioning system is filled, the service machine display shows how much refrigerant and oil is going into the system.

9. Disconnecting the service machine

Turn off both taps on the quick release couplings; so the filling station can empty the service hoses prior to disconnecting them.

Once the refrigerant has been removed from the service hoses, turn off the high and low pressure taps located on the filling station. Then you can remove the quick release couplings and store the service hoses on the side of the recovery/service machine.

Reinstall the caps over the service connections.

Turn off the recovery/service machine and return it to the equipment storage area.

Fig. 153 Once the service machine has finished charging the air conditioning system, close the coupling on the hoses. Allow the service machine to recover the refrigerant from the service hoses.

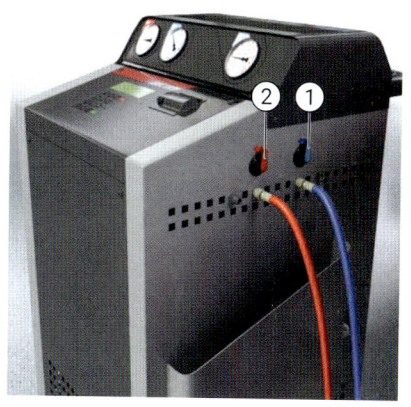

Fig. 154 Close the valves on the filling station: first, the low-pressure valve (1), followed by the high-pressure valve (2).

Fig. 155 Detach the lines from the vehicle and secure them on the side of the service machine.

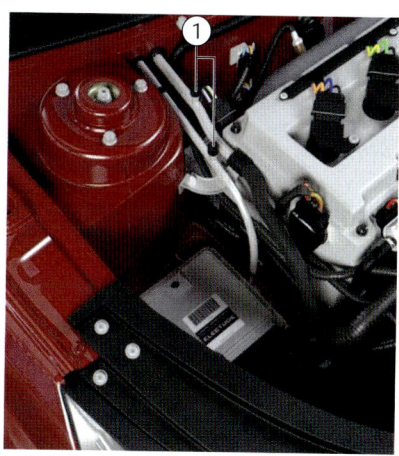

Fig. 156 Next, screw the caps back onto the service connections.

SNIFFER LEAK DETECTION

Fig. 157 Lines, couplings, and components of the air conditioning system may leak.

1. Introduction

If the air conditioning system is leaking refrigerant, the source of the leak can be identified with the aid of an electronic leak detector. This device analyzes the composition of the ambient air.

Where a concentration of refrigerant is found, there also is the source of the leak. In order to detect the leak, it's important to position the detector near to the air conditioning component being tested.

PLEASE NOTE Never carry out maintenance and/or repairs to an air conditioning system without the EPA Section 609 certification and permission from a supervisor.

2. Using the Sniffer

The sniffer analyses the composition of the air. This analysis is most accurate when the ambient air is still. Try therefore, to limit the air flow through the test area. You can limit the air flow by not switching on the engine and closing the shop doors.

Move the sniffer slowly along all components, pipes and hoses of the air conditioning system. If you move the sniffer too quickly, the measurement will be inaccurate.

If a leak is detected, the sniffer reacts by means of a sound and/or light signal.

3. Refrigerant Sniffer

A leak in the air conditioning system can be detected with the aid of a refrigerant sniffer. This type of sniffer detects the presence refrigerant in the air. Because of this, the refrigerant sniffer can be used right away, without having to prepare the air conditioning system.

After switching on, the sniffer must be moved slowly along the components of the air conditioning system. If the sniffer gives a signal, refrigerant has been detected and a leak has been found.

If a leak has been found, the system must first be evacuated. In this way, the remaining refrigerant is extracted from the air conditioning system without harming the environment. When the system is empty, the leak can be repaired.

Fig. 158 A refrigerant detector: 1. Measuring element. 2. Light. 3. Display.

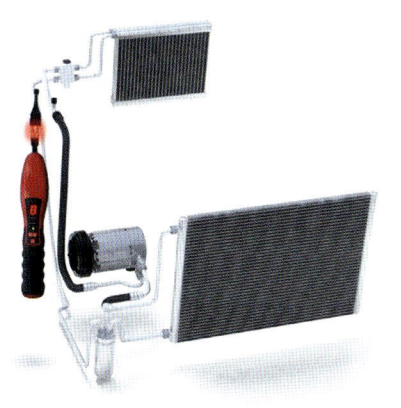

Fig. 159 If the measuring element detects refrigerant, the detector will emit a light and/or audible signal. The number shown on the display gives an indication of the size of the leakage.

4. Hydrogen Sniffer

A hydrogen sniffer is often used to detect very small leaks. However, before the air conditioning system can be filled with hydrogen, the air conditioning system must be evacuated.

The empty air conditioning system is filled with a mixture of 95% nitrogen and 5% hydrogen. This gas mixture is known as forming gas. An air conditioning system should never be filled with compressed air; this could damage the air conditioning system.

If the pressure goes down, the air conditioning system is leaking. Hydrogen consists of very small particles; this makes it possible to detect the smallest of leaks with the aid of a hydrogen sniffer.

After the leak has been found, the system can be emptied. Forming gas is harmless; therefore it does not need to be collected separately. However, it is important that the space be well ventilated before releasing the gas into open air.

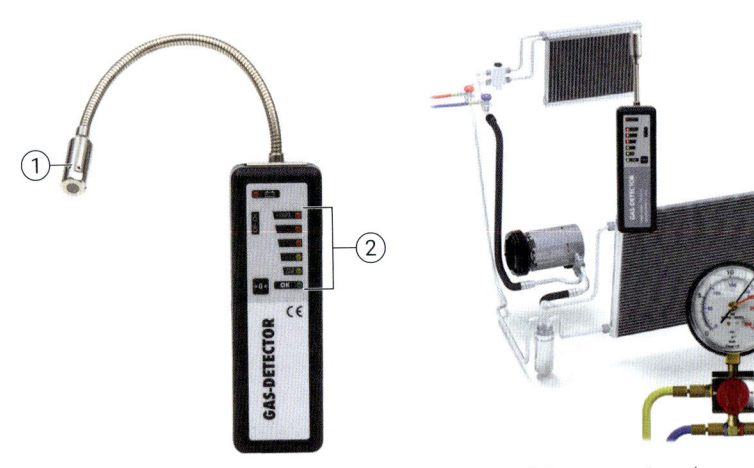

Fig. 160 A hydrogen detector: 1. Measuring element. 2. LED indicators.

Fig. 161 If the measuring element detects hydrogen, the LEDs on the detector will be activated. The number of LEDs activated will indicate the size of the leakage.

NITROGEN LEAK DETECTION

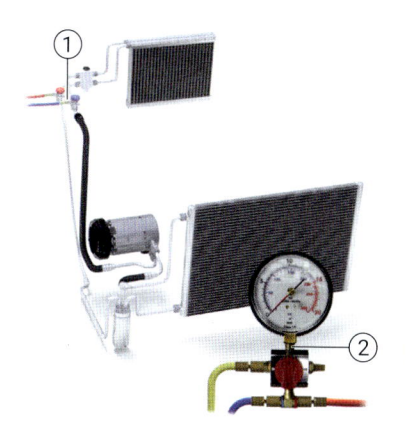

1. Introduction

Leaks in the air conditioning system can be detected using nitrogen. Before filling the system with nitrogen, the system must be empty

The nitrogen source is connected to the air conditioning system via a pressure regulating valve. The regulating valve reduces the pressure, for safe filling of the air conditioning system.

Fig. 162 The pressure reduction valve (2) is connected to the air conditioning system via quick-release couplings (1).

PLEASE NOTE Never perform maintenance and/or repairs to an air conditioning system, without the permission of a supervisor.

2. Leak Detection

The empty air conditioning system is filled with nitrogen. An air conditioning system should never be filled with compressed air. Compressed air contains moisture; this affects the air conditioning system. Nitrogen is clean and dry

If the pressure goes down, the air conditioning system has a leak. A leak can be detected using special leak spray. If the spray begins to bubble, the system is leaking at that location.

After the leak has been found, the system can be emptied. Nitrogen gas is harmless and therefore does not need to be recovered. It is important though, that during emptying, the area is well ventilated.

PLEASE NOTE When the air conditioning system is pressurized with nitrogen, the compressor must **never** be switched on.

Fig. 163 Leak detection spray in a spray bottle.

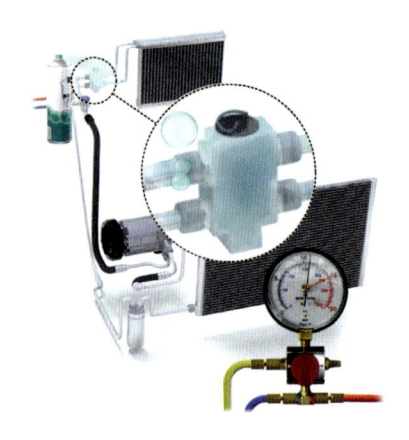

Fig. 164 If leak detection spray is sprayed onto a leak, it will start bubbling.

UV LEAK DETECTION

1. UV leak detection dye

A leak in the air conditioning system can be detected with UV leak detection dye. The UV dye is added to the refrigerant, where it mixes with the existing lubricating oil.

Leak detection dye glows a bright fluorescent yellow-green color when exposed to UV light; thereby identifying the source of the leak.

Both the quantity and quality of the UV dye used is important. Good quality UV dyes should meet SAE J2297 requirements. These requirements apply to UV dyes that can be used for both R134a and R1234YF refrigerants. The air conditioning system is negatively affected by the addition of a poor quality and/or too much UV dye.

Fig. 165 UV leak detection fluid in a measuring cup.

Fig. 166 Without UV light, the UV leak detection fluid is barely visible in the dark.

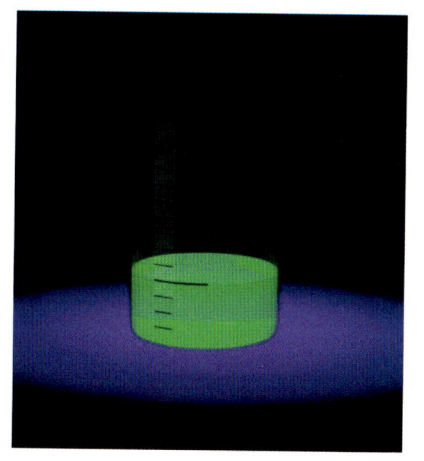

Fig. 167 The UV leak detection fluid becomes luminescent when illuminated with UV light.

2. UV Dye Use

UV leak detection dye can be added to an air conditioning system before a leak develops; it mixes and remains with the lubricating oil until all the oil in the system is replaced. At the moment that the system develops a leak, the source can be easily identified with the aid of a UV lamp and UV protective goggles.

UV protective goggles protect the eyes from the harmful UV light. The color of the goggles also ensures that the dye has a much sharper contrast against the background.

A leak is detected by wearing UV protective goggles and running over all parts of the air conditioning system with the UV lamp. The leak is identified by a fluorescent yellow-green trace at the source of the leak.

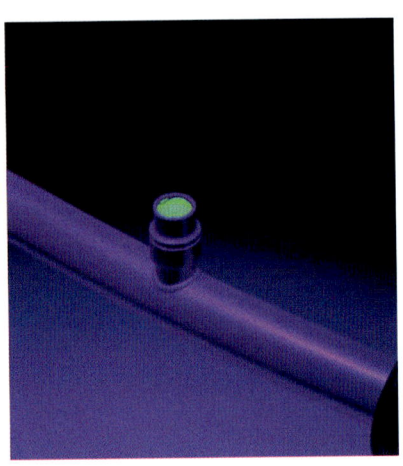

Fig. 168 UV leak detection fluid is left in the service connection.

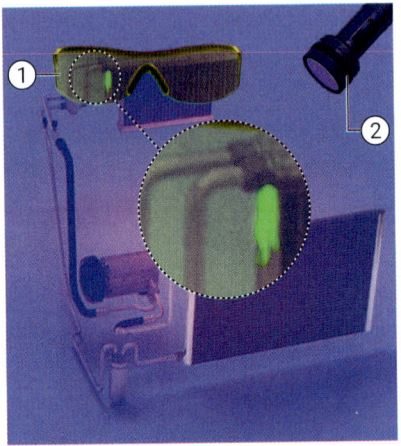

Fig. 169 UV protective glasses (1) make the UV leak detection fluid clearly visible when viewed under a UV light (2).

DIAGNOSING A MALFUNCTIONING AIR CONDITIONER

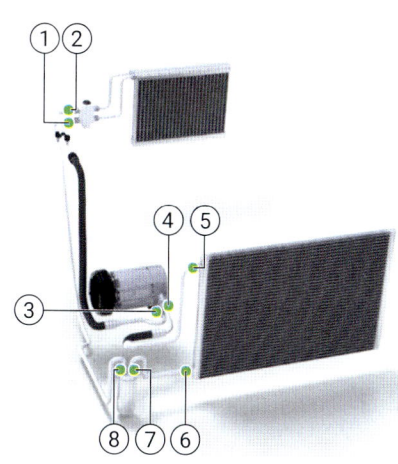

Fig. 170 Diagram of the air conditioning system with potential touch/inspection locations:
1. Evaporator inlet.
2. Evaporator outlet.
3. Compressor inlet.
4. Compressor outlet.
5. Condenser inlet.
6. Condenser outlet.
7. Filter dryer inlet.
8. Filter dryer outlet.

During the warm summer months the number of complaints about poor performing air conditioning systems will increase. As the air conditioning system is integrated into one single climate control system, the automotive technician needs to determine if this is a refrigeration or electrical problem. Checking the systems related to climate control for stored faults is a good first step, and a scan tool can be used for this. If there are air conditioning-related problems present, there are a few basic checks that can be carried out. For instance:

— Check the compressor drive.
— Check the plug and cable connections.
— Check for contamination or blockage of the condenser.
— A greasy residue on air conditioner components could indicate leakage.

If the air conditioning is operational:
— Does the compressor switch on normally?
— Does the condenser fan switch on normally?

In addition to the above-mentioned visual checks, you can also check for failure or defects in the A/C system by hand with simple temperature checks. To be able to determine and judge the temperatures at these touch locations, some basic knowledge of the A/C system is necessary. Generally speaking, components and pipes under high pressure will feel warm or hot to the touch. Pipes and components that are part of the low-pressure circuit are (freezing) cold.

1. Table of touch locations

When checking the air conditioning system using the touch locations, there are a few conditions that must first be met:
— Air conditioning compressor is switched on.
— Recirculation door is closed
— Climate control set to maximum cooling.
— System has been operating for at least 10 min.
— Engine at operating temperature.

An easy way to check if the A/C system is cooling sufficiently is to measure the temperature of the air flowing out of the dash vents. The airflow temperature should be 50 to 59 °F (10 to 15°C) lower than the exterior temperature.

NOTE Before conducting the test, the engine must be running and have reached operating temperature. Be careful not to touch any hot or moving parts.

The pipe between the condenser outlet and the evaporator inlet: This pipe contains liquid refrigerant under high pressure. Temperature approx. 104-140°F (40-60°C).

The pipe between the compressor outlet and the condenser inlet: This pipe contains gaseous refrigerant under high pressure. Temperature approx. 140-194°F (60-90°C).

The pipe between the evaporator outlet and the compressor inlet: This pipe contains gaseous refrigerant under low pressure.

— Evaporator surface temperature 32-41°F (0-5°C).
— Expansion valve on the evaporator 35.6-41°F (2-5°C).
— Compressor intake side 41-59°F (5-15°C).

The receiver/drier is situated between the condenser and the evaporator: A temperature difference between the inlet and outlet of the receiver/drier indicates a blockage!

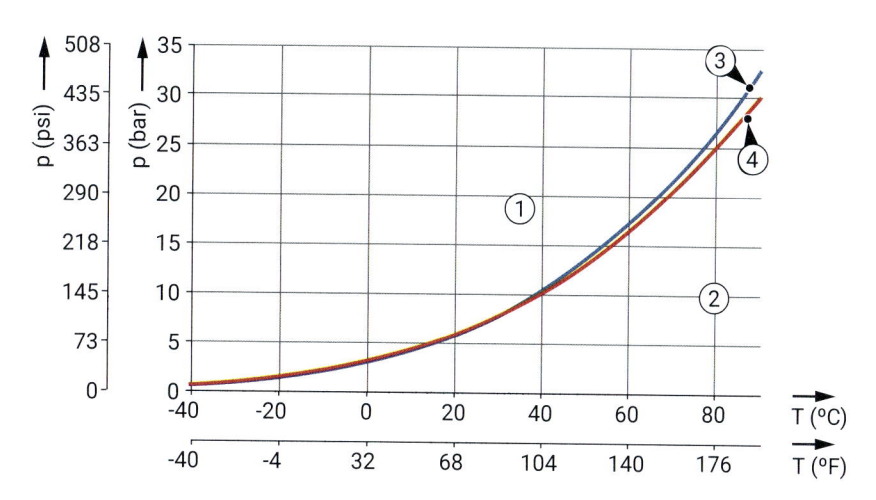

Fig. 171 Relation between boiling point and pressure:
1. Liquid. 2. Gaseous. 3. R134a. 4. R1234yf.

Exterior air temperature.					
Air temperature at outlet vents.					
	Touch locations	Ice Cold	Cold	Warm	Hot
1.	Evaporator inlet			X	
2.	Evaporator outlet	X			
3.	Compressor inlet	X	X		
4.	Compressor outlet				X
5.	Condenser inlet				X
6.	Condenser outlet			X	
7.	Receiver/drier inlet			X	
8.	Receiver/drier outlet			X	

Fig. 172 Table of touch locations.

Fig. 173 Surface thermometer with a clamp.

2. Pressure and Temperature

It is important to measure both the temperature as well as the pressures for systems with variable output compressors. Temperatures that are too high will affect the operation and life span of the system. It is possible to diagnose the system if we can determine the exact temperature and the corresponding pressures. The system pressures (low and high pressures) can be read using a gauge manifold set.

A multimeter with a thermocouple can be used to measure the temperature. A surface thermometer with a clamp can be used to make a precise temperature measurements. The pressures will depend on the ambient temperature and the type of compressor.

	Engine turned off		Engine running			
			Ideal pressure		Possible range	
	bar	psi	bar	psi	bar	psi
Low pressure (psi)	min. 1.5	min. 21.8	2	29	0.5 - 3.5	7.3 - 50.8
High pressure (psi)	min. 1.5	min. 21.8	18	261	9.5 - 25	137.8 - 362.6

Fig. 174 General guide values for pressure.

In the above chart, the low pressures (suction pressure or evaporation pressure) and the high pressures (compression pressure or condensation pressure) correspond to each temperature reading. For example, a pressure of 145 psi has a corresponding condensation temperature of 109.4°F (43°C (R134a)).

The low pressure reading corresponds the temperature to the temperature of the evaporator. These temperature values are important for determining the amount of subcooling and superheat present in the system.

Touch locations		Operating Temperature		System pressure	
		°C	°F	bar	psi
1.	Evaporator inlet	44	111.2	13.8	200.15
2.	Evaporator outlet	4	39.2	1.3	18.85
3.	Compressor inlet	4	39.2	1.3	18.85
4.	Compressor outlet	70	158	13.8	200.15
5.	Condenser inlet	70	158	13.8	200.15
6.	Condenser outlet	44	111.2	13.8	200.15
7.	Receiver/drier inlet	44	111.2	13.8	200.15
8.	Receiver/drier outlet	44	111.2	13.8	200.15

Fig. 175 Example for measurement of the temperature and pressure of R134a.

5. HVAC SERVICE AND MAINTENANCE

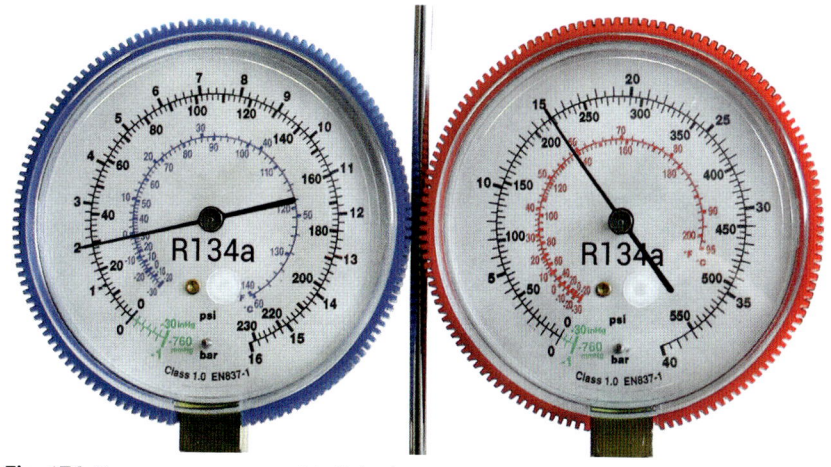

Fig. 176 Pressure gauge set with dials showing pressure and temperature.

Pressure		Temp.		Pressure		Temp.		Pressure		Temp.	
bar	psi	°C	°F	bar	psi	°C	°F	bar	psi	°C	°F
1	14.5	-26.4	-15.5	4.43	62.37	12	53.6	13.85	200.9	52	125.6
1.06	15.37	-25	-13	4.72	68.46	14	57.2	14.55	211.09	54	129.2
1.16	16.82	-23	-9.4	5.04	73.06	16	60.8	15.28	221.62	56	132.8
1.27	18.42	-21	-5.8	5.54	80.35	19	66.2	16.04	232.6	58	136.4
1.39	20.16	-19	-2.2	5.89	85.41	21	69.8	16.82	243.95	60	140
1.51	21.9	-17	1.4	6.26	90.79	23	73.4	17.22	249.78	61	141.8
1.64	23.79	-15	5	6.65	96.41	25	77	18.47	267.91	64	147.2
1.78	25.82	-13	8.6	7.05	102.28	27	80.6	19.34	280.55	66	150.8
1.93	27.99	-11	12.2	7.48	108.43	29	84.2	20.24	293.61	68	154.4
2.08	30.17	-9	15.8	7.92	114.84	31	87.8	21.18	307.15	70	158
2.25	32.63	-7	19.4	8.15	118.16	32	89.6	22.142	321.14	72	161.6
2.43	35.24	-5	23	8.62	125.01	34	93.2	23.14	335.6	74	165.2
2.62	38	-3	26.6	9.11	132.13	36	96.8	24.17	350.57	76	168.8
2.82	40.9	-1	30.2	9.63	139.6	38	100.4	25.24	366.03	78	172.4
3.03	43.95	1	33.8	10.16	147.34	40	104	26.34	282.01	80	176
3.14	45.54	2	35.6	10.72	155.48	42	107	27.48	398.53	82	179.6
3.37	48.88	4	39.2	11.3	163.83	44	111.2	28.65	415.59	84	183.2
3.62	52.5	6	42.8	11.9	172.57	46	114.8	29.87	433.21	86	186.8
3.87	56.13	8	46.4	12.53	181.73	48	118.4	31.12	451.42	88	190.4
4.14	60.05	10	50	13.18	191.1	50	122	32.42	470.21	90	194

Fig. 177 Temperature-pressure table for R134a.

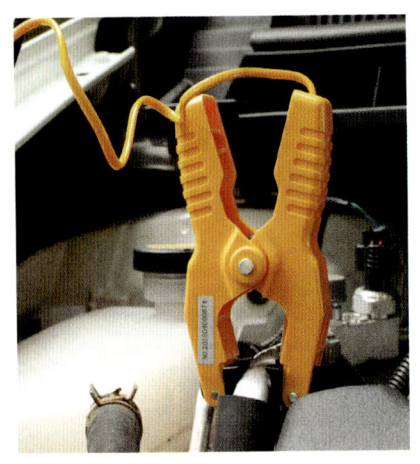

Fig. 178
A surface thermometer is clamped onto the pipe.

Superheat

To prevent any possible liquid discharge in the compressor, the refrigerant is heated above its boiling point in the evaporator. Superheat is calculated by determining the difference between the evaporation temperature of the refrigerant at a given pressure, and the temperature of the refrigerant at the evaporator outlet. In a properly functioning system, superheat will be between 41 and 50°F (5 and 10°C).

Subcooling

To prevent any gaseous refrigerant from entering the evaporator, the condenser must be able to cool the refrigerant adequately. Subcooling is calculated by determining the difference between the condensation temperature of the refrigerant and the temperature of the pipe leaving the condenser. In a properly functioning system, subcooling will be between 50 and 86°F (10 and 30°C) (the temperature difference when entering and exiting the compressor should be approx. 30%).

AIR CONDITIONING LUBRICATION OIL TYPES

1. Compressor Oil

The compressor needs to be lubricated with oil. This oil is added to the refrigerant, and circulates through the entire system. The amount of oil is specified by the manufacturer.
We need to pay attention not only to the specified amount of oil, but also to the type of oil that is required.

There are several types of oil used in air conditioning systems:
- Mineral oil
- PAG oil
- POE oil
- PAO oil

2. Mineral Oil

In vehicles with an R12 air conditioning system the compressor is lubricated with a mineral oil. Mineral oils are naturally based oils, and will not affect the black rubber seals of the R12 lines.

3. PAG Oil

Mineral oil cannot be used in cars using R134a or R1234yf refrigerants. This mineral oil will not blend with R134a or R1234yf. Synthetic PAG oil is usually used with these refrigerants. PAG stands for Polyalkayne Glycol. PAG oils are extremely hygroscopic and will conduct electricity. Hygroscopic means that the oil will attract moisture.

4. PAO Oil

PAO oil, or Poly-alpha-olefin oil, is a synthetic oil. This oil is often referred to as a universal air conditioning oil. PAO oil is not hygroscopic. This oil can be used with R12, R134a, and R1234yf.

Fig. 179 PAG 100 oil bottle

	[-- --]		[-- --]	
	R134a	R1234yf	[-- --]	[-- --]
PAG	V	X	V	X
PAG YF	V	V	V	X
PAG SP-A2	V	V	V	V
PAO	V	V	V	X
PAO AA1	V	V	V	V
POE	V	V	X	V

5. POE Oil

POE oil is a polyolester oil. This oil is used in electrical air conditioning compressors. The windings in the electric motor consist of a copper wire covered with an insulating coating. This coating can be damaged by PAG oil. Additionally, PAG oils conduct electricity. Due to this, only POE oil must be used with electrical air conditioning compressors.

6. Oil Viscosity

Just like engine oil, air conditioning compressor oil is available in various kinds of viscosity. The viscosity of air conditioning compressor oils is defined in the ISO standard. Typical oils are: PAG 46, PAG 100, and PAG 150. Of these, PAG 46 has a low viscosity and PAG 150 has a high viscosity. Therefore, PAG 46 is a very thin oil, whereas PAG 150 is a thicker oil.

7. Amount of Oil

When replacing a component of an air conditioning system, there will always be a residual amount of oil present inside the part. When the air conditioner is refilled with refrigerant, the amount of oil must be replenished. Depending on the situation, the manufacturer either indicates that a standard amount of oil should be added, or that the residual amount of oil in the old component should be drained and then measured. The latter is usually the case when replacing a compressor.

The amount of fresh oil to be added will therefore be based on the amount measured. When replacing an air conditioning compressor, it is also important to check whether the new compressor is pre-charged with oil or not. If not enough compressor oil is used, the air conditioning compressor will wear quickly and fail. If too much oil is used, the air conditioning system will not be able to cool as well, and there is a risk of hydro-locking the air conditioning compressor with the excess of refrigerant oil.

Compressor oil	Refill quantity
After replacement of all pipes and parts.	200 ml (6.8 fl oz)
A/C compressor - Amount drained from defective compressor	150 ml (5.1 fl oz)
A/C compressor - Amount drained from defective compressor > 150ml (5.1 fl oz)	200 ml (6.8 fl oz)
Condenser air conditioning	30 ml (1 fl oz)
Evaporator air conditioning	30 ml (1 fl oz)
Always when coolant has been drained.	= quantity collected
Please note!	
Refill quantity should not exceed filling quantity of compressor oil.	
If, besides the compressor, other parts of the air-conditioning system are also replaced, apart from filling the compressor, compressor oil should not be topped up any further.	
The compressor oil in the air conditioning compressor must be drained due to the different amounts.	

Fig. 180 An example of oil capacities for compressor oil.

HOW TO: DETECT A LEAK IN THE AIR CONDITIONING SYSTEM

1. Detecting a Leak in the Air Conditioning System

You can read the system to determine if the air conditioning is not working. Failure codes are not always saved, but you can often infer something from the current values.

It is a good idea to check the connection valves before connecting the air conditioning filling station. Use a UV lamp to check for fluorine on the valves. This is how you can determine if there is any fluorine in the system. You can also use soap bubbles to check for leaking valves.

Fig. 182 Reading out a car with air conditioning issues can provide information that can help you diagnose the problem. For example, you can see if the engine fan is operational when the air conditioning is on. If this is not the case, it could be a problem.

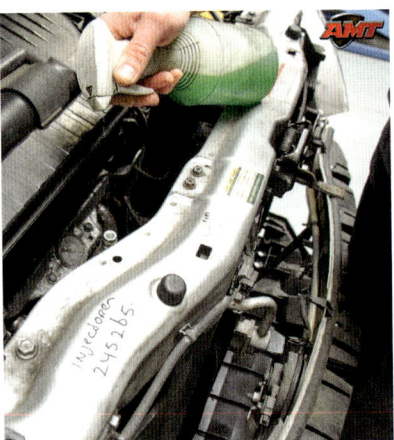

Fig. 183 Use soap bubbles to determine whether the air conditioning system filling valves are leaking. Protective goggles must be worn when using UV light.

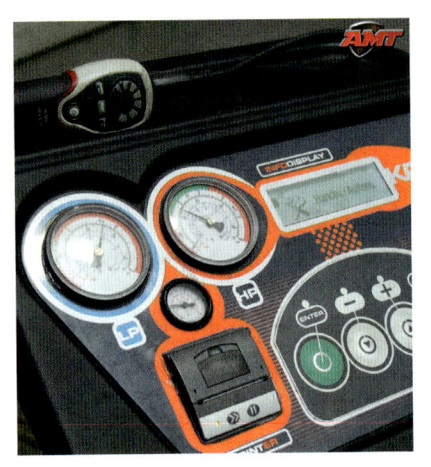

Fig. 184 Connect the air conditioning filling station and check the pressures when the engine is not running. The pressure for both the low and the high pressure sections should be the same when the engine is stationary. You can read it here: between about 90 and 130 psi. It should be lower than 30 psi and higher than 220 psi with the engine running.

2. Using Fluorine or Forming Gas to Detect Leaks

You can use a UV lamp to check for leaks if you have determined that the system already contains fluorine. If there is no fluorine in the system, you will need to empty the system and fill it with fluorine. The system will need to run for a while before any fluorine from a leak will become visible.

Forming Gas

Empty the system using the air conditioning filling station and then fill it with forming gas. Forming gas is 95 percent nitrogen and 5 percent hydrogen. Hydrogen is a small molecule and can fit through any leak. Hydrogen is detected using a sniffer.

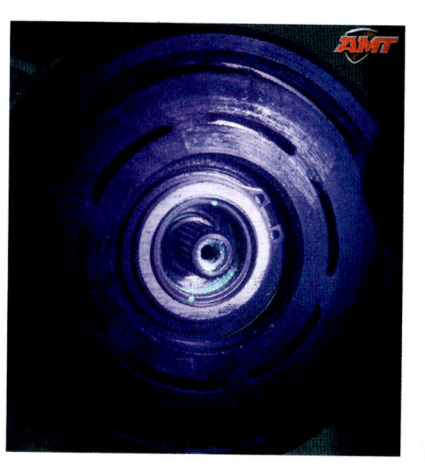

Fig. 185 Leaks in the system can be detected in a number of different ways. In this example, you add fluorine to the compressor oil. Use a UV lamp to find (small) leaks. Put on UV protective goggles if you are using a UV light.

Fig. 186 Fill the air conditioning system with forming gas. A pressure of 115 psi is sufficient for detecting leaks.

Fig. 187 Slowly move the forming gas sniffer over the air conditioning system components and see if you can find a leak. You can also use this method in the interior.

3. Using Soap Bubbles to Detect Small Leaks

Fill the high-pressure hose with liquid soap and water (1:10 ratio) and spray it on the condenser and all of the connectors. Bubbles or suds may form after a few minutes, while in some cases it can take up to an hour.

Fig. 188 Spray the condenser and all of the connectors using the high-pressure hose and wait for bubbles to form.

Fig. 189 This lets you see where the bubbles form on the condenser. The condenser needs to be replaced.

4. Filling the Air Conditioning System

Replace the component that has a leak. Depressurize the system and refill it with coolant. Add oil to replace the amount that was lost. Follow the manufacturer's specifications when doing so.

Fig. 190 Replace the component as soon as you find the leak. Use new O-rings after coating them with compressor oil. Depressurize the system again before pulling the vacuum.

Fig. 191 Fill coolant and add the correct amount of oil. The oil can be pre-mixed with fluorine so that any new leaks will be easier to find. Limit its use; the oil must never contain more than 5% fluorine.

HOW TO: MEASURE THE AIR CONDITIONING TEMPERATURE

1. Turn on the air conditioning.

Turn on the air conditioning to test its performance.

The engine drives the air conditioning compressor. This means that you need to start the engine in order to turn on the air conditioning.

Fig. 192 If possible, check the performance of the air conditioning system indoors, in a well-ventilated area with exhaust extraction. If not, check it outside (out of direct sunlight).

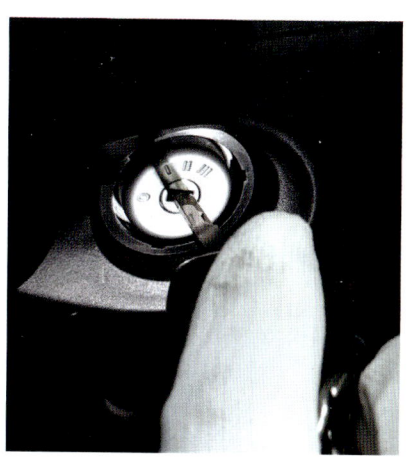

Fig. 193 Start the engine to turn on the air conditioning.

Fig. 194 Turn on the air conditioning system (A/C), reduce the fan speed, set the interior temperature to the lowest setting and aim the airflow at the passengers.

Fig. 195 The air conditioning compressor clutch is switched off in this photo. The air conditioning compressor is not running.

Fig. 196 The air conditioning compressor clutch is now switched on. The air conditioning compressor is being driven by the serpentine belt.

2. Manufacturer Information

An air conditioning system has a specific capacity for cooling external air. This means that the minimum air temperature at the air vents greatly depends on the temperature outside the vehicle.

Consult the manufacturer information for the minimum amount the air conditioning needs to be able to cool the air.
The air conditioning system will need maintenance/repairs if the air vent temperature is too high.

External air temperature compared to the minimum interior air temperature.					
outside air temperature	21°C	27°C	32°C	38°C	43°C
Air temperature at air vent	-3 to 3°C	-1 to 7°C	3 to 9°C	6 to 13°C	10 to 18°C

Fig. 197 The table lists the temperature that the air conditioning system should be able to achieve at a given exterior air temperature.

3. Measuring Temperatures

Measure the air conditioning system's performance by comparing the temperature outside the vehicle with the temperature of the air flowing from the vents.
If possible, use the middle (central) air vent.

Fig. 198 Measure the air temperature outside the car. The thermometer reading is 21.3°C.

Fig. 199 Close the other air vents and allow some time for the air conditioning to work.

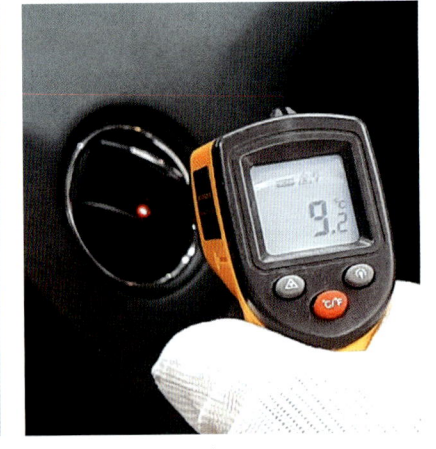

Fig. 200 Measure the temperature in the air vent outlet. The temperature measured is about 9°C. That is not cold enough.

The air temperature measured in the air vents is too high. The air conditioning needs to be serviced.

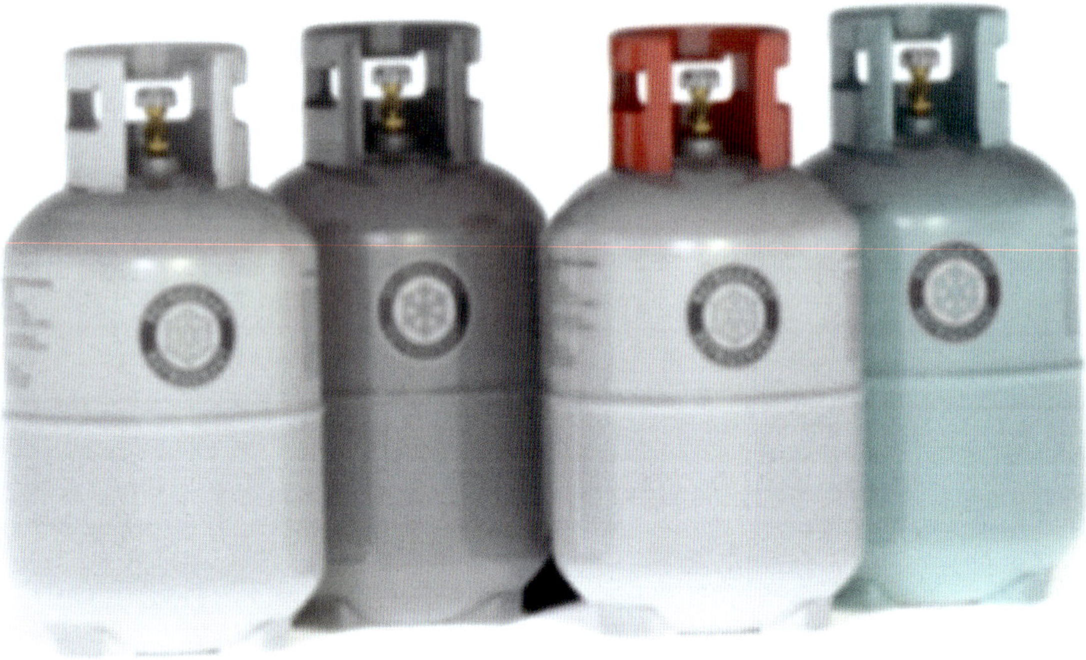

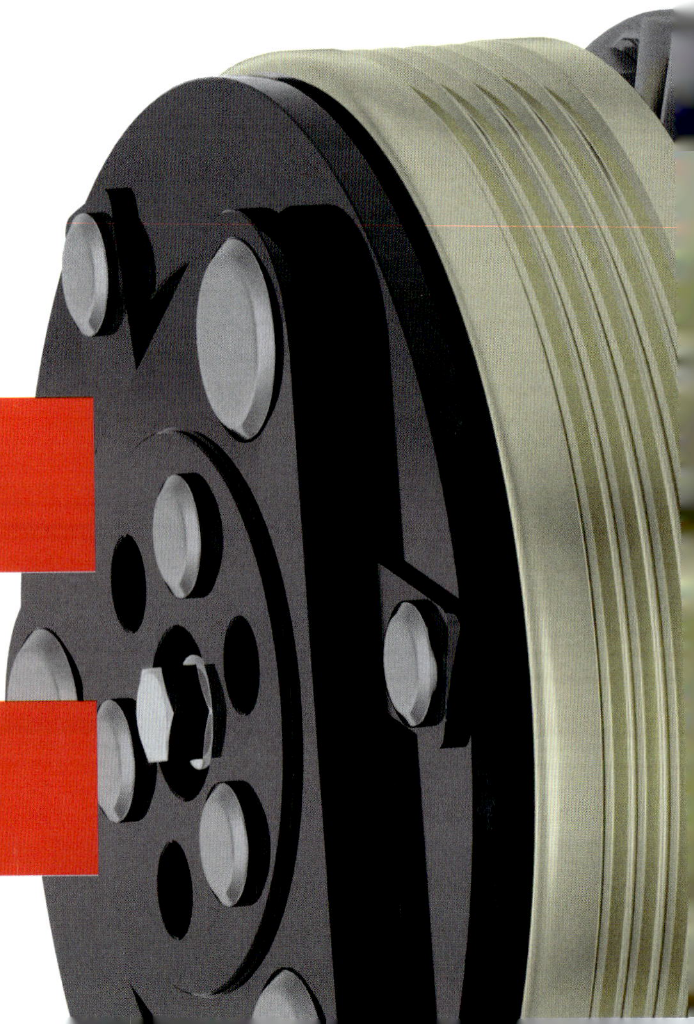

6. Safety Systems

INTRODUCTION TO SAFETY SYSTEMS

1. Safety Systems

Modern vehicles are getting safer with each passing year. New or improved safety systems are constantly being developed and installed. These systems ensure the safety of a car's occupants in various conditions the vehicle may be subjected to. They can reduce the chances of the vehicle being involved in an accident or of the occupants getting injured or killed if an accident occurs.

There are two types of safety systems installed in today's vehicles: active safety systems and passive safety systems.

2. Active Safety Systems

Active safety systems are designed to help prevent accidents. These systems can assist the driver in stopping the vehicle or taking evasive action to avoid a collision. These systems can also improve the visibility of the vehicle. Some examples of active safety systems include:
— Anti-lock braking systems (ABS).
— Traction control system (TCR).
— Electronic stability programs (ESP).
— Radar systems that warn and/or intervene in order to prevent collisions.
— Daytime running lights for better visibility.
— Intelligent lighting such as automatic lighting and dynamic corner lighting.
— Climate systems (air conditioning) to help keep the driver alert.

3. Passive Safety Systems

Passive safety systems help reduce the effects of an accident on the vehicle occupants. When the car is involved in an accident, these safety systems will activate in order to protect the occupants. There are also safety features incorporated into the construction of the car that provide extra strength or absorb impact forces.

Some examples of passive safety systems include:
— Seat belts to keep occupants in their seats.
— Belt pre-tensioners to improve the functioning of the seat belts.
— Airbags to form a cushion between the occupants and the interior.
— Active headrests.
— Retractable steering column to keep the steering wheel away from the driver.
— Crumple zones for absorbing the force of a collision.
— Cage construction to keep the roof rigid when a car rolls over.
— Reinforcement in the doors for extra strength in the event of a side impact.

SRS: AIRBAGS

1. Introduction

An airbag is a protective cushion which inflates automatically in the event of an accident. In its inflated state, the airbag can protect the driver during a collision. This reduces the chance of injury.

This system is commonly referred to as the Supplemental Restraint System or SRS.
Some manufacturers also refer to this system as SIR (Supplemental Inflatable Restraint) or AIR (Automotive Inflatable Restraint) system.

Look for the abbreviations SRS, SIR, AIR or the word 'Airbag' visible on the steering wheel to learn if the vehicle is equipped with a driver's airbag. Similar lettering found on the dash, seats, and pillar moldings indicate the vehicle is also equipped with passenger and side impact protection.

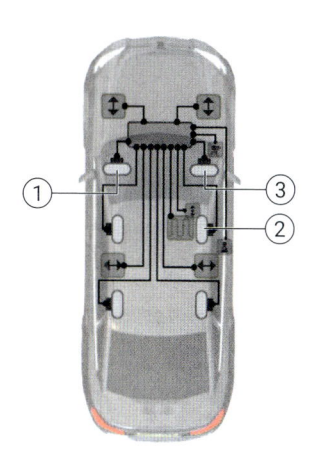

Fig. 202 The airbag system restrains the driver in a collision: 1. Driver airbag. 2. Side airbag. 3. Passenger airbag.

2. Position of the Airbag

Airbags are fitted at various places in the vehicle.
The people in the car are then protected on several sides.

The airbags which protect the people in the car are:
— driver airbag
— passenger airbag
— side airbags
— knee airbags
— curtain airbags

Fig. 203 Airbags can be mounted in different places in the car: 1. Side airbag. 2. Curtain airbag. 3. Passenger airbag. 4. Driver airbag.

Fig. 204 The airbags when inflated: 1. Side airbag. 2. Curtain airbag. 3. Passenger airbag. 4. Driver airbag.

3. Activation of the Airbag

An airbag is activated in three steps.

1. The collision sensor detects a collision and transmits a signal to the control unit.

2. The control unit processes the sensor signal (input) and compares this with the stored data in the control unit.
If the sensor signal is recognized as a collision, a signal is transmitted to the airbag (output).

3. The actuator converts the output signal from the control unit into a mechanical action. The airbag is inflated.

Fig. 205 The collision sensor detects the impact.

Fig. 206 The control unit processes the signal and determines whether the airbag needs to be activated.

Fig. 207 The airbag (actuator) is sent a signal and it inflates.

4. Airbag System

Not all airbags are activated during a collision. If there is a collision in the longitudinal direction, it is superfluous to activate the side airbags.

The forward collision sensor detects a collision of the car in the longitudinal direction. The sensor signal is sent to the control unit and this unit decides whether the driver or passenger airbag must be activated.

The lateral sensor detects a collision of the car in the lateral direction. The sensor signal is sent to the control unit and this unit decides whether the side airbags must be activated.

The seat occupancy sensor detects whether somebody is sitting on a car seat. If nobody is sitting on the seat, the relevant airbags are not activated.

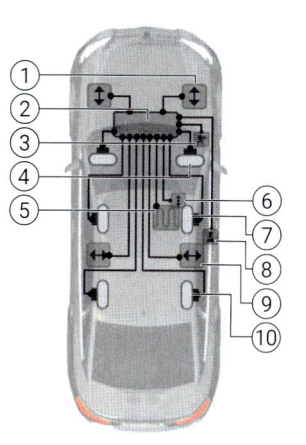

Fig. 208 The components of the airbag system: 1. Collision sensor. 2. Control unit. 3. Airbag lock. 4. Airbag. 5. Seat position sensor. 6. Seat occupation sensor. 7. Side airbag. 8. Belt sensor. 9. Lateral force sensor. 10. Side airbag for passengers.

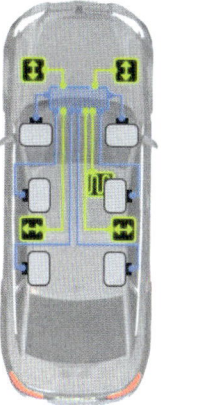

Fig. 209 In the event of a frontal collision in a diagonal direction, the sensors are activated in a longitudinal and a transverse direction. This causes all of the airbags to be activated.

5. Disabling the Passenger Airbag

There are situations when you must disable the passenger airbag.
— If there is a baby in a baby seat.
— If the child is smaller than 1.4 meters (4 feet, 9 inches).

If you do not disable the airbag in these situations, there is a greater risk of injury in the event of a car collision.

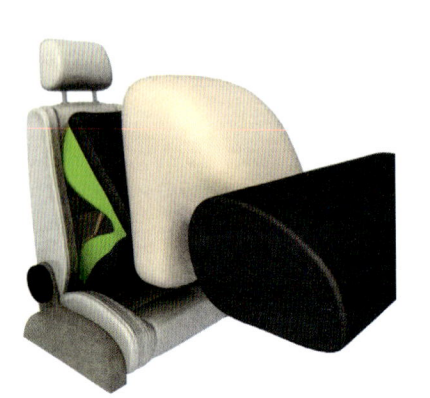

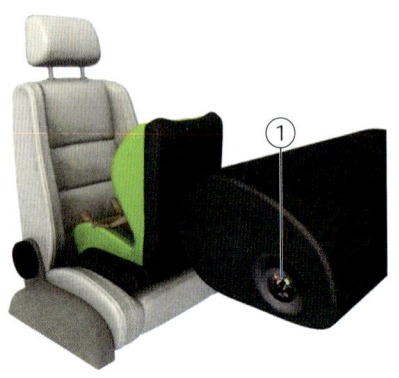

Fig. 210 The airbag pushes the child seat against the backrest of the seat.

Fig. 211 The switch for the airbag lock (1) is often located on the side of the dashboard.

ACCELERATION SENSOR

1. Operating Principle

An acceleration sensor is used to measure the acceleration of the vehicle in a specific direction.

An arrow can be found on the acceleration sensor. The sensor measures acceleration along this axis.

The sensor has a measuring element that converts the acceleration into an electric signal.

There are different acceleration sensor types. The acceleration that must be measured will determine which acceleration sensor is suitable.

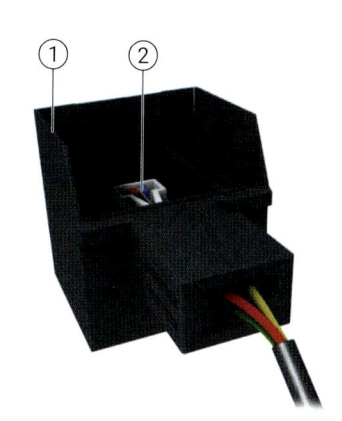

Fig. 212 The acceleration sensor: 1. Housing. 2. Measurement element.

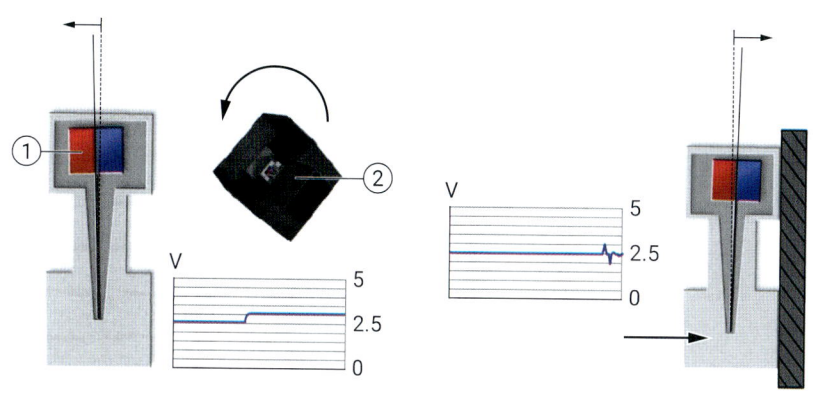

Fig. 213 The mobile part (1) in the measurement element moves when the sensor (2) is rotated. This changes the voltage emitted.

Fig. 214 When the sensor comes to a sudden halt, the mobile part of the measurement element will move.

2. Different Types of Acceleration Sensors

There are different types of acceleration sensors. They can be divided into two different principles:
— Electronic acceleration sensors.
— Electromechanical acceleration sensors or safety switches.

Electronic acceleration sensors measure the acceleration/deceleration and sends an electric signal to the control unit. The size of this signal indicates how great the deceleration is.

The measurement element in the sensor moves if it detects deceleration. This changes the characteristics of the measurement element. This ensures that a certain voltage is emitted.

Electromechanical acceleration sensors are also called safety switches. They make contact when the limit value of the deceleration is exceeded. These sensors usually work with a small weight which moves due to inertia of mass. If deceleration is great enough (in the event of a collision), the weight will move far enough to operate a switch. This is measured by the control unit that decides whether one or more airbags should be activated.

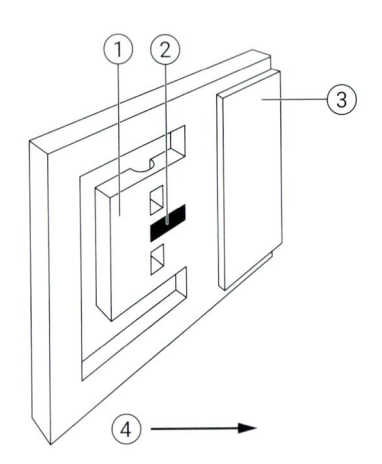

Fig. 215 An electronic acceleration sensor. (4) indicates the driving direction. In the event of a collision, the plate (1) moves forwards due to inertia of mass. This causes the measurement element (2) to deform. The electronic circuit (3) converts this information into a signal and sends it to the control unit.

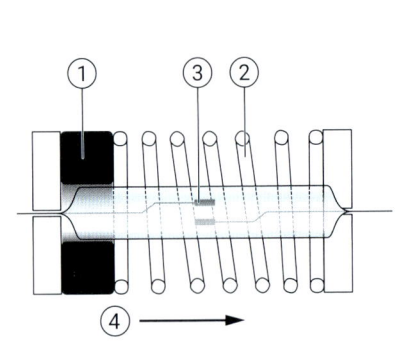

Fig. 216 A commonly used electromechanical acceleration sensor has a Reed switch and a magnet. In the event of a collision, the magnet (1) moves in the driving direction (4) against the force of the spring (2). If the magnet (1) moves far enough, the Reed switch (3) is activated.

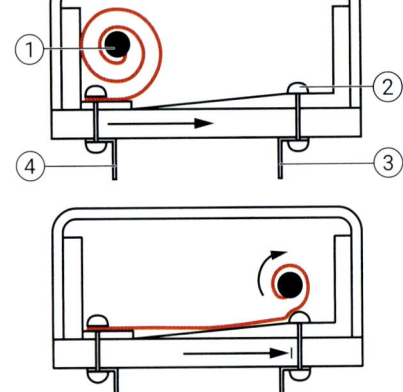

Fig. 217 An electromechanical acceleration sensor. The weight is rolled in a leaf spring (1). In the event of a collision, the weight moves to the right and the leaf spring uncoils. This then makes contact with contact (2). Connections (3) and (4) are connected in the process.

3. Acceleration

Multiple acceleration sensors are installed in a vehicle because one sensor can only measure vehicle acceleration in one direction.

The vehicle can accelerate in different directions:
— Transverse direction
— Longitudinal direction
— Elevation direction

4. Airbags

The airbag control unit uses the signals of the acceleration sensors in the longitudinal and transverse directions.

This control unit processes the signals of the longitudinal and transverse acceleration sensors and drives the correct airbags.

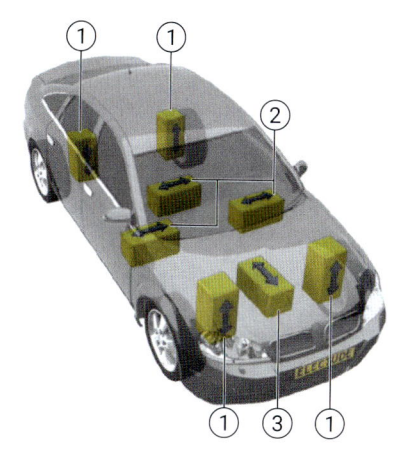

Fig. 218 Acceleration sensors in different directions: 1. Up/down direction. 2. Transverse direction. 3. Longitudinal direction.

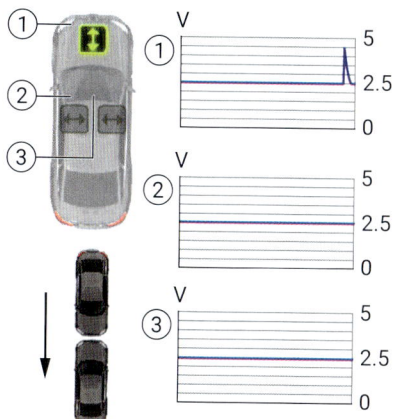

Fig. 219 In the event of a frontal collision, only the longitudinal acceleration sensor (1) is activated.

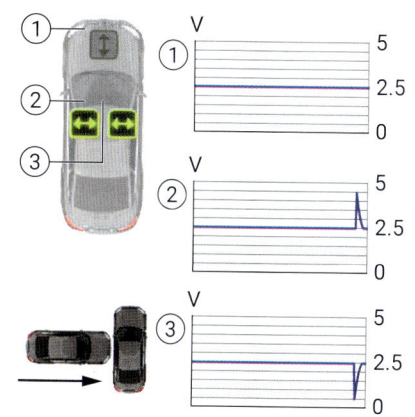

Fig. 220 In the event of a collision from the side, transverse acceleration sensors (2 and 3) are activated. The signals are opposed because the sensors are mounted in opposite directions. This allows them to detect which side the collision is coming from.

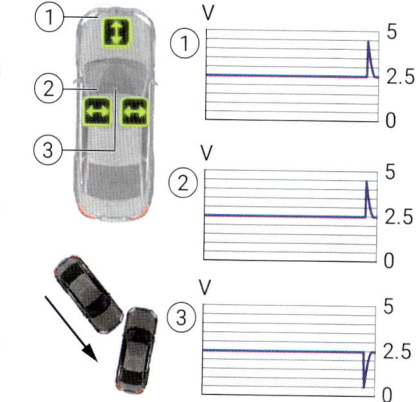

Fig. 221 In the event of a collision that is from the front and diagonal, the transverse acceleration sensors and the longitudinal acceleration sensor are activated. The size of the signal from the sensors is smaller, because the force of the collision is spread across the longitudinal and transverse directions.

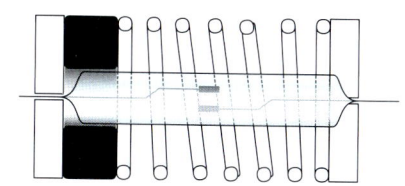

Fig. 222 Acceleration sensors with a Reed switch are often used as a safety switch.

5. Deceleration Sensor in the Control Device

A safety switch is included in the airbag control unit. The electronic acceleration sensors can be located in the control unit, but they can also be connected as separate sensors.

The safety switch ensures that the airbag cannot accidentally go off as a result of a failure in an acceleration sensor. So both of them need to register the collision for the airbag to activate.

SRS: GAS GENERATOR

1. SRS: Gas Generator

The gas generator can be found behind the folded airbag. The control unit will actuate the gas generator during an accident.

The gas generator provides the gas required for filling the airbag.

2. Gas Generator Construction

The gas generator comprises a:
— Housing
— Ignition element
— Gas pellets
— Metal filter

The ignition element has a heat wire and an ignition pellet with a boost charge.
The control unit transmits a current through the heat wire that activates the ignition pellet using the boost charge. The heat of the boost charge ignites the solid propellant. The solid propellant comprises compressed fuel and oxygen.

Gas is released when the solid propellant is ignited. The gas flows through a metal filter to the airbag under pressure. The metal filter helps to clean and cool the gas entering the airbag. The gas generator will burn all the solid propellant within 40 ms.

Fig. 223 The gas generator (2) is located in the steering wheel, behind the folded airbag (1).

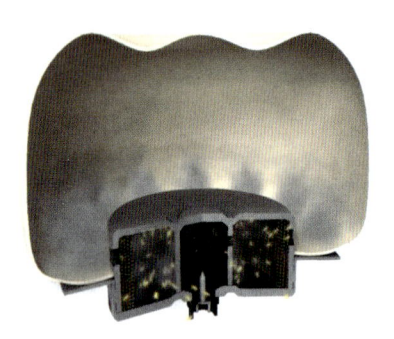

Fig. 224 The heat from the amplification charge ensures that the solid charge is burned and produces gas. The gas fills the airbag.

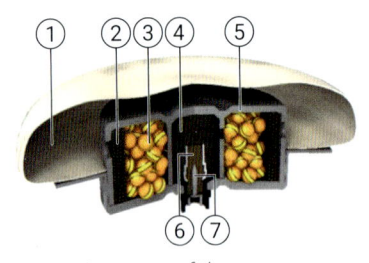

Fig. 225 Structure of the gas generator: 1. Airbag. 2. Metal filter. 3. Solid charge. 4. Amplification charge. 5. Housing. 6. Igniter pellet. 7. Heating wire.

Fig. 226 The amplification charge is ignited and produces heat.

Fig. 227 The heating wire ensures that the igniter pellet is ignited.

SRS: WORKING ON AIRBAGS

Fig. 229 Recognition points for a vehicle with airbags: 1. SRS or AIRBAG where an airbag is mounted. 2. Switch for passenger airbag. 3. Airbag diagnostic light. 4. Chassis number.

1. Vehicle with Airbag

There are features in and around the vehicle which enable you to determine whether the vehicle is equipped with airbags.

These features are as follows:
- airbag warning light on the dashboard.
- places where an airbag is fitted are indicated by the letters SRS or SIR and/or the word 'Airbag'.
- indication on the chassis number.
- on/off switch for passenger airbag.

2. Removing

Before you remove an airbag, you must look up the step-by-step procedure in the service manual. The procedure is different for every make and model of vehicle.

Step-by-step procedure for removing an airbag.
- First turn off the ignition.
- Then remove the battery terminals (neg. first) and look up the waiting period for the airbag control unit in the service manual. It's important to wait prior to disconnecting the airbag from the control unit, because the control unit can activate the airbag within the waiting period.
- Once the waiting period is over, you can safely disconnect and remove the airbag from the vehicle.
- **Warning:** Never set an airbag on a conductive surface and always place it with the bag side up.

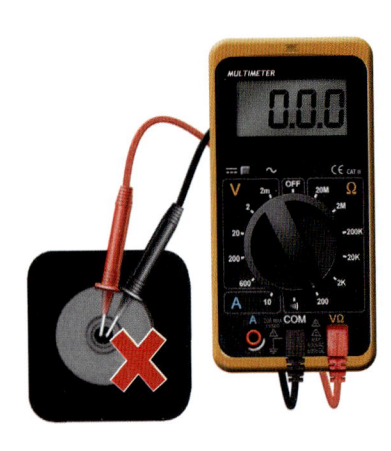

Fig. 230 NEVER connect a multimeter to (parts of) the airbag system.

3. Installing

Before you install an airbag, look up the step-by-step procedure in the service manual. The procedure is different for every make/model of car.

Step-by-step procedure for installing an airbag:
— First install the airbag.
— Connect the airbag to the control unit.
— Connect the positive terminal of the battery. Then connect the negative terminal of the battery.

Warning: Never use a multimeter to test the airbag system. This may cause activation of the airbag.

SEAT BELT

1. Seat Belt

The seat belt ensures that the vehicle occupant remains securely seated when the vehicle suddenly decelerates. This reduces the probability of the person sustaining injuries.

The width of the seat belt is made rather wide, so pressure from deceleration is more equally distributed across the body during sudden deceleration, for example, in the event of an accident.

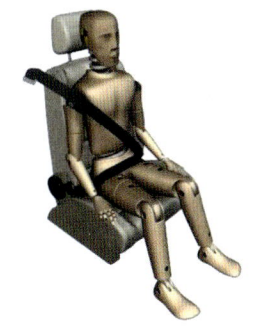

Fig. 235 The seat belt.

Fig. 236 In the event of quick deceleration, such as a collision, the occupant is held in the seat.

2. Three-Point Seat Belt

The seat belt used most often in vehicles is the three-point seat belt. This seat belt design is secured to three fixed points in the vehicle.

There are also seat belts that are secured to more than three fixed points.

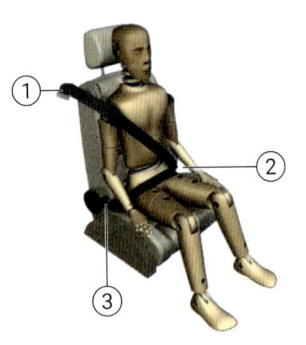

Fig. 237 A three-point belt attaches to the car at three points.

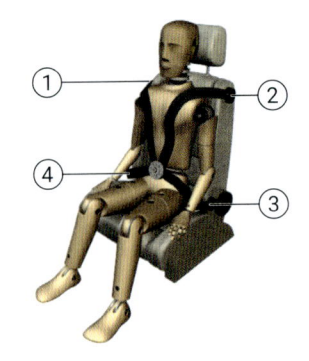

Fig. 238 A four-point belt attaches to the car at four points.

3. Reeling Device

The seat belt has a reeling device. This device is required to extend and automatically retract the seat belt.

When you put on your seat belt, you pull it forward. The pulley allows the seat belt to extend. This action winds the spring tight.
When you unbuckle the seat belt, the spring unwinds, causing the pulley to retract the seat belt automatically.

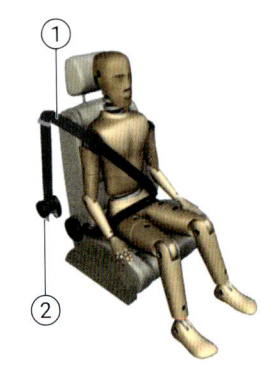

Fig. 239 The seat belt (1) is equipped with a retractor (2).

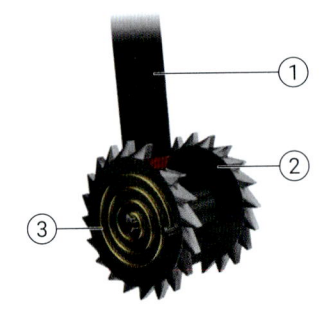

Fig. 240 The seat belt (1) is rolled up on a pulley (2) that is tensioned by a spring (3).

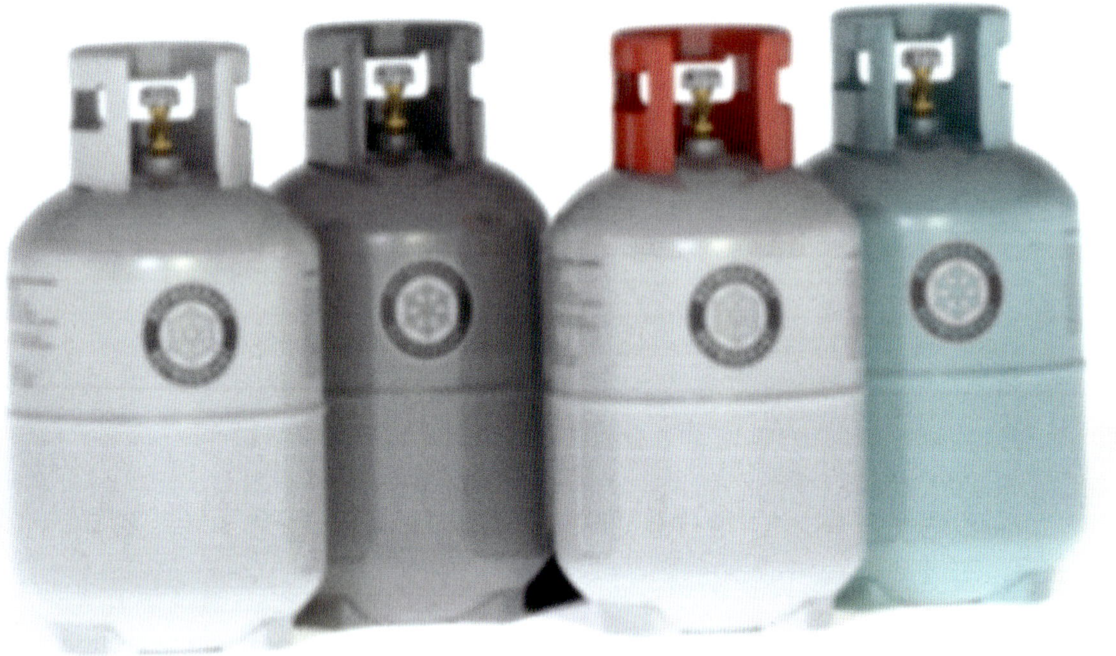

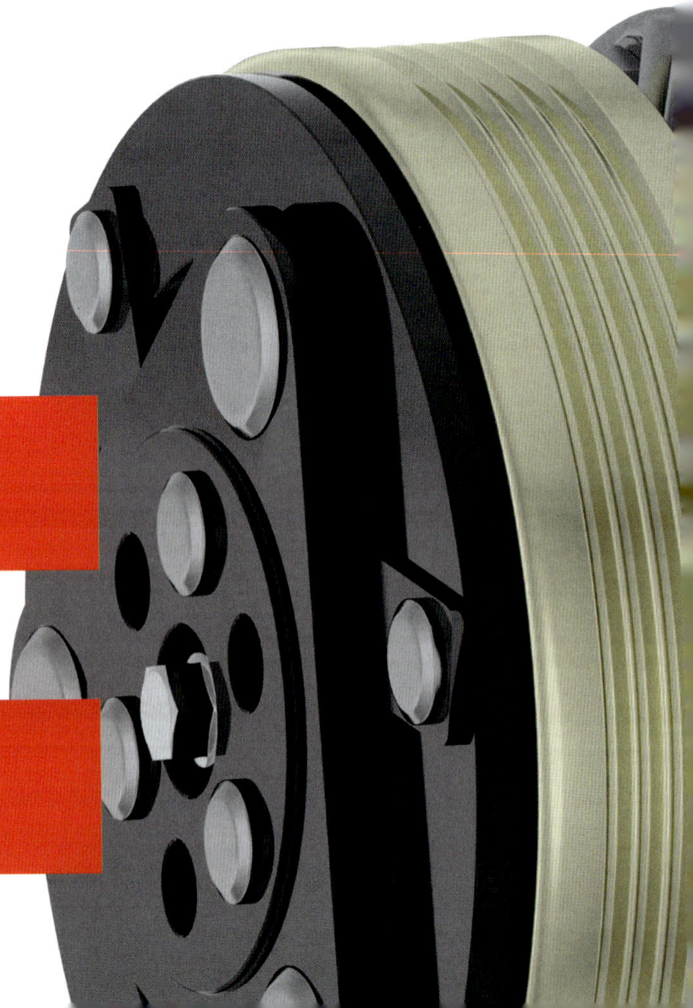

7. Electrical Accessories

CENTRAL LOCKING SYSTEM

1. Introduction

The history of the central door lock (CDL) dates back to around 1950. CDLs were not standard on production cars at that time. Many developments took place in the years that followed. In modern times, you will find a central door lock on almost every newly produced car.

Historically, the doors were centrally locked and unlocked with a traditional key.

Until 1990, some manufacturers used vacuum (negative pressure) or positive pressure to operate the locks. Other manufacturers used magnetic coils or electric motors.

Developments in the field of electronics made it possible in the 90s to remotely lock and unlock the doors with a handheld transmitter. Current systems work with a smart key or smart card.

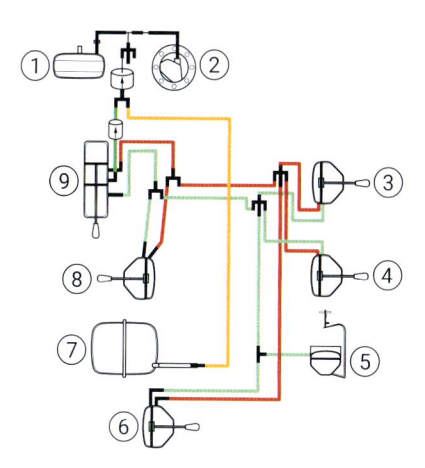

Fig. 245 Vacuum system schematic: 1. Brake booster. 2. Vacuum pump. 3. Right front door lock. 4. Right rear door lock. 5. Fuel flap. 6. Trunk lock. 7. Vacuum tank. 8. Left front door lock. 9. Driver's door.

Fig. 246 Control integrated in the key.

Fig. 247 Separate handheld transmitter and smart card.

2. Systems

Current systems are electric and cars often come with a key that has a built-in radio transmitter that can be used for "open" and "close" functions as standard equipment.

With the application of CAN bus and LIN bus networks, only a software connection is needed to perform the following actions remotely:
– Open the trunk.
– Switch the lights on.
– Switch the alarm on or off.
– Start the engine.

Extended systems have a transponder (transmitter) in a smart key or smart card. The locks are then automatically unlocked when you approach the vehicle or locked when you leave it.

ELECTRIC WINDOWS

1. Introduction

Mercedes-Benz introduced the first car with electric windows in 1948. In modern vehicles, electric windows come as standard equipment in most cases.

They are operated with a spring-loaded, three-position switch. The positions are: down, rest and up. The power windows can be operated after the ignition has been turned on in the accessory position.

The power windows operate using a DC motor, and the direction of window travel is controlled by the polarity of the electrical current supplied to the motor. The type of circuit that makes the reversal of polarity possible is called an H-bridge circuit.

The polarity is determined by the position of four switches and alternates between the positive and negative. An H-bridge makes it possible to run a DC motor such as a window motor in both directions.

As a rule, all of the windows can be operated from the driver's seat. Passengers can operate their own windows from their respective position.

Fig. 252 Operation from the driver's position.

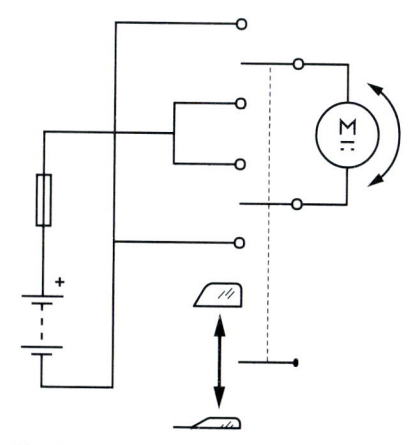

Fig. 253 H-bridge switch.

2. Construction

Scissor Mechanism

The door window can be moved using cables or a scissor mechanism. Scissor mechanisms are much heavier than a cable system, and contain a spring, a rack-and-pinion style of gear, and a scissor-shaped device that expands and contracts as the window travels up and down.

Cable System

In cable systems, the gear on the window motor moves a cable. The cable is attached to the window glass and it runs over guide rollers through a guide rail. This system is much lighter than scissor-type systems.

When the window motor rotates counterclockwise, the inner cable moves from the window motor to the left across the top green guide roller. In the left guide rail, the left cable attachment will lower the window. The cable then goes through the lower guide roller in the left rail to the upper guide roller in the right rail. This will also cause the right side of the window to move down.

The cable returns to the gear on the window motor via the lower guide roller in the right rail.

If the window is operated to raise it, everything is done in reverse order.

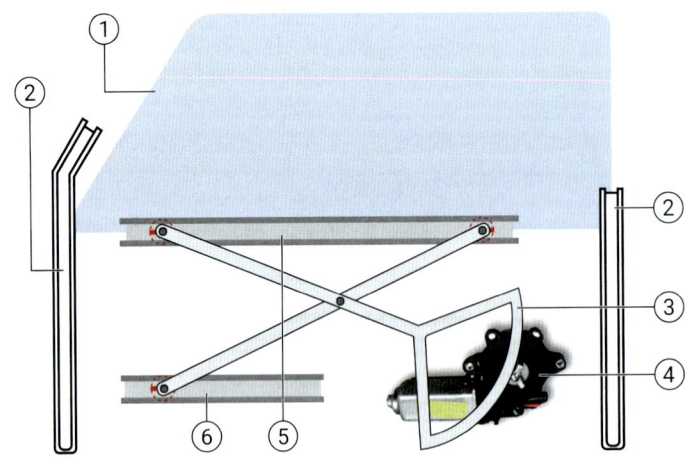

Fig. 254 Window mechanism with scissor system: 1. Window glass. 2. Window guide. 3. Ring gear. 4. Window motor. 5. Window mounting rail. 6. Fixed rail on the door.

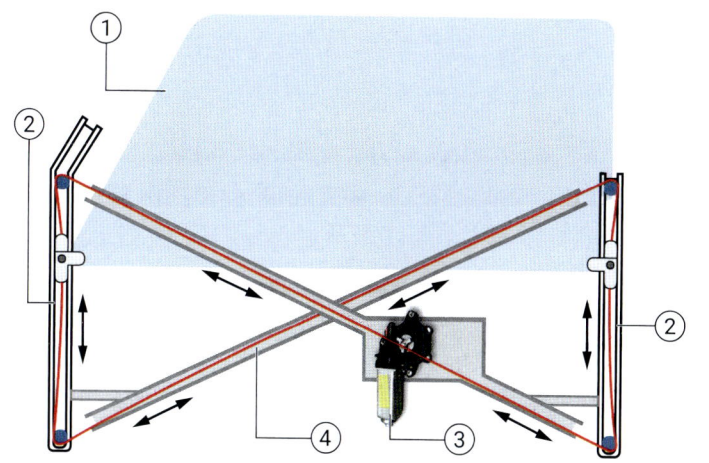

Fig. 255 Window mechanism with cable system: 1. Window glass. 2. Window guide. 3. Window motor. 4. Cable.

3. Motor.

The window motor is linked to a system that allows the electric windows to be operated after switching on the ignition.

When the spring-loaded window switch is moved down, the top contact connects to the negative of the electric motor. The bottom contact in the window switch connects to the positive of the electric motor. This causes the motor to rotate and the window to move down.
If the switch continues to be operated after the window has reached the end of its travel, there is a risk of the motor burning out or damage to the mechanism. To avoid this, the electric motor is equipped with a thermal contact. This is a switch that breaks when the temperature exceeds a certain value.
Once the thermal contact has cooled, the window can be operated again. A thermal contact can also prevent damage to an object that comes between the window and the door frame.

The electric motor has two directions of rotation due to the polarity reversal (switching between positive and negative). There is no connection to the electric motor in the middle position of the window switch.

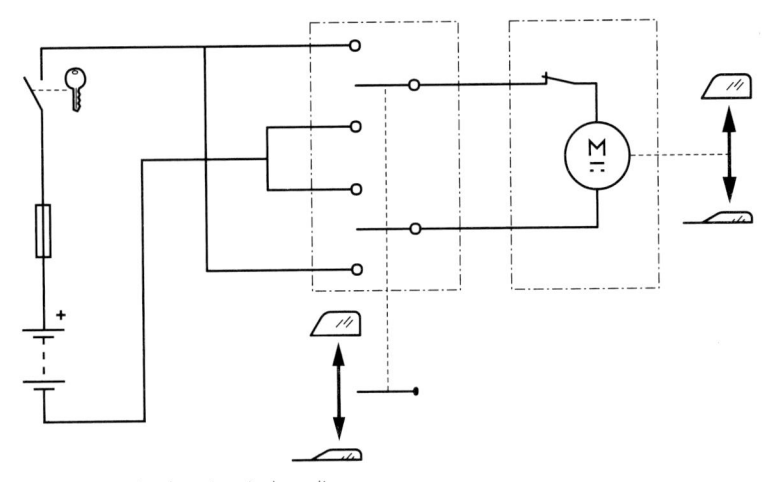

Fig. 256 Basic electric window diagram.

MIRRORS

1. Side Mirrors

Passenger vehicles are legally required to have exterior mirrors. Door mirrors on the driver's side of the vehicle were mandatory in the US in the early stages. Since the 1960s, most states also require door mirrors on the passenger side of new vehicles.

Door mirrors improve visibility around the vehicle and therefore road safety. In addition, the mirrors are good to have when parking, backing up or changing lanes.

Even with these mirrors, there are still blind spots where visibility is limited.

Fig. 259 Door mirror with curved glass to reduce the blind spot.

Fig. 260 Flat door mirror.

Mirrors often feature "accessories" on newer vehicles, including:
— Mirror heating.
  In the winter, mirrors are electrically heated with a heating element. The ice, water or mist on the mirrors will evaporate. This increases road safety significantly.
— Entry lighting.
  Extra lighting for entry, but also turn signals to indicate more clearly when changing direction.
— Folding mechanism.
  Mirrors are protruding objects on vehicles, and can be an obstacle for parking vehicles or for passers-by.
  An additional motor in the mirror folds the mirror in. This reduces the risk of damage.

– Outside temperature sensor.
  Mirrors are located at a favorable height so they are less affected by radiant heat from the road surface. The sensors are often installed at the bottom of the mirror.

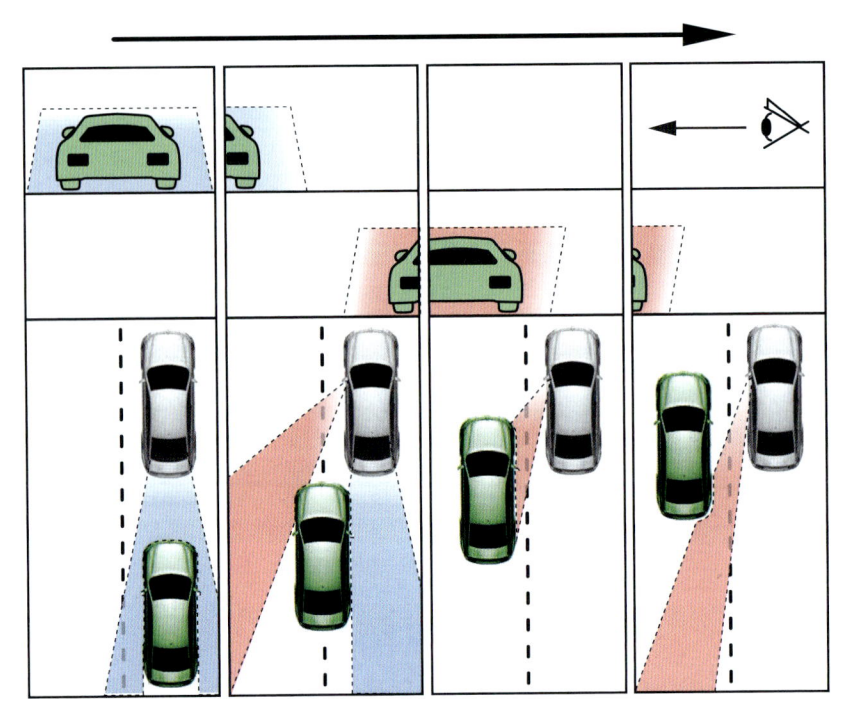

Fig. 261 The mirrors' blind spots.

2. Interior Mirrors

Interior mirrors are also installed in vehicles with rear windows. This provides the driver with a view of what is happening behind them. During night driving there is a risk of being blinded by the headlights of the vehicle behind you. To combat this, many interior mirrors can be manually set to a glare-free position by tilting them.

This happens automatically in some vehicles. A light sensor (LDR) registers the light from the vehicle behind. The mirror is then colored by a liquid between two glass plates. This liquid darkens as soon as it comes into contact with electricity.

A second method uses a thin transparent layer that lies across the mirror. If a current flows through it, this layer gradually darkens. This can dim the reflected light from 7% to 85%. As soon as the light source disappears, the current is switched off and the mirror becomes clear again.

Fig. 262 Temperature sensor in the door mirror.

Fig. 263 Automatically dimmed interior mirror.

3. 360° Surround View

Various technological developments are constantly improving the road safety of todays vehicles. Some vehicles come equipped with camera systems that display a 360° surround view of the car. These systems are referred to by technical marketing names such as the 360° Surround View Camera.

These systems provide a projected image of the entire perimeter around the car.
This is achieved using four wide-angle cameras: one in front of the grille, one under each of the two door mirrors and one above the license plate on the rear of the car. The images are projected onto a large color monitor in the dashboard. You can use a selector switch to choose between the four cameras. This allows drivers to see where the obstacles are and at what distance from the vehicle.

In addition, there is the "Bird View" (birds eye view) function. The image is like that of a drone hovering above the car showing the immediate surrounding area. This is a computer animation composed of the images from the four cameras combined and literally gives drivers 360° line of sight around the vehicle.

Fig. 264 360° "Bird View" function (bird's eye view).

MIRROR OPERATION

1. Manually Operated Door Mirrors

There is no legal requirement for mirrors to be operable from the inside of the vehicle. However, today's vehicles are almost all equipped with electrically adjustable door mirrors.

2. Electrically Operated Door Mirrors

The control panel is located within the driver's reach. The driver can choose to adjust the left or right mirror using a selector knob.

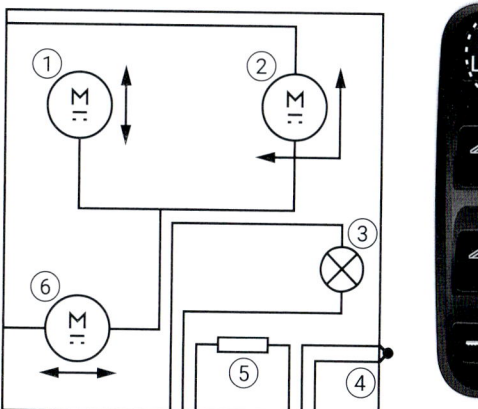

Fig. 265 Basic electric mirror operation: 1. Y-axis motor. 2. Fold-in motor. 3. Lamp. 4. Temperature sensor. 5. Heating element. 6. X-axis motor.

Fig. 266 Mirror control in left door.

Electrically operated mirrors are equipped with at least two electric motors. One is for the two directions in the horizontal plane (turning from left to right along the x-axis).
The other is for the two directions in the vertical plane (tilting from top to bottom along the y-axis). The motors are often equipped with a freewheel control to prevent them from burning out.

Mirrors are optionally equipped with mirror heating. This is achieved with a PTC foil heating element of approximately 5-18 W. The PTC heats the mirror quickly, which helps clear fog and ice from the mirror in poor weather conditions. Additional components in the mirror may include an outside temperature sensor, additional entry and turn signals, and a motor to fold the mirror in.

3. Door Mirrors With Memory

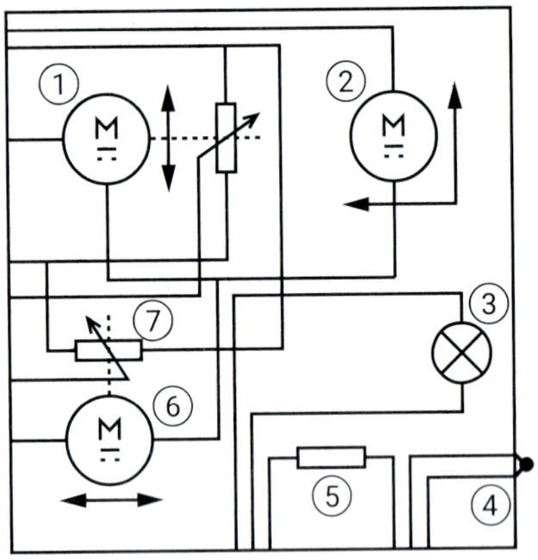

Electrically operated mirrors with position memory are equipped with electric servo motors. In addition to the electric motor, servo motors also have a position sensor on the output shaft. This position sensor feeds the position of the mirror back to the electronics. The advantage of this is that after the mirror is set, the position can be stored in memory. If this position memory is linked to a handheld transmitter, key transponder or smart card/smart key, the mirror will assume the position stored in the associated memory. This allows each driver to have his/her own settings.

Fig. 267 High-optioned electric mirror operation: 1. Y-axis motor. 2. Fold-in motor. 3. Lamp. 4. Temperature sensor. 5. Heating element. 6. X-axis motor. 7. Position sensor/potentiometer.

SEAT CONTROL

1. Introduction

Car seats have been adjustable for decades. A properly adjusted seat ensures comfort and increases road safety. Visibility is improved and it is less tiring for the driver. In addition, all of the buttons in the car are easier to operate.
The angle of the backrest is adjustable as a standard and the seat can be adjusted manually from front to back.

In mid-range cars, the car seat is optionally equipped with height adjustment, adjustable lumbar support, two-piece backrest adjustment, tilt adjustment of the seat and even more options. In the higher segment you will find electric seat adjustment with memory positions.

Fig. 270 Car seat operation.

2. Electrically Adjustable Seat

The basic adjustments of an electrically adjustable seat are:

1. Height of the seat at the front.
2. Height of the seat at the rear.
3. Longitudinal position in the horizontal direction (distance from the pedals).
4. Tilt angle of the backrest.

With these four adjustment options, the seat can be adjusted to a position where the driver feels most comfortable.

Electric motors with permanent magnets with two directions of rotation are used for seat adjustment. These are operated by H-bridge switches. Power protection devices in the form of position sensors, circuit breakers, PTC resistors, or module programming ensures that the power is switched off from the seat motor when the seat reaches the end of the travel. This prevents the switches and electric motors from burning out.
Worm gear transmissions are primarily used as the transmissions for the electrically adjustable seat functions.

Fig. 271 Worm gear

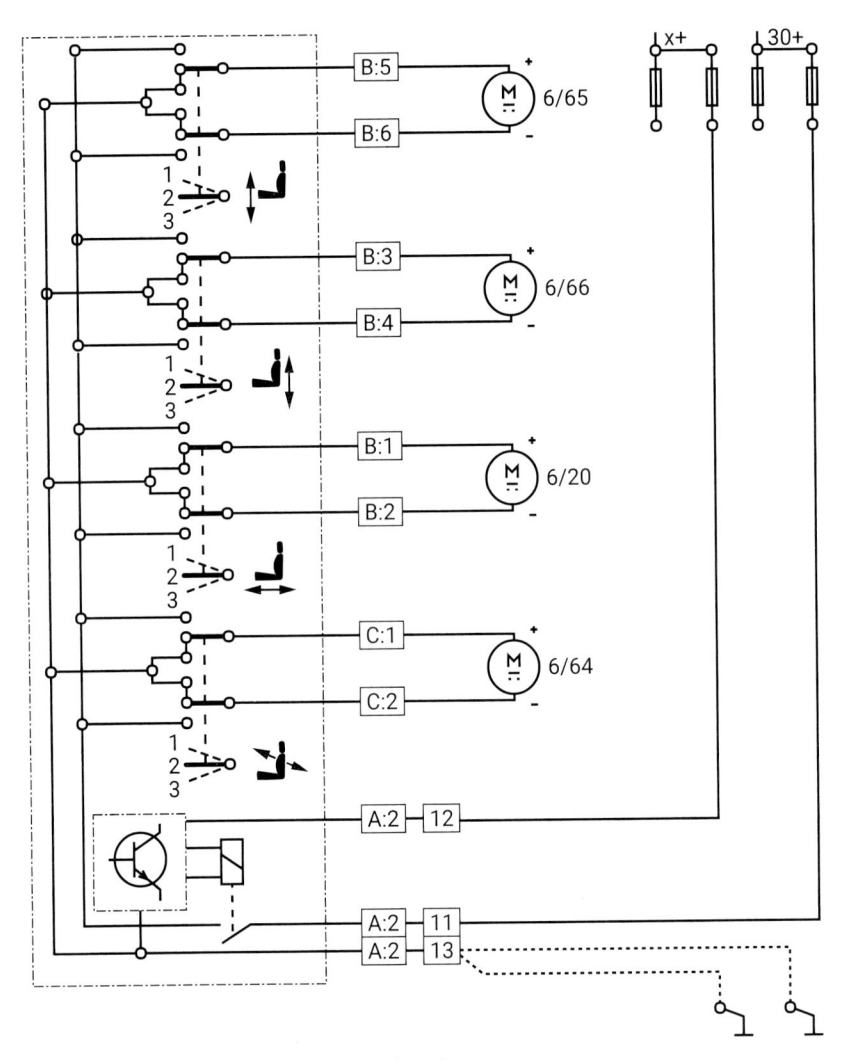

Fig. 272 Basic operation of the electrically adjustable car seat.

SEAT HEATING AND VENTILATION

1. Introduction

A relaxed driver is an alert driver who is less likely to become tired. This increases road safety. Drivers can travel longer distances in a relaxed and comfortable manner. For these reasons, car seats in the more expensive price range come with fully equipped seats. Seat heating and ventilation are standard.

2. Seat Ventilation

These types of seats are equipped with at least two fans in the backrest and seat; these blow or draw in air to cool the occupant. These systems can be adjusted in steps or they can be infinitely variable with regard to the fan speed. This is done by a PWM/duty cycle control where the speed is controlled. The fans will be switched on and off approximately 400 times per second for a shorter or longer period of time.

In addition, there are active seat ventilators in which the suction and blowing direction of the ventilation can be reversed. Several fans are used for this. When the ventilation is switched on, cooler ambient air is sucked along the surfaces of the seat and backrest. After some time, the ventilation direction is reversed and ventilation is blown instead.

Fig. 274 Car seat.

Fig. 275 Seat heating element.

3. Seat Heating

Seat heating uses heating elements. In terms of their construction, these can be compared to mirror heating. The wires form one element with long flexible loops. A PTC resistor is used as the series resistor in the wires. There are also seat heating elements with a thermal contact. A disadvantage of these elements is that there is a greater difference between the activating and deactivating temperature. This makes it less comfortable.

A temperature-controlled system is used in intermediate level cars. The system has a temperature sensor and a control unit for setting the desired temperature. There are often two or more steps or the control is infinitely variable.
A temperature limit has been set for the surface of the seat: 100° F. In cars in the more expensive segment, the armrests and inner door panel are also heated.

4. Massage

Seats in the more expensive price range can be equipped with a massage function. In these seats, air pumps move air between several inflatable cushions. These cushions are mainly found in the backrest.
There are also seats in which four to fourteen individually inflatable cushions provide a relaxing massage. The selection sometimes consists of five or more massage programs. There are systems in which the four most centrally located sections around the spine can be heated to 130° F for a hot stone experience.

Advanced Automotive Electronics

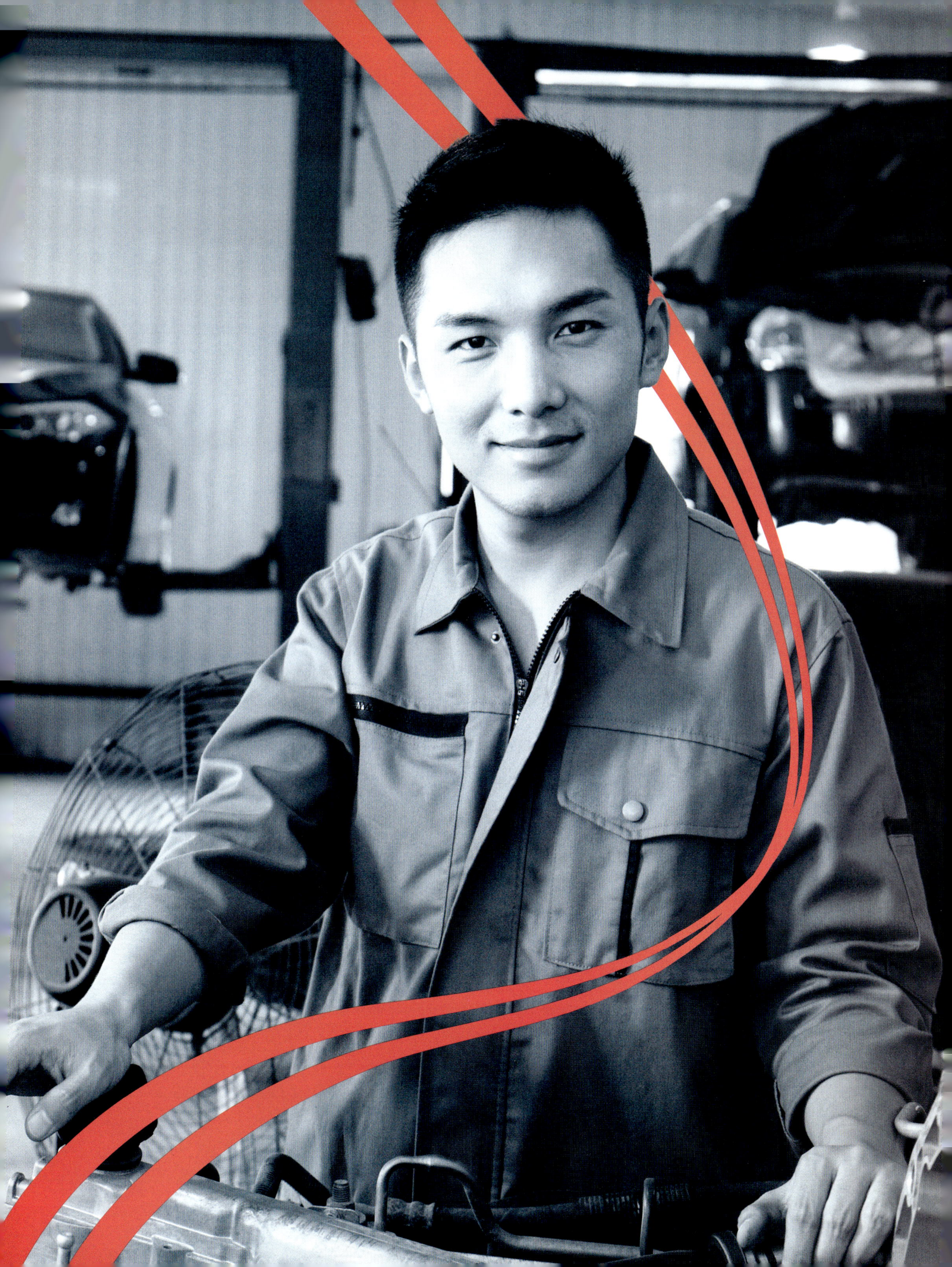

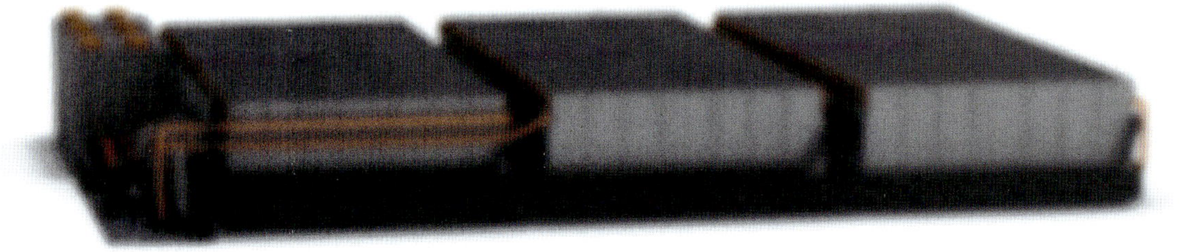

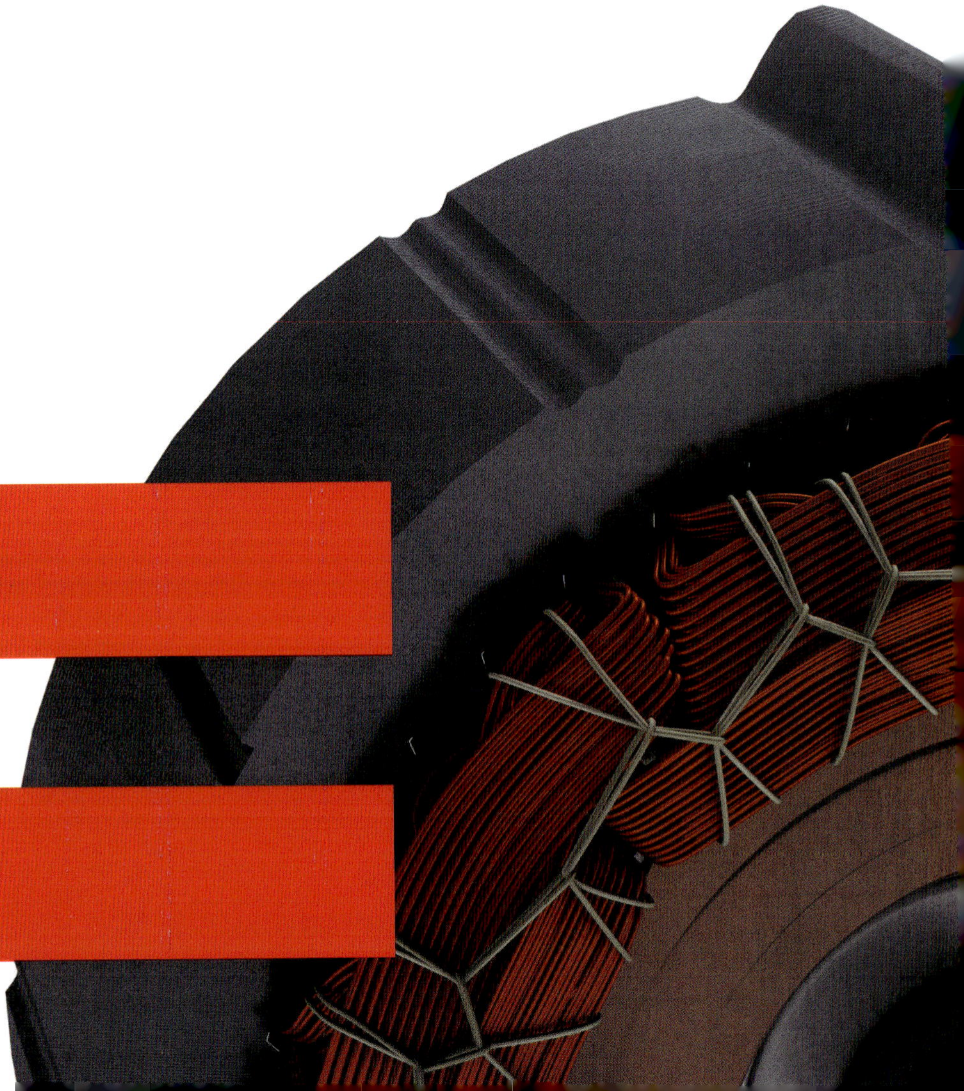

1. Advanced Electrical and Electronic Components

NTC THERMISTOR

1. Introduction

An NTC resistor is type of thermistor. This means that the resistance depends on the temperature.

An NTC (Negative Temperature Coefficient) thermistor has the following property: as its temperature increases, its resistance decreases.

NTC resistors are often used as:

- coolant temperature sensors
- intake air temperature sensors
- evaporator temperature sensors
- ambient air temperature sensors
- battery temperature sensors

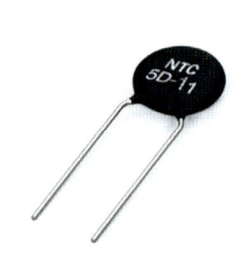

Fig. 1 NTC resistor.

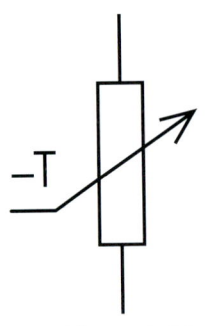

Fig. 2 The symbol for an NTC resistor

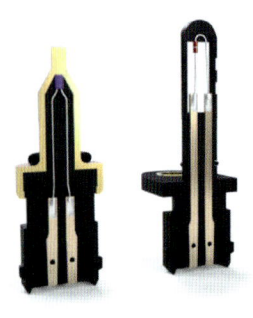

Fig. 3 An NTC resistor as coolant temperature sensor and as an air temperature sensor.

2. Negative Temperature Coefficient

NTC thermistors are often used as a temperature sensor because they have a range of -4° F (-20° C) to 248° F (120° C).

With an NTC thermistor, the resistance decreases with increasing temperature.

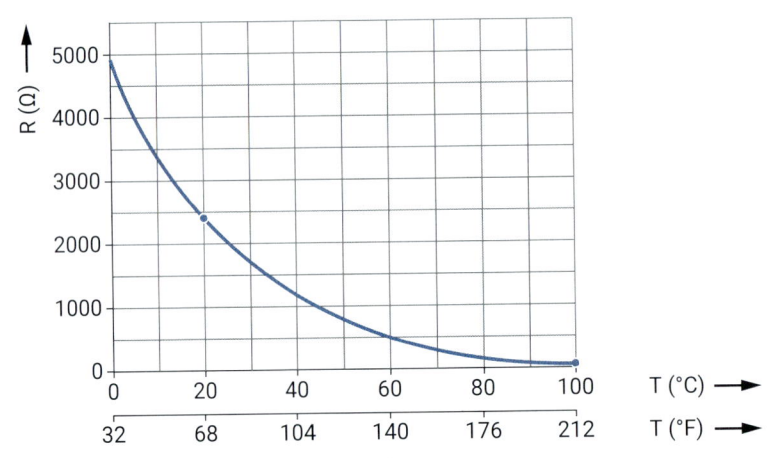

Fig. 4 The characteristic of an NTC resistor

If you look at the graph, you will see that the resistance at room temperature (68° F / 20° C) is approximately 2.4 kΩ.

At the boiling point of water (212° F / 100° C) the resistance is approximately 65 Ω.

PTC THERMISTOR

1. Introduction

A PTC resistor is a thermistor. This means that the resistance depends on the temperature.

A PTC (Positive Temperature Coefficient) increases its resistance as temperature rises.

You will often find PTC resistors used in the construction of:

- fluid level sensors
- air flow sensors
- air heating elements
- circuit protectors

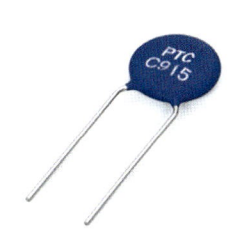

Fig. 5 PTC Thermistor

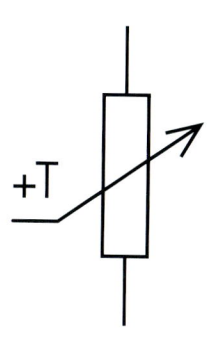

Fig. 6 The symbol of a PTC resistor

Fig. 7 An exhaust gas temperature sensor with a PTC sensor

2. Positive Temperature Coefficient

PTC resistors are often used as a temperature sensor. They can have a measuring range from -328° F to 1832° F.

With a PTC resistor, the resistance increases with increasing temperature.

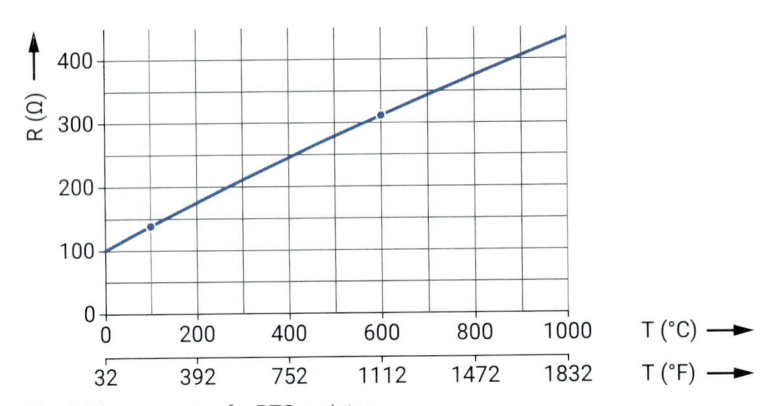

Fig. 8 The property of a PTC resistor

If you read the graph, you will see that the resistance at 212° F (100 °C) is approximately 140 Ω.

If the sensor is heated to 1112° F (600 °C), the resistance increases to approximately 320 Ω.

The resistance increases almost linearly with this sensor.

LIGHT DEPENDENT RESISTOR

An LDR is a resistor that responds to the intensity of light.

When the LDR (**L**ight **D**ependent **R**esistor) absorbs light, the resistance decreases.

In the dark, the resistance can reach 10,000,000 Ω (10 MΩ). As soon as light falls on the sensor, the resistance value quickly drops to 1000 Ω or lower.

An LDR sensor is used in, among other things, a self-dimming interior mirror, light sensor, sun sensor, and a camera.

Fig. 9 An LDR with a resistance of 2.49 kΩ

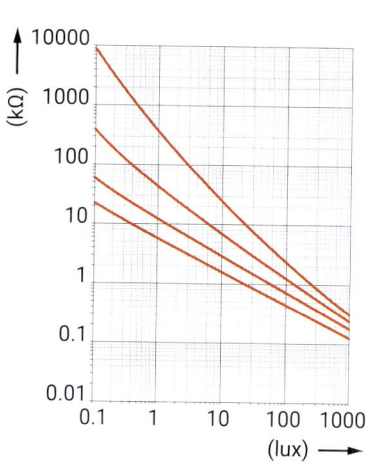

Fig. 10 Characteristic of an LDR

MAGNETIC DEPENDENT RESISTOR

A MDR (**M**agnetic **D**ependent **R**esistor) is a resistor that responds to magnetism.
When the magnetic field changes, the resistance also changes.
They are commonly used in modern ABS systems.

The resistance is at its maximum at an angle of 0° between the direction of the current through the resistor and the magnetic field lines.

The resistance is at its minimum at an angle of 90° between the direction of the current through the resistor and the magnetic field lines.

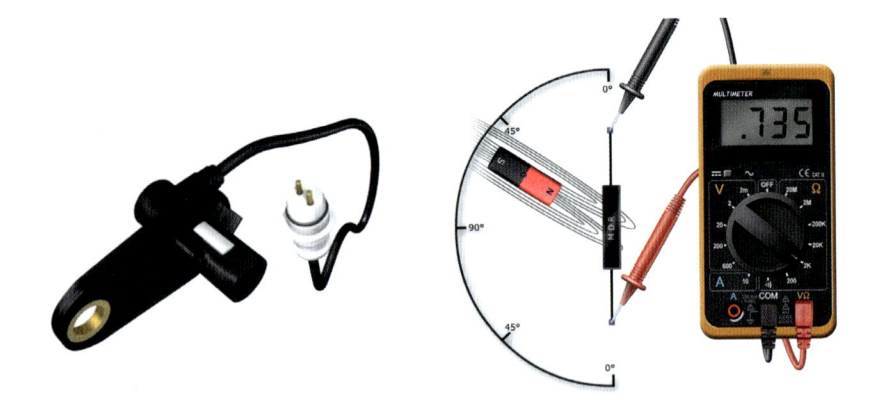

Fig. 11 MRE wheel sensors (Magneto Resistive Element) also contain magnetically dependent resistors.

Fig. 12 Resistance measurement on a MDR resistor

Magnetically dependent resistors can be used to determine position. A permanent magnet is often used to generate the magnetic field.

Wheel sensors contain MDR resistors, but the position of the throttle valve can also be easily determined with a magnetically dependent resistor.

POSITIVE TEMPERATURE COEFFICIENT (PTC) HEATER

1. Function and Application

A component can be quickly heated to operating temperature and kept at that temperature with the use of a positive temperature coefficient (PTC) heating element. The temperature of the heating element is determined by the current flowing through it, which in turn is controlled by a PTC resistor.

PTC heaters can be found in numerous components, such as:

- interior heating element
  The interior can be heated, even when the engine is cold.
- Heated wide-band oxygen sensor
  An oxygen sensor must reach a predetermined operating temperature before it functions correctly.

2. PTC principle

A PTC (**P**ositive **T**emperature **C**oefficient) resistor is a resistor in which the resistance value is dependent on the temperature.

The characteristics of a PTC resistor are that the resistance increases as the temperature increases.

3. How a positive temperature coefficient (PTC) heater functions

A positive temperature coefficient (PTC) heater uses the properties of a PTC resistor to control the current flowing through a heating element. In this way the temperature can be controlled.

A heated oxygen sensor must be heated to 400°C. Due to the current flowing through the heating element the oxygen sensor is heated. The supply Voltage is constant. The amount of current depends on the resistance of the PTC resistor.

When the sensor is cold, the resistance value of the PTC resistor is low. The current is then high, so the heating element warms up quickly.

As the sensor nears operating temperature of 400°C, the current decreases, because the resistance increases.

The current flowing through the heating element depends on the supply voltage and the resistance of the positive temperature coefficient (PTC) resistor. This current can be used to heat the heating element. The current decreases as the temperature increases.

The heating element must be brought to operating temperature and kept at that temperature. For this more current is required. The more current necessary to keep the element at operating temperature, the less is available to increase the heat the element.

At a certain temperature an equilibrium point is reached. The current flowing through the component is exactly enough to keep it at operating temperature.

The resistance properties of the chosen PTC resistor are such that the required end temperature is reached.

4. Supply Voltage

Until now we have assumed that the supply voltage remains at a constant 12 Volts. In reality the supply voltage can vary.

If the supply voltage changes, then so does the end temperature. Because of this you cannot accurately control the temperature with a positive temperature coefficient (PTC) heater. If accuracy is required, then a duty-cycle controlled PTC heater is used.

Because it is self regulating, a PTC heater ensures the component never gets too hot.

LED

An LED is a special diode, designed to emit light. LED stands for: **L**ight **E**mitting **D**iode and means *light-emitting diode*.
The threshold voltage for an LED differs per color and is approximately:
— Red = 1.6 V
— Yellow = 2 V
— Blue = 4 V

In order for an LED to emit adequate light the correct current flow is important. For most LEDs this is about 10 mA.

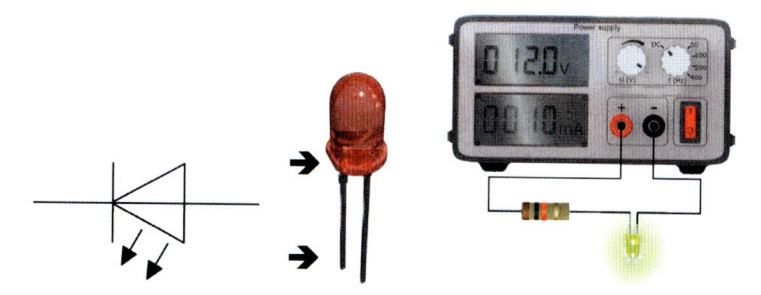

Fig. 13 The cathode can be identified by a shorter connection pin and the flattened off housing.

Fig. 14 Example

An LED does not have a colored ring to identify the cathode. Instead, the cathode of an LED can be identified by:
— a shorter connection pin
— housing that is flattened on the cathode side

The current through an LED can be limited by placing a resistor, called a ballast resistor, in front of it. The value of this resistor can be calculated.

EXAMPLE

Given:
A yellow LED is connected to a voltage of 12 V. The current through the LED must not exceed 10 mA.

Requested:
What is the value of the ballast resistor?

Answer:

A yellow LED is used. That is to say, the threshold voltage is 2 V.

$V_R = V_{source} - V_{led}$
$V_R = 12 - 2$
$V_R = 10$ V

$R = V_R / I$
$R = 10/0.01$
$R = 1000 \, \Omega$

1. Application

Here you see a printed circuit board of an amplifier.

Various electronic components are used for the correct functioning of this amplifier.

Use your acquired knowledge to identify the components on the circuit board.

Fig. 15 Printed circuit board with LED

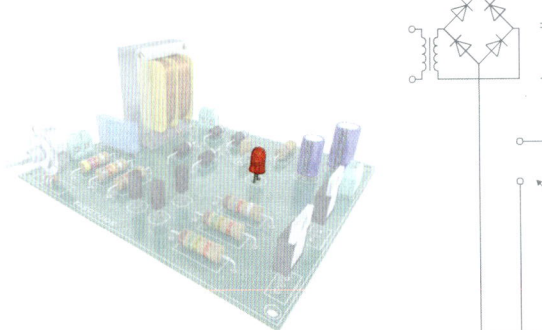

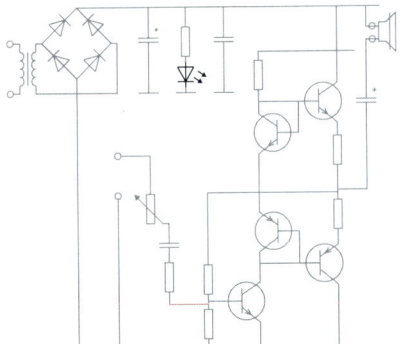

Fig. 16 Electrical diagram with LED

An LED is used on this printed circuit board.

In the diagram you can identify this by the code D5. You can see a red LED mounted on the printed circuit board.

ZENER DIODE

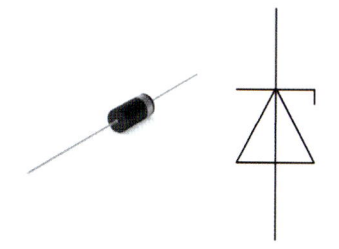

Fig. 17 The symbol for a zener diode

A zener diode is designed to block current in one direction until a certain "break-down" (zener voltage) is reached. Once the break-down or zener voltage is surpassed, the diode becomes conductive in both directions. Zener diodes are connected in reverse polarity.

Each zener diode has a maximum power rating. When this rating is exceeded, the diode gets too hot and becomes inoperative.

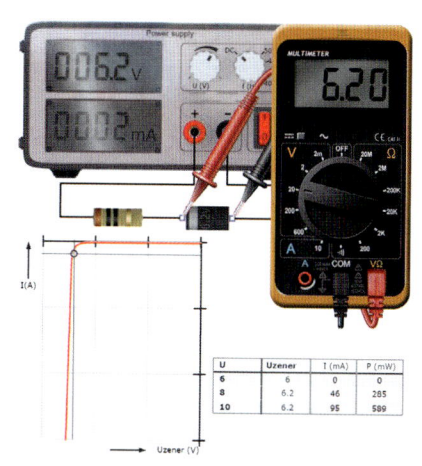

Fig. 18 A current will only flow when the zener voltage is reached.

Fig. 19 Example

The power developed in the zener diode can be calculated with the formula:

$P_{zener} = V_{zener} \times I$

An example:
Given:

V_{source} = 9 V
V_{zener} = 6.2 V
I = 71 mA

Requested: What is the power consumption of the zener diode?
Answer:

$P_{zener} = V_{zener} \times I$
$P_{zener} = 6.2 \times 71$
$P_{zener} = 440.2$ mW

TRANSISTOR

1. Introduction

A transistor is an electronic component. It can control a large current with a small current. Therefore, a transistor is a type of current amplifier.

Because it uses a PN transition, a transistor belongs to the category of semiconductors.

Many electronic devices use transistors, such as computers, calculators, and amplifiers.

The two types of transistors are PNP and NPN. You can identify the PNP transistor by the direction of the arrow in the symbol.

A bipolar transistor has three connections. Every connection has a name. The abbreviations are:

- B, base
- C, collector
- E, emitter

Transistors may have different types of housing/cases. A larger housing indicates a larger capacity. In some transistors (TO-3), the housing/case is the connection for the collector (C).

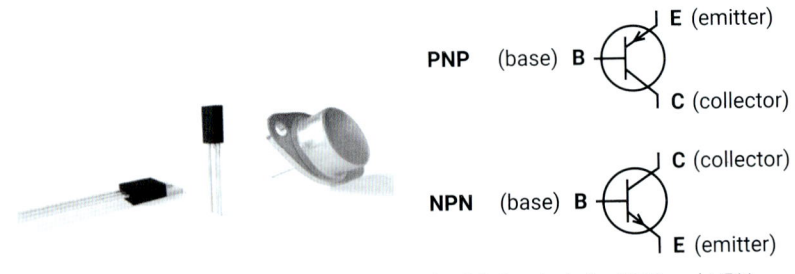

Fig. 20 Different types of transistors

Fig. 21 Symbols for PNP and NPN transistors

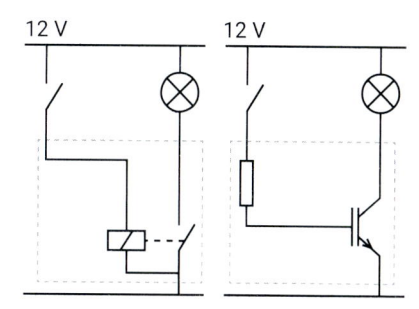

Fig. 22 Transistor as a switch

2. Transistor as a Switch

When a transistor is used as a switch it has the same function as a relay, but without the moving parts. A small control current switches the larger main current. The control current flows through the base connection.

Like a switch, a transistor has only two states, conductive and non-conductive. Therefore all the available voltage is transferred and consumed by the bulb.

Like a diode, there is a PN transition between base and emitter, so a small threshold voltage (V_{BE}) is necessary to make the transistor conductive.
– germanium: 0.3 V
– silicon: 0.7 V

You can calculate the capacity in a transistor by multiplying the current by the voltage over the transistor. This voltage is named V_{CE}.

3. Transistor as a Semiconductor

A transistor is a current amplifier when used as a semiconductor.

In this way, the collector current depends on the strength of the base current. This current is multiplied a fixed number of times, up to a maximum level. This coefficient of amplification is named h_{FE}.

To calculate the collector current you use the following formula:

$$I_C = h_{FE} \times I_B$$

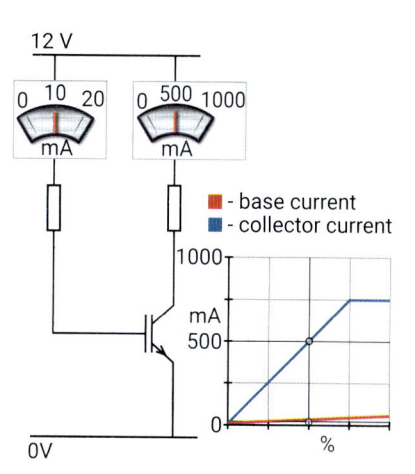

Fig. 23 A transistor as an amplifier

To adjust the current you can use a variable resistor.

When the collector current reaches its maximum level, the transistor is said to be *saturated*. From this point, any further increase in the base current will have no further influence over the collector current.

Calculation example 1
A transistor with an amplification factor (h_{FE}) of 400 has a base current (I_B) 0.1 mA.

Calculate the collector current (I_C).

$I_C = h_{FE} \times I_B$
$I_C = 400 \times 0.1$ mA
$I_C = 40$ mA

Calculation example 2
The transistor works as an amplifier. The base current (I_B) is 10 mA and the collector current (I_C) is 500 mA.
What is the amplification factor (h_{FE}) of this transistor?

$h_{FE} = I_C / I_B$
$h_{FE} = 500$ mA $/ 10$ mA
$h_{FE} = 50$

By adjusting the base current (I_B) you can control the collector current (I_C). The transistor now behaves like an amplifier.

4. Application

Here you see a printed circuit board of an amplifier. Various components are used for its correct functioning. You will use your acquired knowledge to identify the components on the circuit board.

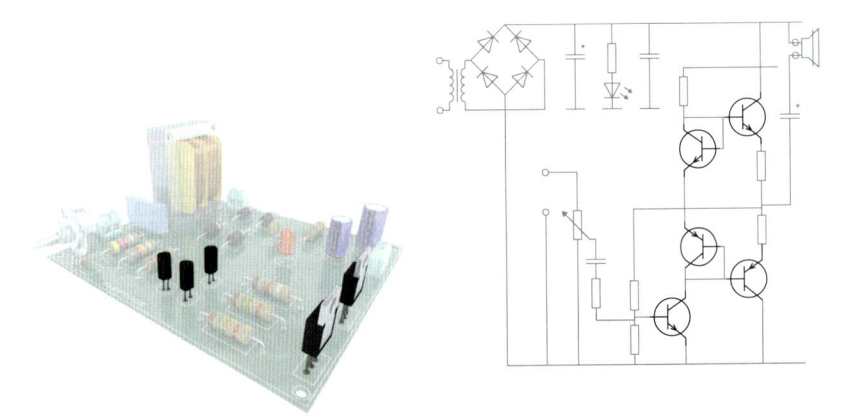

Fig. 24 Printed circuit board with transistors

Fig. 25 Electrical diagram with transistors

There are five transistors in this circuit. Both PNP and NPN transistors are used to amplify the signal.

CAPACITOR

1. Capacitors in Practice

A capacitor is an electronic component. It is often used to suppress and filter interfering signals.

You will find capacitors in *electric motors*, in some *microphones*, and in the *ignition system* of vehicles with distributor ignition.

A *microphone* has a special capacitor that can change by sound vibrations. In this way sound recording is possible.

Fig. 26 Components that contain capacitors

2. Introduction

A capacitor is a component that easily stores and releases electric energy.

Each capacitor has a value, referred to as capacitance (C). The unit of capacitance is farad (F). Capacitors have a maximum operating voltage. Both capacitance and voltage are specified on the casing.

There are various types of capacitors. Most have a fixed capacitance, with the exception of variable capacitors.

Capacitors of 1 farad are very large. In practice capacitors are typically found in the range from pico farads (pF) to micro farads (μF):
- 1 pF = pico farad = 10^{-12} F (one trillionth of a farad, or .001 nF)
- 1 nF = nano Farad = 10^{-9} F (one billionth of a farad, or .001 μF)
- 1 μF = micro farad = 10^{-6} F (one millionth of a farad, or 1000 nF)

The maximum voltage is in the range of a few Volts to 1000 Volts.

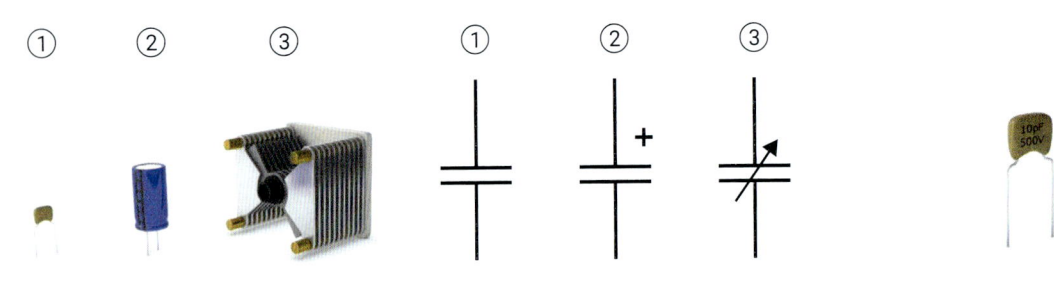

Fig. 27 1. Capacitor 2. Polar Capacitor 3. Variable Capacitor

Fig. 28 Symbol of a: 1. Capacitor 2. Polar Capacitor 3. Variable Capacitor

Fig. 29 A capacitor with a capacity of 10 pF

3. Construction

A capacitor consists of two connecting leads: *electrodes*, or *plates*, and a *dielectric* between the plates.

The capacitance of a capacitor is determined by three factors:
— Surface area of the electrodes
— Distance between the plates
— Material of the dielectric

The dielectric is the insulation between the two electrodes. Each material has its own constant:

— Air: 1
— Mica: 7
— Paper: 3.5
— Polyester: 3
— Aluminium-oxide: 24

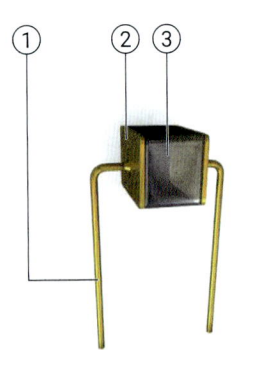

Fig. 30 Construction of a capacitor: 1. Connection 2. Electrode or plate 3. Dielectric.

Fig. 31 The capacity of the first capacitor is small, and the capacity of the last capacitor is large.

Fig. 32 Film capacitor: 1. Electrode 2. Dielectric

4. Types

There are four commonly used types of capacitors.

Plastic-film capacitors: This capacitor consists of two thin layers of plastic as a dielectric and two layers of metal foil as an electrode. The width and the number of turns (length) determine the capacitance.

Ceramic capacitors: A plate ceramic material (dielectric) is metalized (electrode) on both sides. These capacitors are relatively small. The ceramic material has a high resistance. The dielectric constant is high.

Electrolytic capacitors: Anode and cathode consist of aluminum foil. The anode is roughened to increase the surface area over which a layer of aluminum-oxide is placed (the dielectric). Paper filled with electrolyte is placed between these plates to ensure a good connection.
Electrolytic capacitors are polarity sensitive and therefore not suitable for use with alternating current.

Variable capacitor: By rotating the plates, the active surfaces of the plates changes. In this way the capacity can be adjusted. The dielectric is often mica, plastic, or air.

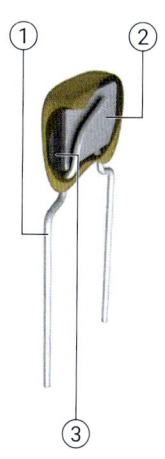

Fig. 33 Ceramic capacitor: 1. Connection 2. Electrode 3. Dielectric

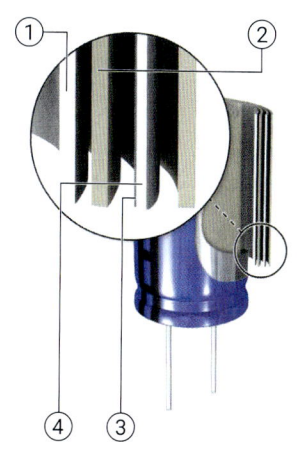

Fig. 34 Electrolytic capacitor: 1. Cathode 2. Electrolyte plates 3. Dielectric 4. Anode

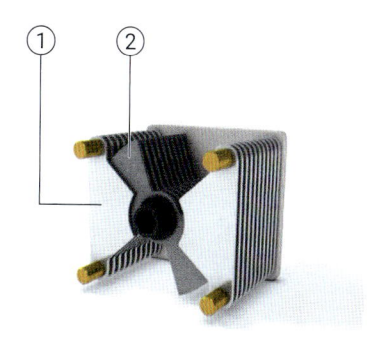

Fig. 35 Variable capacitor: 1. Fixed plate 2. Moving plate

5. Operation

The resistance of a capacitor, also known as "capacitive reactance," depends on two factors:
— capacity
— frequency

A capacitor blocks DC voltage. In an alternating current, the capacitance will decrease as the frequency increases. This allows a larger current to flow.

A capacitor can be used to suppress interference of electric devices, but also to filter signals, since low frequencies are blocked.

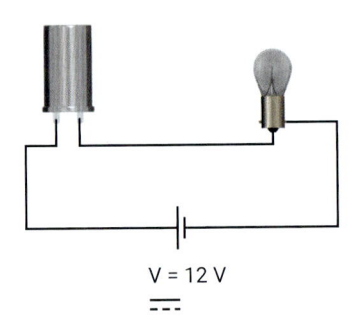

Fig. 36 DC voltage cannot flow through a capacitor.

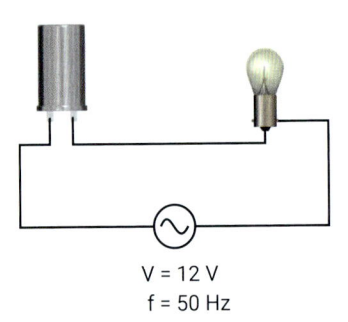

Fig. 37 The current flows with more difficulty through a capacitor when the frequency is low.

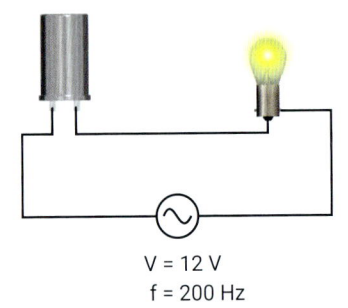

Fig. 38 The current flows more easily through a capacitor when the frequency is high.

6. Application

Here you see a printed circuit board of an amplifier.

Various electronic components are used for the correct functioning of this amplifier.

Use your acquired knowledge to identify the components on the circuit board.

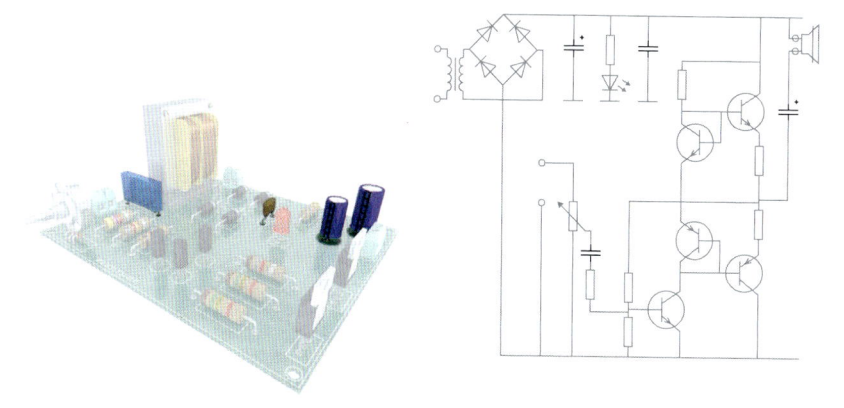

Fig. 39 Printed circuit board with capacitors

Fig. 40 Electrical diagram with capacitors

You will find several capacitors on the printed circuit board. All capacitors are visible in the electrical diagram.

In automotive electronics, the capacitor is used more as a buffer. It can temporarily store electrical charge. This allows it to pick up pulses or hold a relay.

7. Inspecting a Capacitor

You may suspect that a capacitor is not functioning properly.

What can you do to inspect it?
You can measure the resistance with a multimeter. If the resistance of the capacitor is high, this is a good sign. The dielectric between the two plates acts as an insulator.

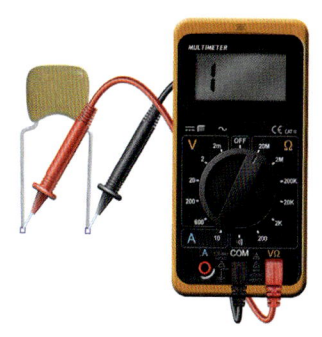

Fig. 41 Checking a capacitor with a resistance measurement

The capacity of a capacitor can only be checked with a special meter. Once you have checked this, you know the capacitor is okay.

COIL

1. Coils in Practice

Coils play a large role in our daily lives. When listening to music a coil creates vibrations in the speaker. A coil is used in a **relay** to switch a contact. Coils in electric motors convert electricity into a revolving movement.

All these examples convert *electrical energy* in *movement*.

A **transformer** uses two coils to transform voltage upwards or downwards.

Fig. 42 Components that contain coils

2. Introduction

Coils exist with and without a core. When two coils are connected and wound around a core, you have a transformer. This is shown by the straight line drawn in the diagrams below.

Each coil has a constant or coefficient of self-induction (L). Meaning, the strength of the self-induced voltage is predictable.

The coefficient of self-induction is based on the properties of the coil and whether or not it has a core.

The unit of self-induction is called the **Henry (H)**.

There are coils ranging from µH (micro Henry) up to several Henry.
- 1 µH = micro Henry = 10^{-6} H
- 1 mH = milli Henry = 10^{-3} H
- 1 H = Henry = 1 H

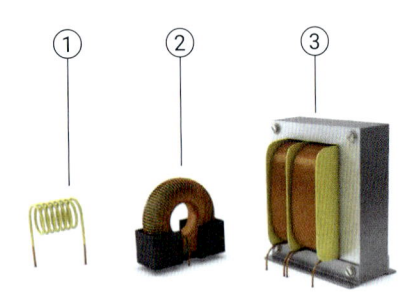

Fig. 43 1. coil without core 2. coil with core 3. transformer

In general terms, the larger the Henry, the greater the self induced voltage will be.

Fig. 44 Symbol of a: 1. coil without core 2. coil with core 3. transformer

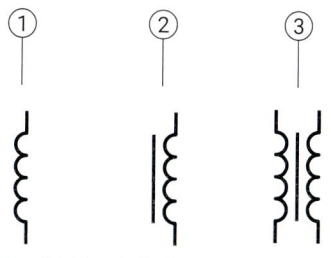

Fig. 45 A coil with a self-induction coefficient of 22 mH

Fig. 46 The coefficient of self-induction of coil 1 is small and is large for coil 3.

3. Construction

A coil consists of an electric conductor spooled into the shape of a coil.

The coefficient of self-induction of a coil is determined by four factors:
- properties of the core
- number of coil windings
- core cross-section
- core length

The properties of a core are identified by the *permeability* (μ), pronounced as "mu." This number determines how easily a magnetic field can pass through it.

4. Operation

The "resistance" of a coil depends on two factors:
- the coefficient of self-induction
- the frequency

This resistance at a coil is named the inductive resistance.

A coil lets a direct voltage through without problems. If the frequency increases, the inductive resistance increases.

A Coil can be used to suppress interfering signals and as a filter to block high frequencies.

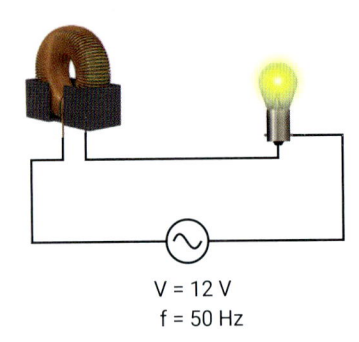

Fig. 47 The current flows more easily through a coil if the frequency is low.

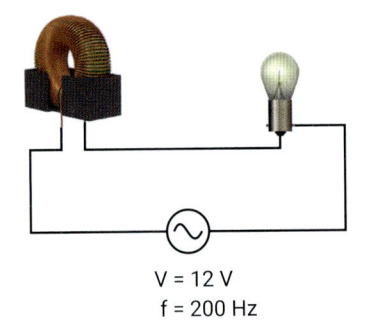

Fig. 48 The current flows less easily through a coil if the frequency is high.

5. Application

Here you see a printed circuit board of an amplifier.

Various components are used for the correct functioning of this amplifier.

You will use your acquired knowledge to identify the components on the circuit board.

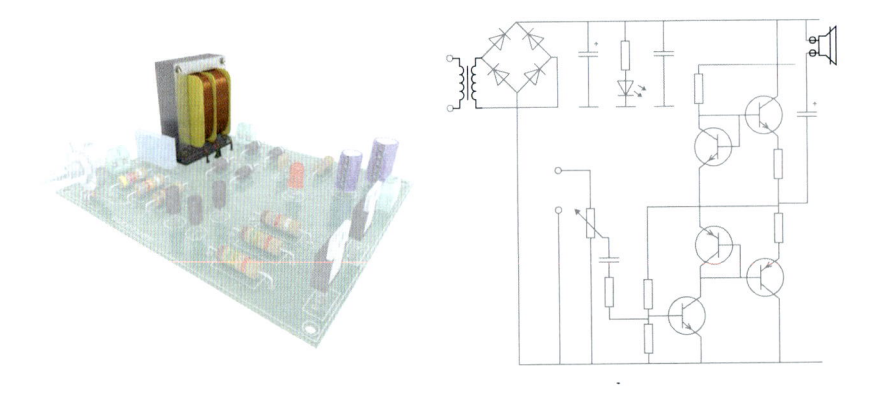

Fig. 49 Printed circuit board with a transformer

Fig. 50 Electrical diagram with a transformer and a speaker

On the printed circuit board you will find a transformer in which coils are incorporated.

In the electrical diagram you can find the transformer using the symbol. Coils are also incorporated in the speaker.

Fig. 51 Checking a coil with a resistance measurement

6. Testing a Coil

Sometimes you may have doubts about the functioning of a coil.

What do you do?
You can measure the resistance of the coil with an ohmmeter, and it must comply with the factory data.

To determine the self-induction of a coil and the surrounding material, you need a special meter. This meter works with an alternating current that generates self-induction (and is not usually present in the workplace).

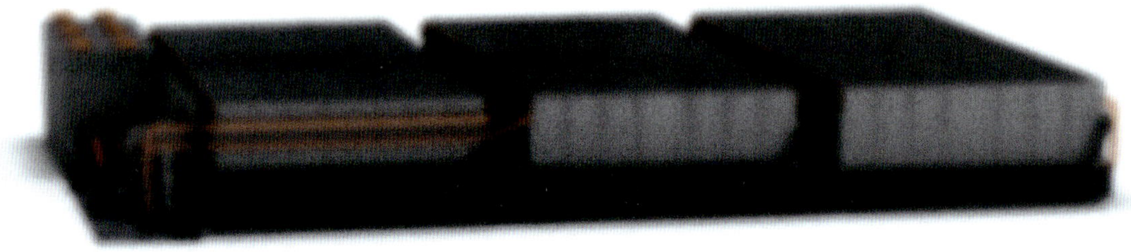

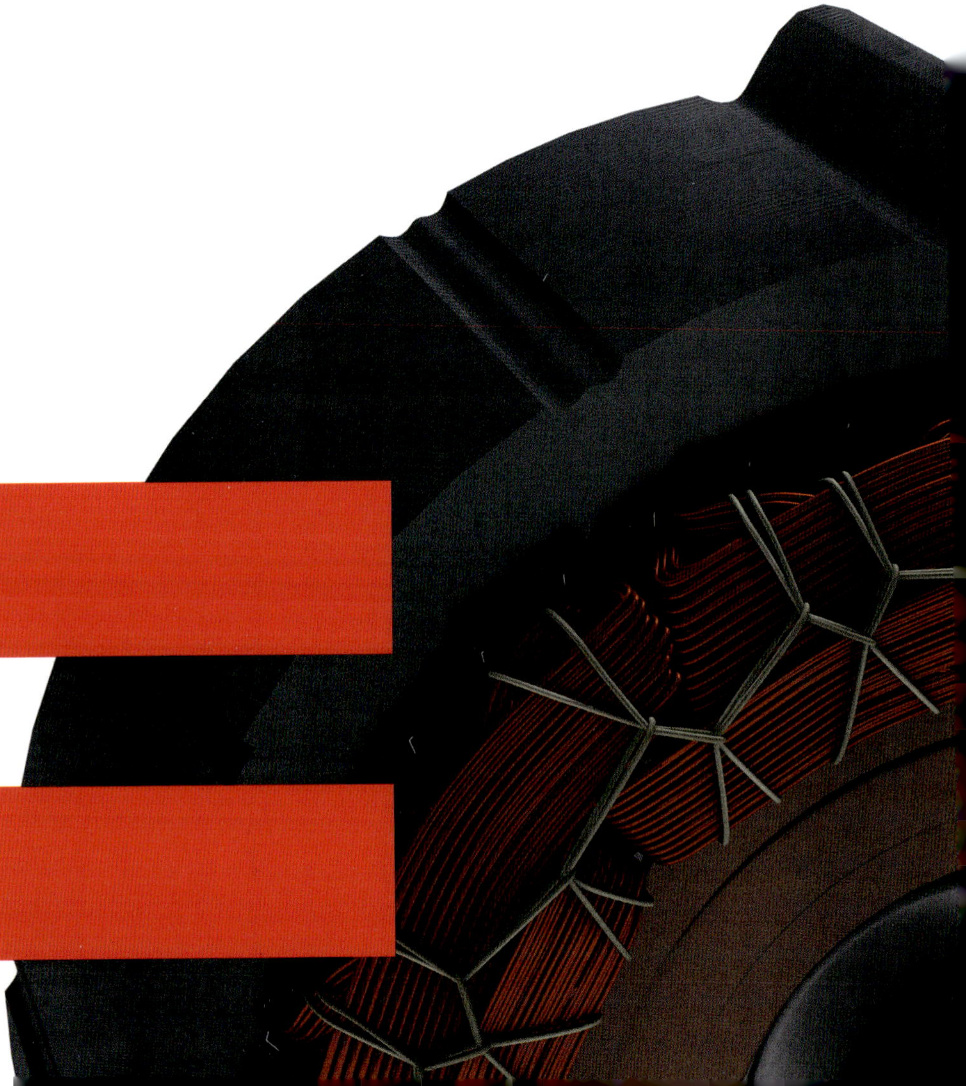

2. Oscilloscope

OSCILLOSCOPE: INTRODUCTION

1. Power and Information

Electrical wires transport two different things: electrical power and information.

This difference can be clearly seen in the example of a television. There's a wire that transports power to the television (120 VAC) and there's a wire that transports information (which appears on the screen) to the television.

Fig. 52 Power and information supply in a television: 1. Information (signal). 2. Power (main supply).

Fig. 53 You can measure power or information using a variety of different measuring instruments: 1. Multimeter (measures energy). 2. Oscilloscope (measures information).

12.43 VDC

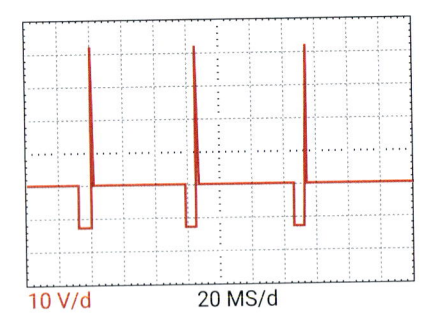

10 V/d   20 MS/d

Fig. 54 The voltage signature of an injector's operation, visualized on oscilloscope screen.

2. Oscilloscope

An oscilloscope is a measuring instrument that converts electrical signals into a graphical display.

The time is displayed on the horizontal axis, and the voltage on the vertical axis.

If you are going to measure across the injector with an oscilloscope, you can clearly see how high the induction voltage rises when the injector is switched off. The voltage is in the vertical direction. The signal can then be assessed for any deviations.

If you look in the horizontal direction, you can see how long the injector is open.

3. Engine Management

A vehicle has wires that carry power and information that cannot be identified by looking at them from the outside.
Identification requires a wiring diagram.

A multimeter is the tool used most often to check a wire carrying power. You usually use an oscilloscope for a wire carrying information.

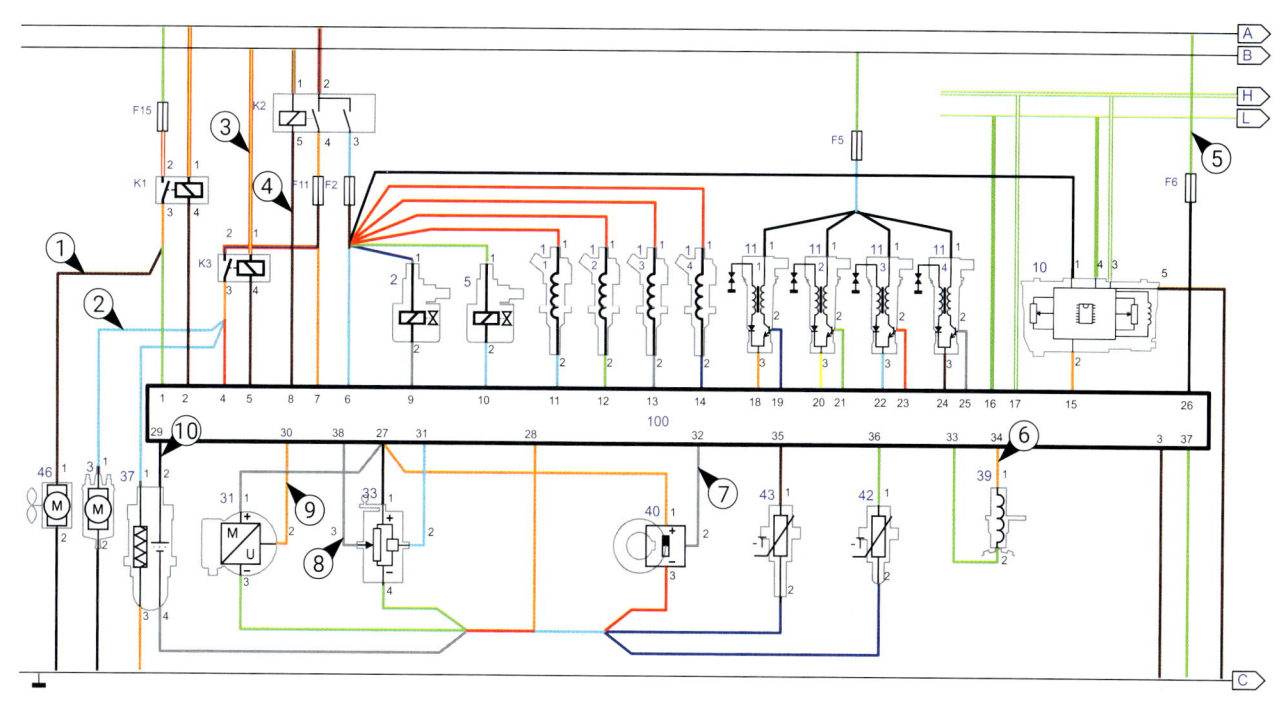

Fig. 55 Wiring diagram of an engine management system

Example of power supply wires in an engine management system:
1. Cooling fan power supply.
2. Fuel pump power supply.
3. Pump relay power supply.
4. Main relay ground.
5. ECU power supply.

Example of information supply wires in an engine management system:
6. Crankshaft sensor signal.
7. Hall sensor signal.
8. Throttle valve position sensor.
9. Mass air flow meter.
10. Lambda sensor signal.

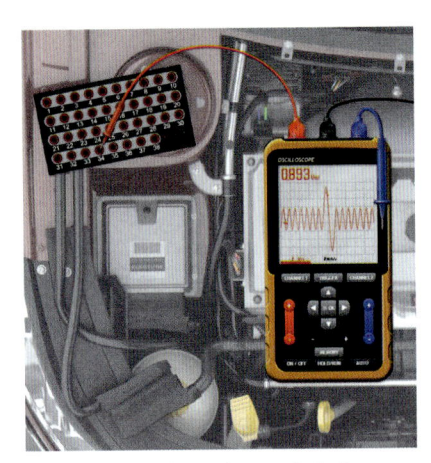

Fig. 56 Signal from the crankshaft sensor

4. Measurement

If you want to measure the signal from the crankshaft sensor via the breakout box, then connect the oscilloscope the following way.

OSCILLOSCOPE: GUIDED TOUR

1. Setting up an Oscilloscope

The main parts of this oscilloscope or DSO (digital storage oscilloscope) are the measuring connections (measuring probes), the screen, and the control buttons.

With this scope you can perform two measurements at the same time; for this, you need two channels.

Channel 1 is red, the connection, the data on the screen, and the buttons for the settings.

All blue parts belong to channel 2.

Explanation for the Basic Functionality of an Oscilloscope

1. Measuring connection 1: with this the first signal can be measured.
2. Ground connection, the ground for both channels
3. Measuring connection 2: the second signal can be measured with this.
4. Signal 1: graphical representation of measurement 1.
5. Signal 2: graphical representation of measurement 2.
6. Settings for channel 2: the position can be determined using the arrows.
7. Settings for the trigger: the signal can be "aligned" with this. The trigger can be positioned with the arrows.
8. The setting for the number of volts per division: this is called sensitivity (vertical). You set the number of boxes per volt for channel 2.
9. The setting for the duration per division: set the number (milli) seconds per box (horizontal).
10. On-off button for the oscilloscope.
11. Number of volts per division for channel 1.
12. Select settings for channel 1: the position can be determined using the arrows.

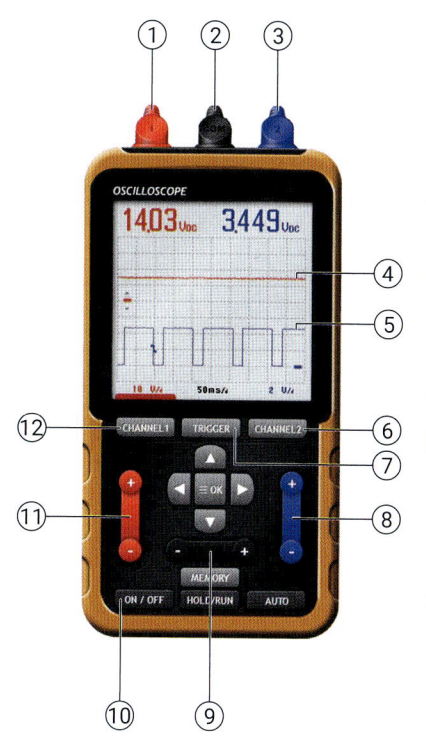

Fig. 57 Basic functionality of an oscilloscope

2. Oscilloscope as Multimeter

The scope can also function as a multimeter.

At the top of the screen, a measurement value is displayed that the scope calculates from the signal.

If you select "CHANNEL 1" and then press this button again, you will get the menu where you can set the multimeter.

If you measure an AC voltage with an oscilloscope, the actual value is always displayed graphically. If you measure the voltage with the multimeter function, the effective value is calculated and displayed.

Fig. 58 Settings for measuring a DC voltage

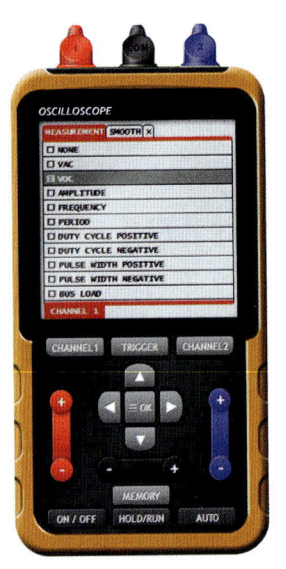

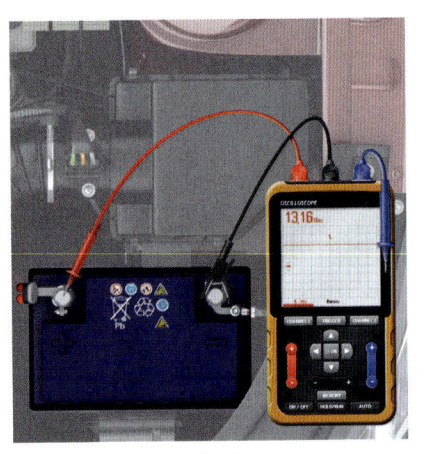

Fig. 59 Measuring the battery voltage

For measuring a DC voltage, select V_{DC} and for measuring an AC voltage select V_{AC}. You can also perform a few other measurements.

This onboard battery has a voltage of 13.16 V.

Fig. 60 Other functionality.
1. HOLD/RUN function. 2. AUTO function. 3. MEMORY function.

3. Other Functionality

In addition to the oscilloscope and multimeter function, a few other functions are important.

The HOLD/RUN button operates a pause function that freezes the signal image for closer inspection and then displays a live image when pressed again.

The AUTO function (auto range) allows the oscilloscope to find the most ideal settings for a certain signal.

With the SMOOTH function, noise is filtered from the signal. With this setting you have to be careful; it is possible that important information is filtered out.

The control buttons for this are located at the bottom, near the ON/OFF switch.

With the MEMORY button you can save scope images and recall them later, so that you can easily compare multiple measurements with each other.

OSCILLOSCOPE: STEP-BY-STEP PLAN

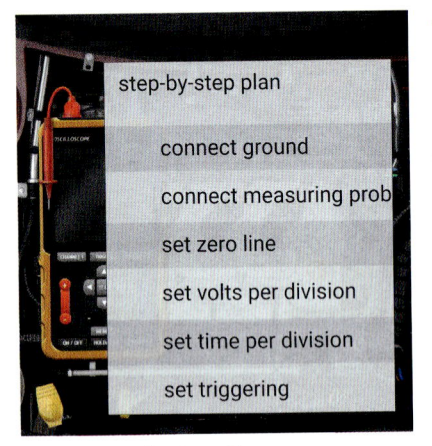

Fig. 61 Step-by-Step Plan

1. Connect Ground

In order to correctly measure with an oscilloscope, you must use a consistent procedure to connect and set up the oscilloscope.

We are going to connect the oscilloscope in accordance with a step-by-step plan, and will measure the starting voltage.

The first step is to connect the ground correctly.

This can be done in two ways, via the non-shielded common ground (COM) or with a shielded ground via the coax connection.

Make sure that the ground is positioned at a logical point in the circuit, just as you would do with a multimeter.

Fig. 62 Connecting the ground

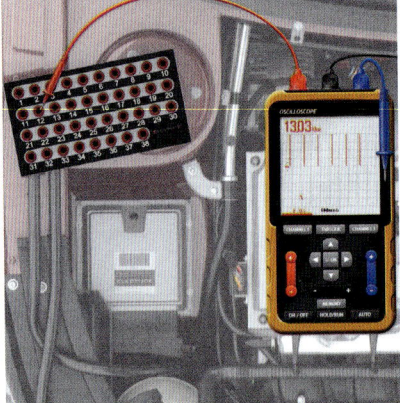

Fig. 63 Connecting the measuring probe to the breakout box

2. Connect the Measuring Probe

The second step is to connect the measuring probes of the oscilloscope.

Make sure you choose the correct connection point in the circuit and that you use the measuring probe of channel A (red) on the scope.

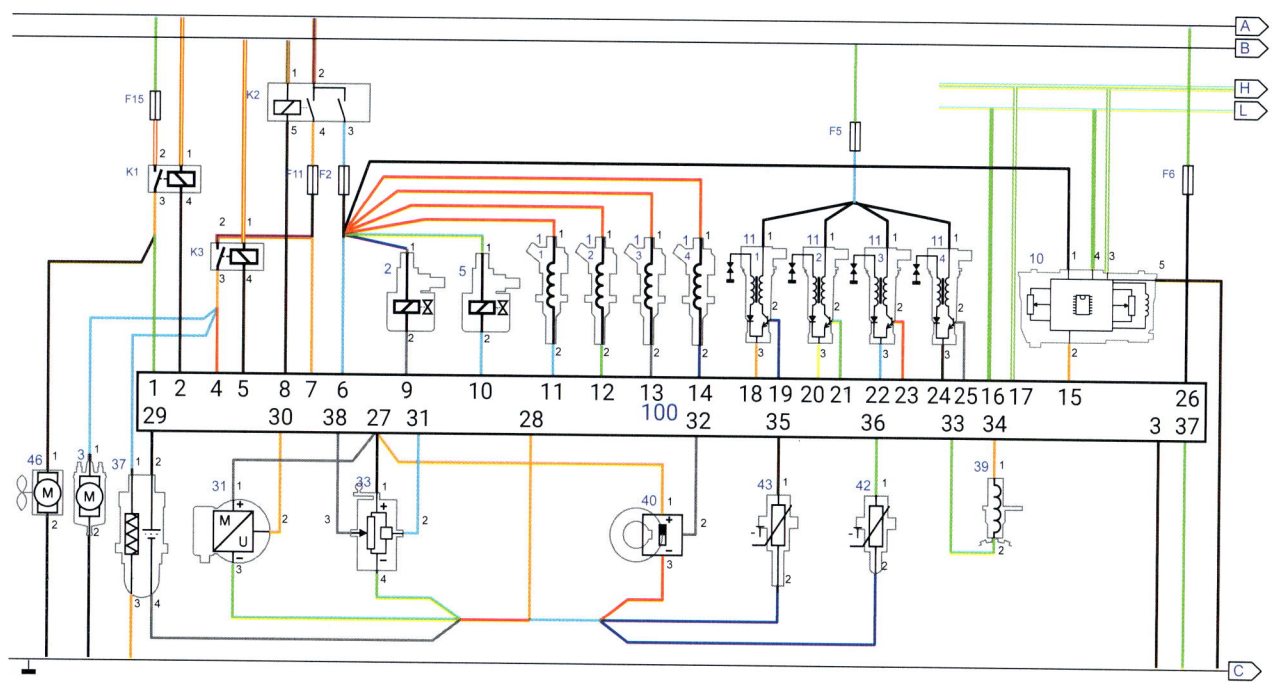

Fig. 64 Wiring Diagram

Connect the oscilloscope in a way that you can measure the control of the second injector (pin 12 breakout box).

3. Set the Zero Line

The third step is to correctly set the zero line of the signal.

In principle, there are two places where you can put the zero line. For direct voltage measurements it's best to put the zero line near the bottom of the screen.

For alternating voltage it's more convenient to place the zero line in the center of the screen.

4. Set the Sensitivity

The fourth step is to set the volts per division. Once again, there are two basic settings.

The first basic setting is for measuring sensors and the CAN bus. The usual setting for this is 1 volt per division.

The other basic setting is for measuring actuators and the LIN bus. The setting for this is 5 volts per division.

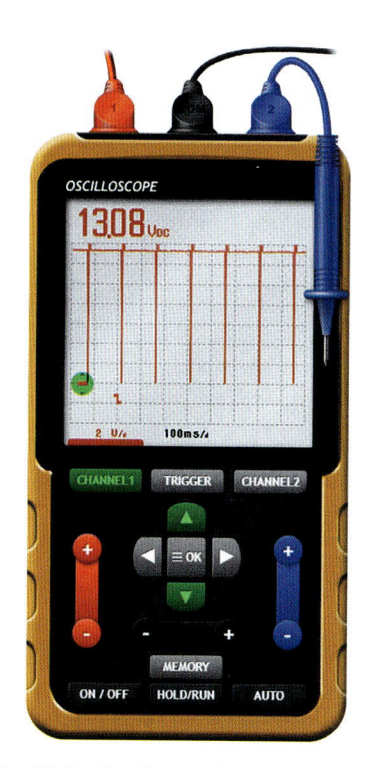

Fig. 65 Setting the zero line

Note: These are basic settings. If these settings do not work suitably for a certain signal then you can always refine the setting.

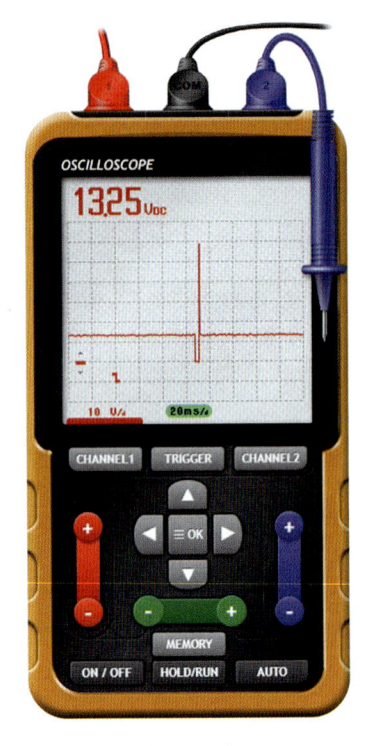

Fig. 66 Setting the sensitivity

Fig. 67 Setting the time base

5. Set the Time Base

The fifth step is to set the time per division. Once again, there are two basic settings for most measurements.

For measuring slow signals, the usual setting is 1 second per division.

Slow signals are, for example, lambda, MAP, air mass, temperature and throttle position.

For measuring fast signals, the usual setting is 10 milliseconds per division.

Fast signals are, for example, the crankshaft signal, camshaft signal, injectors, ignition, CAN, and LIN.

Note: These are basic settings. If these settings do not work suitably for a certain signal then you can always adjust the setting.

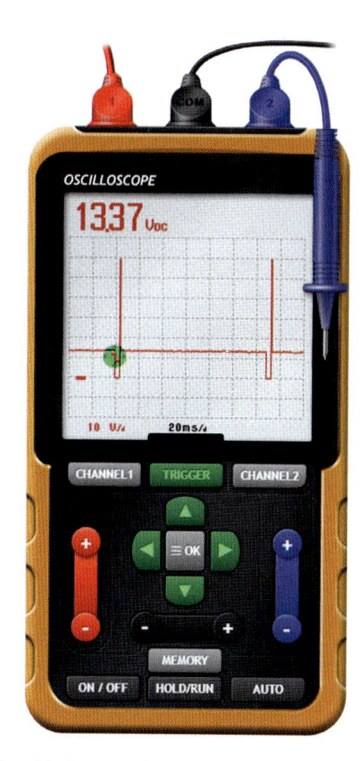

Fig. 68 Setting the trigger

6. Set the Trigger

The aim of the sixth step is to set the triggering correctly.

If an oscilloscope "triggers" a signal then the oscilloscope does not display the signal until a certain condition is met. This condition is passing through (either rising or falling edge, as required) a certain voltage value.

For correct triggering you have to select the correct voltage value (trigger level) and whether this has to be a rising or falling voltage (slope).

Triggering is primarily used for fast signals or signals that periodically look the same.

OSCILLOSCOPE: USING TWO CHANNELS

With this oscilloscope you can measure two signals at the same time. Three things are important here.

The first thing to keep in mind is the ground for channel 1 and channel 2 are interconnected. This is to prevent short circuit.

The second important point is the positioning of the zero line for channel 1 and 2. It's common to place the zero line of channel 1 just above the center line of the screen and the zero line of channel 2 near the bottom.

When using two channels of an oscilloscope, you must select which channel to trigger from. It's not possible to trigger on both channels. For example, you cannot set the timebase separately for two channels.

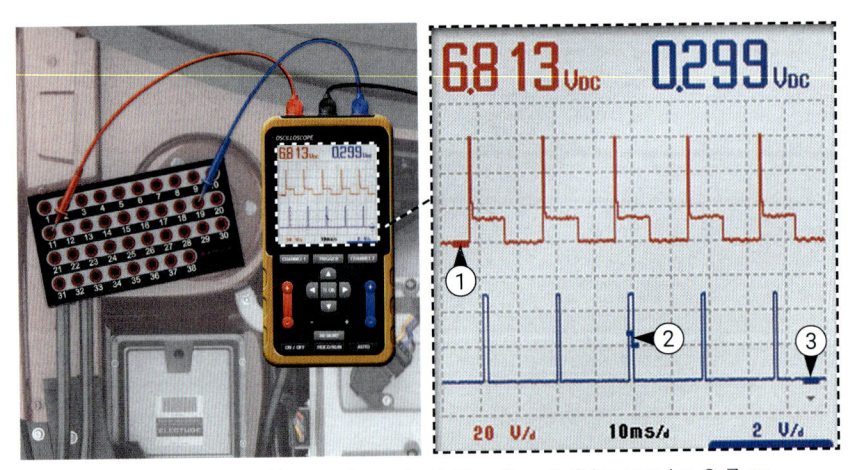

Fig. 69 A measurement with two channels. 1. Zero line. 2. Trigger point. 3. Zero line.

Measuring with Two Channels

The oscilloscope is connected via a breakout box. The signal from injector 1 (pin 11) becomes visible on channel 1 (red), the control of the ignition coil 1 (pin 19) on channel 2 (blue).

As you can see, the time base of both channels is 10 ms./div.; this always remains the same for both channels but the measuring sensitivity can be set separately. For the measurement on the injector (channel 1), it is at 20 V/div so that the entire signal is clearly visible. The sensitivity is set to 2 V/div for measuring the control of the ignition coil.

When measuring this signal, the triggering is set on channel 2. You can see this by the blue "trigger" symbol in the screen.

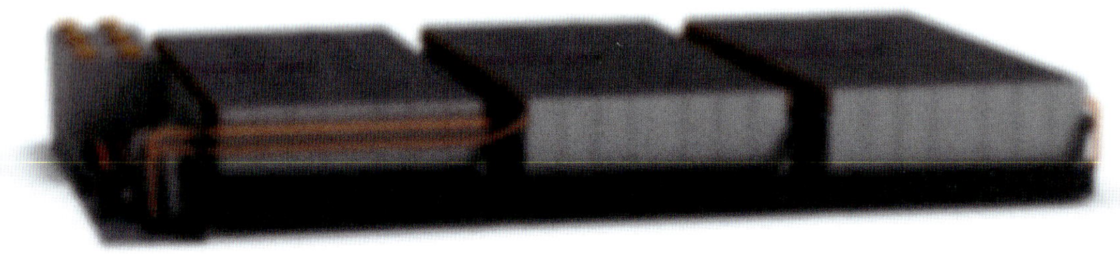

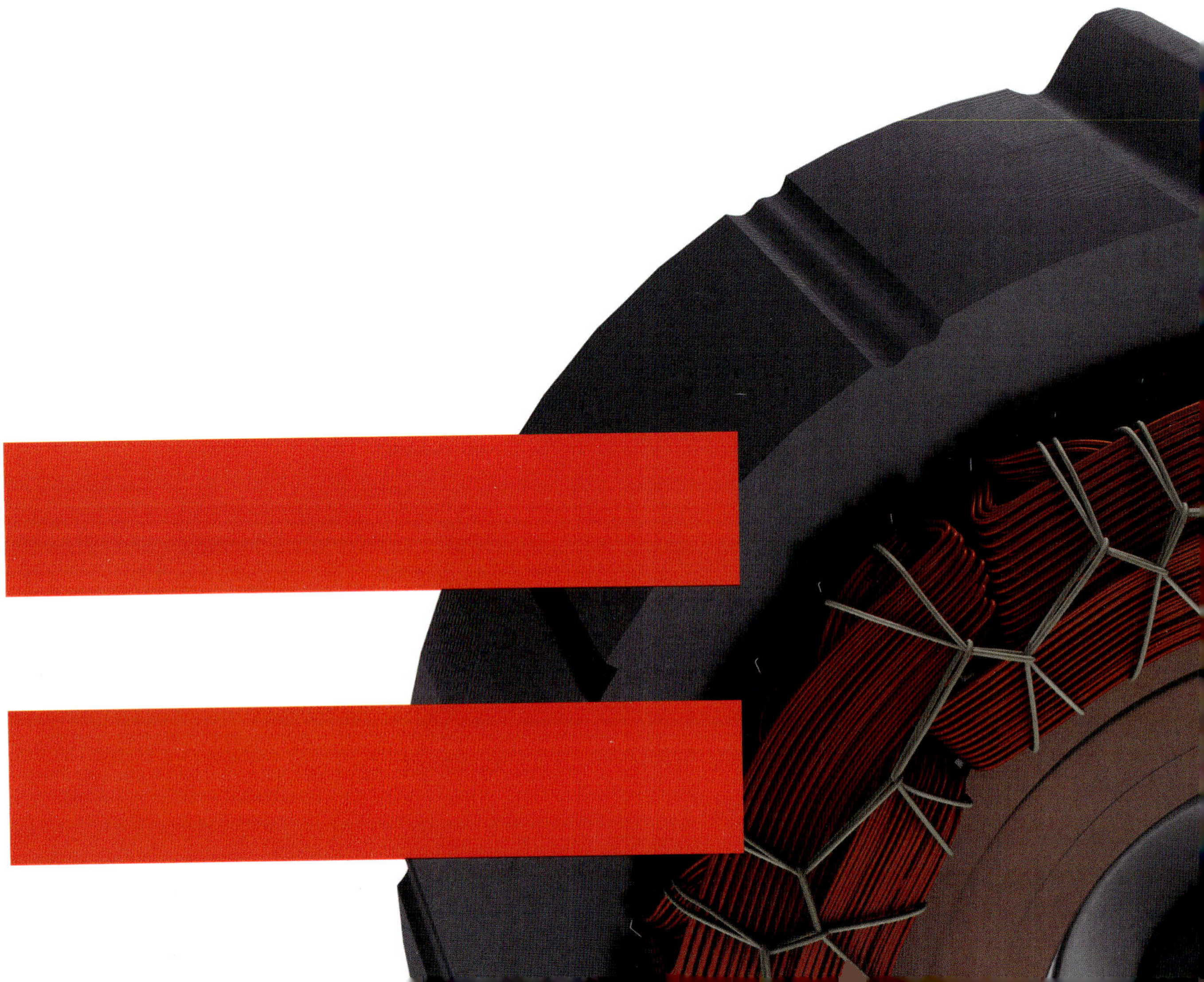

3. Sensors, Signals and Actuators

INTRODUCTION TO SENSORS

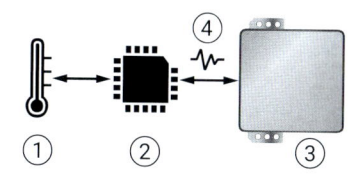

Fig. 70 Sensor converts variable to voltage difference: 1. Variable 2. Sensor 3. Control unit 4. Digital signal

1. What is a Sensor?

A sensor is an instrument that detects and responds to changes in the physical environment (variables) and converts them into changes in voltage or current that are sent to other devices. The variable can be heat, pressure, air flow, rotational speed, and so on. The voltage difference that the sensor generates is usually converted into a digital signal in the control unit. However, this can also occur in the sensor. The voltage difference can then be a PWM, Duty Cycle, Lin bus or SENT protocol.

The following variables are important for engine management:
— accelerator pedal position
— throttle valve position
— intake air mass
— crankshaft and camshaft position
— engine temperature
— engine vibration frequency (knocking)
— percentage of oxygen in the exhaust gas

2. Physical Sensors and Need for Additional Sensors

The more variables measured, the more information the engine control unit receives and uses to make the engine improve power, efficiency, and emissions. However, measuring additional variables requires more physical sensors.

The disadvantages of having more sensors include:
— extra cost
— reduced reliability
— space consumption

Associated costs have a major influence over the design of new sensors. An average modern vehicle contains around sixty to one hundred sensors. This number will only increase in the near future. It is estimated that in the near future an average car will have around two hundred sensors, part of which will be used for engine management. Two hundred sensors per car means that around twenty-two billion sensors are used throughout the automotive industry. That is quite a cost, and if the industry can save on that, it will certainly do so.

The extreme conditions under which the sensors perform their tasks have a negative influence on service life. Consider, for example, the high temperatures and extreme vibrations in the engine compartment. It is easy to understand that the sensors of the engine management system often have a shorter service life than that of other sensors. Although it would be difficult to achieve because of all the variables that need to be measured, limiting the number of sensors would improve the reliability of the engine management system. The increasingly tight engine spaces required for aerodynamics also limits available space for additional sensors. For example, the mass air flow sensor must be mounted in a relatively long and straight inlet tube to guarantee precise measurements. This takes up a lot of space.

3. Virtual Sensors

The desire to measure more variables and the disadvantages of physical sensors have led to the increased use of the virtual sensor. The virtual sensor replaces the physical sensor where possible. It uses information that is available via other measurements and process parameters. On the basis of this information, the software in the engine management control unit makes a calculation to determine the variable.

Determining the compression stroke for cylinder 1 is a well-known example of a physical sensor that is being replaced by a virtual one. As a rule, this is determined by the combined signal from the camshaft and crankshaft sensors. The crankshaft position indicates which cylinder pairs are at TDC. The camshaft position indicates which of these two cylinders is on the compression stroke.

The virtual sensor for determining the compression stroke is based on calculations from the crankshaft signal. Via the crankshaft signal, the engine management control unit knows when cylinder 1 is at TDC. By counting pulses from the crankshaft signal, the management also knows when the other cylinders are at TDC.

With this data, the engine management control unit is able to start the engine. This is because it ensures the fuel injection and ignition occur simultaneously in the two paired cylinders. With a four-cylinder engine, engine management control unit therefore looks at the pulse for cylinder 1. Based on this, the fuel injection and ignition of cylinders 1 and 4 are controlled at the same time. By counting the pulses from the crankshaft signal, the control unit can also determine the injection and ignition of cylinder pairs 2 and 3.

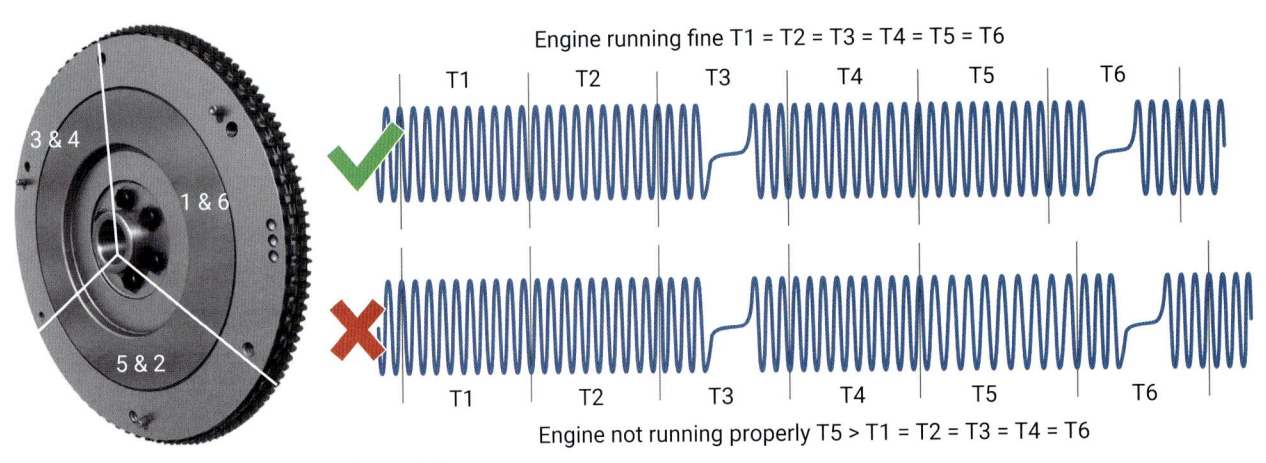

Fig. 71 Above: Crankshaft signal without misfire.
Below: Crankshaft signal with misfire in cylinder 5.

The engine is now running, but the engine management control unit does not yet know which cylinder is on the compression/power stroke. To find out, the management control unit switches off the injection at one of the cylinders of the cylinder pairs. For example, the control unit turns off cylinder 1 injection. If cylinder 1 is not injected with fuel, a "misfire" will occur.

The engine management control unit can see on the basis of the crankshaft signal whether a combustion occurs. When a combustion has taken place, the crankshaft will rotate a little faster. By continuously viewing the crankshaft signal and strategically turning off the fuel injection, the control unit finds out within a number of revolutions which cylinder is on the compression stroke. Once the control unit knows about one cylinder, it can easily determine the same thing for all the other cylinders.

In this way, it is possible to eliminate the camshaft sensor on an engine without variable valve timing. In the future, additional parameters—wherever possible—will be measured with the help of virtual sensors.

SIGNALS

1. Introduction

Modern cars require more and more control units due to the wide use of electronically controlled actuators. Like any computer, the powertrain control module (PCM)needs information to accurately command solenoids and actuators. The PCM depends on strategically placed input sensors for speed, position, pressure, driver demand, and so on.

There are basically three different types of sensors:
- Passive sensors
- Active sensors
- Intelligent sensors

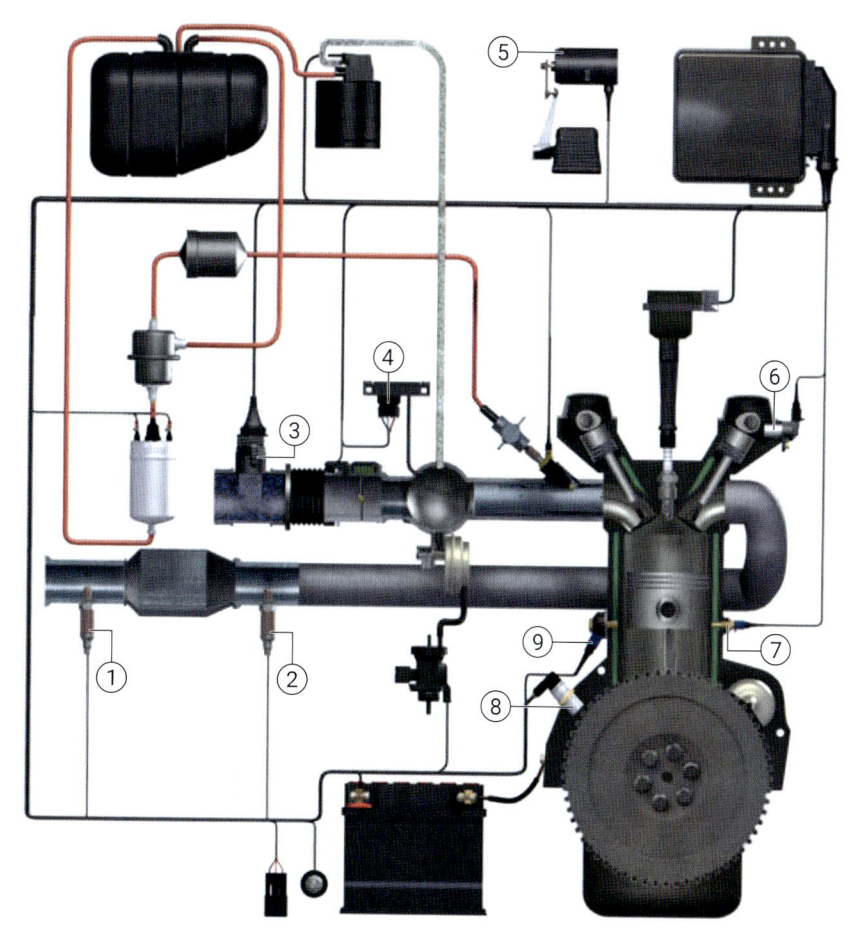

Fig. 72 Engine management sensors: 1. & 2. Oxygen sensor. 3. Mass air flow sensor. 4. Manifold pressure sensor. 5. Accelerator pedal position sensor. 6. Camshaft position sensor. 7. Engine temperature sensor. 8. Crankshaft sensor. 9. Knock sensor.

Control Unit

The control unit consists of the following:

- An **input circuit (terminal)** for each sensor signal. It is important to note that the Engine Control Unit's Central Processing Unit (CPU) cannot process analog signals; therefore, within the Engine Control Unit's circuitry, signals are digitized through the use of an interface and analog to digital (A/D) converter before being sent to the CPU.
- The **central processing unit (CPU)** is the "heart" of the PCM (like the processor in a desktop computer) and receives data from the various input circuits. Applying the input values, the CPU uses algorithms to determine actuator commands.
- The **output circuit** is the part of the PCM that receives and carries out the command from the CPU (for example, activating an injector). Actuators are usually hardwired to B+, and the commands are carried out by switching the actuator's ground circuit. However, in some cases output actuators are hardwired to ground and receive power from the PCM. Asian transmission solenoids tend to be wired that way.

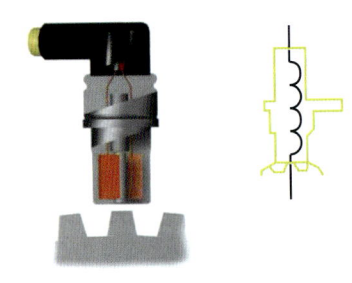

Fig. 73 An inductive crankshaft sensor has two connections.

2. Passive Sensor

A passive sensor is a sensor that does not require a power supply or ground to emit a signal. A passive sensor has a magnetic core in the center of a copper winding that creates a signal when the magnetic field shifts each time a tooth passes the tip of the sensor. The shift in the magnetic field induces AC voltage.

A passive sensor can be used to measure a parameter, such as engine rpm. The alternating current (AC) analog signal is received and conditioned into a usable signal by means of an interface. The signal is then fully digitized (i.e., turned into data) by the PCM's A/D converter.

Following conversion, this data is sent to the CPU.

A passive sensor has one or two wires to the control unit: Examples of passive sensors include the following:
- Inductive crankshaft sensor

– Coolant temperature sensor
– Intake air temperature sensor

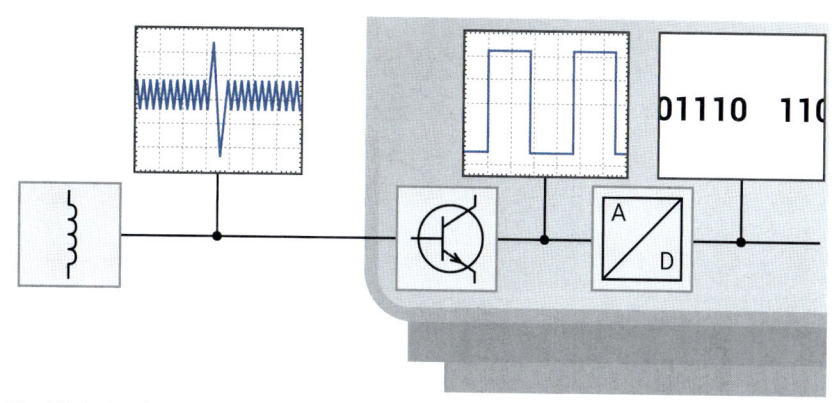

Fig. 74 Inductive sensor: Interfacing and digitization take place in the control unit.

3. Active Sensor

An active sensor must have a power supply and ground to emit a signal.

The interfacing takes place in the sensor.
The data conversion occurs in the control unit. The active sensor still requires a trigger wheel much the way the inductive sensor does, but produces a direct current (DC) digital signal that can be directly fed to the CPU without being processed by an A/D converter.

The interfacing ensures that the signal is amplified between 0 and 5 V (DC). This is the working range of the control unit.

The active sensor can also contain electronics to filter or amplify the signal before it is passed to the control unit.

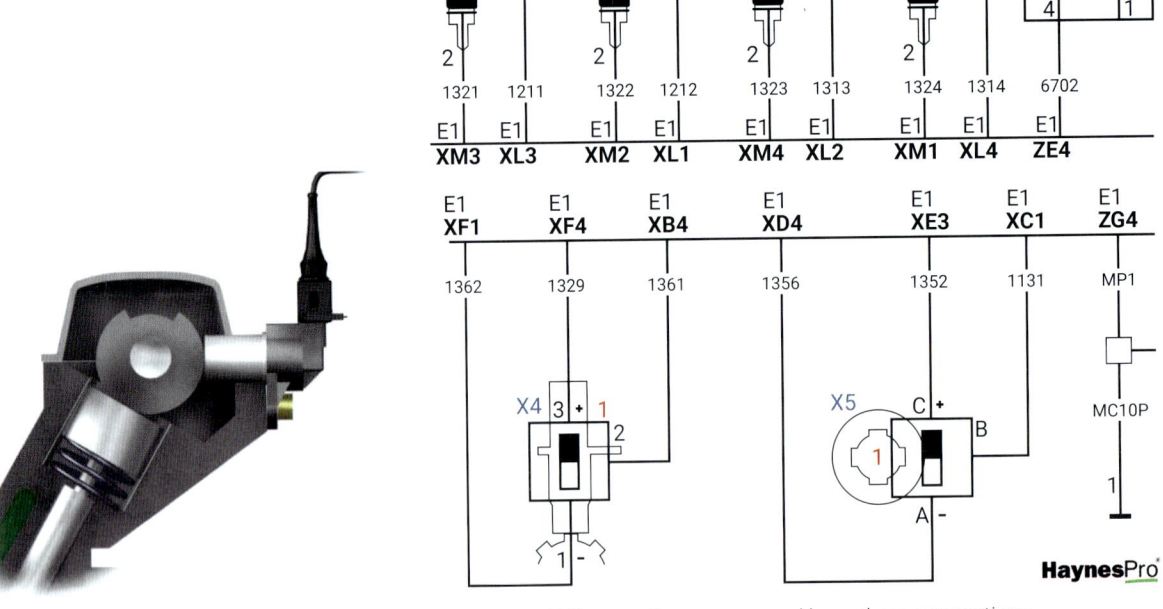

Fig. 75 A Hall effect camshaft position sensor.

Fig. 76 X4 and X5 are active sensors and have three connections.

An active sensor usually has three wires that are connected to the control unit: power supply, ground, and signal.

These are examples of active sensors:
— Hall effect camshaft position sensor
— Mass Air Flow sensor
— Manifold Absolute Pressure sensor

Some active sensors have two wires. This type of sensor has a power supply and a ground. The signal is transmitted by means of an internal circuit sent through either the power supply or ground wire, and a square wave signal is generated as the teeth pass. The Magnetic Resistant Element (MRE) sensor is an example of an active two-wire sensor. MRE sensors are commonly used as wheel speed sensors for the ABS/ESP system.

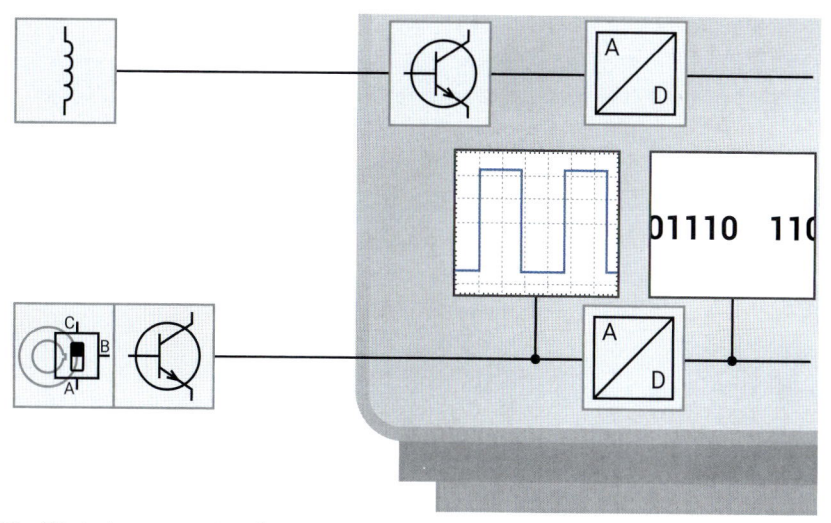

Fig. 77 Active sensor: Interfacing takes place in the sensor, and digitization takes place in the control unit.

4. Intelligent Sensor

The intelligent sensor is named as such because it can communicate (digitally) back and forth with the control unit.

When several intelligent sensors are connected to a control unit, this forms a network. Sometimes one control unit will relay sensor information to another control unit over the vehicle network.

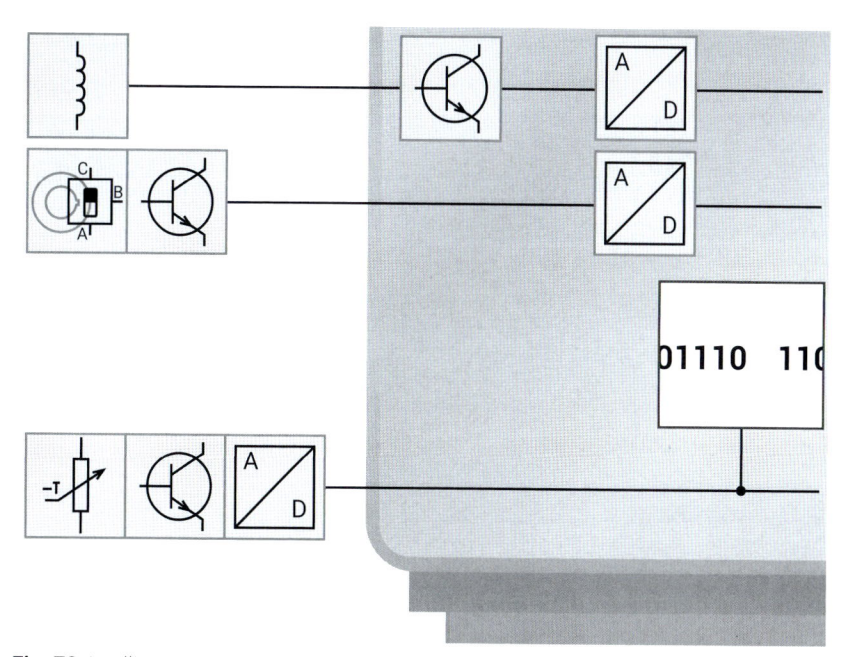

Fig. 78 Intelligent sensor: Interfacing and digitization take place in the sensor.

The signal from an intelligent sensor is digital, so interfacing and digitization take place inside the sensor.

An intelligent sensor has three connections with the control unit: power supply, ground, and data.

These are examples of intelligent sensors:
— Battery Monitor Sensor
— Rain sensor
— Oil quality sensor

Communication of the sensor information can be sent between modules via pulse width modulated (PWM) signal on the vehicle's network bus.

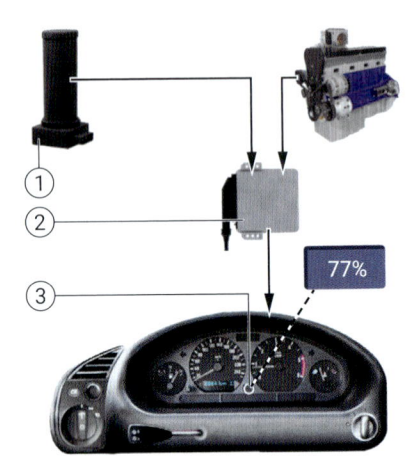

Fig. 79 1. Oil quality sensor. 2. Control unit. 3. Instrument panel.

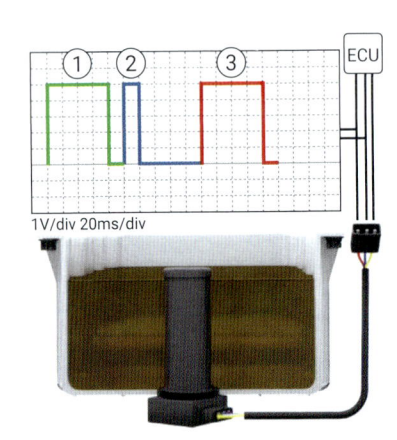

Fig. 80 PWM signal from the oil quality sensor: 1. Oil level high. 2. Oil temperature low. 3. Oil quality good.

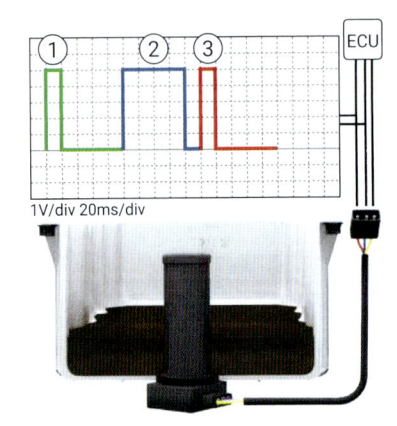

Fig. 81 1. Oil level low. 2. Oil temperature high. 3. Oil quality poor.

AMPLITUDE MODULATION

1. Amplitude Modulation

Analogue information transfer is the most common method by which communication between sensor and control unit takes place. The information is transferred in the height (amplitude) of the signal. Examples of AM signals:

— Throttle position sensor
— Engine temperature sensor
— Pressure sensor
— Oxygen sensor

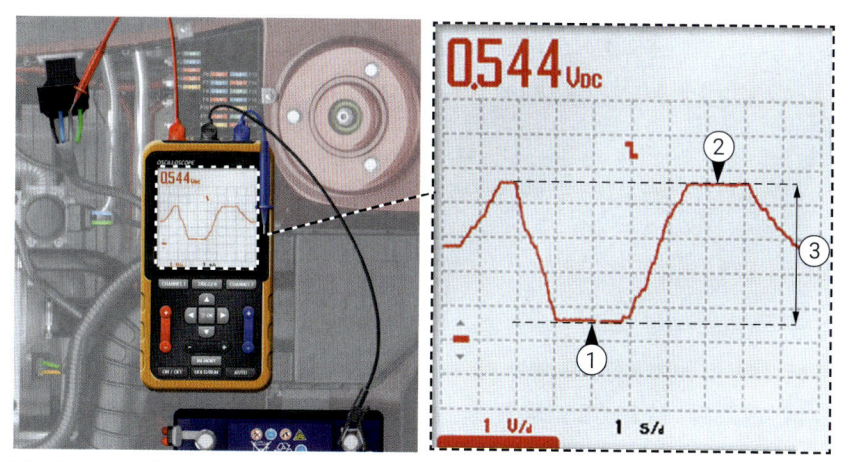

Fig. 82 Signal from the throttle position sensor. 1. Throttle not used. 2. Throttle fully operation. Amplitude signal.

Measurement example:

In the measurement shown, the signal from the accelerator pedal position sensor is being measured.
When the accelerator pedal is released, the signal voltage is 0.5 V. If the pedal is fully depressed, the voltage is 4.5 V. If the accelerator pedal is pressed halfway, the sensor will emit a voltage of 2.5 V.

With this signal you can clearly see that the height (amplitude) of the voltage signal is equal to the position of the accelerator pedal. The basic time of the measured signal is very slow, 1 S/d. This means that every square on the horizontal axis of the scope lasts one second.

FREQUENCY MODULATION

1. Frequency Modulation

For an FM signal, the information is transferred by varying the frequency of a signal.
The frequency of the signal then becomes a measure for the value of the measured unit.

There are two types of FM signals:

- Passive
- Active

A passive FM signal comes from a sensor that does not require a power supply or earth connection in order to be able to emit a signal.

An active FM signal comes from a sensor that does require a power supply and earth connection in order to be able to emit a signal.

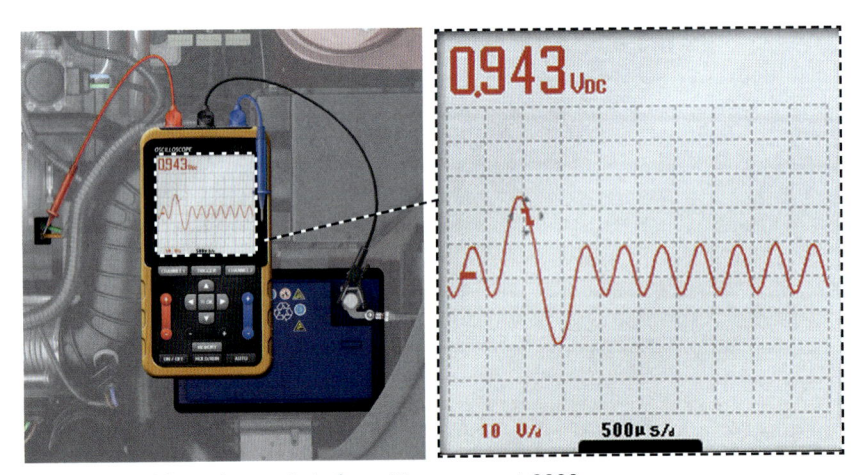

Fig. 83 Signal from the crankshaft position sensor at 2000 rpm

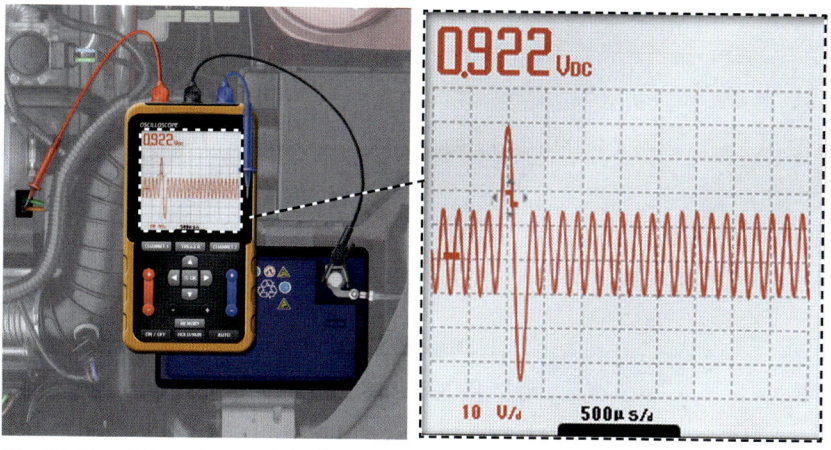

Fig. 84 Signal from the crankshaft position sensor at 5000 rpm

Measurement example:

You can see two measurements on the crankshaft position sensor. This is a passive sensor. As a result, the amplitude can also vary, but the control unit does not use this portion of the signal.

In the first measurement, the internal combustion engine has a low speed; the frequency of the sensor is also low.

The second measurement has a high speed; the frequency that the sensor emits is higher.

PULSE WIDTH MODULATION

1. Pulse Width Modulation

A pulse width modulated (PWM) signal is a square wave voltage signal with a varying width of the signal.
The amplitude and frequency of the signal stay the same, and the information is contained in the amount of time the signal is pulsed on and off.

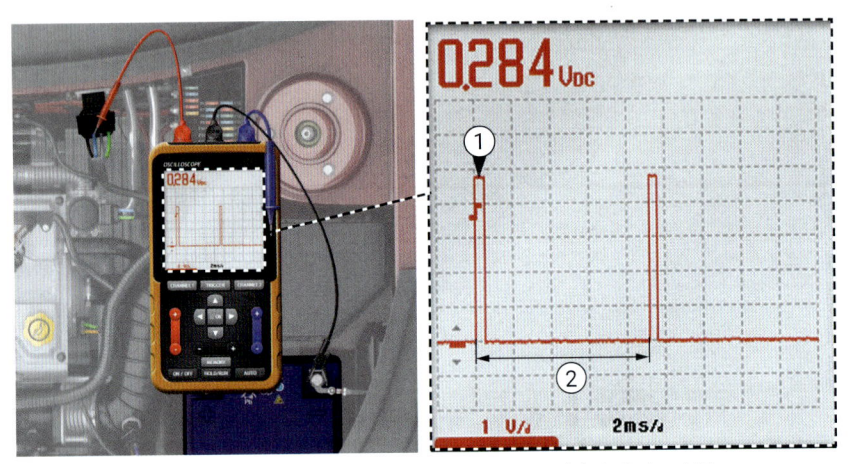

Fig. 85 Measurement with a non-operated accelerator pedal. 1. Puls width. 2. Period.

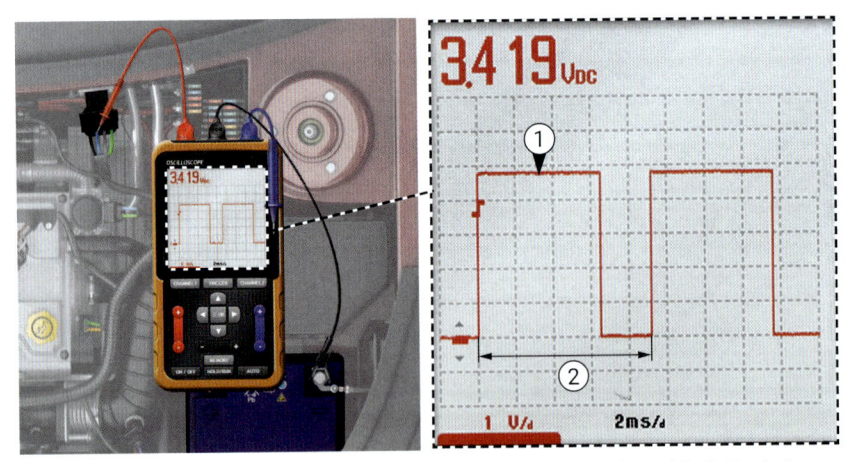

Fig. 86 Measurement with an operated accelerator pedal. 1. Puls Width. 2. Period.

Sensors can use a Puls Width signal to active send information. For that the sensors need 3 wires: Power supply, ground and a signal wire.

An example is the throttle position sensor.

Actuators, valves and electric motor speeds can also be controlled by modulating the pulse width of the voltage supply.

The time that something is controlled this way is referred to as the duration. In this example, the duration is about 9 milliseconds.

PRINCIPLE OPERATION OF ACTUATORS

1. Introduction

The engine management system controls and regulates multiple processes. To influence a process, action must be taken. These types of actions are called steering or control actions. The command for performing them comes from the control unit. The steering and control actions are performed by actuators.

An actuator is a component that uses an electrical signal to set a mechanism in motion. An electrical relay is an example of this. The engine management control unit ensures a voltage difference across the relay. The coil in the relay therefore becomes magnetic and pulls the switch, or the mechanism, to a certain position.

While there are many types of actuators, their operation is based on only three different principles:
— electromagnetic (coil)
— electrostatic (piezo)
— electric heating

Of these, the electromagnetic principle is the most important. It is often applied in the engine management actuators. Imagine how a throttle valve motor works. This direct current actuator operates based on the principle of electromagnetism. The injector also uses this principle by opening the injector needle. In a final example, electromagnetism is also used in the ignition coil to generate the high voltage required for a spark plug.

To understand the electromagnetic principle, an explanation of the following terms is necessary:
— magnetic field
— electromagnetism
— coil
— self-induction

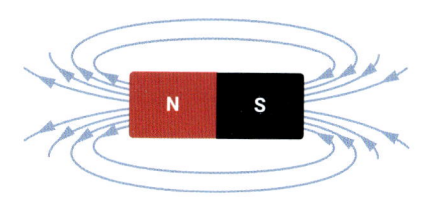

Fig. 87 A magnet and the field lines

2. Magnetic Field

A magnet exerts a force on steel objects. There are two types of magnets:
- Permanent magnets: hold their magnetic charge without an inducing field or current
- Electromagnets: a metal core made into a magnet by passing current through a coil wrapped around it

The force effect of a magnet is caused by the magnetic field that is present around the magnet. This can be represented by field lines. The field lines are imaginary lines that indicate the flow of the magnetic field. The field lines run from the north pole to the south pole. The concentration of lines indicates how strong the field is. A high density of field lines gives the magnet great force.

3. Electromagnetism

The magnetic field that arises around an electromagnet is called electromagnetism. A live conductor is shown in the image. Field lines are drawn around the conductor. The direction of the field lines around the conductor depends on the direction of current in the conductor.

Fig. 88 Magnetic field with field lines around a live conductor

The corkscrew rule is a handy mnemonic aid to determine the direction of the field around a live conductor.

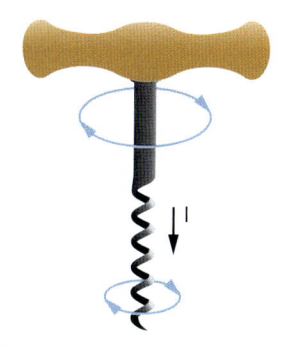

Fig. 89 The direction of the corkscrew is the direction of the lines of force.

If we draw a cross-section of a live conductor, we can show the current direction through the conductor in the following way. A cross indicates that the current direction has diverted away from us. A point in the middle indicates that the current direction has turned

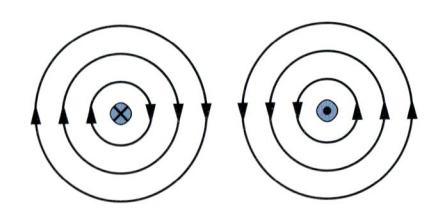

Fig. 90 Left: Current directed away from us, field lines to the right. Right: Current directed towards us, field lines to the left.

towards us. The image shows a cross-section of a conductor and the direction of the field.

4. Coil

A coil is a conductor (copper wire) that is wound into a coil. With the help of the corkscrew rule, the direction of the field around the coil is constructed.

The entirety of the field lines covered by the coil is called the magnetic flux, indicated by the Greek letter Φ (Phi). A strong magnetic field has many field lines; the flux Φ is then large.

An actuator consists of a coil that is wound around a core of soft iron. The electromagnetic field generated by the coil will attract the iron core to the center of the coil. In short, the coil sets the iron core in motion, converting an electric current into movement. This principle is used in numerous actuators, such as injectors, relays, and EGR valves. The direct current motor of a throttle valve also works on this principle.

The strength of the electromagnetic field generated by the coil depends on the:
— current strength that flows through the coil
— number of windings or threads
— type of material of the core.

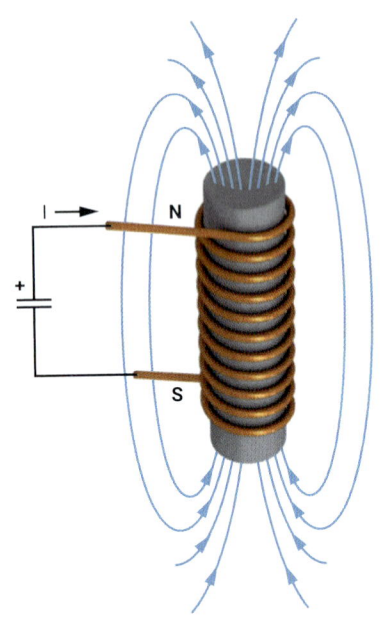

Fig. 91 The magnetic field around a coil.

5. Self-induction

Switching the current on and off through a conductor changes the magnetic field around the conductor. Due to this changing magnetic field, an electric voltage is generated in the conductor. This is called self-induction. The self-induction tries to maintain the situation that was there.

Switching on the current:
The switch was open and is now closing. The coil was not magnetic and will become magnetic. The inductance tries to maintain the 'not being magnetic' with the generation of voltage. The polarity of the induced voltage is now opposite to that of the battery. This (temporarily) stops the build-up of the current and thus the build-up of the magnetic field.

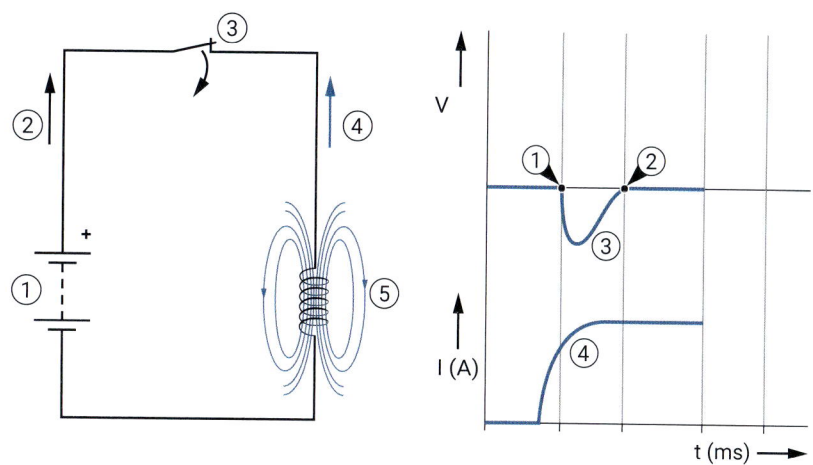

Fig. 92 1. battery 2. energy from battery 3. switch closes 4. energy through self-induction voltage 5. building up magnetic field in coil.

Fig. 93 1. switch closing 2. end of inductance, maximum current reached 3. self-induction voltage in coil 4. build-up of current through coil.

Switching off the current:

The switch opens, the coil used to be magnetic and should now become non-magnetic. The inductance tries to maintain 'being magnetic' by regenerating the voltage. The polarity of the generated voltage is now the same as that of the battery. As a result, the reduction of the current and thus the reduction of the magnetic field is (temporarily) stopped.

The level of the inductance voltage depends on:
— The rate at which the magnetic field changes (the faster, the higher the generated voltage).
— The strength of the magnetic field (the stronger, the higher the generated voltage).
— The length of the conductor in the magnetic field (the more windings, the higher the voltage generated).

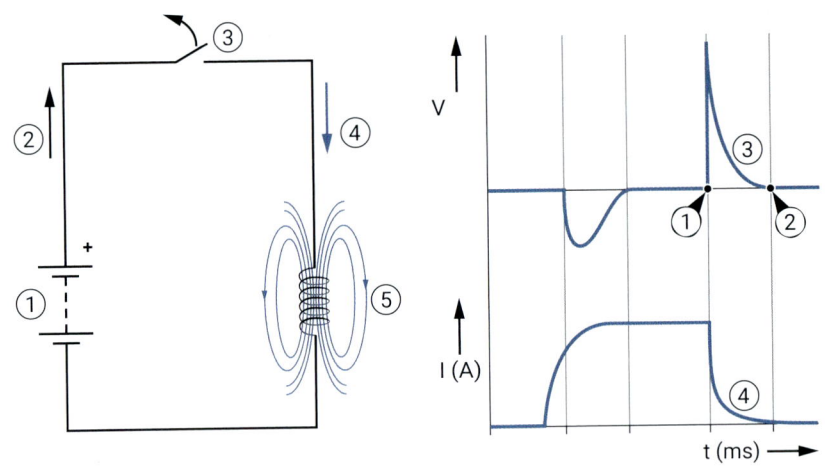

Fig. 94 1. battery 2. energy from battery drops 3. switch opens 4. energy through self-induction voltage 5. decreasing magnetic field in coil.

Fig. 95 1. opening of switch 2. end of self-inductance, magnetic field reduced 3. self-induction voltage in coil 4. reduction of current through coil.

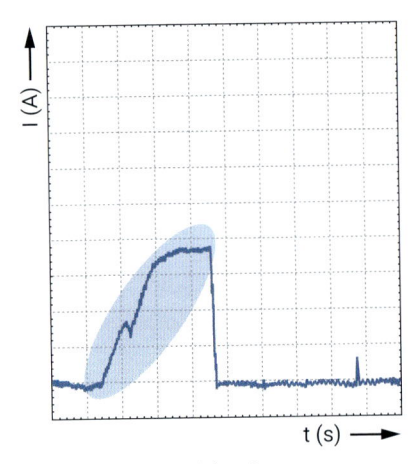

Fig. 96 Current build-up in an injector

The image shows that the current through an injector (a coil with a soft-iron core) is not immediately at its maximum capability, but instead, starts slowly as a result of self-induction. The self-induction phenomenon applies to all coil-based actuators.

The result of the delayed current build-up is that the actuator will not immediately move as soon as the current is switched on. The engine management control unit must, therefore, take into account a delay in switching on actuators based on a coil. During the development of this type of actuator, all attempts have been made to minimize this delay.

SWITCHING ACTUATORS ON AND OFF

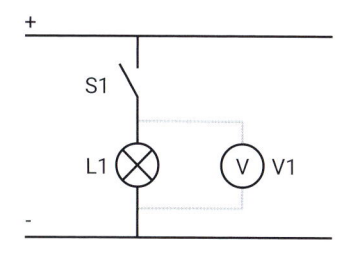

Fig. 97 Positive Control

1. Positive Control

The image shows a lamp (L1) that is continuously connected to ground. A switch establishes the connection between the supply voltage and the lamp. If switch S1 is open, no current is flowing. The voltage across lamp L1 is 0 volts, and the lamp is not lit up. Because in a series connection the sum of the voltages is equal to the supply voltage, the voltage across the switch is 12 volts. When switch S1 is closed, a current flows through the lamp. Voltmeter V1 shows 12 volts and across the switch is 0 volts. This circuit is called positive control.

2. Own Power Supply

Some positive control systems use direct injection. Because with direct injection the voltage is often higher than the supply voltage of 14.4 volts, there is no direct connection with the positive control switch, but the voltage is controlled by the ECU (high-side driver). This can often be recognized in the electrical diagram. Both connections of the injector come from the ECU.

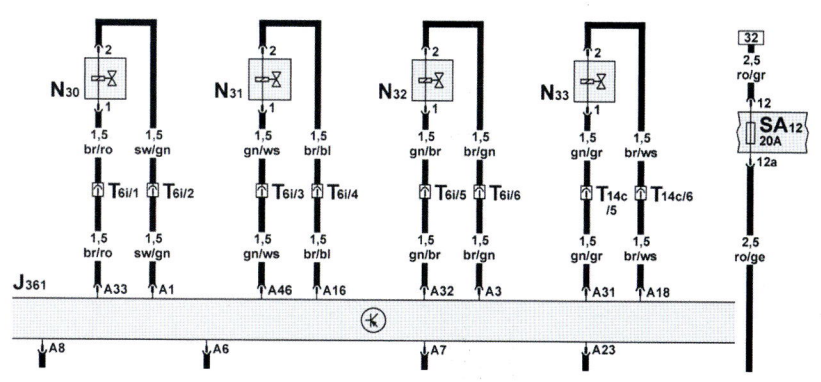

2009, source: erWin, author: Audi AG

Fig. 98 Wiring of injector comes from the ECU

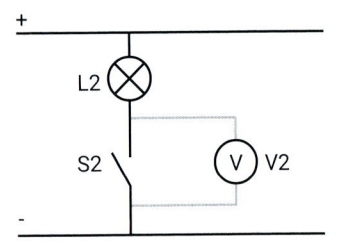

Fig. 99 Ground Control

3. Ground Control

A ground circuit is shown in the image. Lamp L2 is continuously connected to the positive supply voltage. Switch S2 switches on the current by establishing the connection between the lamp and the ground. If the switch is open, the lamp is not lit up. The voltage across the lamp is then 0 volt. The voltmeter across the switch then shows 12 volts. As soon as the switch is closed, the voltage across the lamp is 12 volts, and the voltage across the switch is 0 volt. The voltmeter shows 0 volt.

An example of a ground control is the circuit of an injector. The diagram shows the flow diagram of an engine management. The control unit (100) controls the injector (1). The ground of the injector is connected to the control unit via pin 21 (low-side driver). The control unit is connected to ground via pin 10.

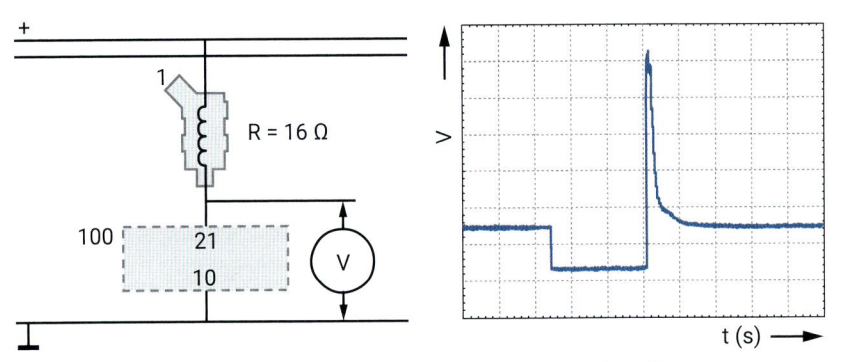

Fig. 100 The injector in the circuit diagram with the associated oscilloscope image

Before the control unit activates the injector, the voltage at terminal 21 is 12 volts.

At the time of turning on, the voltage at terminal 21 drops to 0 volt because the control unit connects terminal 21 to ground terminal 10. During the time that the power through the injector remains on, there is 0 volt at terminal 21. This is also clearly visible in the oscilloscope image in the picture.

The moment that the power is interrupted, the magnetic field collapses and the injector closes. The change in the field strength causes an induction voltage in the coil. After this induction voltage peak, the voltage at terminal 21 drops again to 12 volts.

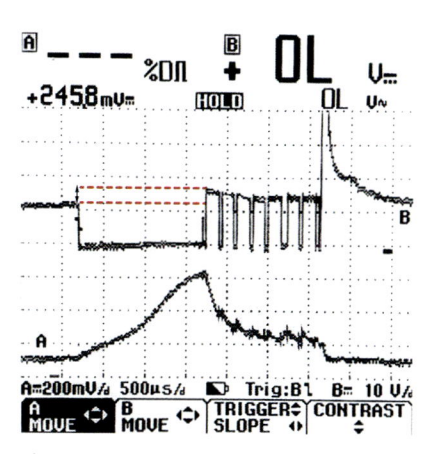

Fig. 101 The voltage is slightly higher during current control.

4. Switching On and Off With Current Limitation

Due to their self-inductive behavior, actuators have a time delay between switching on the current and the actual presence of the magnetic field. In order to keep that time as short as possible, low-resistance actuators are used in combination with a current limiting circuit.

For example, reducing the resistance of an injector results in a fast injector with a current that is too high. This current can be limited by switching the injector on and off. The engine management control unit does this by interrupting the ground after the current is strong enough to lift the needle.

Due to the characteristics of the coil, it now generates an induction voltage. It is important to prevent the induction voltage from becoming too high or the injector needle will close. This is prevented by including a two-driver circuit to control the injector action. This circuit in the control unit ensures that the energy that is released in the injector, after the current is interrupted, is used to preserve the coil's magnetic field. This keeps the needle tightened, and the injector continues to inject.

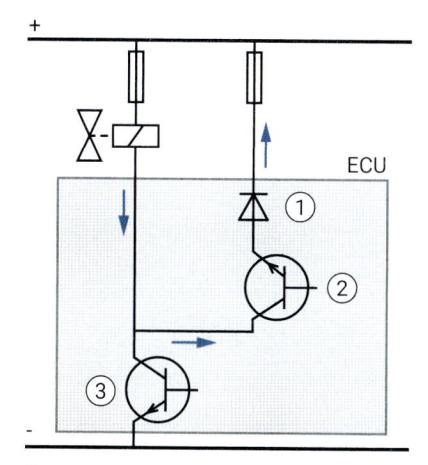

Fig. 102 Electrical diagram for the current control.
1. diode
2. output stage current control
3. output stage control injector

The operation of this circuit can be seen in the picture. Output stage 3 connects the ground side of the injector with ground. With output stage 2 we can connect the ground side of the injector to the power supply side of the injector. Placing diode 1 in between prevents a short circuit from occurring.

As output stage 3 conducts, a current starts to flow, just like with a conventionally switched injector, and the needle is lifted by the magnetic field against the spring force.

Before the current rises too high, output stage 3 is switched off. The voltage on the ground side now increases due to the induction in the coil. If the voltage exceeds the battery voltage plus 0.7 volts from the diode, a current will flow through output stage 2 via diode 1 to the power supply side of the injector. The current direction through the coil therefore stays the same.
The magnetic field is thereby maintained. This is not a permanent situation, and the strength of the magnetic field does weaken.

Before the spring force of the needle overcomes the force of the magnetic field and the needle closes, output stage 3 is activated again. The magnetic field recovers; the current rises, and output stage 3 is interrupted. This cycle is repeated until the injector has to close. Then both output stages 2 and 3 will no longer be controlled.

An actuator controlled in this way is called a peak hold circuit. In this way the actuator reacts with much less delay without a large current generating a lot of heat.

PLEASE NOTE These types of low-resistance actuators, such as this injector, must never be checked by connecting them to a battery.

5. Duty Cycle Control

Using a duty cycle control makes regulating the current intensity by a consumer possible. The term duty cycle is basically self-explanatory. Duty means service or activity, and cycle means cycle or period. It indicates how long there is activity (current) per period. A period in this case means that the voltage has been high once and zero once.

Concepts and details related to duty cycle control include:
— It uses a pulsating DC voltage.
— The level of these voltage pulses does not change; for example, in a car it is 12 volts.
— The width of the pulses determines the current strength because the current remains switched on for longer or shorter.

This concept is also referred to as "the duty cycle of a signal." This is then expressed as a percentage that represents the ratio between the time the power is on and off. The ratio between switching the power on and off can be changed with a duty cycle control. This regulates the current intensity. With a duty cycle of 90%, the power is switched on 90% of the time per period and switched off 10% of the time.

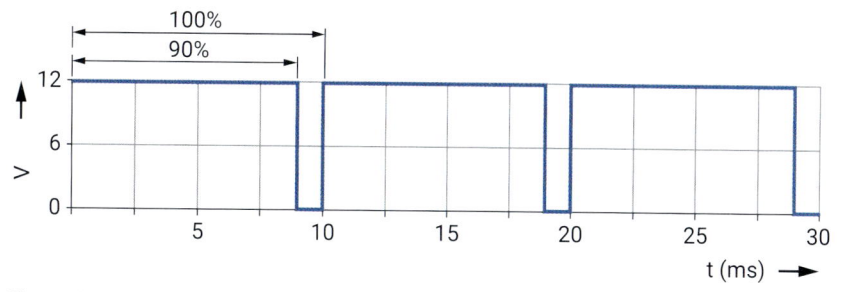

Fig. 103 A signal with a duty cycle of 90% and a frequency of 100 Hz

The "making" of a duty cycle signal is done by a piece of electronics that controls a transistor. The transistor switches the current on and off.

The picture shows how a duty cycle signal changes. In the first graph, the ratio between switched on (12 volts) and switched off (0 volt) is 25%. In the next one, the ratio is 50%, and in the last one it is 75%. This ratio or duty cycle can be adjusted continuously between 0 and 100%.

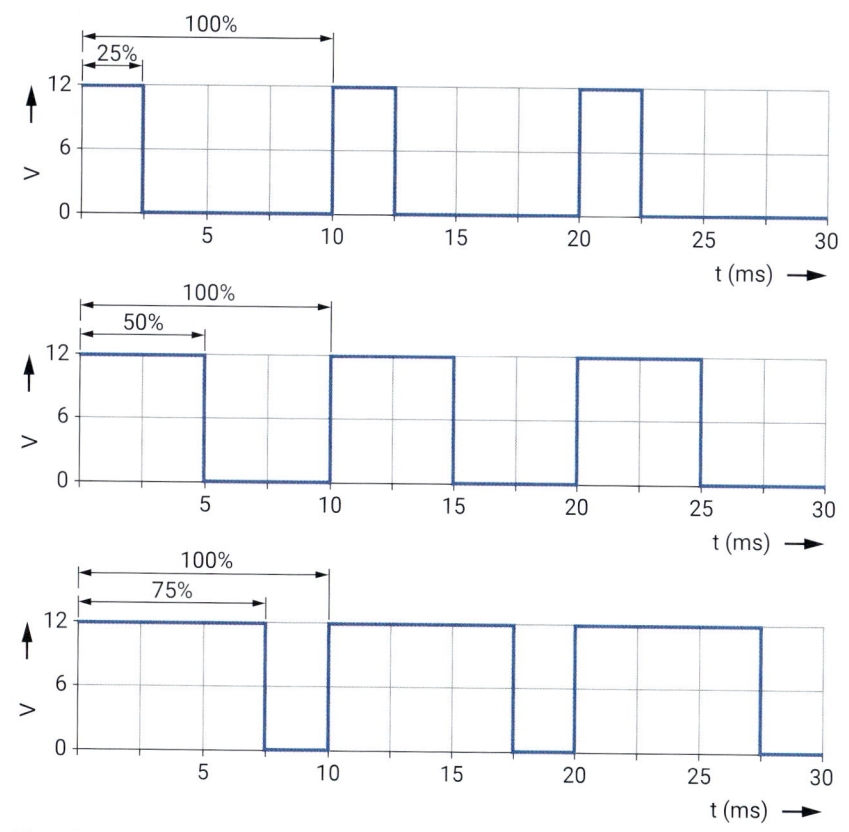

Fig. 104 Control power by varying the width of the pulse

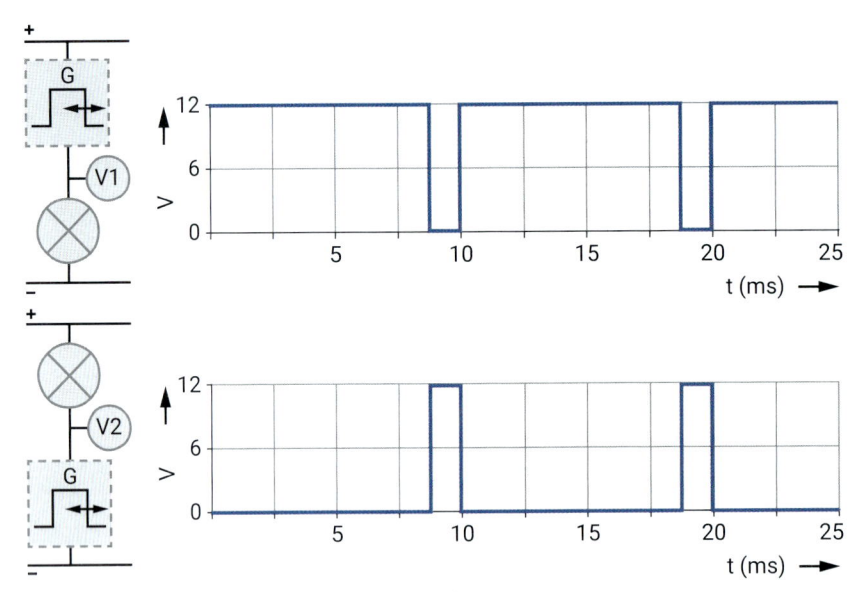

Fig. 105 Positive and ground control duty cycle

This circuit can be placed in both the positive and ground connections. When the duty cycle circuit is connected to the ground connection, the signal will look exactly the other way around. During the time that V2 is grounded, the current flows through the lamp. If the voltage on V2 has become 12 volts, the connection is broken.

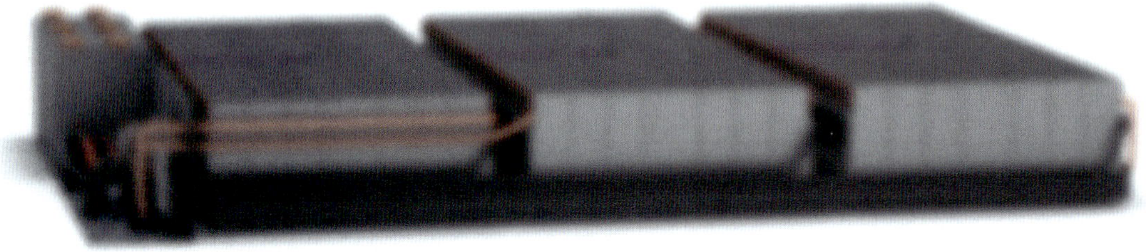

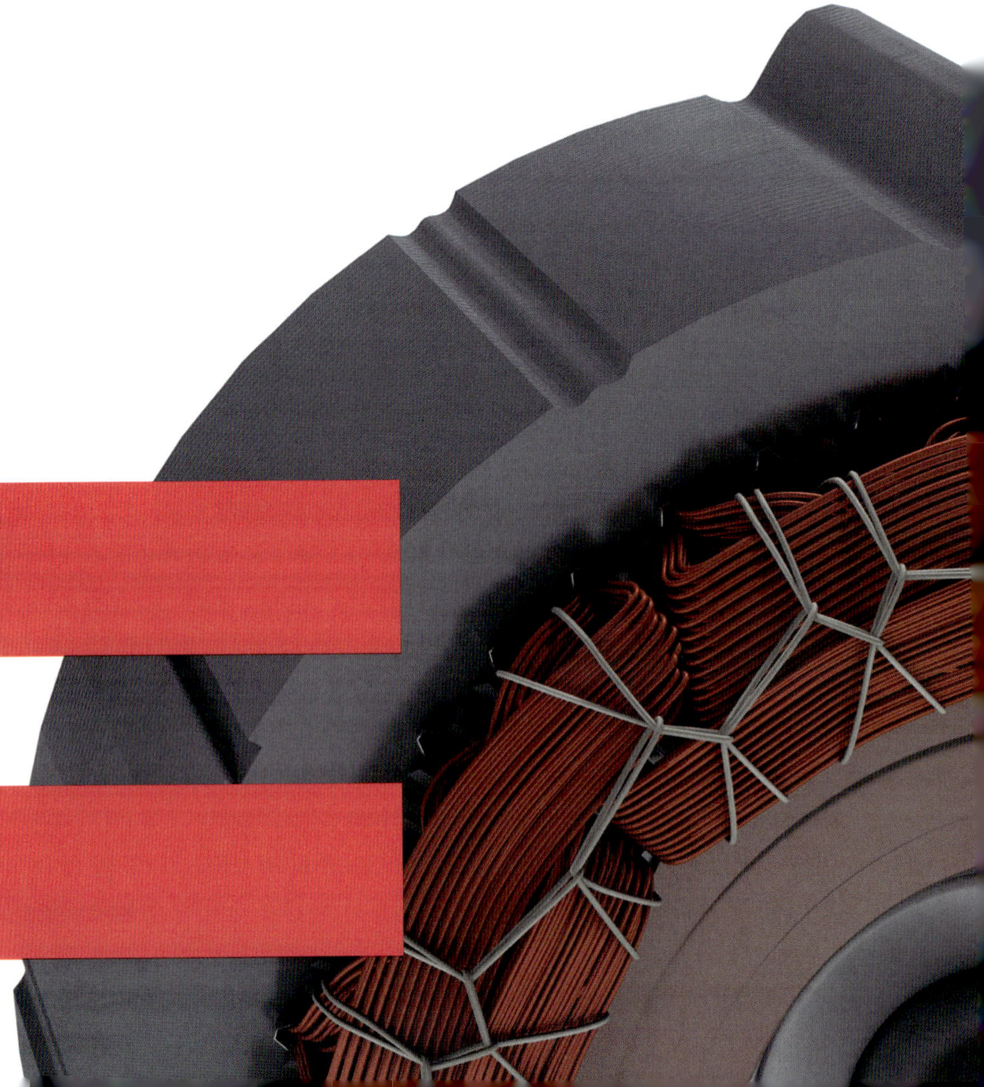

4. In-vehicle Network Communication

CAN BUS: INTRODUCTION

1. Increasing Complexity

With the increasing complexity of vehicles, it has become necessary to be able to exchange information quickly and efficiently. Instead of having a unique wire for each piece of information, a solution has been found in the development of communication networks.

These networks allow various pieces of information to be transported via a single circuit, which means multiple pieces of information can be transmitted over a single path.

CAN bus is an application of a communication network in motor vehicles. An example of a CAN bus application is the sharing of information between various control units; thereby controlling windshield wipers, washers, headlights, and turn signals operation with only a single circuit.

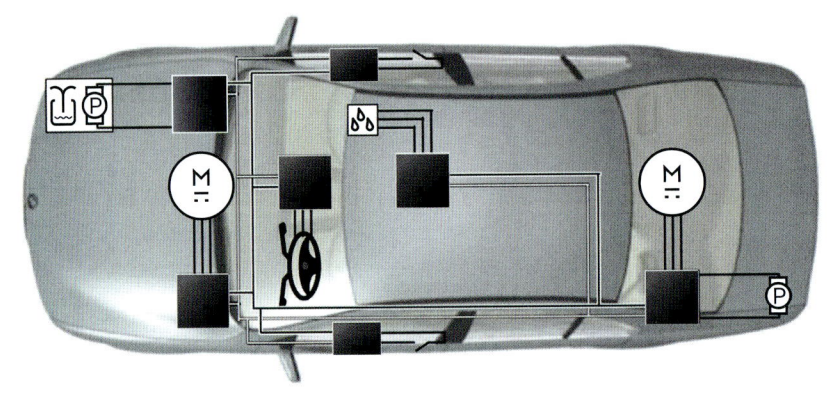

Fig. 106 Vehicle with CAN bus system connecting various control units

2. CAN Bus.

CAN bus is a communication network; the letters CAN stand for Controller Area Network.

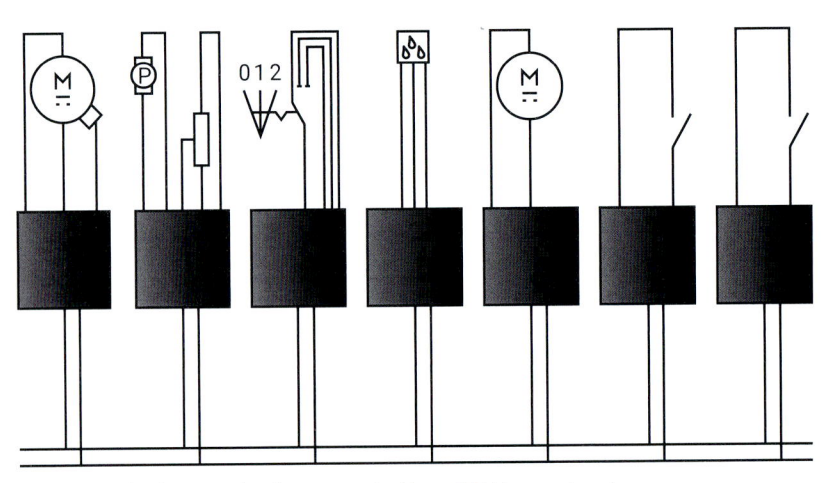

Fig. 107 Multiple control units connected by a CAN bus network

The difference between a system which operates with a CAN bus network and one that does not becomes clear when we zoom in on a component with a number of functions.

If we look at a door mirror of a fully equipped vehicle, we find the following functions:
— mirror adjustment
— mirror heating
— camera for 360° view
— warning car in blind spot
— indicator
— outside temperature sensor
— folding motor
— automatic dimming function

— ground lighting

If this information were to be sent over a parallel communication network, a lot of wires would be needed to carry each signal. This would be two or three wires per function.

If we equip the mirror with a module that is connected to the CAN bus network, then in principle we only need four wires to carry out all of the functions: one positive wire, one negative wire, and two communication wires.

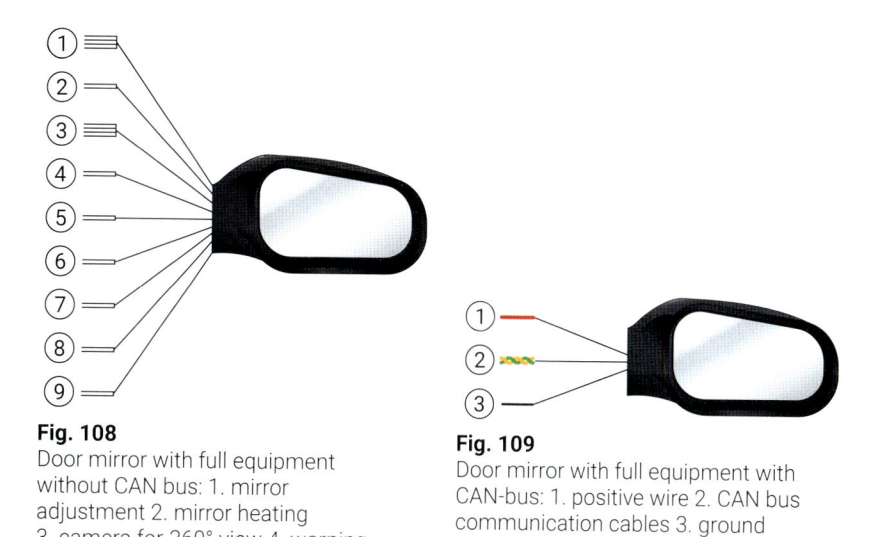

Fig. 108
Door mirror with full equipment without CAN bus: 1. mirror adjustment 2. mirror heating 3. camera for 360° view 4. warning car in blind spot 5. turn signal 6. outside temperature sensor 7. folding motor 8. automatic dimming function 9. ground lighting

Fig. 109
Door mirror with full equipment with CAN-bus: 1. positive wire 2. CAN bus communication cables 3. ground wire

3. Network Variants

Other network variants besides CAN can also be used.

Examples include:
— Local Interconnect Network (LIN)
— Media Oriented System Transport (MOST)
— FlexRay
— ByteFlight (BMW)

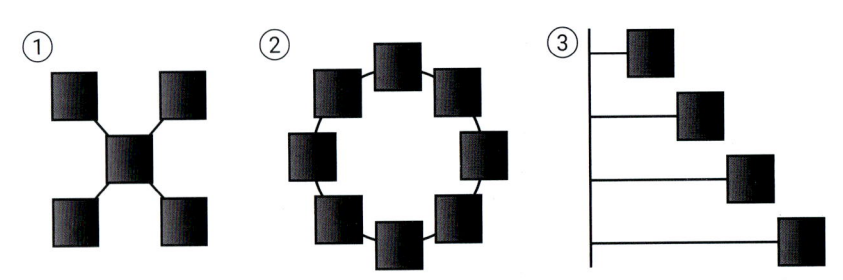

Fig. 110 1. star network 2. ring network 3. bus network

The control units can be connected to each other in different ways. The middle control unit often takes the lead in a star network. In a ring network, all control units are connected in series via a ring-shaped network that is used to pass all information through one module to the next. Finally, in a bus network, each control unit receives the information at the same time, and there is no control unit in charge.

4. Star Network

The star network is based on the Master-Slave principle. The master is responsible for diverting the data from one control unit to the other.

The disadvantage of a star network is that it is tricky to expand. This is because the hardware of a master needs to be modified with each function that is added (e.g. the number of connections).

However, the star network is used as a subnetwork or in places where operating reliability is paramount (e.g. brake systems).

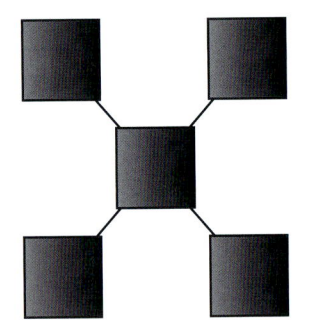

Fig. 111 Star network

5. Ring Network

In a ring network, the data line runs from control unit to control unit in a loop.

Information is passed from one control unit to another, until the information is received back at the original transmitter. The flow of information is always in the same direction.

A master control unit determines which component can transmit a message and at what time.

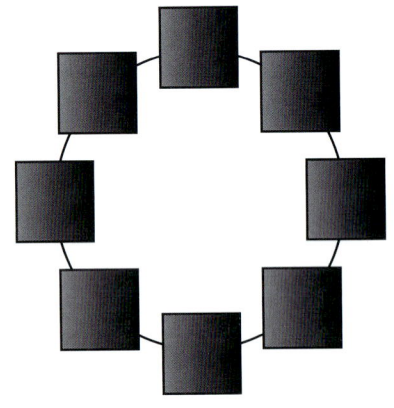

Fig. 112 Ring network

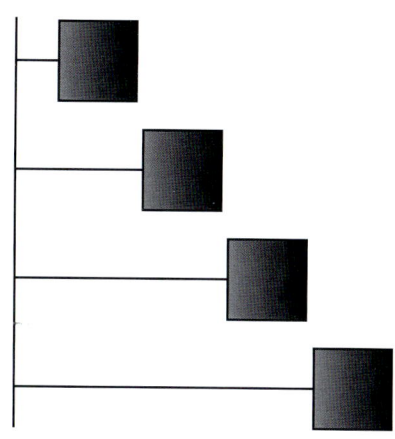

Fig. 113 Bus network

6. Bus Network

In contrast to a ring network, all control units in a bus network are connected with each other in parallel.

The messages therefore do not pass from control unit to control unit, but rather are put on the bus where every control unit receives the information at the same time.

An advantage of the bus network is that it is easy to extend, without the disadvantage of the ring network.

CAN BUS: NETWORK TOPOLOGY

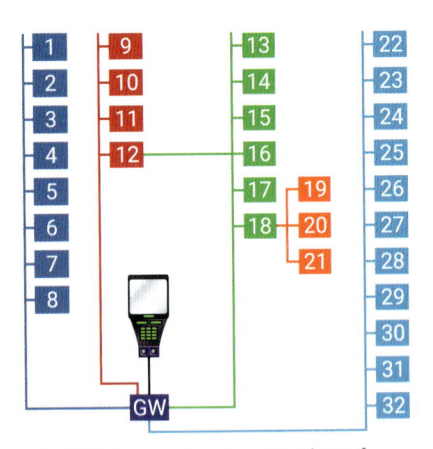

Fig. 114 Due to the large number of control units in vehicles, multiple networks are required for communication.

1. Introduction

The degree to which a CAN bus is used varies from manufacturer to manufacturer. There are vehicles with fewer than ten control units, and there are some with almost 100 control units.

When the number of control units increases, a designer must take account of the number of messages that must be spread across the bus, i.e. the traffic on the bus. This traffic is also called the bus load.

In order to limit the bus load, there are often several CAN networks in a single vehicle. Control units which have to exchange a lot of information between each other are linked together by a designer to form a single network. With these types of networks, a single controller is connected to all the networks and serves as a 'gateway' for diagnostic equipment.

The topology of a network is much like a road map. It refers to how the network is laid out and which control unit is connected to which network.

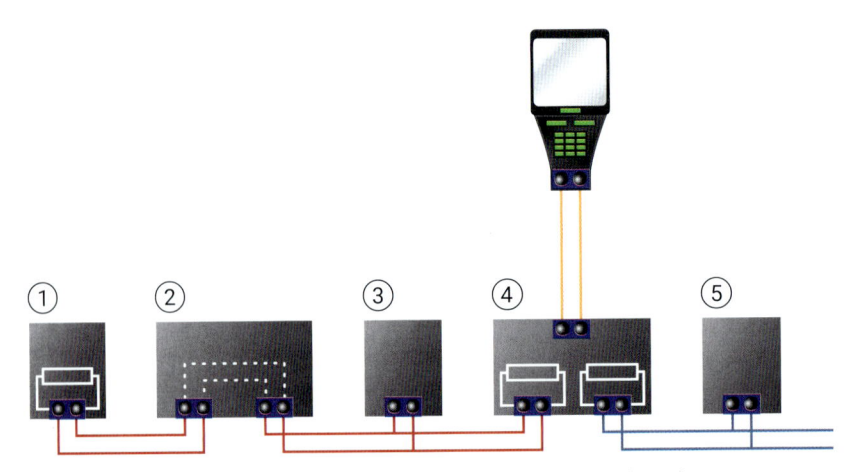

Fig. 115 In control unit 2, the network runs via the printed circuit board. Disconnecting the plug from control unit 2 has a different effect than disconnecting the plug from control unit 3.

2. Need for Topology

While troubleshooting in networks it is necessary to have access to the topology of all networks. This information allows you to understand the paths of communication through the various networks in the vehicle. Furthermore, with the help of topology you can predict the effect of disconnecting plugs in the wiring harness or on control units when attempting to diagnose network faults.

Depending on the topology, the disconnection of plugs from some control units can cause an interruption in the network because the bus runs through the printed circuit board in the control unit.

3. Exchange of Information

In order to make a limited exchange of information between the networks possible, they are connected to each other via a gateway. The gateway acts like a translator with a filter. Only certain messages (identifiers) are allowed to pass through. The gateway also adjusts the speed of the communication. The gateway functionality is often added to an existing control unit and runs as a separate piece of software in the control unit.

One possible extra function of the gateway is to enable communication between the diagnostic tester and the control units. This communication takes place over the CAN bus.

Multiple control units can also have the function of a gateway. You will only find this out after studying a diagram of the entire network.

It's also possible that a control unit is connected to two networks without fulfilling the gateway function. In these cases the control unit needs a lot of information from both networks. If you were to only connect this control unit to one of the two networks, then too much data must be copied to the second network; making the bus load on the second network too high.
In fact, this one control unit is then given a private connection to both networks.

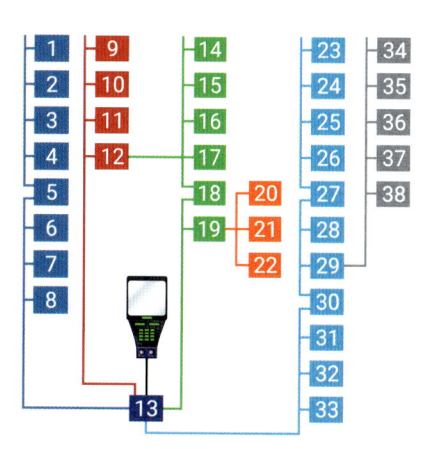

Fig. 116 Control units 13, 19, and 29 have the gateway function. Control units 5, 12, 27, and 30 each appear to be a gateway, but they are not. With control units 5, 27, and 30, the network runs through the printed circuit board without acting as a filter. Control unit 12 requires a lot of information from two networks and therefore gets its own connection to both networks.

CAN BUS: TRANSMISSION LINES

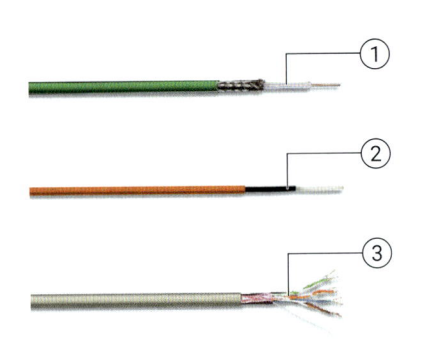

Fig. 117 1. Coax cable. 2. Optical cable. 3. Copper cable.

1. Introduction

The connections between the control units are called transmission lines. Transmission lines are used for transporting:
– electrical energy (current)
– signals (information)

Signals can be analog or digital, and the application determines the choice of transmission line.
Examples of transmission lines:
– coax cable
– optical cable
– copper wire

The choice of one of the cables depends on the requirements that are imposed on the communication system.

2. Coax Cable

Coax cable is widely used for connecting antennas to receivers such as radio and television sets. The coax cable is comprised of an insulated copper or aluminum core surrounded by a metal sheath.

The sheath is connected to ground, diverting interference voltages or noise (such as from the high voltage ignition system) directly to ground. The signal voltage is thus transmitted and received uninterrupted.

A Faraday cage is created by placing a mantle around the core. Interference from outside cannot pass through this.

3. Optical Cable

'Glass fiber' or fiber optic is a type of cable through which data is transported in the form of light signals. Fiber optic is not actually made of glass but rather of plastic (optical fiber).

A light source at one end of the cable shoots a beam of light through the plastic core. The light is repeatedly reflected by the sheath that surrounds the core until it reaches the receiver at the other end.

A light flash is considered to be a '1' and a pause (no light beam) a '0'.

The main advantage of fiber optic communication is light signals are not influenced by electric fields.

If connected correctly, the fiberoptic cable can transmit at the speed of light. This makes fiberoptic cables very suitable if large quantities of data need to be transported, such as when sending moving images. Optical cables are also not affected by electrical interference sources.

4. Copper Wire

Copper is by far the most commonly used conductor in a car. The advantages of copper are:

— low specific resistance
— easy to repair
— suitable for data and current
— flexible

5. Twisted pair

A way of protecting copper wire from external influences is to use a 'twisted pair' cable.
This is two copper wires twisted together.
CAN bus uses twisted pair cables.

The two data lines are called
CAN-L (Low) and CAN-H (High).

The ends of the CAN-L and CAN-H are connected with terminating resistances. This is done to prevent interference.

There are often multiple "twisted pair cables" in the wiring harness between the control units of the vehicle.

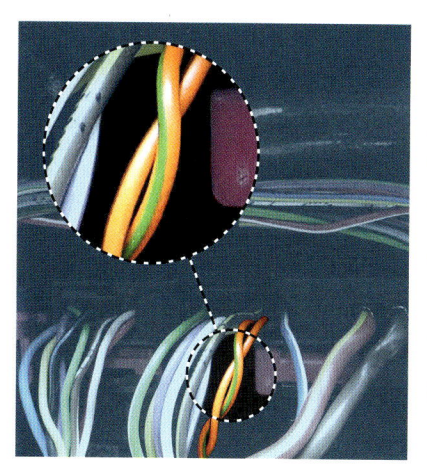

Fig. 118 There are often multiple "twisted pair cables" in a wiring harness to a computer.

CAN BUS: ELECTRICAL OPERATION

1. The telegraph line

The CAN bus can be compared to the telegraph line from long ago. Connected in parallel with the telegraph line are small telegraph offices (control units), which can receive and transmit messages.

Each telegraph office has an operator to whom information is delivered. The telegraph operator puts the information onto the telegraph line in a suitable format.

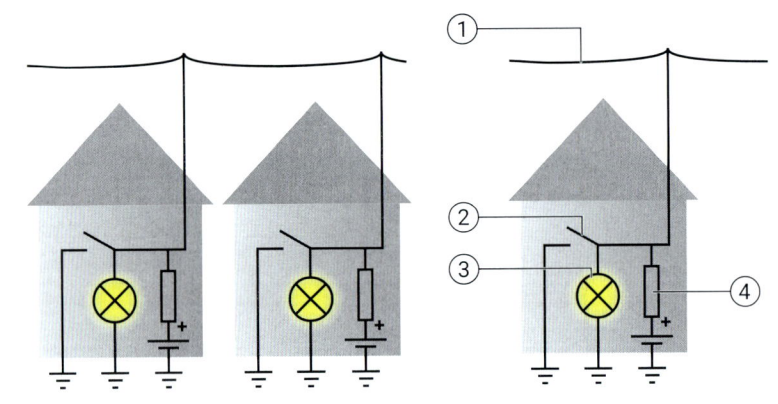

Fig. 119 A CAN bus can be compared with the telegraph lines of the past.

Fig. 120 A post office consists of: 1. voltage source 2. signal key 3. lamp 4. resistor

All post offices can send and receive a message. Every sent piece of information is seen by all post offices.

2. Sending Messages

To send a telegraph, the operator uses a signal key to draw the idle voltage on the line to ground. The recipient can see who is sending the message; this information is encrypted in the message itself.

The lamp serves as the recipient of the messages. If a telegraph operator somewhere starts sending, the message can be read with the lamp in every post office. This is also a feedback to the telegraph operator when they are transmitting; they can immediately see what they are sending.

Now all post offices need agreements in place that determine when someone can start sending (timing), and who can send first if several telegraph operators want to start messages simultaneously (arbitration). These agreements together are called a protocol.

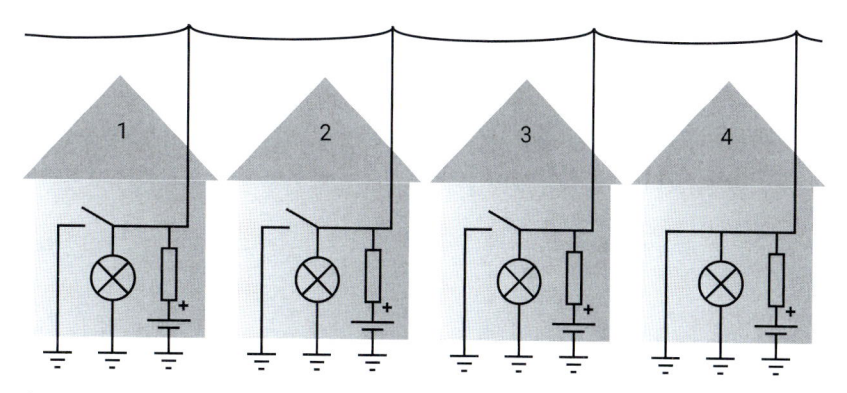

Fig. 121 Telegraph operator (4) operates the signal key, which causes the lamp to go out in all post offices.

3. Digital Messages

With CAN, normal copper wire is used to transmit digital messages. Digital means that only two states are recognized on the bus: "0" and "1." These two states are made visible on the bus by two different voltage levels (high/low).

Only the control units in the car are connected to the CAN bus.

Each control unit contains a CAN interface which makes it possible to transmit and receive digital messages.

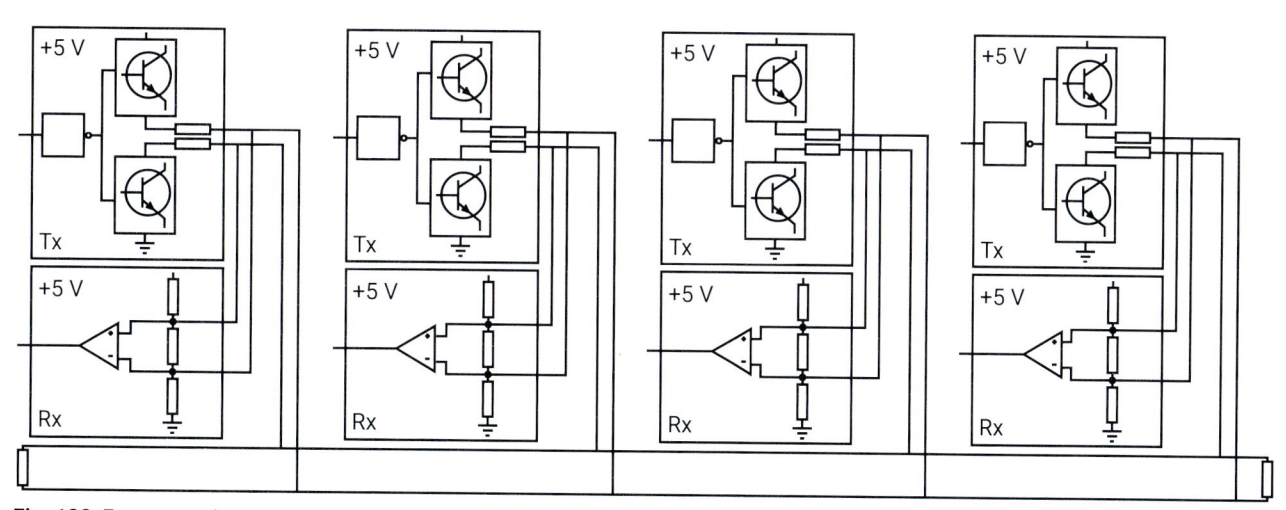

Fig. 122 Four control units are connected to the CAN bus.

4. Data Line

Four control units are connected to a data line in the same way telegraph offices are connected to a telegraph line.

Instead of one data line, the CAN bus consists of two lines, called CAN-High and CAN-Low. A receiver uses the voltage difference between CAN-H and CAN-L to determine whether a bit has the value '1' or the value '0'. This method contributes to the operating reliability of CAN.

At both ends of the bus, CAN-H and CAN-L are connected to each other via two 120 ohm terminating resistors. These resistors prevent the reflection of messages on the bus and are mounted in a control unit or in the cable harness.

5. Sending and Receiving Messages

Like a telegraph office, each control unit contains a telegraph key (transmitter) and a receiver.

The quiescent voltage comes from the supply source which is integrated into the receiver. Together, they form the electrical connection between the CAN controller (telegraph operator) and the CAN bus (telegraph line).

This connection is called the CAN interface. This CAN interface makes the ones and zeros electrically visible on the bus.

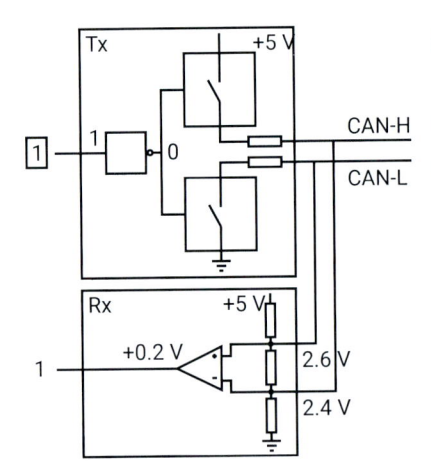

Fig. 123 Each control unit contains a signal key (Transmitter Tx) and a receiver (Receiver Rx).

The transmitter (Tx) is comprised of two electronic switches which are always operated simultaneously via the output of an inverter.

If a '1' is passed to the input of the inverter, the output will be "0." If a "0" is passed, the output will be "1."

The receiver (Rx) consists of a voltage divider with three resistors and a differential amplifier (operational amplifier).

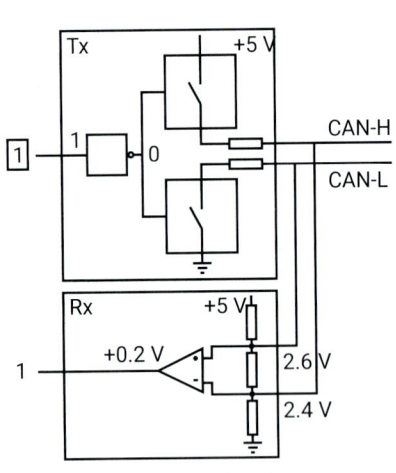

Fig. 124 A "1" is passed to the inverter, so the output is "0."

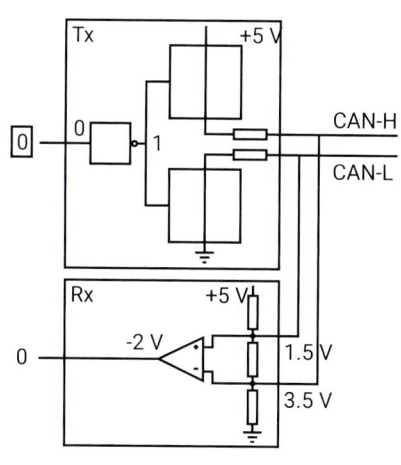

Fig. 125 The control unit sends a "0"

6. State of the Bus

The state of the bus is called *recessive* when a logical "1" is sent. When a logical "0' is sent, the state of the bus is *dominant*.

The control unit can send a message by making a series of ones and zeroes: a series of bits. A bit is the smallest piece of information that a computer can understand, and is comprised of either a 0 or 1.

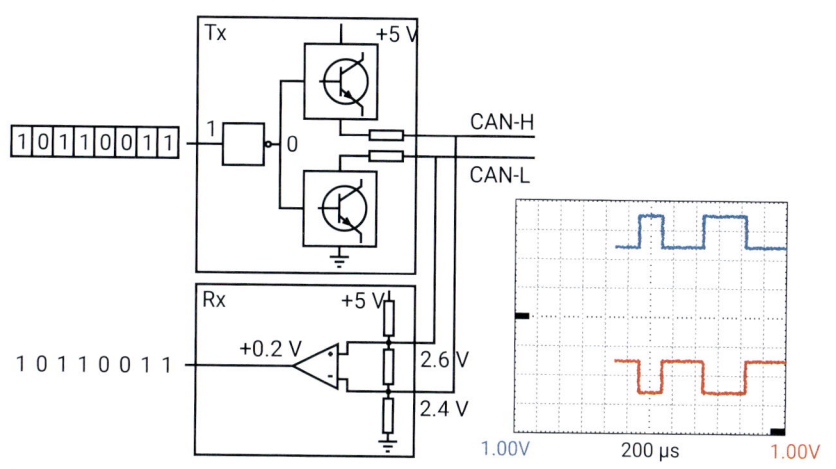

Fig. 126 The control unit sends a message (a series of bits)

The receiver in the CAN interface processes the difference between CAN-H and CAN-L. As both data lines are twisted, electrical interference on either line has an equally strong effect.

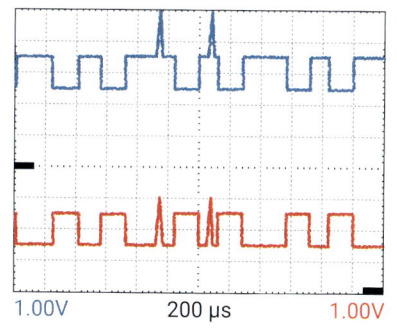

Fig. 127 The influence of electrical interference is the same on both lines.

CAN BUS: NETWORK PROTOCOL INTRODUCTION

There can easily be 10 or more control units connected to a CAN network.
When data is transmitted, certain agreements are required. For example:

- the origin of the data
- the start and end of a message

These agreements are called a protocol.

A phone conversation, for example, has a fixed sequence of events.

You can also call this a protocol.

Globally, the CAN protocol is as follows:
- start: start bit
- identification: identifier
- message: data field
- stop: stop bit

In a car network, a message is often used by more than one control unit.
For example, the ABS unit measures the vehicle speed and puts this data on the network. This data is then accessible and used by the dashboard unit, engine unit and radio.

You have just seen that it's awkward transmitting the same message in turn to different units.
In order to solve this, the identifier has been added to the data.

Each message (such as vehicle speed, engine speed, turn signal, engine temperature) has its own code.
The transmitter transmits the identifier + message. All units on the network see the message and from the identifier can see whether the message contains useful information for them.

From this it is clear that some messages must take priority.
The CAN protocol therefore requires more than just a start bit,

identifier, data and a stop bit.

The CAN protocol is more extensive than has been described here. It is, however, too complex to deal with here.

CAN BUS: NETWORK PROTOCOL

1. Introduction

The communication rules that are necessary when exchanging information between control units are referred to as the network communication protocol.
This protocol is an essential part of module communication.

CAN bus networks operate on their own established protocol, and the following attributes of communication are addressed:
- The form of a CAN message: How is the message structured?
- Access to a network: Who can send first if multiple control units start sending at the same time?
- Error detection and handling: How does a sender know whether the message is received? What does a sender need to do if no one receives the message?
- Bit-timing and synchronization: How is it ensured that all control units read the ones and zeros on the CAN network at the same speed and at the same time?

2. Data Frame

One of the purposes of the CAN protocol is to determine in what form the data will be transmitted in over the bus.

CAN communication is similar to our spoken language in that a data frame can be compared to a sentence.
These sentences are composed of fields, which are similar to the words that form a sentence. The bits are the letters from which a word is composed.

A complete message on the CAN bus is called a data frame. A frame is composed of nine pieces, which are called fields. These fields each contain a certain number of bits.

A bit is the smallest piece of information that a computer can understand: 0 or 1.

The nine fields are:

- start field (1 bit)
- arbitration field / identifier (11 bits)
- remote transmission request (RTR) field (1 bit)
- identifier Extension (IDE) field (1 bit)
- control field (4 bits)
- data field (0 to 64 bits)
- error check (CRC) field (16 bits)
- confirmation (ACK) field (2 bits)
- end of message (EOF) field (7 bits)

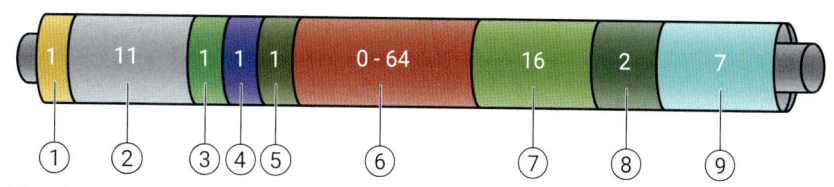

Fig. 128 A data frame consists of nine fields, each made up of one or more bits: 1. Start bit. 2. Arbitration field/identifier. 3. RTR bit. 4. IDE bit. 5. Control field. 6. Data field. 7. CRC field. 8. Confirmation field. 9. End-of-message field.

3. Start Bit

When beginning communication, the transmitting control unit will have to be aware of every other control unit on the CAN bus before it can transmit the message. The start bit is how the control unit indicates to every control unit on the CAN bus that a message is being started. The start bit is one bit long and is always a dominant (0) bit.

4. Arbitration / Identifier

Messages on the CAN bus have no address and/or transmitter information. They are put on the bus and each control unit determines for itself whether the message is interesting enough to read in full. The field after the start bit is used by all control units to determine whether the message which follows is interesting. This field is called the arbitration field or *identifier*.

Two pieces of information are indicated by the identifier:

- the identity of the message
- the priority of the message

The identity of the message (the name) actually indicates what type of data the message contains. For example, in the message from the dashboard control unit with the identity "Position Windshield Wiper Switch," the identity itself already indicates what information the message will contain.

When merely seeing "Position Windshield Wiper Switch," every control unit can determine whether it is worthwhile to read the message or not without seeing the actual data (the state of the switch) provided.

The identifier determines how important a message is, i.e. its priority.
Imagine what would occur when the dashboard control unit and another control unit start sending at the same moment. In this case, the control units would be talking across each other, resulting in nothing being understood by any modules on the bus.

Therefore, the identifier also sets the overall arbitration (access to the network). The convention is that the more dominant bits (0) located in the front of the identifier, the more important the message is. The identifier with the lowest decimal value has the highest priority.

Messages with a high priority have priority over messages with a lower priority and therefore earlier access to the network.

How the bits of the identifier are used depends on the application. The designer of the network software has complete freedom here.

For a standard CAN message (CAN version 2.0A) the identifier consists of 11 bits. There is a more comprehensive (extended) version of CAN (version 2.0B) that uses 29 bits. The extended version was developed to meet the requirements of the American SAE and makes it possible to send more complex messages.
With 11 bits, you can make 2048 unique combinations. Due to an error in the design of an Intel CAN controller, it was documented in the CAN protocol that it is only possible to distinguish 2032 different identifiers (and therefore messages). With 29 bits, it is possible to generate 536 million different identifiers.

5. RTR bit

Suppose that the control unit on the left side of the engine compartment wishes to know the status of the front right door contact; it places a request for this information on the bus. This request is called a remote frame.

A data frame is a message that contains information. A remote frame has the same identifier as the data frame, but contains no information. The Remote Transmission Request (RTR) bit indicates whether a message is a data frame (information) or a remote frame (request). The RTR bit is one bit long and is dominant (0) for a data frame and recessive (1) for a remote frame.

6. IDE bit

The Identifier Extension (IDE) bit is one bit long and is used to indicate whether the message identifier is a standard identifier of 11 bits or an extended identifier of 29 bits.

The IDE bit is dominant (0) to indicate the standard identifier and recessive (1) to indicate the extended identifier.

7. Control Field

The length of the data field (the number of data bytes) can vary. This depends on the quantity of information which the transmitter wishes to put in the message. The length of the data field can vary from 0 up to 8 bytes.

Every control unit that receives the message uses the control field to determine when the data field stops and when the CRC field begins.

8. Data Field

The data field contains the actual information and can be 0 - 64 bits (0 - 8 bytes) long. This immediately explains why not all messages on the CAN bus are equally long. The variation is in the length of the data field.

For a remote frame, the data field is 0 bits long.

9. CRC field

In order to ensure that all zeros and ones have been correctly received, the Cyclic Redundancy Check (CRC) field is added.

The CRC is the result of a calculation which the transmitting control unit has carried out, using all the zeros and ones right up to the CRC field and added to the message.
Every receiver of the message makes the same calculation and compares this with the received CRC.
For a correctly transmitted message, both values must be the same.

The CRC field is 16 bits long and contains a 15-bit Cyclic Redundancy Code and a CRC end bit.

10. ACK field

The transmitting control unit requires an acknowledgement from at least one receiver that the message has been received correctly. During the Acknowledge field (ACK), the transmitting control unit keeps quiet and waits for an acknowledgement. The ACK field is two bits long and consists of an acknowledgement bit (ACK slot) and delimiter (ACK delimiter). Both bits are transmitted as recessive (1) by the control unit.

Once a receiver has received the message correctly, the receiver transmits a dominant bit (0) during the ACK slot. This is acknowledgement to the transmitter that the message has been received correctly by at least one receiver.

11. EOF

If the receipt is acknowledged during the ACK field, the transmitting control unit ends the message with the End Of Frame (EOF) field.

The EOF field is seven recessive bits (1) long and indicates to the other control units on the bus that the message has now ended.

CAN BUS: NETWORK ARBITRATION

1. Introduction

Any control unit connected to the CAN network may transmit a message at anytime, as long as the bus is free (no other control unit transmitting). This is called the multimaster principle.

When the bus is busy (a control unit is transmitting) other control units needing to send a message must wait until the transmitting control unit is finished.

Often, just after one control unit ends a message, several other control units simultaneously want to transmit their message.

An arbitration mechanism is used to prevent messages from being transmitted at the same time over the bus.

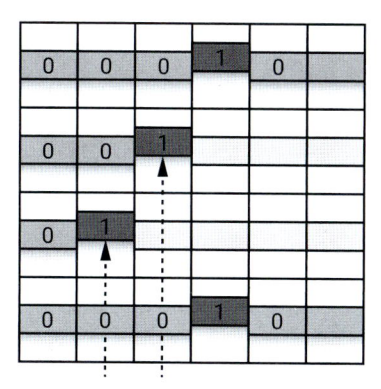

Fig. 129 The identifier with the most dominant bits (0) has the highest priority.

2. Identifier and Arbitration

After a message is transmitted over the bus, each control unit has the opportunity to transmit a new message once a minimum 3-bit time frame has passed.

The control units on the bus are always listening for messages waiting to be transmitted. Identifiers are assigned to the beginning of each message, designating the importance of the transmission.

The highest priority message is always transmitted first. For example, a message regarding air bag deployment would receive a much higher priority than a request to turn on the air conditioning compressor.

This is arranged by giving the identifier with the most dominant bits (0) the highest priority. So the more bits with the value zero (0) at the start of the identifier, the more important the message. Because of the electrical function of a CAN bus, a dominant bit (0) automatically has priority over a recessive bit (1).

CAN BUS: ERROR DETECTION AND RECTIFICATION

1. Introduction

Among other things, the CAN protocol specifies how transmitters and receivers (control units) must deal with communication errors during transmission. The error handling is aimed at detecting incorrect or corrupt messages on the bus, and when these types of messages are detected the transmitter re-sends the message.

First, every transmitting control unit listens "live" to what it puts on the CAN network. For example, if the control unit sends a "1" but hears a "0," then it stops transmitting and starts again. Second, the transmitter of a message wants to receive a confirmation message from at least one recipient. If the transmitter doesn't receive it, they send the message again.

All listening receivers on the CAN network also check the message that appears on the network. If a listening control unit detects an error, it interrupts the message by sending what is called an error frame. The transmitter of the message responds by re-sending the message.

2. Error Frame

By sending an error frame, CAN communication is temporarily stopped. If other control units have not detected the error yet, each control unit on the bus knows that the current message contains an error, and that they must ignore the information they received.

The CAN protocol contains five different error checks:
— bit monitoring
— bit stuffing check
— frame check
— acknowledgement check
— crc check

3. Bit Monitoring

In the communication activities of CAN, each transmitter directly listens to what it transmits.

If, while transmitting, a transmitter detects a difference between what it is transmitting and receiving, this means there is a Bit Error (exception: the arbitration field). The transmitter then stops transmitting and sends an error frame to the bus to indicate to the other control units that the information they have received must be ignored. The transmitter then transmits the message again.

4. Temporary and Permanent Errors

A distinction is made between temporary and permanent errors by the raising and lowering of counters inside of each control unit.

A permanent communication error could result in a control unit having to keep repeating its message. The CAN bus would then be flooded with error messages and/or repeats of the same message.

In order to prevent this, each control unit on the bus has two counters; one counter for erroneous received messages (Rx counter) and one for erroneous transmitted messages (Tx counter).

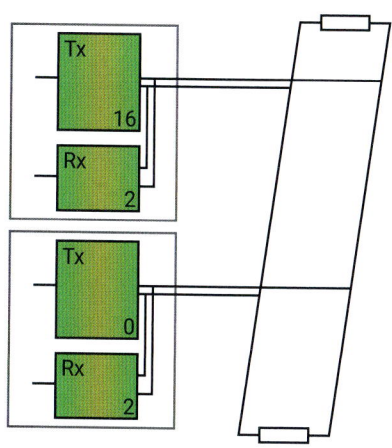

Fig. 130 Each control unit has two counters: Tx: transmitter Rx: receiver

5. Error Counters

Depending on the position of the counters, each control unit on the bus has three states:

— Error Active: When the Tx counter or Rx counter is lower than 127 the control unit can set an Error Flag

— Error Passive: When the Tx counter or Rx counter higher than or equal to 127 the control unit is stopped from setting an Error Flag

— Bus Off: When the Tx counter reaches 255 the control unit no longer transmits.

Transmission is only possible again after a reset of the CAN controller. Cycling the ignition switch is often sufficient. If the error persists, the Tx counter quickly rises again and the transmitter switches itself to "bus off" again.

Fig. 131 With control unit 1, the Tx counter has risen so high that it switches itself to "bus off."

6. Bit Stuffing

If a transmitter transmits a long sequence of the same bits in a message, the chance of bit errors at the receivers increases. For this reason, the protocol specifies that if a transmitter transmits five identical bits (five zeros or five ones), the transmitter must append an extra bit (stuff bit) of a different value as the sixth bit.

Receivers of the message recognise the sixth bit as a stuff bit and ignore it. If a receiver detects more than five identical bits in a sequence, the receiver interrupts the communication by means of an error frame. The transmitter then knows that it must transmit the message again.

7. Frame Check

A number of parts of a CAN message have a fixed form (number of bits and value of the bits). If these parts have an invalid value or form, this is called a Form Error.

If a receiver detects an invalid value in these parts, it interrupts the communication with an error frame. The transmitter then knows that it must transmit the message again.

8. CRC and acknowledgment of receipt (ACK)

If the CRC (Cyclic Redundancy Check) does not match the CRC sent to any receiver, the transmitter will not receive a confirmation message from any control unit during the confirmation field (ACKnowledgement field).

The transmission is now interrupted by the transmitter with an error frame.
Each control unit on the network knows that the information just received must be ignored and the transmitter sends the message again.

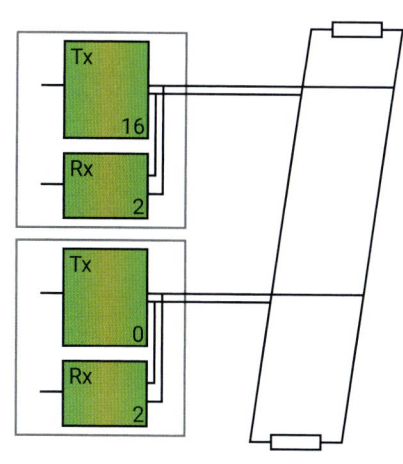

Fig. 132 Each control unit has two counters: Tx: transmitter Rx: receiver

9. Temporary and Permanent Errors

A distinction is made between temporary and permanent errors by the raising and lowering of counters inside of each control unit.

A permanent communication error could result in a control unit having to keep repeating its message. The CAN bus would then be flooded with error messages and/or repeats of the same message.

In order to prevent this, each control unit on the bus has two counters; one counter for erroneous received messages (Rx counter) and one for erroneous transmitted messages (Tx counter).

CAN BUS: DIAGNOSIS

1. Introduction

The introduction of the CAN bus has changed the way we think about a communication network. Where a system previously had one control unit that was relatively easy to test and access, a system is now composed of several control units. Without a system overview (e.g. a block diagram), it is impossible to diagnose malfunctions. Control units that show up as disconnected or inactive within a certain system may well be the cause of the network malfunction you are attempting to find. In addition to a system overview, a functional description of the system is needed for effective diagnosis.

Using a scan tool is the quickest way to assess the bus communication, and reading the error codes should provide an initial indication of which components are active, and which units are not communicating via the bus.

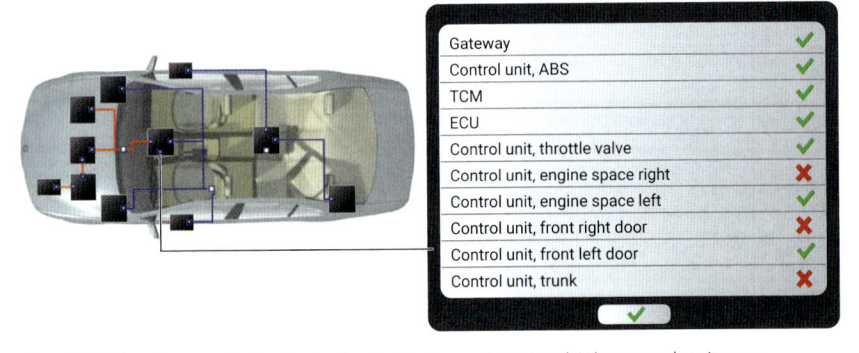

Fig. 133 The diagnostic tester is the fastest way to see which control units are communicating in the bus and which are not.

2. Measurements

Besides reading error codes, you can also perform measurements on the CAN, preferably with an oscilloscope.

The three points used to analyze a scope image are:
— the shape of the signal
— the voltage levels of the signal
— the bus load

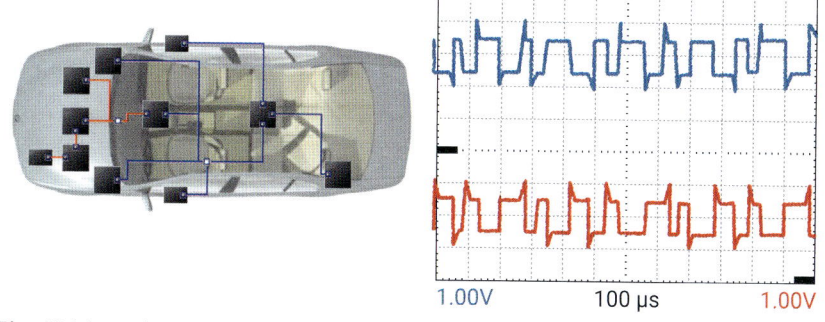

Fig. 134 Impedance peaks on the flanks of the block voltage.

The shape of the signal needs to be a clean block shape, where CAN-H and CAN-L are the inverse of each other. Terminating resistors ensure that the data cable does not carry too much current during communication, which minimizes the induction effect and signal interference as much a possible.

Two control units are connected to the CAN bus and each of them has a resistance of 120 Ω. If there is no problem with the data cable, you will measure a resistance of 60 Ω. If one of the CAN wires is interrupted, you will measure a resistance of 120 Ω. With a short circuit between the CAN wires you will measure a resistance of 0 Ω.

Attention: Never measure resistance in a circuit where the power supply is connected.

Fig. 135 Data cables are okay.

Fig. 136 Data cables interrupted.

3. Voltage Level

The voltage level can show whether there is a short circuit to the ground, to the power supply, or between CAN-High and CAN-Low. You can check which control unit is involved by disconnecting control units.

PLEASE NOTE Voltage levels can only be checked with a scope. A multimeter only indicates the mean voltage!

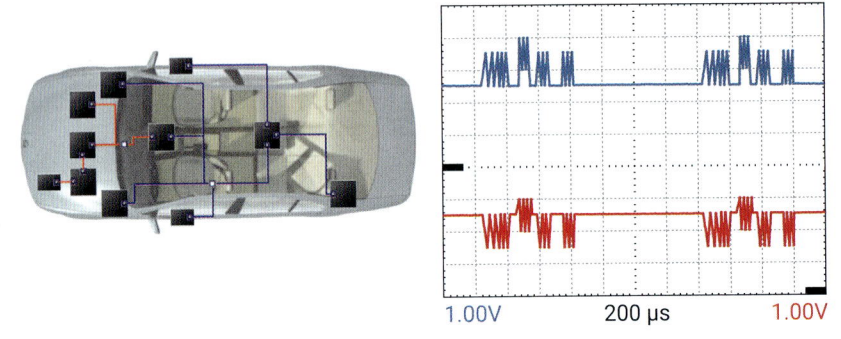

Fig. 137 A message has a different voltage level.

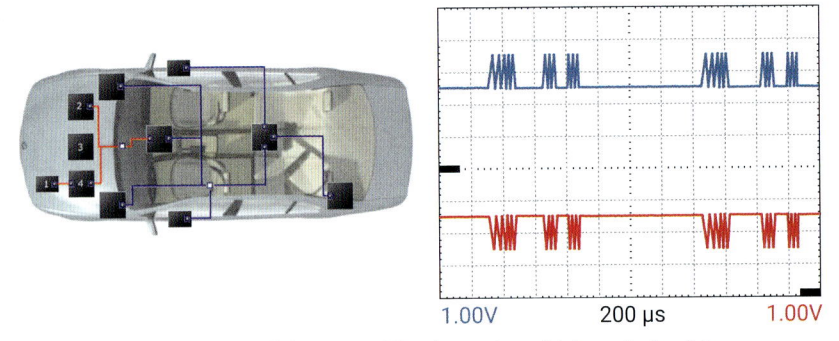

Fig. 138 Use the topology of the network to determine which control unit is involved.

4. Bus Load

The traffic on the CAN bus (bus load) can also only be seen with the scope. The bus load, expressed as a percentage, is the space that messages will take up on the network. In other words: Is there still enough space between the messages? The busier the message transfer becomes, the more difficult it becomes to get a message directly on the bus.

With a high bus load, it becomes difficult for messages with a low priority to appear on the bus without waiting.

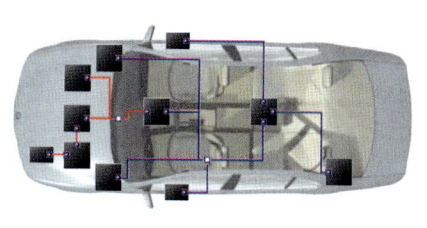

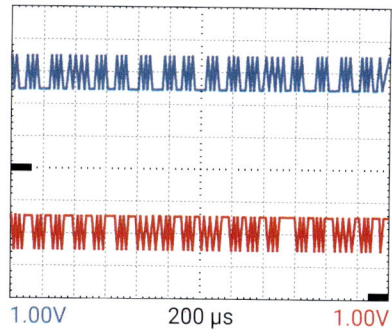

Fig. 139 The bus load is high.

CAN BUS AND FLEXRAY

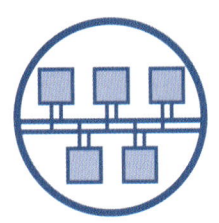

Fig. 140 Networks.

1. CAN Bus.

The control units on the CAN bus are basically the same and are also referred to as multi-master. The bit-wise arbitration system of the CAN bus ensures that only one control unit is assigned to the network at a time. It's possible that different control units want to send a message simultaneously. In that case, the control unit with the highest priority is assigned to the network. Then the message with the smallest binary number (the number with the most zeros in front) takes precedence over any other message. Next comes the message with the second smallest number and so on. It is therefore a bit-wise control of the priority, with which a 0 is dominant and a 1 is recessive.

EXAMPLE The ABS control unit, the engine control unit, and the transmission control unit want to transmit simultaneously.
The three control units will simultaneously place a dominant 0 on the network. As a result, the network remains dominant 0. When the second bit is sent, the transmission control unit places a recessive 1, and the engine control unit and the ABS control unit place a dominant 0. The transmission control unit has lost and stops the communication. When transmitting the third bit, the engine control unit places a recessive 1, and the ABS control unit places a 0. The engine control unit has lost the arbitration, and the ABS control unit may continue to transmit.

In the example, the transmission control unit and the engine control unit may try to transmit a message again at a subsequent time. The arbitration system means that a control unit has no certainty whether and when a message can be transmitted.

Linear networks are widely used in CAN bus systems. A disadvantage of this is that an open or short circuit in the network leads directly to system failure. To make a network redundant (so that it continues to function properly in the event of a failure), an additional network is created, such as the local CAN.

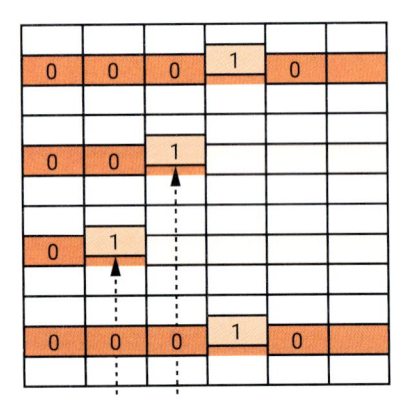

Fig. 141 CAN bus arbitration system The message with the most zeros is given priority.

Autonomous functions, online connections, and "x-by-wire" not only require a network with a high data rate, but also a network that is redundant. Despite the powerful CAN bus protocol and a baud rate (data rate) of 500 kbit/s, this network is not sufficient and has therefore reached the limits of its ability. The Flexray and ethernet networks are more suitable.

2. Flexray

Flexray has been developed by a consortium of various vehicle and semi-conductor manufacturers, including Motorola and Philips. Flexray is a communication system for applications that work on the basis of a powerful real-time data transfer between the control units.

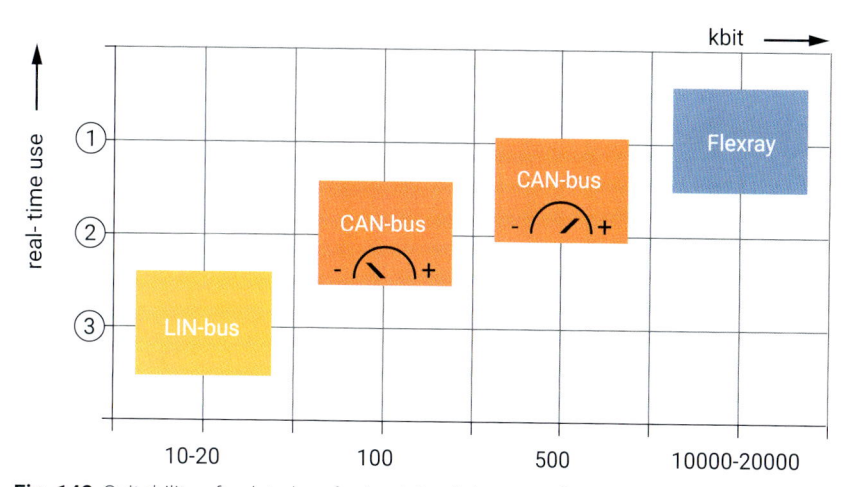

Fig. 142 Suitability of a data bus for "real-time" data transfer.
1. "Real-time," deterministic and redundant 2. Limited suitability for 'real-time'
3. Not suitable for "real-time"

"Real-time" means direct communication; Information is shared and processed and leads to action without delays or waiting time. The graph shows the "real-time" suitability of LIN-bus, CAN-bus, and Flexray relative to the baud rate (bit/s). Due to the low rate of 20 kbit/s, LIN bus is not suitable for "real-time" communication and CAN-bus is suitable only to a limited extent, while Flexray complies with the high data speed of 10 Mbit/s. In addition to a high data rate and suitability for "real-time" communication, Flexray also has a high degree of redundancy and is deterministic (predictable).

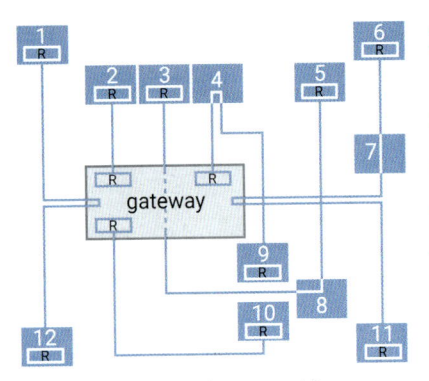

Fig. 143 Flexray with star and linear network

3. Flexray Topology

Flexray can be installed in the car in the following different topology forms:
— Linear network - star network
— Tree network

The depicted Flexray network can be described as a tree network. The network is in fact a combination of several topology forms. The gateway forms the central control unit for the star network, with control units 2, 4, 9, and 10. Among other things, a linear network forms the gateway together with control units 1 and 12.

Like a high speed CAN bus, Flexray uses terminating resistors. The resistors are fitted at the ends of the wires to prevent reflection of the messages. The value of these terminating resistors is determined by the data rate and the length of the wires. The terminating resistors are located in the control units.

If the Flexray connection to the control unit is not the physical end point, this Flexray section is called a supply and transit wire. This control unit also has resistors, which are called "non-terminating resistors."

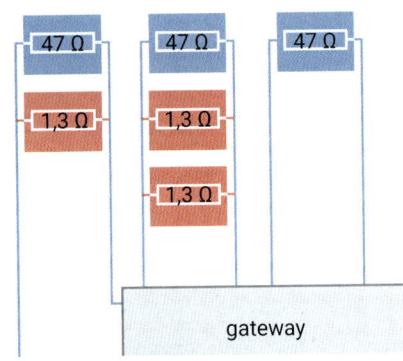

Fig. 144 Terminating resistors (47Ω) and non-terminating resistors (1.3Ω)

4. Redundant Communication

With safety systems, reliable communication must still be guaranteed when a network wire is interrupted. This is achieved via a second pair of network wires. A redundant Flexray network uses two independent pairs of network wires. In the event of a failure of one pair, the information of the defective pair can be transmitted via the other pair.

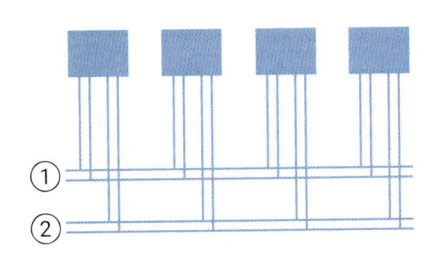

Fig. 145 A dual pair of network wires are installed for safety systems.

5. Deterministic Communication

A CAN bus is an event-driven bus system. Messages are placed on the network when an event is available. This may be an error message in the event of a perceived failure or a kick-down message when fully pressing the accelerator pedal. An increase in events can cause delays with CAN bus, so it can take some time before more messages can be sent. If messages are sent across the CAN network unsuccessfully and without interference, they continue being sent until they have been sent successfully. This can lead to overloading of the CAN network and serious delays. This would not be acceptable in time-critical applications such as driving assistance systems.

Flexray is a system that is both time-driven and event-driven. The time-driven part uses reserved data blocks, or time slots, that are are assigned certain information. A time slot is a fixed period that is kept free for speed, for example. The time slots are also called the static segment. This means that important periodic information is passed on in a fixed timetable in Flexray, so that Flexray cannot get overloaded. This creates a schedule of when certain information is sent and received.

Other messages, of which the processing time is less important, are event-driven. Think here of information about the content of the fuel tank. This section is also referred to as the dynamic segment.

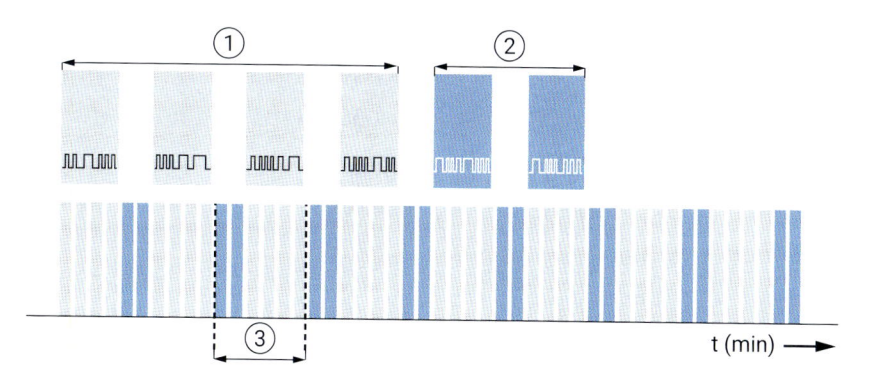

Fig. 146 Deterministic communication.
1. Time-driven 2. Event-driven 3. Cycle (5 ms)

EXAMPLE A Flexray cycle has a duration of 5 ms, of which 3 ms are static (time-driven) and 2 ms dynamic (event-driven). By way of example, four parameters are reserved in the static segment, namely: revs, ignition angle, temperature, and speed. Event-driven information can

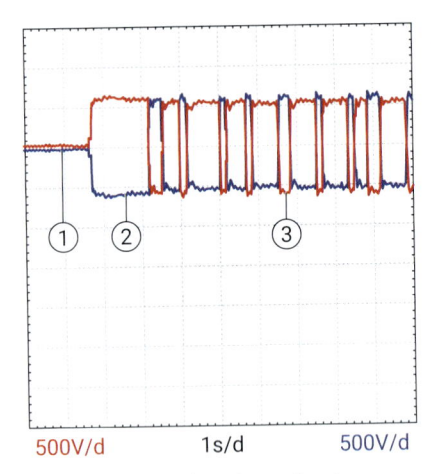

Fig. 147 Flexray has three signal states:
1. Idle
2. Data 1
3. Data 0

be sent in the dynamic segment. In this way the deterministic communication is created. After all, it is predictable which information is shared and when.

6. Signal Characteristics

Flexray works with three signal states:
— Idle
— Data 0
— Data 1

The signal state "idle" is reached when there is no communication. The voltage is then 2.5 V.
The signal levels "data 0" and "data 1" vary between 1.5 V and 3.5 V. During the transmission of a message, the control units "look" at the voltage difference between the maximum value and the minimum value, also known as differential voltage. Typical values for this are 1.8 V and 2.0 V.
The differential voltage must be at least 1.2 V on the transmitter and 0.8 V on the receiver.
The high signal is also called bus plus (+) and the low signal bus minus (-).

LIN BUS

1. Introduction

LIN stands for: Local Interconnect Network. The LIN bus operates on a single wire and is connected to an ECU/node that is in contact with one of the other networks, such as CAN [Controller Area Network] bus.

Actuators and sensors are connected to the LIN bus; they provide information or perform actions at the request of the ECU. For example, you can find the LIN bus in a seat to control the various actuators and the heating. Another example is the control of the fan and the ventilation ducts of a climate control system and the checking or control of the mirrors.

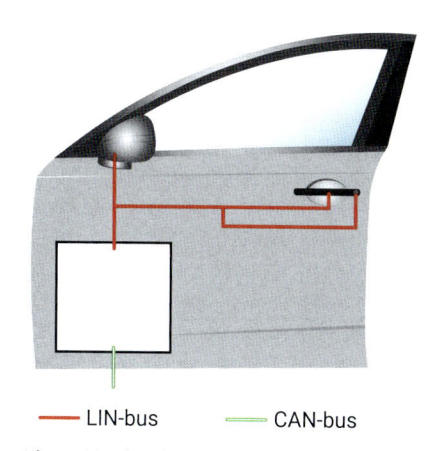

Fig. 148 The door control unit is connected to the CAN bus network. The mirror adjustment, door lock and door control are connected to the control unit via LIN bus.

2. LIN master and slave

LIN bus systems use a master ECU. The master is in contact with other ECUs via MOST or CAN bus. The master module has 1 or more slave modules. These are intelligent sensors and actuators or control devices.

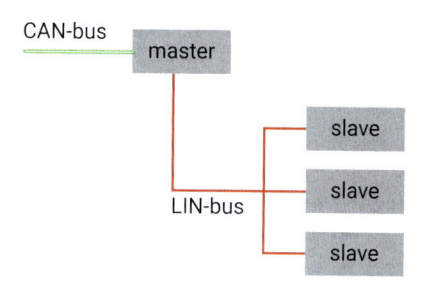

Fig. 149 The master is connected to the CAN bus network. Slaves are connected to the LIN bus network.

3. LIN bus data

LIN bus has a relatively low communication speed. The speed varies per system from 1 to 20 Kbit/s. This means that at the fastest, 20,000 ones or zeros can be sent in 1 second.

Recessive

When no information is sent between the master and a slave, there is a voltage on the bus (wire) of approximately 12 volts. This voltage is called the recessive voltage.

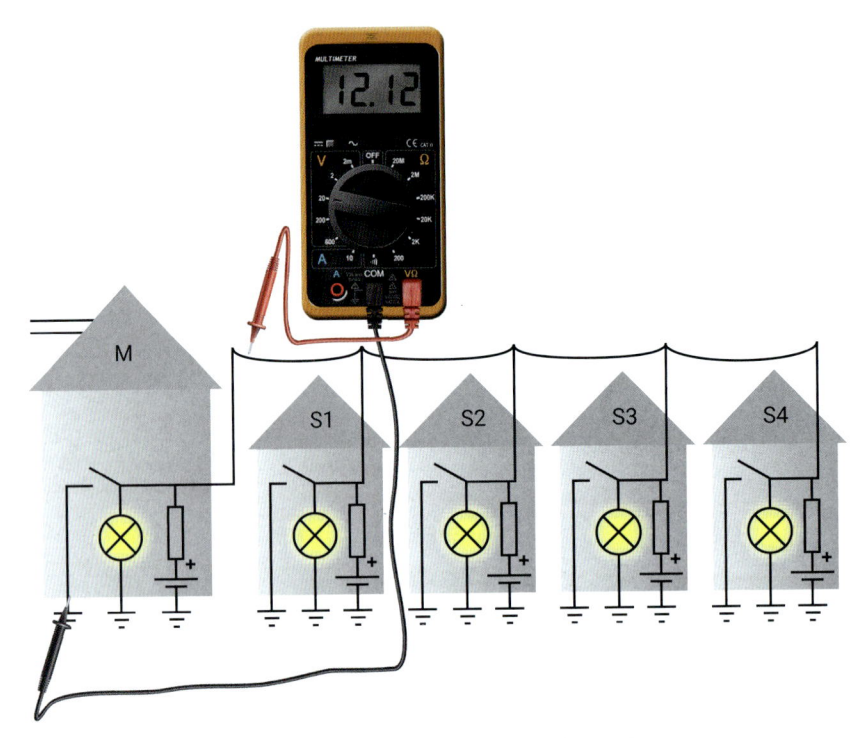

Fig. 150 The base voltage is approximately 12 volts on the LIN bus.

Dominant

By pulling the voltage down to ground, there is approximately 0.5 volts on the bus (wire).

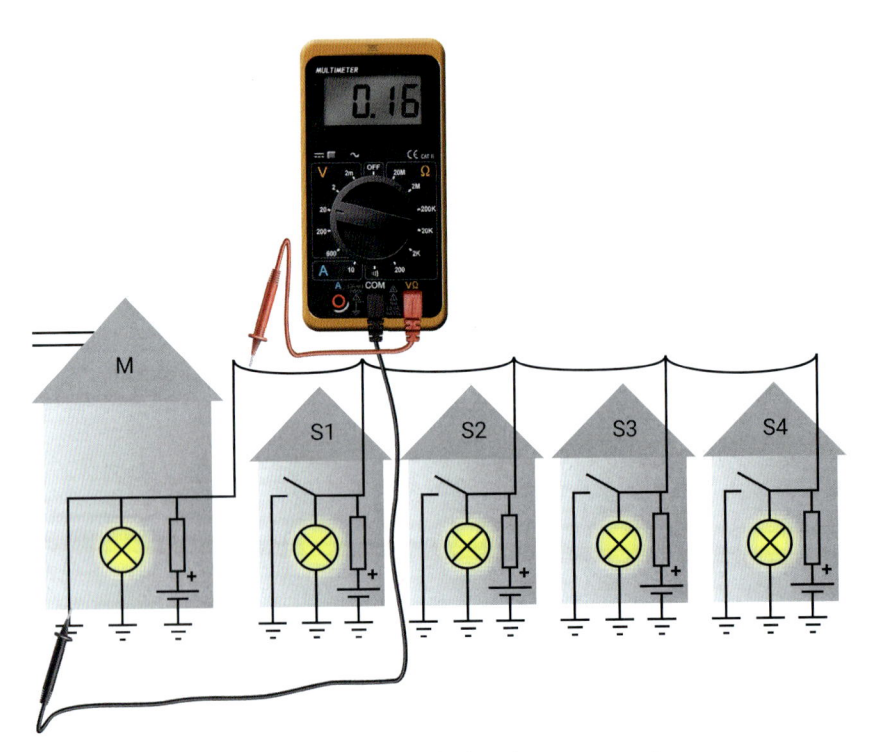

Fig. 151 The voltage when a master pulls the bus down to ground.

Message

By repeating this you will get a switching voltage depending on the position of the switch of the master or of a slave.

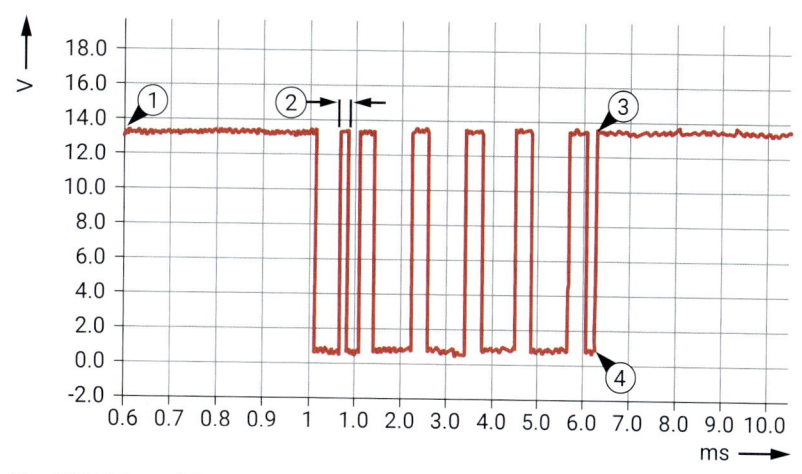

Fig. 152 Voltage (1) is 13 volts. The moment the ECU starts sending information (3), the ECU switches the bus to ground (4). The voltage drops to 0.5 volts. The time (2) is one sent bit.

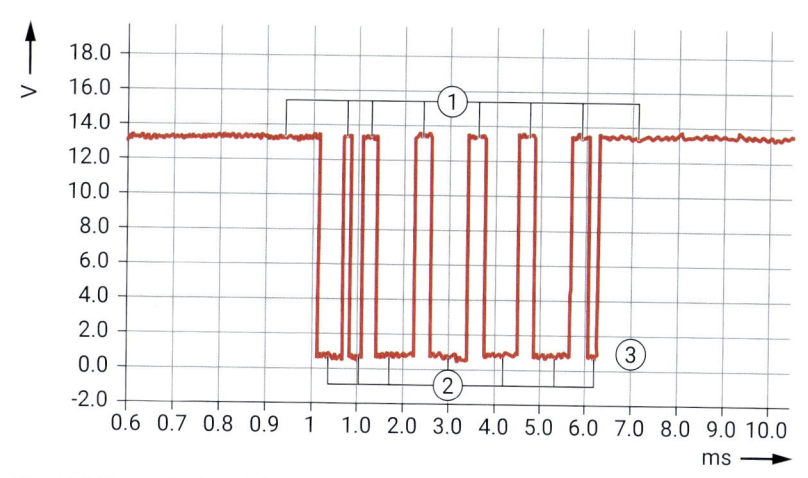

Fig. 153 Recessive bits (1) and dominant bits (2). The message that was sent (3).

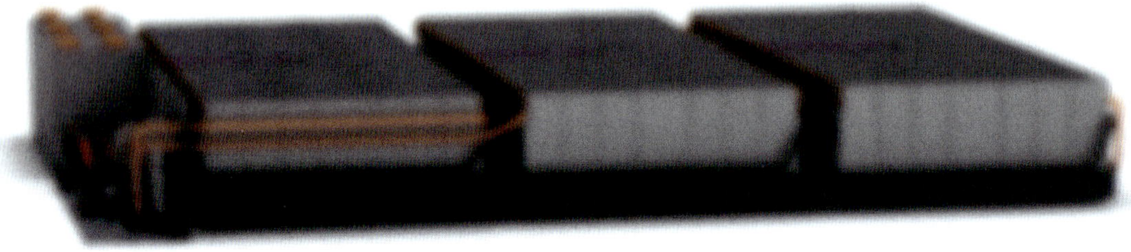

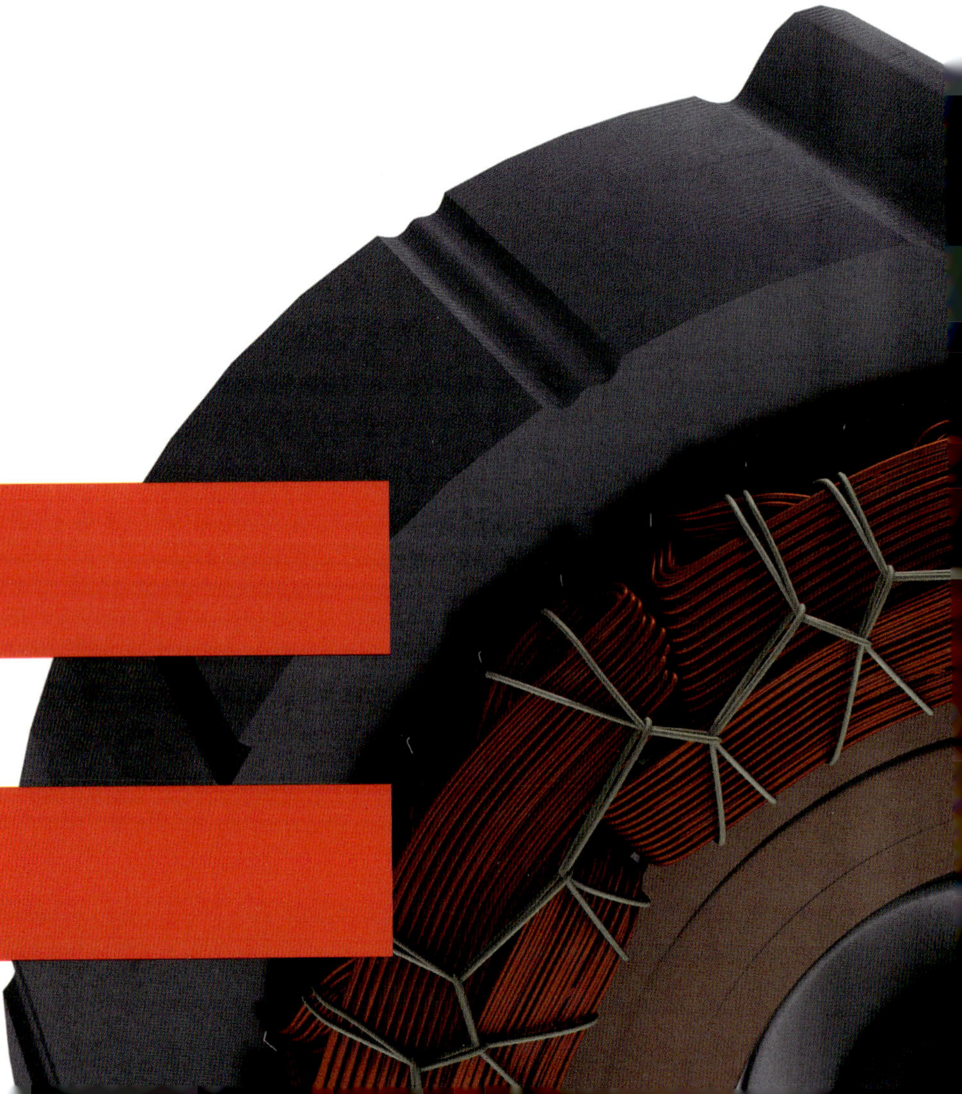

5. Introduction to Hybrid/EV Safety

WORKING WITH VOLTAGE

1. Introduction

Contact with electricity can be life-threatening. It can cause severe burns and may even result in death. This is dependent upon:
— Current strength.
— Alternating or direct voltage.
— Duration of contact.
— Body's resistance.
— Route of the current through the body.
— Individual factors.

It is therefore important that you observe the proper safety precautions.

There is a special symbol that indicates that you are dealing with a life-threatening voltage.

Fig. 154 Hazardous voltage warning.

2. Electrical Contact

The duration and the current strength through the human body are the greatest hazards.

Because a greater current can easily flow when the voltage increases, higher voltages are also dangerous!

The safe voltage is 120 V for direct voltage (DC) and 50 V for AC voltage (AC). The human body reacts differently to these voltages.

Legend:
— **Green**: not externally noticeable
— **Yellow**: externally noticeable, muscles cramp
— **Orange**: difficulty breathing, letting go no longer possible
— **Red**: life-threatening, burns, respiratory arrest, cardiac arrest.

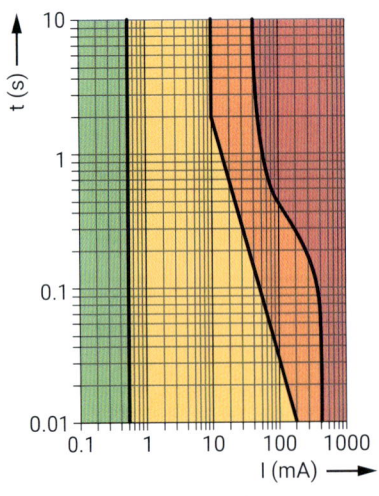

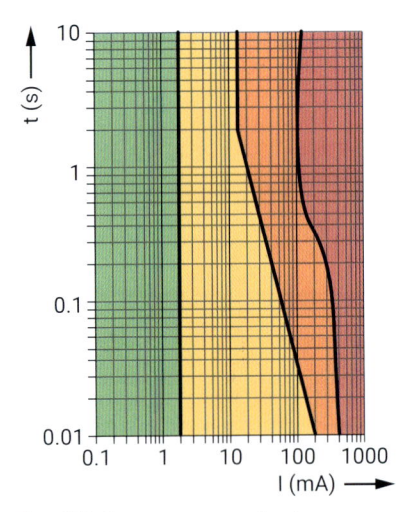

Fig. 155 Consequences due to electrocution with alternating current (AC)

Fig. 156 Consequences due to electrocution with direct current (DC)

Consequences with alternating current:
— Under 0.5 mA, not detectable by human senses.
— 50 mA can be tolerated for about 100 ms before your muscles start to contract.
— 500 mA is immediately life-threatening.

Consequences for direct current:
— Under 2 mA, observation with the human body is not possible.
— 80 mA can be tolerated for about 100 ms before your muscles start to cramp.

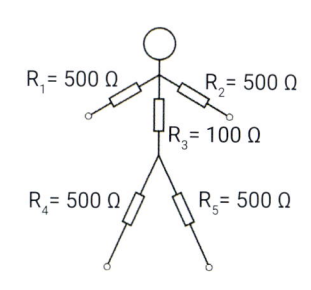

Fig. 157 Limbs expressed in resistance.

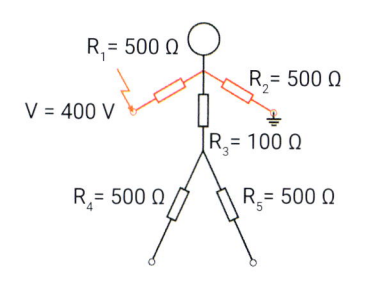

Fig. 158 Calculation Example 1

3. Physical Resistance

The human body has a resistance. As you've already learned, this resistance depends on several factors. To make it easy, we have taken an average here.

Attention! The equivalent resistance for two equal parallel resistors (such as the legs), you calculate by dividing one of these resistors by two.

4. Dangers in Practice

In practice, you encounter situations where electrical contact can lead to dangerous situations.

Here are two calculation examples with practical situations.

Calculation example 1
A technician has opened the HV battery of a hybrid vehicle. The HV voltage of 400 V (DC) is now between two hands.

$$R_{to} = R_1 + R_2 \Rightarrow R_{to} = 500\Omega + 500\Omega$$
$$R_{to} = 1000\Omega$$

What is the current running through the mechanic?

$$I = \frac{U}{R} \Rightarrow I = \frac{400V}{1000\Omega}$$
$$I = 0.4A \quad of \quad 400mA$$

If you compare this in the direct current voltage graph, you can conclude that it is immediately life-threatening!

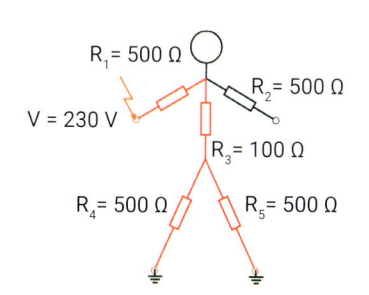

Calculation example 2
An electrician touches the 230 V (AC) conduit with one hand; the current runs away through his feet. What is the resistance from hand to foot for the electrician?

$$\frac{1}{R_v} = \frac{1}{R_4} + \frac{1}{R_5}$$

$$\frac{1}{R_v} = \frac{1}{500}\Omega + \frac{1}{500}\Omega \Rightarrow \frac{1}{R_v} = 0.002 + 0.002\Omega$$

Fig. 159 Calculation Example 2

$$\frac{1}{R_v} = 0.004\Omega \Rightarrow R_v = \frac{1}{0.004}\Omega \Rightarrow R_v = 250\Omega$$

$$R_{to} = R_1 + R_3 + R_v \Rightarrow R_{to} = 500\Omega + 100\Omega + 250\Omega$$

$$R_{to} = 850\Omega$$

What is the current running through the electrician?

$$I = \frac{U}{R} \Rightarrow I = \frac{230V}{850\Omega}$$
$$I = 0.27A \quad of \quad 270mA$$

If you compare this in the graph, you can tolerate this for about 0.2 seconds before it becomes dangerous.

INTRODUCTION TO HYBRID AND ELECTRIC POWERTRAINS

1. Hybrid Drive

To reduce fuel consumption, almost all manufacturers are choosing to build some of their platforms as hybrid vehicles.

In automotive technology, the word "hybrid" means the combination of an internal combustion engine and an electric motor that work together to provide the drive. Depending on prevailing circumstances, operating modes may or may not use the power of the Internal Combustion Engine (ICE) These vehicles are designed to use the ICE as little as possible, but it's necessary most of the time.

The electric motor not only provides the drive, but can also convert kinetic energy into electrical energy while braking to boost the energy stored in the battery. This recovered energy can then be used to power the electric motors so that whenever possible, the internal combustion engine will consume less fuel.

Hybrid cars are available in various types. The most well-known are the full hybrid and the plug-in hybrid, also known as PHEV (Plug-in Hybrid Electric Vehicle).
A PHEV has a larger battery that can be charged at an outlet so that larger distances can be driven completely electrically.

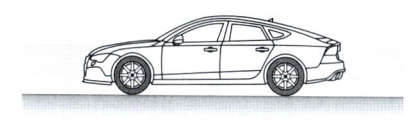

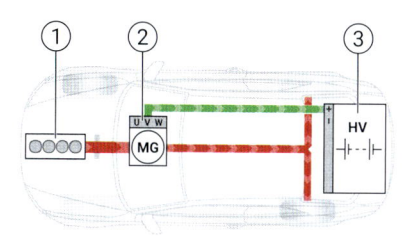

Fig. 160 Hybrid drive. 1. internal combustion engine 2. electric motor 3. battery.

2. Hybrid and Electric Drive

Electric cars are fully powered by the battery and therefore no longer use fuel other than the fuel indirectly used for recharging the battery. They only use one or more electric motors for the drive.
This type of car is also referred to as an EV (Electric Vehicle) or BEV (Battery Electric Vehicle).

The High Voltage energy required to power the electric motor is stored in a very large main battery with a capacity of hundreds of volts. This battery is charged at the outlet, charging post, or charging station. Like the full hybrid, a fully electric car can also convert braking energy and store it in the battery.

There is typically a small (12 V) battery as well. This battery gives power to all systems a driver can use.

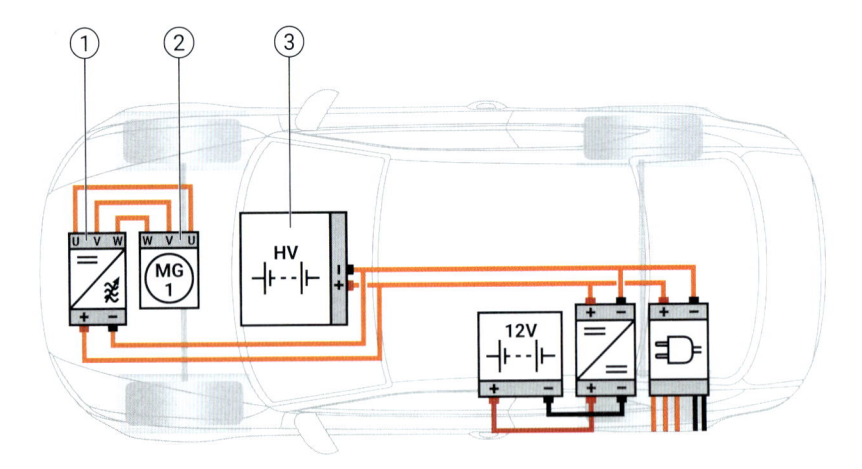

Fig. 161 Electrical drive. 1. inverter 2. electric motor 3. battery

ELECTRIC DRIVE - RECOGNITION

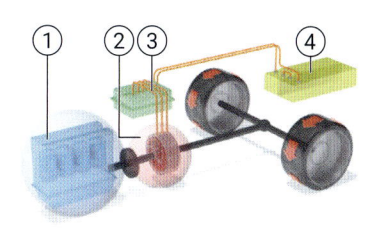

Fig. 162 Semi-hybrid. 1. internal combustion engine 2. electric motor/ generator 3. inverter 4. HV battery

1. Categories

Alternative drives are available in different types.

They differ in the structure of the powertrain and the energy source used.

Semi-hybrid
The internal combustion engine always provides the drive but is supported by an electric motor.

Full hybrid
The internal combustion engine and the electric motor, depending on the situation, provide the drive individually or together.

Plug-in hybrid (PHEV)
The drive is equal to that of a full hybrid car. A plug-in hybrid can drive a greater distance completely electrically because the battery is larger and can be charged at an outlet.

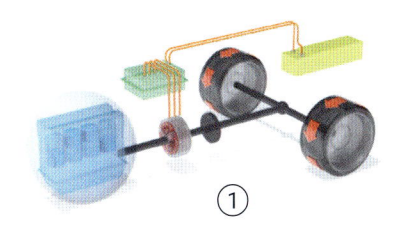

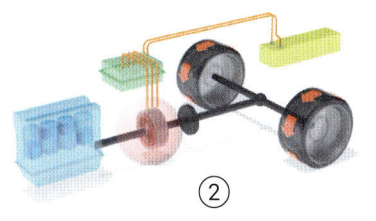

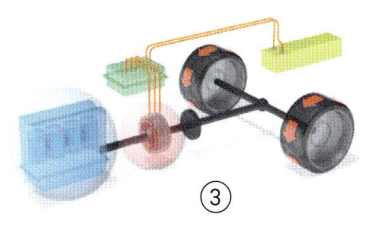

Fig. 163 Full hybrid. 1. The internal combustion engine powers the vehicle. 2. The electric motor drives the vehicle. 3. The internal combustion engine and electric motor power the vehicle together.

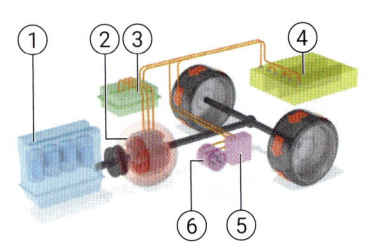

Fig. 164 Plug-in hybrid 1. internal combustion engine 2. electric motor/generator 3. inverter 4. HV battery 5. internal charger 6. charging connection

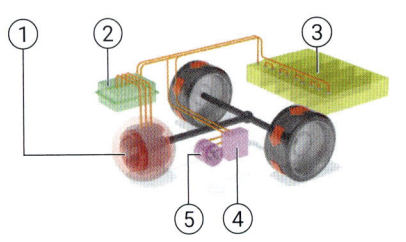

Fig. 165 Electric car 1. electric motor 2. inverter 3. HV battery 4. internal charger 5. charging connection

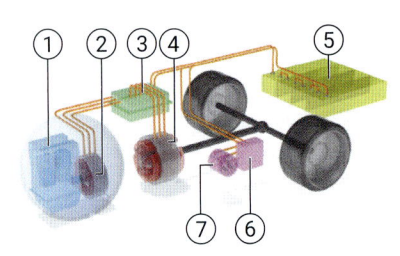

Fig. 166 Electric car with range extender 1. small internal combustion engine 2. generator 3. inverter 4. electric motor 5. HV battery 6. internal charger 7. charging connection

Electric car

The drive is completely electric. The battery is charged at the outlet or charging station.

Electric car with range extender

The drive is the same as that of an electric car, but there is also a small internal combustion engine with generator available that can recharge the battery if it goes dead. This gives the car a larger range.

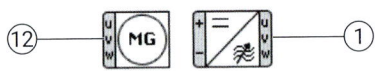

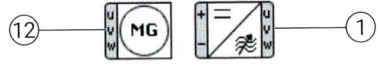

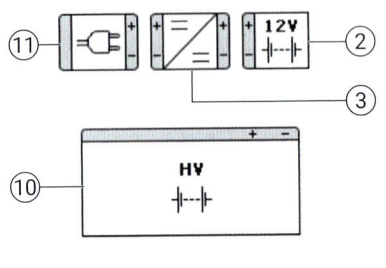

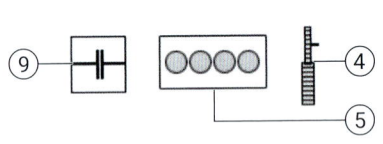

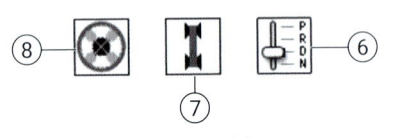

Fig. 167 Explanation of the symbols. 1. inverter 2. 12 V battery 3. DC/DC converter 4. fixed transmission 5. internal combustion engine 6. automatic transmission 7. continuous variable transmission 8. planetary gear system 9. coupling 10. HV battery 11. charging station 12. electric motor / generator

WORKING ON HYBRID VEHICLES

1. Hybrid Automobile

A hybrid vehicle can be recognized by:
- "Hybrid" badging on the vehicle's exterior
- The word "hybrid" printed on the engine cover
- Orange high voltage cables visible from the engine compartment

Like all cars, hybrids require regular maintenance; so it's important for service technicians to be ware of several key points prior to performing maintenance on one of these vehicles.

The first point to remember is hybrid cars have two batteries. A 12 V battery that provides the power for the on-board computers and an HV (high-voltage) battery that supplies power to the electric motor(s). A minimum of 200 V or more may be specified on the HV battery, so one must take care; **this is a lethal amount of voltage!**

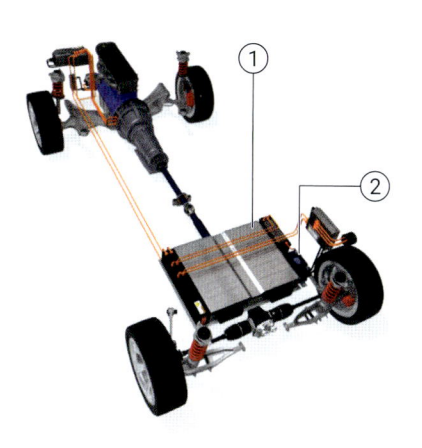

Fig. 180 Hybrid car with two batteries. 1. HV battery 2. 12 V battery

2. High Voltage Components

The high-voltage components can be recognized by:
- The high-voltage symbol (triangle with the lightning bolt)
- Orange HV cables

Important considerations:
- **Towing**: the hybrid motor/generator can generate a current whenever the drive wheels are turning. Therefore, always make sure that the driven axle is off the ground when towing.
- **Paint booth drying chamber**: if the hybrid car is left too long in a paint booth drying chamber the temperature in the car can increase to a very high level. This can cause damage to the HV battery.
- **Factory scan tool**: There are a few actions that may require the use of an OE factory scan tool or aftermarket equivalent, to ensure your safety.

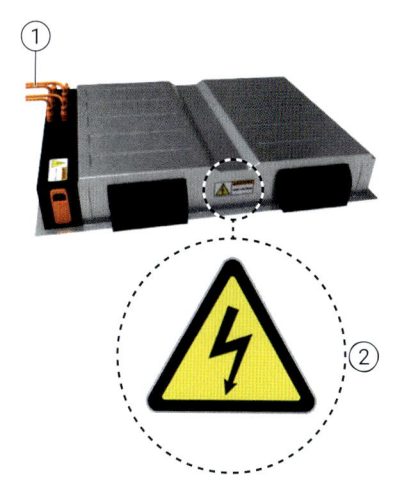

Fig. 181 High-voltage components identification points. 1. orange cables 2. high-voltage symbol.

3. Working Safely Around High-Voltage

You must follow the step-by-step plan in the service manual to ensure you take the appropriate precautions when working around HV components.
This information will vary depending on the vehicle make and model!

General safety rules for working on or around HV components:

First check your tools:
- Inflate the insulating gloves so that you can determine whether there are cracks in the gloves. This can be done by rolling the glove tightly from the open end. **Do not use shop air!**
- Remove the key from the ignition and keep it with you: this will ensure that nobody else will attempt to start the vehicle while you're working on it.
- Put on the HV insulated gloves.
- Test the specified CAT III voltmeter on the 12 V battery.
- Switch off the main power switch to the HV battery. Wait the prescribed number of minutes to allow the capacitors to discharge.
- Measure the voltage over the HV battery, using a CAT III voltmeter. When the voltage is approximately 0 V, you can remove the HV gloves and work safely around the high-voltage parts.

Rule of thumb	
1	Check hybrid tools
2	Key from the ignition
3	HV insulated gloves on
4	Turn HV battery disconnect switch off
5	Waiting time
6	Measuring the HV battery voltage

Fig. 182 Rules of thumb for working on the high-voltage section

In the Netherlands, there are different standards for working on hybrid vehicles. The Dutch standard NEN 9140: this standard is not a law, but is seen as a requirement.

HV SAFETY SWITCH

1. Disconnecting

One of the cables of the HV system is damaged. The HV system needs to be isolated to replace this cable.

You can use this check list:

1. Consult the vehicle service information.
2. Check the tools available.
3. Make sure the ignition switch is off.
4. Remove the negative terminal of the 12 V battery.
5. Put on the insulating gloves.
6. Remove the service plug.
7. Wait for the required time to pass.
8. Check for residual voltage.

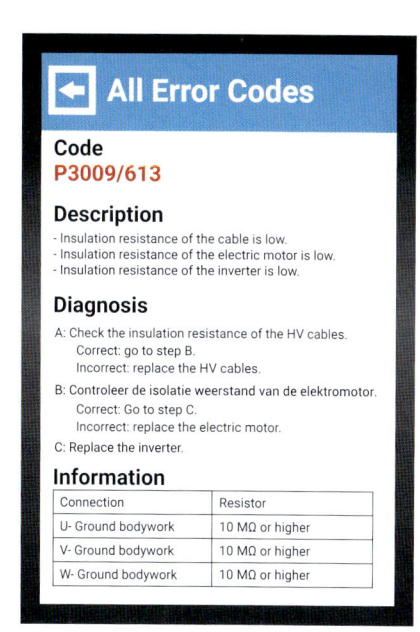

Fig. 183 Error code P3009/613 means that the insulation resistance of the cabling is too low.

The error code panel shows:

Code: P3009/613

Description
- Insulation resistance of the cable is low.
- Insulation resistance of the electric motor is low.
- Insulation resistance of the inverter is low.

Diagnosis
A: Check the insulation resistance of the HV cables.
   Correct: go to step B.
   Incorrect: replace the HV cables.
B: Controleer de isolatie weerstand van de elektromotor.
   Correct: Go to step C.
   Incorrect: replace the electric motor.
C: Replace the inverter.

Information

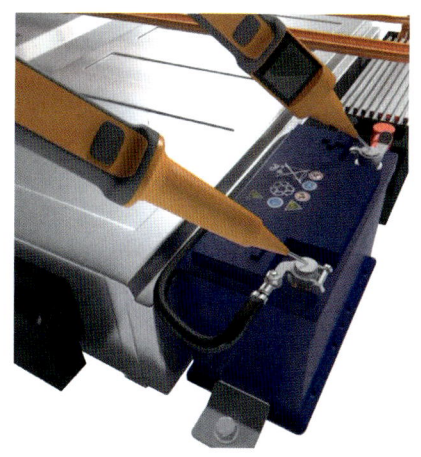

Connection	Resistor
U- Ground bodywork	10 MΩ or higher
V- Ground bodywork	10 MΩ or higher
W- Ground bodywork	10 MΩ or higher

Fig. 184 Check the operation of the voltmeter by measuring the voltage of the 12 V battery.

Fig. 185 Check the insulating gloves by inflating them and listening for escaping air.

Fig. 186 Switch off the ignition of the vehicle by pressing the Power button.

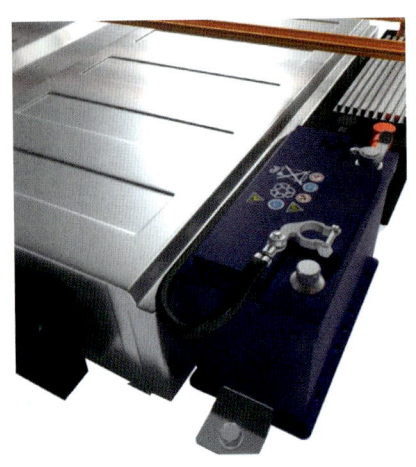

Fig. 187 Disconnect the negative terminal of the 12 V battery.

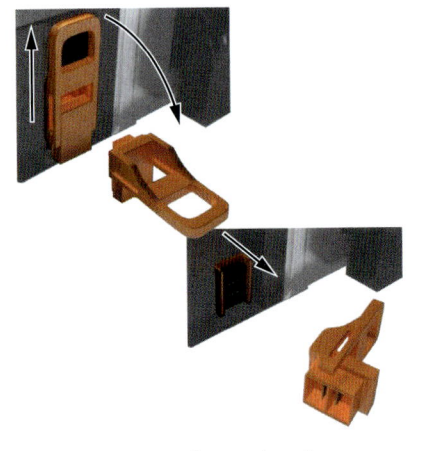

Fig. 188 Remove the service plug from the HV battery.

Fig. 189 Measure the residual voltage in the HV system. There should be no voltage on the connections that are connected to the HV battery

2. Measure Insulation Resistance

The scan tool shows an error code indicating a problem with the insulation resistance in one of the cables from the inverter to the electric motor.

To check the insulation resistance, follow these steps:

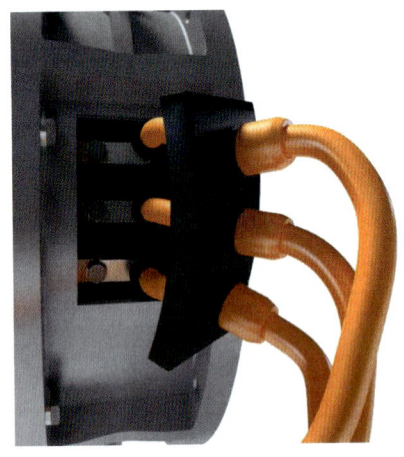

1. Disconnect the cables from the motor.
2. Disconnect the cables from the inverter.
3. Set the insulation resistance meter to 500 V.
4. Connect the black probe to the housing.
5. Connect the red probe to the U cable.
6. Press 'Test' to start the measurement.
7. Record the measured values.
8. Measure the insulation resistance of the V cable and the W cable in the same way.
9. Assess the measured values.
10. Replace the cable with the poor insulation resistance.
11. Connect the cables with the inverter.
12. Connect the cables with the motor.

Fig. 190 Disconnect the cables from the motor.

Fig. 191 Disconnect the cables from the inverter.

Fig. 192 Set the insulation resistor meter to 500 V.

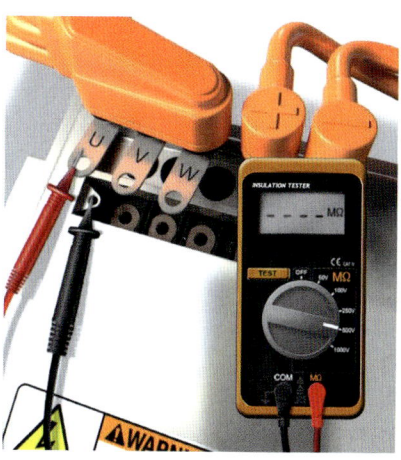

Fig. 193 Connect the measuring pins.

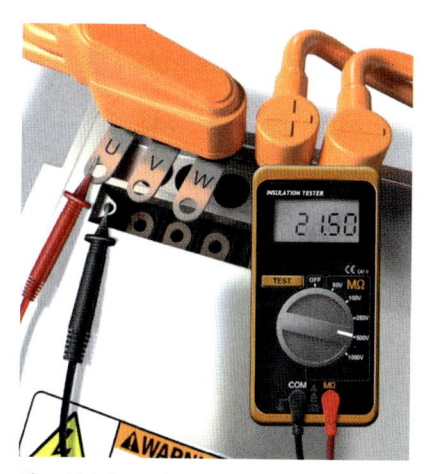

Fig. 194 Press 'Test' to start the measurement.

3. Switching On

You've carried out the repairs and now you're going to check if the repairs were successful.

Switch the system back on using these steps:
— Connect ground to the 12 V battery.
— Install the service plug.
— Take off the insulating gloves.
— Switch the ignition on.
— Verify that the fault is repaired.

976 ADVANCED AUTOMOTIVE ELECTRONICS

Fig. 195 Connect the negative terminal of the 12 V battery.

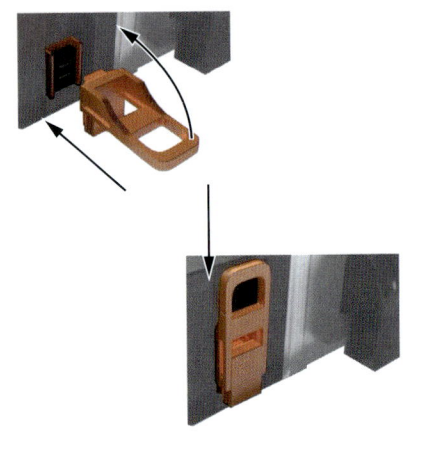

Fig. 196 Install the service plug.

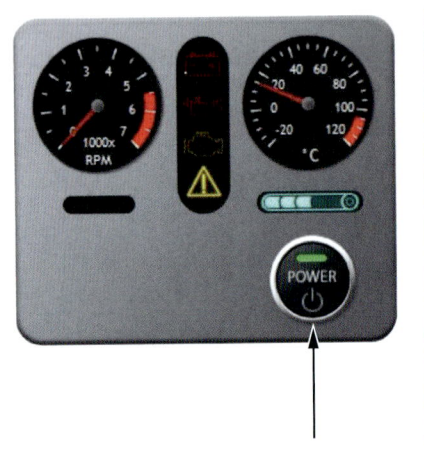

Fig. 197 Press the Power button to switch on the ignition.

Fig. 198 Erase the error codes and verify that none of the error codes return.

HOW TO: DE-ENERGIZE A HYBRID CAR'S HV CIRCUIT

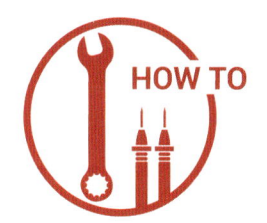

1. Procedure for de-energizing a Toyota Prius 3.

When the workshop manual specifies that a car must be disconnected from the voltage, follow the procedure in the workshop manual. For the Toyota Prius 3, this is done as follows.

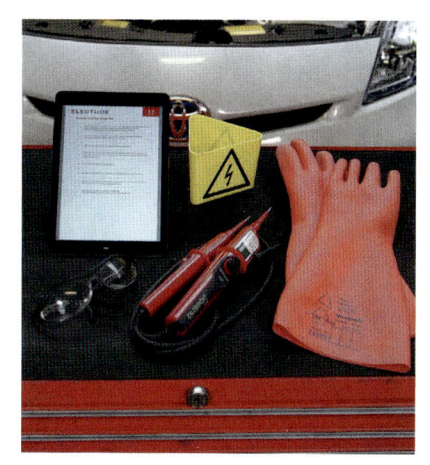

Fig. 199 Make sure you have the required tools.

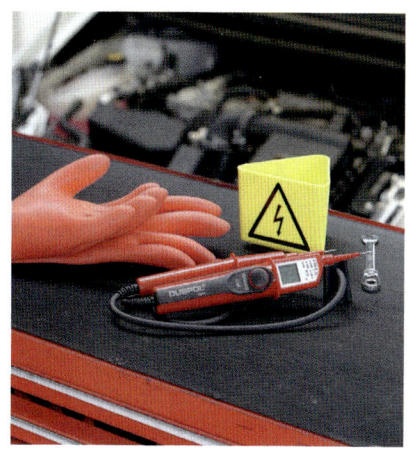

Fig. 200 Inflate the gloves one at a time and pressurize them by rolling them up, starting where they open. Squeeze them and make sure that no air is escaping.

Fig. 201 Place the safety warning placard on the car to make it clear to fellow mechanics that the vehicle is being worked on.

2. Check the HV multimeter, disconnect the negative terminal of the 12 V battery, put on the insulating gloves and unlock the service plug

Fig. 202 Switch off the car's ignition. Check the HV multimeter by measuring the voltage on the 12 V battery. Check the display to see if the meter is showing 12 V. If so, then the meter is okay.

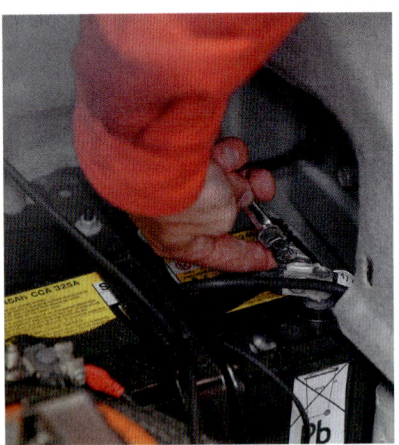

Fig. 203 Disconnect the negative pole of the 12 V battery.

Fig. 204 Put on the insulating gloves. Remove the service plug by unlocking it and then pulling on it to remove it.

3. Check whether the HV circuit is voltage-free

Wait 5 to 10 minutes after the service plug is unlocked. The high voltage capacitors need to discharge before you can check whether the HV circuit is voltage free.

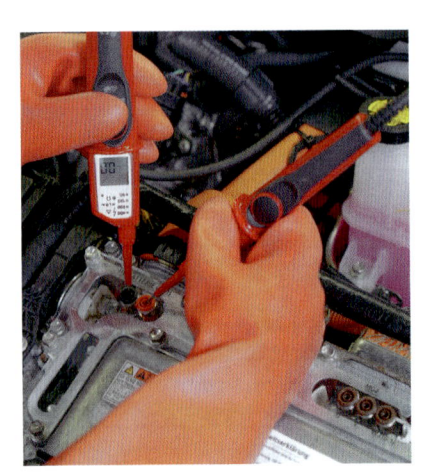

Fig. 205 Measure the voltage at the measuring points of the converter and make sure that voltage is no longer present. It is now safe to work on this car.

HOW TO: TURN ON A HYBRID CAR'S HV CIRCUIT

1. Procedure for turning on a Toyota Prius 3 HV circuit

After a hybrid car has been repaired, consult the workshop manual to learn how to turn the HV circuit back on. For the Toyota Prius 3, this can be done as follows.

2. Check the gloves and install the service plug

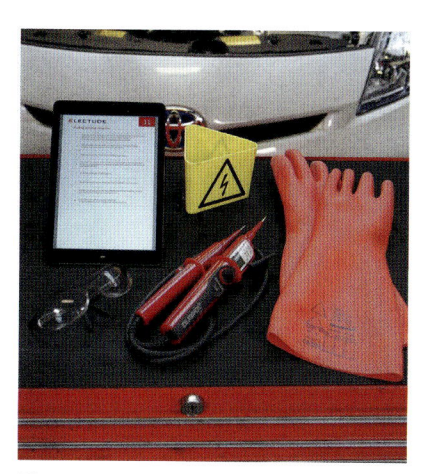

Fig. 208 Make sure you have the required tools.

Fig. 209 Inflate the gloves one at a time and pressurize them by rolling them up, starting where they open. Squeeze them and make sure that no air is escaping.

Fig. 210 Put on the insulating gloves. Check that no tools are left behind. Install the service plug.

980 ADVANCED AUTOMOTIVE ELECTRONICS

3. Connect the negative pole of the 12 V battery and switch on the ignition

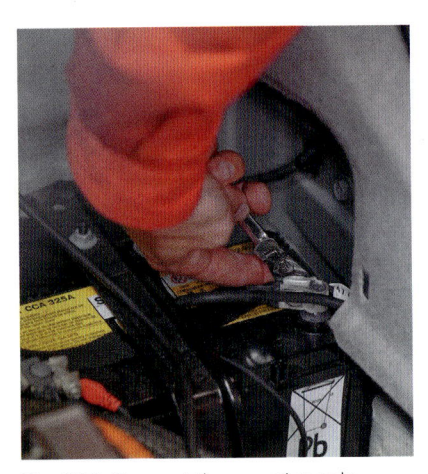

Fig. 211 Connect the negative pole of the 12 V battery.

Fig. 212 Turn on the ignition.

Fig. 213 Check whether the system indicates "ready" on the dashboard. Then turn the ignition off.

4. Remove the safety warning placard from the car

Fig. 214 Remove the safety warning placard. The car is now ready for use.

TOWING A HYBRID VEHICLE

1. Introduction

A car with a hybrid drive differs at various points from a car with a manual gearbox. For example, when working on a hybrid vehicle, special attention must be paid to safety. Extra attention must also be paid when towing a hybrid vehicle. Certain hybrid vehicles may only be towed at low speed to prevent damage to the drive. Other Hybrid vehicles must be towed with the drive wheels off the ground. For all-wheel drive models, only flatbed towing is allowed. Consult the vehicle manual to see how the vehicle can be towed.

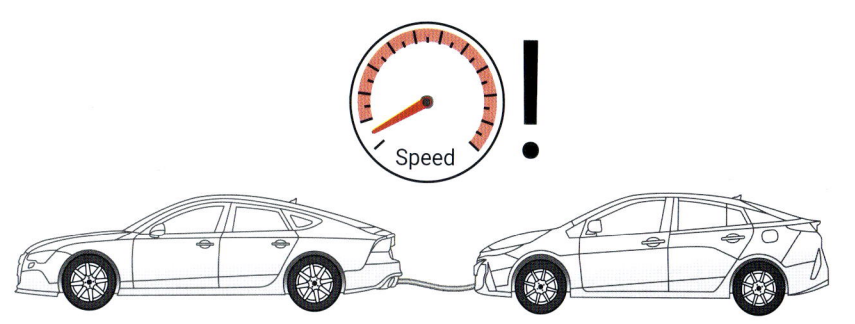

Fig. 217 Not every hybrid vehicle can just be towed.

2. Precautions

Hybrid vehicles that work with a planetary gear set can only be towed at low speeds.

The internal combustion engine (ICE) and two electric motors/generators (MG1 and MG2) have a fixed gear ratio through a planetary gear set.
If the internal combustion engine can not be started due to a failure, the speed of MG2 may be too high (as a result of the high gear ratio).
This results in the bearings becoming heavily loaded as well as the voltage generated in MG1 becoming too high.

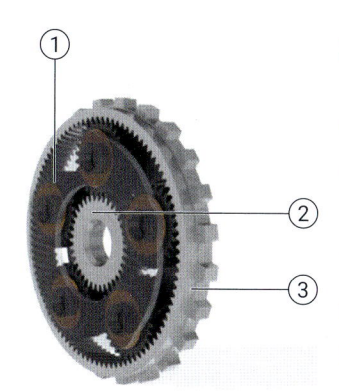

Fig. 218 Planetary gear set.
1. planet carrier, connected with the internal combustion engine 2. sun gear, connected with MG1 3. ring gear, connected with MG2.

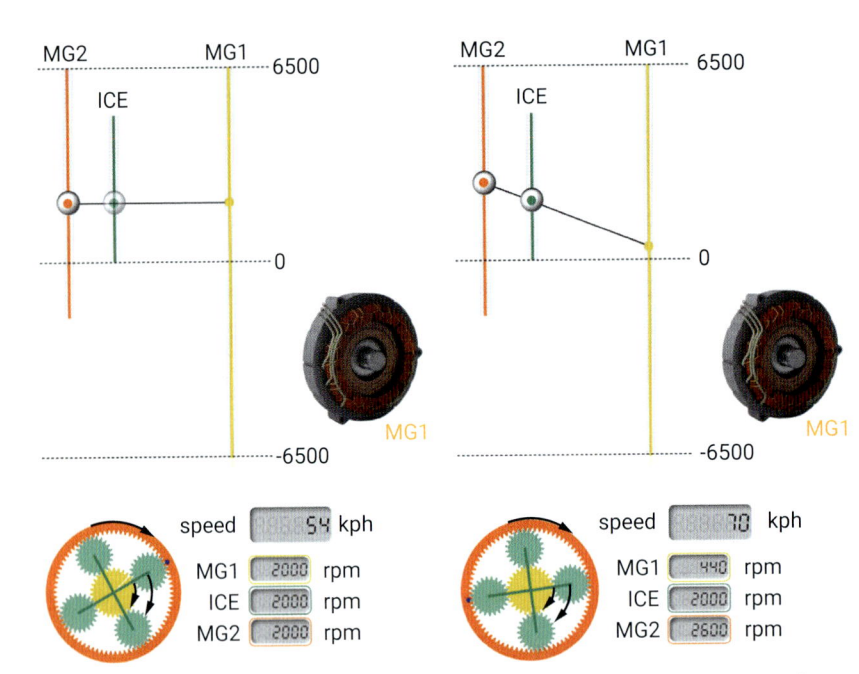

Fig. 219 When driving at a speed of 54 km/hr and an engine speed of 2000 rpm, MG1 and MG2 also run at 2000 rpm.

Fig. 220 When driving at a speed of 70 km/hr and an engine speed of 2000 rpm, MG1 runs at a speed of 440 rpm and MG2 at 2600 rpm.

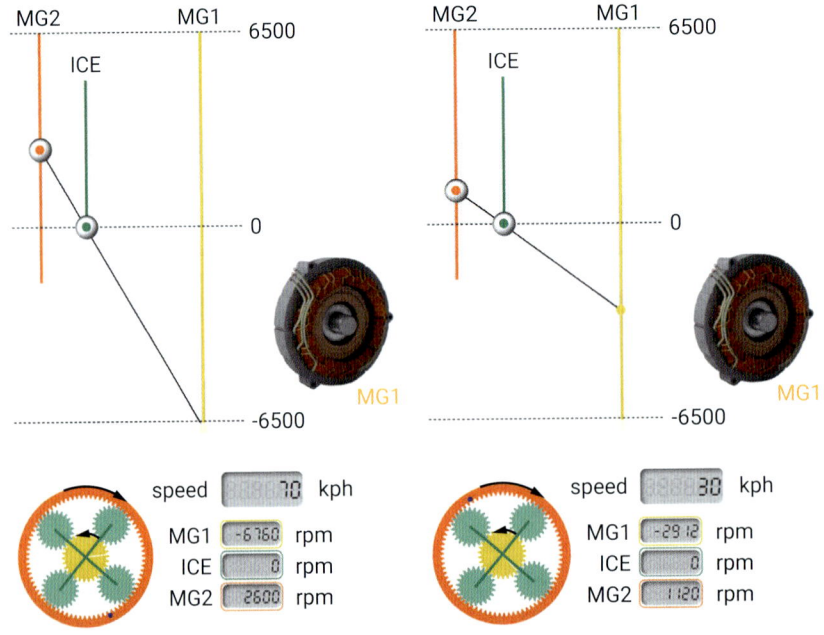

Fig. 221 If, at a speed of 70 km/hr, the internal combustion engine would not run, then due to the transmission, MG1 would have a speed of 6760 rpm. MG2 still runs at 2600 rpm because this is directly proportional to the vehicle speed.

Fig. 222 When driving with a maximum specified towing speed of 30 km/hr and stationary engine, then MG1 runs at less than 3000 rpm and MG2 at just over 1100 rpm.

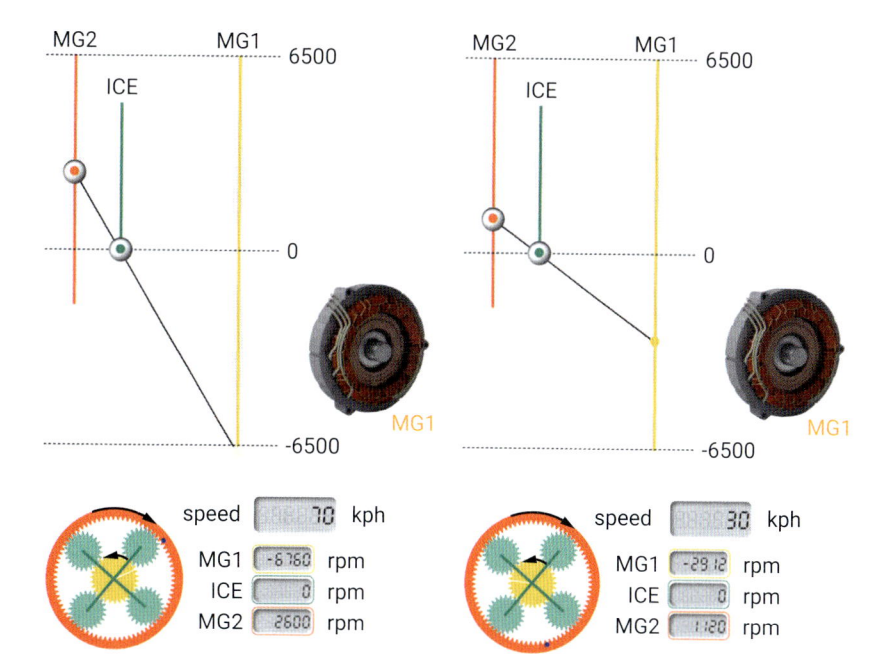

Fig. 223 If, at a speed of 70 km/hr, the internal combustion engine would not run, the generated voltage in MG1 would be almost 400 V.

Fig. 224 When driving with a maximum specified towing speed of 30 km/hr and stationary engine, then the generated voltage in MG1 is only 170 V.